W9-DGR-532

ACP

ISBN-13: 978-0-324-57108-0
ISBN-10: 0-324-57108-9
90000
9 780324 571080

THOMSON™

Visit Thomson
Custom Solutions online at
www.thomsoncustom.com

For your lifelong learning needs:
www.thomsonlearning--.com

Statistics and Quantitative Methods for Business and Economics

Anderson/Sweeney/Williams

THOMSON
SOUTH-WESTERN

Australia · Canada · Mexico · Singapore · Spain · United Kingdom · United States

THOMSON
SOUTH-WESTERN

Statistics and Quantitative Methods for Business and Economics
Anderson/Sweeney/Williams

Executive Editors:
Michele Baird, Maureen Staudt & Michael Stranz

Project Development Manager:
Linda deStefano

Sr. Marketing Coordinators:
Lindsay Annett and Sara Mercurio

Production/Manufacturing Manager:
Donna M. Brown

Production Editorial Manager:
Dan Plofchan

Pre-Media Services Supervisor:
Becki Walker

Rights and Permissions Specialist:
Kalina Ingham Hintz

Cover Image
Getty Images*

Printed in the
United States of America
1 2 3 4 5 6 7 10 09 08 07

For more information, please contact Thomson Custom Solutions, 5191 Natorp Boulevard, Mason, OH 45040. Or you can visit our Internet site at http://www.thomsoncustom.com

The Adaptable Courseware Program consists of products and additions to existing Thomson products that are produced from camera-ready copy. Peer review, class testing, and accuracy are primarily the responsibility of the author(s).

ISBN 978-0-324-57108-0
(0-324-57108-9)

International Divisions List

Asia (Including India):
Thomson Learning
(a division of Thomson Asia Pte Ltd)
5 Shenton Way #01-01
UIC Building
Singapore 068808
Tel: (65) 6410-1200
Fax: (65) 6410-1208

Australia/New Zealand:
Thomson Learning Australia
102 Dodds Street
Southbank, Victoria 3006
Australia

Latin America:
Thomson Learning
Seneca 53
Colonia Polano
11560 Mexico, D.F., Mexico
Tel (525) 281-2906
Fax (525) 281-2656

Canada:
Thomson Nelson
1120 Birchmount Road
Toronto, Ontario
Canada M1K 5G4
Tel (416) 752-9100
Fax (416) 752-8102

UK/Europe/Middle East/Africa:
Thomson Learning
High Holborn House
50-51 Bedford Row
London, WC1R 4LS
United Kingdom
Tel 44 (020) 7067-2500
Fax 44 (020) 7067-2600

Spain (Includes Portugal):
Thomson Paraninfo
Calle Magallanes 25
28015 Madrid
España
Tel 34 (0)91 446-3350
Fax 34 (0)91 445-6218

Brief Contents

From Statistics for Business and Economics, 10e

From Quantitative Methods for Business, 10e

CHAPTER 1

Data and Statistics

CONTENTS

STATISTICS *in* PRACTICE

BUSINESSWEEK*
NEW YORK, NEW YORK

With a global circulation of more than 1 million, *BusinessWeek* is the most widely read business magazine in the world. More than 200 dedicated reporters and editors in 26 bureaus worldwide deliver a variety of articles of interest to the business and economic community. Along with feature articles on current topics, the magazine contains regular sections on International Business, Economic Analysis, Information Processing, and Science & Technology. Information in the feature articles and the regular sections helps readers stay abreast of current developments and assess the impact of those developments on business and economic conditions.

Most issues of *BusinessWeek* provide an in-depth report on a topic of current interest. Often, the in-depth reports contain statistical facts and summaries that help the reader understand the business and economic information. For example, the December 6, 2004, issue included a special report on the pricing of goods made in China; the January 3, 2005, issue provided information about where to invest in 2005; and the April 4, 2005, issue provided an overview of the *BusinessWeek* 50, a diverse group of top-performing companies. In addition, the weekly *BusinessWeek Investor* provides statistics about the state of the economy, including production indexes, stock prices, mutual funds, and interest rates.

BusinessWeek also uses statistics and statistical information in managing its own business. For example, an annual survey of subscribers helps the company learn about subscriber demographics, reading habits, likely purchases, lifestyles, and so on. *BusinessWeek* managers use statistical summaries from the survey to provide better services to subscribers and advertisers. One recent North American subscriber survey indicated that 90% of *BusinessWeek* subscribers use a personal computer at home and that 64% of *BusinessWeek* subscribers are involved with computer purchases at work. Such statistics alert *BusinessWeek* managers to subscriber interest in articles about new developments in computers. The results of the survey are also made available to potential advertisers. The high percentage of subscribers using personal computers at home and the high percentage of subscribers involved with computer purchases at work would be an incentive for a computer manufacturer to consider advertising in *BusinessWeek*.

In this chapter, we discuss the types of data available for statistical analysis and describe how the data are obtained. We introduce descriptive statistics and statistical inference as ways of converting data into meaningful and easily interpreted statistical information.

BusinessWeek uses statistical facts and summaries in many of its articles. © Terri Miller/E-Visual Communications, Inc.

*The authors are indebted to Charlene Trentham, Research Manager at *BusinessWeek*, for providing this Statistics in Practice.

Frequently, we see the following types of statements in newspapers and magazines:

- The National Association of Realtors reported that the median selling price for a house in the United States was $215,000 (*The Wall Street Journal,* January 16, 2006).
- The average cost of a 30-second television commercial during the 2006 Super Bowl game was $2.5 million (*USA Today,* January 27, 2006).

- A Jupiter Media survey found 31% of adult males watch television 10 or more hours a week. For adult women it was 26% (*The Wall Street Journal,* January 26, 2004).
- General Motors, a leader in automotive cash rebates, provided an average cash incentive of $4300 per vehicle (*USA Today,* January 27, 2006).
- More than 40% of Marriott International managers work their way up through the ranks (*Fortune*, January 20, 2003).
- The New York Yankees have the highest payroll in major league baseball. In 2005, the team payroll was $208,306,817, with a median of $5,833,334 per player (*USA Today* Salary Database, February 2006).
- The Dow Jones Industrial Average closed at 11,577 (*Barron's,* May 6, 2006).

The numerical facts in the preceding statements ($215,000; $2.5 million; 31%; 26%; $4300; 40%; $5,833,334; and 11,577) are called statistics. In this usage, the term *statistics* refers to numerical facts such as averages, medians, percents, and index numbers that help us understand a variety of business and economic conditions. However, as you will see, the field, or subject, of statistics involves much more than numerical facts. In a broader sense, **statistics** is defined as the art and science of collecting, analyzing, presenting, and interpreting data. Particularly in business and economics, the information provided by collecting, analyzing, presenting, and interpreting data gives managers and decision makers a better understanding of the business and economic environment and thus enables them to make more informed and better decisions. In this text, we emphasize the use of statistics for business and economic decision making.

Chapter 1 begins with some illustrations of the applications of statistics in business and economics. In Section 1.2 we define the term *data* and introduce the concept of a data set. This section also introduces key terms such as *variables* and *observations,* discusses the difference between quantitative and qualitative data, and illustrates the uses of cross-sectional and time series data. Section 1.3 discusses how data can be obtained from existing sources or through survey and experimental studies designed to obtain new data. The important role that the Internet now plays in obtaining data is also highlighted. The uses of data in developing descriptive statistics and in making statistical inferences are described in Sections 1.4 and 1.5.

1.1 Applications in Business and Economics

In today's global business and economic environment, anyone can access vast amounts of statistical information. The most successful managers and decision makers understand the information and know how to use it effectively. In this section, we provide examples that illustrate some of the uses of statistics in business and economics.

Accounting

Public accounting firms use statistical sampling procedures when conducting audits for their clients. For instance, suppose an accounting firm wants to determine whether the amount of accounts receivable shown on a client's balance sheet fairly represents the actual amount of accounts receivable. Usually the large number of individual accounts receivable makes reviewing and validating every account too time-consuming and expensive. As common practice in such situations, the audit staff selects a subset of the accounts called a sample. After reviewing the accuracy of the sampled accounts, the auditors draw a conclusion as to whether the accounts receivable amount shown on the client's balance sheet is acceptable.

Finance

Financial analysts use a variety of statistical information to guide their investment recommendations. In the case of stocks, the analysts review a variety of financial data including price/earnings ratios and dividend yields. By comparing the information for an individual stock with information about the stock market averages, a financial analyst can begin to draw a conclusion as to whether an individual stock is over- or underpriced. For example, *Barron's* (September 12, 2005) reported that the average price/earnings ratio for the 30 stocks in the Dow Jones Industrial Average was 16.5. JPMorgan showed a price/earnings ratio of 11.8. In this case, the statistical information on price/earnings ratios indicated a lower price in comparison to earnings for JPMorgan than the average for the Dow Jones stocks. Therefore, a financial analyst might conclude that JPMorgan was underpriced. This and other information about JPMorgan would help the analyst make a buy, sell, or hold recommendation for the stock.

Marketing

Electronic scanners at retail checkout counters collect data for a variety of marketing research applications. For example, data suppliers such as ACNielsen and Information Resources, Inc., purchase point-of-sale scanner data from grocery stores, process the data, and then sell statistical summaries of the data to manufacturers. Manufacturers spend hundreds of thousands of dollars per product category to obtain this type of scanner data. Manufacturers also purchase data and statistical summaries on promotional activities such as special pricing and the use of in-store displays. Brand managers can review the scanner statistics and the promotional activity statistics to gain a better understanding of the relationship between promotional activities and sales. Such analyses often prove helpful in establishing future marketing strategies for the various products.

Production

Today's emphasis on quality makes quality control an important application of statistics in production. A variety of statistical quality control charts are used to monitor the output of a production process. In particular, an x-bar chart can be used to monitor the average output. Suppose, for example, that a machine fills containers with 12 ounces of a soft drink. Periodically, a production worker selects a sample of containers and computes the average number of ounces in the sample. This average, or x-bar value, is plotted on an x-bar chart. A plotted value above the chart's upper control limit indicates overfilling, and a plotted value below the chart's lower control limit indicates underfilling. The process is termed "in control" and allowed to continue as long as the plotted x-bar values fall between the chart's upper and lower control limits. Properly interpreted, an x-bar chart can help determine when adjustments are necessary to correct a production process.

Economics

Economists frequently provide forecasts about the future of the economy or some aspect of it. They use a variety of statistical information in making such forecasts. For instance, in forecasting inflation rates, economists use statistical information on such indicators as the Producer Price Index, the unemployment rate, and manufacturing capacity utilization. Often these statistical indicators are entered into computerized forecasting models that predict inflation rates.

Applications of statistics such as those described in this section are an integral part of this text. Such examples provide an overview of the breadth of statistical applications. To supplement these examples, practitioners in the fields of business and economics provided chapter-opening Statistics in Practice articles that introduce the material covered in each chapter. The Statistics in Practice applications show the importance of statistics in a wide variety of business and economic situations.

1.2 Data

Data are the facts and figures collected, analyzed, and summarized for presentation and interpretation. All the data collected in a particular study are referred to as the **data set** for the study. Table 1.1 shows a data set containing information for 25 companies that are part of the S&P 500. The S&P 500 is made up of 500 companies selected by Standard & Poor's. These companies account for 76% of the market capitalization of all U.S. stocks. S&P 500 stocks are closely followed by investors and Wall Street analysts.

TABLE 1.1 DATA SET FOR 25 S&P 500 COMPANIES

CD file BWS&P

Company	Exchange	Ticker	*BusinessWeek* Rank	Share Price ($)	Earnings per Share ($)
Abbott Laboratories	N	ABT	90	46	2.02
Altria Group	N	MO	148	66	4.57
Apollo Group	NQ	APOL	174	74	0.90
Bank of New York	N	BK	305	30	1.85
Bristol-Myers Squibb	N	BMY	346	26	1.21
Cincinnati Financial	NQ	CINF	161	45	2.73
Comcast	NQ	CMCSA	296	32	0.43
Deere	N	DE	36	71	5.77
eBay	NQ	EBAY	19	43	0.57
Federated Dept. Stores	N	FD	353	56	3.86
Hasbro	N	HAS	373	21	0.96
IBM	N	IBM	216	93	4.94
International Paper	N	IP	370	37	0.98
Knight-Ridder	N	KRI	397	66	4.13
Manor Care	N	HCR	285	34	1.90
Medtronic	N	MDT	53	52	1.79
National Semiconductor	N	NSM	155	20	1.03
Novellus Systems	NQ	NVLS	386	30	1.06
Pitney Bowes	N	PBI	339	46	2.05
Pulte Homes	N	PHM	12	78	7.67
SBC Communications	N	SBC	371	24	1.52
St. Paul Travelers	N	STA	264	38	1.53
Teradyne	N	TER	412	15	0.84
UnitedHealth Group	N	UNH	5	91	3.94
Wells Fargo	N	WFC	159	59	4.09

Source: BusinessWeek (April 4, 2005).

Elements, Variables, and Observations

Elements are the entities on which data are collected. For the data set in Table 1.1, each individual company's stock is an element; the element names appear in the first column. With 25 stocks, the data set contains 25 elements.

A **variable** is a characteristic of interest for the elements. The data set in Table 1.1 includes the following five variables:

- *Exchange:* Where the stock is traded—N (New York Stock Exchange) and NQ (Nasdaq National Market)
- *Ticker Symbol:* The abbreviation used to identify the stock on the exchange listing
- *BusinessWeek Rank:* A number from 1 to 500 that is a measure of company strength
- *Share Price ($):* The closing price (February 28, 2005)
- *Earnings per Share ($):* The earnings per share for the most recent 12 months

Measurements collected on each variable for every element in a study provide the data. The set of measurements obtained for a particular element is called an **observation.** Referring to Table 1.1, we see that the set of measurements for the first observation (Abbott Laboratories) is N, ABT, 90, 46, and 2.02. The set of measurements for the second observation (Altria Group) is N, MO, 148, 66, and 4.57, and so on. A data set with 25 elements contains 25 observations.

Scales of Measurement

Data collection requires one of the following scales of measurement: nominal, ordinal, interval, or ratio. The scale of measurement determines the amount of information contained in the data and indicates the most appropriate data summarization and statistical analyses.

When the data for a variable consist of labels or names used to identify an attribute of the element, the scale of measurement is considered a **nominal scale**. For example, referring to the data in Table 1.1, we see that the scale of measurement for the exchange variable is nominal because N and NQ are labels used to identify where the company's stock is traded. In cases where the scale of measurement is nominal, a numeric code as well as nonnumeric labels may be used. For example, to facilitate data collection and to prepare the data for entry into a computer database, we might use a numeric code by letting 1 denote the New York Stock Exchange and 2 denote the Nasdaq National Market. In this case the numeric values 1 and 2 provide the labels used to identify where the stock is traded. The scale of measurement is nominal even though the data appear as numeric values.

The scale of measurement for a variable is called an **ordinal scale** if the data exhibit the properties of nominal data and the order or rank of the data is meaningful. For example, Eastside Automotive sends customers a questionnaire designed to obtain data on the quality of its automotive repair service. Each customer provides a repair service rating of excellent, good, or poor. Because the data obtained are the labels—excellent, good, or poor—the data have the properties of nominal data. In addition, the data can be ranked, or ordered, with respect to the service quality. Data recorded as excellent indicate the best service, followed by good and then poor. Thus, the scale of measurement is ordinal. Note that the ordinal data can also be recorded using a numeric code. For example, the *BusinessWeek* rank for the data in Table 1.1 is ordinal data. It provides a rank from 1 to 500 based on *BusinessWeek*'s assessment of the company's strength.

The scale of measurement for a variable becomes an **interval scale** if the data show the properties of ordinal data and the interval between values is expressed in terms of a fixed unit of measure. Interval data are always numeric. Scholastic Aptitude Test (SAT) scores are an example of interval-scaled data. For example, three students with SAT math scores of 620, 550, and 470 can be ranked or ordered in terms of best performance to poorest performance. In addition, the differences between the scores are meaningful. For instance, student 1 scored $620 - 550 = 70$ points more than student 2, while student 2 scored $550 - 470 = 80$ points more than student 3.

The scale of measurement for a variable is a **ratio scale** if the data have all the properties of interval data and the ratio of two values is meaningful. Variables such as distance, height, weight, and time use the ratio scale of measurement. This scale requires that a zero value be included to indicate that nothing exists for the variable at the zero point. For example, consider the cost of an automobile. A zero value for the cost would indicate that the automobile has no cost and is free. In addition, if we compare the cost of \$30,000 for one automobile to the cost of \$15,000 for a second automobile, the ratio property shows that the first automobile is \$30,000/\$15,000 = 2 times, or twice, the cost of the second automobile.

Qualitative and Quantitative Data

Qualitative data are often referred to as categorical data.

Data can also be classified as either qualitative or quantitative. **Qualitative data** include labels or names used to identify an attribute of each element. Qualitative data use either the nominal or ordinal scale of measurement and may be nonnumeric or numeric. **Quantitative data** require numeric values that indicate how much or how many. Quantitative data are obtained using either the interval or ratio scale of measurement.

The statistical method appropriate for summarizing data depends upon whether the data are qualitative or quantitative.

A **qualitative variable** is a variable with qualitative data, and a **quantitative variable** is a variable with quantitative data. The statistical analysis appropriate for a particular variable depends upon whether the variable is qualitative or quantitative. If the variable is qualitative, the statistical analysis is rather limited. We can summarize qualitative data by counting the number of observations in each qualitative category or by computing the proportion of the observations in each qualitative category. However, even when the qualitative data use a numeric code, arithmetic operations such as addition, subtraction, multiplication, and division do not provide meaningful results. Section 2.1 discusses ways for summarizing qualitative data.

On the other hand, arithmetic operations often provide meaningful results for a quantitative variable. For example, for a quantitative variable, the data may be added and then divided by the number of observations to compute the average value. This average is usually meaningful and easily interpreted. In general, more alternatives for statistical analysis are possible when the data are quantitative. Section 2.2 and Chapter 3 provide ways of summarizing quantitative data.

Cross-Sectional and Time Series Data

For purposes of statistical analysis, distinguishing between cross-sectional data and time series data is important. **Cross-sectional data** are data collected at the same or approximately the same point in time. The data in Table 1.1 are cross-sectional because they describe the five variables for the 25 S&P 500 companies at the same point in time. **Time series data** are data collected over several time periods. For example, Figure 1.1 provides a graph of the U.S. city average price per gallon for unleaded regular gasoline. The graph shows gasoline price in a fairly stable band between \$1.80 and \$2.00 from May 2004 through February 2005. After that gasoline price became more volatile. It rose significantly, culminating with a sharp spike in September 2005.

Graphs of time series data are frequently found in business and economic publications. Such graphs help analysts understand what happened in the past, identify any trends over

FIGURE 1.1 U.S. CITY AVERAGE PRICE PER GALLON FOR CONVENTIONAL REGULAR GASOLINE

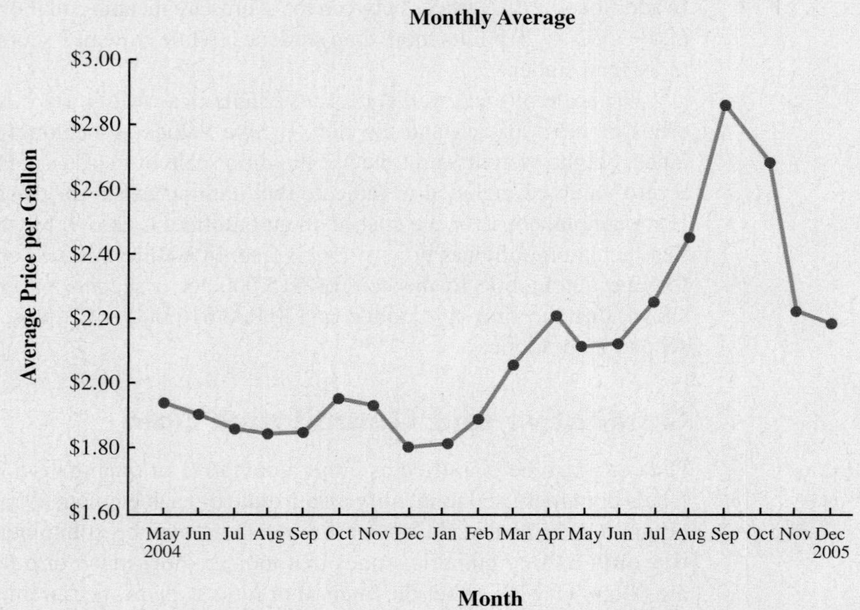

Source: U.S. Energy Information Administration, January 2006.

time, and project future levels for the time series. The graphs of time series data can take on a variety of forms, as shown in Figure 1.2. With a little study, these graphs are usually easy to understand and interpret.

For example, Panel (A) in Figure 1.2 is a graph showing the interest rate for student Stafford Loans between 2000 and 2006. After 2000, the interest rate declined and reached its lowest level of 3.2% in 2004. However, after 2004, the interest rate for student loans showed a steep increase, reaching 6.8% in 2006. With the U.S. Department of Education estimating that more than 50% of undergraduate students graduate with debt, this increasing interest rate places a greater financial burden on many new college graduates.

The graph in Panel (B) shows a rather disturbing increase in the average credit card debt per household over the 10-year period from 1995 to 2005. Notice how the time series shows an almost steady annual increase in the average credit card debt per household from $4500 in 1995 to $9500 in 2005. In 2005, an average credit card debt per household of $10,000 appeared not far off. Most credit card companies offer relatively low introductory interest rates. After this initial period, however, annual interest rates of 18%, 20%, or more are common. These rates make the credit card debt difficult for households to handle.

Panel (C) shows a graph of the time series for the occupancy rate of hotels in South Florida during a typical one-year period. Note that the form of the graph in Panel (C) is different from the graphs in Panels (A) and (B), with the time in months shown on the vertical, rather than the horizontal axis. The highest occupancy rates of 95% to 98% occur during the months of February and March when the climate of South Florida is attractive to tourists. In fact, January to April is the typical high occupancy season for South Florida hotels. On the other hand, note the low occupancy rates in August to October; the lowest occupancy of 50% occurring in September. Higher temperatures and the hurricane season are the primary reasons for the drop in hotel occupancy during this period.

FIGURE 1.2 A VARIETY OF GRAPHS OF TIME SERIES DATA

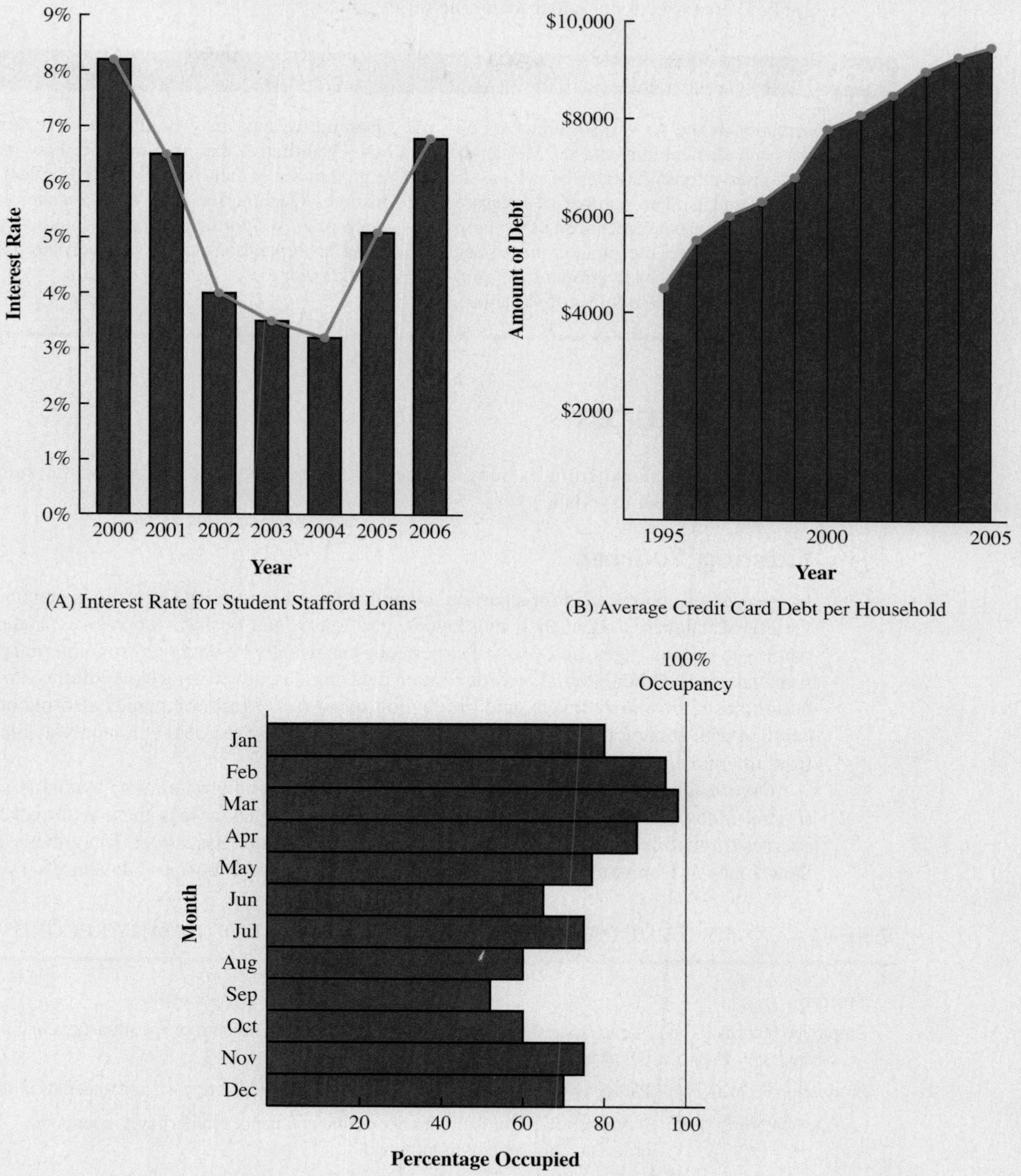

(A) Interest Rate for Student Stafford Loans

(B) Average Credit Card Debt per Household

(C) Occupancy Rate of South Florida Hotels

We will study times series and the forecasting of time series when we discuss forecasting methods in Chapter 16. Other than Chapter 16, the statistical methods presented in this text apply to cross-sectional rather than time series data.

NOTES AND COMMENTS

1. An observation is the set of measurements obtained for each element in a data set. Hence, the number of observations is always the same as the number of elements. The number of measurements obtained for each element equals the number of variables. Hence, the total number of data items can be determined by multiplying the number of observations by the number of variables.
2. Quantitative data may be discrete or continuous. Quantitative data that measure how many (e.g., number of calls received in 5 minutes) are discrete. Quantitative data that measure how much (e.g., weight or time) are continuous because no separation occurs between the possible data values.

1.3 Data Sources

Data can be obtained from existing sources or from surveys and experimental studies designed to collect new data.

Existing Sources

In some cases, data needed for a particular application already exist. Companies maintain a variety of databases about their employees, customers, and business operations. Data on employee salaries, ages, and years of experience can usually be obtained from internal personnel records. Other internal records contain data on sales, advertising expenditures, distribution costs, inventory levels, and production quantities. Most companies also maintain detailed data about their customers. Table 1.2 shows some of the data commonly available from internal company records.

Organizations that specialize in collecting and maintaining data make available substantial amounts of business and economic data. Companies access these external data sources through leasing arrangements or by purchase. Dun & Bradstreet, Bloomberg, and Dow Jones & Company are three firms that provide extensive business database services

TABLE 1.2 EXAMPLES OF DATA AVAILABLE FROM INTERNAL COMPANY RECORDS

Source	Some of the Data Typically Available
Employee records	Name, address, social security number, salary, number of vacation days, number of sick days, and bonus
Production records	Part or product number, quantity produced, direct labor cost, and materials cost
Inventory records	Part or product number, number of units on hand, reorder level, economic order quantity, and discount schedule
Sales records	Product number, sales volume, sales volume by region, and sales volume by customer type
Credit records	Customer name, address, phone number, credit limit, and accounts receivable balance
Customer profile	Age, gender, income level, household size, address, and preferences

to clients. ACNielsen and Information Resources, Inc., built successful businesses collecting and processing data that they sell to advertisers and product manufacturers.

Data are also available from a variety of industry associations and special interest organizations. The Travel Industry Association of America maintains travel-related information such as the number of tourists and travel expenditures by states. Such data would be of interest to firms and individuals in the travel industry. The Graduate Management Admission Council maintains data on test scores, student characteristics, and graduate management education programs. Most of the data from these types of sources are available to qualified users at a modest cost.

The Internet continues to grow as an important source of data and statistical information. Almost all companies maintain Web sites that provide general information about the company as well as data on sales, number of employees, number of products, product prices, and product specifications. In addition, a number of companies now specialize in making information available over the Internet. As a result, one can obtain access to stock quotes, meal prices at restaurants, salary data, and an almost infinite variety of information.

Government agencies are another important source of existing data. For instance, the U.S. Department of Labor maintains considerable data on employment rates, wage rates, size of the labor force, and union membership. Table 1.3 lists selected governmental agencies and some of the data they provide. Most government agencies that collect and process data also make the results available through a Web site. For instance, the U.S. Census Bureau has a wealth of data at its Web site, www.census.gov. Figure 1.3 shows the homepage for the U.S. Census Bureau.

Statistical Studies

Sometimes the data needed for a particular application are not available through existing sources. In such cases, the data can often be obtained by conducting a statistical study. Statistical studies can be classified as either *experimental* or *observational.*

The largest experimental statistical study ever conducted is believed to be the 1954 Public Health Service experiment for the Salk polio vaccine. Nearly 2 million children in grades 1, 2, and 3 were selected from throughout the United States.

In an experimental study, a variable of interest is first identified. Then one or more other variables are identified and controlled so that data can be obtained about how they influence the variable of interest. For example, a pharmaceutical firm might be interested in conducting an experiment to learn about how a new drug affects blood pressure. Blood pressure is the variable of interest in the study. The dosage level of the new drug is another variable that is hoped to have a causal effect on blood pressure. To obtain data about the effect of the new drug, researchers select a sample of individuals. The dosage level of the new drug is controlled, as different groups of individuals are given different dosage levels. Before and after

TABLE 1.3 EXAMPLES OF DATA AVAILABLE FROM SELECTED GOVERNMENT AGENCIES

Government Agency	Some of the Data Available
Census Bureau *www.census.gov*	Population data, number of households, and household income
Federal Reserve Board *www.federalreserve.gov*	Data on the money supply, installment credit, exchange rates, and discount rates
Office of Management and Budget *www.whitehouse.gov/omb*	Data on revenue, expenditures, and debt of the federal government
Department of Commerce *www.doc.gov*	Data on business activity, value of shipments by industry, level of profits by industry, and growing and declining industries
Bureau of Labor Statistics *www.bls.gov*	Consumer spending, hourly earnings, unemployment rate, safety records, and international statistics

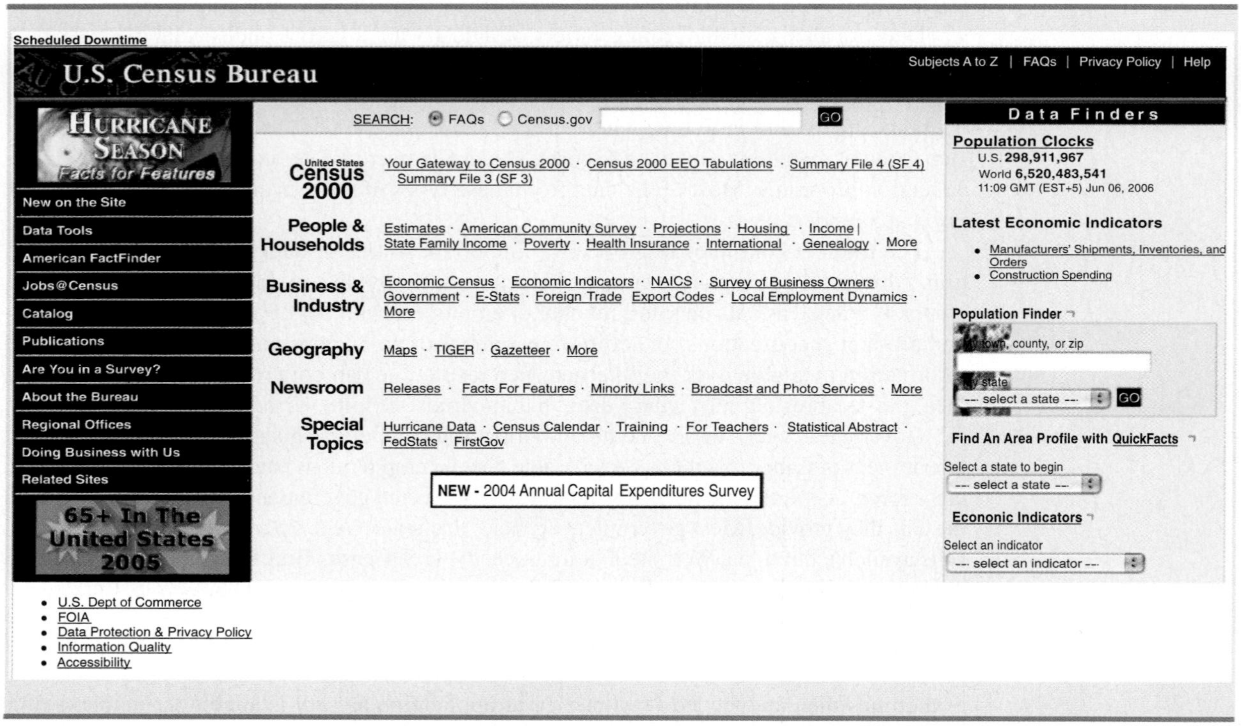

FIGURE 1.3 U.S. CENSUS BUREAU HOMEPAGE

data on blood pressure are collected for each group. Statistical analysis of the experimental data can help determine how the new drug affects blood pressure.

Studies of smokers and nonsmokers are observational studies because researchers do not determine or control who will smoke and who will not smoke.

Nonexperimental, or observational, statistical studies make no attempt to control the variables of interest. A survey is perhaps the most common type of observational study. For instance, in a personal interview survey, research questions are first identified. Then a questionnaire is designed and administered to a sample of individuals. Some restaurants use observational studies to obtain data about their customers' opinions of the quality of food, service, atmosphere, and so on. A questionnaire used by the Lobster Pot Restaurant in Redington Shores, Florida, is shown in Figure 1.4. Note that the customers completing the questionnaire are asked to provide ratings for five variables: food quality, friendliness of service, promptness of service, cleanliness, and management. The response categories of excellent, good, satisfactory, and unsatisfactory provide ordinal data that enable Lobster Pot's managers to assess the quality of the restaurant's operation.

Managers wanting to use data and statistical analysis as aids to decision making must be aware of the time and cost required to obtain the data. The use of existing data sources is desirable when data must be obtained in a relatively short period of time. If important data are not readily available from an existing source, the additional time and cost involved in obtaining the data must be taken into account. In all cases, the decision maker should consider the contribution of the statistical analysis to the decision-making process. The cost of data acquisition and the subsequent statistical analysis should not exceed the savings generated by using the information to make a better decision.

Data Acquisition Errors

Managers should always be aware of the possibility of data errors in statistical studies. Using erroneous data can be worse than not using any data at all. An error in data acquisition occurs whenever the data value obtained is not equal to the true or actual value that would be obtained with a correct procedure. Such errors can occur in a number of ways.

FIGURE 1.4 CUSTOMER OPINION QUESTIONNAIRE USED BY THE LOBSTER POT RESTAURANT, REDINGTON SHORES, FLORIDA

The LOBSTER Pot

RESTAURANT

We are happy you stopped by the Lobster Pot Restaurant and want to make sure you will come back. So, if you have a little time, we will really appreciate it if you will fill out this card. Your comments and suggestions are extremely important to us. Thank you!

Server's Name ______________

	Excellent	Good	Satisfactory	Unsatisfactory
Food Quality	❑	❑	❑	❑
Friendly Service	❑	❑	❑	❑
Prompt Service	❑	❑	❑	❑
Cleanliness	❑	❑	❑	❑
Management	❑	❑	❑	❑

Comments ______________

What prompted your visit to us? ______________

Please drop in suggestion box at entrance. Thank you.

For example, an interviewer might make a recording error, such as a transposition in writing the age of a 24-year-old person as 42, or the person answering an interview question might misinterpret the question and provide an incorrect response.

Experienced data analysts take great care in collecting and recording data to ensure that errors are not made. Special procedures can be used to check for internal consistency of the data. For instance, such procedures would indicate that the analyst should review the accuracy of data for a respondent shown to be 22 years of age but reporting 20 years of work experience. Data analysts also review data with unusually large and small values, called outliers, which are candidates for possible data errors. In Chapter 3 we present some of the methods statisticians use to identify outliers.

Errors often occur during data acquisition. Blindly using any data that happen to be available or using data that were acquired with little care can result in misleading information and bad decisions. Thus, taking steps to acquire accurate data can help ensure reliable and valuable decision-making information.

1.4 Descriptive Statistics

Most of the statistical information in newspapers, magazines, company reports, and other publications consists of data that are summarized and presented in a form that is easy for the reader to understand. Such summaries of data, which may be tabular, graphical, or numerical, are referred to as **descriptive statistics**.

TABLE 1.4 FREQUENCIES AND PERCENT FREQUENCIES FOR THE EXCHANGE VARIABLE

Exchange	Frequency	Percent Frequency
New York Stock Exchange	20	80
Nasdaq National Market	5	20
Totals	25	100

Refer again to the data set in Table 1.1 showing data on 25 S&P 500 companies. Methods of descriptive statistics can be used to provide summaries of the information in this data set. For example, a tabular summary of the data for the qualitative variable Exchange is shown in Table 1.4. A graphical summary of the same data, called a bar graph, is shown in Figure 1.5. These types of tabular and graphical summaries generally make the data easier to interpret. Referring to Table 1.4 and Figure 1.5, we can see easily that the majority of the stocks in the data set are traded on the New York Stock Exchange. On a percentage basis, 80% are traded on the New York Stock Exchange and 20% are traded on the Nasdaq National Market.

A graphical summary of the data for the quantitative variable Share Price for the S&P stocks, called a histogram, is provided in Figure 1.6. The histogram makes it easy to see that the share prices range from \$0 to \$100, with the highest concentrations between \$20 and \$60.

In addition to tabular and graphical displays, numerical descriptive statistics are used to summarize data. The most common numerical descriptive statistic is the average, or mean. Using the data on the variable Earnings per Share for the S&P stocks in Table 1.1, we can compute the average by adding the earnings per share for all 25 stocks and dividing

FIGURE 1.5 BAR GRAPH FOR THE EXCHANGE VARIABLE

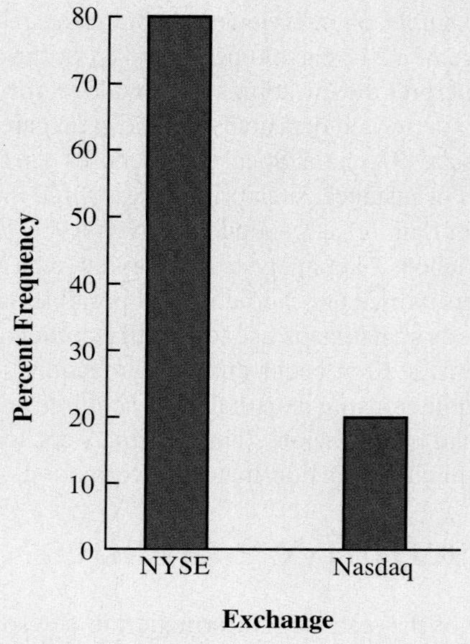

FIGURE 1.6 HISTOGRAM OF SHARE PRICE FOR 25 S&P STOCKS

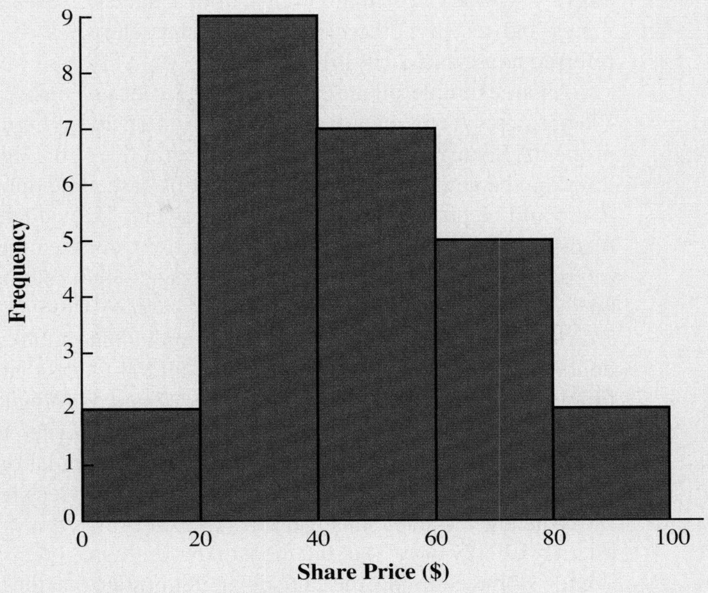

the sum by 25. Doing so provides an average earnings per share of $2.49. This average demonstrates a measure of the central tendency, or central location, of the data for that variable.

In a number of fields, interest continues to grow in statistical methods that can be used for developing and presenting descriptive statistics. Chapters 2 and 3 devote attention to the tabular, graphical, and numerical methods of descriptive statistics.

1.5 Statistical Inference

Many situations require information about a large group of elements (individuals, companies, voters, households, products, customers, and so on). But, because of time, cost, and other considerations, data can be collected from only a small portion of the group. The larger group of elements in a particular study is called the **population**, and the smaller group is called the **sample**. Formally, we use the following definitions.

POPULATION

A population is the set of all elements of interest in a particular study.

SAMPLE

A sample is a subset of the population.

The U.S. government conducts a census every 10 years. Market research firms conduct sample surveys every day.

The process of conducting a survey to collect data for the entire population is called a **census**. The process of conducting a survey to collect data for a sample is called a **sample survey**. As one of its major contributions, statistics uses data from a sample to make estimates and test hypotheses about the characteristics of a population through a process referred to as **statistical inference**.

As an example of statistical inference, let us consider the study conducted by Norris Electronics. Norris manufactures a high-intensity lightbulb used in a variety of electrical products. In an attempt to increase the useful life of the lightbulb, the product design group developed a new lightbulb filament. In this case, the population is defined as all lightbulbs that could be produced with the new filament. To evaluate the advantages of the new filament, 200 bulbs with the new filament were manufactured and tested. Data collected from this sample showed the number of hours each lightbulb operated before filament burnout. See Table 1.5.

Suppose Norris wants to use the sample data to make an inference about the average hours of useful life for the population of all lightbulbs that could be produced with the new filament. Adding the 200 values in Table 1.5 and dividing the total by 200 provides the sample average lifetime for the lightbulbs: 76 hours. We can use this sample result to estimate that the average lifetime for the lightbulbs in the population is 76 hours. Figure 1.7 provides a graphical summary of the statistical inference process for Norris Electronics.

Whenever statisticians use a sample to estimate a population characteristic of interest, they usually provide a statement of the quality, or precision, associated with the estimate. For the Norris example, the statistician might state that the point estimate of the average lifetime for the population of new lightbulbs is 76 hours with a margin of error of ± 4 hours. Thus, an interval estimate of the average lifetime for all lightbulbs produced with the new filament is 72 hours to 80 hours. The statistician can also state how confident he or she is that the interval from 72 hours to 80 hours contains the population average.

TABLE 1.5 HOURS UNTIL BURNOUT FOR A SAMPLE OF 200 LIGHTBULBS FOR THE NORRIS ELECTRONICS EXAMPLE

CD file
Norris

107	73	68	97	76	79	94	59	98	57
54	65	71	70	84	88	62	61	79	98
66	62	79	86	68	74	61	82	65	98
62	116	65	88	64	79	78	79	77	86
74	85	73	80	68	78	89	72	58	69
92	78	88	77	103	88	63	68	88	81
75	90	62	89	71	71	74	70	74	70
65	81	75	62	94	71	85	84	83	63
81	62	79	83	93	61	65	62	92	65
83	70	70	81	77	72	84	67	59	58
78	66	66	94	77	63	66	75	68	76
90	78	71	101	78	43	59	67	61	71
96	75	64	76	72	77	74	65	82	86
66	86	96	89	81	71	85	99	59	92
68	72	77	60	87	84	75	77	51	45
85	67	87	80	84	93	69	76	89	75
83	68	72	67	92	89	82	96	77	102
74	91	76	83	66	68	61	73	72	76
73	77	79	94	63	59	62	71	81	65
73	63	63	89	82	64	85	92	64	73

FIGURE 1.7 THE PROCESS OF STATISTICAL INFERENCE FOR THE NORRIS ELECTRONICS EXAMPLE

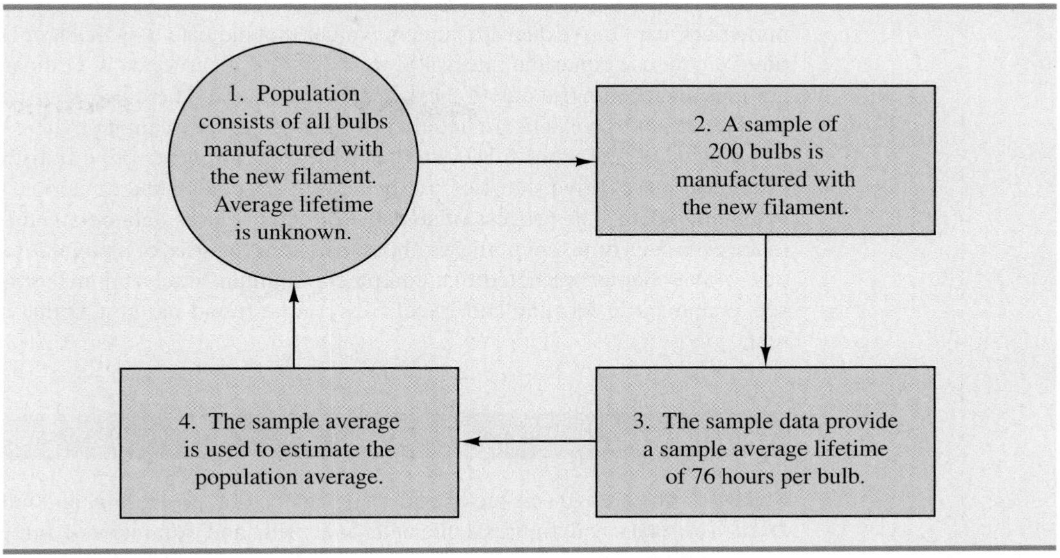

1.6 Computers and Statistical Analysis

Because statistical analysis typically involves large amounts of data, analysts frequently use computer software for this work. For instance, computing the average lifetime for the 200 lightbulbs in the Norris Electronics example (see Table 1.5) would be quite tedious without a computer. To facilitate computer usage, the larger data sets in this book are available on the CD that accompanies the text. A logo in the left margin of the text (e.g., Norris) identifies each of these data sets. The data files are available in both Minitab and Excel formats. In addition, we provide instructions in chapter appendixes for carrying out many of the statistical procedures using Minitab and Excel.

Summary

Statistics is the art and science of collecting, analyzing, presenting, and interpreting data. Nearly every college student majoring in business or economics is required to take a course in statistics. We began the chapter by describing typical statistical applications for business and economics.

Data consist of the facts and figures that are collected and analyzed. Four scales of measurement used to obtain data on a particular variable include nominal, ordinal, interval, and ratio. The scale of measurement for a variable is nominal when the data are labels or names used to identify an attribute of an element. The scale is ordinal if the data demonstrate the properties of nominal data and the order or rank of the data is meaningful. The scale is interval if the data demonstrate the properties of ordinal data and the interval between values is expressed in terms of a fixed unit of measure. Finally, the scale of measurement is ratio if the data show all the properties of interval data and the ratio of two values is meaningful.

For purposes of statistical analysis, data can be classified as qualitative or quantitative. Qualitative data use labels or names to identify an attribute of each element. Qualitative data use either the nominal or ordinal scale of measurement and may be nonnumeric or numeric. Quantitative data are numeric values that indicate how much or how many. Quantitative data use either the interval or ratio scale of measurement. Ordinary arithmetic operations are meaningful only if the data are quantitative. Therefore, statistical computations used for quantitative data are not always appropriate for qualitative data.

In Sections 1.4 and 1.5 we introduced the topics of descriptive statistics and statistical inference. Descriptive statistics are the tabular, graphical, and numerical methods used to summarize data. The process of statistical inference uses data obtained from a sample to make estimates or test hypotheses about the characteristics of a population. In the last section of the chapter we noted that computers facilitate statistical analysis. The larger data sets contained in Minitab and Excel files can be found on the CD that accompanies the text.

Glossary

Statistics The art and science of collecting, analyzing, presenting, and interpreting data.
Data The facts and figures collected, analyzed, and summarized for presentation and interpretation.
Data set All the data collected in a particular study.
Elements The entities on which data are collected.
Variable A characteristic of interest for the elements.
Observation The set of measurements obtained for a particular element.
Nominal scale The scale of measurement for a variable when the data are labels or names used to identify an attribute of an element. Nominal data may be nonnumeric or numeric.
Ordinal scale The scale of measurement for a variable if the data exhibit the properties of nominal data and the order or rank of the data is meaningful. Ordinal data may be nonnumeric or numeric.
Interval scale The scale of measurement for a variable if the data demonstrate the properties of ordinal data and the interval between values is expressed in terms of a fixed unit of measure. Interval data are always numeric.
Ratio scale The scale of measurement for a variable if the data demonstrate all the properties of interval data and the ratio of two values is meaningful. Ratio data are always numeric.
Qualitative data Labels or names used to identify an attribute of each element. Qualitative data use either the nominal or ordinal scale of measurement and may be nonnumeric or numeric.
Quantitative data Numeric values that indicate how much or how many of something. Quantitative data are obtained using either the interval or ratio scale of measurement.
Qualitative variable A variable with qualitative data.
Quantitative variable A variable with quantitative data.
Cross-sectional data Data collected at the same or approximately the same point in time.
Time series data Data collected over several time periods.
Descriptive statistics Tabular, graphical, and numerical summaries of data.
Population The set of all elements of interest in a particular study.
Sample A subset of the population.
Census A survey to collect data on the entire population.
Sample survey A survey to collect data on a sample.
Statistical inference The process of using data obtained from a sample to make estimates or test hypotheses about the characteristics of a population.

Supplementary Exercises

1. Discuss the differences between statistics as numerical facts and statistics as a discipline or field of study.

SELF test

2. *Condé Nast Traveler* magazine conducts an annual survey of subscribers in order to determine the best places to stay throughout the world. Table 1.6 shows a sample of nine European hotels (*Condé Nast Traveler,* January 2000). The price of a standard double room during the hotel's high season ranges from $ (lowest price) to $$$$ (highest price). The overall score includes subscribers' evaluations of each hotel's rooms, service, restaurants, location/atmosphere, and public areas; a higher overall score corresponds to a higher level of satisfaction.
   a. How many elements are in this data set?
   b. How many variables are in this data set?
   c. Which variables are qualitative and which variables are quantitative?
   d. What type of measurement scale is used for each of the variables?

SELF test

3. Refer to Table 1.6.
   a. What is the average number of rooms for the nine hotels?
   b. Compute the average overall score.
   c. What is the percentage of hotels located in England?
   d. What is the percentage of hotels with a room rate of $$?

4. All-in-one sound systems, called minisystems, typically include an AM/FM tuner, a dual-cassette tape deck, and a CD changer in a book-sized box with two separate speakers. The data in Table 1.7 show the retail price, sound quality, CD capacity, FM tuning sensitivity and selectivity, and the number of tape decks for a sample of 10 minisystems (*Consumer Reports Buying Guide 2002*).
   a. How many elements does this data set contain?
   b. What is the population?
   c. Compute the average price for the sample.
   d. Using the results in part (c), estimate the average price for the population.

5. Consider the data set for the sample of 10 minisystems in Table 1.7.
   a. How many variables are in the data set?
   b. Which of the variables are quantitative and which are qualitative?
   c. What is the average CD capacity for the sample?
   d. What percentage of the minisystems provides an FM tuning rating of very good or excellent?
   e. What percentage of the minisystems includes two tape decks?

TABLE 1.6 RATINGS FOR NINE PLACES TO STAY IN EUROPE

CD file
Hotel

Name of Property	Country	Room Rate	Number of Rooms	Overall Score
Graveteye Manor	England	$$	18	83.6
Villa d'Este	Italy	$$$$	166	86.3
Hotel Prem	Germany	$	54	77.8
Hotel d'Europe	France	$$	47	76.8
Palace Luzern	Switzerland	$$	326	80.9
Royal Crescent Hotel	England	$$$	45	73.7
Hotel Sacher	Austria	$$$	120	85.5
Duc de Bourgogne	Belgium	$	10	76.9
Villa Gallici	France	$$	22	90.6

Source: Condé Nast Traveler, January 2000.

TABLE 1.7 A SAMPLE OF 10 MINISYSTEMS

Brand and Model	Price ($)	Sound Quality	CD Capacity	FM Tuning	Tape Decks
Aiwa NSX-AJ800	250	Good	3	Fair	2
JVC FS-SD1000	500	Good	1	Very Good	0
JVC MX-G50	200	Very Good	3	Excellent	2
Panasonic SC-PM11	170	Fair	5	Very Good	1
RCA RS 1283	170	Good	3	Poor	0
Sharp CD-BA2600	150	Good	3	Good	2
Sony CHC-CL1	300	Very Good	3	Very Good	1
Sony MHC-NX1	500	Good	5	Excellent	2
Yamaha GX-505	400	Very Good	3	Excellent	1
Yamaha MCR-E100	500	Very Good	1	Excellent	0

CD file
Minisystems

6. Columbia House provides CDs to its mail-order club members. A Columbia House Music Survey asked new club members to complete an 11-question survey. Some of the questions asked were:
   a. How many CDs have you bought in the last 12 months?
   b. Are you currently a member of a national mail-order book club? (Yes or No)
   c. What is your age?
   d. Including yourself, how many people (adults and children) are in your household?
   e. What kind of music are you interested in buying? Fifteen categories were listed, including hard rock, soft rock, adult contemporary, heavy metal, rap, and country.

   Comment on whether each question provides qualitative or quantitative data.
7. The Ritz-Carlton Hotel used a customer opinion questionnaire to obtain performance data about its dining and entertainment services (The Ritz-Carrolton Hotel, Naples, Florida, February 2006). Customers were asked to rate six factors: Welcome, Service, Food, Menu Appeal, Atmosphere, and Overall Experience. Data were recorded for each factor with 1 for Fair, 2 for Average, 3 for Good, and 4 for Excellent.
   a. The customer responses provided data for six variables. Are the variables qualitative or quantitative?
   b. What measurement scale is used?
8. The Gallup organization conducted a telephone survey with a randomly selected national sample of 1005 adults, 18 years and older. The survey asked the respondents, "How would you describe your own physical health at this time?" (www.gallup.com, February 7, 2002). Response categories were Excellent, Good, Only Fair, Poor, and No Opinion.
   a. What was the sample size for this survey?
   b. Are the data qualitative or quantitative?
   c. Would it make more sense to use averages or percentages as a summary of the data for this question?
   d. Of the respondents, 29% said their personal health was excellent. How many individuals provided this response?
9. The Commerce Department reported receiving the following applications for the Malcolm Baldrige National Quality Award: 23 from large manufacturing firms, 18 from large service firms, and 30 from small businesses.
   a. Is type of business a qualitative or quantitative variable?
   b. What percentage of the applications came from small businesses?
10. *The Wall Street Journal* subscriber survey (October 13, 2003) asked 46 questions about subscriber characteristics and interests. State whether each of the following questions

provided qualitative or quantitative data and indicate the measurement scale appropriate for each.

a. What is your age?
b. Are you male or female?
c. When did you first start reading the *WSJ*? High school, college, early career, mid-career, late career, or retirement?
d. How long have you been in your present job or position?
e. What type of vehicle are you considering for your next purchase? Nine response categories include sedan, sports car, SUV, minivan, and so on.

11. State whether each of the following variables is qualitative or quantitative and indicate its measurement scale.
a. Annual sales
b. Soft drink size (small, medium, large)
c. Employee classification (GS1 through GS18)
d. Earnings per share
e. Method of payment (cash, check, credit card)

12. The Hawaii Visitors Bureau collects data on visitors to Hawaii. The following questions were among 16 asked in a questionnaire handed out to passengers during incoming airline flights in June 2003.
   - This trip to Hawaii is my: 1st, 2nd, 3rd, 4th, etc.
   - The primary reason for this trip is: (10 categories including vacation, convention, honeymoon)
   - Where I plan to stay: (11 categories including hotel, apartment, relatives, camping)
   - Total days in Hawaii

a. What is the population being studied?
b. Is the use of a questionnaire a good way to reach the population of passengers on incoming airline flights?
c. Comment on each of the four questions in terms of whether it will provide qualitative or quantitative data.

SELF test

13. Figure 1.8 provides a bar graph summarizing the earnings for Volkswagen for the years 1997 to 2005 (*BusinessWeek,* December 26, 2005).

FIGURE 1.8 EARNINGS FOR VOLKSWAGEN

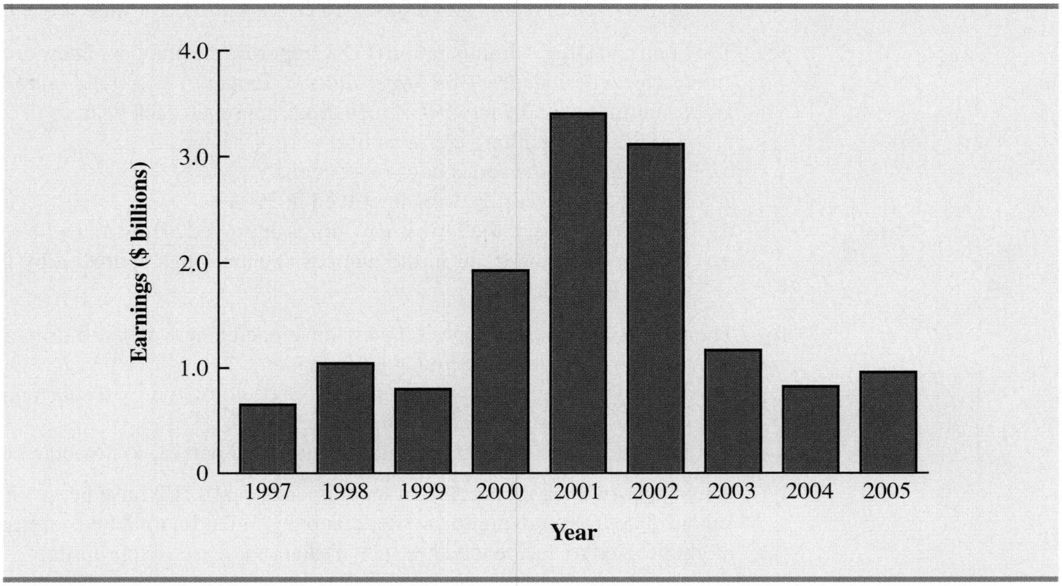

a. Are the data qualitative or quantitative?
b. Are the data time series or cross-sectional?
c. What is the variable of interest?
d. Comment on the trend in Volkswagen's earnings over time. The *BusinessWeek* article (December 26, 2005) estimated earnings for 2006 at $600 million or $.6 billion. Does Figure 1.8 indicate whether this estimate appears to be reasonable?
e. A similar article that appeared in *BusinessWeek* on July 23, 2001, only had the data from 1997 to 2000 along with higher earnings projected for 2001. What was the outlook for Volkswagen's earnings in July 2001? Did an investment in Volkswagen look promising in 2001? Explain.
f. What warning does this graph suggest about projecting data such as Volkswagen's earnings into the future?

14. CSM Worldwide forecasts global production for all automobile manufacturers. The following CSM data show the forecast of global auto production for General Motors, Ford, DaimlerChrysler, and Toyota for the years 2004 to 2007 (*USA Today,* December 21, 2005). Data are in millions of vehicles.

Manufacturer	2004	2005	2006	2007
General Motors	8.9	9.0	8.9	8.8
Ford	7.8	7.7	7.8	7.9
DaimlerChrysler	4.1	4.2	4.3	4.6
Toyota	7.8	8.3	9.1	9.6

a. Construct a time series graph for the years 2004 to 2007 showing the number of vehicles manufactured by each automotive company. Show the time series for all four manufacturers on the same graph.
b. General Motors has been the undisputed production leader of automobiles since 1931. What does the time series graph show about who is the world's biggest car company? Discuss.
c. Construct a bar graph showing vehicles produced by automobile manufacturer using the 2007 data. Is this graph based on cross-sectional or time series data?

15. The Food and Drug Administration (FDA) reported the number of new drugs approved over an eight-year period (*The Wall Street Journal,* January 12, 2004). Figure 1.9 provides a bar graph summarizing the number of new drugs approved each year.
a. Are the data qualitative or quantitative?
b. Are the data time series or cross-sectional?
c. How many new drugs were approved in 2003?
d. In what year were the fewest new drugs approved? How many?
e. Comment on the trend in the number of new drugs approved by the FDA over the eight-year period.

16. The marketing group at your company developed a new diet soft drink that it claims will capture a large share of the young adult market.
a. What data would you want to see before deciding to invest substantial funds in introducing the new product into the marketplace?
b. How would you expect the data mentioned in part (a) to be obtained?

17. A manager of a large corporation recommends a $10,000 raise be given to keep a valued subordinate from moving to another company. What internal and external sources of data might be used to decide whether such a salary increase is appropriate?

FIGURE 1.9 NUMBER OF NEW DRUGS APPROVED BY THE FOOD AND DRUG ADMINISTRATION

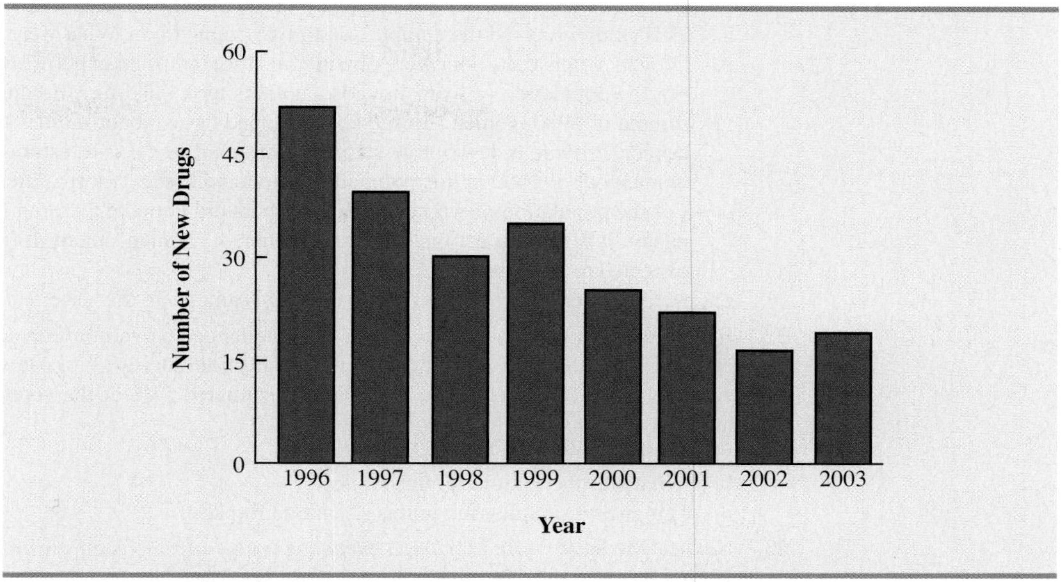

18. A survey of 430 business travelers found 155 business travelers used a travel agent to make the travel arrangements (*USA Today,* November 20, 2003).
    a. Develop a descriptive statistic that can be used to estimate the percentage of all business travelers who use a travel agent to make travel arrangements.
    b. The survey reported that the most frequent way business travelers make travel arrangements is by using an online travel site. If 44% of business travelers surveyed made their arrangements this way, how many of the 430 business travelers used an online travel site?
    c. Are the data on how travel arrangements are made qualitative or quantitative?
19. A *BusinessWeek* North American subscriber study collected data from a sample of 2861 subscribers. Fifty-nine percent of the respondents indicated an annual income of $75,000 or more, and 50% reported having an American Express credit card.
    a. What is the population of interest in this study?
    b. Is annual income a qualitative or quantitative variable?
    c. Is ownership of an American Express card a qualitative or quantitative variable?
    d. Does this study involve cross-sectional or time series data?
    e. Describe any statistical inferences *BusinessWeek* might make on the basis of the survey.
20. A survey of 131 investment managers in *Barron's* Big Money poll revealed the following (*Barron's,* October 28, 2002):
    - 43% of managers classified themselves as bullish or very bullish on the stock market.
    - The average expected return over the next 12 months for equities was 11.2%.
    - 21% selected health care as the sector most likely to lead the market in the next 12 months.
    - When asked to estimate how long it would take for technology and telecom stocks to resume sustainable growth, the managers' average response was 2.5 years.

    a. Cite two descriptive statistics.
    b. Make an inference about the population of all investment managers concerning the average return expected on equities over the next 12 months.
    c. Make an inference about the length of time it will take for technology and telecom stocks to resume sustainable growth.

21. A seven-year medical research study reported that women whose mothers took the drug DES during pregnancy were twice as likely to develop tissue abnormalities that might lead to cancer as were women whose mothers did not take the drug.
    a. This study involved the comparison of two populations. What were the populations?
    b. Do you suppose the data were obtained in a survey or an experiment?
    c. For the population of women whose mothers took the drug DES during pregnancy, a sample of 3980 women showed 63 developed tissue abnormalities that might lead to cancer. Provide a descriptive statistic that could be used to estimate the number of women out of 1000 in this population who have tissue abnormalities.
    d. For the population of women whose mothers did not take the drug DES during pregnancy, what is the estimate of the number of women out of 1000 who would be expected to have tissue abnormalities?
    e. Medical studies often use a relatively large sample (in this case, 3980). Why?
22. In the fall of 2003, Arnold Schwarzenegger challenged Governor Gray Davis for the governorship of California. A Policy Institute of California survey of registered voters reported Arnold Schwarzenegger in the lead with an estimated 54% of the vote (*Newsweek,* September 8, 2003).
    a. What was the population for this survey?
    b. What was the sample for this survey?
    c. Why was a sample used in this situation? Explain.
23. Nielsen Media Research conducts weekly surveys of television viewing throughout the United States, publishing both rating and market share data. The Nielsen rating is the percentage of households with televisions watching a program, while the Nielsen share is the percentage of households watching a program among those households with televisions in use. For example, Nielsen Media Research results for the 2003 Baseball World Series between the New York Yankees and the Florida Marlins showed a rating of 12.8% and a share of 22% (Associated Press, October 27, 2003). Thus, 12.8% of households with televisions were watching the World Series and 22% of households with televisions in use were watching the World Series. Based on the rating and share data for major television programs, Nielsen publishes a weekly ranking of television programs as well as a weekly ranking of the four major networks: ABC, CBS, NBC, and Fox.
    a. What is Nielsen Media Research attempting to measure?
    b. What is the population?
    c. Why would a sample be used in this situation?
    d. What kinds of decisions or actions are based on the Nielsen rankings?
24. A sample of midterm grades for five students showed the following results: 72, 65, 82, 90, 76. Which of the following statements are correct, and which should be challenged as being too generalized?
    a. The average midterm grade for the sample of five students is 77.
    b. The average midterm grade for all students who took the exam is 77.
    c. An estimate of the average midterm grade for all students who took the exam is 77.
    d. More than half of the students who take this exam will score between 70 and 85.
    e. If five other students are included in the sample, their grades will be between 65 and 90.
25. Table 1.8 shows a data set containing information for 25 of the shadow stocks tracked by the American Association of Individual Investors (aaii.com, February 2002). Shadow stocks are common stocks of smaller companies that are not closely followed by Wall Street analysts. The data set is also on the CD accompanying the text in the file named Shadow02.
    a. How many variables are in the data set?
    b. Which of the variables are qualitative and which are quantitative?

TABLE 1.8 DATA SET FOR 25 SHADOW STOCKS

CD file
Shadow02

Company	Exchange	Ticker Symbol	Market Cap ($ millions)	Price/ Earnings Ratio	Gross Profit Margin (%)
DeWolfe Companies	AMEX	DWL	36.4	8.4	36.7
North Coast Energy	OTC	NCEB	52.5	6.2	59.3
Hansen Natural Corp.	OTC	HANS	41.1	14.6	44.8
MarineMax, Inc.	NYSE	HZO	111.5	7.2	23.8
Nanometrics Incorporated	OTC	NANO	228.6	38.0	53.3
TeamStaff, Inc.	OTC	TSTF	92.1	33.5	4.1
Environmental Tectonics	AMEX	ETC	51.1	35.8	35.9
Measurement Specialties	AMEX	MSS	101.8	26.8	37.6
SEMCO Energy, Inc.	NYSE	SEN	193.4	18.7	23.6
Party City Corporation	OTC	PCTY	97.2	15.9	36.4
Embrex, Inc.	OTC	EMBX	136.5	18.9	59.5
Tech/Ops Sevcon, Inc.	AMEX	TO	23.2	20.7	35.7
ARCADIS NV	OTC	ARCAF	173.4	8.8	9.6
Qiao Xing Universal Tele.	OTC	XING	64.3	22.1	30.8
Energy West Incorporated	OTC	EWST	29.1	9.7	16.3
Barnwell Industries, Inc.	AMEX	BRN	27.3	7.4	73.4
Innodata Corporation	OTC	INOD	66.1	11.0	29.6
Medical Action Industries	OTC	MDCI	137.1	26.9	30.6
Instrumentarium Corp.	OTC	INMRY	240.9	3.6	52.1
Petroleum Development	OTC	PETD	95.9	6.1	19.4
Drexler Technology Corp.	OTC	DRXR	233.6	45.6	53.6
Gerber Childrenswear Inc.	NYSE	GCW	126.9	7.9	25.8
Gaiam, Inc.	OTC	GAIA	295.5	68.2	60.7
Artesian Resources Corp.	OTC	ARTNA	62.8	20.5	45.5
York Water Company	OTC	YORW	92.2	22.9	74.2

c. For the Exchange variable, show the frequency and the percent frequency for AMEX, NYSE, and OTC. Construct a bar graph similar to Figure 1.5 for the Exchange variable.
d. Show the frequency distribution for the Gross Profit Margin using the five intervals: 0–14.9, 15–29.9, 30–44.9, 45–59.9, and 60–74.9. Construct a histogram similar to Figure 1.6.
e. What is the average price/earnings ratio?

CHAPTER 2

Descriptive Statistics: Tabular and Graphical Presentations

CONTENTS

STATISTICS *in* PRACTICE

COLGATE-PALMOLIVE COMPANY*
NEW YORK, NEW YORK

The Colgate-Palmolive Company started as a small soap and candle shop in New York City in 1806. Today, Colgate-Palmolive employs more than 40,000 people working in more than 200 countries and territories around the world. Although best known for its brand names of Colgate, Palmolive, Ajax, and Fab, the company also markets Mennen, Hill's Science Diet, and Hill's Prescription Diet products.

The Colgate-Palmolive Company uses statistics in its quality assurance program for home laundry detergent products. One concern is customer satisfaction with the quantity of detergent in a carton. Every carton in each size category is filled with the same amount of detergent by weight, but the volume of detergent is affected by the density of the detergent powder. For instance, if the powder density is on the heavy side, a smaller volume of detergent is needed to reach the carton's specified weight. As a result, the carton may appear to be underfilled when opened by the consumer.

To control the problem of heavy detergent powder, limits are placed on the acceptable range of powder density. Statistical samples are taken periodically, and the density of each powder sample is measured. Data summaries are then provided for operating personnel so that corrective action can be taken if necessary to keep the density within the desired quality specifications.

A frequency distribution for the densities of 150 samples taken over a one-week period and a histogram are shown in the accompanying table and figure. Density levels above .40 are unacceptably high. The frequency distribution and histogram show that the operation is meeting its quality guidelines with all of the densities less than or equal to .40. Managers viewing these statistical summaries would be pleased with the quality of the detergent production process.

In this chapter, you will learn about tabular and graphical methods of descriptive statistics such as frequency distributions, bar graphs, histograms, stem-and-leaf displays, crosstabulations, and others. The goal of these methods is to summarize data so that the data can be easily understood and interpreted.

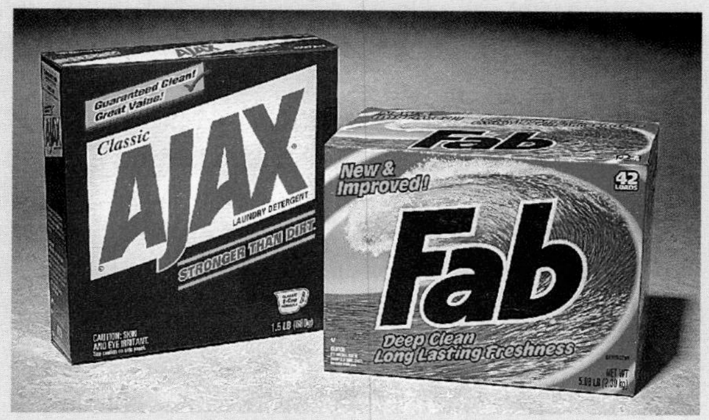

Statistical summaries help maintain the quality of these Colgate-Palmolive products. © Joe Higgins/South-Western.

Frequency Distribution of Density Data

Density	Frequency
.29–.30	30
.31–.32	75
.33–.34	32
.35–.36	9
.37–.38	3
.39–.40	1
Total	150

Histogram of Density Data

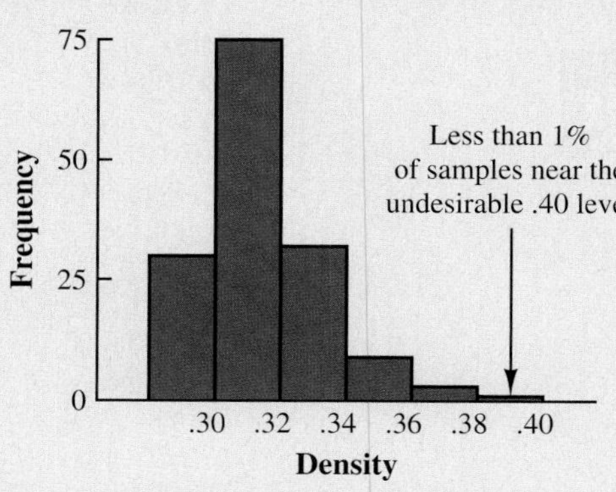

*The authors are indebted to William R. Fowle, Manager of Quality Assurance, Colgate-Palmolive Company, for providing this Statistics in Practice.

As indicated in Chapter 1, data can be classified as either qualitative or quantitative. **Qualitative data** use labels or names to identify categories of like items. **Quantitative data** are numerical values that indicate how much or how many.

This chapter introduces tabular and graphical methods commonly used to summarize both qualitative and quantitative data. Tabular and graphical summaries of data can be found in annual reports, newspaper articles, and research studies. Everyone is exposed to these types of presentations. Hence, it is important to understand how they are prepared and how they should be interpreted. We begin with tabular and graphical methods for summarizing data concerning a single variable. The last section introduces methods for summarizing data when the relationship between two variables is of interest.

Modern statistical software packages provide extensive capabilities for summarizing data and preparing graphical presentations. Minitab and Excel are two packages that are widely available. In the chapter appendixes, we show some of their capabilities.

2.1 Summarizing Qualitative Data

Frequency Distribution

We begin the discussion of how tabular and graphical methods can be used to summarize qualitative data with the definition of a **frequency distribution**.

> FREQUENCY DISTRIBUTION
>
> A frequency distribution is a tabular summary of data showing the number (frequency) of items in each of several nonoverlapping classes.

Let us use the following example to demonstrate the construction and interpretation of a frequency distribution for qualitative data. Coke Classic, Diet Coke, Dr. Pepper, Pepsi, and Sprite are five popular soft drinks. Assume that the data in Table 2.1 show the soft drink selected in a sample of 50 soft drink purchases.

CD file SoftDrink

TABLE 2.1 DATA FROM A SAMPLE OF 50 SOFT DRINK PURCHASES

Coke Classic	Sprite	Pepsi
Diet Coke	Coke Classic	Coke Classic
Pepsi	Diet Coke	Coke Classic
Diet Coke	Coke Classic	Coke Classic
Coke Classic	Diet Coke	Pepsi
Coke Classic	Coke Classic	Dr. Pepper
Dr. Pepper	Sprite	Coke Classic
Diet Coke	Pepsi	Diet Coke
Pepsi	Coke Classic	Pepsi
Pepsi	Coke Classic	Pepsi
Coke Classic	Coke Classic	Pepsi
Dr. Pepper	Pepsi	Pepsi
Sprite	Coke Classic	Coke Classic
Coke Classic	Sprite	Dr. Pepper
Diet Coke	Dr. Pepper	Pepsi
Coke Classic	Pepsi	Sprite
Coke Classic	Diet Coke	

TABLE 2.2

FREQUENCY DISTRIBUTION OF SOFT DRINK PURCHASES

Soft Drink	Frequency
Coke Classic	19
Diet Coke	8
Dr. Pepper	5
Pepsi	13
Sprite	5
Total	50

To develop a frequency distribution for these data, we count the number of times each soft drink appears in Table 2.1. Coke Classic appears 19 times, Diet Coke appears 8 times, Dr. Pepper appears 5 times, Pepsi appears 13 times, and Sprite appears 5 times. These counts are summarized in the frequency distribution in Table 2.2.

This frequency distribution provides a summary of how the 50 soft drink purchases are distributed across the five soft drinks. This summary offers more insight than the original data shown in Table 2.1. Viewing the frequency distribution, we see that Coke Classic is the leader, Pepsi is second, Diet Coke is third, and Sprite and Dr. Pepper are tied for fourth. The frequency distribution summarizes information about the popularity of the five soft drinks.

Relative Frequency and Percent Frequency Distributions

A frequency distribution shows the number (frequency) of items in each of several nonoverlapping classes. However, we are often interested in the proportion, or percentage, of items in each class. The *relative frequency* of a class equals the fraction or proportion of items belonging to a class. For a data set with n observations, the relative frequency of each class can be determined as follows:

RELATIVE FREQUENCY

$$\text{Relative frequency of a class} = \frac{\text{Frequency of the class}}{n} \tag{2.1}$$

The *percent frequency* of a class is the relative frequency multiplied by 100.

A **relative frequency distribution** gives a tabular summary of data showing the relative frequency for each class. A **percent frequency distribution** summarizes the percent frequency of the data for each class. Table 2.3 shows a relative frequency distribution and a percent frequency distribution for the soft drink data. In Table 2.3 we see that the relative frequency for Coke Classic is 19/50 = .38, the relative frequency for Diet Coke is 8/50 = .16, and so on. From the percent frequency distribution, we see that 38% of the purchases were Coke Classic, 16% of the purchases were Diet Coke, and so on. We can also note that 38% + 26% + 16% = 80% of the purchases were the top three soft drinks.

Bar Graphs and Pie Charts

A **bar graph**, or bar chart, is a graphical device for depicting qualitative data summarized in a frequency, relative frequency, or percent frequency distribution. On one axis of the graph (usually the horizontal axis), we specify the labels that are used for the classes (categories). A frequency, relative frequency, or percent frequency scale can be used for the other axis of

TABLE 2.3 RELATIVE FREQUENCY AND PERCENT FREQUENCY DISTRIBUTIONS OF SOFT DRINK PURCHASES

Soft Drink	Relative Frequency	Percent Frequency
Coke Classic	.38	38
Diet Coke	.16	16
Dr. Pepper	.10	10
Pepsi	.26	26
Sprite	.10	10
Total	1.00	100

FIGURE 2.1 BAR GRAPH OF SOFT DRINK PURCHASES

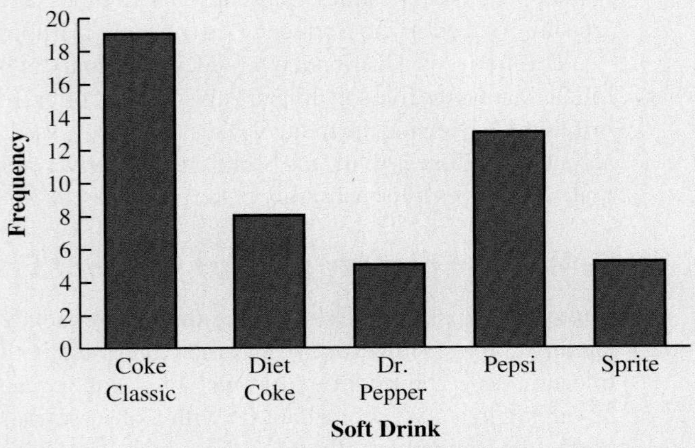

In quality control applications, bar graphs are used to identify the most important causes of problems. When the bars are arranged in descending order of height from left to right with the most frequently occurring cause appearing first, the bar graph is called a pareto diagram. *This diagram is named for its founder, Vilfredo Pareto, an Italian economist.*

the graph (usually the vertical axis). Then, using a bar of fixed width drawn above each class label, we extend the length of the bar until we reach the frequency, relative frequency, or percent frequency of the class. For qualitative data, the bars should be separated to emphasize the fact that each class is separate. Figure 2.1 shows a bar graph of the frequency distribution for the 50 soft drink purchases. Note how the graphical presentation shows Coke Classic, Pepsi, and Diet Coke to be the most preferred brands.

The **pie chart** provides another graphical device for presenting relative frequency and percent frequency distributions for qualitative data. To construct a pie chart, we first draw a circle to represent all of the data. Then we use the relative frequencies to subdivide the circle into sectors, or parts, that correspond to the relative frequency for each class. For example, because a circle contains 360 degrees and Coke Classic shows a relative frequency of .38, the sector of the pie chart labeled Coke Classic consists of .38(360) = 136.8 degrees. The sector of the pie chart labeled Diet Coke consists of .16(360) = 57.6 degrees. Similar calculations for the other classes yield the pie chart in Figure 2.2. The

FIGURE 2.2 PIE CHART OF SOFT DRINK PURCHASES

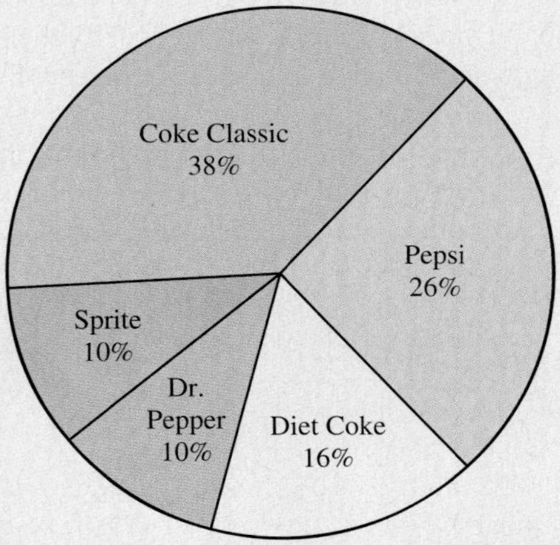

numerical values shown for each sector can be frequencies, relative frequencies, or percent frequencies.

NOTES AND COMMENTS

1. Often the number of classes in a frequency distribution is the same as the number of categories found in the data, as is the case for the soft drink purchase data in this section. The data involve only five soft drinks, and a separate frequency distribution class was defined for each one. Data that included all soft drinks would require many categories, most of which would have a small number of purchases. Most statisticians recommend that classes with smaller frequencies be grouped into an aggregate class called "other." Classes with frequencies of 5% or less would most often be treated in this fashion.

2. The sum of the frequencies in any frequency distribution always equals the number of observations. The sum of the relative frequencies in any relative frequency distribution always equals 1.00, and the sum of the percentages in a percent frequency distribution always equals 100.

Exercises

Methods

1. The response to a question has three alternatives: A, B, and C. A sample of 120 responses provides 60 A, 24 B, and 36 C. Show the frequency and relative frequency distributions.

2. A partial relative frequency distribution is given.

Class	Relative Frequency
A	.22
B	.18
C	.40
D	

   a. What is the relative frequency of class D?
   b. The total sample size is 200. What is the frequency of class D?
   c. Show the frequency distribution.
   d. Show the percent frequency distribution.

SELF test

3. A questionnaire provides 58 Yes, 42 No, and 20 no-opinion answers.
   a. In the construction of a pie chart, how many degrees would be in the section of the pie showing the Yes answers?
   b. How many degrees would be in the section of the pie showing the No answers?
   c. Construct a pie chart.
   d. Construct a bar graph.

Applications

CD file
TVMedia

4. The top four primetime television shows were *CSI, ER, Everybody Loves Raymond,* and *Friends* (*Nielsen Media Research,* January 11, 2004). Data indicating the preferred shows for a sample of 50 viewers follow.

CSI	Friends	CSI	CSI	CSI
CSI	CSI	Raymond	ER	ER
Friends	CSI	ER	Friends	CSI
ER	ER	Friends	CSI	Raymond
CSI	Friends	CSI	CSI	Friends
ER	ER	ER	Friends	Raymond
CSI	Friends	Friends	CSI	Raymond
Friends	Friends	Raymond	Friends	CSI
Raymond	Friends	ER	Friends	CSI
CSI	ER	CSI	Friends	ER

a. Are these data qualitative or quantitative?
b. Provide frequency and percent frequency distributions.
c. Construct a bar graph and a pie chart.
d. On the basis of the sample, which television show has the largest viewing audience? Which one is second?

5. In alphabetical order, the six most common last names in the United States are Brown, Davis, Johnson, Jones, Smith, and Williams (*The World Almanac,* 2006). Assume that a sample of 50 individuals with one of these last names provided the following data.

CD file
Names

Brown	Williams	Williams	Williams	Brown
Smith	Jones	Smith	Johnson	Smith
Davis	Smith	Brown	Williams	Johnson
Johnson	Smith	Smith	Johnson	Brown
Williams	Davis	Johnson	Williams	Johnson
Williams	Johnson	Jones	Smith	Brown
Johnson	Smith	Smith	Brown	Jones
Jones	Jones	Smith	Smith	Davis
Davis	Jones	Williams	Davis	Smith
Jones	Johnson	Brown	Johnson	Davis

Summarize the data by constructing the following:
a. Relative and percent frequency distributions
b. A bar graph
c. A pie chart
d. Based on these data, what are the three most common last names?

6. The Nielsen Media Research television rating measures the percentage of television owners who are watching a particular television program. The highest-rated television program in television history was the *M*A*S*H Last Episode Special* shown on February 28, 1983. A 60.2 rating indicated that 60.2% of all television owners were watching this program. Nielsen Media Research provided the list of the 50 top-rated single shows in television history (*The New York Times Almanac,* 2006). The following data show the television network that produced each of these 50 top-rated shows.

CD file
Networks

ABC	ABC	ABC	NBC	CBS
ABC	CBS	ABC	ABC	NBC
NBC	NBC	CBS	ABC	NBC
CBS	ABC	CBS	NBC	ABC
CBS	NBC	NBC	CBS	NBC
CBS	CBS	CBS	NBC	NBC
FOX	CBS	CBS	ABC	NBC
ABC	ABC	CBS	NBC	NBC
NBC	CBS	NBC	CBS	CBS
ABC	CBS	ABC	NBC	ABC

a. Construct a frequency distribution, percent frequency distribution, and bar graph for the data.

b. Which network or networks have done the best in terms of presenting top-rated television shows? Compare the performance of ABC, CBS, and NBC.

SELF test

7. Leverock's Waterfront Steakhouse in Maderia Beach, Florida, uses a questionnaire to ask customers how they rate the server, food quality, cocktails, prices, and atmosphere at the restaurant. Each characteristic is rated on a scale of outstanding (O), very good (V), good (G), average (A), and poor (P). Use descriptive statistics to summarize the following data collected on food quality. What is your feeling about the food quality ratings at the restaurant?

G	O	V	G	A	O	V	O	V	G	O	V	A
V	O	P	V	O	G	A	O	O	O	G	O	V
V	A	G	O	V	P	V	O	O	G	O	O	V
O	G	A	O	V	O	O	G	V	A	G		

8. Data for a sample of 55 members of the Baseball Hall of Fame in Cooperstown, New York, are shown here. Each observation indicates the primary position played by the Hall of Famers: pitcher (P), catcher (H), 1st base (1), 2nd base (2), 3rd base (3), shortstop (S), left field (L), center field (C), and right field (R).

L	P	C	H	2	P	R	1	S	S	1	L	P	R	P
P	P	P	R	C	S	L	R	P	C	C	P	P	R	P
2	3	P	H	L	P	1	C	P	P	P	S	1	L	R
R	1	2	H	S	3	H	2	L	P					

a. Use frequency and relative frequency distributions to summarize the data.
b. What position provides the most Hall of Famers?
c. What position provides the fewest Hall of Famers?
d. What outfield position (L, C, or R) provides the most Hall of Famers?
e. Compare infielders (1, 2, 3, and S) to outfielders (L, C, and R).

9. About 60% of small and medium-sized businesses are family-owned. A TEC International Inc. survey asked the chief executive officers (CEOs) of family-owned businesses how they became the CEO (*The Wall Street Journal,* December 16, 2003). Responses were that the CEO inherited the business, the CEO built the business, or the CEO was hired by the family-owned firm. A sample of 26 CEOs of family-owned businesses provided the following data on how each became the CEO.

CD file
CEOs

Built	Built	Built	Inherited
Inherited	Built	Inherited	Built
Inherited	Built	Built	Built
Built	Hired	Hired	Hired
Inherited	Inherited	Inherited	Built
Built	Built	Built	Hired
Built	Inherited		

a. Provide a frequency distribution.
b. Provide a percent frequency distribution.
c. Construct a bar graph.
d. What percentage of CEOs of family-owned businesses became the CEO because they inherited the business? What is the primary reason a person becomes the CEO of a family-owned business?

10. Netflix, Inc., of San Jose, California, provides DVD rentals of more than 50,000 titles by mail. Customers go online to create an order list of DVDs they would like to view. Before ordering a particular DVD, the customer may view a description of the DVD and, if desired, a summary of critics' ratings. Netflix uses a five-star rating system with the following descriptions:

1 star	Hated it
2 star	Didn't like it
3 star	Liked it
4 star	Really liked it
5 star	Loved it

Eighteen critics, including Roger Ebert of the *Chicago Sun Times* and Ty Burr of the *Boston Globe,* provided ratings for the movie *Batman Begins* (Netflix.com, March 1, 2006). The ratings for *Batman Begins* were as follows:

4, 2, 5, 2, 4, 3, 3, 4, 4, 3, 4, 4, 4, 2, 4, 4, 5, 4

a. Comment on why these data are qualitative.
b. Provide a frequency distribution and relative frequency distribution for the data.
c. Provide a bar graph.
d. Comment on the critics' evaluation of *Batman Begins.*

2.2 Summarizing Quantitative Data

Frequency Distribution

TABLE 2.4

YEAR-END AUDIT TIMES (IN DAYS)

12	14	19	18
15	15	18	17
20	27	22	23
22	21	33	28
14	18	16	13

As defined in Section 2.1, a frequency distribution is a tabular summary of data showing the number (frequency) of items in each of several nonoverlapping classes. This definition holds for quantitative as well as qualitative data. However, with quantitative data we must be more careful in defining the nonoverlapping classes to be used in the frequency distribution.

For example, consider the quantitative data in Table 2.4. These data show the time in days required to complete year-end audits for a sample of 20 clients of Sanderson and Clifford, a small public accounting firm. The three steps necessary to define the classes for a frequency distribution with quantitative data are:

1. Determine the number of nonoverlapping classes.
2. Determine the width of each class.
3. Determine the class limits.

CD file

Audit

Let us demonstrate these steps by developing a frequency distribution for the audit time data in Table 2.4.

Number of classes Classes are formed by specifying ranges that will be used to group the data. As a general guideline, we recommend using between 5 and 20 classes. For a small number of data items, as few as five or six classes may be used to summarize the data. For a larger number of data items, a larger number of classes is usually required. The goal is to use enough classes to show the variation in the data, but not so many classes that some contain only a few data items. Because the number of data items in Table 2.4 is relatively small ($n = 20$), we chose to develop a frequency distribution with five classes.

Making the classes the same width reduces the chance of inappropriate interpretations by the user.

Width of the classes The second step in constructing a frequency distribution for quantitative data is to choose a width for the classes. As a general guideline, we recommend that the width be the same for each class. Thus the choices of the number of classes and the width of classes are not independent decisions. A larger number of classes means a smaller class width, and vice versa. To determine an approximate class width, we begin by identifying the largest and smallest data values. Then, with the desired number of classes specified, we can use the following expression to determine the approximate class width.

$$\text{Approximate class width} = \frac{\text{Largest data value} - \text{Smallest data value}}{\text{Number of classes}} \tag{2.2}$$

The approximate class width given by equation (2.2) can be rounded to a more convenient value based on the preference of the person developing the frequency distribution. For example, an approximate class width of 9.28 might be rounded to 10 simply because 10 is a more convenient class width to use in presenting a frequency distribution.

For the data involving the year-end audit times, the largest data value is 33 and the smallest data value is 12. Because we decided to summarize the data with five classes, using equation (2.2) provides an approximate class width of $(33 - 12)/5 = 4.2$. We therefore decided to round up and use a class width of five days in the frequency distribution.

No single frequency distribution is best for a data set. Different people may construct different, but equally acceptable, frequency distributions. The goal is to reveal the natural grouping and variation in the data.

In practice, the number of classes and the appropriate class width are determined by trial and error. Once a possible number of classes is chosen, equation (2.2) is used to find the approximate class width. The process can be repeated for a different number of classes. Ultimately, the analyst uses judgment to determine the combination of the number of classes and class width that provides the best frequency distribution for summarizing the data.

For the audit time data in Table 2.4, after deciding to use five classes, each with a width of five days, the next task is to specify the class limits for each of the classes.

Class limits Class limits must be chosen so that each data item belongs to one and only one class. The *lower class limit* identifies the smallest possible data value assigned to the class. The *upper class limit* identifies the largest possible data value assigned to the class. In developing frequency distributions for qualitative data, we did not need to specify class limits because each data item naturally fell into a separate class. But with quantitative data, such as the audit times in Table 2.4, class limits are necessary to determine where each data value belongs.

Using the audit time data in Table 2.4, we selected 10 days as the lower class limit and 14 days as the upper class limit for the first class. This class is denoted 10–14 in Table 2.5. The smallest data value, 12, is included in the 10–14 class. We then selected 15 days as the lower class limit and 19 days as the upper class limit of the next class. We continued defining the lower and upper class limits to obtain a total of five classes: 10–14, 15–19, 20–24, 25–29, and 30–34. The largest data value, 33, is included in the 30–34 class. The difference between the lower class limits of adjacent classes is the class width. Using the first two lower class limits of 10 and 15, we see that the class width is $15 - 10 = 5$.

TABLE 2.5 FREQUENCY DISTRIBUTION FOR THE AUDIT TIME DATA

Audit Time (days)	Frequency
10–14	4
15–19	8
20–24	5
25–29	2
30–34	1
Total	20

With the number of classes, class width, and class limits determined, a frequency distribution can be obtained by counting the number of data values belonging to each class. For example, the data in Table 2.4 show that four values—12, 14, 14, and 13—belong to the 10–14 class. Thus, the frequency for the 10–14 class is 4. Continuing this counting process for the 15–19, 20–24, 25–29, and 30–34 classes provides the frequency distribution in Table 2.5. Using this frequency distribution, we can observe the following:

1. The most frequently occurring audit times are in the class of 15–19 days. Eight of the 20 audit times belong to this class.
2. Only one audit required 30 or more days.

Other conclusions are possible, depending on the interests of the person viewing the frequency distribution. The value of a frequency distribution is that it provides insights about the data that are not easily obtained by viewing the data in their original unorganized form.

Class midpoint In some applications, we want to know the midpoints of the classes in a frequency distribution for quantitative data. The **class midpoint** is the value halfway between the lower and upper class limits. For the audit time data, the five class midpoints are 12, 17, 22, 27, and 32.

Relative Frequency and Percent Frequency Distributions

We define the relative frequency and percent frequency distributions for quantitative data in the same manner as for qualitative data. First, recall that the relative frequency is the proportion of the observations belonging to a class. With n observations,

$$\text{Relative frequency of class} = \frac{\text{Frequency of the class}}{n}$$

The percent frequency of a class is the relative frequency multiplied by 100.

Based on the class frequencies in Table 2.5 and with $n = 20$, Table 2.6 shows the relative frequency distribution and percent frequency distribution for the audit time data. Note that .40

TABLE 2.6 RELATIVE FREQUENCY AND PERCENT FREQUENCY DISTRIBUTIONS FOR THE AUDIT TIME DATA

Audit Time (days)	Relative Frequency	Percent Frequency
10–14	.20	20
15–19	.40	40
20–24	.25	25
25–29	.10	10
30–34	.05	5
Total	1.00	100

of the audits, or 40%, required from 15 to 19 days. Only .05 of the audits, or 5%, required 30 or more days. Again, additional interpretations and insights can be obtained by using Table 2.6.

Dot Plot

One of the simplest graphical summaries of data is a **dot plot**. A horizontal axis shows the range for the data. Each data value is represented by a dot placed above the axis. Figure 2.3 is the dot plot for the audit time data in Table 2.4. The three dots located above 18 on the horizontal axis indicate that an audit time of 18 days occurred three times. Dot plots show the details of the data and are useful for comparing the distribution of the data for two or more variables.

Histogram

A common graphical presentation of quantitative data is a **histogram**. This graphical summary can be prepared for data previously summarized in either a frequency, relative frequency, or percent frequency distribution. A histogram is constructed by placing the variable of interest on the horizontal axis and the frequency, relative frequency, or percent frequency on the vertical axis. The frequency, relative frequency, or percent frequency of each class is shown by drawing a rectangle whose base is determined by the class limits on the horizontal axis and whose height is the corresponding frequency, relative frequency, or percent frequency.

Figure 2.4 is a histogram for the audit time data. Note that the class with the greatest frequency is shown by the rectangle appearing above the class of 15–19 days. The height of the rectangle shows that the frequency of this class is 8. A histogram for the relative or percent frequency distribution of these data would look the same as the histogram in Figure 2.4 with the exception that the vertical axis would be labeled with relative or percent frequency values.

As Figure 2.4 shows, the adjacent rectangles of a histogram touch one another. Unlike a bar graph, a histogram contains no natural separation between the rectangles of adjacent classes. This format is the usual convention for histograms. Because the classes for the audit

FIGURE 2.3 DOT PLOT FOR THE AUDIT TIME DATA

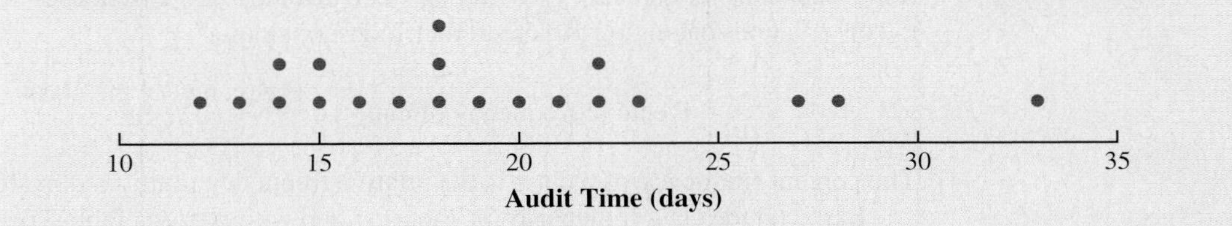

FIGURE 2.4 HISTOGRAM FOR THE AUDIT TIME DATA

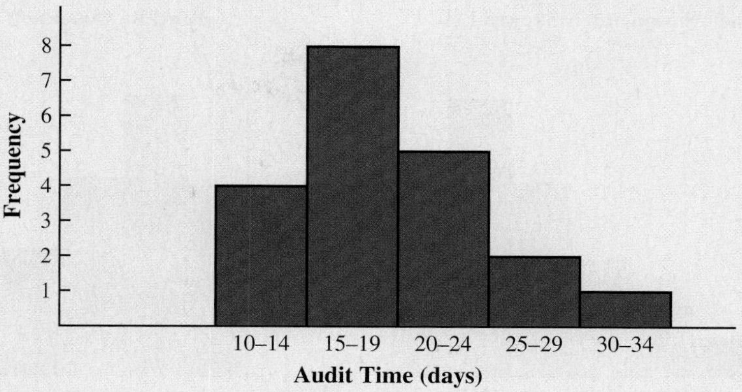

time data are stated as 10–14, 15–19, 20–24, 25–29, and 30–34, one-unit spaces of 14 to 15, 19 to 20, 24 to 25, and 29 to 30 would seem to be needed between the classes. These spaces are eliminated when constructing a histogram. Eliminating the spaces between classes in a histogram for the audit time data helps show that all values between the lower limit of the first class and the upper limit of the last class are possible.

One of the most important uses of a histogram is to provide information about the shape, or form, of a distribution. Figure 2.5 contains four histograms constructed from relative frequency distributions. Panel A shows the histogram for a set of data moderately skewed to the left. A histogram is said to be skewed to the left if its tail extends farther to the left. This histogram is typical for exam scores, with no scores above 100%, most of the scores above 70%, and only a few really low scores. Panel B shows the histogram for a set of data moderately skewed to the right. A histogram is said to be skewed to the right if its tail extends farther to the right. An example of this type of histogram would be for data such as housing prices; a few expensive houses create the skewness in the right tail.

Panel C shows a symmetric histogram. In a symmetric histogram, the left tail mirrors the shape of the right tail. Histograms for data found in applications are never perfectly symmetric, but the histogram for many applications may be roughly symmetric. Data for SAT scores, heights and weights of people, and so on lead to histograms that are roughly symmetric. Panel D shows a histogram highly skewed to the right. This histogram was constructed from data on the amount of customer purchases over one day at a women's apparel store. Data from applications in business and economics often lead to histograms that are skewed to the right. For instance, data on housing prices, salaries, purchase amounts, and so on often result in histograms skewed to the right.

Cumulative Distributions

A variation of the frequency distribution that provides another tabular summary of quantitative data is the **cumulative frequency distribution**. The cumulative frequency distribution uses the number of classes, class widths, and class limits developed for the frequency distribution. However, rather than showing the frequency of each class, the cumulative frequency distribution shows the number of data items with values *less than or equal to the upper class limit* of each class. The first two columns of Table 2.7 provide the cumulative frequency distribution for the audit time data.

FIGURE 2.5 HISTOGRAMS SHOWING DIFFERING LEVELS OF SKEWNESS

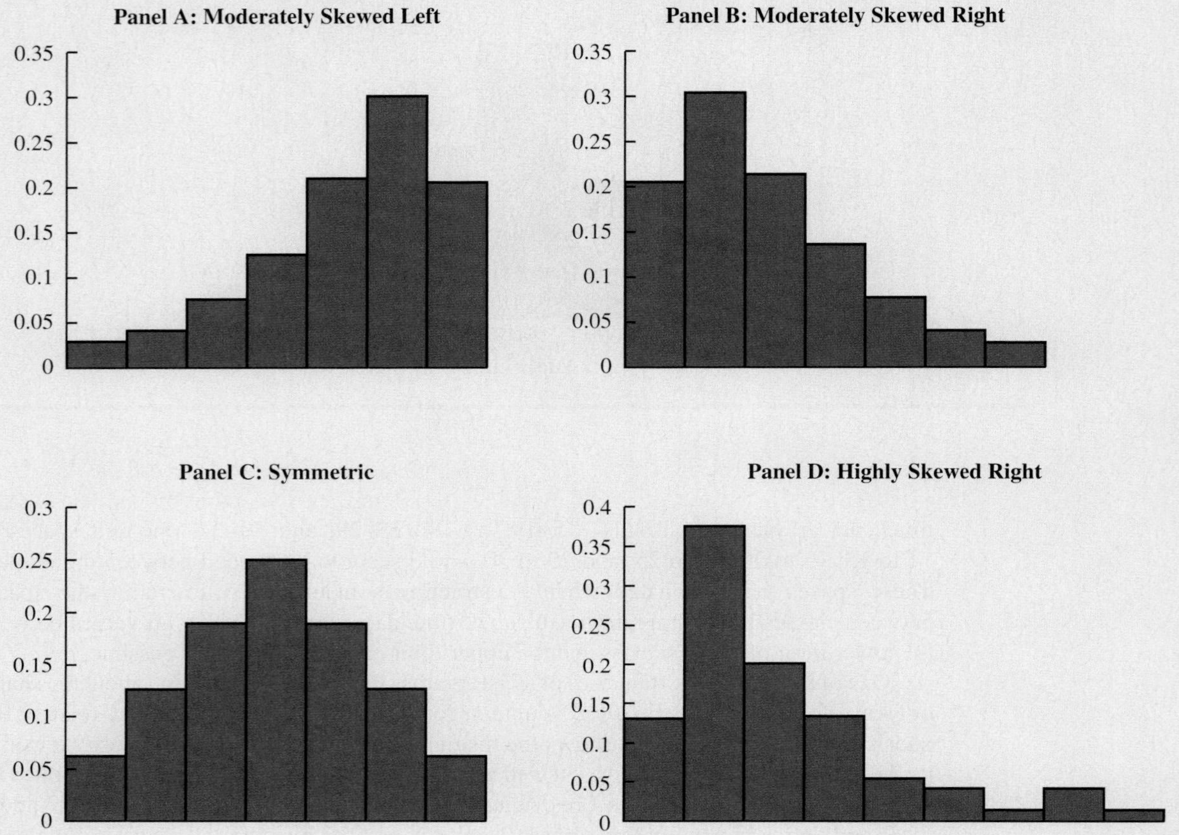

To understand how the cumulative frequencies are determined, consider the class with the description "less than or equal to 24." The cumulative frequency for this class is simply the sum of the frequencies for all classes with data values less than or equal to 24. For the frequency distribution in Table 2.5, the sum of the frequencies for classes 10–14, 15–19, and 20–24 indicates that $4 + 8 + 5 = 17$ data values are less than or equal to 24. Hence,

TABLE 2.7 CUMULATIVE FREQUENCY, CUMULATIVE RELATIVE FREQUENCY, AND CUMULATIVE PERCENT FREQUENCY DISTRIBUTIONS FOR THE AUDIT TIME DATA

Audit Time (days)	Cumulative Frequency	Cumulative Relative Frequency	Cumulative Percent Frequency
Less than or equal to 14	4	.20	20
Less than or equal to 19	12	.60	60
Less than or equal to 24	17	.85	85
Less than or equal to 29	19	.95	95
Less than or equal to 34	20	1.00	100

the cumulative frequency for this class is 17. In addition, the cumulative frequency distribution in Table 2.7 shows that four audits were completed in 14 days or less and 19 audits were completed in 29 days or less.

As a final point, we note that a **cumulative relative frequency distribution** shows the proportion of data items, and a **cumulative percent frequency distribution** shows the percentage of data items with values less than or equal to the upper limit of each class. The cumulative relative frequency distribution can be computed either by summing the relative frequencies in the relative frequency distribution or by dividing the cumulative frequencies by the total number of items. Using the latter approach, we found the cumulative relative frequencies in column 3 of Table 2.7 by dividing the cumulative frequencies in column 2 by the total number of items ($n = 20$). The cumulative percent frequencies were again computed by multiplying the relative frequencies by 100. The cumulative relative and percent frequency distributions show that .85 of the audits, or 85%, were completed in 24 days or less, .95 of the audits, or 95%, were completed in 29 days or less, and so on.

Ogive

A graph of a cumulative distribution, called an **ogive**, shows data values on the horizontal axis and either the cumulative frequencies, the cumulative relative frequencies, or the cumulative percent frequencies on the vertical axis. Figure 2.6 illustrates an ogive for the cumulative frequencies of the audit time data in Table 2.7.

The ogive is constructed by plotting a point corresponding to the cumulative frequency of each class. Because the classes for the audit time data are 10–14, 15–19, 20–24, and so on, one-unit gaps appear from 14 to 15, 19 to 20, and so on. These gaps are eliminated by plotting points halfway between the class limits. Thus, 14.5 is used for the 10–14 class, 19.5 is used for the 15–19 class, and so on. The "less than or equal to 14" class with a cumulative frequency of 4 is shown on the ogive in Figure 2.6 by the point located at 14.5 on the horizontal axis and 4 on the vertical axis. The "less than or equal to 19" class with a cumulative frequency of 12 is shown by the point located at 19.5 on the horizontal axis and 12 on the vertical axis. Note that one additional point is plotted at the left end of the ogive. This point starts the ogive by showing that no data values fall below the 10–14 class. It is plotted at 9.5 on the horizontal axis and 0 on the vertical axis. The plotted points are connected by straight lines to complete the ogive.

FIGURE 2.6 OGIVE FOR THE AUDIT TIME DATA

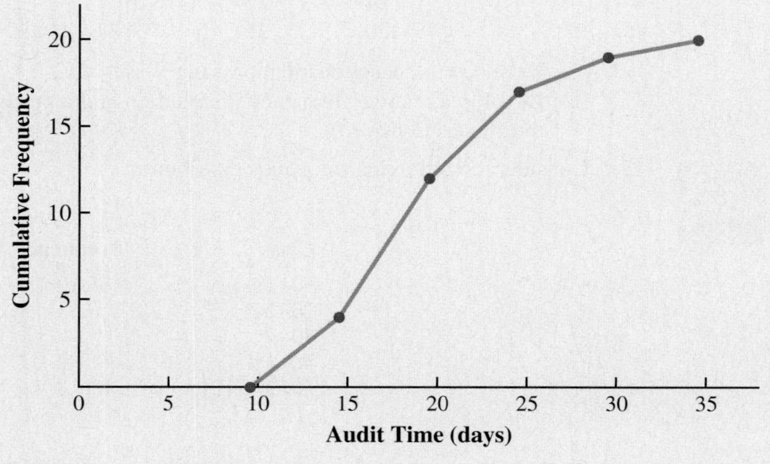

NOTES AND COMMENTS

1. A bar graph and a histogram are essentially the same thing; both are graphical presentations of the data in a frequency distribution. A histogram is just a bar graph with no separation between bars. For some discrete quantitative data, a separation between bars is also appropriate. Consider, for example, the number of classes in which a college student is enrolled. The data may only assume integer values. Intermediate values such as 1.5, 2.73, and so on are not possible. With continuous quantitative data, however, such as the audit times in Table 2.4, a separation between bars is not appropriate.
2. The appropriate values for the class limits with quantitative data depend on the level of accuracy of the data. For instance, with the audit time data of Table 2.4 the limits used were integer values. If the data were rounded to the nearest tenth of a day (e.g., 12.3, 14.4, and so on), then the limits would be stated in tenths of days. For instance, the first class would be 10.0–14.9. If the data were recorded to the nearest hundredth of a day (e.g., 12.34, 14.45, and so on), the limits would be stated in hundredths of days. For instance, the first class would be 10.00–14.99.
3. An *open-end* class requires only a lower class limit or an upper class limit. For example, in the audit time data of Table 2.4, suppose two of the audits had taken 58 and 65 days. Rather than continue with the classes of width 5 with classes 35–39, 40–44, 45–49, and so on, we could simplify the frequency distribution to show an open-end class of "35 or more." This class would have a frequency of 2. Most often the open-end class appears at the upper end of the distribution. Sometimes an open-end class appears at the lower end of the distribution, and occasionally such classes appear at both ends.
4. The last entry in a cumulative frequency distribution always equals the total number of observations. The last entry in a cumulative relative frequency distribution always equals 1.00 and the last entry in a cumulative percent frequency distribution always equals 100.

Exercises

Methods

CD file
Frequency

11. Consider the following data.

14	21	23	21	16
19	22	25	16	16
24	24	25	19	16
19	18	19	21	12
16	17	18	23	25
20	23	16	20	19
24	26	15	22	24
20	22	24	22	20

a. Develop a frequency distribution using classes of 12–14, 15–17, 18–20, 21–23, and 24–26.
b. Develop a relative frequency distribution and a percent frequency distribution using the classes in part (a).

SELF test

12. Consider the following frequency distribution.

Class	Frequency
10–19	10
20–29	14
30–39	17
40–49	7
50–59	2

Construct a cumulative frequency distribution and a cumulative relative frequency distribution.

13. Construct a histogram and an ogive for the data in exercise 12.

14. Consider the following data.

8.9	10.2	11.5	7.8	10.0	12.2	13.5	14.1	10.0	12.2
6.8	9.5	11.5	11.2	14.9	7.5	10.0	6.0	15.8	11.5

a. Construct a dot plot.
b. Construct a frequency distribution.
c. Construct a percent frequency distribution.

Applications

SELF test

15. A doctor's office staff studied the waiting times for patients who arrive at the office with a request for emergency service. The following data with waiting times in minutes were collected over a one-month period.

2 5 10 12 4 4 5 17 11 8 9 8 12 21 6 8 7 13 18 3

Use classes of 0–4, 5–9, and so on in the following:
a. Show the frequency distribution.
b. Show the relative frequency distribution.
c. Show the cumulative frequency distribution.
d. Show the cumulative relative frequency distribution.
e. What proportion of patients needing emergency service wait 9 minutes or less?

16. Consider the following two frequency distributions. The first frequency distribution provides an approximation of the annual adjusted gross income in the United States (Internal Revenue Service, March 2003). The second frequency distribution shows exam scores for students in a college statistics course.

Income ($1000s)	Frequency (millions)	Exam Score	Frequency
0–24	60	20–29	2
25–49	33	30–39	5
50–74	20	40–49	6
75–99	6	50–59	13
100–124	4	60–69	32
125–149	2	70–79	78
150–174	1	80–89	43
175–199	1	90–99	21
Total	127	Total	200

a. Develop a histogram for the annual income data. What evidence of skewness does it show? Does this skewness make sense? Explain.
b. Develop a histogram for the exam score data. What evidence of skewness does it show? Explain.
c. Develop a histogram for the data in exercise 11. What evidence of skewness does it show? What is the general shape of the distribution?

17. What is the typical price for a share of stock for the 30 Dow Jones Industrial Average companies? The following data show the price for a share of stock to the nearest dollar in January 2006 (*The Wall Street Journal,* January 16, 2006).

CD file
PriceShare

Company	$/Share	Company	$/Share
AIG	70	Home Depot	42
Alcoa	29	Honeywell	37
Altria Group	76	IBM	83
American Express	53	Intel	26
AT&T	25	Johnson & Johnson	62
Boeing	69	JPMorgan Chase	40
Caterpillar	62	McDonald's	35
Citigroup	49	Merck	33
Coca-Cola	41	Microsoft	27
Disney	26	3M	78
DuPont	40	Pfizer	25
ExxonMobil	61	Procter & Gamble	59
General Electric	35	United Technologies	56
General Motors	20	Verizon	32
Hewlett-Packard	32	Wal-Mart	45

a. Prepare a frequency distribution of the data.
b. Prepare a histogram of the data. Interpret the histogram, including a discussion of the general shape of the histogram, the mid-price per share range, the most frequent price per share range, and the high and low extreme prices per share.
c. What are the highest-priced and the lowest-priced stocks?
d. Use *The Wall Street Journal* to find the current price per share for these companies. Prepare a histogram of the data and discuss any changes since January 2006.

18. NRF/BIG research provided results of a consumer holiday spending survey (*USA Today,* December 20, 2005). The following data provide the dollar amount of holiday spending for a sample of 25 consumers.

CD file
Holiday

1200	850	740	590	340
450	890	260	610	350
1780	180	850	2050	770
800	1090	510	520	220
1450	280	1120	200	350

a. What is the lowest holiday spending? The highest?
b. Use a class width of $250 to prepare a frequency distribution and a percent frequency distribution for the data.
c. Prepare a histogram and comment on the shape of the distribution.
d. What observations can you make about holiday spending?

19. Sorting through unsolicited e-mail and spam affects the productivity of office workers. An InsightExpress survey monitored office workers to determine the unproductive time per day devoted to unsolicited e-mail and spam (*USA Today,* November 13, 2003). The following data show a sample of time in minutes devoted to this task.

2	4	8	4
8	1	2	32
12	1	5	7
5	5	3	4
24	19	4	14

Summarize the data by constructing the following:
a. A frequency distribution (Classes 1–5, 6–10, 11–15, 16–20, and so on)
b. A relative frequency distribution
c. A cumulative frequency distribution

d. A cumulative relative frequency distribution
e. An ogive
f. What percentage of office workers spend 5 minutes or less on unsolicited e-mail and spam? What percentage of office workers spend more than 10 minutes a day on this task?

20. The top 20 concert tours and their average ticket price for shows in North America are shown here. The list is based on data provided to the trade publication *Pollstar* by concert promoters and venue managers (*Associated Press,* November 21, 2003).

CD file Concerts

Concert Tour	Ticket Price	Concert Tour	Ticket Price
Bruce Springsteen	$72.40	Toby Keith	$37.76
Dave Matthews Band	44.11	James Taylor	44.93
Aerosmith/KISS	69.52	Alabama	40.83
Shania Twain	61.80	Harper/Johnson	33.70
Fleetwood Mac	78.34	50 Cent	38.89
Radiohead	39.50	Steely Dan	36.38
Cher	64.47	Red Hot Chili Peppers	56.82
Counting Crows	36.48	R.E.M.	46.16
Timberlake/Aguilera	74.43	American Idols Live	39.11
Mana	46.48	Mariah Carey	56.08

Summarize the data by constructing the following:
a. A frequency distribution and a percent frequency distribution
b. A histogram
c. What concert had the most expensive average ticket price? What concert had the least expensive average ticket price?
d. Comment on what the data indicate about the average ticket prices of the top concert tours.

21. The *Nielsen Home Technology Report* provided information about home technology and its usage. The following data are the hours of personal computer usage during one week for a sample of 50 persons.

CD file Computer

4.1	1.5	10.4	5.9	3.4	5.7	1.6	6.1	3.0	3.7
3.1	4.8	2.0	14.8	5.4	4.2	3.9	4.1	11.1	3.5
4.1	4.1	8.8	5.6	4.3	3.3	7.1	10.3	6.2	7.6
10.8	2.8	9.5	12.9	12.1	0.7	4.0	9.2	4.4	5.7
7.2	6.1	5.7	5.9	4.7	3.9	3.7	3.1	6.1	3.1

Summarize the data by constructing the following:
a. A frequency distribution (use a class width of three hours)
b. A relative frequency distribution
c. A histogram
d. An ogive
e. Comment on what the data indicate about personal computer usage at home.

2.3 Exploratory Data Analysis: The Stem-and-Leaf Display

The techniques of **exploratory data analysis** consist of simple arithmetic and easy-to-draw graphs that can be used to summarize data quickly. One technique—referred to as a **stem-and-leaf display**—can be used to show both the rank order and shape of a data set simultaneously.

TABLE 2.8 NUMBER OF QUESTIONS ANSWERED CORRECTLY ON AN APTITUDE TEST

CD file
ApTest

112	72	69	97	107
73	92	76	86	73
126	128	118	127	124
82	104	132	134	83
92	108	96	100	92
115	76	91	102	81
95	141	81	80	106
84	119	113	98	75
68	98	115	106	95
100	85	94	106	119

To illustrate the use of a stem-and-leaf display, consider the data in Table 2.8. These data result from a 150-question aptitude test given to 50 individuals recently interviewed for a position at Haskens Manufacturing. The data indicate the number of questions answered correctly.

To develop a stem-and-leaf display, we first arrange the leading digits of each data value to the left of a vertical line. To the right of the vertical line, we record the last digit for each data value. Based on the top row of data in Table 2.8 (112, 72, 69, 97, and 107), the first five entries in constructing a stem-and-leaf display would be as follows:

6	9
7	2
8	
9	7
10	7
11	2
12	
13	
14	

For example, the data value 112 shows the leading digits 11 to the left of the line and the last digit 2 to the right of the line. Similarly, the data value 72 shows the leading digit 7 to the left of the line and last digit 2 to the right of the line. Continuing to place the last digit of each data value on the line corresponding to its leading digit(s) provides the following:

6	9 8
7	2 3 6 3 6 5
8	6 2 3 1 1 0 4 5
9	7 2 2 6 2 1 5 8 8 5 4
10	7 4 8 0 2 6 6 0 6
11	2 8 5 9 3 5 9
12	6 8 7 4
13	2 4
14	1

With this organization of the data, sorting the digits on each line into rank order is simple. Doing so provides the stem-and-leaf display shown here.

6	8 9
7	2 3 3 5 6 6
8	0 1 1 2 3 4 5 6
9	1 2 2 2 4 5 5 6 7 8 8
10	0 0 2 4 6 6 6 7 8
11	2 3 5 5 8 9 9
12	4 6 7 8
13	2 4
14	1

The numbers to the left of the vertical line (6, 7, 8, 9, 10, 11, 12, 13, and 14) form the *stem*, and each digit to the right of the vertical line is a *leaf*. For example, consider the first row with a stem value of 6 and leaves of 8 and 9.

6 | 8 9

This row indicates that two data values have a first digit of six. The leaves show that the data values are 68 and 69. Similarly, the second row

7 | 2 3 3 5 6 6

indicates that six data values have a first digit of seven. The leaves show that the data values are 72, 73, 73, 75, 76, and 76.

To focus on the shape indicated by the stem-and-leaf display, let us use a rectangle to contain the leaves of each stem. Doing so, we obtain the following.

6	8 9
7	2 3 3 5 6 6
8	0 1 1 2 3 4 5 6
9	1 2 2 2 4 5 5 6 7 8 8
10	0 0 2 4 6 6 6 7 8
11	2 3 5 5 8 9 9
12	4 6 7 8
13	2 4
14	1

Rotating this page counterclockwise onto its side provides a picture of the data that is similar to a histogram with classes of 60–69, 70–79, 80–89, and so on.

Although the stem-and-leaf display may appear to offer the same information as a histogram, it has two primary advantages.

1. The stem-and-leaf display is easier to construct by hand.
2. Within a class interval, the stem-and-leaf display provides more information than the histogram because the stem-and-leaf shows the actual data.

Just as a frequency distribution or histogram has no absolute number of classes, neither does a stem-and-leaf display have an absolute number of rows or stems. If we believe that our original stem-and-leaf display condensed the data too much, we can easily stretch the display by using two or more stems for each leading digit. For example, to use two stems for each leading digit,

In a stretched stem-and-leaf display, whenever a stem value is stated twice, the first value corresponds to leaf values of 0–4, and the second value corresponds to leaf values of 5–9.

we would place all data values ending in 0, 1, 2, 3, and 4 in one row and all values ending in 5, 6, 7, 8, and 9 in a second row. The following stretched stem-and-leaf display illustrates this approach.

```
 6 | 8 9
 7 | 2 3 3
 7 | 5 6 6
 8 | 0 1 1 2 3 4
 8 | 5 6
 9 | 1 2 2 2 4
 9 | 5 5 6 7 8 8
10 | 0 0 2 4
10 | 6 6 6 7 8
11 | 2 3
11 | 5 5 8 9 9
12 | 4
12 | 6 7 8
13 | 2 4
13 |
14 | 1
```

Note that values 72, 73, and 73 have leaves in the 0–4 range and are shown with the first stem value of 7. The values 75, 76, and 76 have leaves in the 5–9 range and are shown with the second stem value of 7. This stretched stem-and-leaf display is similar to a frequency distribution with intervals of 65–69, 70–74, 75–79, and so on.

The preceding example showed a stem-and-leaf display for data with as many as three digits. Stem-and-leaf displays for data with more than three digits are possible. For example, consider the following data on the number of hamburgers sold by a fast-food restaurant for each of 15 weeks.

1565	1852	1644	1766	1888	1912	2044	1812
1790	1679	2008	1852	1967	1954	1733	

A stem-and-leaf display of these data follows.

```
Leaf unit = 10
15 | 6
16 | 4 7
17 | 3 6 9
18 | 1 5 5 8
19 | 1 5 6
20 | 0 4
```

A single digit is used to define each leaf in a stem-and-leaf display. The leaf unit indicates how to multiply the stem-and-leaf numbers in order to approximate the original data. Leaf units may be 100, 10, 1, 0.1, and so on.

Note that a single digit is used to define each leaf and that only the first three digits of each data value have been used to construct the display. At the top of the display we have specified Leaf unit = 10. To illustrate how to interpret the values in the display, consider the first stem, 15, and its associated leaf, 6. Combining these numbers, we obtain 156. To reconstruct an approximation of the original data value, we must multiply this number by 10, the value of the *leaf unit*. Thus, $156 \times 10 = 1560$ is an approximation of the original data value used to construct the stem-and-leaf display. Although it is not possible to reconstruct the exact data value from this stem-and-leaf display, the convention of using a single digit for each leaf enables stem-and-leaf displays to be constructed for data having a large number of digits. For stem-and-leaf displays where the leaf unit is not shown, the leaf unit is assumed to equal 1.

Exercises

Methods

22. Construct a stem-and-leaf display for the following data.

70	72	75	64	58	83	80	82
76	75	68	65	57	78	85	72

SELF test

23. Construct a stem-and-leaf display for the following data.

11.3	9.6	10.4	7.5	8.3	10.5	10.0
9.3	8.1	7.7	7.5	8.4	6.3	8.8

24. Construct a stem-and-leaf display for the following data. Use a leaf unit of 10.

1161	1206	1478	1300	1604	1725	1361	1422
1221	1378	1623	1426	1557	1730	1706	1689

Applications

SELF test

25. A psychologist developed a new test of adult intelligence. The test was administered to 20 individuals, and the following data were obtained.

114	99	131	124	117	102	106	127	119	115
98	104	144	151	132	106	125	122	118	118

Construct a stem-and-leaf display for the data.

26. The American Association of Individual Investors conducts an annual survey of discount brokers. The following prices charged are from a sample of 24 discount brokers (*AAII Journal,* January 2003). The two types of trades are a broker-assisted trade of 100 shares at $50 per share and an online trade of 500 shares at $50 per share.

CD file
Broker

Broker	Broker-Assisted 100 Shares at $50/Share	Online 500 Shares at $50/Share	Broker	Broker-Assisted 100 Shares at $50/Share	Online 500 Shares at $50/Share
Accutrade	30.00	29.95	Merrill Lynch Direct	50.00	29.95
Ameritrade	24.99	10.99	Muriel Siebert	45.00	14.95
Banc of America	54.00	24.95	NetVest	24.00	14.00
Brown & Co.	17.00	5.00	Recom Securities	35.00	12.95
Charles Schwab	55.00	29.95	Scottrade	17.00	7.00
CyberTrader	12.95	9.95	Sloan Securities	39.95	19.95
E*TRADE Securities	49.95	14.95	Strong Investments	55.00	24.95
First Discount	35.00	19.75	TD Waterhouse	45.00	17.95
Freedom Investments	25.00	15.00	T. Rowe Price	50.00	19.95
Harrisdirect	40.00	20.00	Vanguard	48.00	20.00
Investors National	39.00	62.50	Wall Street Discount	29.95	19.95
MB Trading	9.95	10.55	York Securities	40.00	36.00

a. Round the trading prices to the nearest dollar and develop a stem-and-leaf display for 100 shares at $50 per share. Comment on what you learned about broker-assisted trading prices.

b. Round the trading prices to the nearest dollar and develop a stretched stem-and-leaf display for 500 shares online at $50 per share. Comment on what you learned about online trading prices.

27. Most major ski resorts offer family programs that provide ski and snowboarding instruction for children. The typical classes provide four to six hours on the snow with a certified instructor. The daily rate for a group lesson at 15 ski resorts follows (*The Wall Street Journal,* January 20, 2006).

Resort	Location	Daily Rate	Resort	Location	Daily Rate
Beaver Creek	Colorado	$ 137	Okemo	Vermont	$ 86
Deer Valley	Utah	115	Park City	Utah	145
Diamond Peak	California	95	Butternut	Massachusetts	75
Heavenly	California	145	Steamboat	Colorado	98
Hunter	New York	79	Stowe	Vermont	104
Mammoth	California	111	Sugar Bowl	California	100
Mount Sunapee	New Hampshire	96	Whistler-Blackcomb	British Columbia	104
Mount Bachelor	Oregon	83			

a. Develop a stem-and-leaf display for the data.
b. Interpret the stem-and-leaf display in terms of what it tells you about the daily rate for these ski and snowboarding instruction programs.

28. The 2004 Naples, Florida, mini marathon (13.1 miles) had 1228 registrants (*Naples Daily News,* January 17, 2004). Competition was held in six age groups. The following data show the ages for a sample of 40 individuals who participated in the marathon.

CD file
Marathon

49	33	40	37	56
44	46	57	55	32
50	52	43	64	40
46	24	30	37	43
31	43	50	36	61
27	44	35	31	43
52	43	66	31	50
72	26	59	21	47

a. Show a stretched stem-and-leaf display.
b. What age group had the largest number of runners?
c. What age occurred most frequently?
d. A *Naples Daily News* feature article emphasized the number of runners who were "20-something." What percentage of the runners were in the 20-something age group? What do you suppose was the focus of the article?

2.4 Crosstabulations and Scatter Diagrams

Crosstabulations and scatter diagrams are used to summarize data in a way that reveals the relationship between two variables.

Thus far in this chapter, we have focused on tabular and graphical methods used to summarize the data for *one variable at a time.* Often a manager or decision maker requires tabular and graphical methods that will assist in the understanding of the *relationship between two variables.* Crosstabulation and scatter diagrams are two such methods.

Crosstabulation

A **crosstabulation** is a tabular summary of data for two variables. Let us illustrate the use of a crosstabulation by considering the following application based on data from Zagat's Restaurant Review. The quality rating and the meal price data were collected for a sample of 300 restaurants located in the Los Angeles area. Table 2.9 shows the data for the first 10 restaurants. Data on a restaurant's quality rating and typical meal price are reported. Quality rating is a qualitative variable with rating categories of good, very good, and excellent. Meal price is a quantitative variable that ranges from $10 to $49.

A crosstabulation of the data for this application is shown in Table 2.10. The left and top margin labels define the classes for the two variables. In the left margin, the row labels (good, very good, and excellent) correspond to the three classes of the quality rating variable. In the top margin, the column labels ($10–19, $20–29, $30–39, and $40–49) correspond to

TABLE 2.9 QUALITY RATING AND MEAL PRICE FOR 300 LOS ANGELES RESTAURANTS

CD file
Restaurant

Restaurant	Quality Rating	Meal Price ($)
1	Good	18
2	Very Good	22
3	Good	28
4	Excellent	38
5	Very Good	33
6	Good	28
7	Very Good	19
8	Very Good	11
9	Very Good	23
10	Good	13
⋮	⋮	⋮

the four classes of the meal price variable. Each restaurant in the sample provides a quality rating and a meal price. Thus, each restaurant in the sample is associated with a cell appearing in one of the rows and one of the columns of the crosstabulation. For example, restaurant 5 is identified as having a very good quality rating and a meal price of $33. This restaurant belongs to the cell in row 2 and column 3 of Table 2.10. In constructing a crosstabulation, we simply count the number of restaurants that belong to each of the cells in the crosstabulation table.

In reviewing Table 2.10, we see that the greatest number of restaurants in the sample (64) have a very good rating and a meal price in the $20–29 range. Only two restaurants have an excellent rating and a meal price in the $10–19 range. Similar interpretations of the other frequencies can be made. In addition, note that the right and bottom margins of the crosstabulation provide the frequency distributions for quality rating and meal price separately. From the frequency distribution in the right margin, we see that data on quality ratings show 84 good restaurants, 150 very good restaurants, and 66 excellent restaurants. Similarly, the bottom margin shows the frequency distribution for the meal price variable.

Dividing the totals in the right margin of the crosstabulation by the total for that column provides a relative and percent frequency distribution for the quality rating variable.

Quality Rating	Relative Frequency	Percent Frequency
Good	.28	28
Very Good	.50	50
Excellent	.22	22
Total	1.00	100

TABLE 2.10 CROSSTABULATION OF QUALITY RATING AND MEAL PRICE FOR 300 LOS ANGELES RESTAURANTS

	Meal Price				
Quality Rating	**$10–19**	**$20–29**	**$30–39**	**$40–49**	**Total**
Good	42	40	2	0	84
Very Good	34	64	46	6	150
Excellent	2	14	28	22	66
Total	78	118	76	28	300

From the percent frequency distribution we see that 28% of the restaurants were rated good, 50% were rated very good, and 22% were rated excellent.

Dividing the totals in the bottom row of the crosstabulation by the total for that row provides a relative and percent frequency distribution for the meal price variable.

Meal Price	Relative Frequency	Percent Frequency
$10–19	.26	26
$20–29	.39	39
$30–39	.25	25
$40–49	.09	9
Total	1.00	100

Note that the sum of the values in each column does not add exactly to the column total, because the values being summed are rounded. From the percent frequency distribution we see that 26% of the meal prices are in the lowest price class ($10–19), 39% are in the next higher class, and so on.

The frequency and relative frequency distributions constructed from the margins of a crosstabulation provide information about each of the variables individually, but they do not shed any light on the relationship between the variables. The primary value of a crosstabulation lies in the insight it offers about the relationship between the variables. A review of the crosstabulation in Table 2.10 reveals that higher meal prices are associated with the higher quality restaurants, and the lower meal prices are associated with the lower quality restaurants.

Converting the entries in a crosstabulation into row percentages or column percentages can provide more insight into the relationship between the two variables. For row percentages, the results of dividing each frequency in Table 2.10 by its corresponding row total are shown in Table 2.11. Each row of Table 2.11 is a percent frequency distribution of meal price for one of the quality rating categories. Of the restaurants with the lowest quality rating (good), we see that the greatest percentages are for the less expensive restaurants (50% have $10–19 meal prices and 47.6% have $20–29 meal prices). Of the restaurants with the highest quality rating (excellent), we see that the greatest percentages are for the more expensive restaurants (42.4% have $30–39 meal prices and 33.4% have $40–49 meal prices). Thus, we continue to see that the more expensive meals are associated with the higher quality restaurants.

Crosstabulation is widely used for examining the relationship between two variables. In practice, the final reports for many statistical studies include a large number of crosstabulation tables. In the Los Angeles restaurant survey, the crosstabulation is based on one qualitative variable (quality rating) and one quantitative variable (meal price). Crosstabulations can also be developed when both variables are qualitative and when both variables are quantitative. When quantitative variables are used, however, we must first create classes for the values of the variable. For instance, in the restaurant example we grouped the meal prices into four classes ($10–19, $20–29, $30–39, and $40–49).

TABLE 2.11 ROW PERCENTAGES FOR EACH QUALITY RATING CATEGORY

	Meal Price				
Quality Rating	**$10–19**	**$20–29**	**$30–39**	**$40–49**	**Total**
Good	50.0	47.6	2.4	0.0	100
Very Good	22.7	42.7	30.6	4.0	100
Excellent	3.0	21.2	42.4	33.4	100

Simpson's Paradox

The data in two or more crosstabulations are often combined or aggregated to produce a summary crosstabulation showing how two variables are related. In such cases, we must be careful in drawing conclusions about the relationship between the two variables in the aggregated crosstabulation. In some cases the conclusions based upon the aggregated crosstabulation can be completely reversed if we look at the unaggregated data, an occurrence known as **Simpson's paradox**. To provide an illustration of Simpson's paradox we consider an example involving the analysis of verdicts for two judges in two types of courts.

Judges Ron Luckett and Dennis Kendall presided over cases in Common Pleas Court and Municipal Court during the past three years. Some of the verdicts they rendered were appealed. In most of these cases the appeals court upheld the original verdicts, but in some cases those verdicts were reversed. For each judge a crosstabulation was developed based upon two variables: Verdict (upheld or reversed) and Type of Court (Common Pleas and Municipal). Suppose that the two crosstabulations were then combined by aggregating the type of court data. The resulting aggregated crosstabulation contains two variables: Verdict (upheld or reversed) and Judge (Luckett or Kendall). This crosstabulation shows the number of appeals in which the verdict was upheld and the number in which the verdict was reversed for both judges. The following crosstabulation shows these results along with the column percentages in parentheses next to each value.

	Judge		
Verdict	**Luckett**	**Kendall**	**Total**
Upheld	129 (86%)	110 (88%)	239
Reversed	21 (14%)	15 (12%)	36
Total (%)	150 (100%)	125 (100%)	275

A review of the column percentages shows that 14% of the verdicts were reversed for Judge Luckett, but only 12% of the verdicts were reversed for Judge Kendall. Thus, we might conclude that Judge Kendall is doing a better job because a higher percentage of his verdicts are being upheld. A problem arises with this conclusion, however.

The following crosstabulations show the cases tried by Luckett and Kendall in the two courts; column percentages are also shown in parentheses next to each value.

	Judge Luckett		
Verdict	**Common Pleas**	**Municipal Court**	**Total**
Upheld	29 (91%)	100 (85%)	129
Reversed	3 (9%)	18 (15%)	21
Total (%)	32 (100%)	118 (100%)	150

	Judge Kendall		
Verdict	**Common Pleas**	**Municipal Court**	**Total**
Upheld	90 (90%)	20 (80%)	110
Reversed	10 (10%)	5 (20%)	15
Total (%)	100 (100%)	25 (100%)	125

From the crosstabulation and column percentages for Luckett, we see that his verdicts were upheld in 91% of the Common Pleas Court cases and in 85% of the Municipal Court cases. From the crosstabulation and column percentages for Kendall, we see that his verdicts were upheld in 90% of the Common Pleas Court cases and in 80% of the Municipal Court cases. Comparing the column percentages for the two judges, we see that Judge Luckett demonstrates a better record than Judge Kendall in both courts. This result contradicts the conclusion we reached when we aggregated the data across both courts for the original crosstabulation. It appeared then that Judge Kendall had the better record. This example illustrates Simpson's paradox.

The original crosstabulation was obtained by aggregating the data in the separate crosstabulations for the two courts. Note that for both judges the percentage of appeals that resulted in reversals was much higher in Municipal Court than in Common Pleas Court. Because Judge Luckett tried a much higher percentage of his cases in Municipal Court, the aggregated data favored Judge Kendall. When we look at the crosstabulations for the two courts separately, however, Judge Luckett clearly shows the better record. Thus, for the original crosstabulation, we see that the *type of court* is a hidden variable that cannot be ignored when evaluating the records of the two judges.

Because of Simpson's paradox, we need to be especially careful when drawing conclusions using aggregated data. Before drawing any conclusions about the relationship between two variables shown for a crosstabulation involving aggregated data, you should investigate whether any hidden variables could affect the results.

Scatter Diagram and Trendline

A **scatter diagram** is a graphical presentation of the relationship between two quantitative variables, and a **trendline** is a line that provides an approximation of the relationship. As an illustration, consider the advertising/sales relationship for a stereo and sound equipment store in San Francisco. On 10 occasions during the past three months, the store used weekend television commercials to promote sales at its stores. The managers want to investigate whether a relationship exists between the number of commercials shown and sales at the store during the following week. Sample data for the 10 weeks with sales in hundreds of dollars are shown in Table 2.12.

Figure 2.7 shows the scatter diagram and the trendline* for the data in Table 2.12. The number of commercials (x) is shown on the horizontal axis and the sales (y) are shown on the vertical axis. For week 1, $x = 2$ and $y = 50$. A point with those coordinates is plotted on the scatter diagram. Similar points are plotted for the other nine weeks. Note that during two of the weeks one commercial was shown, during two of the weeks two commercials were shown, and so on.

The completed scatter diagram in Figure 2.7 indicates a positive relationship between the number of commercials and sales. Higher sales are associated with a higher number of commercials. The relationship is not perfect in that all points are not on a straight line. However, the general pattern of the points and the trendline suggest that the overall relationship is positive.

Some general scatter diagram patterns and the types of relationships they suggest are shown in Figure 2.8. The top left panel depicts a positive relationship similar to the one for

TABLE 2.12 SAMPLE DATA FOR THE STEREO AND SOUND EQUIPMENT STORE

Week	Number of Commercials x	Sales ($100s) y
1	2	50
2	5	57
3	1	41
4	3	54
5	4	54
6	1	38
7	5	63
8	3	48
9	4	59
10	2	46

CD file
Stereo

*The equation of the trendline is $y = 36.15 + 4.95x$. The slope of the trendline is 4.95 and the y-intercept (the point where the line intersects the y axis) is 36.15. We will discuss in detail the interpretation of the slope and y-intercept for a linear trendline in Chapter 12 when we study simple linear regression.

FIGURE 2.7 SCATTER DIAGRAM AND TRENDLINE FOR THE STEREO AND SOUND EQUIPMENT STORE

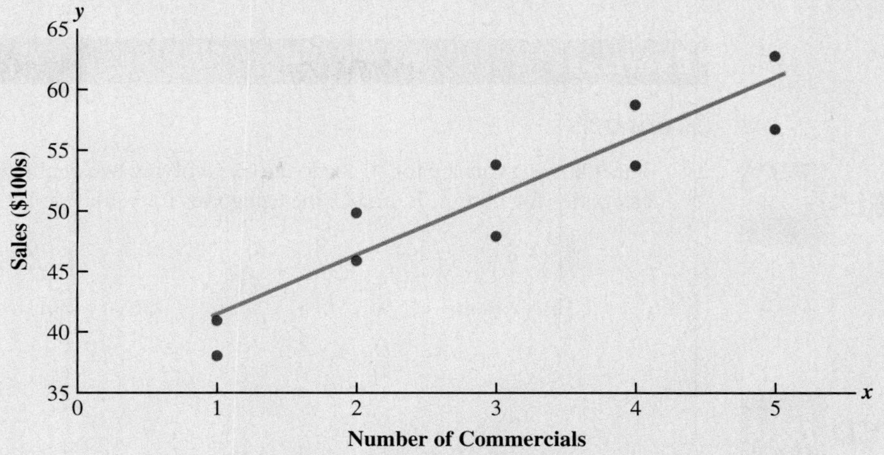

FIGURE 2.8 TYPES OF RELATIONSHIPS DEPICTED BY SCATTER DIAGRAMS

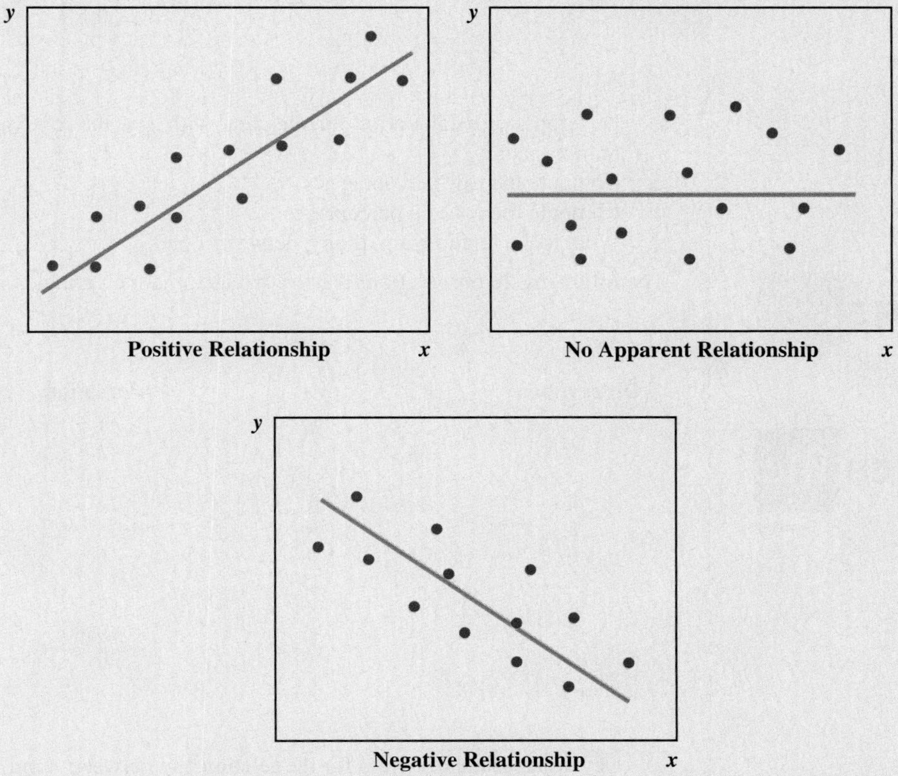

the number of commercials and sales example. In the top right panel, the scatter diagram shows no apparent relationship between the variables. The bottom panel depicts a negative relationship where y tends to decrease as x increases.

Exercises

Methods

SELF test

29. The following data are for 30 observations involving two qualitative variables, x and y. The categories for x are A, B, and C; the categories for y are 1 and 2.

CD file Crosstab

Observation	x	y	Observation	x	y
1	A	1	16	B	2
2	B	1	17	C	1
3	B	1	18	B	1
4	C	2	19	C	1
5	B	1	20	B	1
6	C	2	21	C	2
7	B	1	22	B	1
8	C	2	23	C	2
9	A	1	24	A	1
10	B	1	25	B	1
11	A	1	26	C	2
12	B	1	27	C	2
13	C	2	28	A	1
14	C	2	29	B	1
15	C	2	30	B	2

a. Develop a crosstabulation for the data, with x as the row variable and y as the column variable.
b. Compute the row percentages.
c. Compute the column percentages.
d. What is the relationship, if any, between x and y?

SELF test

30. The following 20 observations are for two quantitative variables, x and y.

CD file Scatter

Observation	x	y	Observation	x	y
1	−22	22	11	−37	48
2	−33	49	12	34	−29
3	2	8	13	9	−18
4	29	−16	14	−33	31
5	−13	10	15	20	−16
6	21	−28	16	−3	14
7	−13	27	17	−15	18
8	−23	35	18	12	17
9	14	−5	19	−20	−11
10	3	−3	20	−7	−22

a. Develop a scatter diagram for the relationship between x and y.
b. What is the relationship, if any, between x and y?

Applications

31. The following crosstabulation shows household income by educational level of the head of household (*Statistical Abstract of the United States: 2002*).

	Household Income ($1000s)					
Educational Level	Under 25	25.0–49.9	50.0–74.9	75.0–99.9	100 or more	Total
Not H.S. graduate	9285	4093	1589	541	354	15862
H.S. graduate	10150	9821	6050	2737	2028	30786
Some college	6011	8221	5813	3215	3120	26380
Bachelor's degree	2138	3985	3952	2698	4748	17521
Beyond bach. deg.	813	1497	1815	1589	3765	9479
Total	28397	27617	19219	10780	14015	100028

a. Compute the row percentages and identify the percent frequency distributions of income for households in which the head is a high school graduate and in which the head holds a bachelor's degree.

b. What percentage of households headed by high school graduates earn $75,000 or more? What percentage of households headed by bachelor's degree recipients earn $75,000 or more?

c. Construct percent frequency histograms of income for households headed by persons with a high school degree and for those headed by persons with a bachelor's degree. Is any relationship evident between household income and educational level?

32. Refer again to the crosstabulation of household income by educational level shown in exercise 31.

a. Compute column percentages and identify the percent frequency distributions displayed. What percentage of the heads of households did not graduate from high school?

b. What percentage of the households earning $100,000 or more were headed by a person having schooling beyond a bachelor's degree? What percentage of the households headed by a person with schooling beyond a bachelor's degree earned over $100,000? Why are these two percentages different?

c. Compare the percent frequency distributions for those households earning "Under 25," "100 or more," and for "Total." Comment on the relationship between household income and educational level of the head of household.

33. Recently, management at Oak Tree Golf Course received a few complaints about the condition of the greens. Several players complained that the greens are too fast. Rather than react to the comments of just a few, the Golf Association conducted a survey of 100 male and 100 female golfers. The survey results are summarized here.

Male Golfers

	Greens Condition	
Handicap	Too Fast	Fine
Under 15	10	40
15 or more	25	25

Female Golfers

	Greens Condition	
Handicap	Too Fast	Fine
Under 15	1	9
15 or more	39	51

a. Combine these two crosstabulations into one with Male and Female as the row labels and Too Fast and Fine as the column labels. Which group shows the highest percentage saying that the greens are too fast?

b. Refer to the initial crosstabulations. For those players with low handicaps (better players), which group (male or female) shows the highest percentage saying the greens are too fast?

c. Refer to the initial crosstabulations. For those players with higher handicaps, which group (male or female) shows the highest percentage saying the greens are too fast?

d. What conclusions can you draw about the preferences of men and women concerning the speed of the greens? Are the conclusions you draw from part (a) as compared with parts (b) and (c) consistent? Explain any apparent inconsistencies.

34. Table 2.13 provides financial data for a sample of 36 companies whose stocks trade on the New York Stock Exchange (*Investor's Business Daily,* April 7, 2000). The data on Sales/Margins/ROE are a composite rating based on a company's sales growth rate, its profit margins, and its return on equity (ROE). EPS Rating is a measure of growth in earnings per share for the company.

CD file IBD

TABLE 2.13 FINANCIAL DATA FOR A SAMPLE OF 36 COMPANIES

Company	EPS Rating	Relative Price Strength	Industry Group Relative Strength	Sales/Margins/ ROE
Advo	81	74	B	A
Alaska Air Group	58	17	C	B
Alliant Tech	84	22	B	B
Atmos Energy	21	9	C	E
Bank of Am.	87	38	C	A
Bowater PLC	14	46	C	D
Callaway Golf	46	62	B	E
Central Parking	76	18	B	C
Dean Foods	84	7	B	C
Dole Food	70	54	E	C
Elec. Data Sys.	72	69	A	B
Fed. Dept. Store	79	21	D	B
Gateway	82	68	A	A
Goodyear	21	9	E	D
Hanson PLC	57	32	B	B
ICN Pharm.	76	56	A	D
Jefferson Plt.	80	38	D	C
Kroger	84	24	D	A
Mattel	18	20	E	D
McDermott	6	6	A	C
Monaco	97	21	D	A
Murphy Oil	80	62	B	B
Nordstrom	58	57	B	C
NYMAGIC	17	45	D	D
Office Depot	58	40	B	B
Payless Shoes	76	59	B	B
Praxair	62	32	C	B
Reebok	31	72	C	E
Safeway	91	61	D	A
Teco Energy	49	48	D	B
Texaco	80	31	D	C
US West	60	65	B	A
United Rental	98	12	C	A
Wachovia	69	36	E	B
Winnebago	83	49	D	A
York International	28	14	D	B

Source: Investor's Business Daily, April 7, 2000.

a. Prepare a crosstabulation of the data on Sales/Margins/ROE (rows) and EPS Rating (columns). Use classes of 0–19, 20–39, 40–59, 60–79, and 80–99 for EPS Rating.
b. Compute row percentages and comment on any relationship between the variables.

35. Refer to the data in Table 2.13.
a. Prepare a crosstabulation of the data on Sales/Margins/ROE and Industry Group Relative Strength.
b. Prepare a frequency distribution for the data on Sales/Margins/ROE.
c. Prepare a frequency distribution for the data on Industry Group Relative Strength.
d. How has the crosstabulation helped in preparing the frequency distributions in parts (b) and (c)?

36. Refer to the data in Table 2.13.
a. Prepare a scatter diagram of the data on EPS Rating and Relative Price Strength.
b. Comment on the relationship, if any, between the variables. (The meaning of the EPS Rating is described in exercise 34. Relative Price Strength is a measure of the change in the stock's price over the past 12 months. Higher values indicate greater strength.)

37. The National Football League rates prospects position by position on a scale that ranges from 5 to 9. The ratings are interpreted as follows: 8–9 should start the first year; 7.0–7.9 should start; 6.0–6.9 will make the team as a backup; and 5.0–5.9 can make the club and contribute. Table 2.14 shows the position, weight, time (seconds to run 40 yards), and rating for 40 NFL prospects (*USA Today,* April 14, 2000).
a. Prepare a crosstabulation of the data on Position (rows) and Time (columns). Use classes of 4.00–4.49, 4.50–4.99, 5.00–5.49, and 5.50–5.99 for Time.
b. Comment on the relationship between Position and Time based upon the crosstabulation developed in part (a).
c. Develop a scatter diagram of the data on Time and Rating. Use the vertical axis for Rating.
d. Comment on the relationship, if any, between Time and Rating.

Summary

A set of data, even if modest in size, is often difficult to interpret directly in the form in which it is gathered. Tabular and graphical methods provide procedures for organizing and summarizing data so that patterns are revealed and the data are more easily interpreted. Frequency distributions, relative frequency distributions, percent frequency distributions, bar graphs, and pie charts were presented as tabular and graphical procedures for summarizing qualitative data. Frequency distributions, relative frequency distributions, percent frequency distributions, histograms, cumulative frequency distributions, cumulative relative frequency distributions, cumulative percent frequency distributions, and ogives were presented as ways of summarizing quantitative data. A stem-and-leaf display provides an exploratory data analysis technique that can be used to summarize quantitative data. Crosstabulation was presented as a tabular method for summarizing data for two variables. The scatter diagram was introduced as a graphical method for showing the relationship between two quantitative variables. Figure 2.9 shows the tabular and graphical methods presented in this chapter.

With large data sets, computer software packages are essential in constructing tabular and graphical summaries of data. In the two chapter appendixes, we show how Minitab and Excel can be used for this purpose.

CD file
NFL

TABLE 2.14 NATIONAL FOOTBALL LEAGUE RATINGS FOR 40 DRAFT PROSPECTS

Observation	Name	Position	Weight	Time	Rating
1	Peter Warrick	Wide receiver	194	4.53	9
2	Plaxico Burress	Wide receiver	231	4.52	8.8
3	Sylvester Morris	Wide receiver	216	4.59	8.3
4	Travis Taylor	Wide receiver	199	4.36	8.1
5	Laveranues Coles	Wide receiver	192	4.29	8
6	Dez White	Wide receiver	218	4.49	7.9
7	Jerry Porter	Wide receiver	221	4.55	7.4
8	Ron Dugans	Wide receiver	206	4.47	7.1
9	Todd Pinkston	Wide receiver	169	4.37	7
10	Dennis Northcutt	Wide receiver	175	4.43	7
11	Anthony Lucas	Wide receiver	194	4.51	6.9
12	Darrell Jackson	Wide receiver	197	4.56	6.6
13	Danny Farmer	Wide receiver	217	4.6	6.5
14	Sherrod Gideon	Wide receiver	173	4.57	6.4
15	Trevor Gaylor	Wide receiver	199	4.57	6.2
16	Cosey Coleman	Guard	322	5.38	7.4
17	Travis Claridge	Guard	303	5.18	7
18	Kaulana Noa	Guard	317	5.34	6.8
19	Leander Jordan	Guard	330	5.46	6.7
20	Chad Clifton	Guard	334	5.18	6.3
21	Manula Savea	Guard	308	5.32	6.1
22	Ryan Johanningmeir	Guard	310	5.28	6
23	Mark Tauscher	Guard	318	5.37	6
24	Blaine Saipaia	Guard	321	5.25	6
25	Richard Mercier	Guard	295	5.34	5.8
26	Damion McIntosh	Guard	328	5.31	5.3
27	Jeno James	Guard	320	5.64	5
28	Al Jackson	Guard	304	5.2	5
29	Chris Samuels	Offensive tackle	325	4.95	8.5
30	Stockar McDougle	Offensive tackle	361	5.5	8
31	Chris McIngosh	Offensive tackle	315	5.39	7.8
32	Adrian Klemm	Offensive tackle	307	4.98	7.6
33	Todd Wade	Offensive tackle	326	5.2	7.3
34	Marvel Smith	Offensive tackle	320	5.36	7.1
35	Michael Thompson	Offensive tackle	287	5.05	6.8
36	Bobby Williams	Offensive tackle	332	5.26	6.8
37	Darnell Alford	Offensive tackle	334	5.55	6.4
38	Terrance Beadles	Offensive tackle	312	5.15	6.3
39	Tutan Reyes	Offensive tackle	299	5.35	6.1
40	Greg Robinson-Ran	Offensive tackle	333	5.59	6

FIGURE 2.9 TABULAR AND GRAPHICAL METHODS FOR SUMMARIZING DATA

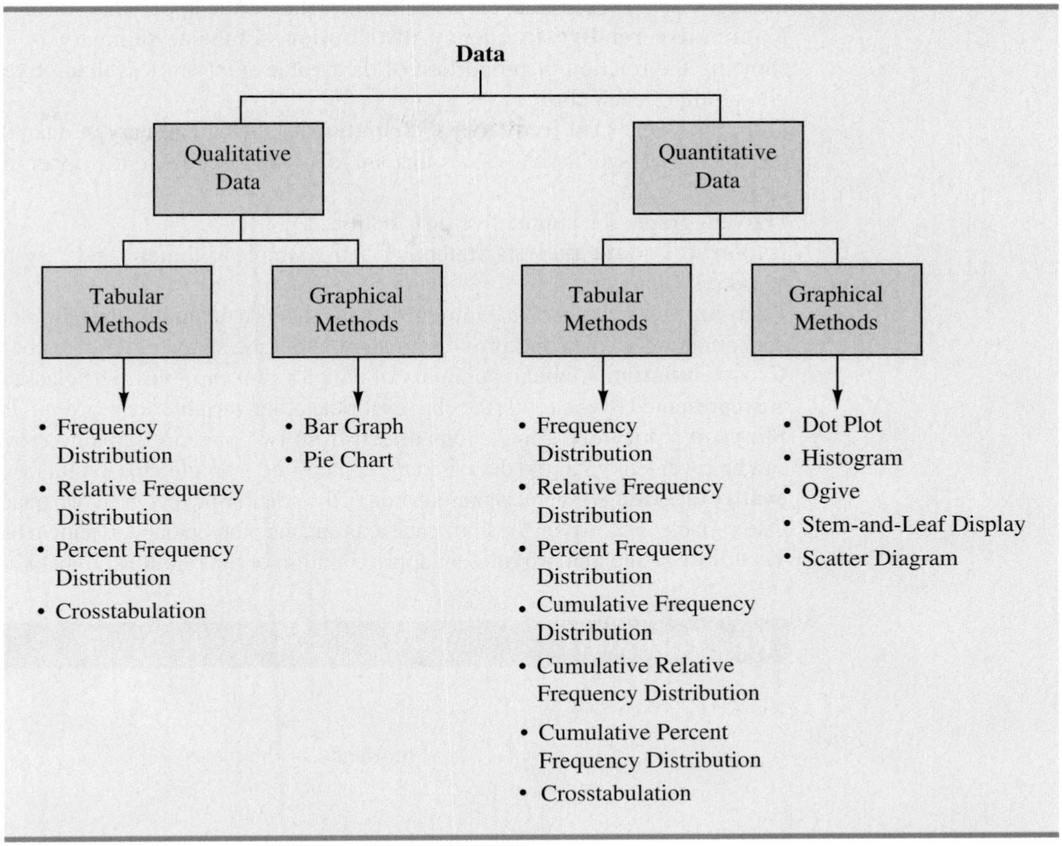

Glossary

Qualitative data Labels or names used to identify categories of like items.
Quantitative data Numerical values that indicate how much or how many.
Frequency distribution A tabular summary of data showing the number (frequency) of data values in each of several nonoverlapping classes.
Relative frequency distribution A tabular summary of data showing the fraction or proportion of data values in each of several nonoverlapping classes.
Percent frequency distribution A tabular summary of data showing the percentage of data values in each of several nonoverlapping classes.
Bar graph A graphical device for depicting qualitative data that have been summarized in a frequency, relative frequency, or percent frequency distribution.
Pie chart A graphical device for presenting data summaries based on subdivision of a circle into sectors that correspond to the relative frequency for each class.
Class midpoint The value halfway between the lower and upper class limits.
Dot plot A graphical device that summarizes data by the number of dots above each data value on the horizontal axis.
Histogram A graphical presentation of a frequency distribution, relative frequency distribution, or percent frequency distribution of quantitative data constructed by placing the class intervals on the horizontal axis and the frequencies, relative frequencies, or percent frequencies on the vertical axis.

Cumulative frequency distribution A tabular summary of quantitative data showing the number of data values that are less than or equal to the upper class limit of each class.

Cumulative relative frequency distribution A tabular summary of quantitative data showing the fraction or proportion of data values that are less than or equal to the upper class limit of each class.

Cumulative percent frequency distribution A tabular summary of quantitative data showing the percentage of data values that are less than or equal to the upper class limit of each class.

Ogive A graph of a cumulative distribution.

Exploratory data analysis Methods that use simple arithmetic and easy-to-draw graphs to summarize data quickly.

Stem-and-leaf display An exploratory data analysis technique that simultaneously rank orders quantitative data and provides insight about the shape of the distribution.

Crosstabulation A tabular summary of data for two variables. The classes for one variable are represented by the rows; the classes for the other variable are represented by the columns.

Simpson's paradox Conclusions drawn from two or more separate crosstabulations that can be reversed when the data are aggregated into a single crosstabulation.

Scatter diagram A graphical presentation of the relationship between two quantitative variables. One variable is shown on the horizontal axis and the other variable is shown on the vertical axis.

Trendline A line that provides an approximation of the relationship between two variables.

Key Formulas

Relative Frequency

$$\frac{\text{Frequency of the class}}{n} \tag{2.1}$$

Approximate Class Width

$$\frac{\text{Largest data value} - \text{Smallest data value}}{\text{Number of classes}} \tag{2.2}$$

Supplementary Exercises

38. The five top-selling vehicles during 2003 were the Chevrolet Silverado/C/K pickup, Dodge Ram pickup, Ford F-Series pickup, Honda Accord, and Toyota Camry (*Motor Trend,* 2003). Data from a sample of 50 vehicle purchases are presented in Table 2.15.

CD file
AutoData

TABLE 2.15 DATA FOR 50 VEHICLE PURCHASES

Silverado	Ram	Accord	Camry	Camry
Silverado	Silverado	Camry	Ram	F-Series
Ram	F-Series	Accord	Ram	Ram
Silverado	F-Series	F-Series	Silverado	Ram
Ram	Ram	Accord	Silverado	Camry
F-Series	Ram	Silverado	Accord	Silverado
Camry	F-Series	F-Series	F-Series	Silverado
F-Series	Silverado	F-Series	F-Series	Ram
Silverado	Silverado	Camry	Camry	F-Series
Silverado	F-Series	F-Series	Accord	Accord

a. Develop a frequency and percent frequency distribution.
b. What is the best-selling pickup truck, and what is the best-selling passenger car?
c. Show a pie chart.

39. The Higher Education Research Institute at UCLA provides statistics on the most popular majors among incoming college freshmen. The five most popular majors are Arts and Humanities (A), Business Administration (B), Engineering (E), Professional (P), and Social Science (S) (*The New York Times Almanac,* 2006). A broad range of other (O) majors, including biological science, physical science, computer science, and education, are grouped together. The majors selected for a sample of 64 college freshmen follow.

CD file
Major

S	P	P	O	B	E	O	E	P	O	O	B	O	O	O	A
O	E	E	B	S	O	B	O	A	O	E	O	E	O	B	P
B	A	S	O	E	A	B	O	S	S	O	O	E	B	O	B
A	E	B	E	A	A	P	O	O	E	O	B	B	O	P	B

a. Show a frequency distribution and percent frequency distribution.
b. Show a bar graph.
c. What percentage of freshmen selects one of the five most popular majors?
d. What is the most popular major for incoming freshmen? What percentage of freshmen select this major?

40. *Golf Magazine*'s Top 100 Teachers were asked the question, "What is the most critical area that prevents golfers from reaching their potential?" The possible responses were lack of accuracy, poor approach shots, poor mental approach, lack of power, limited practice, poor putting, poor short game, and poor strategic decisions. The data obtained follow (*Golf Magazine,* February 2002):

CD file
Golf

Mental approach	Mental approach	Short game	Short game	Short game
Practice	Accuracy	Mental approach	Accuracy	Putting
Power	Approach shots	Accuracy	Short game	Putting
Accuracy	Mental approach	Mental approach	Accuracy	Power
Accuracy	Accuracy	Short game	Power	Short game
Accuracy	Putting	Mental approach	Strategic decisions	Accuracy
Short game	Power	Mental approach	Approach shots	Short game
Practice	Practice	Mental approach	Power	Power
Mental approach	Short game	Mental approach	Short game	Strategic decisions
Accuracy	Short game	Accuracy	Mental approach	Short game
Mental approach	Putting	Mental approach	Mental approach	Putting
Practice	Putting	Practice	Short game	Putting
Power	Mental approach	Short game	Practice	Strategic decisions
Accuracy	Short game	Accuracy	Practice	Putting
Accuracy	Short game	Accuracy	Short game	Putting
Accuracy	Approach shots	Short game	Mental approach	Practice
Short game	Short game	Strategic decisions	Short game	Short game
Practice	Practice	Short game	Practice	Strategic decisions
Mental approach	Strategic decisions	Strategic decisions	Power	Short game
Accuracy	Practice	Practice	Practice	Accuracy

a. Develop a frequency and percent frequency distribution.
b. Which four critical areas most often prevent golfers from reaching their potential?

41. Dividend yield is the annual dividend paid by a company expressed as a percentage of the price of the stock (Dividend/Stock Price × 100). The dividend yield for the Dow Jones Industrial Average companies is shown in Table 2.16 (*The Wall Street Journal,* March 3, 2006).
a. Construct a frequency distribution and percent frequency distribution.
b. Construct a histogram.
c. Comment on the shape of the distribution.

TABLE 2.16 DIVIDEND YIELD FOR DOW JONES INDUSTRIAL AVERAGE COMPANIES

CD file DivYield

Company	Dividend Yield %	Company	Dividend Yield %
AIG	0.9	Home Depot	1.4
Alcoa	2.0	Honeywell	2.2
Altria Group	4.5	IBM	1.0
American Express	0.9	Intel	2.0
AT&T	4.7	Johnson & Johnson	2.3
Boeing	1.6	JPMorgan Chase	3.3
Caterpillar	1.3	McDonald's	1.9
Citigroup	4.3	Merck	4.3
Coca-Cola	3.0	Microsoft	1.3
Disney	1.0	3M	2.5
DuPont	3.6	Pfizer	3.7
ExxonMobil	2.1	Procter & Gamble	1.9
General Electric	3.0	United Technologies	1.5
General Motors	5.2	Verizon	4.8
Hewlett-Packard	0.9	Wal-Mart Stores	1.3

d. What do the tabular and graphical summaries tell about the dividend yields among the Dow Jones Industrial Average companies?

e. What company has the highest dividend yield? If the stock for this company currently sells for $20 per share and you purchase 500 shares, how much dividend income will this investment generate in one year?

42. Approximately 1.5 million high school students take the Scholastic Aptitude Test (SAT) each year and nearly 80% of the college and universities without open admissions policies use SAT scores in making admission decisions (*College Board,* March 2006). A sample of SAT scores for the combined math and verbal portions of the test are as follows:

CD file SATScores

1025	1042	1195	880	945
1102	845	1095	936	790
1097	913	1245	1040	998
998	940	1043	1048	1130
1017	1140	1030	1171	1035

a. Show a frequency distribution and histogram for the SAT scores. Begin the first class with an SAT score of 750 and use a class width of 100.

b. Comment on the shape of the distribution.

c. What other observations can be made about SAT scores based on the tabular and graphical summaries?

43. Ninety-four shadow stocks were reported by the American Association of Individual Investors. The term *shadow* indicates stocks for small to medium-sized firms not followed closely by the major brokerage houses. Information on where the stock was traded—New York Stock Exchange (NYSE), American Stock Exchange (AMEX), and over-the-counter (OTC)—the earnings per share, and the price/earnings ratio was provided for the following sample of 20 shadow stocks.

CD file Shadow

Stock	Exchange	Earnings per Share ($)	Price/Earnings Ratio
Chemi-Trol	OTC	.39	27.30
Candie's	OTC	.07	36.20
TST/Impreso	OTC	.65	12.70

(continued)

Stock	Exchange	Earnings per Share ($)	Price/Earnings Ratio
Unimed Pharm.	OTC	.12	59.30
Skyline Chili	AMEX	.34	19.30
Cyanotech	OTC	.22	29.30
Catalina Light.	NYSE	.15	33.20
DDL Elect.	NYSE	.10	10.20
Euphonix	OTC	.09	49.70
Mesa Labs	OTC	.37	14.40
RCM Tech.	OTC	.47	18.60
Anuhco	AMEX	.70	11.40
Hello Direct	OTC	.23	21.10
Hilite Industries	OTC	.61	7.80
Alpha Tech.	OTC	.11	34.60
Wegener Group	OTC	.16	24.50
U.S. Home & Garden	OTC	.24	8.70
Chalone Wine	OTC	.27	44.40
Eng. Support Sys.	OTC	.89	16.70
Int. Remote Imaging	AMEX	.86	4.70

a. Provide frequency and relative frequency distributions for the exchange data. Where are most shadow stocks listed?

b. Provide frequency and relative frequency distributions for the earnings per share and price/earnings ratio data. Use classes of 0.00–0.19, 0.20–0.39, and so on for the earnings per share data and classes of 0.0–9.9, 10.0–19.9, and so on for the price/earnings ratio data. What observations and comments can you make about the shadow stocks?

44. Data from the U.S. Census Bureau provides the population by state in millions of people (*The World Almanac,* 2006).

CD file
Population

State	Population	State	Population	State	Population
Alabama	4.5	Louisiana	4.5	Ohio	11.5
Alaska	0.7	Maine	1.3	Oklahoma	3.5
Arizona	5.7	Maryland	5.6	Oregon	3.6
Arkansas	2.8	Massachusetts	6.4	Pennsylvania	12.4
California	35.9	Michigan	10.1	Rhode Island	1.1
Colorado	4.6	Minnesota	5.1	South Carolina	4.2
Connecticut	3.5	Mississippi	2.9	South Dakota	0.8
Delaware	0.8	Missouri	5.8	Tennessee	5.9
Florida	17.4	Montana	0.9	Texas	22.5
Georgia	8.8	Nebraska	1.7	Utah	2.4
Hawaii	1.3	Nevada	2.3	Vermont	0.6
Idaho	1.4	New Hampshire	1.3	Virginia	7.5
Illinois	12.7	New Jersey	8.7	Washington	6.2
Indiana	6.2	New Mexico	1.9	West Virginia	1.8
Iowa	3.0	New York	19.2	Wisconsin	5.5
Kansas	2.7	North Carolina	8.5	Wyoming	0.5
Kentucky	4.1	North Dakota	0.6		

a. Develop a frequency distribution, a percent frequency distribution, and a histogram. Use a class width of 2.5 million.

b. Discuss the skewness in the distribution.

c. What observations can you make about the population of the 50 states?

45. *Drug Store News* (September 2002) provided data on annual pharmacy sales for the leading pharmacy retailers in the United States. The following data are annual sales in millions.

Retailer	Sales	Retailer	Sales
Ahold USA	$ 1700	Medicine Shoppe	$ 1757
CVS	12700	Rite-Aid	8637
Eckerd	7739	Safeway	2150
Kmart	1863	Walgreens	11660
Kroger	3400	Wal-Mart	7250

a. Show a stem-and-leaf display.
b. Identify the annual sales levels for the smallest, medium, and largest drug retailers.
c. What are the two largest drug retailers?

46. The daily high and low temperatures for 20 cities follow (*USA Today,* March 3, 2006).

CD file
CityTemp

City	High	Low	City	High	Low
Albuquerque	66	39	Los Angeles	60	46
Atlanta	61	35	Miami	84	65
Baltimore	42	26	Minneapolis	30	11
Charlotte	60	29	New Orleans	68	50
Cincinnati	41	21	Oklahoma City	62	40
Dallas	62	47	Phoenix	77	50
Denver	60	31	Portland	54	38
Houston	70	54	St. Louis	45	27
Indianapolis	42	22	San Francisco	55	43
Las Vegas	65	43	Seattle	52	36

a. Prepare a stem-and-leaf display of the high temperatures.
b. Prepare a stem-and-leaf display of the low temperatures.
c. Compare the two stem-and-leaf displays and make comments about the difference between the high and low temperatures.
d. Provide a frequency distribution for both high and low temperatures.

47. Refer to the data set for high and low temperatures for 20 cities in exercise 46.
a. Develop a scatter diagram to show the relationship between the two variables, high temperature and low temperature.
b. Comment on the relationship between high and low temperatures.

48. A study of job satisfaction was conducted for four occupations. Job satisfaction was measured using an 18-item questionnaire with each question receiving a response score of 1 to 5 with higher scores indicating greater satisfaction. The sum of the 18 scores provides the job satisfaction score for each individual in the sample. The data are as follow.

CD file
OccupSat

Occupation	Satisfaction Score	Occupation	Satisfaction Score	Occupation	Satisfaction Score
Lawyer	42	Physical Therapist	78	Systems Analyst	60
Physical Therapist	86	Systems Analyst	44	Physical Therapist	59
Lawyer	42	Systems Analyst	71	Cabinetmaker	78
Systems Analyst	55	Lawyer	50	Physical Therapist	60

(continued)

Occupation	Satisfaction Score	Occupation	Satisfaction Score	Occupation	Satisfaction Score
Lawyer	38	Lawyer	48	Physical Therapist	50
Cabinetmaker	79	Cabinetmaker	69	Cabinetmaker	79
Lawyer	44	Physical Therapist	80	Systems Analyst	62
Systems Analyst	41	Systems Analyst	64	Lawyer	45
Physical Therapist	55	Physical Therapist	55	Cabinetmaker	84
Systems Analyst	66	Cabinetmaker	64	Physical Therapist	62
Lawyer	53	Cabinetmaker	59	Systems Analyst	73
Cabinetmaker	65	Cabinetmaker	54	Cabinetmaker	60
Lawyer	74	Systems Analyst	76	Lawyer	64
Physical Therapist	52				

a. Provide a crosstabulation of occupation and job satisfaction score.
b. Compute the row percentages for your crosstabulation in part (a).
c. What observations can you make concerning the level of job satisfaction for these occupations?

49. Do larger companies generate more revenue? The following data show the number of employees and annual revenue for a sample of 20 *Fortune* 1000 companies (*Fortune*, April 17, 2000).

CD file
RevEmps

Company	Employees	Revenue ($ millions)	Company	Employees	Revenue ($ millions)
Sprint	77,600	19,930	American Financial	9,400	3,334
Chase Manhattan	74,801	33,710	Fluor	53,561	12,417
Computer Sciences	50,000	7,660	Phillips Petroleum	15,900	13,852
Wells Fargo	89,355	21,795	Cardinal Health	36,000	25,034
Sunbeam	12,200	2,398	Borders Group	23,500	2,999
CBS	29,000	7,510	MCI Worldcom	77,000	37,120
Time Warner	69,722	27,333	Consolidated Edison	14,269	7,491
Steelcase	16,200	2,743	IBP	45,000	14,075
Georgia-Pacific	57,000	17,796	Super Value	50,000	17,421
Toro	1,275	4,673	H&R Block	4,200	1,669

a. Prepare a scatter diagram to show the relationship between the variables Revenue and Employees.
b. Comment on any relationship between the variables.

50. A survey of commercial buildings served by the Cincinnati Gas & Electric Company asked what main heating fuel was used and what year the building was constructed. A partial crosstabulation of the findings follows.

Year Constructed	Fuel Type				
	Electricity	Natural Gas	Oil	Propane	Other
1973 or before	40	183	12	5	7
1974–1979	24	26	2	2	0
1980–1986	37	38	1	0	6
1987–1991	48	70	2	0	1

a. Complete the crosstabulation by showing the row totals and column totals.
b. Show the frequency distributions for year constructed and for fuel type.
c. Prepare a crosstabulation showing column percentages.
d. Prepare a crosstabulation showing row percentages.
e. Comment on the relationship between year constructed and fuel type.

51. Table 2.17 contains a portion of the data on the file named Fortune on the CD that accompanies the text. It provides data on stockholders' equity, market value, and profits for a sample of 50 *Fortune* 500 companies.

CD file

Fortune

TABLE 2.17 DATA FOR A SAMPLE OF 50 *FORTUNE* 500 COMPANIES

Company	Stockholders' Equity ($1000s)	Market Value ($1000s)	Profit ($1000s)
AGCO	982.1	372.1	60.6
AMP	2698.0	12017.6	2.0
Apple Computer	1642.0	4605.0	309.0
Baxter International	2839.0	21743.0	315.0
Bergen Brunswick	629.1	2787.5	3.1
Best Buy	557.7	10376.5	94.5
Charles Schwab	1429.0	35340.6	348.5
.	.	.	.
.	.	.	.
.	.	.	.
Walgreen	2849.0	30324.7	511.0
Westvaco	2246.4	2225.6	132.0
Whirlpool	2001.0	3729.4	325.0
Xerox	5544.0	35603.7	395.0

a. Prepare a crosstabulation for the variables Stockholders' Equity and Profit. Use classes of 0–200, 200–400, . . . , 1000–1200 for Profit, and classes of 0–1200, 1200–2400, . . . , 4800–6000 for Stockholders' Equity.
b. Compute the row percentages for your crosstabulation in part (a).
c. What relationship, if any, do you notice between Profit and Stockholders' Equity?

52. Refer to the data set in Table 2.17.
a. Prepare a crosstabulation for the variables Market Value and Profit.
b. Compute the row percentages for your crosstabulation in part (a).
c. Comment on any relationship between the variables.

53. Refer to the data set in Table 2.17.
a. Prepare a scatter diagram to show the relationship between the variables Profit and Stockholders' Equity.
b. Comment on any relationship between the variables.

54. Refer to the data set in Table 2.17.
a. Prepare a scatter diagram to show the relationship between the variables Market Value and Stockholders' Equity.
b. Comment on any relationship between the variables.

Case Problem 1 Pelican Stores

Pelican Stores, a division of National Clothing, is a chain of women's apparel stores operating throughout the country. The chain recently ran a promotion in which discount coupons were sent to customers of other National Clothing stores. Data collected for a sample of 100 in-store credit card transactions at Pelican Stores during one day while the promotion was

TABLE 2.18 DATA FOR A SAMPLE OF 100 CREDIT CARD PURCHASES AT PELICAN STORES

CD file
PelicanStores

Customer	Type of Customer	Items	Net Sales	Method of Payment	Gender	Marital Status	Age
1	Regular	1	39.50	Discover	Male	Married	32
2	Promotional	1	102.40	Proprietary Card	Female	Married	36
3	Regular	1	22.50	Proprietary Card	Female	Married	32
4	Promotional	5	100.40	Proprietary Card	Female	Married	28
5	Regular	2	54.00	MasterCard	Female	Married	34
.	.	.	.	.	.	.	.
.	.	.	.	.	.	.	.
.	.	.	.	.	.	.	.
96	Regular	1	39.50	MasterCard	Female	Married	44
97	Promotional	9	253.00	Proprietary Card	Female	Married	30
98	Promotional	10	287.59	Proprietary Card	Female	Married	52
99	Promotional	2	47.60	Proprietary Card	Female	Married	30
100	Promotional	1	28.44	Proprietary Card	Female	Married	44

running are contained in the file named PelicanStores. Table 2.18 shows a portion of the data set. The Proprietary Card method of payment refers to charges made using a National Clothing charge card. Customers who made a purchase using a discount coupon are referred to as promotional customers and customers who made a purchase but did not use a discount coupon are referred to as regular customers. Because the promotional coupons were not sent to regular Pelican Stores customers, management considers the sales made to people presenting the promotional coupons as sales it would not otherwise make. Of course, Pelican also hopes that the promotional customers will continue to shop at its stores.

Most of the variables shown in Table 2.18 are self-explanatory, but two of the variables require some clarification.

Items	The total number of items purchased
Net Sales	The total amount ($) charged to the credit card

Pelican's management would like to use this sample data to learn about its customer base and to evaluate the promotion involving discount coupons.

Managerial Report

Use the tabular and graphical methods of descriptive statistics to help management develop a customer profile and to evaluate the promotional campaign. At a minimum, your report should include the following:

1. Percent frequency distribution for key variables.
2. A bar graph or pie chart showing the number of customer purchases attributable to the method of payment.
3. A crosstabulation of type of customer (regular or promotional) versus net sales. Comment on any similarities or differences present.
4. A scatter diagram to explore the relationship between net sales and customer age.

Case Problem 2 Motion Picture Industry

The motion picture industry is a competitive business. More than 50 studios produce a total of 300 to 400 new motion pictures each year, and the financial success of each motion picture varies considerably. The opening weekend gross sales ($millions), the total gross sales ($millions), the number of theaters the movie was shown in, and the number of weeks the motion picture was in the top 60 for gross sales are common variables used to measure

TABLE 2.19 PERFORMANCE DATA FOR 10 MOTION PICTURES

Motion Picture	Opening Gross Sales ($millions)	Total Gross Sales ($millions)	Number of Theaters	Weeks in Top 60
Coach Carter	29.17	67.25	2574	16
Ladies in Lavender	0.15	6.65	119	22
Batman Begins	48.75	205.28	3858	18
Unleashed	10.90	24.47	1962	8
Pretty Persuasion	0.06	0.23	24	4
Fever Pitch	12.40	42.01	3275	14
Harry Potter and the Goblet of Fire	102.69	287.18	3858	13
Monster-in-Law	23.11	82.89	3424	16
White Noise	24.11	55.85	2279	7
Mr. and Mrs. Smith	50.34	186.22	3451	21

CD file
Movies

the success of a motion picture. Data collected for a sample of 100 motion pictures produced in 2005 are contained in the file named Movies. Table 2.19 shows the data for the first 10 motion pictures in this file.

Managerial Report

Use the tabular and graphical methods of descriptive statistics to learn how these variables contribute to the success of a motion picture. Include the following in your report.

1. Tabular and graphical summaries for each of the four variables along with a discussion of what each summary tells us about the motion picture industry.
2. A scatter diagram to explore the relationship between Total Gross Sales and Opening Weekend Gross Sales. Discuss.
3. A scatter diagram to explore the relationship between Total Gross Sales and Number of Theaters. Discuss.
4. A scatter diagram to explore the relationship between Total Gross Sales and Number of Weeks in the Top 60. Discuss.

Appendix 2.1 Using Minitab for Tabular and Graphical Presentations

Minitab offers extensive capabilities for constructing tabular and graphical summaries of data. In this appendix we show how Minitab can be used to construct several graphical summaries and the tabular summary of a crosstabulation. The graphical methods presented include the dot plot, the histogram, the stem-and-leaf display, and the scatter diagram.

Dot Plot

CD file
Audit

We use the audit time data in Table 2.4 to demonstrate. The data are in column C1 of a Minitab worksheet. The following steps will generate a dot plot.

Step 1. Select the **Graph** menu and choose **Dotplot**
Step 2. Select **One Y, Simple** and click **OK**
Step 3. When the Dotplot-One Y, Simple dialog box appears:
Enter C1 in the **Graph Variables** box
Click **OK**

Histogram

CD file Audit

We show how to construct a histogram with frequencies on the vertical axis using the audit time data in Table 2.4. The data are in column C1 of a Minitab worksheet. The following steps will generate a histogram for audit times.

Step 1. Select the **Graph** menu
Step 2. Choose **Histogram**
Step 3. Select **Simple** and click **OK**
Step 4. When the Histogram-Simple dialog box appears:
Enter C1 in the **Graph Variables** box
Click **OK**
Step 5. When the Histogram appears:
Position the mouse pointer over any one of the bars
Double-click
Step 6. When the Edit Bars dialog box appears:
Click on the **Binning** tab
Select **Cutpoint** for Interval Type
Select **Midpoint/Cutpoint positions** for Interval Definition
Enter 10:35/5 in the **Midpoint/Cutpoint positions** box*
Click **OK**

Note that Minitab also provides the option of scaling the x-axis so that the numerical values appear at the midpoints of the histogram rectangles. If this option is desired, modify step 6 to include Select **Midpoint** for Interval Type and Enter 12:32/5 in the **Midpoint/Cutpoint positions** box. These steps provide the same histogram with the midpoints of the histogram rectangles labeled 12, 17, 22, 27, and 32.

Stem-and-Leaf Display

CD file ApTest

We use the aptitude test data in Table 2.8 to demonstrate the construction of a stem-and-leaf display. The data are in column C1 of a Minitab worksheet. The following steps will generate the stretched stem-and-leaf display shown in Section 2.3.

Step 1. Select the **Graph** menu
Step 2. Choose **Stem-and-Leaf**
Step 3. When the Stem-and-Leaf dialog box appears:
Enter C1 in the **Graph Variables** box
Click **OK**

Scatter Diagram

CD file Stereo

We use the stereo and sound equipment store data in Table 2.12 to demonstrate the construction of a scatter diagram. The weeks are numbered from 1 to 10 in column C1, the data for number of commercials are in column C2, and the data for sales are in column C3 of a Minitab worksheet. The following steps will generate the scatter diagram shown in Figure 2.7.

*The entry 10:35/5 indicates that 10 is the starting value for the histogram, 35 is the ending value for the histogram, and 5 is the class width.

Step 1. Select the **Graph** menu
Step 2. Choose **Scatterplot**
Step 3. Select **Simple** and click **OK**
Step 4. When the Scatterplot-Simple dialog box appears:
Enter C3 under **Y variables** and C2 under **X variables**
Click **OK**

Crosstabulation

CD file
Restaurant

We use the data from Zagat's restaurant review, part of which is shown in Table 2.9, to demonstrate. The restaurants are numbered from 1 to 300 in column C1 of the Minitab worksheet. The quality ratings are in column C2, and the meal prices are in column C3.

Minitab can only create a crosstabulation for qualitative variables and meal price is a quantitative variable. So we need to first code the meal price data by specifying the class to which each meal price belongs. The following steps will code the meal price data to create four classes of meal price in column C4: \$10–19, \$20–29, \$30–39, and \$40–49.

Step 1. Select the **Data** menu
Step 2. Choose **Code**
Step 3. Choose **Numeric to Text**
Step 4. When the Code-Numeric to Text dialog box appears:
Enter C3 in the **Code data from columns** box
Enter C4 in the **Into columns** box
Enter 10:19 in the first **Original values** box and \$10-19 in the adjacent **New** box
Enter 20:29 in the second **Original values** box and \$20-29 in the adjacent **New** box
Enter 30:39 in the third **Original values** box and \$30-39 in the adjacent **New** box
Enter 40:49 in the fourth **Original values** box and \$40-49 in the adjacent **New** box
Click **OK**

For each meal price in column C3 the associated meal price category will now appear in column C4. We can now develop a crosstabulation for quality rating and the meal price categories by using the data in columns C2 and C4. The following steps will create a crosstabulation containing the same information as shown in Table 2.10.

Step 1. Select the **Stat** menu
Step 2. Choose **Tables**
Step 3. Choose **Cross Tabulation and Chi-Square**
Step 4. When the Cross Tabulation and Chi-Square dialog box appears:
Enter C2 in the **For rows** box and C4 in the **For columns** box
Select **Counts** under Display
Click **OK**

Appendix 2.2 Using Excel for Tabular and Graphical Presentations

Excel offers extensive capabilities for constructing tabular and graphical summaries of data. In this appendix, we show how Excel can be used to construct a frequency distribution, bar graph, pie chart, histogram, crosstabulation, and scatter diagram. We will demonstrate two of Excel's most powerful tools: the Chart Wizard and the PivotTable Report.

Frequency Distribution and Bar Graph for Qualitative Data

In this section we show how Excel can be used to construct a frequency distribution and a bar graph for qualitative data. We illustrate each using the data on soft drink purchases in Table 2.1.

Frequency distribution We begin by showing how the COUNTIF function can be used to construct a frequency distribution for the data in Table 2.1. Refer to Figure 2.10 as we describe the steps involved. The formula worksheet (showing the functions and formulas used) is set in the background, and the value worksheet (showing the results obtained using the functions and formulas) appears in the foreground.

CD file

SoftDrink

The label "Brand Purchased" and the data for the 50 soft drink purchases are in cells A1:A51. We also entered the labels "Soft Drink" and "Frequency" in cells C1:D1. The five soft drink names are entered into cells C2:C6. Excel's COUNTIF function can now be used to count the number of times each soft drink appears in cells A2:A51. The following steps are used.

Step 1. Select cell D2
Step 2. Enter =COUNTIF($A$2:$A$51,C2)
Step 3. Copy cell D2 to cells D3:D6

FIGURE 2.10 FREQUENCY DISTRIBUTION FOR SOFT DRINK PURCHASES CONSTRUCTED USING EXCEL'S COUNTIF FUNCTION

Note: Rows 11–44 are hidden.

	A	B	C	D	E
1	**Brand Purchased**		**Soft Drink**	**Frequency**	
2	Coke Classic		Coke Classic	=COUNTIF($A$2:$A$51,C2)	
3	Diet Coke		Diet Coke	=COUNTIF($A$2:$A$51,C3)	
4	Pepsi		Dr. Pepper	=COUNTIF($A$2:$A$51,C4)	
5	Diet Coke		Pepsi	=COUNTIF($A$2:$A$51,C5)	
6	Coke Classic		Sprite	=COUNTIF($A$2:$A$51,C6)	
7	Coke Classic				
8	Dr. Pepper				
9	Diet Coke				
10	Pepsi				
45	Pepsi				
46	Pepsi				
47	Pepsi				
48	Coke Classic				
49	Dr. Pepper				
50	Pepsi				
51	Sprite				
52					

	A	B	C	D	E
1	**Brand Purchased**		**Soft Drink**	**Frequency**	
2	Coke Classic		Coke Classic	19	
3	Diet Coke		Diet Coke	8	
4	Pepsi		Dr. Pepper	5	
5	Diet Coke		Pepsi	13	
6	Coke Classic		Sprite	5	
7	Coke Classic				
8	Dr. Pepper				
9	Diet Coke				
10	Pepsi				
45	Pepsi				
46	Pepsi				
47	Pepsi				
48	Coke Classic				
49	Dr. Pepper				
50	Pepsi				
51	Sprite				
52					

The formula worksheet in Figure 2.10 shows the cell formulas inserted by applying these steps. The value worksheet shows the values computed by the cell formulas. This worksheet shows the same frequency distribution that we developed in Table 2.2.

CD file
SoftDrink

Bar graph Here we show how Excel's Chart Wizard can be used to construct a bar graph for the soft drink data. Refer to the frequency distribution shown in the value worksheet of Figure 2.10. The bar chart that we are going to develop is an extension of this worksheet. The worksheet and the bar graph developed using the Chart Wizard as shown in Figure 2.11. The steps are as follows:

Step 1. Select cells C1:D6
Step 2. Click the **Chart Wizard** button on the Standard toolbar (or select the **Insert** menu and choose the **Chart** option)
Step 3. When the Chart Wizard - Step 1 of 4 - Chart Type dialog box appears:
Choose **Column** in the **Chart type** list
Choose **Clustered Column** from the **Chart sub-type** display
Click **Next >**
Step 4. When the Chart Wizard - Step 2 of 4 - Chart Source Data dialog box appears:
Click **Next >**

FIGURE 2.11 BAR GRAPH OF SOFT DRINK PURCHASES CONSTRUCTED USING EXCEL'S CHART WIZARD

	A	B	C	D	E	F	G	H	I
1	**Brand Purchased**		**Soft Drink**	**Frequency**					
2	Coke Classic		Coke Classic	19					
3	Diet Coke		Diet Coke	8					
4	Pepsi		Dr. Pepper	5					
5	Diet Coke		Pepsi	13					
6	Coke Classic		Sprite	5					
7	Coke Classic								
8	Dr. Pepper								
9	Diet Coke								
10	Pepsi								
45	Pepsi								
46	Pepsi								
47	Pepsi								
48	Coke Classic								
49	Dr. Pepper								
50	Pepsi								
51	Sprite								
52									
53									
54									
55									
56									
57									

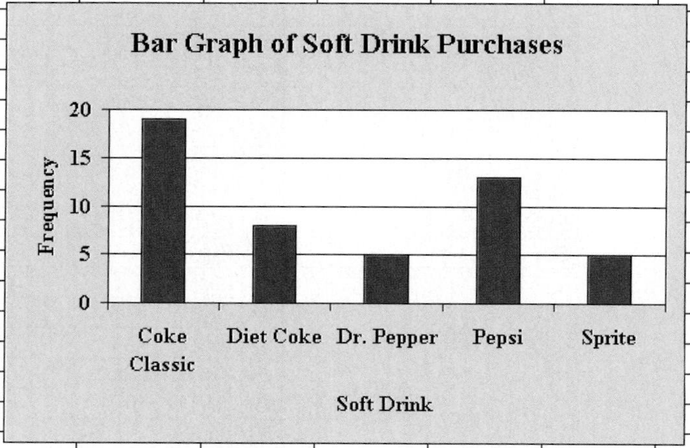

Step 5. When the Chart Wizard - Step 3 of 4 - Chart Options dialog box appears:
Select the **Titles** tab and then
Type Bar Graph of Soft Drink Purchases in the **Chart title** box
Type Soft Drink in the **Category (X)** axis box
Type Frequency in the **Value (Y)** axis box
Select the **Legend** tab and then
Remove the check in the **Show legend** box
Click **Next >**
Step 6. When the Chart Wizard - Step 4 of 4 - Chart Location dialog box appears:
Specify a location for the new chart (we used the current worksheet by selecting **As object in**)
Click **Finish**

The resulting bar graph (chart) is shown in Figure 2.11.*

Excel's Chart Wizard can produce a pie chart for the soft drink data in a similar fashion. The major difference is that in step 3 we would choose **Pie** in the Chart type list.

Frequency Distribution and Histogram for Quantitative Data

In this section we show how Excel can be used to construct a frequency distribution and a histogram for quantitative data. We illustrate each using the audit time data shown in Table 2.4.

CD file
Audit

Frequency distribution Excel's FREQUENCY function can be used to construct a frequency distribution for quantitative data. Refer to Figure 2.12 as we describe the steps involved. The formula worksheet is in the background, and the value worksheet is in the foreground. The label "Audit Time" is in cell A1 and the data for the 20 audits are in cells A2:A21. Using the procedures describe in the text, we make the five classes 10–14, 15–19, 20–24, 25–29, and 30–34. The label "Audit Time" and the five classes are entered in cells C1:C6. The label "Upper Limit" and the five class upper limits are entered in cells D1:D6. We also entered the label "Frequency" in cell E1. Excel's FREQUENCY function will be used to show the class frequencies in cells E2:E6. The following steps describe how to develop a frequency distribution for the audit time data.

You must hold down the Ctrl and Shift keys while pressing the Enter key to enter an array formula.

Step 1. Select cells E2:E6
Step 2. Type, but do not enter, the following formula:

=FREQUENCY(A2:A21,D2:D6)

Step 3. Press CTRL + SHIFT + ENTER and the array formula will be entered into each of the cells E2:E6

The results are shown in Figure 2.12. The values displayed in the cells E2:E6 indicate frequencies for the corresponding classes. Referring to the FREQUENCY function, we see that the range of cells for the upper class limits (D2:D6) provides input to the function. These upper class limits, which Excel refers to as *bins,* tell Excel which frequency to put into the cells of the output range (E2:E6). For example, the frequency for the class with an upper limit, or bin, of 14 is placed in the first cell (E2), the frequency for the class with an upper limit, or bin, of 19 is placed in the second cell (E3), and so on.

---

*The bar graph in Figure 2.11 is a different size than the one provided by Excel after selecting **Finish**. Resizing an Excel chart is not difficult. First, select the chart. Small black squares, called sizing handles, will appear on the chart border. Click on the sizing handles and drag them to resize the figure to your preference.

FIGURE 2.12 FREQUENCY DISTRIBUTION FOR AUDIT TIME DATA CONSTRUCTED USING EXCEL'S FREQUENCY FUNCTION

	A	B	C	D	E
1	Audit Time		Audit Time	Upper Limit	Frequency
2	12		10-14	14	=FREQUENCY(A2:A21,D2:D6)
3	15		15-19	19	=FREQUENCY(A2:A21,D2:D6)
4	20		20-24	24	=FREQUENCY(A2:A21,D2:D6)
5	22		25-29	29	=FREQUENCY(A2:A21,D2:D6)
6	14		30-34	34	=FREQUENCY(A2:A21,D2:D6)
7	14				
8	15				
9	27				
10	21				
11	18				
12	19				
13	18				
14	22				
15	33				
16	16				
17	18				
18	17				
19	23				
20	28				
21	13				

	A	B	C	D	E
1	Audit Times		Audit Times	Upper Limit	Frequency
2	12		10-14	14	4
3	15		15-19	19	8
4	20		20-24	24	5
5	22		25-29	29	2
6	14		30-34	34	1
7	14				
8	15				
9	27				
10	21				
11	18				
12	19				
13	18				
14	22				
15	33				
16	16				
17	18				
18	17				
19	23				
20	28				
21	13				

Histogram To use Excel's Chart Wizard to construct a histogram for the audit time data, we begin with the frequency distribution as shown in Figure 2.12. The frequency distribution worksheet and the histogram output are shown in Figure 2.13. The following steps describe how to use the Chart Wizard to develop the histogram of the audit time data.

Step 1. Select cells E2:E6

Step 2. Click the **Chart Wizard** button on the Standard toolbar (or select the **Insert** menu and choose the **Chart** option)

Step 3. When the Chart Wizard - Step 1 of 4 - Chart Type dialog box appears:
Choose **Column** in the **Chart type** list
Choose **Clustered Column** from the **Chart sub-type** display
Click **Next >**

Step 4. When the Chart Wizard - Step 2 of 4 - Chart Source Data dialog box appears:
Select the **Series** tab and then
Click in the **Category (X) axis labels** box
Select cells C2:C6
Click **Next >**

FIGURE 2.13 EXCEL HISTOGRAM FOR THE AUDIT TIME DATA

	A	B	C	D	E	F	G
1	Audit Times		Audit Times	Upper Limit	Frequency		
2	12		10-14	14	4		
3	15		15-19	19	8		
4	20		20-24	24	5		
5	22		25-29	29	2		
6	14		30-34	34	1		
7	14						
8	15						
9	27						
10	21						
11	18						
12	19						
13	18						
14	22						
15	33						
16	16						
17	18						
18	17						
19	23						
20	28						
21	13						
22							

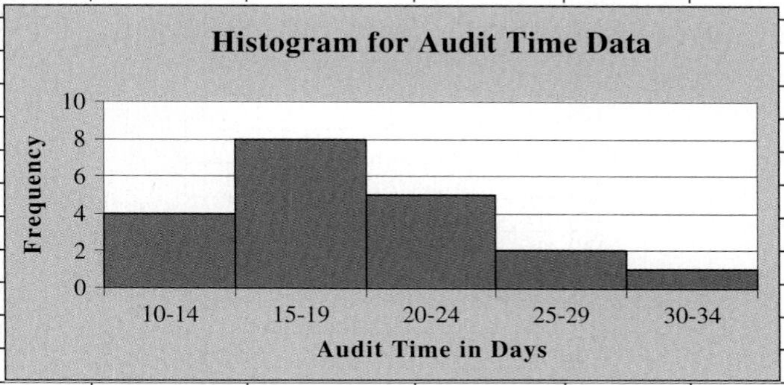

Step 5. When the Chart Wizard - Step 3 of 4 - Chart Options dialog box appears:
Select the **Titles** tab and then
Type Histogram for Audit Time Data in the **Chart title** box
Type Audit Time in Days in the **Category (X)** axis box
Type Frequency in the **Value (Y)** axis box
Select the **Legend** tab and then
Remove the check in the **Show legend** box
Click **Next >**

Step 6. When the Chart Wizard - Step 4 of 4 - Chart Location dialog box appears:
Specify a location for the chart (we used the current worksheet by selecting **As object in**)
Click **Finish**

At this point, the worksheet will show a column chart produced by Excel. However, gaps will appear between the rectangles. Because the adjacent rectangles in a histogram touch, we need to edit the chart in order to eliminate the gaps between the rectangles. The following steps describe this process.

Step 1. Double-click on any rectangle in the column chart

Step 2. When the Format Data Series dialog box appears:
Select the **Options** tab
Enter 0 in the **Cap width** box
Click **OK**

The histogram will appear as shown in Table 2.13.

Finally, an interesting aspect of the worksheet in Figure 2.13 is that Excel has linked the data in cells A2:A21 to the frequencies in cells E2:E6 and to the histogram. If an edit or revision of the data in cells A2:A21 occurs, the frequencies in cells E2:E6 and the histogram

FIGURE 2.14 SCATTER DIAGRAM FOR STEREO AND SOUND EQUIPMENT STORE USING EXCEL'S CHART WIZARD

	A	B	C	D	E	F	G	H
1	Week	No. of Commercials	Sales Volume					
2	1	2	50					
3	2	5	57					
4	3	1	41					
5	4	3	54					
6	5	4	54					
7	6	1						
8	7	5						
9	8	3						
10	9	4						
11	10	2						
12								
13								
14								
15								
16								
17								
18								
19								
20								
21								

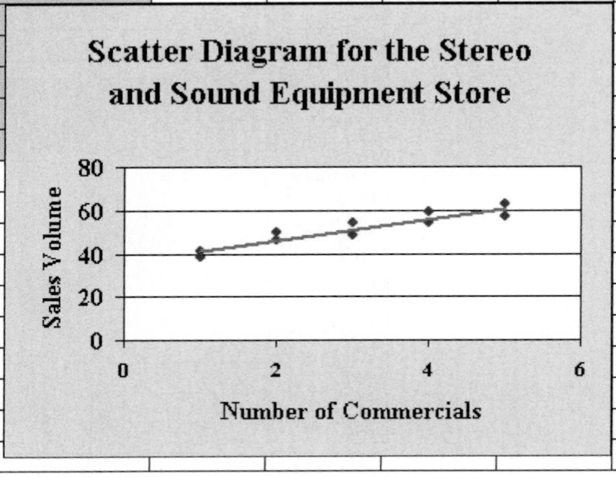

will be updated automatically to display a revised frequency distribution and histogram. Try one or two data edits to see how this automatic updating works.

Scatter Diagram

CD file
Stereo

We use the stereo and sound equipment store data in Table 2.12 to demonstrate the use of Excel's Chart Wizard to construct a scatter diagram. Refer to Figure 2.14 as we describe the tasks involved. The value worksheet is set in the background, and the scatter diagram produced by the Chart Wizard appears in the foreground. The following steps will produce the scatter diagram.

Step 1. Select cells B1:C11

Step 2. Select the **Chart Wizard** button on the standard toolbar (or select the **Insert** menu and choose the **Chart** option)

Step 3. When the Chart Wizard - Step 1 of 4 - Chart Type dialog box appears:
Choose **XY (Scatter)** in the **Chart type:** display
Choose **Scatter** from the **Chart sub-type** display
Click **Next**

Step 4. When the Chart Wizard - Step 2 of 4 - Chart Source Data dialog box appears:
Click **Next**

Step 5. When the Chart Wizard - Step 3 of 4 - Chart Options dialog box appears:
Select the **Titles** tab
Type Scatter Diagram for the Stereo and Sound Equipment Store in the **Chart title** box
Type Number of Commercials in the **Value (X) axis** box
Type Sales Volume in the **Value (Y) axis** box
Select the **Legend** tab
Remove the check in the **Show legend** box
Click **Next**

Step 6. When the Chart Wizard - Step 4 of 4 - Chart Location dialog box appears:
Specify a location for the new chart (we used the current worksheet by selecting **As object in**)
Click **Finish**

A trendline can be added to the scatter diagram as follows.

Step 1. Position the mouse pointer over any data point in the scatter diagram and right-click to display a list of options
Step 2. Choose **Add Trendline**
Step 3. When the Add Trendline dialog box appears:
Select the **Type** tab
Choose **Linear** from the **Trend/Regression type** display
Click **OK**

The worksheet in Figure 2.14 shows the scatter diagram with the trendline added.

PivotTable Report

Excel's PivotTable Report provides a valuable tool for managing data sets involving more than one variable. We will illustrate its use by showing how to develop a crosstabulation.

Crosstabulation We illustrate the construction of a crosstabulation using the restaurant data in Figure 2.15. Labels are entered in row 1, and the data for each of the 300 restaurants are entered into cells A2:C301.

FIGURE 2.15 EXCEL WORKSHEET CONTAINING RESTAURANT DATA

CD file
Restaurant

Note: Rows 12–291 are hidden.

	A	B	C	D
1	**Restaurant**	**Quality Rating**	**Meal Price ($)**	
2	1	Good	18	
3	2	Very Good	22	
4	3	Good	28	
5	4	Excellent	38	
6	5	Very Good	33	
7	6	Good	28	
8	7	Very Good	19	
9	8	Very Good	11	
10	9	Very Good	23	
11	10	Good	13	
292	291	Very Good	23	
293	292	Very Good	24	
294	293	Excellent	45	
295	294	Good	14	
296	295	Good	18	
297	296	Good	17	
298	297	Good	16	
299	298	Good	15	
300	299	Very Good	38	
301	300	Very Good	31	
302				

Step 1. Select the **Data** menu
Step 2. Choose **PivotTable and PivotChart Report**
Step 3. When the PivotTable and PivotChart Wizard - Step 1 of 3 - dialog box appears:
Choose **Microsoft Office Excel list or database**
Choose **PivotTable**
Click **Next**
Step 4. When the PivotTable and PivotChart Wizard - Step 2 of 3 - dialog box appears:
Enter A1:C301 in the **Range** box
Click **Next**
Step 5. When the PivotTable and PivotChart Wizard - Step 3 of 3 - dialog box appears:
Select **New Worksheet**
Click **Layout**
Step 6. When the PivotTable and PivotChart Wizard - Layout diagram appears (see Figure 2.16):
Drag the **Quality Rating** field button to the **ROW** section of the diagram
Drag the **Meal Price ($)** field button to the **COLUMN** section of the diagram
Drag the **Restaurant** field button to the **DATA** section of the diagram
Double-click the **Sum of Restaurant** field button in the DATA section
When the PivotTable Field dialog box appears:
Choose **Count** under **Summarize by**
Click **OK** (Figure 2.17 shows the completed layout diagram)
Click **OK**
Step 7. When the PivotTable and PivotChart Wizard - Step 3 of 3 - dialog box reappears:
Click **Finish**

A portion of the output generated by Excel is shown in Figure 2.18. Note that the output that appears in columns D through AK is hidden so the results can be shown in a reasonably sized figure. The row labels (Excellent, Good, and Very Good) and row totals

FIGURE 2.16 PIVOTTABLE AND PIVOTCHART WIZARD - LAYOUT DIAGRAM

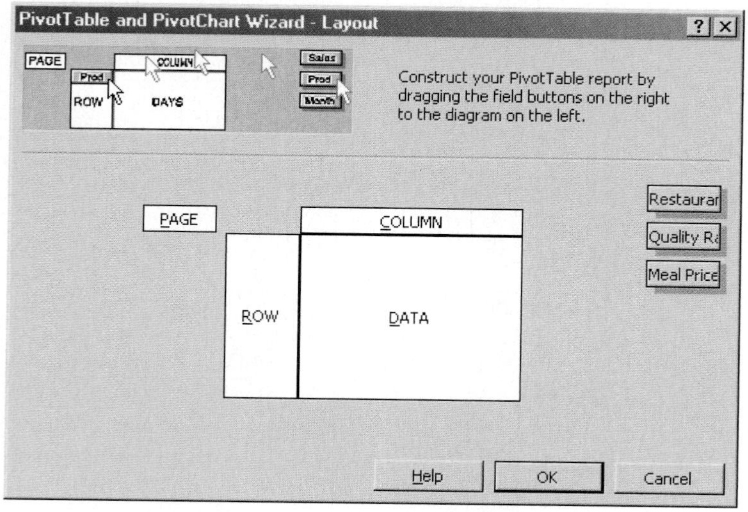

FIGURE 2.17 COMPLETED LAYOUT DIAGRAM

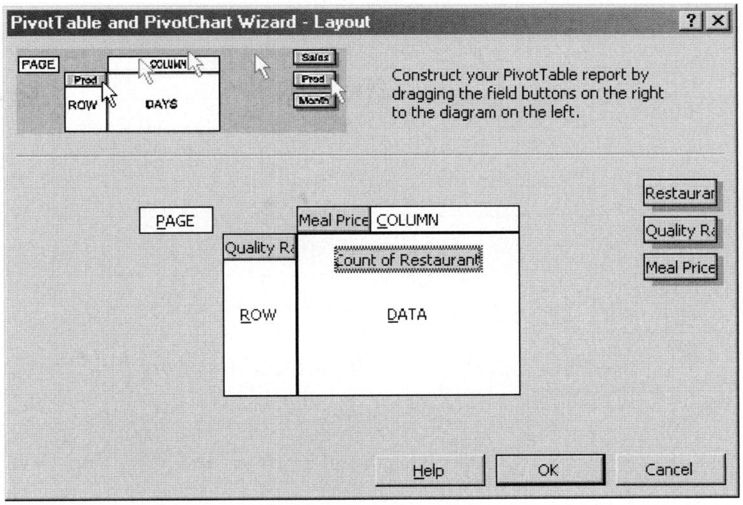

FIGURE 2.18 INITIAL PIVOTTABLE REPORT OUTPUT (COLUMNS D:AK ARE HIDDEN)

	A	B	C	AL	AM	AN	AO
1							
2							
3	Count of Restaurant	Meal Price ($) ▼					
4	Quality Rating ▼	10	11	47	48	Grand Total	
5	Excellent			2	2	66	
6	Good	6	4			84	
7	Very Good	1	4		1	150	
8	Grand Total	7	8	2	3	300	
9							
10							
11							
12		PivotTable					
13		PivotTable ▾					
14							
15							
16							
17							
18							
19							
20							

FIGURE 2.19 FINAL PIVOTTABLE REPORT FOR RESTAURANT DATA

	A	B	C	D	E	F	G
1							
2							
3	Count of Restaurant	Meal Price ($) ▼					
4	Quality Rating ▼	10-19	20-29	30-39	40-49	Grand Total	
5	Good	42	40	2		84	
6	Very Good	34	64	46	6	150	
7	Excellent	2	14	28	22	66	
8	Grand Total	78	118	76	28	300	
9							
10							
11							
12							
13							
14							
15							
16							
17							
18							
19							
20							

(66, 84, 150, and 300) that appear in Figure 2.18 are the same as the row labels and row totals shown in Table 2.10, but they are in a different order. To put them in the order Good, Very Good, Excellent, follow these steps.

Step 1. Right-click on Excellent in cell A5
Step 2. Choose **Order**
Step 3. Select **Move to End**

In Figure 2.18, one column is designated for each possible value of meal price. For example, column B contains a count of restaurants with a $10 meal price, column C contains a count of restaurants with an $11 meal price, and so on. To view the PivotTable Report in a form similar to that shown in Table 2.10, we must group the columns into four price categories: $10–19, $20–29, $30–39, and $40–49. The steps necessary to group the columns for the worksheet shown in Figure 2.18 follow.

Step 1. Right-click on Meal Price ($) in cell B3 of the PivotTable
Step 2. Choose **Group and Show Detail**
Choose **Group**
Step 3. When the **Grouping** dialog box appears
Enter 10 in the **Starting at** box
Enter 49 in the **Ending at** box
Enter 10 in the **By** box
Click **OK**

The revised PivotTable output is shown in Figure 2.19. It is the final PivotTable. Note that it provides the same information as the crosstabulation shown in Table 2.10.

CHAPTER 3

Descriptive Statistics: Numerical Measures

CONTENTS

STATISTICS *in* PRACTICE

SMALL FRY DESIGN*
SANTA ANA, CALIFORNIA

Founded in 1997, Small Fry Design is a toy and accessory company that designs and imports products for infants. The company's product line includes teddy bears, mobiles, musical toys, rattles, and security blankets and features high-quality soft toy designs with an emphasis on color, texture, and sound. The products are designed in the United States and manufactured in China.

Small Fry Design uses independent representatives to sell the products to infant furnishing retailers, children's accessory and apparel stores, gift shops, upscale department stores, and major catalog companies. Currently, Small Fry Design products are distributed in more than 1000 retail outlets throughout the United States.

Cash flow management is one of the most critical activities in the day-to-day operation of this company. Ensuring sufficient incoming cash to meet both current and ongoing debt obligations can mean the difference between business success and failure. A critical factor in cash flow management is the analysis and control of accounts receivable. By measuring the average age and dollar value of outstanding invoices, management can predict cash availability and monitor changes in the status of accounts receivable. The company set the following goals: the average age for outstanding invoices should not exceed 45 days, and the dollar value of invoices more than 60 days old should not exceed 5% of the dollar value of all accounts receivable.

In a recent summary of accounts receivable status, the following descriptive statistics were provided for the age of outstanding invoices:

Mean	40 days
Median	35 days
Mode	31 days

*The authors are indebted to John A. McCarthy, President of Small Fry Design, for providing this Statistics in Practice.

Small Fry Design's "King of the Jungle" mobile.
© Photo courtesy of Small Fry Design, Inc.

Interpretation of these statistics shows that the mean or average age of an invoice is 40 days. The median shows that half of the invoices remain outstanding 35 days or more. The mode of 31 days, the most frequent invoice age, indicates that the most common length of time an invoice is outstanding is 31 days. The statistical summary also showed that only 3% of the dollar value of all accounts receivable was more than 60 days old. Based on the statistical information, management was satisfied that accounts receivable and incoming cash flow were under control.

In this chapter, you will learn how to compute and interpret some of the statistical measures used by Small Fry Design. In addition to the mean, median, and mode, you will learn about other descriptive statistics such as the range, variance, standard deviation, percentiles, and correlation. These numerical measures will assist in the understanding and interpretation of data.

In Chapter 2 we discussed tabular and graphical presentations used to summarize data. In this chapter, we present several numerical measures that provide additional alternatives for summarizing data.

We start by developing numerical summary measures for data sets consisting of a single variable. When a data set contains more than one variable, the same numerical measures can be computed separately for each variable. However, in the two-variable case, we will also develop measures of the relationship between the variables.

Numerical measures of location, dispersion, shape, and association are introduced. If the measures are computed for data from a sample, they are called **sample statistics**. If the measures are computed for data from a population, they are called **population parameters**. In statistical inference, a sample statistic is referred to as the **point estimator** of the corresponding population parameter. In Chapter 7 we will discuss in more detail the process of point estimation.

In the two chapter appendixes we show how Minitab and Excel can be used to compute many of the numerical measures described in the chapter.

3.1 Measures of Location

Mean

Perhaps the most important measure of location is the **mean**, or average value, for a variable. The mean provides a measure of central location for the data. If the data are for a sample, the mean is denoted by $\bar{x}$; if the data are for a population, the mean is denoted by the Greek letter μ.

In statistical formulas, it is customary to denote the value of variable x for the first observation by x_1, the value of variable x for the second observation by x_2, and so on. In general, the value of variable x for the ith observation is denoted by x_i. For a sample with n observations, the formula for the sample mean is as follows.

The sample mean $\bar{x}$ is a sample statistic.

SAMPLE MEAN

$$\bar{x} = \frac{\Sigma x_i}{n} \tag{3.1}$$

In the preceding formula, the numerator is the sum of the values of the n observations. That is,

$$\Sigma x_i = x_1 + x_2 + \cdots + x_n$$

The Greek letter Σ is the summation sign.

To illustrate the computation of a sample mean, let us consider the following class size data for a sample of five college classes.

46 54 42 46 32

We use the notation x_1, x_2, x_3, x_4, x_5 to represent the number of students in each of the five classes.

$$x_1 = 46 \qquad x_2 = 54 \qquad x_3 = 42 \qquad x_4 = 46 \qquad x_5 = 32$$

Hence, to compute the sample mean, we can write

$$\bar{x} = \frac{\Sigma x_i}{n} = \frac{x_1 + x_2 + x_3 + x_4 + x_5}{5} = \frac{46 + 54 + 42 + 46 + 32}{5} = 44$$

The sample mean class size is 44 students.

Another illustration of the computation of a sample mean is given in the following situation. Suppose that a college placement office sent a questionnaire to a sample of business school graduates requesting information on monthly starting salaries. Table 3.1 shows the

TABLE 3.1 MONTHLY STARTING SALARIES FOR A SAMPLE OF 12 BUSINESS SCHOOL GRADUATES

Graduate	Monthly Starting Salary ($)	Graduate	Monthly Starting Salary ($)
1	3450	7	3490
2	3550	8	3730
3	3650	9	3540
4	3480	10	3925
5	3355	11	3520
6	3310	12	3480

CD file
StartSalary

collected data. The mean monthly starting salary for the sample of 12 business college graduates is computed as

$$\bar{x} = \frac{\Sigma x_i}{n} = \frac{x_1 + x_2 + \cdots + x_{12}}{12}$$

$$= \frac{3450 + 3550 + \cdots + 3480}{12}$$

$$= \frac{42{,}480}{12} = 3540$$

Equation (3.1) shows how the mean is computed for a sample with n observations. The formula for computing the mean of a population remains the same, but we use different notation to indicate that we are working with the entire population. The number of observations in a population is denoted by N and the symbol for a population mean is μ.

The sample mean $\bar{x}$ is a point estimator of the population mean μ.

POPULATION MEAN

$$\mu = \frac{\Sigma x_i}{N} \tag{3.2}$$

Median

The **median** is another measure of central location. The median is the value in the middle when the data are arranged in ascending order (smallest value to largest value). With an odd number of observations, the median is the middle value. An even number of observations has no single middle value. In this case, we follow convention and define the median as the average of the values for the middle two observations. For convenience the definition of the median is restated as follows.

MEDIAN

Arrange the data in ascending order (smallest value to largest value).

(a) For an odd number of observations, the median is the middle value.
(b) For an even number of observations, the median is the average of the two middle values.

Let us apply this definition to compute the median class size for the sample of five college classes. Arranging the data in ascending order provides the following list.

32 42 46 46 54

Because $n = 5$ is odd, the median is the middle value. Thus the median class size is 46 students. Even though this data set contains two observations with values of 46, each observation is treated separately when we arrange the data in ascending order.

Suppose we also compute the median starting salary for the 12 business college graduates in Table 3.1. We first arrange the data in ascending order.

$$3310 \quad 3355 \quad 3450 \quad 3480 \quad 3480 \quad \underbrace{3490 \quad 3520}_{\text{Middle Two Values}} \quad 3540 \quad 3550 \quad 3650 \quad 3730 \quad 3925$$

Because $n = 12$ is even, we identify the middle two values: 3490 and 3520. The median is the average of these values.

$$\text{Median} = \frac{3490 + 3520}{2} = 3505$$

The median is the measure of location most often reported for annual income and property value data because a few extremely large incomes or property values can inflate the mean. In such cases, the median is the preferred measure of central location.

Although the mean is the more commonly used measure of central location, in some situations the median is preferred. The mean is influenced by extremely small and large data values. For instance, suppose that one of the graduates (see Table 3.1) had a starting salary of \$10,000 per month (maybe the individual's family owns the company). If we change the highest monthly starting salary in Table 3.1 from \$3925 to \$10,000 and recompute the mean, the sample mean changes from \$3540 to \$4046. The median of \$3505, however, is unchanged, because \$3490 and \$3520 are still the middle two values. With the extremely high starting salary included, the median provides a better measure of central location than the mean. We can generalize to say that whenever a data set contains extreme values, the median is often the preferred measure of central location.

Mode

A third measure of location is the **mode**. The mode is defined as follows.

MODE

The mode is the value that occurs with greatest frequency.

To illustrate the identification of the mode, consider the sample of five class sizes. The only value that occurs more than once is 46. Because this value, occurring with a frequency of 2, has the greatest frequency, it is the mode. As another illustration, consider the sample of starting salaries for the business school graduates. The only monthly starting salary that occurs more than once is \$3480. Because this value has the greatest frequency, it is the mode.

Situations can arise for which the greatest frequency occurs at two or more different values. In these instances more than one mode exists. If the data contain exactly two modes, we say that the data are *bimodal*. If data contain more than two modes, we say that the data are *multimodal*. In multimodal cases the mode is almost never reported because listing three or more modes would not be particularly helpful in describing a location for the data.

Percentiles

A **percentile** provides information about how the data are spread over the interval from the smallest value to the largest value. For data that do not contain numerous repeated values, the pth percentile divides the data into two parts. Approximately p percent of the observations have values less than the pth percentile; approximately $(100 - p)$ percent of the observations have values greater than the pth percentile. The pth percentile is formally defined as follows.

PERCENTILE

The pth percentile is a value such that *at least* p percent of the observations are less than or equal to this value and *at least* $(100 - p)$ percent of the observations are greater than or equal to this value.

Colleges and universities frequently report admission test scores in terms of percentiles. For instance, suppose an applicant obtains a raw score of 54 on the verbal portion of an admission test. How this student performed in relation to other students taking the same test may not be readily apparent. However, if the raw score of 54 corresponds to the 70th percentile, we know that approximately 70% of the students scored lower than this individual and approximately 30% of the students scored higher than this individual.

The following procedure can be used to compute the pth percentile.

Following these steps makes it easy to calculate percentiles.

CALCULATING THE pTH PERCENTILE

Step 1. Arrange the data in ascending order (smallest value to largest value).

Step 2. Compute an index i

$$i = \left(\frac{p}{100}\right)n$$

where p is the percentile of interest and n is the number of observations.

Step 3. (a) If *i is not an integer, round up.* The next integer *greater* than i denotes the position of the pth percentile.

(b) If *i is an integer,* the pth percentile is the average of the values in positions i and $i + 1$.

As an illustration of this procedure, let us determine the 85th percentile for the starting salary data in Table 3.1.

Step 1. Arrange the data in ascending order.

3310 3355 3450 3480 3480 3490 3520 3540 3550 3650 3730 3925

Step 2.

$$i = \left(\frac{p}{100}\right)n = \left(\frac{85}{100}\right)12 = 10.2$$

Step 3. Because i is not an integer, *round up.* The position of the 85th percentile is the next integer greater than 10.2, the 11th position.

Returning to the data, we see that the 85th percentile is the data value in the 11th position, or 3730.

FIGURE 3.1 LOCATION OF THE QUARTILES

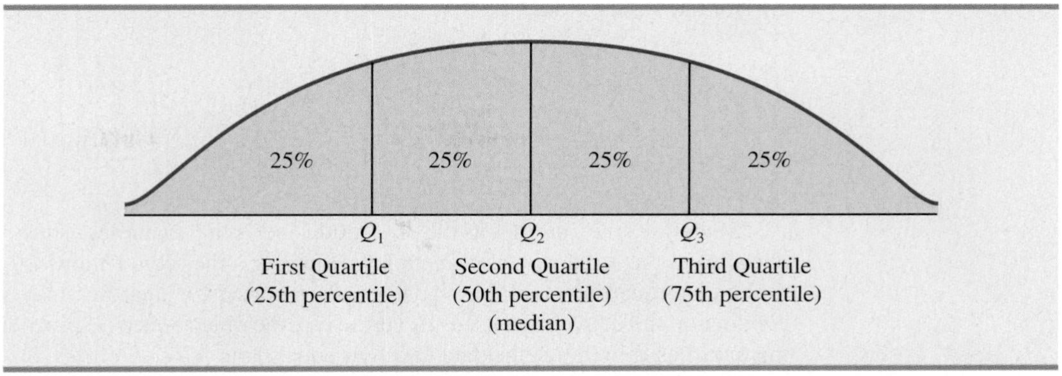

As another illustration of this procedure, let us consider the calculation of the 50th percentile for the starting salary data. Applying step 2, we obtain

$$i = \left(\frac{50}{100}\right)12 = 6$$

Because i is an integer, step 3(b) states that the 50th percentile is the average of the sixth and seventh data values; thus the 50th percentile is (3490 + 3520)/2 = 3505. Note that the *50th percentile is also the median.*

Quartiles

Quartiles are just specific percentiles; thus, the steps for computing percentiles can be applied directly in the computation of quartiles.

It is often desirable to divide data into four parts, with each part containing approximately one-fourth, or 25% of the observations. Figure 3.1 shows a data distribution divided into four parts. The division points are referred to as the **quartiles** and are defined as

Q_1 = first quartile, or 25th percentile
Q_2 = second quartile, or 50th percentile (also the median)
Q_3 = third quartile, or 75th percentile.

The starting salary data are again arranged in ascending order. We already identified Q_2, the second quartile (median), as 3505.

3310 3355 3450 3480 3480 3490 3520 3540 3550 3650 3730 3925

The computations of quartiles Q_1 and Q_3 require the use of the rule for finding the 25th and 75th percentiles. These calculations follow.

For Q_1,

$$i = \left(\frac{p}{100}\right)n = \left(\frac{25}{100}\right)12 = 3$$

Because i is an integer, step 3(b) indicates that the first quartile, or 25th percentile, is the average of the third and fourth data values; thus, $Q_1 = (3450 + 3480)/2 = 3465$.

For Q_3,

$$i = \left(\frac{p}{100}\right)n = \left(\frac{75}{100}\right)12 = 9$$

Again, because i is an integer, step 3(b) indicates that the third quartile, or 75th percentile, is the average of the ninth and tenth data values; thus, $Q_3 = (3550 + 3650)/2 = 3600$.

The quartiles divide the starting salary data into four parts, with each part containing 25% of the observations.

3310 3355 3450 | 3480 3480 3490 | 3520 3540 3550 | 3650 3730 3925

$Q_1 = 3465$ $\qquad$ $Q_2 = 3505$ (Median) $\qquad$ $Q_3 = 3600$

We defined the quartiles as the 25th, 50th, and 75th percentiles. Thus, we computed the quartiles in the same way as percentiles. However, other conventions are sometimes used to compute quartiles, and the actual values reported for quartiles may vary slightly depending on the convention used. Nevertheless, the objective of all procedures for computing quartiles is to divide the data into four equal parts.

NOTES AND COMMENTS

It is better to use the median than the mean as a measure of central location when a data set contains extreme values. Another measure, sometimes used when extreme values are present, is the *trimmed mean*. It is obtained by deleting a percentage of the smallest and largest values from a data set and then computing the mean of the remaining values. For example, the 5% trimmed mean is obtained by removing the smallest 5% and the largest 5% of the data values and then computing the mean of the remaining values. Using the sample with $n = 12$ starting salaries, $0.05(12) = 0.6$. Rounding this value to 1 indicates that the 5% trimmed mean would remove the 1 smallest data value and the 1 largest data value. The 5% trimmed mean using the 10 remaining observations is 3524.50.

Exercises

Methods

1. Consider a sample with data values of 10, 20, 12, 17, and 16. Compute the mean and median.
2. Consider a sample with data values of 10, 20, 21, 17, 16, and 12. Compute the mean and median.

SELF test

3. Consider a sample with data values of 27, 25, 20, 15, 30, 34, 28, and 25. Compute the 20th, 25th, 65th, and 75th percentiles.
4. Consider a sample with data values of 53, 55, 70, 58, 64, 57, 53, 69, 57, 68, and 53. Compute the mean, median, and mode.

Applications

5. The Dow Jones Travel Index reported what business travelers pay for hotel rooms per night in major U.S. cities (*The Wall Street Journal,* January 16, 2004). The average hotel room rates for 20 cities are as follows:

CD file
Hotels

Atlanta	$163	Minneapolis	$125
Boston	177	New Orleans	167
Chicago	166	New York	245
Cleveland	126	Orlando	146
Dallas	123	Phoenix	139
Denver	120	Pittsburgh	134
Detroit	144	San Francisco	167
Houston	173	Seattle	162
Los Angeles	160	St. Louis	145
Miami	192	Washington, D.C.	207

a. What is the mean hotel room rate?
b. What is the median hotel room rate?
c. What is the mode?
d. What is the first quartile?
e. What is the third quartile?

6. The National Association of Colleges and Employers compiled information about annual starting salaries for college graduates by major. The mean starting salary for business administration graduates was $39,850 (*CNNMoney.com,* February 15, 2006). Samples with annual starting data for marketing majors and accounting majors follow (data are in thousands):

CD file BASalary

Marketing Majors

34.2	45.0	39.5	28.4	37.7	35.8	30.6	35.2	34.2	42.4

Accounting Majors

33.5	57.1	49.7	40.2	44.2	45.2	47.8	38.0
53.9	41.1	41.7	40.8	55.5	43.5	49.1	49.9

a. Compute the mean, median, and mode of the annual starting salary for both majors.
b. Compute the first and third quartiles for both majors.
c. Business administration students with accounting majors generally obtain the highest annual salary after graduation. What do the sample data indicate about the difference between the annual starting salaries for marketing and accounting majors?

7. The American Association of Individual Investors conducted an annual survey of discount brokers (*AAII Journal,* January 2003). The commissions charged by 24 discount brokers for two types of trades, a broker-assisted trade of 100 shares at $50 per share and an online trade of 500 shares at $50 per share, are shown in Table 3.2.
a. Compute the mean, median, and mode for the commission charged on a broker-assisted trade of 100 shares at $50 per share.
b. Compute the mean, median, and mode for the commission charged on an online trade of 500 shares at $50 per share.
c. Which costs more, a broker-assisted trade of 100 shares at $50 per share or an online trade of 500 shares at $50 per share?
d. Is the cost of a transaction related to the amount of the transaction?

TABLE 3.2 COMMISSIONS CHARGED BY DISCOUNT BROKERS

CD file Broker

Broker	**Broker-Assisted 100 Shares at $50/Share**	**Online 500 Shares at $50/Share**	**Broker**	**Broker-Assisted 100 Shares at $50/Share**	**Online 500 Shares at $50/Share**
Accutrade	30.00	29.95	Merrill Lynch Direct	50.00	29.95
Ameritrade	24.99	10.99	Muriel Siebert	45.00	14.95
Banc of America	54.00	24.95	NetVest	24.00	14.00
Brown & Co.	17.00	5.00	Recom Securities	35.00	12.95
Charles Schwab	55.00	29.95	Scottrade	17.00	7.00
CyberTrader	12.95	9.95	Sloan Securities	39.95	19.95
E*TRADE Securities	49.95	14.95	Strong Investments	55.00	24.95
First Discount	35.00	19.75	TD Waterhouse	45.00	17.95
Freedom Investments	25.00	15.00	T. Rowe Price	50.00	19.95
Harrisdirect	40.00	20.00	Vanguard	48.00	20.00
Investors National	39.00	62.50	Wall Street Discount	29.95	19.95
MB Trading	9.95	10.55	York Securities	40.00	36.00

Source: AAII Journal, January 2003.

8. Millions of Americans work from offices in their homes. Following is a sample of age data for individuals who work at home.

SELF test

18	54	20	46	25	48	53	27	26	37
40	36	42	25	27	33	28	40	45	25

a. Compute the mean and mode.
b. The median age of the population of all adults is 36 years (*The World Almanac,* 2006). Use the median age of the preceding data to comment on whether the at-home workers tend to be younger or older than the population of all adults.
c. Compute the first and third quartiles.
d. Compute and interpret the 32nd percentile.

9. J. D. Powers and Associates surveyed cell phone users in order to learn about the minutes of cell phone usage per month (Associated Press, June 2002). Minutes per month for a sample of 15 cell phone users are shown here.

615	135	395
430	830	1180
690	250	420
265	245	210
180	380	105

a. What is the mean number of minutes of usage per month?
b. What is the median number of minutes of usage per month?
c. What is the 85th percentile?
d. J. D. Powers and Associates reported that the average wireless subscriber plan allows up to 750 minutes of usage per month. What do the data suggest about cell phone subscribers' utilization of their monthly plan?

10. An American Hospital Association survey found that most hospital emergency rooms are operating at full capacity (Associated Press, April 9, 2002). The survey collected data on the emergency room waiting times for hospitals where the emergency room is operating at full capacity and for hospitals where the emergency room is in balance and rarely operates at capacity. Sample data showing waiting times in minutes are as follows.

ER Waiting Times for Hospitals at Full Capacity		ER Waiting Times for Hospitals in Balance	
87	59	60	39
80	110	54	32
47	83	18	56
73	79	29	26
50	50	45	37
93	66	34	38
72	115		

a. Compute the mean and median emergency room waiting times for hospitals operating at full capacity.
b. Compute the mean and median emergency room waiting times for hospitals operating in balance.
c. What observations can you make about emergency room waiting times based on these results? Would the American Hospital Association express concern with the statistical results shown here?

11. In automobile mileage and gasoline-consumption testing, 13 automobiles were road tested for 300 miles in both city and highway driving conditions. The following data were recorded for miles-per-gallon performance.

City:	16.2	16.7	15.9	14.4	13.2	15.3	16.8	16.0	16.1	15.3	15.2	15.3	16.2
Highway:	19.4	20.6	18.3	18.6	19.2	17.4	17.2	18.6	19.0	21.1	19.4	18.5	18.7

Use the mean, median, and mode to make a statement about the difference in performance for city and highway driving.

12. Walt Disney Company bought Pixar Animation Studios, Inc., in a deal worth $7.4 billion (*CNNMoney.com,* January 24, 2006). The animated movies produced by Disney and Pixar during the previous 10 years are listed below. The box office revenues are in millions of dollars. Compute the total revenue, the mean, the median, and the quartiles to compare the box office success of the movies produced by both companies. Do the statistics suggest at least one of the reasons Disney was interested in buying Pixar? Discuss.

CD file
Disney

Disney Movies	**Revenue ($millions)**	**Pixar Movies**	**Revenue ($millions)**
Pocahontas	346	*Toy Story*	362
Hunchback of Notre Dame	325	*A Bug's Life*	363
Hercules	253	*Toy Story 2*	485
Mulan	304	*Monsters, Inc.*	525
Tarzan	448	*Finding Nemo*	865
Dinosaur	354	*The Incredibles*	631
The Emperor's New Groove	169		
Lilo & Stitch	273		
Treasure Planet	110		
The Jungle Book 2	136		
Brother Bear	250		
Home on the Range	104		
Chicken Little	249		

3.2 Measures of Variability

The variability in the delivery time creates uncertainty for production scheduling. Methods in this section help measure and understand variability.

In addition to measures of location, it is often desirable to consider measures of variability, or dispersion. For example, suppose that you are a purchasing agent for a large manufacturing firm and that you regularly place orders with two different suppliers. After several months of operation, you find that the mean number of days required to fill orders is 10 days for both of the suppliers. The histograms summarizing the number of working days required to fill orders from the suppliers are shown in Figure 3.2. Although the mean number of days is 10 for both suppliers, do the two suppliers demonstrate the same degree of reliability in terms of making deliveries on schedule? Note the dispersion, or variability, in delivery times indicated by the histograms. Which supplier would you prefer?

For most firms, receiving materials and supplies on schedule is important. The seven- or eight-day deliveries shown for J.C. Clark Distributors might be viewed favorably; however, a few of the slow 13- to 15-day deliveries could be disastrous in terms of keeping

FIGURE 3.2 HISTORICAL DATA SHOWING THE NUMBER OF DAYS REQUIRED TO FILL ORDERS

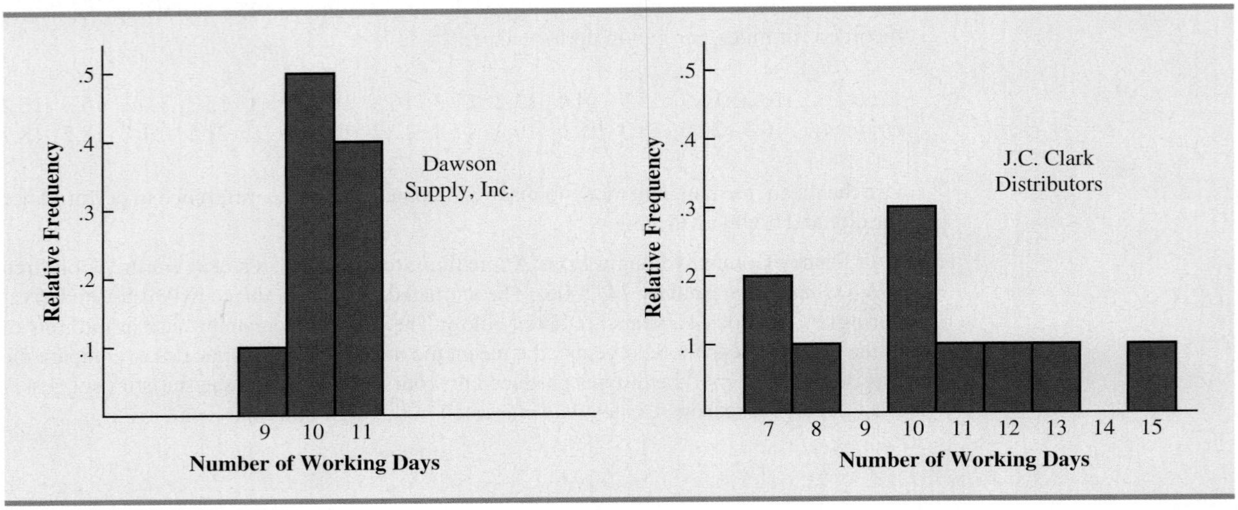

a workforce busy and production on schedule. This example illustrates a situation in which the variability in the delivery times may be an overriding consideration in selecting a supplier. For most purchasing agents, the lower variability shown for Dawson Supply, Inc., would make Dawson the preferred supplier.

We turn now to a discussion of some commonly used measures of variability.

Range

The simplest measure of variability is the **range**.

RANGE

$$\text{Range} = \text{Largest value} - \text{Smallest value}$$

Let us refer to the data on starting salaries for business school graduates in Table 3.1. The largest starting salary is 3925 and the smallest is 3310. The range is $3925 - 3310 = 615$.

Although the range is the easiest of the measures of variability to compute, it is seldom used as the only measure. The reason is that the range is based on only two of the observations and thus is highly influenced by extreme values. Suppose one of the graduates received a starting salary of \$10,000 per month. In this case, the range would be $10,000 - 3310 = 6690$ rather than 615. This large value for the range would not be especially descriptive of the variability in the data because 11 of the 12 starting salaries are closely grouped between 3310 and 3730.

Interquartile Range

A measure of variability that overcomes the dependency on extreme values is the **interquartile range (IQR)**. This measure of variability is the difference between the third quartile, Q_3, and the first quartile, Q_1. In other words, the interquartile range is the range for the middle 50% of the data.

INTERQUARTILE RANGE

$$\text{IQR} = Q_3 - Q_1 \tag{3.3}$$

For the data on monthly starting salaries, the quartiles are $Q_3 = 3600$ and $Q_1 = 3465$. Thus, the interquartile range is $3600 - 3465 = 135$.

Variance

The **variance** is a measure of variability that utilizes all the data. The variance is based on the difference between the value of each observation (x_i) and the mean. The difference between each x_i and the mean ($\bar{x}$ for a sample, μ for a population) is called a *deviation about the mean.* For a sample, a deviation about the mean is written $(x_i - \bar{x})$; for a population, it is written $(x_i - \mu)$. In the computation of the variance, the deviations about the mean are *squared.*

If the data are for a population, the average of the squared deviations is called the *population variance.* The population variance is denoted by the Greek symbol σ^2. For a population of N observations and with μ denoting the population mean, the definition of the population variance is as follows.

POPULATION VARIANCE

$$\sigma^2 = \frac{\Sigma(x_i - \mu)^2}{N} \tag{3.4}$$

In most statistical applications, the data being analyzed are for a sample. When we compute a sample variance, we are often interested in using it to estimate the population variance σ^2. Although a detailed explanation is beyond the scope of this text, it can be shown that if the sum of the squared deviations about the sample mean is divided by $n - 1$, and not n, the resulting sample variance provides an unbiased estimate of the population variance. For this reason, the *sample variance,* denoted by s^2, is defined as follows.

The sample variance s^2 is the estimator of the population variance σ^2.

SAMPLE VARIANCE

$$s^2 = \frac{\Sigma(x_i - \bar{x})^2}{n - 1} \tag{3.5}$$

To illustrate the computation of the sample variance, we will use the data on class size for the sample of five college classes as presented in Section 3.1. A summary of the data, including the computation of the deviations about the mean and the squared deviations about the mean, is shown in Table 3.3. The sum of squared deviations about the mean is $\Sigma(x_i - \bar{x})^2 = 256$. Hence, with $n - 1 = 4$, the sample variance is

$$s^2 = \frac{\Sigma(x_i - \bar{x})^2}{n - 1} = \frac{256}{4} = 64$$

Before moving on, let us note that the units associated with the sample variance often cause confusion. Because the values being summed in the variance calculation, $(x_i - \bar{x})^2$, are squared, the units associated with the sample variance are also *squared.* For instance, the

TABLE 3.3 COMPUTATION OF DEVIATIONS AND SQUARED DEVIATIONS ABOUT THE MEAN FOR THE CLASS SIZE DATA

Number of Students in Class (x_i)	Mean Class Size ($\bar{x}$)	Deviation About the Mean ($x_i - \bar{x}$)	Squared Deviation About the Mean $(x_i - \bar{x})^2$
46	44	2	4
54	44	10	100
42	44	−2	4
46	44	2	4
32	44	−12	144
		0	256
		$\Sigma(x_i - \bar{x})$	$\Sigma(x_i - \bar{x})^2$

sample variance for the class size data is $s^2 = 64$ (students)^2. The squared units associated with variance make it difficult to obtain an intuitive understanding and interpretation of the numerical value of the variance. We recommend that you think of the variance as a measure useful in comparing the amount of variability for two or more variables. In a comparison of the variables, the one with the largest variance shows the most variability. Further interpretation of the value of the variance may not be necessary.

The variance is useful in comparing the variability of two or more variables.

As another illustration of computing a sample variance, consider the starting salaries listed in Table 3.1 for the 12 business school graduates. In Section 3.1, we showed that the sample mean starting salary was 3540. The computation of the sample variance ($s^2 = 27{,}440.91$) is shown in Table 3.4.

TABLE 3.4 COMPUTATION OF THE SAMPLE VARIANCE FOR THE STARTING SALARY DATA

Monthly Salary (x_i)	Sample Mean ($\bar{x}$)	Deviation About the Mean ($x_i - \bar{x}$)	Squared Deviation About the Mean $(x_i - \bar{x})^2$
3450	3540	−90	8,100
3550	3540	10	100
3650	3540	110	12,100
3480	3540	−60	3,600
3355	3540	−185	34,225
3310	3540	−230	52,900
3490	3540	−50	2,500
3730	3540	190	36,100
3540	3540	0	0
3925	3540	385	148,225
3520	3540	−20	400
3480	3540	−60	3,600
		0	301,850
		$\Sigma(x_i - \bar{x})$	$\Sigma(x_i - \bar{x})^2$

Using equation (3.5),

$$s^2 = \frac{\Sigma(x_i - \bar{x})^2}{n - 1} = \frac{301{,}850}{11} = 27{,}440.91$$

In Tables 3.3 and 3.4 we show both the sum of the deviations about the mean and the sum of the squared deviations about the mean. For any data set, the sum of the deviations about the mean will *always equal zero.* Note that in Tables 3.3 and 3.4, $\Sigma(x_i - \bar{x}) = 0$. The positive deviations and negative deviations cancel each other, causing the sum of the deviations about the mean to equal zero.

Standard Deviation

The **standard deviation** is defined to be the positive square root of the variance. Following the notation we adopted for a sample variance and a population variance, we use s to denote the sample standard deviation and σ to denote the population standard deviation. The standard deviation is derived from the variance in the following way.

The sample standard deviation s is the estimator of the population standard deviation σ.

STANDARD DEVIATION

$$\text{Sample standard deviation} = s = \sqrt{s^2} \tag{3.6}$$

$$\text{Population standard deviation} = \sigma = \sqrt{\sigma^2} \tag{3.7}$$

Recall that the sample variance for the sample of class sizes in five college classes is $s^2 = 64$. Thus, the sample standard deviation is $s = \sqrt{64} = 8$. For the data on starting salaries, the sample standard deviation is $s = \sqrt{27{,}440.91} = 165.65$.

The standard deviation is easier to interpret than the variance because the standard deviation is measured in the same units as the data.

What is gained by converting the variance to its corresponding standard deviation? Recall that the units associated with the variance are squared. For example, the sample variance for the starting salary data of business school graduates is $s^2 = 27{,}440.91$ (dollars)^2. Because the standard deviation is the square root of the variance, the units of the variance, dollars squared, are converted to dollars in the standard deviation. Thus, the standard deviation of the starting salary data is \$165.65. In other words, the standard deviation is measured in the same units as the original data. For this reason the standard deviation is more easily compared to the mean and other statistics that are measured in the same units as the original data.

Coefficient of Variation

The coefficient of variation is a relative measure of variability; it measures the standard deviation relative to the mean.

In some situations we may be interested in a descriptive statistic that indicates how large the standard deviation is relative to the mean. This measure is called the **coefficient of variation** and is usually expressed as a percentage.

COEFFICIENT OF VARIATION

$$\left(\frac{\text{Standard deviation}}{\text{Mean}} \times 100\right)\% \tag{3.8}$$

For the class size data, we found a sample mean of 44 and a sample standard deviation of 8. The coefficient of variation is $[(8/44) \times 100]\% = 18.2\%$. In words, the coefficient of variation tells us that the sample standard deviation is 18.2% of the value of the sample mean. For the starting salary data with a sample mean of 3540 and a sample standard deviation of 165.65, the coefficient of variation, $[(165.65/3540) \times 100]\% = 4.7\%$, tells us the sample standard deviation is only 4.7% of the value of the sample mean. In general, the coefficient of variation is a useful statistic for comparing the variability of variables that have different standard deviations and different means.

NOTES AND COMMENTS

1. Statistical software packages and spreadsheets can be used to develop the descriptive statistics presented in this chapter. After the data are entered into a worksheet, a few simple commands can be used to generate the desired output. In Appendixes 3.1 and 3.2, we show how Minitab and Excel can be used to develop descriptive statistics.
2. The standard deviation is a commonly used measure of the risk associated with investing in stock and stock funds (*BusinessWeek,* January 17, 2000). It provides a measure of how monthly returns fluctuate around the long-run average return.
3. Rounding the value of the sample mean $\bar{x}$ and the values of the squared deviations $(x_i - \bar{x})^2$ may introduce errors when a calculator is used in the computation of the variance and standard deviation. To reduce rounding errors, we recommend carrying at least six significant digits during intermediate calculations. The resulting variance or standard deviation can then be rounded to fewer digits.
4. An alternative formula for the computation of the sample variance is

$$s^2 = \frac{\Sigma x_i^2 - n\bar{x}^2}{n - 1}$$

where $\Sigma x_i^2 = x_1^2 + x_2^2 + \cdots + x_n^2$.

Exercises

Methods

13. Consider a sample with data values of 10, 20, 12, 17, and 16. Compute the range and interquartile range.
14. Consider a sample with data values of 10, 20, 12, 17, and 16. Compute the variance and standard deviation.
15. Consider a sample with data values of 27, 25, 20, 15, 30, 34, 28, and 25. Compute the range, interquartile range, variance, and standard deviation.

SELF test

Applications

16. A bowler's scores for six games were 182, 168, 184, 190, 170, and 174. Using these data as a sample, compute the following descriptive statistics.

SELF test

   a. Range
   b. Variance
   c. Standard deviation
   d. Coefficient of variation
17. A home theater in a box is the easiest and cheapest way to provide surround sound for a home entertainment center. A sample of prices is shown here (*Consumer Reports Buying Guide,* 2004). The prices are for models with a DVD player and for models without a DVD player.

Models with DVD Player	Price	Models without DVD Player	Price
Sony HT-1800DP	$450	Pioneer HTP-230	$300
Pioneer HTD-330DV	300	Sony HT-DDW750	300
Sony HT-C800DP	400	Kenwood HTB-306	360
Panasonic SC-HT900	500	RCA RT-2600	290
Panasonic SC-MTI	400	Kenwood HTB-206	300

   a. Compute the mean price for models with a DVD player and the mean price for models without a DVD player. What is the additional price paid to have a DVD player included in a home theater unit?
   b. Compute the range, variance, and standard deviation for the two samples. What does this information tell you about the prices for models with and without a DVD player?

18. Car rental rates per day for a sample of seven Eastern U.S. cities are as follows (*The Wall Street Journal,* January 16, 2004).

City	Daily Rate
Boston	$43
Atlanta	35
Miami	34
New York	58
Orlando	30
Pittsburgh	30
Washington, D.C.	36

a. Compute the mean, variance, and standard deviation for the car rental rates.
b. A similar sample of seven Western U.S. cities showed a sample mean car rental rate of $38 per day. The variance and standard deviation were 12.3 and 3.5, respectively. Discuss any difference between the car rental rates in Eastern and Western U.S. cities.

19. The *Los Angeles Times* regularly reports the air quality index for various areas of Southern California. A sample of air quality index values for Pomona provided the following data: 28, 42, 58, 48, 45, 55, 60, 49, and 50.
a. Compute the range and interquartile range.
b. Compute the sample variance and sample standard deviation.
c. A sample of air quality index readings for Anaheim provided a sample mean of 48.5, a sample variance of 136, and a sample standard deviation of 11.66. What comparisons can you make between the air quality in Pomona and that in Anaheim on the basis of these descriptive statistics?

20. The following data were used to construct the histograms of the number of days required to fill orders for Dawson Supply, Inc., and J.C. Clark Distributors (see Figure 3.2).

Dawson Supply Days for Delivery:	11	10	9	10	11	11	10	11	10	10
Clark Distributors Days for Delivery:	8	10	13	7	10	11	10	7	15	12

Use the range and standard deviation to support the previous observation that Dawson Supply provides the more consistent and reliable delivery times.

21. How do grocery costs compare across the country? Using a market basket of 10 items including meat, milk, bread, eggs, coffee, potatoes, cereal, and orange juice, *Where to Retire* magazine calculated the cost of the market basket in six cities and in six retirement areas across the country (*Where to Retire,* November/December 2003). The data with market basket cost to the nearest dollar are as follows:

City	Cost	Retirement Area	Cost
Buffalo, NY	$33	Biloxi-Gulfport, MS	$29
Des Moines, IA	27	Asheville, NC	32
Hartford, CT	32	Flagstaff, AZ	32
Los Angeles, CA	38	Hilton Head, SC	34
Miami, FL	36	Fort Myers, FL	34
Pittsburgh, PA	32	Santa Fe, NM	31

a. Compute the mean, variance, and standard deviation for the sample of cities and the sample of retirement areas.
b. What observations can be made based on the two samples?

CD file

Broker

22. The American Association of Individual Investors conducted an annual survey of discount brokers (*AAII Journal,* January 2003). The commissions charged by 24 discount brokers for two types of trades, a broker-assisted trade of 100 shares at \$50 per share and an online trade of 500 shares at \$50 per share, are shown in Table 3.2.
    a. Compute the range and interquartile range for each type of trade.
    b. Compute the variance and standard deviation for each type of trade.
    c. Compute the coefficient of variation for each type of trade.
    d. Compare the variability of cost for the two types of trades.
23. Scores turned in by an amateur golfer at the Bonita Fairways Golf Course in Bonita Springs, Florida, during 2005 and 2006 are as follows:

2005 Season	74	78	79	77	75	73	75	77
2006 Season	71	70	75	77	85	80	71	79

    a. Use the mean and standard deviation to evaluate the golfer's performance over the two-year period.
    b. What is the primary difference in performance between 2005 and 2006? What improvement, if any, can be seen in the 2006 scores?
24. The following times were recorded by the quarter-mile and mile runners of a university track team (times are in minutes).

Quarter-Mile Times:	.92	.98	1.04	.90	.99
Mile Times:	4.52	4.35	4.60	4.70	4.50

    After viewing this sample of running times, one of the coaches commented that the quarter-milers turned in the more consistent times. Use the standard deviation and the coefficient of variation to summarize the variability in the data. Does the use of the coefficient of variation indicate that the coach's statement should be qualified?

3.3 Measures of Distribution Shape, Relative Location, and Detecting Outliers

We have described several measures of location and variability for data. In addition, it is often important to have a measure of the shape of a distribution. In Chapter 2 we noted that a histogram provides a graphical display showing the shape of a distribution. An important numerical measure of the shape of a distribution is called **skewness**.

Distribution Shape

Shown in Figure 3.3 are four histograms constructed from relative frequency distributions. The histograms in Panels A and B are moderately skewed. The one in Panel A is skewed to the left; its skewness is −.85. The histogram in Panel B is skewed to the right; its skewness is +.85. The histogram in Panel C is symmetric; its skewness is zero. The histogram in Panel D is highly skewed to the right; its skewness is 1.62. The formula used to compute skewness is somewhat complex.* However, the skewness can be easily computed using

*The formula for the skewness of sample data:

$$\text{Skewness} = \frac{n}{(n-1)(n-2)} \sum \left(\frac{x_i - \bar{x}}{s} \right)^3$$

FIGURE 3.3 HISTOGRAMS SHOWING THE SKEWNESS FOR FOUR DISTRIBUTIONS

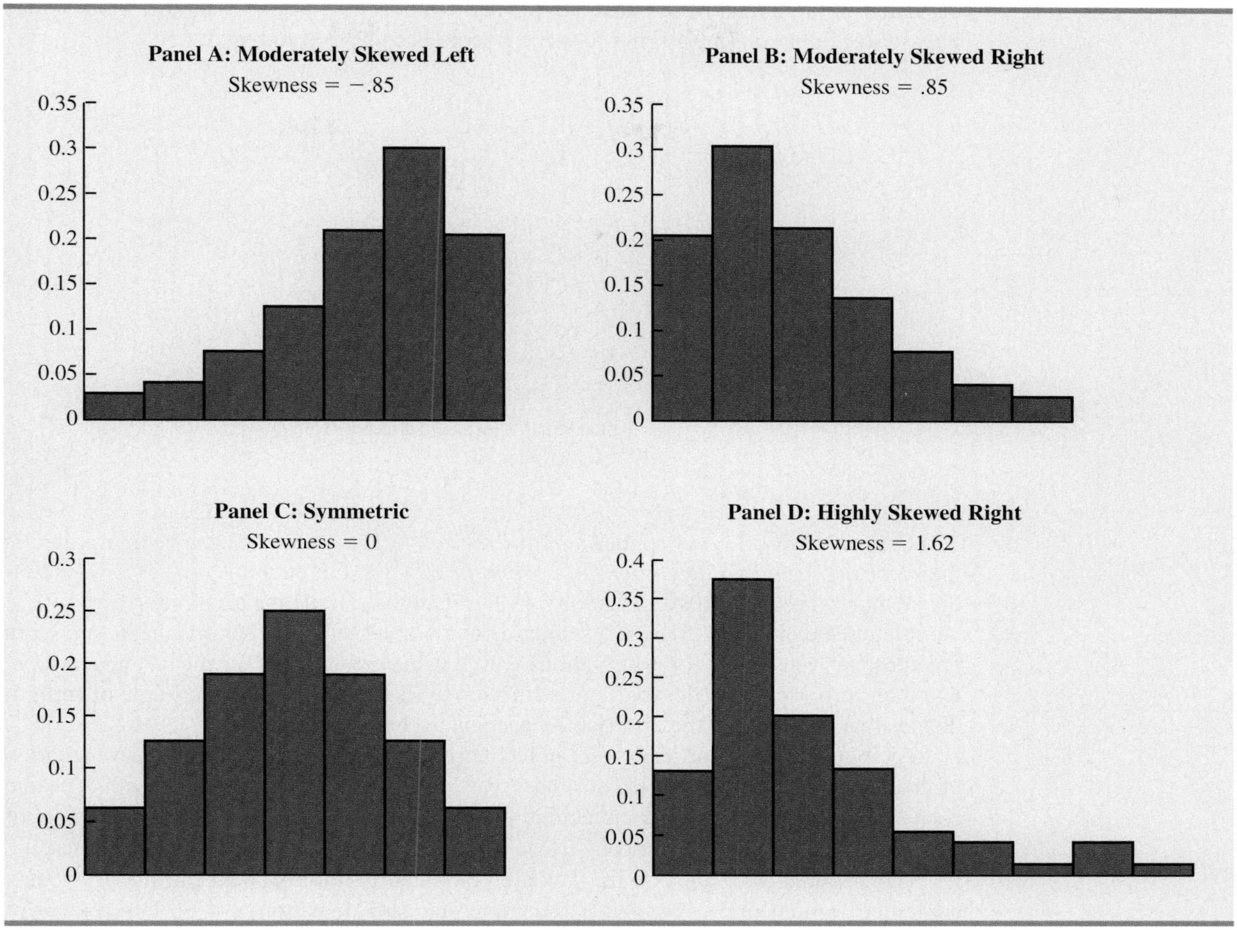

statistical software (see Appendixes 3.1 and 3.2). For data skewed to the left, the skewness is negative; for data skewed to the right, the skewness is positive. If the data are symmetric, the skewness is zero.

For a symmetric distribution, the mean and the median are equal. When the data are positively skewed, the mean will usually be greater than the median; when the data are negatively skewed, the mean will usually be less than the median. The data used to construct the histogram in Panel D are customer purchases at a women's apparel store. The mean purchase amount is $77.60 and the median purchase amount is $59.70. The relatively few large purchase amounts tend to increase the mean, while the median remains unaffected by the large purchase amounts. The median provides the preferred measure of location when the data are highly skewed.

z-Scores

In addition to measures of location, variability, and shape, we are also interested in the relative location of values within a data set. Measures of relative location help us determine how far a particular value is from the mean.

By using both the mean and standard deviation, we can determine the relative location of any observation. Suppose we have a sample of n observations, with the values denoted by $x_1, x_2, \ldots, x_n$. In addition, assume that the sample mean, $\bar{x}$, and the sample standard deviation, s, are already computed. Associated with each value, x_i, is another value called its **z-score**. Equation (3.9) shows how the z-score is computed for each x_i.

z-SCORE

$$z_i = \frac{x_i - \bar{x}}{s} \tag{3.9}$$

where

z_i = the z-score for x_i
$\bar{x}$ = the sample mean
s = the sample standard deviation

The z-score is often called the *standardized value*. The z-score, z_i, can be interpreted as the *number of standard deviations x_i is from the mean $\bar{x}$*. For example, $z_1 = 1.2$ would indicate that x_1 is 1.2 standard deviations greater than the sample mean. Similarly, $z_2 = -.5$ would indicate that x_2 is .5, or 1/2, standard deviation less than the sample mean. A z-score greater than zero occurs for observations with a value greater than the mean, and a z-score less than zero occurs for observations with a value less than the mean. A z-score of zero indicates that the value of the observation is equal to the mean.

The z-score for any observation can be interpreted as a measure of the relative location of the observation in a data set. Thus, observations in two different data sets with the same z-score can be said to have the same relative location in terms of being the same number of standard deviations from the mean.

The z-scores for the class size data are computed in Table 3.5. Recall the previously computed sample mean, $\bar{x} = 44$, and sample standard deviation, $s = 8$. The z-score of -1.50 for the fifth observation shows it is farthest from the mean; it is 1.50 standard deviations below the mean.

Chebyshev's Theorem

Chebyshev's theorem enables us to make statements about the proportion of data values that must be within a specified number of standard deviations of the mean.

TABLE 3.5 z-SCORES FOR THE CLASS SIZE DATA

Number of Students in Class (x_i)	Deviation About the Mean ($x_i - \bar{x}$)	z-Score $\left(\frac{x_i - \bar{x}}{s}\right)$
46	2	2/8 = .25
54	10	10/8 = 1.25
42	−2	−2/8 = −.25
46	2	2/8 = .25
32	−12	−12/8 = −1.50

CHEBYSHEV'S THEOREM

At least $(1 - 1/z^2)$ of the data values must be within z standard deviations of the mean, where z is any value greater than 1.

Some of the implications of this theorem, with $z = 2$, 3, and 4 standard deviations, follow.

- At least .75, or 75%, of the data values must be within $z = 2$ standard deviations of the mean.
- At least .89, or 89%, of the data values must be within $z = 3$ standard deviations of the mean.
- At least .94, or 94%, of the data values must be within $z = 4$ standard deviations of the mean.

For an example using Chebyshev's theorem, suppose that the midterm test scores for 100 students in a college business statistics course had a mean of 70 and a standard deviation of 5. How many students had test scores between 60 and 80? How many students had test scores between 58 and 82?

For the test scores between 60 and 80, we note that 60 is two standard deviations below the mean and 80 is two standard deviations above the mean. Using Chebyshev's theorem, we see that at least .75, or at least 75%, of the observations must have values within two standard deviations of the mean. Thus, at least 75% of the students must have scored between 60 and 80.

Chebyshev's theorem requires $z > 1$; but z need not be an integer.

For the test scores between 58 and 82, we see that $(58 - 70)/5 = -2.4$ indicates 58 is 2.4 standard deviations below the mean and that $(82 - 70)/5 = +2.4$ indicates 82 is 2.4 standard deviations above the mean. Applying Chebyshev's theorem with $z = 2.4$, we have

$$\left(1 - \frac{1}{z^2}\right) = \left(1 - \frac{1}{(2.4)^2}\right) = .826$$

At least 82.6% of the students must have test scores between 58 and 82.

Empirical Rule

The empirical rule is based on the normal probability distribution, which will be discussed in Chapter 6. The normal distribution is used extensively throughout the text.

One of the advantages of Chebyshev's theorem is that it applies to any data set regardless of the shape of the distribution of the data. Indeed, it could be used with any of the distributions in Figure 3.3. In many practical applications, however, data sets exhibit a symmetric mound-shaped or bell-shaped distribution like the one shown in Figure 3.4. When the data are believed to approximate this distribution, the **empirical rule** can be used to determine the percentage of data values that must be within a specified number of standard deviations of the mean.

EMPIRICAL RULE

For data having a bell-shaped distribution:

- Approximately 68% of the data values will be within one standard deviation of the mean.
- Approximately 95% of the data values will be within two standard deviations of the mean.
- Almost all of the data values will be within three standard deviations of the mean.

FIGURE 3.4 A SYMMETRIC MOUND-SHAPED OR BELL-SHAPED DISTRIBUTION

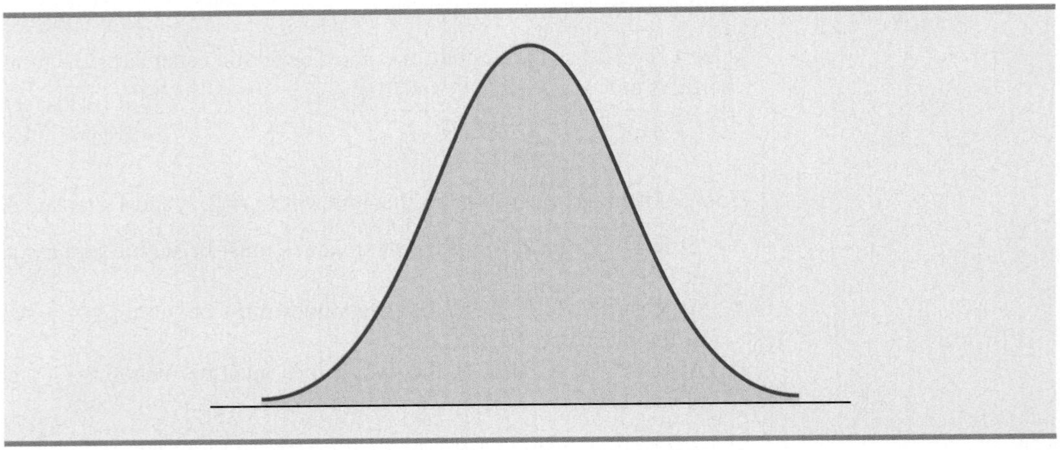

For example, liquid detergent cartons are filled automatically on a production line. Filling weights frequently have a bell-shaped distribution. If the mean filling weight is 16 ounces and the standard deviation is .25 ounces, we can use the empirical rule to draw the following conclusions.

- Approximately 68% of the filled cartons will have weights between 15.75 and 16.25 ounces (within one standard deviation of the mean).
- Approximately 95% of the filled cartons will have weights between 15.50 and 16.50 ounces (within two standard deviations of the mean).
- Almost all filled cartons will have weights between 15.25 and 16.75 ounces (within three standard deviations of the mean).

Detecting Outliers

Sometimes a data set will have one or more observations with unusually large or unusually small values. These extreme values are called **outliers**. Experienced statisticians take steps to identify outliers and then review each one carefully. An outlier may be a data value that has been incorrectly recorded. If so, it can be corrected before further analysis. An outlier may also be from an observation that was incorrectly included in the data set; if so, it can be removed. Finally, an outlier may be an unusual data value that has been recorded correctly and belongs in the data set. In such cases it should remain.

It is a good idea to check for outliers before making decisions based on data analysis. Errors are often made in recording data and entering data into the computer. Outliers should not necessarily be deleted, but their accuracy and appropriateness should be verified.

Standardized values (z-scores) can be used to identify outliers. Recall that the empirical rule allows us to conclude that for data with a bell-shaped distribution, almost all the data values will be within three standard deviations of the mean. Hence, in using z-scores to identify outliers, we recommend treating any data value with a z-score less than -3 or greater than $+3$ as an outlier. Such data values can then be reviewed for accuracy and to determine whether they belong in the data set.

Refer to the z-scores for the class size data in Table 3.5. The z-score of -1.50 shows the fifth class size is farthest from the mean. However, this standardized value is well within the -3 to $+3$ guideline for outliers. Thus, the z-scores do not indicate that outliers are present in the class size data.

NOTES AND COMMENTS

1. Chebyshev's theorem is applicable for any data set and can be used to state the minimum number of data values that will be within a certain number of standard deviations of the mean. If the data are known to be approximately bell-shaped, more can be said. For instance, the

empirical rule allows us to say that *approximately* 95% of the data values will be within two standard deviations of the mean; Chebyshev's theorem allows us to conclude only that at least 75% of the data values will be in that interval.

2. Before analyzing a data set, statisticians usually make a variety of checks to ensure the validity of data. In a large study it is not uncommon for errors to be made in recording data values or in entering the values into a computer. Identifying outliers is one tool used to check the validity of the data.

Exercises

Methods

25. Consider a sample with data values of 10, 20, 12, 17, and 16. Compute the z-score for each of the five observations.

26. Consider a sample with a mean of 500 and a standard deviation of 100. What are the z-scores for the following data values: 520, 650, 500, 450, and 280?

SELF test

27. Consider a sample with a mean of 30 and a standard deviation of 5. Use Chebyshev's theorem to determine the percentage of the data within each of the following ranges.
    a. 20 to 40
    b. 15 to 45
    c. 22 to 38
    d. 18 to 42
    e. 12 to 48

28. Suppose the data have a bell-shaped distribution with a mean of 30 and a standard deviation of 5. Use the empirical rule to determine the percentage of data within each of the following ranges.
    a. 20 to 40
    b. 15 to 45
    c. 25 to 35

Applications

SELF test

29. The results of a national survey showed that on average, adults sleep 6.9 hours per night. Suppose that the standard deviation is 1.2 hours.
    a. Use Chebyshev's theorem to calculate the percentage of individuals who sleep between 4.5 and 9.3 hours.
    b. Use Chebyshev's theorem to calculate the percentage of individuals who sleep between 3.9 and 9.9 hours.
    c. Assume that the number of hours of sleep follows a bell-shaped distribution. Use the empirical rule to calculate the percentage of individuals who sleep between 4.5 and 9.3 hours per day. How does this result compare to the value that you obtained using Chebyshev's theorem in part (a)?

30. The Energy Information Administration reported that the mean retail price per gallon of regular grade gasoline was $2.30 (*Energy Information Administration,* February 27, 2006). Suppose that the standard deviation was $.10 and that the retail price per gallon has a bell-shaped distribution.
    a. What percentage of regular grade gasoline sold between $2.20 and $2.40 per gallon?
    b. What percentage of regular grade gasoline sold between $2.20 and $2.50 per gallon?
    c. What percentage of regular grade gasoline sold for more than $2.50 per gallon?

31. The national average for the verbal portion of the College Board's Scholastic Aptitude Test (SAT) is 507 (*The World Almanac,* 2006). The College Board periodically rescales the test scores such that the standard deviation is approximately 100. Answer the following questions using a bell-shaped distribution and the empirical rule for the verbal test scores.

a. What percentage of students have an SAT verbal score greater than 607?
b. What percentage of students have an SAT verbal score greater than 707?
c. What percentage of students have an SAT verbal score between 407 and 507?
d. What percentage of students have an SAT verbal score between 307 and 607?

32. The high costs in the California real estate market have caused families who cannot afford to buy bigger homes to consider backyard sheds as an alternative form of housing expansion. Many are using the backyard structures for home offices, art studios, and hobby areas as well as for additional storage. The mean price of a customized wooden, shingled backyard structure is $3100 (*Newsweek,* September 29, 2003). Assume that the standard deviation is $1200.
    a. What is the z-score for a backyard structure costing $2300?
    b. What is the z-score for a backyard structure costing $4900?
    c. Interpret the z-scores in parts (a) and (b). Comment on whether either should be considered an outlier.
    d. The *Newsweek* article described a backyard shed-office combination built in Albany, California, for $13,000. Should this structure be considered an outlier? Explain.

33. Florida Power & Light (FP&L) Company has enjoyed a reputation for quickly fixing its electric system after storms. However, during the hurricane seasons of 2004 and 2005, a new reality was that the company's historical approach to emergency electric system repairs was no longer good enough (*The Wall Street Journal,* January 16, 2006). Data showing the days required to restore electric service after seven hurricanes during 2004 and 2005 follow.

Hurricane	Days to Restore Service
Charley	13
Frances	12
Jeanne	8
Dennis	3
Katrina	8
Rita	2
Wilma	18

Based on this sample of seven, compute the following descriptive statistics:
    a. Mean, median, and mode
    b. Range and standard deviation
    c. Should Wilma be considered an outlier in terms of the days required to restore electric service?
    d. The seven hurricanes resulted in 10 million service interruptions to customers. Do the statistics show that FP&L should consider updating its approach to emergency electric system repairs? Discuss.

34. A sample of 10 NCAA college basketball game scores provided the following data (*USA Today,* January 26, 2004).

CD file
NCAA

Winning Team	Points	Losing Team	Points	Winning Margin
Arizona	90	Oregon	66	24
Duke	85	Georgetown	66	19
Florida State	75	Wake Forest	70	5
Kansas	78	Colorado	57	21
Kentucky	71	Notre Dame	63	8
Louisville	65	Tennessee	62	3
Oklahoma State	72	Texas	66	6

Winning Team	Points	Losing Team	Points	Winning Margin
Purdue	76	Michigan State	70	6
Stanford	77	Southern Cal	67	10
Wisconsin	76	Illinois	56	20

a. Compute the mean and standard deviation for the points scored by the winning team.
b. Assume that the points scored by the winning teams for all NCAA games follow a bell-shaped distribution. Using the mean and standard deviation found in part (a), estimate the percentage of all NCAA games in which the winning team scores 84 or more points. Estimate the percentage of NCAA games in which the winning team scores more than 90 points.
c. Compute the mean and standard deviation for the winning margin. Do the data contain outliers? Explain.

35. *Consumer Review* posts reviews and ratings of a variety of products on the Internet. The following is a sample of 20 speaker systems and their ratings (www.audioreview.com). The ratings are on a scale of 1 to 5, with 5 being best.

CD file
Speakers

Speaker	Rating	Speaker	Rating
Infinity Kappa 6.1	4.00	ACI Sapphire III	4.67
Allison One	4.12	Bose 501 Series	2.14
Cambridge Ensemble II	3.82	DCM KX-212	4.09
Dynaudio Contour 1.3	4.00	Eosone RSF1000	4.17
Hsu Rsch. HRSW12V	4.56	Joseph Audio RM7si	4.88
Legacy Audio Focus	4.32	Martin Logan Aerius	4.26
Mission 73li	4.33	Omni Audio SA 12.3	2.32
PSB 400i	4.50	Polk Audio RT12	4.50
Snell Acoustics D IV	4.64	Sunfire True Subwoofer	4.17
Thiel CS1.5	4.20	Yamaha NS-A636	2.17

a. Compute the mean and the median.
b. Compute the first and third quartiles.
c. Compute the standard deviation.
d. The skewness of this data is -1.67. Comment on the shape of the distribution.
e. What are the z-scores associated with Allison One and Omni Audio?
f. Do the data contain any outliers? Explain.

3.4 Exploratory Data Analysis

In Chapter 2 we introduced the stem-and-leaf display as a technique of exploratory data analysis. Recall that exploratory data analysis enables us to use simple arithmetic and easy-to-draw pictures to summarize data. In this section we continue exploratory data analysis by considering five-number summaries and box plots.

Five-Number Summary

In a **five-number summary**, the following five numbers are used to summarize the data.

1. Smallest value
2. First quartile (Q_1)
3. Median (Q_2)

4. Third quartile (Q_3)
5. Largest value

The easiest way to develop a five-number summary is to first place the data in ascending order. Then it is easy to identify the smallest value, the three quartiles, and the largest value. The monthly starting salaries shown in Table 3.1 for a sample of 12 business school graduates are repeated here in ascending order.

3310	3355	3450	3480	3480	3490	3520	3540	3550	3650	3730	3925

$Q_1 = 3465$ $\quad$ $Q_2 = 3505$ (Median) $\quad$ $Q_3 = 3600$

The median of 3505 and the quartiles $Q_1 = 3465$ and $Q_3 = 3600$ were computed in Section 3.1. Reviewing the data shows a smallest value of 3310 and a largest value of 3925. Thus the five-number summary for the salary data is 3310, 3465, 3505, 3600, 3925. Approximately one-fourth, or 25%, of the observations are between adjacent numbers in a five-number summary.

Box Plot

A **box plot** is a graphical summary of data that is based on a five-number summary. A key to the development of a box plot is the computation of the median and the quartiles, Q_1 and Q_3. The interquartile range, IQR $= Q_3 - Q_1$, is also used. Figure 3.5 is the box plot for the monthly starting salary data. The steps used to construct the box plot follow.

Box plots provide another way to identify outliers. But they do not necessarily identify the same values as those with a z-score less than −3 or greater than +3. Either or both procedures may be used.

1. A box is drawn with the ends of the box located at the first and third quartiles. For the salary data, $Q_1 = 3465$ and $Q_3 = 3600$. This box contains the middle 50% of the data.
2. A vertical line is drawn in the box at the location of the median (3505 for the salary data).
3. By using the interquartile range, IQR $= Q_3 - Q_1$, *limits* are located. The limits for the box plot are 1.5(IQR) below Q_1 and 1.5(IQR) above Q_3. For the salary data, IQR $= Q_3 - Q_1 = 3600 - 3465 = 135$. Thus, the limits are $3465 - 1.5(135) = 3262.5$ and $3600 + 1.5(135) = 3802.5$. Data outside these limits are considered *outliers.*
4. The dashed lines in Figure 3.5 are called *whiskers.* The whiskers are drawn from the ends of the box to the smallest and largest values *inside the limits* computed in step 3. Thus, the whiskers end at salary values of 3310 and 3730.
5. Finally, the location of each outlier is shown with the symbol *. In Figure 3.5 we see one outlier, 3925.

FIGURE 3.5 BOX PLOT OF THE STARTING SALARY DATA WITH LINES SHOWING THE LOWER AND UPPER LIMITS

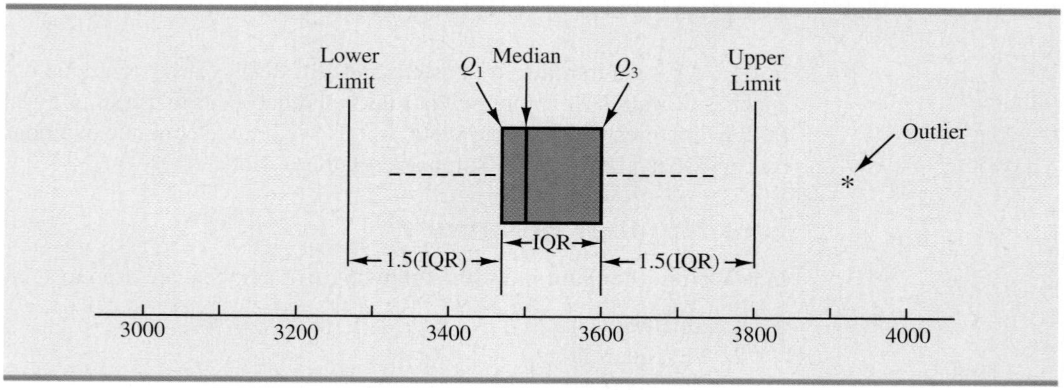

In Figure 3.5 we included lines showing the location of the upper and lower limits. These lines were drawn to show how the limits are computed and where they are located for the salary data. Although the limits are always computed, generally they are not drawn on the box plots. Figure 3.6 shows the usual appearance of a box plot for the salary data.

FIGURE 3.6 BOX PLOT OF THE STARTING SALARY DATA

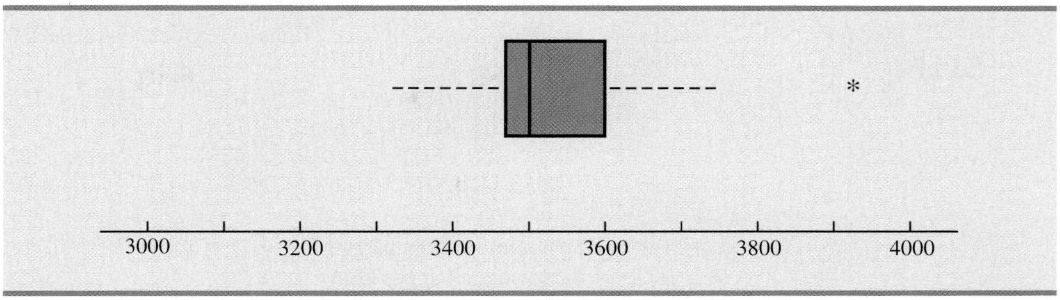

NOTES AND COMMENTS

1. An advantage of the exploratory data analysis procedures is that they are easy to use; few numerical calculations are necessary. We simply sort the data values into ascending order and identify the five-number summary. The box plot can then be constructed. It is not necessary to compute the mean and the standard deviation for the data.
2. In Appendix 3.1, we show how to construct a box plot for the starting salary data using Minitab. The box plot obtained looks just like the one in Figure 3.6, but turned on its side.

Exercises

Methods

36. Consider a sample with data values of 27, 25, 20, 15, 30, 34, 28, and 25. Provide the five-number summary for the data.

37. Show the box plot for the data in exercise 36.

SELF test

38. Show the five-number summary and the box plot for the following data: 5, 15, 18, 10, 8, 12, 16, 10, 6.

39. A data set has a first quartile of 42 and a third quartile of 50. Compute the lower and upper limits for the corresponding box plot. Should a data value of 65 be considered an outlier?

Applications

40. Ebby Halliday Realtors provide advertisements for distinctive properties and estates located throughout the United States. The prices listed for 22 distinctive properties and estates are shown here (*The Wall Street Journal,* January 16, 2004). Prices are in thousands.

CD file
Property

1500	700	2995
895	619	880
719	725	3100
619	739	1699
625	799	1120
4450	2495	1250
2200	1395	912
1280		

a. Provide a five-number summary.
b. Compute the lower and upper limits.
c. The highest priced property, $4,450,000, is listed as an estate overlooking White Rock Lake in Dallas, Texas. Should this property be considered an outlier? Explain.
d. Should the second highest priced property, listed for $3,100,000, be considered an outlier? Explain.
e. Show a box plot.

SELF test

41. Annual sales, in millions of dollars, for 21 pharmaceutical companies follow.

8408	1374	1872	8879	2459	11413
608	14138	6452	1850	2818	1356
10498	7478	4019	4341	739	2127
3653	5794	8305			

a. Provide a five-number summary.
b. Compute the lower and upper limits.
c. Do the data contain any outliers?
d. Johnson & Johnson's sales are the largest on the list at $14,138 million. Suppose a data entry error (a transposition) had been made and the sales had been entered as $41,138 million. Would the method of detecting outliers in part (c) identify this problem and allow for correction of the data entry error?
e. Show a box plot.

42. Major League Baseball payrolls continue to escalate. Team payrolls in millions are as follows (*USA Today* Online Database, March 2006).

CD file
Baseball

Team	Payroll	Team	Payroll
Arizona	$ 62	Milwaukee	$ 40
Atlanta	86	Minnesota	56
Baltimore	74	NY Mets	101
Boston	124	NY Yankees	208
Chi Cubs	87	Oakland	55
Chi White Sox	75	Philadelphia	96
Cincinnati	62	Pittsburgh	38
Cleveland	42	San Diego	63
Colorado	48	San Francisco	90
Detroit	69	Seattle	88
Florida	60	St. Louis	92
Houston	77	Tampa Bay	30
Kansas City	37	Texas	56
LA Angels	98	Toronto	46
LA Dodgers	83	Washington	49

a. What is the median team payroll?
b. Provide a five-number summary.
c. Is the $208 million payroll for the New York Yankees an outlier? Explain.
d. Show a box plot.

43. New York Stock Exchange (NYSE) Chairman Richard Grasso and NYSE Board of Directors came under fire for the large compensation package being paid to Grasso. When it comes to salary plus bonus, Grasso's $8.5 million out-earned the top executives of all major financial services companies. The data that follow show total annual salary plus bonus

FIGURE 3.9 INTERPRETATION OF SAMPLE COVARIANCE

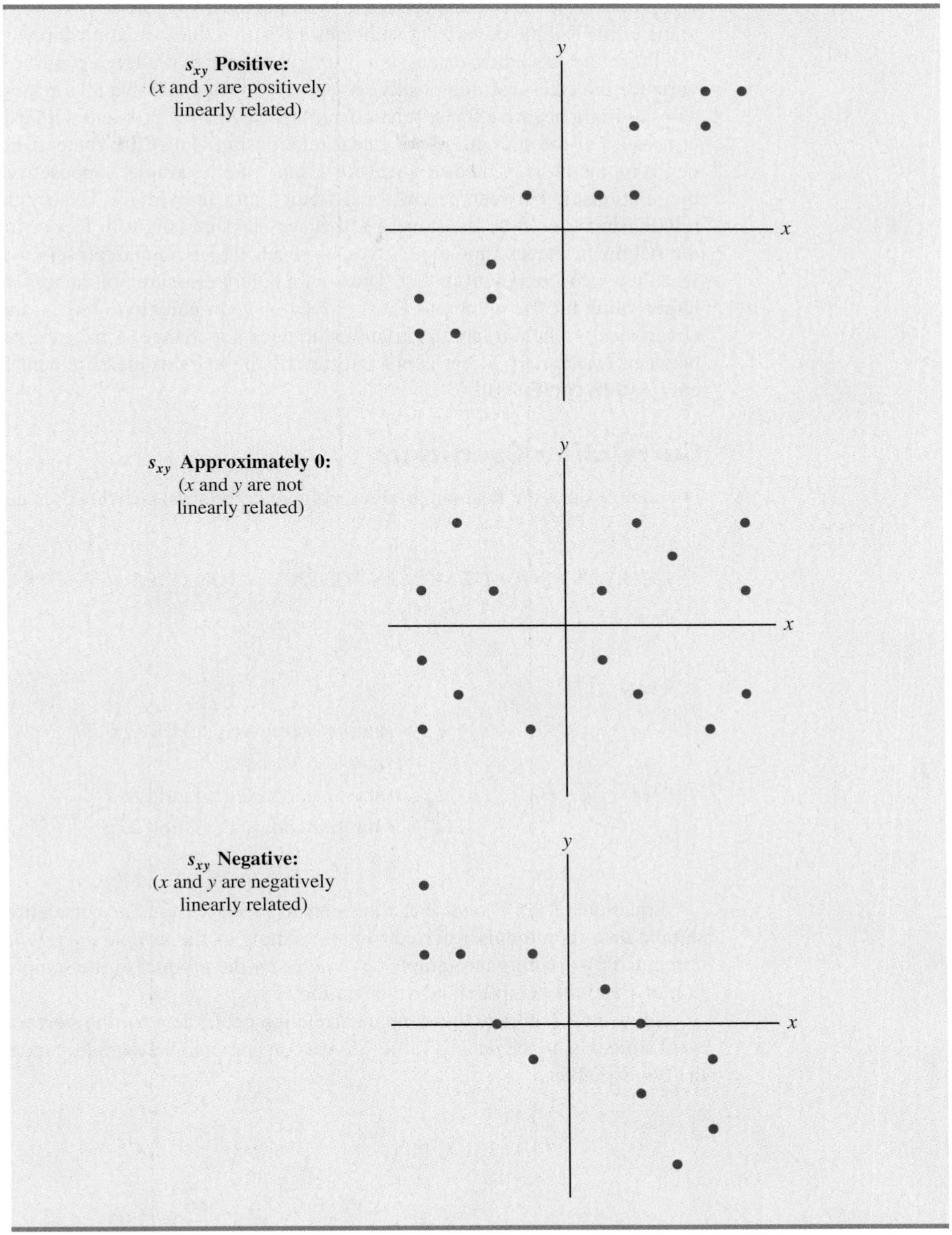

Referring again to Figure 3.8, we see that the scatter diagram for the stereo and sound equipment store follows the pattern in the top panel of Figure 3.9. As we should expect, the value of the sample covariance indicates a positive linear relationship with $s_{xy} = 11$.

From the preceding discussion, it might appear that a large positive value for the covariance indicates a strong positive linear relationship and that a large negative value indicates a strong negative linear relationship. However, one problem with using covariance as a measure of the strength of the linear relationship is that the value of the covariance depends on the units of measurement for x and y. For example, suppose we are interested in the relationship between height x and weight y for individuals. Clearly the strength of the relationship should be the same whether we measure height in feet or inches. Measuring the height in inches, however, gives us much larger numerical values for $(x_i - \bar{x})$ than when we measure height in feet. Thus, with height measured in inches, we would obtain a larger value for the numerator $\Sigma(x_i - \bar{x})(y_i - \bar{y})$ in equation (3.10)—and hence a larger covariance—when in fact the relationship does not change. A measure of the relationship between two variables that is not affected by the units of measurement for x and y is the **correlation coefficient**.

Correlation Coefficient

For sample data, the Pearson product moment correlation coefficient is defined as follows.

PEARSON PRODUCT MOMENT CORRELATION COEFFICIENT: SAMPLE DATA

$$r_{xy} = \frac{s_{xy}}{s_x s_y} \tag{3.12}$$

where

r_{xy} = sample correlation coefficient
s_{xy} = sample covariance
s_x = sample standard deviation of x
s_y = sample standard deviation of y

Equation (3.12) shows that the Pearson product moment correlation coefficient for sample data (commonly referred to more simply as the *sample correlation coefficient*) is computed by dividing the sample covariance by the product of the sample standard deviation of x and the sample standard deviation of y.

Let us now compute the sample correlation coefficient for the stereo and sound equipment store. Using the data in Table 3.8, we can compute the sample standard deviations for the two variables.

$$s_x = \sqrt{\frac{\Sigma(x_i - \bar{x})^2}{n - 1}} = \sqrt{\frac{20}{9}} = 1.49$$

$$s_y = \sqrt{\frac{\Sigma(y_i - \bar{y})^2}{n - 1}} = \sqrt{\frac{566}{9}} = 7.93$$

Now, because $s_{xy} = 11$, the sample correlation coefficient equals

$$r_{xy} = \frac{s_{xy}}{s_x s_y} = \frac{11}{(1.49)(7.93)} = +.93$$

The formula for computing the correlation coefficient for a population, denoted by the Greek letter ρ_{xy} (rho, pronounced "row"), follows.

The sample correlation coefficient r_{xy} is the estimator of the population correlation coefficient ρ_{xy}.

PEARSON PRODUCT MOMENT CORRELATION COEFFICIENT: POPULATION DATA

$$\rho_{xy} = \frac{\sigma_{xy}}{\sigma_x \sigma_y} \tag{3.13}$$

where

ρ_{xy} = population correlation coefficient
σ_{xy} = population covariance
σ_x = population standard deviation for x
σ_y = population standard deviation for y

The sample correlation coefficient r_{xy} provides an estimate of the population correlation coefficient ρ_{xy}.

Interpretation of the Correlation Coefficient

First let us consider a simple example that illustrates the concept of a perfect positive linear relationship. The scatter diagram in Figure 3.10 depicts the relationship between x and y based on the following sample data.

x_i	y_i
5	10
10	30
15	50

FIGURE 3.10 SCATTER DIAGRAM DEPICTING A PERFECT POSITIVE LINEAR RELATIONSHIP

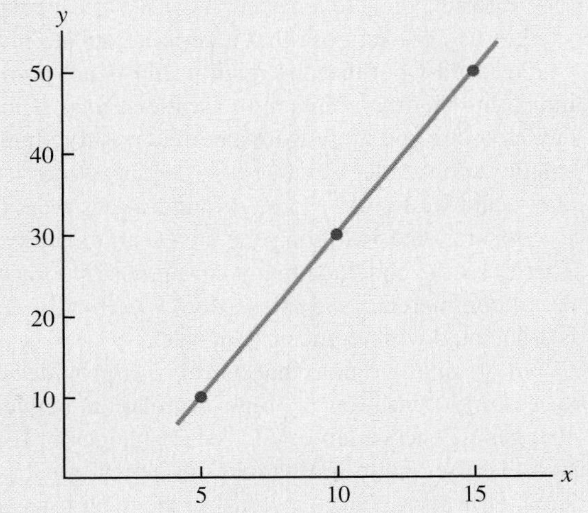

TABLE 3.9 COMPUTATIONS USED IN CALCULATING THE SAMPLE CORRELATION COEFFICIENT

	x_i	y_i	$x_i - \bar{x}$	$(x_i - \bar{x})^2$	$y_i - \bar{y}$	$(y_i - \bar{y})^2$	$(x_i - \bar{x})(y_i - \bar{y})$
	5	10	−5	25	−20	400	100
	10	30	0	0	0	0	0
	15	50	5	25	20	400	100
Totals	30	90	0	50	0	800	200
	$\bar{x} = 10$	$\bar{y} = 30$					

The straight line drawn through each of the three points shows a perfect linear relationship between x and y. In order to apply equation (3.12) to compute the sample correlation we must first compute s_{xy}, s_x, and s_y. Some of the computations are shown in Table 3.9. Using the results in Table 3.9, we find

$$s_{xy} = \frac{\Sigma(x_i - \bar{x})(y_i - \bar{y})}{n - 1} = \frac{200}{2} = 100$$

$$s_x = \sqrt{\frac{\Sigma(x_i - \bar{x})^2}{n - 1}} = \sqrt{\frac{50}{2}} = 5$$

$$s_y = \sqrt{\frac{\Sigma(y_i - \bar{y})^2}{n - 1}} = \sqrt{\frac{800}{2}} = 20$$

$$r_{xy} = \frac{s_{xy}}{s_x s_y} = \frac{100}{5(20)} = 1$$

The correlation coefficient ranges from −1 to +1. Values close to −1 or +1 indicate a strong linear relationship. The closer the correlation is to zero, the weaker the relationship.

Thus, we see that the value of the sample correlation coefficient is 1.

In general, it can be shown that if all the points in a data set fall on a positively sloped straight line, the value of the sample correlation coefficient is +1; that is, a sample correlation coefficient of +1 corresponds to a perfect positive linear relationship between x and y. Moreover, if the points in the data set fall on a straight line having negative slope, the value of the sample correlation coefficient is −1; that is, a sample correlation coefficient of −1 corresponds to a perfect negative linear relationship between x and y.

Let us now suppose that a certain data set indicates a positive linear relationship between x and y but that the relationship is not perfect. The value of r_{xy} will be less than 1, indicating that the points in the scatter diagram are not all on a straight line. As the points deviate more and more from a perfect positive linear relationship, the value of r_{xy} becomes smaller and smaller. A value of r_{xy} equal to zero indicates no linear relationship between x and y, and values of r_{xy} near zero indicate a weak linear relationship.

For the data involving the stereo and sound equipment store, recall that $r_{xy} = +.93$. Therefore, we conclude that a strong positive linear relationship occurs between the number of commercials and sales. More specifically, an increase in the number of commercials is associated with an increase in sales.

In closing, we note that correlation provides a measure of linear association and not necessarily causation. A high correlation between two variables does not mean that changes in one variable will cause changes in the other variable. For example, we may find that the quality rating and the typical meal price of restaurants are positively correlated. However, simply increasing the meal price at a restaurant will not cause the quality rating to increase.

Exercises

Methods

SELF test

45. Five observations taken for two variables follow.

x_i	4	6	11	3	16
y_i	50	50	40	60	30

a. Develop a scatter diagram with x on the horizontal axis.
b. What does the scatter diagram developed in part (a) indicate about the relationship between the two variables?
c. Compute and interpret the sample covariance.
d. Compute and interpret the sample correlation coefficient.

46. Five observations taken for two variables follow.

x_i	6	11	15	21	27
y_i	6	9	6	17	12

a. Develop a scatter diagram for these data.
b. What does the scatter diagram indicate about a relationship between x and y?
c. Compute and interpret the sample covariance.
d. Compute and interpret the sample correlation coefficient.

Applications

47. Nielsen Media Research provides two measures of the television viewing audience: a television program *rating,* which is the percentage of households with televisions watching a program, and a television program *share,* which is the percentage of households watching a program among those with televisions in use. The following data show the Nielsen television ratings and share data for the Major League Baseball World Series over a nine-year period (Associated Press, October 27, 2003).

Rating	19	17	17	14	16	12	15	12	13
Share	32	28	29	24	26	20	24	20	22

a. Develop a scatter diagram with rating on the horizontal axis.
b. What is the relationship between rating and share? Explain.
c. Compute and interpret the sample covariance.
d. Compute the sample correlation coefficient. What does this value tell us about the relationship between rating and share?

48. A department of transportation's study on driving speed and mileage for midsize automobiles resulted in the following data.

Driving Speed	30	50	40	55	30	25	60	25	50	55
Mileage	28	25	25	23	30	32	21	35	26	25

Compute and interpret the sample correlation coefficient.

49. *PC World* provided ratings for 15 notebook PCs (*PC World,* February 2000). The performance score is a measure of how fast a PC can run a mix of common business applications as compared to a baseline machine. For example, a PC with a performance score of 200 is twice as fast as the baseline machine. A 100-point scale was used to provide an overall rating for each notebook tested in the study. A score in the 90s is exceptional, while one in the 70s is good. Table 3.10 shows the performance scores and the overall ratings for the 15 notebooks.

TABLE 3.10 PERFORMANCE SCORES AND OVERALL RATINGS FOR 15 NOTEBOOK PCs

CD file PCs

Notebook	Performance Score	Overall Rating
AMS Tech Roadster 15CTA380	115	67
Compaq Armada M700	191	78
Compaq Prosignia Notebook 150	153	79
Dell Inspiron 3700 C466GT	194	80
Dell Inspiron 7500 R500VT	236	84
Dell Latitude Cpi A366XT	184	76
Enpower ENP-313 Pro	184	77
Gateway Solo 9300LS	216	92
HP Pavilion Notebook PC	185	83
IBM ThinkPad I Series 1480	183	78
Micro Express NP7400	189	77
Micron TransPort NX PII-400	202	78
NEC Versa SX	192	78
Sceptre Soundx 5200	141	73
Sony VAIO PCG-F340	187	77

a. Compute the sample correlation coefficient.
b. What does the sample correlation coefficient tell about the relationship between the performance score and the overall rating?

50. The Dow Jones Industrial Average (DJIA) and the Standard & Poor's 500 Index (S&P 500) are both used to measure the performance of the stock market. The DJIA is based on the price of stocks for 30 large companies; the S&P 500 is based on the price of stocks for 500 companies. If both the DJIA and S&P 500 measure the performance of the stock market, how are they correlated? The following data show the daily percent increase or daily percent decrease in the DJIA and S&P 500 for a sample of nine days over a three-month period (*The Wall Street Journal,* January 15 to March 10, 2006).

CD file StockMarket

DJIA	.20	.82	−.99	.04	−.24	1.01	.30	.55	−.25
S&P 500	.24	.19	−.91	.08	−.33	.87	.36	.83	−.16

a. Show a scatter diagram.
b. Compute the sample correlation coefficient for these data.
c. Discuss the association between the DJIA and S&P 500. Do you need to check both before having a general idea about the daily stock market performance?

51. The daily high and low temperatures for 12 U.S. cities are as follows (Weather Channel, January 25, 2004).

CD file Temperature

City	High	Low	City	High	Low
Albany	9	−8	Los Angeles	62	47
Boise	32	26	New Orleans	71	55
Cleveland	21	19	Portland	43	36
Denver	37	10	Providence	18	8
Des Moines	24	16	Raleigh	28	24
Detroit	20	17	Tulsa	55	38

a. What is the sample mean daily high temperature?
b. What is the sample mean daily low temperature?
c. What is the correlation between the high and low temperatures?

3.6 The Weighted Mean and Working with Grouped Data

In Section 3.1, we presented the mean as one of the most important measures of central location. The formula for the mean of a sample with n observations is restated as follows.

$$\bar{x} = \frac{\Sigma x_i}{n} = \frac{x_1 + x_2 + \cdots + x_n}{n} \tag{3.14}$$

In this formula, each x_i is given equal importance or weight. Although this practice is most common, in some instances, the mean is computed by giving each observation a weight that reflects its importance. A mean computed in this manner is referred to as a **weighted mean**.

Weighted Mean

The weighted mean is computed as follows:

WEIGHTED MEAN

$$\bar{x} = \frac{\Sigma w_i x_i}{\Sigma w_i} \tag{3.15}$$

where

$$x_i = \text{value of observation } i$$
$$w_i = \text{weight for observation } i$$

When the data are from a sample, equation (3.15) provides the weighted sample mean. When the data are from a population, μ replaces $\bar{x}$ and equation (3.15) provides the weighted population mean.

As an example of the need for a weighted mean, consider the following sample of five purchases of a raw material over the past three months.

Purchase	Cost per Pound ($)	Number of Pounds
1	3.00	1200
2	3.40	500
3	2.80	2750
4	2.90	1000
5	3.25	800

Note that the cost per pound varies from \$2.80 to \$3.40, and the quantity purchased varies from 500 to 2750 pounds. Suppose that a manager asked for information about the mean cost per pound of the raw material. Because the quantities ordered vary, we must use the formula for a weighted mean. The five cost-per-pound data values are $x_1 = 3.00$, $x_2 = 3.40$, $x_3 = 2.80$, $x_4 = 2.90$, and $x_5 = 3.25$. The weighted mean cost per pound is found by weighting each cost by its corresponding quantity. For this example, the weights are $w_1 = 1200$, $w_2 = 500$, $w_3 = 2750$, $w_4 = 1000$, and $w_5 = 800$. Based on equation (3.15), the weighted mean is calculated as follows:

$$\bar{x} = \frac{1200(3.00) + 500(3.40) + 2750(2.80) + 1000(2.90) + 800(3.25)}{1200 + 500 + 2750 + 1000 + 800}$$

$$= \frac{18{,}500}{6250} = 2.96$$

Thus, the weighted mean computation shows that the mean cost per pound for the raw material is \$2.96. Note that using equation (3.14) rather than the weighted mean formula would have provided misleading results. In this case, the mean of the five cost-per-pound values is $(3.00 + 3.40 + 2.80 + 2.90 + 3.25)/5 = 15.35/5 = \$3.07$, which overstates the actual mean cost per pound purchased.

The choice of weights for a particular weighted mean computation depends upon the application. An example that is well known to college students is the computation of a grade point average (GPA). In this computation, the data values generally used are 4 for an A grade, 3 for a B grade, 2 for a C grade, 1 for a D grade, and 0 for an F grade. The weights are the number of credits hours earned for each grade. Exercise 54 at the end of this section provides an example of this weighted mean computation. In other weighted mean computations, quantities such as pounds, dollars, or volume are frequently used as weights. In any case, when observations vary in importance, the analyst must choose the weight that best reflects the importance of each observation in the determination of the mean.

Computing a grade point average is a good example of the use of a weighted mean.

Grouped Data

In most cases, measures of location and variability are computed by using the individual data values. Sometimes, however, data are available only in a grouped or frequency distribution form. In the following discussion, we show how the weighted mean formula can be used to obtain approximations of the mean, variance, and standard deviation for **grouped data**.

In Section 2.2 we provided a frequency distribution of the time in days required to complete year-end audits for the public accounting firm of Sanderson and Clifford. The frequency distribution of audit times based on a sample of 20 clients is shown again in Table 3.11. Based on this frequency distribution, what is the sample mean audit time?

To compute the mean using only the grouped data, we treat the midpoint of each class as being representative of the items in the class. Let M_i denote the midpoint for class i and let f_i denote the frequency of class i. The weighted mean formula (3.15) is then used with the data values denoted as M_i and the weights given by the frequencies f_i. In this case, the denominator of equation (3.15) is the sum of the frequencies, which is the

TABLE 3.11 FREQUENCY DISTRIBUTION OF AUDIT TIMES

Audit Time (days)	Frequency
10–14	4
15–19	8
20–24	5
25–29	2
30–34	1
Total	20

sample size n. That is, $\Sigma f_i = n$. Thus, the equation for the sample mean for grouped data is as follows.

SAMPLE MEAN FOR GROUPED DATA

$$\bar{x} = \frac{\Sigma f_i M_i}{n} \tag{3.16}$$

where

M_i = the midpoint for class i
f_i = the frequency for class i
n = the sample size

With the class midpoints, M_i, halfway between the class limits, the first class of 10–14 in Table 3.11 has a midpoint at $(10 + 14)/2 = 12$. The five class midpoints and the weighted mean computation for the audit time data are summarized in Table 3.12. As can be seen, the sample mean audit time is 19 days.

To compute the variance for grouped data, we use a slightly altered version of the formula for the variance provided in equation (3.5). In equation (3.5), the squared deviations of the data about the sample mean $\bar{x}$ were written $(x_i - \bar{x})^2$. However, with grouped data, the values are not known. In this case, we treat the class midpoint, M_i, as being representative of the x_i values in the corresponding class. Thus, the squared deviations about the sample mean, $(x_i - \bar{x})^2$, are replaced by $(M_i - \bar{x})^2$. Then, just as we did with the sample mean calculations for grouped data, we weight each value by the frequency of the class, f_i. The sum of the squared deviations about the mean for all the data is approximated by $\Sigma f_i(M_i - \bar{x})^2$. The term $n - 1$ rather than n appears in the denominator in order to make the sample variance the estimate of the population variance. Thus, the following formula is used to obtain the sample variance for grouped data.

SAMPLE VARIANCE FOR GROUPED DATA

$$s^2 = \frac{\Sigma f_i(M_i - \bar{x})^2}{n - 1} \tag{3.17}$$

TABLE 3.12 COMPUTATION OF THE SAMPLE MEAN AUDIT TIME FOR GROUPED DATA

Audit Time (days)	Class Midpoint (M_i)	Frequency (f_i)	f_iM_i
10–14	12	4	48
15–19	17	8	136
20–24	22	5	110
25–29	27	2	54
30–34	32	1	32
		20	380

$$\text{Sample mean } \bar{x} = \frac{\Sigma f_i M_i}{n} = \frac{380}{20} = 19 \text{ days}$$

TABLE 3.13 COMPUTATION OF THE SAMPLE VARIANCE OF AUDIT TIMES FOR GROUPED DATA (SAMPLE MEAN $\bar{x} = 19$)

Audit Time (days)	Class Midpoint (M_i)	Frequency (f_i)	Deviation ($M_i - \bar{x}$)	Squared Deviation ($M_i - \bar{x})^2$	$f_i(M_i - \bar{x})^2$
10–14	12	4	−7	49	196
15–19	17	8	−2	4	32
20–24	22	5	3	9	45
25–29	27	2	8	64	128
30–34	32	1	13	169	169
		20			570
					$\Sigma f_i(M_i - \bar{x})^2$

$$\text{Sample variance } s^2 = \frac{\Sigma f_i(M_i - \bar{x})^2}{n - 1} = \frac{570}{19} = 30$$

The calculation of the sample variance for audit times based on the grouped data from Table 3.11 is shown in Table 3.13. As can be seen, the sample variance is 30.

The standard deviation for grouped data is simply the square root of the variance for grouped data. For the audit time data, the sample standard deviation is $s = \sqrt{30} = 5.48$.

Before closing this section on computing measures of location and dispersion for grouped data, we note that formulas (3.16) and (3.17) are for a sample. Population summary measures are computed similarly. The grouped data formulas for a population mean and variance follow.

POPULATION MEAN FOR GROUPED DATA

$$\mu = \frac{\Sigma f_i M_i}{N} \tag{3.18}$$

POPULATION VARIANCE FOR GROUPED DATA

$$\sigma^2 = \frac{\Sigma f_i(M_i - \mu)^2}{N} \tag{3.19}$$

NOTES AND COMMENTS

In computing descriptive statistics for grouped data, the class midpoints are used to approximate the data values in each class. As a result, the descriptive statistics for grouped data approximate the descriptive statistics that would result from using the original data directly. We therefore recommend computing descriptive statistics from the original data rather than from grouped data whenever possible.

Exercises

Methods

52. Consider the following data and corresponding weights.

x_i	Weight (w_i)
3.2	6
2.0	3
2.5	2
5.0	8

a. Compute the weighted mean.
b. Compute the sample mean of the four data values without weighting. Note the difference in the results provided by the two computations.

SELF test

53. Consider the sample data in the following frequency distribution.

Class	Midpoint	Frequency
3–7	5	4
8–12	10	7
13–17	15	9
18–22	20	5

a. Compute the sample mean.
b. Compute the sample variance and sample standard deviation.

Applications

SELF test

54. The grade point average for college students is based on a weighted mean computation. For most colleges, the grades are given the following data values: A (4), B (3), C (2), D (1), and F (0). After 60 credit hours of course work, a student at State University earned 9 credit hours of A, 15 credit hours of B, 33 credit hours of C, and 3 credit hours of D.
a. Compute the student's grade point average.
b. Students at State University must maintain a 2.5 grade point average for their first 60 credit hours of course work in order to be admitted to the business college. Will this student be admitted?

55. *Bloomberg Personal Finance* (July/August 2001) included the following companies in its recommended investment portfolio. For a portfolio value of \$25,000, the recommended dollar amounts allocated to each stock are shown.

Company	Portfolio (\$)	Estimated Growth Rate (%)	Dividend Yield (%)
Citigroup	3000	15	1.21
General Electric	5500	14	1.48
Kimberly-Clark	4200	12	1.72
Oracle	3000	25	0.00
Pharmacia	3000	20	0.96
SBC Communications	3800	12	2.48
WorldCom	2500	35	0.00

a. Using the portfolio dollar amounts as the weights, what is the weighted average estimated growth rate for the portfolio?
b. What is the weighted average dividend yield for the portfolio?

56. A survey of subscribers to *Fortune* magazine asked the following question: "How many of the last four issues have you read?" Suppose that the following frequency distribution summarizes 500 responses.

Number Read		Frequency
0		15
1		10
2		40
3		85
4		350
	Total	500

a. What is the mean number of issues read by a *Fortune* subscriber?
b. What is the standard deviation of the number of issues read?

57. The following frequency distribution shows the price per share for the 30 companies in the Dow Jones Industrial Average (*The Wall Street Journal,* January 16, 2006).

Price per Share	Frequency
\$20–29	7
\$30–39	6
\$40–49	6
\$50–59	3
\$60–69	4
\$70–79	3
\$80–89	1

Compute the mean price per share and the standard deviation of the price per share for the Dow Jones Industrial Average companies.

Summary

In this chapter we introduced several descriptive statistics that can be used to summarize the location, variability, and shape of a data distribution. Unlike the tabular and graphical procedures introduced in Chapter 2, the measures introduced in this chapter summarize the data in terms of numerical values. When the numerical values obtained are for a sample, they are called sample statistics. When the numerical values obtained are for a population, they are called population parameters. Some of the notation used for sample statistics and population parameters follow.

In statistical inference, the sample statistic is referred to as the point estimator of the population parameter.

	Sample Statistic	Population Parameter
Mean	$\bar{x}$	μ
Variance	s^2	σ^2
Standard deviation	s	σ
Covariance	s_{xy}	σ_{xy}
Correlation	r_{xy}	ρ_{xy}

As measures of central location, we defined the mean, median, and mode. Then the concept of percentiles was used to describe other locations in the data set. Next, we presented the range, interquartile range, variance, standard deviation, and coefficient of variation as measures of variability or dispersion. Our primary measure of the shape of a data distribution was the skewness. Negative values indicate a data distribution skewed to the left. Positive values indicate a data distribution skewed to the right. We then described how the mean and standard deviation could be used, applying Chebyshev's theorem and the empirical rule, to provide more information about the distribution of data and to identify outliers.

In Section 3.4 we showed how to develop a five-number summary and a box plot to provide simultaneous information about the location, variability, and shape of the distribution. In Section 3.5 we introduced covariance and the correlation coefficient as measures of association between two variables. In the final section, we showed how to compute a weighted mean and how to calculate a mean, variance, and standard deviation for grouped data.

The descriptive statistics we discussed can be developed using statistical software packages and spreadsheets. In Appendix 3.1 we show how to develop most of the descriptive statistics introduced in the chapter using Minitab. In Appendix 3.2, we demonstrate the use of Excel for the same purpose.

Glossary

Sample statistic A numerical value used as a summary measure for a sample (e.g., the sample mean, $\bar{x}$, the sample variance, s^2, and the sample standard deviation, s).

Population parameter A numerical value used as a summary measure for a population (e.g., the population mean, μ, the population variance, σ^2, and the population standard deviation, σ).

Point estimator The sample statistic, such as $\bar{x}$, s^2, and s, when used to estimate the corresponding population parameter.

Mean A measure of central location computed by summing the data values and dividing by the number of observations.

Median A measure of central location provided by the value in the middle when the data are arranged in ascending order.

Mode A measure of location, defined as the value that occurs with greatest frequency.

Percentile A value such that at least p percent of the observations are less than or equal to this value and at least $(100 - p)$ percent of the observations are greater than or equal to this value. The 50th percentile is the median.

Quartiles The 25th, 50th, and 75th percentiles, referred to as the first quartile, the second quartile (median), and third quartile, respectively. The quartiles can be used to divide a data set into four parts, with each part containing approximately 25% of the data.

Range A measure of variability, defined to be the largest value minus the smallest value.

Interquartile range (IQR) A measure of variability, defined to be the difference between the third and first quartiles.

Variance A measure of variability based on the squared deviations of the data values about the mean.

Standard deviation A measure of variability computed by taking the positive square root of the variance.

Coefficient of variation A measure of relative variability computed by dividing the standard deviation by the mean and multiplying by 100.

Skewness A measure of the shape of a data distribution. Data skewed to the left result in negative skewness; a symmetric data distribution results in zero skewness; and data skewed to the right result in positive skewness.

z-score A value computed by dividing the deviation about the mean $(x_i - \bar{x})$ by the standard deviation s. A z-score is referred to as a standardized value and denotes the number of standard deviations x_i is from the mean.
Chebyshev's theorem A theorem that can be used to make statements about the proportion of data values that must be within a specified number of standard deviations of the mean.
Empirical rule A rule that can be used to compute the percentage of data values that must be within one, two, and three standard deviations of the mean for data that exhibit a bell-shaped distribution.
Outlier An unusually small or unusually large data value.
Five-number summary An exploratory data analysis technique that uses five numbers to summarize the data: smallest value, first quartile, median, third quartile, and largest value.
Box plot A graphical summary of data based on a five-number summary.
Covariance A measure of linear association between two variables. Positive values indicate a positive relationship; negative values indicate a negative relationship.
Correlation coefficient A measure of linear association between two variables that takes on values between -1 and $+1$. Values near $+1$ indicate a strong positive linear relationship; values near -1 indicate a strong negative linear relationship; and values near zero indicate the lack of a linear relationship.
Weighted mean The mean obtained by assigning each observation a weight that reflects its importance.
Grouped data Data available in class intervals as summarized by a frequency distribution. Individual values of the original data are not available.

Key Formulas

Sample Mean

$$\bar{x} = \frac{\Sigma x_i}{n} \tag{3.1}$$

Population Mean

$$\mu = \frac{\Sigma x_i}{N} \tag{3.2}$$

Interquartile Range

$$\text{IQR} = Q_3 - Q_1 \tag{3.3}$$

Population Variance

$$\sigma^2 = \frac{\Sigma(x_i - \mu)^2}{N} \tag{3.4}$$

Sample Variance

$$s^2 = \frac{\Sigma(x_i - \bar{x})^2}{n - 1} \tag{3.5}$$

Standard Deviation

$$\text{Sample standard deviation} = s = \sqrt{s^2} \tag{3.6}$$

$$\text{Population standard deviation} = \sigma = \sqrt{\sigma^2} \tag{3.7}$$

Coefficient of Variation

$$\left(\frac{\text{Standard deviation}}{\text{Mean}} \times 100\right)\% \tag{3.8}$$

z-Score

$$z_i = \frac{x_i - \bar{x}}{s} \tag{3.9}$$

Sample Covariance

$$s_{xy} = \frac{\Sigma(x_i - \bar{x})(y_i - \bar{y})}{n - 1} \tag{3.10}$$

Population Covariance

$$\sigma_{xy} = \frac{\Sigma(x_i - \mu_x)(y_i - \mu_y)}{N} \tag{3.11}$$

Pearson Product Moment Correlation Coefficient: Sample Data

$$r_{xy} = \frac{s_{xy}}{s_x s_y} \tag{3.12}$$

Pearson Product Moment Correlation Coefficient: Population Data

$$\rho_{xy} = \frac{\sigma_{xy}}{\sigma_x \sigma_y} \tag{3.13}$$

Weighted Mean

$$\bar{x} = \frac{\Sigma w_i x_i}{\Sigma w_i} \tag{3.15}$$

Sample Mean for Grouped Data

$$\bar{x} = \frac{\Sigma f_i M_i}{n} \tag{3.16}$$

Sample Variance for Grouped Data

$$s^2 = \frac{\Sigma f_i (M_i - \bar{x})^2}{n - 1} \tag{3.17}$$

Population Mean for Grouped Data

$$\mu = \frac{\Sigma f_i M_i}{N} \tag{3.18}$$

Population Variance for Grouped Data

$$\sigma^2 = \frac{\Sigma f_i (M_i - \mu)^2}{N} \tag{3.19}$$

Supplementary Exercises

58. According to the 2003 Annual Consumer Spending Survey, the average monthly Bank of America Visa credit card charge was $1838 (*U.S. Airways Attaché Magazine,* December 2003). A sample of monthly credit card charges provides the following data.

CD file Visa

236	1710	1351	825	7450
316	4135	1333	1584	387
991	3396	170	1428	1688

a. Compute the mean and median.
b. Compute the first and third quartiles.
c. Compute the range and interquartile range.
d. Compute the variance and standard deviation.
e. The skewness measure for these data is 2.12. Comment on the shape of this distribution. Is it the shape you would expect? Why or why not?
f. Do the data contain outliers?

59. The U.S. Census Bureau provides statistics on family life in the United States, including the age at the time of first marriage, current marital status, and size of household (www.census.gov, March 20, 2006). The following data show the age at the time of first marriage for a sample of men and a sample of women.

CD file Ages

Men	26	23	28	25	27	30	26	35	28
	21	24	27	29	30	27	32	27	25
Women	20	28	23	30	24	29	26	25	
	22	22	25	23	27	26	19		

a. Determine the median age at the time of first marriage for men and women.
b. Compute the first and third quartiles for both men and women.
c. Twenty-five years ago the median age at the time of first marriage was 25 for men and 22 for women. What insight does this information provide about the decision of when to marry among young people today?

60. Dividend yield is the annual dividend per share a company pays divided by the current market price per share expressed as a percentage. A sample of 10 large companies provided the following dividend yield data (*The Wall Street Journal,* January 16, 2004).

Company	Yield %	Company	Yield %
Altria Group	5.0	General Motors	3.7
American Express	0.8	JPMorgan Chase	3.5
Caterpillar	1.8	McDonald's	1.6
Eastman Kodak	1.9	United Technology	1.5
ExxonMobil	2.5	Wal-Mart Stores	0.7

a. What are the mean and median dividend yields?
b. What are the variance and standard deviation?
c. Which company provides the highest dividend yield?
d. What is the z-score for McDonald's? Interpret this z-score.
e. What is the z-score for General Motors? Interpret this z-score.
f. Based on z-scores, do the data contain any outliers?

61. The U.S. Department of Education reports that about 50% of all college students use a student loan to help cover college expenses (*National Center for Educational Studies,* January 2006). A sample of students who graduated with student loan debt is shown here. The data, in thousands of dollars, show typical amounts of debt upon graduation.

10.1	14.8	5.0	10.2	12.4	12.2	2.0	11.5	17.8	4.0

a. For those students who use a student loan, what is the mean loan debt upon graduation?
b. What is the variance? Standard deviation?

62. Small business owners often look to payroll service companies to handle their employee payroll. Reasons are that small business owners face complicated tax regulations and penalties for employment tax errors are costly. According to the Internal Revenue Service, 26% of all small business employment tax returns contained errors that resulted in a tax penalty to the owner (*The Wall Street Journal,* January 30, 2006). The tax penalty for a sample of 20 small business owners follows:

CD file Penalty

820	270	450	1010	890	700	1350	350	300	1200
390	730	2040	230	640	350	420	270	370	620

a. What is the mean tax penalty for improperly filed employment tax returns?
b. What is the standard deviation?
c. Is the highest penalty, $2040, an outlier?
d. What are some of the advantages of a small business owner hiring a payroll service company to handle employee payroll services, including the employment tax returns?

63. Public transportation and the automobile are two methods an employee can use to get to work each day. Samples of times recorded for each method are shown. Times are in minutes.

Public Transportation:	28	29	32	37	33	25	29	32	41	34
Automobile:	29	31	33	32	34	30	31	32	35	33

a. Compute the sample mean time to get to work for each method.
b. Compute the sample standard deviation for each method.
c. On the basis of your results from parts (a) and (b), which method of transportation should be preferred? Explain.
d. Develop a box plot for each method. Does a comparison of the box plots support your conclusion in part (c)?

64. The National Association of Realtors reported the median home price in the United States and the increase in median home price over a five-year period (*The Wall Street Journal,* January 16, 2006). Use the sample home prices shown here to answer the following questions.

CD file Homes

995.9	48.8	175.0	263.5	298.0	218.9	209.0
628.3	111.0	212.9	92.6	2325.0	958.0	212.5

a. What is the sample median home price?
b. In January 2001, the National Association of Realtors reported a median home price of $139,300 in the United States. What was the percentage increase in the median home price over the five-year period?
c. What are the first quartile and the third quartile for the sample data?
d. Provide a five-number summary for the home prices.
e. Do the data contain any outliers?
f. What is the mean home price for the sample? Why does the National Association of Realtors prefer to use the median home price in its reports?

65. The following data show the media expenditures ($ millions) and shipments in millions of barrels (bbls.) for 10 major brands of beer.

CD file

Beer

Brand	Media Expenditures ($millions)	Shipments in bbls. (millions)
Budweiser	120.0	36.3
Bud Light	68.7	20.7
Miller Lite	100.1	15.9
Coors Light	76.6	13.2
Busch	8.7	8.1
Natural Light	0.1	7.1
Miller Genuine Draft	21.5	5.6
Miller High Life	1.4	4.4
Busch Lite	5.3	4.3
Milwaukee's Best	1.7	4.3

a. What is the sample covariance? Does it indicate a positive or negative relationship?
b. What is the sample correlation coefficient?

66. *Road & Track* provided the following sample of the tire ratings and load-carrying capacity of automobiles tires.

Tire Rating	Load-Carrying Capacity
75	853
82	1047
85	1135
87	1201
88	1235
91	1356
92	1389
93	1433
105	2039

a. Develop a scatter diagram for the data with tire rating on the x-axis.
b. What is the sample correlation coefficient, and what does it tell you about the relationship between tire rating and load-carrying capacity?

67. The following data show the trailing 52-week primary share earnings and book values as reported by 10 companies (*The Wall Street Journal,* March 13, 2000).

Company	Book Value	Earnings
Am Elec	25.21	2.69
Columbia En	23.20	3.01
Con Ed	25.19	3.13
Duke Energy	20.17	2.25
Edison Int'l	13.55	1.79
Enron Cp.	7.44	1.27
Peco	13.61	3.15
Pub Sv Ent	21.86	3.29
Southn Co.	8.77	1.86
Unicom	23.22	2.74

a. Develop a scatter diagram for the data with book value on the x-axis.
b. What is the sample correlation coefficient, and what does it tell you about the relationship between the earnings per share and the book value?

68. A forecasting technique referred to as moving averages uses the average or mean of the most recent n periods to forecast the next value for time series data. With a three-period moving average, the most recent three periods of data are used in the forecast computation. Consider a product with the following demand for the first three months of the current year: January (800 units), February (750 units), and March (900 units).
a. What is the three-month moving average forecast for April?
b. A variation of this forecasting technique is called weighted moving averages. The weighting allows the more recent time series data to receive more weight or more importance in the computation of the forecast. For example, a weighted three-month moving average might give a weight of 3 to data one month old, a weight of 2 to data two months old, and a weight of 1 to data three months old. Use the data given to provide a three-month weighted moving average forecast for April.

69. The days to maturity for a sample of five money market funds are shown here. The dollar amounts invested in the funds are provided. Use the weighted mean to determine the mean number of days to maturity for dollars invested in these five money market funds.

Days to Maturity	Dollar Value ($millions)
20	20
12	30
7	10
5	15
6	10

70. Automobiles traveling on a road with a posted speed limit of 55 miles per hour are checked for speed by a state police radar system. Following is a frequency distribution of speeds.

Speed (miles per hour)	Frequency
45–49	10
50–54	40
55–59	150
60–64	175
65–69	75
70–74	15
75–79	10
Total	475

a. What is the mean speed of the automobiles traveling on this road?
b. Compute the variance and the standard deviation.

Case Problem 1 Pelican Stores

Pelican Stores, a division of National Clothing, is a chain of women's apparel stores operating throughout the country. The chain recently ran a promotion in which discount coupons were sent to customers of other National Clothing stores. Data collected for a sample of 100 in-store credit card transactions at Pelican Stores during one day while the promotion was running are contained in the file named PelicanStores. Table 3.14 shows a portion of the data set. The proprietary card method of payment refers to charges made using a National Clothing charge card. Customers who made a purchase using a discount coupon are referred to as promotional customers and customers who made a purchase but did not use a discount coupon are referred to as regular customers. Because the promotional coupons were not sent to regular Pelican Stores customers, management considers the sales made to people presenting the promotional coupons as sales it would not otherwise make. Of course, Pelican also hopes that the promotional customers will continue to shop at its stores.

Most of the variables shown in Table 3.14 are self-explanatory, but two of the variables require some clarification.

Items	The total number of items purchased
Net Sales	The total amount ($) charged to the credit card

Pelican's management would like to use this sample data to learn about its customer base and to evaluate the promotion involving discount coupons.

Managerial Report

Use the methods of descriptive statistics presented in this chapter to summarize the data and comment on your findings. At a minimum, your report should include the following:

1. Descriptive statistics on net sales and descriptive statistics on net sales by various classifications of customers.
2. Descriptive statistics concerning the relationship between age and net sales.

CD file
PelicanStores

TABLE 3.14 SAMPLE OF 100 CREDIT CARD PURCHASES AT PELICAN STORES

Customer	Type of Customer	Items	Net Sales	Method of Payment	Gender	Marital Status	Age
1	Regular	1	39.50	Discover	Male	Married	32
2	Promotional	1	102.40	Proprietary Card	Female	Married	36
3	Regular	1	22.50	Proprietary Card	Female	Married	32
4	Promotional	5	100.40	Proprietary Card	Female	Married	28
5	Regular	2	54.00	MasterCard	Female	Married	34
6	Regular	1	44.50	MasterCard	Female	Married	44
7	Promotional	2	78.00	Proprietary Card	Female	Married	30
8	Regular	1	22.50	Visa	Female	Married	40
9	Promotional	2	56.52	Proprietary Card	Female	Married	46
10	Regular	1	44.50	Proprietary Card	Female	Married	36
⋮	⋮	⋮	⋮	⋮	⋮	⋮	⋮
96	Regular	1	39.50	MasterCard	Female	Married	44
97	Promotional	9	253.00	Proprietary Card	Female	Married	30
98	Promotional	10	287.59	Proprietary Card	Female	Married	52
99	Promotional	2	47.60	Proprietary Card	Female	Married	30
100	Promotional	1	28.44	Proprietary Card	Female	Married	44

Case Problem 2 Motion Picture Industry

The motion picture industry is a competitive business. More than 50 studios produce a total of 300 to 400 new motion pictures each year, and the financial success of each motion picture varies considerably. The opening weekend gross sales, the total gross sales, the number of theaters the movie was shown in, and the number of weeks the motion picture was in the top 60 for gross sales are common variables used to measure the success of a motion picture. Data collected for a sample of 100 motion pictures produced in 2005 are contained in the file named Movies. Table 3.15 shows the data for the first 10 motion pictures in the file.

Managerial Report

Use the numerical methods of descriptive statistics presented in this chapter to learn how these variables contribute to the success of a motion picture. Include the following in your report.

1. Descriptive statistics for each of the four variables along with a discussion of what the descriptive statistics tell us about the motion picture industry.
2. What motion pictures, if any, should be considered high-performance outliers? Explain.
3. Descriptive statistics showing the relationship between total gross sales and each of the other variables. Discuss.

CD file Movies

TABLE 3.15 PERFORMANCE DATA FOR 10 MOTION PICTURES

Motion Picture	Opening Gross Sales ($millions)	Total Gross Sales ($millions)	Number of Theaters	Weeks in Top 60
Coach Carter	29.17	67.25	2574	16
Ladies in Lavender	0.15	6.65	119	22
Batman Begins	48.75	205.28	3858	18
Unleashed	10.90	24.47	1962	8
Pretty Persuasion	0.06	0.23	24	4
Fever Pitch	12.40	42.01	3275	14
Harry Potter and the Goblet of Fire	102.69	287.18	3858	13
Monster-in-Law	23.11	82.89	3424	16
White Noise	24.11	55.85	2279	7
Mr. and Mrs. Smith	50.34	186.22	3451	21

Case Problem 3 Business Schools of Asia-Pacific

CD file Asian

The pursuit of a higher education degree in business is now international. A survey shows that more and more Asians choose the Master of Business Administration degree route to corporate success. As a result, the number of applicants for MBA courses at Asia-Pacific schools continues to increase.

Across the region, thousands of Asians show an increasing willingness to temporarily shelve their careers and spend two years in pursuit of a theoretical business qualification. Courses in these schools are notoriously tough and include economics, banking, marketing, behavioral sciences, labor relations, decision making, strategic thinking, business law, and more. The data set in Table 3.16 shows some of the characteristics of the leading Asia-Pacific business schools.

TABLE 3.16 DATA FOR 25 ASIA-PACIFIC BUSINESS SCHOOLS

Business School	Full-Time Enrollment	Students per Faculty	Local Tuition ($)	Foreign Tuition ($)	Age	%Foreign	GMAT	English Test	Work Experience	Starting Salary ($)
Melbourne Business School	200	5	24,420	29,600	28	47	Yes	No	Yes	71,400
University of New South Wales (Sydney)	228	4	19,993	32,582	29	28	Yes	No	Yes	65,200
Indian Institute of Management (Ahmedabad)	392	5	4,300	4,300	22	0	No	No	No	7,100
Chinese University of Hong Kong	90	5	11,140	11,140	29	10	Yes	No	No	31,000
International University of Japan (Niigata)	126	4	33,060	33,060	28	60	Yes	Yes	No	87,000
Asian Institute of Management (Manila)	389	5	7,562	9,000	25	50	Yes	No	Yes	22,800
Indian Institute of Management (Bangalore)	380	5	3,935	16,000	23	1	Yes	No	No	7,500
National University of Singapore	147	6	6,146	7,170	29	51	Yes	Yes	Yes	43,300
Indian Institute of Management (Calcutta)	463	8	2,880	16,000	23	0	No	No	No	7,400
Australian National University (Canberra)	42	2	20,300	20,300	30	80	Yes	Yes	Yes	46,600
Nanyang Technological University (Singapore)	50	5	8,500	8,500	32	20	Yes	No	Yes	49,300
University of Queensland (Brisbane)	138	17	16,000	22,800	32	26	No	No	Yes	49,600
Hong Kong University of Science and Technology	60	2	11,513	11,513	26	37	Yes	No	Yes	34,000
Macquarie Graduate School of Management (Sydney)	12	8	17,172	19,778	34	27	No	No	Yes	60,100
Chulalongkorn University (Bangkok)	200	7	17,355	17,355	25	6	Yes	No	Yes	17,600
Monash Mt. Eliza Business School (Melbourne)	350	13	16,200	22,500	30	30	Yes	Yes	Yes	52,500
Asian Institute of Management (Bangkok)	300	10	18,200	18,200	29	90	No	Yes	Yes	25,000
University of Adelaide	20	19	16,426	23,100	30	10	No	No	Yes	66,000
Massey University (Palmerston North, New Zealand)	30	15	13,106	21,625	37	35	No	Yes	Yes	41,400
Royal Melbourne Institute of Technology Business Graduate School	30	7	13,880	17,765	32	30	No	Yes	Yes	48,900
Jamnalal Bajaj Institute of Management Studies (Bombay)	240	9	1,000	1,000	24	0	No	No	Yes	7,000
Curtin Institute of Technology (Perth)	98	15	9,475	19,097	29	43	Yes	No	Yes	55,000
Lahore University of Management Sciences	70	14	11,250	26,300	23	2.5	No	No	No	7,500
Universiti Sains Malaysia (Penang)	30	5	2,260	2,260	32	15	No	Yes	Yes	16,000
De La Salle University (Manila)	44	17	3,300	3,600	28	3.5	Yes	No	Yes	13,100

Managerial Report

Use the methods of descriptive statistics to summarize the data in Table 3.16. Discuss your findings.

1. Include a summary for each variable in the data set. Make comments and interpretations based on maximums and minimums, as well as the appropriate means and proportions. What new insights do these descriptive statistics provide concerning Asia-Pacific business schools?
2. Summarize the data to compare the following:
   a. Any difference between local and foreign tuition costs.
   b. Any difference between mean starting salaries for schools requiring and not requiring work experience.
   c. Any difference between starting salaries for schools requiring and not requiring English tests.
3. Do starting salaries appear to be related to tuition?
4. Present any additional graphical and numerical summaries that will be beneficial in communicating the data in Table 3.16 to others.

Appendix 3.1 Descriptive Statistics Using Minitab

In this appendix, we describe how to use Minitab to develop descriptive statistics. Table 3.1 listed the starting salaries for 12 business school graduates. Panel A of Figure 3.11 shows the descriptive statistics obtained by using Minitab to summarize these data. Definitions of the headings in Panel A follow.

N	number of data values
N*	number of missing data values
Mean	mean
SE Mean	standard error of mean
StDev	standard deviation
Minimum	minimum data value
Q1	first quartile
Median	median
Q3	third quartile
Maximum	maximum data value

The label SE Mean refers to the *standard error of the mean.* It is computed by dividing the standard deviation by the square root of *N*. The interpretation and use of this measure are discussed in Chapter 7 when we introduce the topics of sampling and sampling distributions.

Although the numerical measures of range, interquartile range, variance, and coefficient of variation do not appear on the Minitab output, these values can be easily computed from the results in Figure 3.11 as follows.

$$\text{Range} = \text{Maximum} - \text{Minimum}$$
$$\text{IQR} = Q_3 - Q_1$$
$$\text{Variance} = (\text{StDev})^2$$
$$\text{Coefficient of Variation} = (\text{StDev/Mean}) \times 100$$

Finally, note that Minitab's quartiles $Q_1 = 3457.5$ and $Q_3 = 3625$ are slightly different from the quartiles $Q_1 = 3465$ and $Q_3 = 3600$ computed in Section 3.1. The different

FIGURE 3.11 DESCRIPTIVE STATISTICS AND BOX PLOT PROVIDED BY MINITAB

Panel A: Descriptive Statistics

N	N*	Mean	SEMean	StDev
12	0	3540.0	47.8	165.7
Minimum	**Q1**	**Median**	**Q3**	**Maximum**
3310.0	3457.5	3505.0	3625.0	3925.0

Panel B: Box Plot

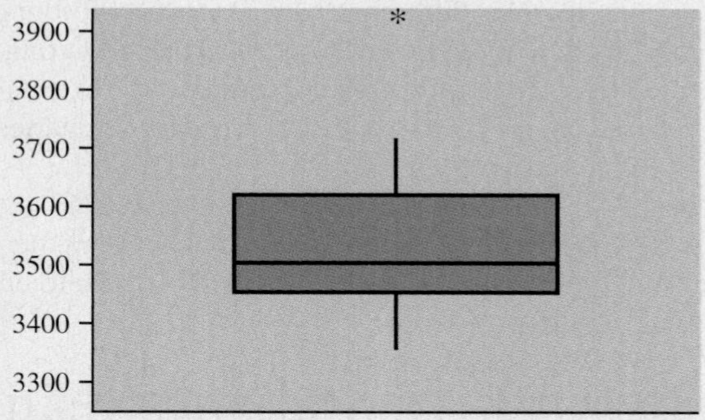

conventions* used to identify the quartiles explain this variation. Hence, the values of Q_1 and Q_3 provided by one convention may not be identical to the values of Q_1 and Q_3 provided by another convention. Any differences tend to be negligible, however, and the results provided should not mislead the user in making the usual interpretations associated with quartiles.

Let us now see how the statistics in Figure 3.11 are generated. The starting salary data are in column C2 of a Minitab worksheet. The following steps can then be used to generate the descriptive statistics.

CD file
StartSalary

Step 1. Select the **Stat** menu
Step 2. Choose **Basic Statistics**
Step 3. Choose **Display Descriptive Statistics**
Step 4. When the Display Descriptive Statistics dialog box appears:
Enter C2 in the **Variables** box
Click **OK**

Panel B of Figure 3.11 is a box plot provided by Minitab. The box drawn from the first to third quartiles contains the middle 50% of the data. The line within the box locates the median. The asterisk indicates an outlier at 3925.

The following steps generate the box plot shown in Panel B of Figure 3.11.

Step 1. Select the **Graph** menu
Step 2. Choose **Boxplot**
Step 3. Select **Simple** and click **OK**
Step 4. When the Boxplot-One Y, Simple dialog box appears:
Enter C2 in the **Graph variables** box
Click **OK**

The skewness measure also does not appear as part of Minitab's standard descriptive statistics output. However, we can include it in the descriptive statistics display by following these steps.

*With the n observations arranged in ascending order (smallest value to largest value), Minitab uses the positions given by $(n + 1)/4$ and $3(n + 1)/4$ to locate Q_1 and Q_3, respectively. When a position is fractional, Minitab interpolates between the two adjacent ordered data values to determine the corresponding quartile.

FIGURE 3.12 COVARIANCE AND CORRELATION PROVIDED BY MINITAB FOR THE NUMBER OF COMMERCIALS AND SALES DATA

```
Covariances: No. of Commercials, Sales Volume

                No. of Comme  Sales Volume
No. of Comme         2.22222
Sales Volume        11.00000      62.88889

Correlations: No. of Commercials, Sales Volume

Pearson correlation of No. of Commercials and Sales Volume = 0.930
P-Value = 0.000
```

Step 1. Select the **Stat** menu
Step 2. Choose **Basic Statistics**
Step 3. Choose **Display Descriptive Statistics**
Step 4. When the Display Descriptive Statistics dialog box appears:
  Click **Statistics**
  Select **Skewness**
  Click **OK**
  Click **OK**

The skewness measure of 1.09 will then appear in your worksheet.

CD file
Stereo

Figure 3.12 shows the covariance and correlation output that Minitab provided for the stereo and sound equipment store data in Table 3.7. In the covariance portion of the figure, No. of Comme denotes the number of weekend television commercials and Sales Volume denotes the sales during the following week. The value in column No. of Comme and row Sales Volume, 11, is the sample covariance as computed in Section 3.5. The value in column No. of Comme and row No. of Comme, 2.22222, is the sample variance for the number of commercials, and the value in column Sales Volume and row Sales Volume, 62.88889, is the sample variance for sales. The sample correlation coefficient, 0.930, is shown in the correlation portion of the output. Note: The interpretation of the p-value $= 0.000$ is discussed in Chapter 9.

Let us now describe how to obtain the information in Figure 3.12. We entered the data for the number of commercials into column C2 and the data for sales volume into column C3 of a Minitab worksheet. The steps necessary to generate the covariance output in the first three rows of Figure 3.12 follow.

Step 1. Select the **Stat** menu
Step 2. Choose **Basic Statistics**
Step 3. Choose **Covariance**
Step 4. When the Covariance dialog box appears:
  Enter C2 C3 in the **Variables** box
  Click **OK**

To obtain the correlation output in Figure 3.12, only one change is necessary in the steps for obtaining the covariance. In step 3, the **Correlation** option is selected.

Appendix 3.2 Descriptive Statistics Using Excel

Excel can be used to generate the descriptive statistics discussed in this chapter. We show how Excel can be used to generate several measures of location and variability for a single variable and to generate the covariance and correlation coefficient as measures of association between two variables.

FIGURE 3.13 USING EXCEL FUNCTIONS FOR COMPUTING THE MEAN, MEDIAN, MODE, VARIANCE, AND STANDARD DEVIATION

	A	B	C	D	E	F
1	Graduate	Starting Salary		Mean	=AVERAGE(B2:B13)	
2	1	3450		Median	=MEDIAN(B2:B13)	
3	2	3550		Mode	=MODE(B2:B13)	
4	3	3650		Variance	=VAR(B2:B13)	
5	4	3480		Standard Deviation	=STDEV(B2:B13)	
6	5	3355				
7	6	3310				
8	7	3490				
9	8	3730				
10	9	3540				
11	10	3925				
12	11	3520				
13	12	3480				
14						

	A	B	C	D	E	F
1	Graduate	Starting Salary		Mean	3540	
2	1	3450		Median	3505	
3	2	3550		Mode	3480	
4	3	3650		Variance	27440.91	
5	4	3480		Standard Deviation	165.65	
6	5	3355				
7	6	3310				
8	7	3490				
9	8	3730				
10	9	3540				
11	10	3925				
12	11	3520				
13	12	3480				
14						

Using Excel Functions

CD file StartSalary

Excel provides functions for computing the mean, median, mode, sample variance, and sample standard deviation. We illustrate the use of these Excel functions by computing the mean, median, mode, sample variance, and sample standard deviation for the starting salary data in Table 3.1. Refer to Figure 3.13 as we describe the steps involved. The data are entered in column B.

Excel's AVERAGE function can be used to compute the mean by entering the following formula into cell E1:

=AVERAGE(B2:B13)

Similarly, the formulas =MEDIAN(B2:B13), =MODE(B2:B13), =VAR(B2:B13), and =STDEV(B2:B13) are entered into cells E2:E5, respectively, to compute the median, mode, variance, and standard deviation. The worksheet in the foreground shows that the values computed using the Excel functions are the same as we computed earlier in the chapter.

Excel also provides functions that can be used to compute the covariance and correlation coefficient. You must be careful when using these functions because the covariance function treats the data as a population and the correlation function treats the data as a sample. Thus, the result obtained using Excel's covariance function must be adjusted to provide the sample covariance. We show here how these functions can be used to compute the sample covariance and the sample correlation coefficient for the stereo and sound equipment store data in Table 3.7. Refer to Figure 3.14 as we present the steps involved.

CD file Stereo

FIGURE 3.14 USING EXCEL FUNCTIONS FOR COMPUTING COVARIANCE AND CORRELATION

	A	B	C	D	E	F	G
1	Week	Commercials	Sales		Population Covariance	=COVAR(B2:B11:C2:C11)	
2	1	2	50		Sample Correlation	=CORREL(B2:B11,C2:C11)	
3	2	5	57				
4	3	1	41				
5	4	3	54				
6	5	4	54				
7	6	1	38				
8	7	5	63				
9	8	3	48				
10	9	4	59				
11	10	2	46				
12							

	A	B	C	D	E	F	G
1	Week	Commercials	Sales		Population Covariance	9.90	
2	1	2	50		Sample Correlation	0.93	
3	2	5	57				
4	3	1	41				
5	4	3	54				
6	5	4	54				
7	6	1	38				
8	7	5	63				
9	8	3	48				
10	9	4	59				
11	10	2	46				
12							

Excel's covariance function, COVAR, can be used to compute the population covariance by entering the following formula into cell F1:

=COVAR(B2:B11,C2:C11)

Similarly, the formula =CORREL(B2:B11,C2:C11) is entered into cell F2 to compute the sample correlation coefficient. The worksheet in the foreground shows the values computed using the Excel functions. Note that the value of the sample correlation coefficient (.93) is the same as computed using equation (3.12). However, the result provided by the Excel COVAR function, 9.9, was obtained by treating the data as a population. Thus, we must adjust the Excel result of 9.9 to obtain the sample covariance. The adjustment is rather simple. First, note that the formula for the population covariance, equation (3.11), requires dividing by the total number of observations in the data set. But the formula for the sample covariance, equation (3.10), requires dividing by the total number of observations minus 1. So, to use the Excel result of 9.9 to compute the sample covariance, we simply multiply 9.9 by $n/(n-1)$. Because $n = 10$, we obtain

$$s_{xy} = \left(\frac{10}{9}\right)9.9 = 11$$

Thus, the sample covariance for the stereo and sound equipment data is 11.

Using Excel's Descriptive Statistics Tool

As we already demonstrated, Excel provides statistical functions to compute descriptive statistics for a data set. These functions can be used to compute one statistic at a time (e.g., mean, variance, etc.). Excel also provides a variety of Data Analysis Tools. One of these tools, called Descriptive Statistics, allows the user to compute a variety of

FIGURE 3.15 EXCEL'S DESCRIPTIVE STATISTICS TOOL OUTPUT

	A	B	C	D	E	F
1	Graduate	Starting Salary		*Starting Salary*		
2	1	3450				
3	2	3550		**Mean**	3540	
4	3	3650		Standard Error	47.82	
5	4	3480		**Median**	3505	
6	5	3355		**Mode**	3480	
7	6	3310		**Standard Deviation**	165.65	
8	7	3490		**Sample Variance**	27440.91	
9	8	3730		Kurtosis	1.7189	
10	9	3540		**Skewness**	1.0911	
11	10	3925		**Range**	615	
12	11	3520		**Minimum**	3310	
13	12	3480		**Maximum**	3925	
14				**Sum**	42480	
15				**Count**	12	
16						

CD file
StartSalary

descriptive statistics at once. We show here how it can be used to compute descriptive statistics for the starting salary data in Table 3.1. Refer to Figure 3.15 as we describe the steps involved.

Step 1. Select the **Tools** menu
Step 2. Choose **Data Analysis**
Step 3. When the Data Analysis dialog box appears:
Choose **Descriptive Statistics**
Click **OK**
Step 4. When the Descriptive Statistics dialog box appears:
Enter B1:B13 in the **Input Range** box
Select **Grouped By Columns**
Select **Labels in First Row**
Select **Output Range**
Enter D1 in the **Output Range** box (to identify the upper left-hand corner of the section of the worksheet where the descriptive statistics will appear)
Select **Summary statistics**
Click **OK**

Cells D1:E15 of Figure 3.15 show the descriptive statistics provided by Excel. The boldface entries are the descriptive statistics we covered in this chapter. The descriptive statistics that are not boldface are either covered subsequently in the text or discussed in more advanced texts.

CHAPTER 4

Introduction to Probability

CONTENTS

STATISTICS *in* PRACTICE

ROHM AND HASS COMPANY*
PHILADELPHIA, PENNSYLVANIA

Rohm and Hass is the world's leading producer of specialty materials, including electronic materials, polymers for paints, and personal care items. Company products enable the creation of leading-edge consumer goods in markets such as pharmaceuticals, retail food, building supplies, communication equipment, and household products. The company has a workforce of more than 17,000 and annual sales of \$8 billion. A network of more than 100 manufacturing, technical research, and customer service sites provide Rohm and Hass products and service in 27 countries worldwide.

In the area of specialty chemical products, the company offers a variety of chemicals designed to meet the unique specifications of its customers. For one particular customer, the company produced an expensive catalyst used in the customer's chemical processing operation. Some, but not all, of the shipments from the company met the customer's specifications for the product. The contract called for the customer to test each shipment after receiving it and determine whether the catalyst would perform the desired function. Shipments that did not pass the customer's test would be returned. Over time, experience showed that the customer was accepting 60% of the shipments, but returning 40% of the shipments. Neither the customer nor the company was pleased with this level of service.

The company explored the possibility of duplicating the customer's test prior to shipment. However, the high cost of the special testing equipment that was required made this alternative infeasible. Company chemists working on the problem proposed a different but relatively low-cost test that could be conducted prior to shipment to the customer. The company believed that the new test would provide an indication of whether the catalyst would pass the customer's more sophisticated test. The probability question was: What is the probability that the catalyst would pass the customer's test given that it passed the new test prior to shipment?

A new test prior to shipment improved customer service. © Keith Wood/Stone.

A sample of the catalyst was produced and subjected to the new company test. Only samples of the catalyst that passed the new test were sent to the customer. Probability analysis of the data indicated that if the catalyst passed the new test prior to shipment, there was a .909 probability that the catalyst would pass the customer's test. Or, if the catalyst passed the new test prior to shipment, there was only a .091 probability that it would fail the customer's test and be returned. The probability analysis provided supporting evidence for the implementation of the testing procedure prior to shipment. This new test resulted in an immediate improvement in customer service and a substantial reduction in shipping and handling costs for the returned shipments.

The probability of a shipment being accepted by the customer given it had passed the new test is called a conditional probability. In this chapter, you will learn how to compute conditional and other probabilities that are helpful in decision making.

*The authors are indebted to Michael Haskell of the Rohm and Hass subsidiary Morton International for providing this statistics in practice.

Managers often base their decisions on an analysis of uncertainties such as the following:

1. What are the chances that sales will decrease if we increase prices?
2. What is the likelihood a new assembly method will increase productivity?
3. How likely is it that the project will be finished on time?
4. What is the chance that a new investment will be profitable?

Some of the earliest work on probability originated in a series of letters between Pierre de Fermat and Blaise Pascal in the 1650s.

Probability is a numerical measure of the likelihood that an event will occur. Thus, probabilities can be used as measures of the degree of uncertainty associated with the four events previously listed. If probabilities are available, we can determine the likelihood of each event occurring.

Probability values are always assigned on a scale from 0 to 1. A probability near zero indicates an event is unlikely to occur; a probability near 1 indicates an event is almost certain to occur. Other probabilities between 0 and 1 represent degrees of likelihood that an event will occur. For example, if we consider the event "rain tomorrow," we understand that when the weather report indicates "a near-zero probability of rain," it means almost no chance of rain. However, if a .90 probability of rain is reported, we know that rain is likely to occur. A .50 probability indicates that rain is just as likely to occur as not. Figure 4.1 depicts the view of probability as a numerical measure of the likelihood of an event occurring.

4.1 Experiments, Counting Rules, and Assigning Probabilities

In discussing probability, we define an **experiment** as a process that generates well-defined outcomes. On any single repetition of an experiment, one and only one of the possible experimental outcomes will occur. Several examples of experiments and their associated outcomes follow.

Experiment	**Experimental Outcomes**
Toss a coin	Head, tail
Select a part for inspection	Defective, nondefective
Conduct a sales call	Purchase, no purchase
Roll a die	1, 2, 3, 4, 5, 6
Play a football game	Win, lose, tie

By specifying all possible experimental outcomes, we identify the **sample space** for an experiment.

SAMPLE SPACE

The sample space for an experiment is the set of all experimental outcomes.

Experimental outcomes are also called sample points.

An experimental outcome is also called a **sample point** to identify it as an element of the sample space.

FIGURE 4.1 PROBABILITY AS A NUMERICAL MEASURE OF THE LIKELIHOOD OF AN EVENT OCCURRING

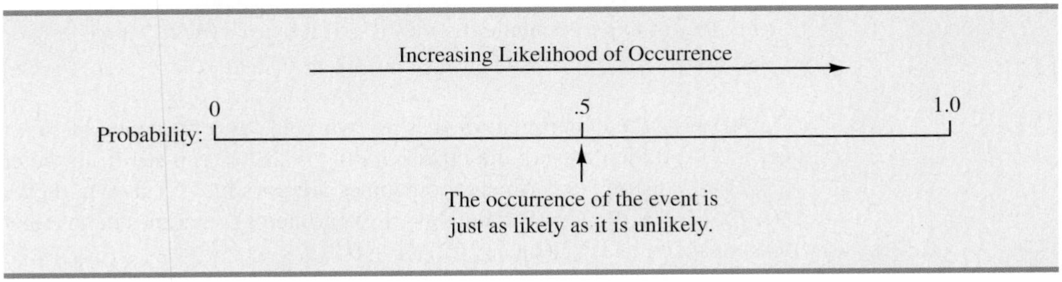

Consider the first experiment in the preceding table—tossing a coin. The upward face of the coin—a head or a tail—determines the experimental outcomes (sample points). If we let S denote the sample space, we can use the following notation to describe the sample space.

$$S = \{\text{Head, Tail}\}$$

The sample space for the second experiment in the table—selecting a part for inspection—can be described as follows:

$$S = \{\text{Defective, Nondefective}\}$$

Both of the experiments just described have two experimental outcomes (sample points). However, suppose we consider the fourth experiment listed in the table—rolling a die. The possible experimental outcomes, defined as the number of dots appearing on the upward face of the die, are the six points in the sample space for this experiment.

$$S = \{1, 2, 3, 4, 5, 6\}$$

Counting Rules, Combinations, and Permutations

Being able to identify and count the experimental outcomes is a necessary step in assigning probabilities. We now discuss three useful counting rules.

Multiple-step experiments The first counting rule applies to multiple-step experiments. Consider the experiment of tossing two coins. Let the experimental outcomes be defined in terms of the pattern of heads and tails appearing on the upward faces of the two coins. How many experimental outcomes are possible for this experiment? The experiment of tossing two coins can be thought of as a two-step experiment in which step 1 is the tossing of the first coin and step 2 is the tossing of the second coin. If we use H to denote a head and T to denote a tail, (H, H) indicates the experimental outcome with a head on the first coin and a head on the second coin. Continuing this notation, we can describe the sample space (S) for this coin-tossing experiment as follows:

$$S = \{(H, H), (H, T), (T, H), (T, T)\}$$

Thus, we see that four experimental outcomes are possible. In this case, we can easily list all of the experimental outcomes.

The counting rule for multiple-step experiments makes it possible to determine the number of experimental outcomes without listing them.

> COUNTING RULE FOR MULTIPLE-STEP EXPERIMENTS
>
> If an experiment can be described as a sequence of k steps with n_1 possible outcomes on the first step, n_2 possible outcomes on the second step, and so on, then the total number of experimental outcomes is given by $(n_1)\,(n_2)\ldots(n_k)$.

Viewing the experiment of tossing two coins as a sequence of first tossing one coin ($n_1 = 2$) and then tossing the other coin ($n_2 = 2$), we can see from the counting rule that $(2)(2) = 4$ distinct experimental outcomes are possible. As shown, they are $S = \{(H, H), (H, T), (T, H), (T, T)\}$. The number of experimental outcomes in an experiment involving tossing six coins is $(2)(2)(2)(2)(2)(2) = 64$.

FIGURE 4.2 TREE DIAGRAM FOR THE EXPERIMENT OF TOSSING TWO COINS

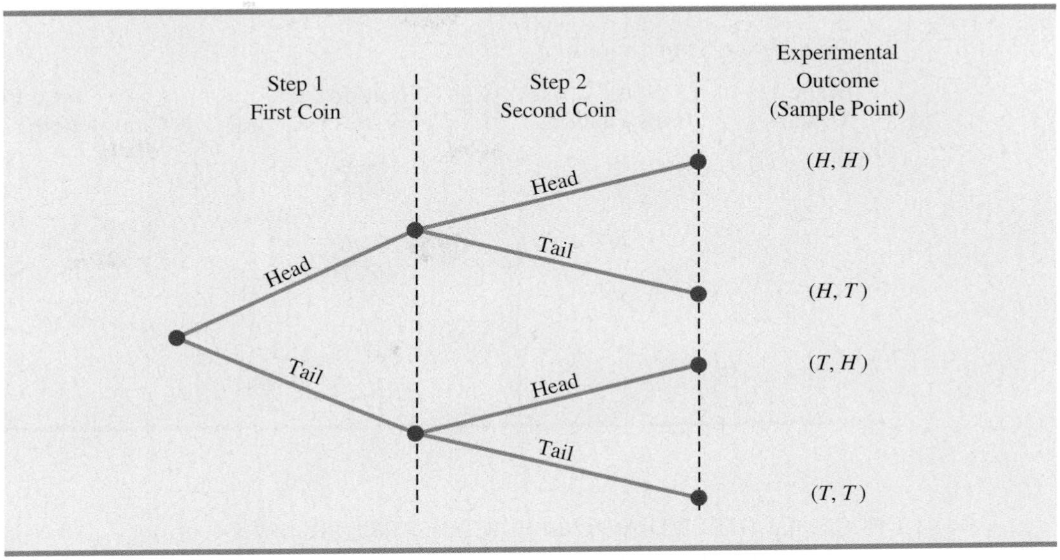

Without the tree diagram, one might think only three experimental outcomes are possible for two tosses of a coin: 0 heads, 1 head, and 2 heads.

A **tree diagram** is a graphical representation that helps in visualizing a multiple-step experiment. Figure 4.2 shows a tree diagram for the experiment of tossing two coins. The sequence of steps moves from left to right through the tree. Step 1 corresponds to tossing the first coin, and step 2 corresponds to tossing the second coin. For each step, the two possible outcomes are head or tail. Note that for each possible outcome at step 1 two branches correspond to the two possible outcomes at step 2. Each of the points on the right end of the tree corresponds to an experimental outcome. Each path through the tree from the leftmost node to one of the nodes at the right side of the tree corresponds to a unique sequence of outcomes.

Let us now see how the counting rule for multiple-step experiments can be used in the analysis of a capacity expansion project for the Kentucky Power & Light Company (KP&L). KP&L is starting a project designed to increase the generating capacity of one of its plants in northern Kentucky. The project is divided into two sequential stages or steps: stage 1 (design) and stage 2 (construction). Even though each stage will be scheduled and controlled as closely as possible, management cannot predict beforehand the exact time required to complete each stage of the project. An analysis of similar construction projects revealed possible completion times for the design stage of 2, 3, or 4 months and possible completion times for the construction stage of 6, 7, or 8 months. In addition, because of the critical need for additional electrical power, management set a goal of 10 months for the completion of the entire project.

Because this project has three possible completion times for the design stage (step 1) and three possible completion times for the construction stage (step 2), the counting rule for multiple-step experiments can be applied here to determine a total of $(3)(3) = 9$ experimental outcomes. To describe the experimental outcomes, we use a two-number notation; for instance, (2, 6) indicates that the design stage is completed in 2 months and the construction stage is completed in 6 months. This experimental outcome results in a total of $2 + 6 = 8$ months to complete the entire project. Table 4.1 summarizes the nine experimental outcomes for the KP&L problem. The tree diagram in Figure 4.3 shows how the nine outcomes (sample points) occur.

The counting rule and tree diagram help the project manager identify the experimental outcomes and determine the possible project completion times. From the information in

TABLE 4.1 EXPERIMENTAL OUTCOMES (SAMPLE POINTS) FOR THE KP&L PROJECT

Completion Time (months)			
Stage 1 Design	Stage 2 Construction	Notation for Experimental Outcome	Total Project Completion Time (months)
2	6	(2, 6)	8
2	7	(2, 7)	9
2	8	(2, 8)	10
3	6	(3, 6)	9
3	7	(3, 7)	10
3	8	(3, 8)	11
4	6	(4, 6)	10
4	7	(4, 7)	11
4	8	(4, 8)	12

FIGURE 4.3 TREE DIAGRAM FOR THE KP&L PROJECT

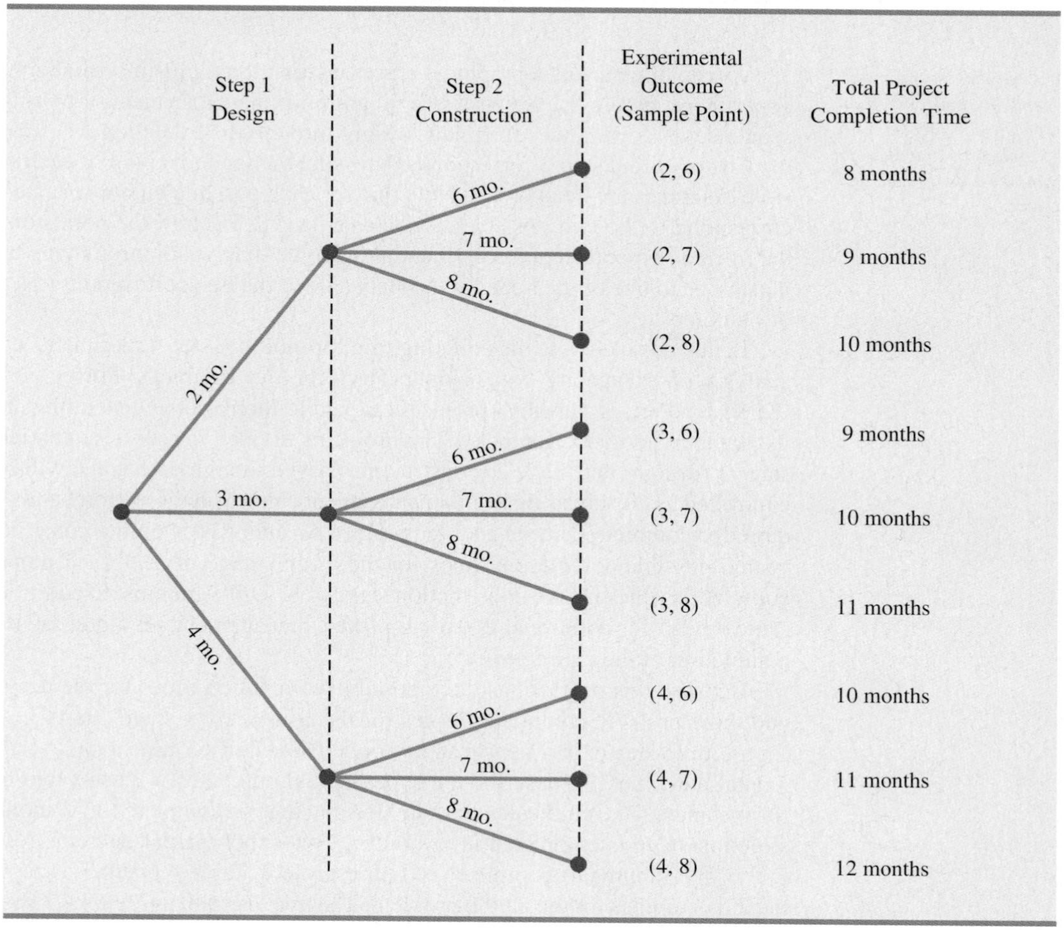

Figure 4.3, we see that the project will be completed in 8 to 12 months, with six of the nine experimental outcomes providing the desired completion time of 10 months or less. Even though identifying the experimental outcomes may be helpful, we need to consider how probability values can be assigned to the experimental outcomes before making an assessment of the probability that the project will be completed within the desired 10 months.

Combinations A second useful counting rule allows one to count the number of experimental outcomes when the experiment involves selecting n objects from a (usually larger) set of N objects. It is called the counting rule for combinations.

COUNTING RULE FOR COMBINATIONS

The number of combinations of N objects taken n at a time is

$$C_n^N = \binom{N}{n} = \frac{N!}{n!(N-n)!} \tag{4.1}$$

where

$$N! = N(N-1)(N-2)\cdots(2)(1)$$
$$n! = n(n-1)(n-2)\cdots(2)(1)$$

and, by definition,

$$0! = 1$$

The notation ! means *factorial;* for example, 5 factorial is $5! = (5)(4)(3)(2)(1) = 120$.

In sampling from a finite population of size N, the counting rule for combinations is used to find the number of different samples of size n that can be selected.

As an illustration of the counting rule for combinations, consider a quality control procedure in which an inspector randomly selects two of five parts to test for defects. In a group of five parts, how many combinations of two parts can be selected? The counting rule in equation (4.1) shows that with $N = 5$ and $n = 2$, we have

$$C_2^5 = \binom{5}{2} = \frac{5!}{2!(5-2)!} = \frac{(5)(4)(3)(2)(1)}{(2)(1)(3)(2)(1)} = \frac{120}{12} = 10$$

Thus, 10 outcomes are possible for the experiment of randomly selecting two parts from a group of five. If we label the five parts as A, B, C, D, and E, the 10 combinations or experimental outcomes can be identified as AB, AC, AD, AE, BC, BD, BE, CD, CE, and DE.

As another example, consider that the Florida lottery system uses the random selection of six integers from a group of 53 to determine the weekly winner. The counting rule for combinations, equation (4.1), can be used to determine the number of ways six different integers can be selected from a group of 53.

$$\binom{53}{6} = \frac{53!}{6!(53-6)!} = \frac{53!}{6!47!} = \frac{(53)(52)(51)(50)(49)(48)}{(6)(5)(4)(3)(2)(1)} = 22{,}957{,}480$$

The counting rule for combinations shows that the chance of winning the lottery is very unlikely.

The counting rule for combinations tells us that almost 23 million experimental outcomes are possible in the lottery drawing. An individual who buys a lottery ticket has 1 chance in 22,957,480 of winning.

Permutations A third counting rule that is sometimes useful is the counting rule for permutations. It allows one to compute the number of experimental outcomes when n objects are to be selected from a set of N objects where the order of selection is important. The same n objects selected in a different order are considered a different experimental outcome.

COUNTING RULE FOR PERMUTATIONS

The number of permutations of N objects taken n at a time is given by

$$P_n^N = n!\binom{N}{n} = \frac{N!}{(N - n)!} \quad \textbf{(4.2)}$$

The counting rule for permutations closely relates to the one for combinations; however, an experiment results in more permutations than combinations for the same number of objects because every selection of n objects can be ordered in $n!$ different ways.

As an example, consider again the quality control process in which an inspector selects two of five parts to inspect for defects. How many permutations may be selected? The counting rule in equation (4.2) shows that with $N = 5$ and $n = 2$, we have

$$P_2^5 = \frac{5!}{(5 - 2)!} = \frac{5!}{3!} = \frac{(5)(4)(3)(2)(1)}{(3)(2)(1)} = \frac{120}{6} = 20$$

Thus, 20 outcomes are possible for the experiment of randomly selecting two parts from a group of five when the order of selection must be taken into account. If we label the parts A, B, C, D, and E, the 20 permutations are AB, BA, AC, CA, AD, DA, AE, EA, BC, CB, BD, DB, BE, EB, CD, DC, CE, EC, DE, and ED.

Assigning Probabilities

Now let us see how probabilities can be assigned to experimental outcomes. The three approaches most frequently used are the classical, relative frequency, and subjective methods. Regardless of the method used, two **basic requirements for assigning probabilities** must be met.

BASIC REQUIREMENTS FOR ASSIGNING PROBABILITIES

1. The probability assigned to each experimental outcome must be between 0 and 1, inclusively. If we let E_i denote the ith experimental outcome and $P(E_i)$ its probability, then this requirement can be written as

$$0 \le P(E_i) \le 1 \text{ for all } i \quad \textbf{(4.3)}$$

2. The sum of the probabilities for all the experimental outcomes must equal 1.0. For n experimental outcomes, this requirement can be written as

$$P(E_1) + P(E_2) + \cdots + P(E_n) = 1 \quad \textbf{(4.4)}$$

The **classical method** of assigning probabilities is appropriate when all the experimental outcomes are equally likely. If n experimental outcomes are possible, a probability of $1/n$ is assigned to each experimental outcome. When using this approach, the two basic requirements for assigning probabilities are automatically satisfied.

For an example, consider the experiment of tossing a fair coin; the two experimental outcomes—head and tail—are equally likely. Because one of the two equally likely outcomes is a head, the probability of observing a head is 1/2, or .50. Similarly, the probability of observing a tail is also 1/2, or .50.

As another example, consider the experiment of rolling a die. It would seem reasonable to conclude that the six possible outcomes are equally likely, and hence each outcome is assigned a probability of 1/6. If $P(1)$ denotes the probability that one dot appears on the upward face of the die, then $P(1) = 1/6$. Similarly, $P(2) = 1/6$, $P(3) = 1/6$, $P(4) = 1/6$, $P(5) = 1/6$, and $P(6) = 1/6$. Note that these probabilities satisfy the two basic requirements of equations (4.3) and (4.4) because each of the probabilities is greater than or equal to zero and they sum to 1.0.

The **relative frequency method** of assigning probabilities is appropriate when data are available to estimate the proportion of the time the experimental outcome will occur if the experiment is repeated a large number of times. As an example, consider a study of waiting times in the X-ray department for a local hospital. A clerk recorded the number of patients waiting for service at 9:00 A.M. on 20 successive days and obtained the following results.

Number Waiting	Number of Days Outcome Occurred
0	2
1	5
2	6
3	4
4	3
Total	20

These data show that on 2 of the 20 days, zero patients were waiting for service; on 5 of the days, one patient was waiting for service; and so on. Using the relative frequency method, we would assign a probability of $2/20 = .10$ to the experimental outcome of zero patients waiting for service, $5/20 = .25$ to the experimental outcome of one patient waiting, $6/20 = .30$ to two patients waiting, $4/20 = .20$ to three patients waiting, and $3/20 = .15$ to four patients waiting. As with the classical method, using the relative frequency method automatically satisfies the two basic requirements of equations (4.3) and (4.4).

The **subjective method** of assigning probabilities is most appropriate when one cannot realistically assume that the experimental outcomes are equally likely and when little relevant data are available. When the subjective method is used to assign probabilities to the experimental outcomes, we may use any information available, such as our experience or intuition. After considering all available information, a probability value that expresses our *degree of belief* (on a scale from 0 to 1) that the experimental outcome will occur is specified. Because subjective probability expresses a person's degree of belief, it is personal. Using the subjective method, different people can be expected to assign different probabilities to the same experimental outcome.

The subjective method requires extra care to ensure that the two basic requirements of equations (4.3) and (4.4) are satisfied. Regardless of a person's degree of belief, the probability value assigned to each experimental outcome must be between 0 and 1, inclusive, and the sum of all the probabilities for the experimental outcomes must equal 1.0.

Consider the case in which Tom and Judy Elsbernd make an offer to purchase a house. Two outcomes are possible:

$$E_1 = \text{their offer is accepted}$$
$$E_2 = \text{their offer is rejected}$$

Judy believes that the probability their offer will be accepted is .8; thus, Judy would set $P(E_1) = .8$ and $P(E_2) = .2$. Tom, however, believes that the probability that their offer will be accepted is .6; hence, Tom would set $P(E_1) = .6$ and $P(E_2) = .4$. Note that Tom's probability estimate for E_1 reflects a greater pessimism that their offer will be accepted.

Bayes' theorem (see Section 4.5) provides a means for combining subjectively determined prior probabilities with probabilities obtained by other means to obtain revised, or posterior, probabilities.

Both Judy and Tom assigned probabilities that satisfy the two basic requirements. The fact that their probability estimates are different emphasizes the personal nature of the subjective method.

Even in business situations where either the classical or the relative frequency approach can be applied, managers may want to provide subjective probability estimates. In such cases, the best probability estimates often are obtained by combining the estimates from the classical or relative frequency approach with subjective probability estimates.

Probabilities for the KP&L Project

To perform further analysis on the KP&L project, we must develop probabilities for each of the nine experimental outcomes listed in Table 4.1. On the basis of experience and judgment, management concluded that the experimental outcomes were not equally likely. Hence, the classical method of assigning probabilities could not be used. Management then decided to conduct a study of the completion times for similar projects undertaken by KP&L over the past three years. The results of a study of 40 similar projects are summarized in Table 4.2.

After reviewing the results of the study, management decided to employ the relative frequency method of assigning probabilities. Management could have provided subjective probability estimates, but felt that the current project was quite similar to the 40 previous projects. Thus, the relative frequency method was judged best.

In using the data in Table 4.2 to compute probabilities, we note that outcome (2, 6)—stage 1 completed in 2 months and stage 2 completed in 6 months—occurred six times in the 40 projects. We can use the relative frequency method to assign a probability of 6/40 = .15 to this outcome. Similarly, outcome (2, 7) also occurred in six of the 40 projects, providing a 6/40 = .15 probability. Continuing in this manner, we obtain the probability assignments for the sample points of the KP&L project shown in Table 4.3. Note that $P(2, 6)$ represents the probability of the sample point (2, 6), $P(2, 7)$ represents the probability of the sample point (2, 7), and so on.

TABLE 4.2 COMPLETION RESULTS FOR 40 KP&L PROJECTS

Completion Time (months)			
Stage 1 Design	**Stage 2 Construction**	**Sample Point**	**Number of Past Projects Having These Completion Times**
2	6	(2, 6)	6
2	7	(2, 7)	6
2	8	(2, 8)	2
3	6	(3, 6)	4
3	7	(3, 7)	8
3	8	(3, 8)	2
4	6	(4, 6)	2
4	7	(4, 7)	4
4	8	(4, 8)	6
		Total	40

TABLE 4.3 PROBABILITY ASSIGNMENTS FOR THE KP&L PROJECT BASED ON THE RELATIVE FREQUENCY METHOD

Sample Point	Project Completion Time	Probability of Sample Point
(2, 6)	8 months	$P(2, 6) = 6/40 =$ .15
(2, 7)	9 months	$P(2, 7) = 6/40 =$ .15
(2, 8)	10 months	$P(2, 8) = 2/40 =$ .05
(3, 6)	9 months	$P(3, 6) = 4/40 =$ .10
(3, 7)	10 months	$P(3, 7) = 8/40 =$ .20
(3, 8)	11 months	$P(3, 8) = 2/40 =$ .05
(4, 6)	10 months	$P(4, 6) = 2/40 =$ .05
(4, 7)	11 months	$P(4, 7) = 4/40 =$ .10
(4, 8)	12 months	$P(4, 8) = 6/40 =$ .15
		Total 1.00

NOTES AND COMMENTS

1. In statistics, the notion of an experiment differs somewhat from the notion of an experiment in the physical sciences. In the physical sciences, researchers usually conduct an experiment in a laboratory or a controlled environment in order to learn about cause and effect. In statistical experiments, probability determines outcomes. Even though the experiment is repeated in exactly the same way, an entirely different outcome may occur. Because of this influence of probability on the outcome, the experiments of statistics are sometimes called *random experiments.*
2. When drawing a random sample without replacement from a population of size N, the counting rule for combinations is used to find the number of different samples of size n that can be selected.

Exercises

Methods

1. An experiment has three steps with three outcomes possible for the first step, two outcomes possible for the second step, and four outcomes possible for the third step. How many experimental outcomes exist for the entire experiment?

SELF test

2. How many ways can three items be selected from a group of six items? Use the letters A, B, C, D, E, and F to identify the items, and list each of the different combinations of three items.
3. How many permutations of three items can be selected from a group of six? Use the letters A, B, C, D, E, and F to identify the items, and list each of the permutations of items B, D, and F.
4. Consider the experiment of tossing a coin three times.
   a. Develop a tree diagram for the experiment.
   b. List the experimental outcomes.
   c. What is the probability for each experimental outcome?
5. Suppose an experiment has five equally likely outcomes: E_1, E_2, E_3, E_4, E_5. Assign probabilities to each outcome and show that the requirements in equations (4.3) and (4.4) are satisfied. What method did you use?

SELF test

6. An experiment with three outcomes has been repeated 50 times, and it was learned that E_1 occurred 20 times, E_2 occurred 13 times, and E_3 occurred 17 times. Assign probabilities to the outcomes. What method did you use?

7. A decision maker subjectively assigned the following probabilities to the four outcomes of an experiment: $P(E_1) = .10$, $P(E_2) = .15$, $P(E_3) = .40$, and $P(E_4) = .20$. Are these probability assignments valid? Explain.

Applications

8. In the city of Milford, applications for zoning changes go through a two-step process: a review by the planning commission and a final decision by the city council. At step 1 the planning commission reviews the zoning change request and makes a positive or negative recommendation concerning the change. At step 2 the city council reviews the planning commission's recommendation and then votes to approve or to disapprove the zoning change. Suppose the developer of an apartment complex submits an application for a zoning change. Consider the application process as an experiment.
   a. How many sample points are there for this experiment? List the sample points.
   b. Construct a tree diagram for the experiment.

SELF test

9. Simple random sampling uses a sample of size *n* from a population of size *N* to obtain data that can be used to make inferences about the characteristics of a population. Suppose that, from a population of 50 bank accounts, we want to take a random sample of four accounts in order to learn about the population. How many different random samples of four accounts are possible?

SELF test

10. Venture capital can provide a big boost in funds available to companies. According to Venture Economics (*Investor's Business Daily,* April 28, 2000), of 2374 venture capital disbursements, 1434 were to companies in California, 390 were to companies in Massachusetts, 217 were to companies in New York, and 112 were to companies in Colorado. Twenty-two percent of the companies receiving funds were in the early stages of development and 55% of the companies were in an expansion stage. Suppose you want to randomly choose one of these companies to learn about how venture capital funds are used.
    a. What is the probability the company chosen will be from California?
    b. What is the probability the company chosen will not be from one of the four states mentioned?
    c. What is the probability the company will not be in the early stages of development?
    d. Assuming the companies in the early stages of development were evenly distributed across the country, how many Massachusetts companies receiving venture capital funds were in their early stages of development?
    e. The total amount of funds invested was $32.4 billion. Estimate the amount that went to Colorado.

11. The National Highway Traffic Safety Administration (NHTSA) conducted a survey to learn about how drivers throughout the United States are using seat belts (Associated Press, August 25, 2003). Sample data consistent with the NHTSA survey are as follows.

	Driver Using Seat Belt?	
Region	**Yes**	**No**
Northeast	148	52
Midwest	162	54
South	296	74
West	252	48
Total	858	228

    a. For the United States, what is the probability that a driver is using a seat belt?
    b. The seat belt usage probability for a U.S. driver a year earlier was .75. NHTSA chief Dr. Jeffrey Runge had hoped for a .78 probability in 2003. Would he have been pleased with the 2003 survey results?

c. What is the probability of seat belt usage by region of the country? What region has the highest seat belt usage?
d. What proportion of the drivers in the sample came from each region of the country? What region had the most drivers selected? What region had the second most drivers selected?
e. Assuming the total number of drivers in each region is the same, do you see any reason why the probability estimate in part (a) might be too high? Explain.

12. The Powerball lottery is played twice each week in 28 states, the Virgin Islands, and the District of Columbia. To play Powerball a participant must purchase a ticket and then select five numbers from the digits 1 through 55 and a Powerball number from the digits 1 through 42. To determine the winning numbers for each game, lottery officials draw five white balls out of a drum with 55 white balls, and one red ball out of a drum with 42 red balls. To win the jackpot, a participant's numbers must match the numbers on the five white balls in any order and the number on the red Powerball. Eight coworkers at the ConAgra Foods plant in Lincoln, Nebraska, claimed the record $365 million jackpot on February 18, 2006, by matching the numbers 15-17-43-44-49 and the Powerball number 29. A variety of other cash prizes are awarded each time the game is played. For instance, a prize of $200,000 is paid if the participant's five numbers match the numbers on the five white balls (www.powerball.com, March 19, 2006).
    a. Compute the number of ways the first five numbers can be selected.
    b. What is the probability of winning a prize of $200,000 by matching the numbers on the five white balls?
    c. What is the probability of winning the Powerball jackpot?

13. A company that manufactures toothpaste is studying five different package designs. Assuming that one design is just as likely to be selected by a consumer as any other design, what selection probability would you assign to each of the package designs? In an actual experiment, 100 consumers were asked to pick the design they preferred. The following data were obtained. Do the data confirm the belief that one design is just as likely to be selected as another? Explain.

Design	Number of Times Preferred
1	5
2	15
3	30
4	40
5	10

4.2 Events and Their Probabilities

In the introduction to this chapter we used the term *event* much as it would be used in everyday language. Then, in Section 4.1 we introduced the concept of an experiment and its associated experimental outcomes or sample points. Sample points and events provide the foundation for the study of probability. As a result, we must now introduce the formal definition of an **event** as it relates to sample points. Doing so will provide the basis for determining the probability of an event.

EVENT

An event is a collection of sample points.

For an example, let us return to the KP&L project and assume that the project manager is interested in the event that the entire project can be completed in 10 months or less. Referring to Table 4.3, we see that six sample points—(2, 6), (2, 7), (2, 8), (3, 6), (3, 7), and (4, 6)—provide a project completion time of 10 months or less. Let C denote the event that the project is completed in 10 months or less; we write

$$C = \{(2, 6), (2, 7), (2, 8), (3, 6), (3, 7), (4, 6)\}$$

Event C is said to occur if *any one* of these six sample points appears as the experimental outcome.

Other events that might be of interest to KP&L management include the following.

$$L = \text{The event that the project is completed in } \textit{less} \text{ than 10 months}$$
$$M = \text{The event that the project is completed in } \textit{more} \text{ than 10 months}$$

Using the information in Table 4.3, we see that these events consist of the following sample points.

$$L = \{(2, 6), (2, 7), (3, 6)\}$$
$$M = \{(3, 8), (4, 7), (4, 8)\}$$

A variety of additional events can be defined for the KP&L project, but in each case the event must be identified as a collection of sample points for the experiment.

Given the probabilities of the sample points shown in Table 4.3, we can use the following definition to compute the probability of any event that KP&L management might want to consider.

PROBABILITY OF AN EVENT

The probability of any event is equal to the sum of the probabilities of the sample points in the event.

Using this definition, we calculate the probability of a particular event by adding the probabilities of the sample points (experimental outcomes) that make up the event. We can now compute the probability that the project will take 10 months or less to complete. Because this event is given by $C = \{(2, 6), (2, 7), (2, 8), (3, 6), (3, 7), (4, 6)\}$, the probability of event C, denoted $P(C)$, is given by

$$P(C) = P(2, 6) + P(2, 7) + P(2, 8) + P(3, 6) + P(3, 7) + P(4, 6)$$

Refer to the sample point probabilities in Table 4.3; we have

$$P(C) = .15 + .15 + .05 + .10 + .20 + .05 = .70$$

Similarly, because the event that the project is completed in less than 10 months is given by $L = \{(2, 6), (2, 7), (3, 6)\}$, the probability of this event is given by

$$\begin{aligned} P(L) &= P(2, 6) + P(2, 7) + P(3, 6) \\ &= .15 + .15 + .10 = .40 \end{aligned}$$

Finally, for the event that the project is completed in more than 10 months, we have $M = \{(3, 8), (4, 7), (4, 8)\}$ and thus

$$\begin{aligned} P(M) &= P(3, 8) + P(4, 7) + P(4, 8) \\ &= .05 + .10 + .15 = .30 \end{aligned}$$

Using these probability results, we can now tell KP&L management that there is a .70 probability that the project will be completed in 10 months or less, a .40 probability that the project will be completed in less than 10 months, and a .30 probability that the project will be completed in more than 10 months. This procedure of computing event probabilities can be repeated for any event of interest to the KP&L management.

Any time that we can identify all the sample points of an experiment and assign probabilities to each, we can compute the probability of an event using the definition. However, in many experiments the large number of sample points makes the identification of the sample points, as well as the determination of their associated probabilities, extremely cumbersome, if not impossible. In the remaining sections of this chapter, we present some basic probability relationships that can be used to compute the probability of an event without knowledge of all the sample point probabilities.

NOTES AND COMMENTS

1. The sample space, S, is an event. Because it contains all the experimental outcomes, it has a probability of 1; that is, $P(S) = 1$.
2. When the classical method is used to assign probabilities, the assumption is that the experimental outcomes are equally likely. In such cases, the probability of an event can be computed by counting the number of experimental outcomes in the event and dividing the result by the total number of experimental outcomes.

Exercises

Methods

14. An experiment has four equally likely outcomes: E_1, E_2, E_3, and E_4.
    a. What is the probability that E_2 occurs?
    b. What is the probability that any two of the outcomes occur (e.g., E_1 or E_3)?
    c. What is the probability that any three of the outcomes occur (e.g., E_1 or E_2 or E_4)?

SELF test

15. Consider the experiment of selecting a playing card from a deck of 52 playing cards. Each card corresponds to a sample point with a 1/52 probability.
    a. List the sample points in the event an ace is selected.
    b. List the sample points in the event a club is selected.
    c. List the sample points in the event a face card (jack, queen, or king) is selected.
    d. Find the probabilities associated with each of the events in parts (a), (b), and (c).
16. Consider the experiment of rolling a pair of dice. Suppose that we are interested in the sum of the face values showing on the dice.
    a. How many sample points are possible? (*Hint:* Use the counting rule for multiple-step experiments.)
    b. List the sample points.
    c. What is the probability of obtaining a value of 7?
    d. What is the probability of obtaining a value of 9 or greater?
    e. Because each roll has six possible even values (2, 4, 6, 8, 10, and 12) and only five possible odd values (3, 5, 7, 9, and 11), the dice should show even values more often than odd values. Do you agree with this statement? Explain.
    f. What method did you use to assign the probabilities requested?

Applications

SELF test

17. Refer to the KP&L sample points and sample point probabilities in Tables 4.2 and 4.3.
    a. The design stage (stage 1) will run over budget if it takes 4 months to complete. List the sample points in the event the design stage is over budget.
    b. What is the probability that the design stage is over budget?
    c. The construction stage (stage 2) will run over budget if it takes 8 months to complete. List the sample points in the event the construction stage is over budget.
    d. What is the probability that the construction stage is over budget?
    e. What is the probability that both stages are over budget?

18. Suppose that a manager of a large apartment complex provides the following subjective probability estimates about the number of vacancies that will exist next month.

Vacancies	Probability
0	.05
1	.15
2	.35
3	.25
4	.10
5	.10

    Provide the probability of each of the following events.
    a. No vacancies
    b. At least four vacancies
    c. Two or fewer vacancies

19. The National Sporting Goods Association conducted a survey of persons 7 years of age or older about participation in sports activities (*Statistical Abstract of the United States: 2002*). The total population in this age group was reported at 248.5 million, with 120.9 million male and 127.6 million female. The number of participants for the top five sports activities appears here.

	Participants (millions)	
Activity	Male	Female
Bicycle riding	22.2	21.0
Camping	25.6	24.3
Exercise walking	28.7	57.7
Exercising with equipment	20.4	24.4
Swimming	26.4	34.4

    a. For a randomly selected female, estimate the probability of participation in each of the sports activities.
    b. For a randomly selected male, estimate the probability of participation in each of the sports activities.
    c. For a randomly selected person, what is the probability the person participates in exercise walking?
    d. Suppose you just happen to see an exercise walker going by. What is the probability the walker is a woman? What is the probability the walker is a man?

20. *Fortune* magazine publishes an annual list of the 500 largest companies in the United States. The following data show the five states with the largest number of *Fortune* 500 companies (*The New York Times Almanac,* 2006).

State	Number of Companies
New York	54
California	52
Texas	48
Illinois	33
Ohio	30

Suppose a *Fortune* 500 company is chosen for a follow-up questionnaire. What are the probabilities of the following events?

a. Let N be the event the company is headquartered in New York. Find $P(N)$.
b. Let T be the event the company is headquartered in Texas. Find $P(T)$.
c. Let B be the event the company is headquartered in one of these five states. Find $P(B)$.

21. The U.S. population by age is as follows (*The World Almanac 2004*). The data are in millions of people.

Age	Number
19 and under	80.5
20 to 24	19.0
25 to 34	39.9
35 to 44	45.2
45 to 54	37.7
55 to 64	24.3
65 and over	35.0

Assume that a person will be randomly chosen from this population.

a. What is the probability the person is 20 to 24 years old?
b. What is the probability the person is 20 to 34 years old?
c. What is the probability the person is 45 years or older?

4.3 Some Basic Relationships of Probability

Complement of an Event

Given an event A, the **complement of A** is defined to be the event consisting of all sample points that are *not* in A. The complement of A is denoted by A^c. Figure 4.4 is a diagram, known as a **Venn diagram**, which illustrates the concept of a complement. The rectangular area represents the sample space for the experiment and as such contains all possible sample points. The circle represents event A and contains only the sample points that belong to A. The shaded region of the rectangle contains all sample points not in event A and is by definition the complement of A.

In any probability application, either event A or its complement A^c must occur. Therefore, we have

$$P(A) + P(A^c) = 1$$

FIGURE 4.4 COMPLEMENT OF EVENT A IS SHADED

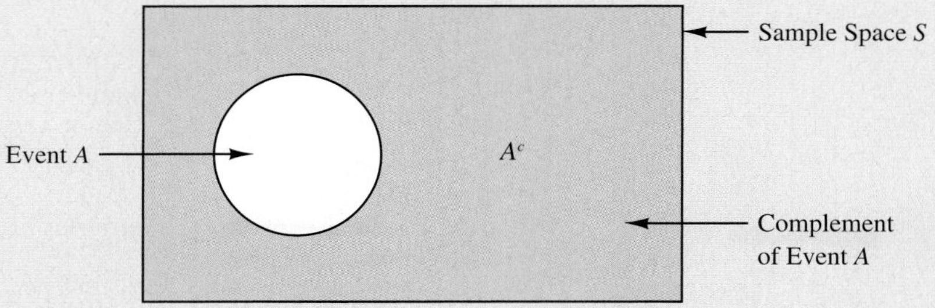

Solving for $P(A)$, we obtain the following result.

COMPUTING PROBABILITY USING THE COMPLEMENT

$$P(A) = 1 - P(A^c) \tag{4.5}$$

Equation (4.5) shows that the probability of an event A can be computed easily if the probability of its complement, $P(A^c)$, is known.

As an example, consider the case of a sales manager who, after reviewing sales reports, states that 80% of new customer contacts result in no sale. By allowing A to denote the event of a sale and A^c to denote the event of no sale, the manager is stating that $P(A^c) = .80$. Using equation (4.5), we see that

$$P(A) = 1 - P(A^c) = 1 - .80 = .20$$

We can conclude that a new customer contact has a .20 probability of resulting in a sale.

In another example, a purchasing agent states a .90 probability that a supplier will send a shipment that is free of defective parts. Using the complement, we can conclude that there is a $1 - .90 = .10$ probability that the shipment will contain defective parts.

Addition Law

The addition law is helpful when we are interested in knowing the probability that at least one of two events occurs. That is, with events A and B we are interested in knowing the probability that event A or event B or both occur.

Before we present the addition law, we need to discuss two concepts related to the combination of events: the *union* of events and the *intersection* of events. Given two events A and B, the **union of A and B** is defined as follows.

UNION OF TWO EVENTS

The *union* of A and B is the event containing *all* sample points belonging to A *or* B *or both.* The union is denoted by $A \cup B$.

The Venn diagram in Figure 4.5 depicts the union of events A and B. Note that the two circles contain all the sample points in event A as well as all the sample points in event B.

FIGURE 4.5 UNION OF EVENTS A AND B IS SHADED

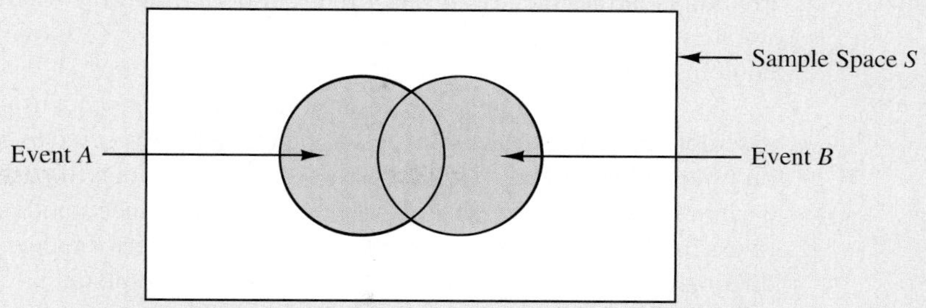

The fact that the circles overlap indicates that some sample points are contained in both A and B.

The definition of the **intersection of A and B** follows.

INTERSECTION OF TWO EVENTS

Given two events A and B, the *intersection* of A and B is the event containing the sample points belonging to *both A and B*. The intersection is denoted by $A \cap B$.

The Venn diagram depicting the intersection of events A and B is shown in Figure 4.6. The area where the two circles overlap is the intersection; it contains the sample points that are in both A and B.

Let us now continue with a discussion of the addition law. The **addition law** provides a way to compute the probability that event A or event B or both occur. In other words, the addition law is used to compute the probability of the union of two events. The addition law is written as follows.

ADDITION LAW

$$P(A \cup B) = P(A) + P(B) - P(A \cap B) \tag{4.6}$$

FIGURE 4.6 INTERSECTION OF EVENTS A AND B IS SHADED

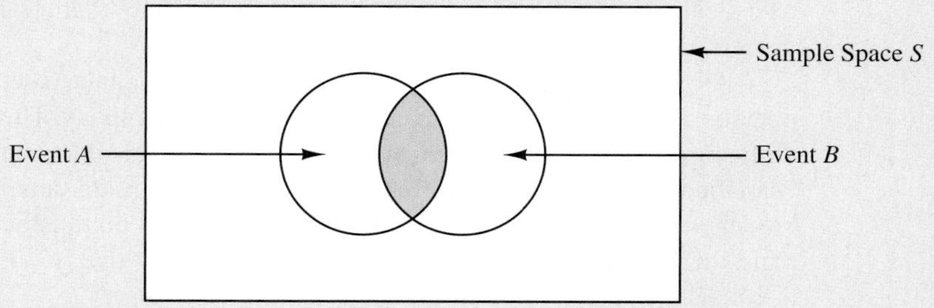

To understand the addition law intuitively, note that the first two terms in the addition law, $P(A) + P(B)$, account for all the sample points in $A \cup B$. However, because the sample points in the intersection $A \cap B$ are in both A and B, when we compute $P(A) + P(B)$, we are in effect counting each of the sample points in $A \cap B$ twice. We correct for this overcounting by subtracting $P(A \cap B)$.

As an example of an application of the addition law, let us consider the case of a small assembly plant with 50 employees. Each worker is expected to complete work assignments on time and in such a way that the assembled product will pass a final inspection. On occasion, some of the workers fail to meet the performance standards by completing work late or assembling a defective product. At the end of a performance evaluation period, the production manager found that 5 of the 50 workers completed work late, 6 of the 50 workers assembled a defective product, and 2 of the 50 workers both completed work late *and* assembled a defective product.

Let

$$L = \text{the event that the work is completed late}$$
$$D = \text{the event that the assembled product is defective}$$

The relative frequency information leads to the following probabilities.

$$P(L) = \frac{5}{50} = .10$$
$$P(D) = \frac{6}{50} = .12$$
$$P(L \cap D) = \frac{2}{50} = .04$$

After reviewing the performance data, the production manager decided to assign a poor performance rating to any employee whose work was either late or defective; thus the event of interest is $L \cup D$. What is the probability that the production manager assigned an employee a poor performance rating?

Note that the probability question is about the union of two events. Specifically, we want to know $P(L \cup D)$. Using equation (4.6), we have

$$P(L \cup D) = P(L) + P(D) - P(L \cap D)$$

Knowing values for the three probabilities on the right side of this expression, we can write

$$P(L \cup D) = .10 + .12 - .04 = .18$$

This calculation tells us that there is a .18 probability that a randomly selected employee received a poor performance rating.

As another example of the addition law, consider a recent study conducted by the personnel manager of a major computer software company. The study showed that 30% of the employees who left the firm within two years did so primarily because they were dissatisfied with their salary, 20% left because they were dissatisfied with their work assignments, and 12% of the former employees indicated dissatisfaction with *both* their salary and their work assignments. What is the probability that an employee who leaves within two years does so because of dissatisfaction with salary, dissatisfaction with the work assignment, or both?

Let

$$S = \text{the event that the employee leaves because of salary}$$
$$W = \text{the event that the employee leaves because of work assignment}$$

We have $P(S) = .30$, $P(W) = .20$, and $P(S \cap W) = .12$. Using equation (4.6), the addition law, we have

$$P(S \cup W) = P(S) + P(W) - P(S \cap W) = .30 + .20 - .12 = .38.$$

We find a .38 probability that an employee leaves for salary or work assignment reasons.

Before we conclude our discussion of the addition law, let us consider a special case that arises for **mutually exclusive events**.

MUTUALLY EXCLUSIVE EVENTS

Two events are said to be mutually exclusive if the events have no sample points in common.

Events A and B are mutually exclusive if, when one event occurs, the other cannot occur. Thus, a requirement for A and B to be mutually exclusive is that their intersection must contain no sample points. The Venn diagram depicting two mutually exclusive events A and B is shown in Figure 4.7. In this case $P(A \cap B) = 0$ and the addition law can be written as follows.

ADDITION LAW FOR MUTUALLY EXCLUSIVE EVENTS

$$P(A \cup B) = P(A) + P(B)$$

FIGURE 4.7 MUTUALLY EXCLUSIVE EVENTS

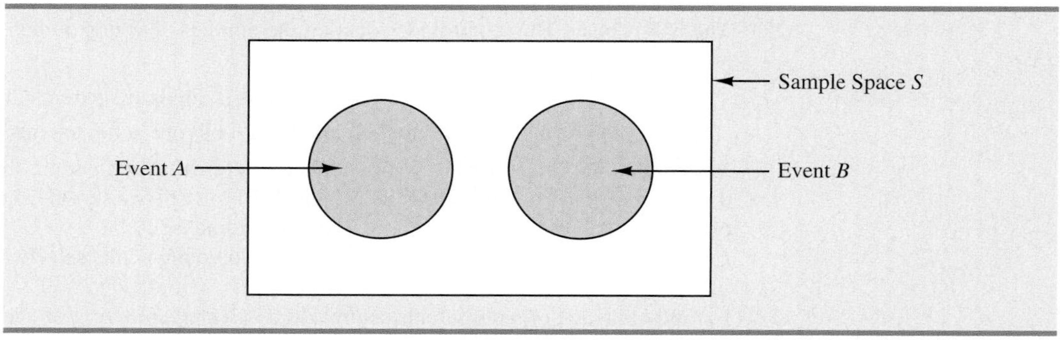

Exercises

Methods

22. Suppose that we have a sample space with five equally likely experimental outcomes: E_1, E_2, E_3, E_4, E_5. Let

$$A = \{E_1, E_2\}$$
$$B = \{E_3, E_4\}$$
$$C = \{E_2, E_3, E_5\}$$

a. Find $P(A)$, $P(B)$, and $P(C)$.
b. Find $P(A \cup B)$. Are A and B mutually exclusive?
c. Find A^c, C^c, $P(A^c)$, and $P(C^c)$.
d. Find $A \cup B^c$ and $P(A \cup B^c)$.
e. Find $P(B \cup C)$.

SELF test

23. Suppose that we have a sample space $S = \{E_1, E_2, E_3, E_4, E_5, E_6, E_7\}$, where $E_1, E_2, \ldots, E_7$ denote the sample points. The following probability assignments apply: $P(E_1) = .05$, $P(E_2) = .20$, $P(E_3) = .20$, $P(E_4) = .25$, $P(E_5) = .15$, $P(E_6) = .10$, and $P(E_7) = .05$. Let

$$A = \{E_1, E_4, E_6\}$$
$$B = \{E_2, E_4, E_7\}$$
$$C = \{E_2, E_3, E_5, E_7\}$$

a. Find $P(A)$, $P(B)$, and $P(C)$.
b. Find $A \cup B$ and $P(A \cup B)$.
c. Find $A \cap B$ and $P(A \cap B)$.
d. Are events A and C mutually exclusive?
e. Find B^c and $P(B^c)$.

Applications

24. Clarkson University surveyed alumni to learn more about what they think of Clarkson. One part of the survey asked respondents to indicate whether their overall experience at Clarkson fell short of expectations, met expectations, or surpassed expectations. The results showed that 4% of the respondents did not provide a response, 26% said that their experience fell short of expectations, and 65% of the respondents said that their experience met expectations (*Clarkson Magazine,* Summer 2001).
    a. If we chose an alumnus at random, what is the probability that the alumnus would say their experience surpassed expectations?
    b. If we chose an alumnus at random, what is the probability that the alumnus would say their experience met or surpassed expectations?

25. The U.S. Census Bureau provides data on the number of young adults, ages 18–24, who are living in their parents' home.* Let

M = the event a male young adult is living in his parents' home
F = the event a female young adult is living in her parents' home

If we randomly select a male young adult and a female young adult, the Census Bureau data enable us to conclude $P(M) = .56$ and $P(F) = .42$ (*The World Almanac,* 2006). The probability that both are living in their parents' home is .24.
    a. What is the probability at least one of the two young adults selected is living in his or her parents' home?
    b. What is the probability both young adults selected are living on their own (neither is living in their parents' home)?

*The data include single young adults who are living in college dormitories because it is assumed these young adults will return to their parents' home when school is not in session.

26. Data on the 30 largest stock and balanced funds provided one-year and five-year percentage returns for the period ending March 31, 2000 (*The Wall Street Journal,* April 10, 2000). Suppose we consider a one-year return in excess of 50% to be high and a five-year return in excess of 300% to be high. Nine of the funds had one-year returns in excess of 50%, seven of the funds had five-year returns in excess of 300%, and five of the funds had both one-year returns in excess of 50% and five-year returns in excess of 300%.
    a. What is the probability of a high one-year return, and what is the probability of a high five-year return?
    b. What is the probability of both a high one-year return and a high five-year return?
    c. What is the probability of neither a high one-year return nor a high five-year return?

27. A 2001 preseason NCAA football poll asked respondents to answer the question, "Will the Big Ten or the Pac-10 have a team in this year's national championship game, the Rose Bowl?" Of the 13,429 respondents, 2961 said the Big Ten would, 4494 said the Pac-10 would, and 6823 said neither the Big Ten nor the Pac-10 would have a team in the Rose Bowl (www.yahoo.com, August 30, 2001).
    a. What is the probability that a respondent said neither the Big Ten nor the Pac-10 would have a team in the Rose Bowl?
    b. What is the probability that a respondent said either the Big Ten or the Pac-10 would have a team in the Rose Bowl?
    c. Find the probability that a respondent said both the Big Ten and the Pac-10 would have a team in the Rose Bowl.

SELF test

28. A survey of magazine subscribers showed that 45.8% rented a car during the past 12 months for business reasons, 54% rented a car during the past 12 months for personal reasons, and 30% rented a car during the past 12 months for both business and personal reasons.
    a. What is the probability that a subscriber rented a car during the past 12 months for business or personal reasons?
    b. What is the probability that a subscriber did not rent a car during the past 12 months for either business or personal reasons?

29. High school seniors with strong academic records apply to the nation's most selective colleges in greater numbers each year. Because the number of slots remains relatively stable, some colleges reject more early applicants. The University of Pennsylvania received 2851 applications for early admission. Of this group, it admitted 1033 students, rejected 854 outright, and deferred 964 to the regular admissions pool. Penn admitted about 18% of the applicants in the regular admissions pool for a total class size (number of early admissions plus number of regular admissions) of 2375 students (*USA Today,* January 24, 2001). Let E, R, and D represent the events that a student who applies for early admission is admitted, rejected outright, or deferred to the regular admissions pool; and let A represent the event that a student in the regular admissions pool is admitted.
    a. Use the data to estimate $P(E)$, $P(R)$, and $P(D)$.
    b. Are events E and D mutually exclusive? Find $P(E \cap D)$.
    c. For the 2375 students admitted to Penn, what is the probability that a randomly selected student was accepted for early admission?
    d. Suppose a student applies to Penn for early admission. What is the probability the student will be admitted for early admission or be accepted for admission in the regular admissions pool?

4.4 Conditional Probability

Often, the probability of an event is influenced by whether a related event already occurred. Suppose we have an event A with probability $P(A)$. If we obtain new information and learn that a related event, denoted by B, already occurred, we will want to take advantage of this information by calculating a new probability for event A. This new probability of event A is called a **conditional probability** and is written $P(A \mid B)$. We use the notation $\mid$ to indicate that we are considering the probability of event A *given* the condition that event B has occurred. Hence, the notation $P(A \mid B)$ reads "the probability of A given B."

As an illustration of the application of conditional probability, consider the situation of the promotion status of male and female officers of a major metropolitan police force in the eastern United States. The police force consists of 1200 officers, 960 men and 240 women. Over the past two years, 324 officers on the police force received promotions. The specific breakdown of promotions for male and female officers is shown in Table 4.4.

After reviewing the promotion record, a committee of female officers raised a discrimination case on the basis that 288 male officers had received promotions but only 36 female officers had received promotions. The police administration argued that the relatively low number of promotions for female officers was due not to discrimination, but to the fact that relatively few females are members of the police force. Let us show how conditional probability could be used to analyze the discrimination charge.

Let

$$M = \text{event an officer is a man}$$
$$W = \text{event an officer is a woman}$$
$$A = \text{event an officer is promoted}$$
$$A^c = \text{event an officer is not promoted}$$

Dividing the data values in Table 4.4 by the total of 1200 officers enables us to summarize the available information with the following probability values.

$P(M \cap A) = 288/1200 = .24 =$ probability that a randomly selected officer is a man *and* is promoted

$P(M \cap A^c) = 672/1200 = .56 =$ probability that a randomly selected officer is a man *and* is not promoted

$P(W \cap A) = 36/1200 = .03 =$ probability that a randomly selected officer is a woman *and* is promoted

$P(W \cap A^c) = 204/1200 = .17 =$ probability that a randomly selected officer is a woman *and* is not promoted

Because each of these values gives the probability of the intersection of two events, the probabilities are called **joint probabilities**. Table 4.5, which provides a summary of the probability information for the police officer promotion situation, is referred to as a *joint probability table*.

The values in the margins of the joint probability table provide the probabilities of each event separately. That is, $P(M) = .80$, $P(W) = .20$, $P(A) = .27$, and $P(A^c) = .73$. These

TABLE 4.4 PROMOTION STATUS OF POLICE OFFICERS OVER THE PAST TWO YEARS

	Men	Women	Total
Promoted	288	36	324
Not Promoted	672	204	876
Total	960	240	1200

TABLE 4.5 JOINT PROBABILITY TABLE FOR PROMOTIONS

Joint probabilities appear in the body of the table.

	Men (M)	Women (W)	Total
Promoted (A)	.24	.03	.27
Not Promoted (A^c)	.56	.17	.73
Total	.80	.20	1.00

Marginal probabilities appear in the margins of the table.

probabilities are referred to as **marginal probabilities** because of their location in the margins of the joint probability table. We note that the marginal probabilities are found by summing the joint probabilities in the corresponding row or column of the joint probability table. For instance, the marginal probability of being promoted is $P(A) = P(M \cap A) + P(W \cap A) = .24 + .03 = .27$. From the marginal probabilities, we see that 80% of the force is male, 20% of the force is female, 27% of all officers received promotions, and 73% were not promoted.

Let us begin the conditional probability analysis by computing the probability that an officer is promoted given that the officer is a man. In conditional probability notation, we are attempting to determine $P(A \mid M)$. To calculate $P(A \mid M)$, we first realize that this notation simply means that we are considering the probability of the event A (promotion) given that the condition designated as event M (the officer is a man) is known to exist. Thus $P(A \mid M)$ tells us that we are now concerned only with the promotion status of the 960 male officers. Because 288 of the 960 male officers received promotions, the probability of being promoted given that the officer is a man is 288/960 = .30. In other words, given that an officer is a man, that officer had a 30% chance of receiving a promotion over the past two years.

This procedure was easy to apply because the values in Table 4.4 show the number of officers in each category. We now want to demonstrate how conditional probabilities such as $P(A \mid M)$ can be computed directly from related event probabilities rather than the frequency data of Table 4.4.

We have shown that $P(A \mid M) = 288/960 = .30$. Let us now divide both the numerator and denominator of this fraction by 1200, the total number of officers in the study.

$$P(A \mid M) = \frac{288}{960} = \frac{288/1200}{960/1200} = \frac{.24}{.80} = .30$$

We now see that the conditional probability $P(A \mid M)$ can be computed as .24/.80. Refer to the joint probability table (Table 4.5). Note in particular that .24 is the joint probability of A and M; that is, $P(A \cap M) = .24$. Also note that .80 is the marginal probability that a randomly selected officer is a man; that is, $P(M) = .80$. Thus, the conditional probability $P(A \mid M)$ can be computed as the ratio of the joint probability $P(A \cap M)$ to the marginal probability $P(M)$.

$$P(A \mid M) = \frac{P(A \cap M)}{P(M)} = \frac{.24}{.80} = .30$$

The fact that conditional probabilities can be computed as the ratio of a joint probability to a marginal probability provides the following general formula for conditional probability calculations for two events A and B.

CONDITIONAL PROBABILITY

$$P(A \mid B) = \frac{P(A \cap B)}{P(B)} \tag{4.7}$$

or

$$P(B \mid A) = \frac{P(A \cap B)}{P(A)} \tag{4.8}$$

The Venn diagram in Figure 4.8 is helpful in obtaining an intuitive understanding of conditional probability. The circle on the right shows that event B has occurred; the portion of the circle that overlaps with event A denotes the event $(A \cap B)$. We know that once event B has occurred, the only way that we can also observe event A is for the event $(A \cap B)$ to occur. Thus, the ratio $P(A \cap B)/P(B)$ provides the conditional probability that we will observe event A given that event B has already occurred.

Let us return to the issue of discrimination against the female officers. The marginal probability in row 1 of Table 4.5 shows that the probability of promotion of an officer is $P(A) = .27$ (regardless of whether that officer is male or female). However, the critical issue in the discrimination case involves the two conditional probabilities $P(A \mid M)$ and $P(A \mid W)$. That is, what is the probability of a promotion *given* that the officer is a man, and what is the probability of a promotion *given* that the officer is a woman? If these two probabilities are equal, a discrimination argument has no basis because the chances of a promotion are the same for male and female officers. However, a difference in the two conditional probabilities will support the position that male and female officers are treated differently in promotion decisions.

We already determined that $P(A \mid M) = .30$. Let us now use the probability values in Table 4.5 and the basic relationship of conditional probability in equation (4.7) to compute

FIGURE 4.8 CONDITIONAL PROBABILITY $P(A \mid B) = P(A \cap B)/P(B)$

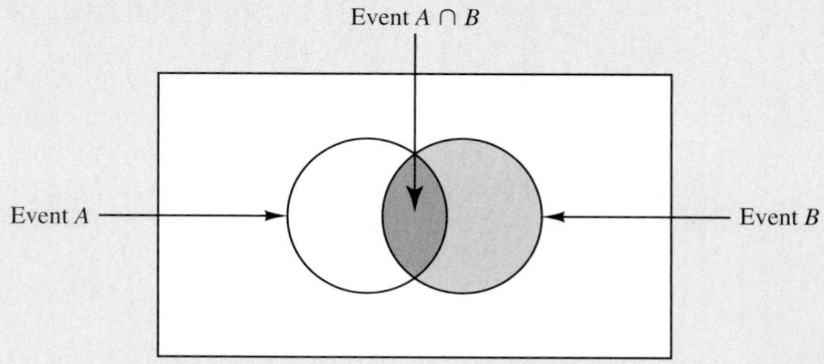

the probability that an officer is promoted given that the officer is a woman; that is, $P(A \mid W)$. Using equation (4.7), with W replacing B, we obtain

$$P(A \mid W) = \frac{P(A \cap W)}{P(W)} = \frac{.03}{.20} = .15$$

What conclusion do you draw? The probability of a promotion given that the officer is a man is .30, twice the .15 probability of a promotion given that the officer is a woman. Although the use of conditional probability does not in itself prove that discrimination exists in this case, the conditional probability values support the argument presented by the female officers.

Independent Events

In the preceding illustration, $P(A) = .27$, $P(A \mid M) = .30$, and $P(A \mid W) = .15$. We see that the probability of a promotion (event A) is affected or influenced by whether the officer is a man or a woman. Particularly, because $P(A \mid M) \neq P(A)$, we would say that events A and M are dependent events. That is, the probability of event A (promotion) is altered or affected by knowing that event M (the officer is a man) exists. Similarly, with $P(A \mid W) \neq P(A)$, we would say that events A and W are *dependent events*. However, if the probability of event A is not changed by the existence of event M—that is, $P(A \mid M) = P(A)$—we would say that events A and M are **independent events**. This situation leads to the following definition of the independence of two events.

INDEPENDENT EVENTS

Two events A and B are independent if

$$P(A \mid B) = P(A) \quad \textbf{(4.9)}$$

or

$$P(B \mid A) = P(B) \quad \textbf{(4.10)}$$

Otherwise, the events are dependent.

Multiplication Law

Whereas the addition law of probability is used to compute the probability of a union of two events, the multiplication law is used to compute the probability of the intersection of two events. The multiplication law is based on the definition of conditional probability. Using equations (4.7) and (4.8) and solving for $P(A \cap B)$, we obtain the **multiplication law**.

MULTIPLICATION LAW

$$P(A \cap B) = P(B)P(A \mid B) \quad \textbf{(4.11)}$$

or

$$P(A \cap B) = P(A)P(B \mid A) \quad \textbf{(4.12)}$$

To illustrate the use of the multiplication law, consider a newspaper circulation department where it is known that 84% of the households in a particular neighborhood subscribe to the daily edition of the paper. If we let D denote the event that a household subscribes to the daily edition, $P(D) = .84$. In addition, it is known that the probability that a household that already holds a daily subscription also subscribes to the Sunday edition (event S) is .75; that is, $P(S \mid D) = .75$.

What is the probability that a household subscribes to both the Sunday and daily editions of the newspaper? Using the multiplication law, we compute the desired $P(S \cap D)$ as

$$P(S \cap D) = P(D)P(S \mid D) = .84(.75) = .63$$

We now know that 63% of the households subscribe to both the Sunday and daily editions.

Before concluding this section, let us consider the special case of the multiplication law when the events involved are independent. Recall that events A and B are independent whenever $P(A \mid B) = P(A)$ or $P(B \mid A) = P(B)$. Hence, using equations (4.11) and (4.12) for the special case of independent events, we obtain the following multiplication law.

MULTIPLICATION LAW FOR INDEPENDENT EVENTS

$$P(A \cap B) = P(A)P(B) \tag{4.13}$$

To compute the probability of the intersection of two independent events, we simply multiply the corresponding probabilities. Note that the multiplication law for independent events provides another way to determine whether A and B are independent. That is, if $P(A \cap B) = P(A)P(B)$, then A and B are independent; if $P(A \cap B) \neq P(A)P(B)$, then A and B are dependent.

As an application of the multiplication law for independent events, consider the situation of a service station manager who knows from past experience that 80% of the customers use a credit card when they purchase gasoline. What is the probability that the next two customers purchasing gasoline will each use a credit card? If we let

A = the event that the first customer uses a credit card
B = the event that the second customer uses a credit card

then the event of interest is $A \cap B$. Given no other information, we can reasonably assume that A and B are independent events. Thus,

$$P(A \cap B) = P(A)P(B) = (.80)(.80) = .64$$

To summarize this section, we note that our interest in conditional probability is motivated by the fact that events are often related. In such cases, we say the events are dependent and the conditional probability formulas in equations (4.7) and (4.8) must be used to compute the event probabilities. If two events are not related, they are independent; in this case neither event's probability is affected by whether the other event occurred.

NOTES AND COMMENTS

Do not confuse the notion of mutually exclusive events with that of independent events. Two events with nonzero probabilities cannot be both mutually exclusive and independent. If one mutually exclusive event is known to occur, the other cannot occur; thus, the probability of the other event occurring is reduced to zero. They are therefore dependent.

Exercises

Methods

SELF test

30. Suppose that we have two events, A and B, with $P(A) = .50$, $P(B) = .60$, and $P(A \cap B) = .40$.
   a. Find $P(A \mid B)$.
   b. Find $P(B \mid A)$.
   c. Are A and B independent? Why or why not?

31. Assume that we have two events, A and B, that are mutually exclusive. Assume further that we know $P(A) = .30$ and $P(B) = .40$.
    a. What is $P(A \cap B)$?
    b. What is $P(A \mid B)$?
    c. A student in statistics argues that the concepts of mutually exclusive events and independent events are really the same, and that if events are mutually exclusive they must be independent. Do you agree with this statement? Use the probability information in this problem to justify your answer.
    d. What general conclusion would you make about mutually exclusive and independent events given the results of this problem?

Applications

32. Due to rising health insurance costs, 43 million people in the United States go without health insurance (*Time,* December 1, 2003). Sample data representative of the national health insurance coverage are shown here.

		Health Insurance	
		Yes	**No**
Age	**18 to 34**	750	170
	35 and older	950	130

    a. Develop a joint probability table for these data and use the table to answer the remaining questions.
    b. What do the marginal probabilities tell you about the age of the U.S. population?
    c. What is the probability that a randomly selected individual does not have health insurance coverage?
    d. If the individual is between the ages of 18 and 34, what is the probability that the individual does not have health insurance coverage?
    e. If the individual is age 35 or older, what is the probability that the individual does not have health insurance coverage?
    f. If the individual does not have health insurance, what is the probability that the individual is in the 18 to 34 age group?
    g. What does the probability information tell you about health insurance coverage in the United States?

SELF test

33. In a survey of MBA students, the following data were obtained on "students' first reason for application to the school in which they matriculated."

		Reason for Application			
		School Quality	**School Cost or Convenience**	**Other**	**Totals**
Enrollment Status	**Full Time**	421	393	76	890
	Part Time	400	593	46	1039
	Totals	821	986	122	1929

    a. Develop a joint probability table for these data.
    b. Use the marginal probabilities of school quality, school cost or convenience, and other to comment on the most important reason for choosing a school.

c. If a student goes full time, what is the probability that school quality is the first reason for choosing a school?
d. If a student goes part time, what is the probability that school quality is the first reason for choosing a school?
e. Let *A* denote the event that a student is full time and let *B* denote the event that the student lists school quality as the first reason for applying. Are events *A* and *B* independent? Justify your answer.

34. The following table shows the probabilities of blood types in the general population (Hoxworth Blood Center, Cincinnati, Ohio, March 2003).

	A	B	AB	O
Rh+	.34	.09	.04	.38
Rh−	.06	.02	.01	.06

a. What is the probability a person will have type O blood?
b. What is the probability a person will be Rh−?
c. What is the probability a person will be Rh− given he or she has type O blood?
d. What is the probability a person will have type B blood given he or she is Rh+?
e. What is the probability a married couple will both be Rh−?
f. What is the probability a married couple will both have type AB blood?

35. The U.S. Bureau of Labor Statistics collected data on the occupations of workers 25 to 64 years old. The following table shows the number of male and female workers (in millions) in each occupation category (*Statistical Abstract of the United States: 2002*).

Occupation	Male	Female
Managerial/Professional	19079	19021
Tech./Sales/Administrative	11079	19315
Service	4977	7947
Precision Production	11682	1138
Operators/Fabricators/Labor	10576	3482
Farming/Forestry/Fishing	1838	514

a. Develop a joint probability table.
b. What is the probability of a female worker being a manager or professional?
c. What is the probability of a male worker being in precision production?
d. Is occupation independent of gender? Justify your answer with a probability calculation.

36. Reggie Miller of the Indiana Pacers is the National Basketball Association's best career free throw shooter, making 89% of his shots (*USA Today,* January 22, 2004). Assume that late in a basketball game, Reggie Miller is fouled and is awarded two shots.
a. What is the probability that he will make both shots?
b. What is the probability that he will make at least one shot?
c. What is the probability that he will miss both shots?
d. Late in a basketball game, a team often intentionally fouls an opposing player in order to stop the game clock. The usual strategy is to intentionally foul the other team's worst free throw shooter. Assume that the Indiana Pacers' center makes 58% of his free throw shots. Calculate the probabilities for the center as shown in parts (a), (b), and (c), and show that intentionally fouling the Indiana Pacers' center is a better strategy than intentionally fouling Reggie Miller.

37. Visa Card USA studied how frequently young consumers, ages 18 to 24, use plastic (debit and credit) cards in making purchases (Associated Press, January 16, 2006). The results of the study provided the following probabilities.

- The probability that a consumer uses a plastic card when making a purchase is .37.
- Given that the consumer uses a plastic card, there is a .19 probability that the consumer is 18 to 24 years old.
- Given that the consumer uses a plastic card, there is a .81 probability that the consumer is more than 24 years old.

U. S. Census Bureau data show that 14% of the consumer population is 18 to 24 years old.

a. Given the consumer is 18 to 24 years old, what is the probability that the consumer use a plastic card?
b. Given the consumer is over 24 years old, what is the probability that the consumer uses a plastic card?
c. What is the interpretation of the probabilities shown in parts (a) and (b)?
d. Should companies such as Visa, MasterCard, and Discover make plastic cards available to the 18 to 24 years old age group before these consumers have had time to establish a credit history? If no, why? If yes, what restrictions might the companies place on this age group?

38. A Morgan Stanley Consumer Research Survey sampled men and women and asked each whether they preferred to drink plain bottled water or a sports drink such as Gatorade or Propel Fitness water (*The Atlanta Journal-Constitution*, December 28, 2005). Suppose 200 men and 200 women participated in the study, and 280 reported they preferred plain bottled water. Of the group preferring a sports drink, 80 were men and 40 were women.

Let

M = the event the consumer is a man
W = the event the consumer is a woman
B = the event the consumer preferred plain bottled water
S = the event the consumer preferred sports drink

a. What is the probability a person in the study preferred plain bottled water?
b. What is the probability a person in the study preferred a sports drink?
c. What are the conditional probabilities $P(M \mid S)$ and $P(W \mid S)$?
d. What are the joint probabilities $P(M \cap S)$ and $P(W \cap S)$?
e. Given a consumer is a man, what is the probability he will prefer a sports drink?
f. Given a consumer is a woman, what is the probability she will prefer a sports drink?
g. Is preference for a sports drink independent of whether the consumer is a man or a woman? Explain using probability information.

4.5 Bayes' Theorem

In the discussion of conditional probability, we indicated that revising probabilities when new information is obtained is an important phase of probability analysis. Often, we begin the analysis with initial or **prior probability** estimates for specific events of interest. Then, from sources such as a sample, a special report, or a product test, we obtain additional information about the events. Given this new information, we update the prior probability values by calculating revised probabilities, referred to as **posterior probabilities. Bayes' theorem** provides a means for making these probability calculations. The steps in this probability revision process are shown in Figure 4.9.

FIGURE 4.9 PROBABILITY REVISION USING BAYES' THEOREM

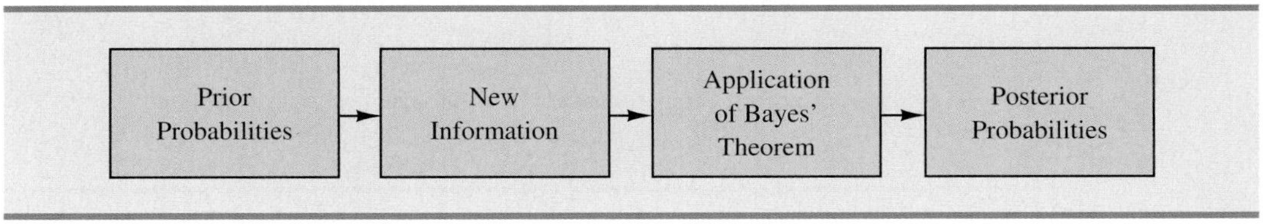

TABLE 4.6 HISTORICAL QUALITY LEVELS OF TWO SUPPLIERS

	Percentage Good Parts	Percentage Bad Parts
Supplier 1	98	2
Supplier 2	95	5

As an application of Bayes' theorem, consider a manufacturing firm that receives shipments of parts from two different suppliers. Let A_1 denote the event that a part is from supplier 1 and A_2 denote the event that a part is from supplier 2. Currently, 65% of the parts purchased by the company are from supplier 1 and the remaining 35% are from supplier 2. Hence, if a part is selected at random, we would assign the prior probabilities $P(A_1) = .65$ and $P(A_2) = .35$.

The quality of the purchased parts varies with the source of supply. Historical data suggest that the quality ratings of the two suppliers are as shown in Table 4.6. If we let G denote the event that a part is good and B denote the event that a part is bad, the information in Table 4.6 provides the following conditional probability values.

$$P(G \mid A_1) = .98 \quad P(B \mid A_1) = .02$$
$$P(G \mid A_2) = .95 \quad P(B \mid A_2) = .05$$

The tree diagram in Figure 4.10 depicts the process of the firm receiving a part from one of the two suppliers and then discovering that the part is good or bad as a two-step experiment. We see that four experimental outcomes are possible; two correspond to the part being good and two correspond to the part being bad.

Each of the experimental outcomes is the intersection of two events, so we can use the multiplication rule to compute the probabilities. For instance,

$$P(A_1, G) = P(A_1 \cap G) = P(A_1)P(G \mid A_1)$$

FIGURE 4.10 TREE DIAGRAM FOR TWO-SUPPLIER EXAMPLE

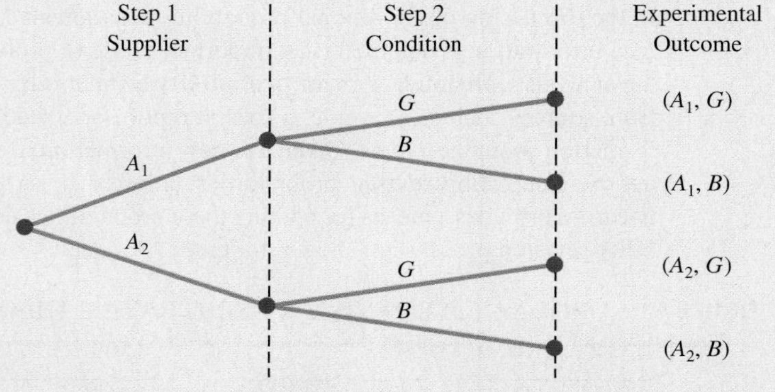

Note: Step 1 shows that the part comes from one of two suppliers, and step 2 shows whether the part is good or bad.

FIGURE 4.11 PROBABILITY TREE FOR TWO-SUPPLIER EXAMPLE

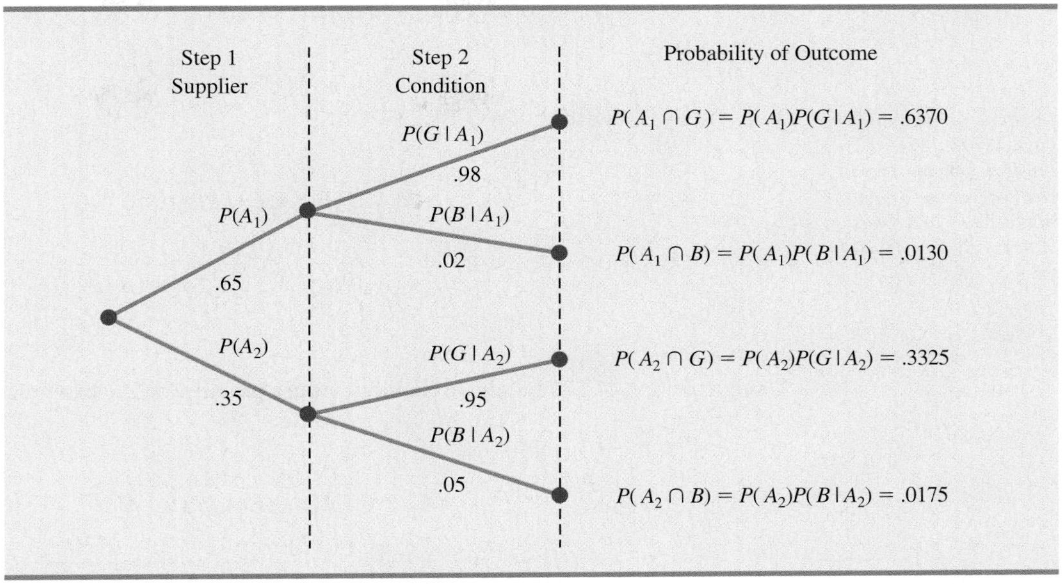

The process of computing these joint probabilities can be depicted in what is called a probability tree (see Figure 4.11). From left to right through the tree, the probabilities for each branch at step 1 are prior probabilities and the probabilities for each branch at step 2 are conditional probabilities. To find the probabilities of each experimental outcome, we simply multiply the probabilities on the branches leading to the outcome. Each of these joint probabilities is shown in Figure 4.11 along with the known probabilities for each branch.

Suppose now that the parts from the two suppliers are used in the firm's manufacturing process and that a machine breaks down because it attempts to process a bad part. Given the information that the part is bad, what is the probability that it came from supplier 1 and what is the probability that it came from supplier 2? With the information in the probability tree (Figure 4.11), Bayes' theorem can be used to answer these questions.

Letting B denote the event that the part is bad, we are looking for the posterior probabilities $P(A_1 \mid B)$ and $P(A_2 \mid B)$. From the law of conditional probability, we know that

$$P(A_1 \mid B) = \frac{P(A_1 \cap B)}{P(B)} \tag{4.14}$$

Referring to the probability tree, we see that

$$P(A_1 \cap B) = P(A_1)P(B \mid A_1) \tag{4.15}$$

To find $P(B)$, we note that event B can occur in only two ways: $(A_1 \cap B)$ and $(A_2 \cap B)$. Therefore, we have

$$\begin{aligned} P(B) &= P(A_1 \cap B) + P(A_2 \cap B) \\ &= P(A_1)P(B \mid A_1) + P(A_2)P(B \mid A_2) \end{aligned} \tag{4.16}$$

Substituting from equations (4.15) and (4.16) into equation (4.14) and writing a similar result for $P(A_2 \mid B)$, we obtain Bayes' theorem for the case of two events.

The Reverend Thomas Bayes (1702–1761), a Presbyterian minister, is credited with the original work leading to the version of Bayes' theorem in use today.

BAYES' THEOREM (TWO-EVENT CASE)

$$P(A_1 \mid B) = \frac{P(A_1)P(B \mid A_1)}{P(A_1)P(B \mid A_1) + P(A_2)P(B \mid A_2)} \tag{4.17}$$

$$P(A_2 \mid B) = \frac{P(A_2)P(B \mid A_2)}{P(A_1)P(B \mid A_1) + P(A_2)P(B \mid A_2)} \tag{4.18}$$

Using equation (4.17) and the probability values provided in the example, we have

$$\begin{aligned} P(A_1 \mid B) &= \frac{P(A_1)P(B \mid A_1)}{P(A_1)P(B \mid A_1) + P(A_2)P(B \mid A_2)} \\ &= \frac{(.65)(.02)}{(.65)(.02) + (.35)(.05)} = \frac{.0130}{.0130 + .0175} \\ &= \frac{.0130}{.0305} = .4262 \end{aligned}$$

In addition, using equation (4.18), we find $P(A_2 \mid B)$.

$$\begin{aligned} P(A_2 \mid B) &= \frac{(.35)(.05)}{(.65)(.02) + (.35)(.05)} \\ &= \frac{.0175}{.0130 + .0175} = \frac{.0175}{.0305} = .5738 \end{aligned}$$

Note that in this application we started with a probability of .65 that a part selected at random was from supplier 1. However, given information that the part is bad, the probability that the part is from supplier 1 drops to .4262. In fact, if the part is bad, it has better than a 50–50 chance that it came from supplier 2; that is, $P(A_2 \mid B) = .5738$.

Bayes' theorem is applicable when the events for which we want to compute posterior probabilities are mutually exclusive and their union is the entire sample space.* For the case of n mutually exclusive events $A_1, A_2, \ldots, A_n$, whose union is the entire sample space, Bayes' theorem can be used to compute any posterior probability $P(A_i \mid B)$ as shown here.

BAYES' THEOREM

$$P(A_i \mid B) = \frac{P(A_i)P(B \mid A_i)}{P(A_1)P(B \mid A_1) + P(A_2)P(B \mid A_2) + \cdots + P(A_n)P(B \mid A_n)} \tag{4.19}$$

*If the union of events is the entire sample space, the events are said to be *collectively exhaustive*.

With prior probabilities $P(A_1), P(A_2), \ldots, P(A_n)$ and the appropriate conditional probabilities $P(B \mid A_1), P(B \mid A_2), \ldots, P(B \mid A_n)$, equation (4.19) can be used to compute the posterior probability of the events $A_1, A_2, \ldots, A_n$.

Tabular Approach

A tabular approach is helpful in conducting the Bayes' theorem calculations. Such an approach is shown in Table 4.7 for the parts supplier problem. The computations shown there are done in the following steps.

Step 1. Prepare the following three columns:
Column 1—The mutually exclusive events A_i for which posterior probabilities are desired
Column 2—The prior probabilities $P(A_i)$ for the events
Column 3—The conditional probabilities $P(B \mid A_i)$ of the new information B given each event

Step 2. In column 4, compute the joint probabilities $P(A_i \cap B)$ for each event and the new information B by using the multiplication law. These joint probabilities are found by multiplying the prior probabilities in column 2 by the corresponding conditional probabilities in column 3; that is, $P(A_i \cap B) = P(A_i)P(B \mid A_i)$.

Step 3. Sum the joint probabilities in column 4. The sum is the probability of the new information, $P(B)$. Thus we see in Table 4.7 that there is a .0130 probability that the part came from supplier 1 and is bad and a .0175 probability that the part came from supplier 2 and is bad. Because these are the only two ways in which a bad part can be obtained, the sum .0130 + .0175 shows an overall probability of .0305 of finding a bad part from the combined shipments of the two suppliers.

Step 4. In column 5, compute the posterior probabilities using the basic relationship of conditional probability.

$$P(A_i \mid B) = \frac{P(A_i \cap B)}{P(B)}$$

Note that the joint probabilities $P(A_i \cap B)$ are in column 4 and the probability $P(B)$ is the sum of column 4.

TABLE 4.7 TABULAR APPROACH TO BAYES' THEOREM CALCULATIONS FOR THE TWO-SUPPLIER PROBLEM

(1) Events A_i	(2) Prior Probabilities $P(A_i)$	(3) Conditional Probabilities $P(B \mid A_i)$	(4) Joint Probabilities $P(A_i \cap B)$	(5) Posterior Probabilities $P(A_i \mid B)$
A_1	.65	.02	.0130	.0130/.0305 = .4262
A_2	.35	.05	.0175	.0175/.0305 = .5738
	1.00		$P(B)$ = .0305	1.0000

NOTES AND COMMENTS

1. Bayes' theorem is used extensively in decision analysis. The prior probabilities are often subjective estimates provided by a decision maker. Sample information is obtained and posterior probabilities are computed for use in choosing the best decision.
2. An event and its complement are mutually exclusive, and their union is the entire sample space. Thus, Bayes' theorem is always applicable for computing posterior probabilities of an event and its complement.

Exercises

Methods

SELF test

39. The prior probabilities for events A_1 and A_2 are $P(A_1) = .40$ and $P(A_2) = .60$. It is also known that $P(A_1 \cap A_2) = 0$. Suppose $P(B \mid A_1) = .20$ and $P(B \mid A_2) = .05$.
    a. Are A_1 and A_2 mutually exclusive? Explain.
    b. Compute $P(A_1 \cap B)$ and $P(A_2 \cap B)$.
    c. Compute $P(B)$.
    d. Apply Bayes' theorem to compute $P(A_1 \mid B)$ and $P(A_2 \mid B)$.
40. The prior probabilities for events A_1, A_2, and A_3 are $P(A_1) = .20$, $P(A_2) = .50$, and $P(A_3) = .30$. The conditional probabilities of event B given A_1, A_2, and A_3 are $P(B \mid A_1) = .50$, $P(B \mid A_2) = .40$, and $P(B \mid A_3) = .30$.
    a. Compute $P(B \cap A_1)$, $P(B \cap A_2)$, and $P(B \cap A_3)$.
    b. Apply Bayes' theorem, equation (4.19), to compute the posterior probability $P(A_2 \mid B)$.
    c. Use the tabular approach to applying Bayes' theorem to compute $P(A_1 \mid B)$, $P(A_2 \mid B)$, and $P(A_3 \mid B)$.

Applications

41. A consulting firm submitted a bid for a large research project. The firm's management initially felt they had a 50–50 chance of getting the project. However, the agency to which the bid was submitted subsequently requested additional information on the bid. Past experience indicates that for 75% of the successful bids and 40% of the unsuccessful bids the agency requested additional information.
    a. What is the prior probability of the bid being successful (that is, prior to the request for additional information)?
    b. What is the conditional probability of a request for additional information given that the bid will ultimately be successful?
    c. Compute the posterior probability that the bid will be successful given a request for additional information.

SELF test

42. A local bank reviewed its credit card policy with the intention of recalling some of its credit cards. In the past approximately 5% of cardholders defaulted, leaving the bank unable to collect the outstanding balance. Hence, management established a prior probability of .05 that any particular cardholder will default. The bank also found that the probability of missing a monthly payment is .20 for customers who do not default. Of course, the probability of missing a monthly payment for those who default is 1.
    a. Given that a customer missed one or more monthly payments, compute the posterior probability that the customer will default.
    b. The bank would like to recall its card if the probability that a customer will default is greater than .20. Should the bank recall its card if the customer misses a monthly payment? Why or why not?

43. Small cars get better gas mileage, but they are not as safe as bigger cars. Small cars accounted for 18% of the vehicles on the road, but accidents involving small cars led to 11,898 fatalities during a recent year (*Reader's Digest,* May 2000). Assume the probability a small car is involved in an accident is .18. The probability of an accident involving a small car leading to a fatality is .128 and the probability of an accident not involving a small car leading to a fatality is .05. Suppose you learn of an accident involving a fatality. What is the probability a small car was involved? Assume that the likelihood of getting into an accident is independent of car size.

44. The American Council of Education reported that 47% of college freshmen earn a degree and graduate within five years (Associated Press, May 6, 2002). Assume that graduation records show women make up 50% of the students who graduated within five years, but only 45% of the students who did not graduate within five years. The students who had not graduated within five years either dropped out or were still working on their degrees.
    a. Let A_1 = the student graduated within five years
       A_2 = the student did not graduate within five years
       W = the student is a female student
       Using the given information, what are the values for $P(A_1)$, $P(A_2)$, $P(W \mid A_1)$, and $P(W \mid A_2)$?
    b. What is the probability that a female student will graduate within five years?
    c. What is the probability that a male student will graduate within five years?
    d. Given the preceding results, what are the percentage of women and the percentage of men in the entering freshman class?

45. In an article about investment growth, *Money* magazine reported that drug stocks show powerful long-term trends and offer investors unparalleled potential for strong and steady gains. The federal Health Care Financing Administration supports this conclusion through its forecast that annual prescription drug expenditures will reach $366 billion by 2010, up from $117 billion in 2000. Many individuals age 65 and older rely heavily on prescription drugs. For this group, 82% take prescription drugs regularly, 55% take three or more prescriptions regularly, and 40% currently use five or more prescriptions. In contrast, 49% of people under age 65 take prescriptions regularly, with 37% taking three or more prescriptions regularly and 28% using five or more prescriptions (*Money,* September 2001). The U.S. Census Bureau reports that of the 281,421,906 people in the United States, 34,991,753 are age 65 years and older (U.S. Census Bureau, *Census 2000*).
    a. Compute the probability that a person in the United States is age 65 or older.
    b. Compute the probability that a person takes prescription drugs regularly.
    c. Compute the probability that a person is age 65 or older and takes five or more prescriptions.
    d. Given a person uses five or more prescriptions, compute the probability that the person is age 65 or older.

Summary

In this chapter we introduced basic probability concepts and illustrated how probability analysis can be used to provide helpful information for decision making. We described how probability can be interpreted as a numerical measure of the likelihood that an event will occur. In addition, we saw that the probability of an event can be computed either by summing the probabilities of the experimental outcomes (sample points) comprising the event or by using the relationships established by the addition, conditional probability, and multiplication laws of probability. For cases in which additional information is available, we showed how Bayes' theorem can be used to obtain revised or posterior probabilities.

Glossary

Probability A numerical measure of the likelihood that an event will occur.
Experiment A process that generates well-defined outcomes.

Sample space The set of all experimental outcomes.
Sample point An element of the sample space. A sample point represents an experimental outcome.
Tree diagram A graphical representation that helps in visualizing a multiple-step experiment.
Basic requirements for assigning probabilities Two requirements that restrict the manner in which probability assignments can be made: (1) for each experimental outcome E_i we must have $0 \leq P(E_i) \leq 1$; (2) considering all experimental outcomes, we must have $P(E_1) + P(E_2) + \cdots + P(E_n) = 1.0$.
Classical method A method of assigning probabilities that is appropriate when all the experimental outcomes are equally likely.
Relative frequency method A method of assigning probabilities that is appropriate when data are available to estimate the proportion of the time the experimental outcome will occur if the experiment is repeated a large number of times.
Subjective method A method of assigning probabilities on the basis of judgment.
Event A collection of sample points.
Complement of *A* The event consisting of all sample points that are not in A.
Venn diagram A graphical representation for showing symbolically the sample space and operations involving events in which the sample space is represented by a rectangle and events are represented as circles within the sample space.
Union of *A* and *B* The event containing all sample points belonging to A or B or both. The union is denoted $A \cup B$.
Intersection of *A* and *B* The event containing the sample points belonging to both A and B. The intersection is denoted $A \cap B$.
Addition law A probability law used to compute the probability of the union of two events. It is $P(A \cup B) = P(A) + P(B) - P(A \cap B)$. For mutually exclusive events, $P(A \cap B) = 0$; in this case the addition law reduces to $P(A \cup B) = P(A) + P(B)$.
Mutually exclusive events Events that have no sample points in common; that is, $A \cap B$ is empty and $P(A \cap B) = 0$.
Conditional probability The probability of an event given that another event already occurred. The conditional probability of A given B is $P(A \mid B) = P(A \cap B)/P(B)$.
Joint probability The probability of two events both occurring; that is, the probability of the intersection of two events.
Marginal probability The values in the margins of a joint probability table that provide the probabilities of each event separately.
Independent events Two events A and B where $P(A \mid B) = P(A)$ or $P(B \mid A) = P(B)$; that is, the events have no influence on each other.
Multiplication law A probability law used to compute the probability of the intersection of two events. It is $P(A \cap B) = P(B)P(A \mid B)$ or $P(A \cap B) = P(A)P(B \mid A)$. For independent events it reduces to $P(A \cap B) = P(A)P(B)$.
Prior probabilities Initial estimates of the probabilities of events.
Posterior probabilities Revised probabilities of events based on additional information.
Bayes' theorem A method used to compute posterior probabilities.

Key Formulas

Counting Rule for Combinations

$$C_n^N = \binom{N}{n} = \frac{N!}{n!(N-n)!} \tag{4.1}$$

Counting Rule for Permutations

$$P_n^N = n!\binom{N}{n} = \frac{N!}{(N-n)!} \tag{4.2}$$

Computing Probability Using the Complement

$$P(A) = 1 - P(A^c) \tag{4.5}$$

Addition Law

$$P(A \cup B) = P(A) + P(B) - P(A \cap B) \tag{4.6}$$

Conditional Probability

$$P(A \mid B) = \frac{P(A \cap B)}{P(B)} \tag{4.7}$$

$$P(B \mid A) = \frac{P(A \cap B)}{P(A)} \tag{4.8}$$

Multiplication Law

$$P(A \cap B) = P(B)P(A \mid B) \tag{4.11}$$

$$P(A \cap B) = P(A)P(B \mid A) \tag{4.12}$$

Multiplication Law for Independent Events

$$P(A \cap B) = P(A)P(B) \tag{4.13}$$

Bayes' Theorem

$$P(A_i \mid B) = \frac{P(A_i)P(B \mid A_i)}{P(A_1)P(B \mid A_1) + P(A_2)P(B \mid A_2) + \cdots + P(A_n)P(B \mid A_n)} \tag{4.19}$$

Supplementary Exercises

46. In a *BusinessWeek*/Harris Poll, 1035 adults were asked about their attitudes toward business (*BusinessWeek,* September 11, 2000). One question asked: "How would you rate large U.S. companies on making good products and competing in a global environment?" The responses were: excellent—18%, pretty good—50%, only fair—26%, poor—5%, and don't know/no answer—1%.
    a. What is the probability that a respondent rated U.S. companies pretty good or excellent?
    b. How many respondents rated U.S. companies poor?
    c. How many respondents did not know or did not answer?

47. A financial manager made two new investments—one in the oil industry and one in municipal bonds. After a one-year period, each of the investments will be classified as either successful or unsuccessful. Consider the making of the two investments as an experiment.
    a. How many sample points exist for this experiment?
    b. Show a tree diagram and list the sample points.
    c. Let O = the event that the oil industry investment is successful and M = the event that the municipal bond investment is successful. List the sample points in O and in M.
    d. List the sample points in the union of the events $(O \cup M)$.
    e. List the sample points in the intersection of the events $(O \cap M)$.
    f. Are events O and M mutually exclusive? Explain.

48. In early 2003, President Bush proposed eliminating the taxation of dividends to shareholders on the grounds that it was double taxation. Corporations pay taxes on the earnings that are later paid out in dividends. In a poll of 671 Americans, TechnoMetrica Market Intelligence found that 47% favored the proposal, 44% opposed it, and 9% were not sure (*Investor's Business Daily,* January 13, 2003). In looking at the responses across party lines the poll showed that 29% of Democrats were in favor, 64% of Republicans were in favor, and 48% of Independents were in favor.
    a. How many of those polled favored elimination of the tax on dividends?
    b. What is the conditional probability in favor of the proposal given the person polled is a Democrat?
    c. Is party affiliation independent of whether one is in favor of the proposal?
    d. If we assume people's responses were consistent with their own self-interest, which group do you believe will benefit most from passage of the proposal?

49. A study of 31,000 hospital admissions in New York State found that 4% of the admissions led to treatment-caused injuries. One-seventh of these treatment-caused injuries resulted in death, and one-fourth were caused by negligence. Malpractice claims were filed in one out of 7.5 cases involving negligence, and payments were made in one out of every two claims.
    a. What is the probability a person admitted to the hospital will suffer a treatment-caused injury due to negligence?
    b. What is the probability a person admitted to the hospital will die from a treatment-caused injury?
    c. In the case of a negligent treatment-caused injury, what is the probability a malpractice claim will be paid?

50. A telephone survey to determine viewer response to a new television show obtained the following data.

Rating	Frequency
Poor	4
Below average	8
Average	11
Above average	14
Excellent	13

    a. What is the probability that a randomly selected viewer will rate the new show as average or better?
    b. What is the probability that a randomly selected viewer will rate the new show below average or worse?

51. The following crosstabulation shows household income by educational level of the head of household (*Statistical Abstract of the United States: 2002*).

	Household Income ($1000s)					
Education Level	Under 25	25.0–49.9	50.0–74.9	75.0–99.9	100 or more	Total
Not H.S. Graduate	9,285	4,093	1,589	541	354	15,862
H.S. Graduate	10,150	9,821	6,050	2,737	2,028	30,786
Some College	6,011	8,221	5,813	3,215	3,120	26,380
Bachelor's Degree	2,138	3,985	3,952	2,698	4,748	17,521
Beyond Bach. Deg.	813	1,497	1,815	1,589	3,765	9,479
Total	28,397	27,617	19,219	10,780	14,015	100,028

a. Develop a joint probability table.
b. What is the probability of a head of household not being a high school graduate?
c. What is the probability of a head of household having a bachelor's degree or more education?
d. What is the probability of a household headed by someone with a bachelor's degree earning \$100,000 or more?
e. What is the probability of a household having income below \$25,000?
f. What is the probability of a household headed by someone with a bachelor's degree earning less than \$25,000?
g. Is household income independent of educational level?

52. A GMAC MBA new-matriculants survey provided the following data for 2018 students.

		Applied to More Than One School	
		Yes	No
Age Group	23 and under	207	201
	24–26	299	379
	27–30	185	268
	31–35	66	193
	36 and over	51	169

a. For a randomly selected MBA student, prepare a joint probability table for the experiment consisting of observing the student's age and whether the student applied to one or more schools.
b. What is the probability that a randomly selected applicant is 23 or under?
c. What is the probability that a randomly selected applicant is older than 26?
d. What is the probability that a randomly selected applicant applied to more than one school?

53. Refer again to the data from the GMAC new-matriculants survey in exercise 52.
a. Given that a person applied to more than one school, what is the probability that the person is 24–26 years old?
b. Given that a person is in the 36-and-over age group, what is the probability that the person applied to more than one school?
c. What is the probability that a person is 24–26 years old or applied to more than one school?
d. Suppose a person is known to have applied to only one school. What is the probability that the person is 31 or more years old?
e. Is the number of schools applied to independent of age? Explain.

54. An IBD/TIPP poll conducted to learn about attitudes toward investment and retirement (*Investor's Business Daily,* May 5, 2000) asked male and female respondents how important they felt level of risk was in choosing a retirement investment. The following joint probability table was constructed from the data provided. "Important" means the respondent said level of risk was either important or very important.

	Male	Female	Total
Important	.22	.27	.49
Not Important	.28	.23	.51
Total	.50	.50	1.00

a. What is the probability a survey respondent will say level of risk is important?
b. What is the probability a male respondent will say level of risk is important?
c. What is the probability a female respondent will say level of risk is important?
d. Is the level of risk independent of the gender of the respondent? Why or why not?
e. Do male and female attitudes toward risk differ?

55. A large consumer goods company ran a television advertisement for one of its soap products. On the basis of a survey that was conducted, probabilities were assigned to the following events.

B = individual purchased the product
S = individual recalls seeing the advertisement
$B \cap S$ = individual purchased the product and recalls seeing the advertisement

The probabilities assigned were $P(B) = .20$, $P(S) = .40$, and $P(B \cap S) = .12$.

a. What is the probability of an individual's purchasing the product given that the individual recalls seeing the advertisement? Does seeing the advertisement increase the probability that the individual will purchase the product? As a decision maker, would you recommend continuing the advertisement (assuming that the cost is reasonable)?
b. Assume that individuals who do not purchase the company's soap product buy from its competitors. What would be your estimate of the company's market share? Would you expect that continuing the advertisement will increase the company's market share? Why or why not?
c. The company also tested another advertisement and assigned it values of $P(S) = .30$ and $P(B \cap S) = .10$. What is $P(B \mid S)$ for this other advertisement? Which advertisement seems to have had the bigger effect on customer purchases?

56. Cooper Realty is a small real estate company located in Albany, New York, specializing primarily in residential listings. They recently became interested in determining the likelihood of one of their listings being sold within a certain number of days. An analysis of company sales of 800 homes in previous years produced the following data.

		Days Listed Until Sold			
		Under 30	31–90	Over 90	Total
Initial Asking Price	Under $150,000	50	40	10	100
	$150,000–$199,999	20	150	80	250
	$200,000–$250,000	20	280	100	400
	Over $250,000	10	30	10	50
	Total	100	500	200	800

a. If A is defined as the event that a home is listed for more than 90 days before being sold, estimate the probability of A.
b. If B is defined as the event that the initial asking price is under $150,000, estimate the probability of B.
c. What is the probability of $A \cap B$?
d. Assuming that a contract was just signed to list a home with an initial asking price of less than $150,000, what is the probability that the home will take Cooper Realty more than 90 days to sell?
e. Are events A and B independent?

57. A company studied the number of lost-time accidents occurring at its Brownsville, Texas, plant. Historical records show that 6% of the employees suffered lost-time accidents last year. Management believes that a special safety program will reduce such accidents to 5% during the current year. In addition, it estimates that 15% of employees who had lost-time accidents last year will experience a lost-time accident during the current year.
    a. What percentage of the employees will experience lost-time accidents in both years?
    b. What percentage of the employees will suffer at least one lost-time accident over the two-year period?

58. The Dallas IRS auditing staff, concerned with identifying potentially fraudulent tax returns, believes that the probability of finding a fraudulent return given that the return contains deductions for contributions exceeding the IRS standard is .20. Given that the deductions for contributions do not exceed the IRS standard, the probability of a fraudulent return decreases to .02. If 8% of all returns exceed the IRS standard for deductions due to contributions, what is the best estimate of the percentage of fraudulent returns?

59. An oil company purchased an option on land in Alaska. Preliminary geologic studies assigned the following prior probabilities.

$$P(\text{high-quality oil}) = .50$$
$$P(\text{medium-quality oil}) = .20$$
$$P(\text{no oil}) = .30$$

    a. What is the probability of finding oil?
    b. After 200 feet of drilling on the first well, a soil test is taken. The probabilities of finding the particular type of soil identified by the test follow.

$$P(\text{soil} \mid \text{high-quality oil}) = .20$$
$$P(\text{soil} \mid \text{medium-quality oil}) = .80$$
$$P(\text{soil} \mid \text{no oil}) = .20$$

    How should the firm interpret the soil test? What are the revised probabilities, and what is the new probability of finding oil?

60. Companies that do business over the Internet can often obtain probability information about Web site visitors from previous Web sites visited. The article "Internet Marketing" (*Interfaces,* March/April 2001) described how clickstream data on Web sites visited could be used in conjunction with a Bayesian updating scheme to determine the gender of a Web site visitor. Par Fore created a Web site to market golf equipment and apparel. Management would like a certain offer to appear for female visitors and a different offer to appear for male visitors. From a sample of past Web site visits, management learned that 60% of the visitors to ParFore.com are male and 40% are female.
    a. What is the prior probability that the next visitor to the Web site will be female?
    b. Suppose you know that the current visitor to ParFore.com previously visited the Dillard's Web site, and that women are three times as likely to visit the Dillard's Web site as men. What is the revised probability that the current visitor to ParFore.com is female? Should you display the offer that appeals more to female visitors or the one that appeals more to male visitors?

Case Problem Hamilton County Judges

Hamilton County judges try thousands of cases per year. In an overwhelming majority of the cases disposed, the verdict stands as rendered. However, some cases are appealed, and of those appealed, some of the cases are reversed. Kristen DelGuzzi of *The Cincinnati Enquirer* conducted a study of cases handled by Hamilton County judges over a three-year period. Shown in Table 4.8 are the results for 182,908 cases handled (disposed) by 38 judges

TABLE 4.8 TOTAL CASES DISPOSED, APPEALED, AND REVERSED IN HAMILTON COUNTY COURTS

CD file
Judge

Common Pleas Court

Judge	Total Cases Disposed	Appealed Cases	Reversed Cases
Fred Cartolano	3,037	137	12
Thomas Crush	3,372	119	10
Patrick Dinkelacker	1,258	44	8
Timothy Hogan	1,954	60	7
Robert Kraft	3,138	127	7
William Mathews	2,264	91	18
William Morrissey	3,032	121	22
Norbert Nadel	2,959	131	20
Arthur Ney, Jr.	3,219	125	14
Richard Niehaus	3,353	137	16
Thomas Nurre	3,000	121	6
John O'Connor	2,969	129	12
Robert Ruehlman	3,205	145	18
J. Howard Sundermann	955	60	10
Ann Marie Tracey	3,141	127	13
Ralph Winkler	3,089	88	6
Total	43,945	1762	199

Domestic Relations Court

Judge	Total Cases Disposed	Appealed Cases	Reversed Cases
Penelope Cunningham	2,729	7	1
Patrick Dinkelacker	6,001	19	4
Deborah Gaines	8,799	48	9
Ronald Panioto	12,970	32	3
Total	30,499	106	17

Municipal Court

Judge	Total Cases Disposed	Appealed Cases	Reversed Cases
Mike Allen	6,149	43	4
Nadine Allen	7,812	34	6
Timothy Black	7,954	41	6
David Davis	7,736	43	5
Leslie Isaiah Gaines	5,282	35	13
Karla Grady	5,253	6	0
Deidra Hair	2,532	5	0
Dennis Helmick	7,900	29	5
Timothy Hogan	2,308	13	2
James Patrick Kenney	2,798	6	1
Joseph Luebbers	4,698	25	8
William Mallory	8,277	38	9
Melba Marsh	8,219	34	7
Beth Mattingly	2,971	13	1
Albert Mestemaker	4,975	28	9
Mark Painter	2,239	7	3
Jack Rosen	7,790	41	13
Mark Schweikert	5,403	33	6
David Stockdale	5,371	22	4
John A. West	2,797	4	2
Total	108,464	500	104

in Common Pleas Court, Domestic Relations Court, and Municipal Court. Two of the judges (Dinkelacker and Hogan) did not serve in the same court for the entire three-year period.

The purpose of the newspaper's study was to evaluate the performance of the judges. Appeals are often the result of mistakes made by judges, and the newspaper wanted to know which judges were doing a good job and which were making too many mistakes. You are called in to assist in the data analysis. Use your knowledge of probability and conditional probability to help with the ranking of the judges. You also may be able to analyze the likelihood of appeal and reversal for cases handled by different courts.

Managerial Report

Prepare a report with your rankings of the judges. Also, include an analysis of the likelihood of appeal and case reversal in the three courts. At a minimum, your report should include the following:

1. The probability of cases being appealed and reversed in the three different courts.
2. The probability of a case being appealed for each judge.
3. The probability of a case being reversed for each judge.
4. The probability of reversal given an appeal for each judge.
5. Rank the judges within each court. State the criteria you used and provide a rationale for your choice.

CHAPTER 5

Discrete Probability Distributions

CONTENTS

STATISTICS *in* PRACTICE

CITIBANK*
LONG ISLAND CITY, NEW YORK

Citibank, a division of Citigroup, makes available a wide range of financial services, including checking and savings accounts, loans and mortgages, insurance, and investment services, within the framework of a unique strategy for delivering those services called Citibanking. Citibanking entails a consistent brand identity all over the world, consistent product offerings, and high-level customer service. Citibanking lets you manage your money anytime, any where, any way you choose. Whether you need to save for the future or borrow for today, you can do it all at Citibank.

Citibank's state-of-the-art automatic teller machines (ATMs) located in Citicard Banking Centers (CBCs) let customers do all their banking in one place with the touch of a finger, 24 hours a day, 7 days a week. More than 150 different banking functions from deposits to managing investments can be performed with ease. Citibanking ATMs are so much more than just cash machines that customers today use them for 80% of their transactions.

Each Citibank CBC operates as a waiting line system with randomly arriving customers seeking service at one of the ATMs. If all ATMs are busy, the arriving customers wait in line. Periodic CBC capacity studies are used to analyze customer waiting times and to determine whether additional ATMs are needed.

Data collected by Citibank showed that the random customer arrivals followed a probability distribution known as the Poisson distribution. Using the Poisson distribution, Citibank can compute probabilities for the number of customers arriving at a CBC during any time period and make decisions concerning the number of ATMs needed. For example, let x = the number of customers arriving during a one-minute period. Assuming that a particular CBC has a mean arrival rate of two customers per minute, the following table shows the probabilities for the number of customers arriving during a one-minute period.

A Citibank state-of-the-art ATM. © Jeff Greenberg/Photo Edit.

x	**Probability**
0	.1353
1	.2707
2	.2707
3	.1804
4	.0902
5 or more	.0527

Discrete probability distributions, such as the one used by Citibank, are the topic of this chapter. In addition to the Poisson distribution, you will learn about the binomial and hypergeometric distributions and how they can be used to provide helpful probability information.

*The authors are indebted to Ms. Stacey Karter, Citibank, for providing this Statistics in Practice.

In this chapter we continue the study of probability by introducing the concepts of random variables and probability distributions. The focus of this chapter is discrete probability distributions. Three special discrete probability distributions—the binomial, Poisson, and hypergeometric—are covered.

5.1 Random Variables

In Chapter 4 we defined the concept of an experiment and its associated experimental outcomes. A random variable provides a means for describing experimental outcomes using numerical values. Random variables must assume numerical values.

Random variables must assume numerical values.

RANDOM VARIABLE

A **random variable** is a numerical description of the outcome of an experiment.

In effect, a random variable associates a numerical value with each possible experimental outcome. The particular numerical value of the random variable depends on the outcome of the experiment. A random variable can be classified as being either *discrete* or *continuous* depending on the numerical values it assumes.

Discrete Random Variables

A random variable that may assume either a finite number of values or an infinite sequence of values such as 0, 1, 2, . . . is referred to as a **discrete random variable**. For example, consider the experiment of an accountant taking the certified public accountant (CPA) examination. The examination has four parts. We can define a random variable as $x =$ the number of parts of the CPA examination passed. It is a discrete random variable because it may assume the finite number of values 0, 1, 2, 3, or 4.

As another example of a discrete random variable, consider the experiment of cars arriving at a tollbooth. The random variable of interest is $x =$ the number of cars arriving during a one-day period. The possible values for x come from the sequence of integers 0, 1, 2, and so on. Hence, x is a discrete random variable assuming one of the values in this infinite sequence.

Although the outcomes of many experiments can naturally be described by numerical values, others cannot. For example, a survey question might ask an individual to recall the message in a recent television commercial. This experiment would have two possible outcomes: the individual cannot recall the message and the individual can recall the message. We can still describe these experimental outcomes numerically by defining the discrete random variable x as follows: let $x = 0$ if the individual cannot recall the message and $x = 1$ if the individual can recall the message. The numerical values for this random variable are arbitrary (we could use 5 and 10), but they are acceptable in terms of the definition of a random variable—namely, x is a random variable because it provides a numerical description of the outcome of the experiment.

Table 5.1 provides some additional examples of discrete random variables. Note that in each example the discrete random variable assumes a finite number of values or an infinite sequence of values such as 0, 1, 2, ... These types of discrete random variables are discussed in detail in this chapter.

TABLE 5.1 EXAMPLES OF DISCRETE RANDOM VARIABLES

Experiment	Random Variable (x)	Possible Values for the Random Variable
Contact five customers	Number of customers who place an order	0, 1, 2, 3, 4, 5
Inspect a shipment of 50 radios	Number of defective radios	0, 1, 2, · · · , 49, 50
Operate a restaurant for one day	Number of customers	0, 1, 2, 3, · · ·
Sell an automobile	Gender of the customer	0 if male; 1 if female

Continuous Random Variables

A random variable that may assume any numerical value in an interval or collection of intervals is called a **continuous random variable**. Experimental outcomes based on measurement scales such as time, weight, distance, and temperature can be described by continuous random variables. For example, consider an experiment of monitoring incoming telephone calls to the claims office of a major insurance company. Suppose the random variable of interest is x = the time between consecutive incoming calls in minutes. This random variable may assume any value in the interval $x \geq 0$. Actually, an infinite number of values are possible for x, including values such as 1.26 minutes, 2.751 minutes, 4.3333 minutes, and so on. As another example, consider a 90-mile section of interstate highway I-75 north of Atlanta, Georgia. For an emergency ambulance service located in Atlanta, we might define the random variable as x = number of miles to the location of the next traffic accident along this section of I-75. In this case, x would be a continuous random variable assuming any value in the interval $0 \leq x \leq 90$. Additional examples of continuous random variables are listed in Table 5.2. Note that each example describes a random variable that may assume any value in an interval of values. Continuous random variables and their probability distributions will be the topic of Chapter 6.

TABLE 5.2 EXAMPLES OF CONTINUOUS RANDOM VARIABLES

Experiment	Random Variable (x)	Possible Values for the Random Variable
Operate a bank	Time between customer arrivals in minutes	$x \geq 0$
Fill a soft drink can (max = 12.1 ounces)	Number of ounces	$0 \leq x \leq 12.1$
Construct a new library	Percentage of project complete after six months	$0 \leq x \leq 100$
Test a new chemical process	Temperature when the desired reaction takes place (min 150° F; max 212° F)	$150 \leq x \leq 212$

NOTES AND COMMENTS

One way to determine whether a random variable is discrete or continuous is to think of the values of the random variable as points on a line segment. Choose two points representing values of the random variable. If the entire line segment between the two points also represents possible values for the random variable, then the random variable is continuous.

Exercises

Methods

SELF test

1. Consider the experiment of tossing a coin twice.
   a. List the experimental outcomes.
   b. Define a random variable that represents the number of heads occurring on the two tosses.
   c. Show what value the random variable would assume for each of the experimental outcomes.
   d. Is this random variable discrete or continuous?

2. Consider the experiment of a worker assembling a product.
   a. Define a random variable that represents the time in minutes required to assemble the product.
   b. What values may the random variable assume?
   c. Is the random variable discrete or continuous?

Applications

SELF test

3. Three students scheduled interviews for summer employment at the Brookwood Institute. In each case the interview results in either an offer for a position or no offer. Experimental outcomes are defined in terms of the results of the three interviews.
   a. List the experimental outcomes.
   b. Define a random variable that represents the number of offers made. Is the random variable continuous?
   c. Show the value of the random variable for each of the experimental outcomes.
4. Suppose we know home mortgage rates for 12 Florida lending institutions. Assume that the random variable of interest is the number of lending institutions in this group that offers a 30-year fixed rate of 8.5% or less. What values may this random variable assume?
5. To perform a certain type of blood analysis, lab technicians must perform two procedures. The first procedure requires either one or two separate steps, and the second procedure requires either one, two, or three steps.
   a. List the experimental outcomes associated with performing the blood analysis.
   b. If the random variable of interest is the total number of steps required to do the complete analysis (both procedures), show what value the random variable will assume for each of the experimental outcomes.
6. Listed is a series of experiments and associated random variables. In each case, identify the values that the random variable can assume and state whether the random variable is discrete or continuous.

Experiment	Random Variable (x)
a. Take a 20-question examination	Number of questions answered correctly
b. Observe cars arriving at a tollbooth for 1 hour	Number of cars arriving at tollbooth
c. Audit 50 tax returns	Number of returns containing errors
d. Observe an employee's work	Number of nonproductive hours in an eight-hour workday
e. Weigh a shipment of goods	Number of pounds

5.2 Discrete Probability Distributions

The **probability distribution** for a random variable describes how probabilities are distributed over the values of the random variable. For a discrete random variable x, the probability distribution is defined by a **probability function**, denoted by $f(x)$. The probability function provides the probability for each value of the random variable.

As an illustration of a discrete random variable and its probability distribution, consider the sales of automobiles at DiCarlo Motors in Saratoga, New York. Over the past 300 days of operation, sales data show 54 days with no automobiles sold, 117 days with 1 automobile sold, 72 days with 2 automobiles sold, 42 days with 3 automobiles sold, 12 days with 4 automobiles sold, and 3 days with 5 automobiles sold. Suppose we consider the experiment of selecting a day of operation at DiCarlo Motors and define the random variable of interest as x = the number of automobiles sold during a day. From historical data, we know

x is a discrete random variable that can assume the values 0, 1, 2, 3, 4, or 5. In probability function notation, $f(0)$ provides the probability of 0 automobiles sold, $f(1)$ provides the probability of 1 automobile sold, and so on. Because historical data show 54 of 300 days with 0 automobiles sold, we assign the value $54/300 = .18$ to $f(0)$, indicating that the probability of 0 automobiles being sold during a day is .18. Similarly, because 117 of 300 days had 1 automobile sold, we assign the value $117/300 = .39$ to $f(1)$, indicating that the probability of exactly 1 automobile being sold during a day is .39. Continuing in this way for the other values of the random variable, we compute the values for $f(2)$, $f(3)$, $f(4)$, and $f(5)$ as shown in Table 5.3, the probability distribution for the number of automobiles sold during a day at DiCarlo Motors.

A primary advantage of defining a random variable and its probability distribution is that once the probability distribution is known, it is relatively easy to determine the probability of a variety of events that may be of interest to a decision maker. For example, using the probability distribution for DiCarlo Motors as shown in Table 5.3, we see that the most probable number of automobiles sold during a day is 1 with a probability of $f(1) = .39$. In addition, there is an $f(3) + f(4) + f(5) = .14 + .04 + .01 = .19$ probability of selling three or more automobiles during a day. These probabilities, plus others the decision maker may ask about, provide information that can help the decision maker understand the process of selling automobiles at DiCarlo Motors.

In the development of a probability function for any discrete random variable, the following two conditions must be satisfied.

These conditions are the analogs to the two basic requirements for assigning probabilities to experimental outcomes presented in Chapter 4.

REQUIRED CONDITIONS FOR A DISCRETE PROBABILITY FUNCTION

$$f(x) \geq 0 \quad (5.1)$$

$$\Sigma f(x) = 1 \quad (5.2)$$

Table 5.3 shows that the probabilities for the random variable x satisfy equation (5.1); $f(x)$ is greater than or equal to 0 for all values of x. In addition, because the probabilities sum to 1, equation (5.2) is satisfied. Thus, the DiCarlo Motors probability function is a valid discrete probability function.

We can also present probability distributions graphically. In Figure 5.1 the values of the random variable x for DiCarlo Motors are shown on the horizontal axis and the probability associated with these values is shown on the vertical axis.

In addition to tables and graphs, a formula that gives the probability function, $f(x)$, for every value of x is often used to describe probability distributions. The simplest example of

TABLE 5.3 PROBABILITY DISTRIBUTION FOR THE NUMBER OF AUTOMOBILES SOLD DURING A DAY AT DICARLO MOTORS

x	$f(x)$
0	.18
1	.39
2	.24
3	.14
4	.04
5	.01
Total	1.00

FIGURE 5.1 GRAPHICAL REPRESENTATION OF THE PROBABILITY DISTRIBUTION FOR THE NUMBER OF AUTOMOBILES SOLD DURING A DAY AT DICARLO MOTORS

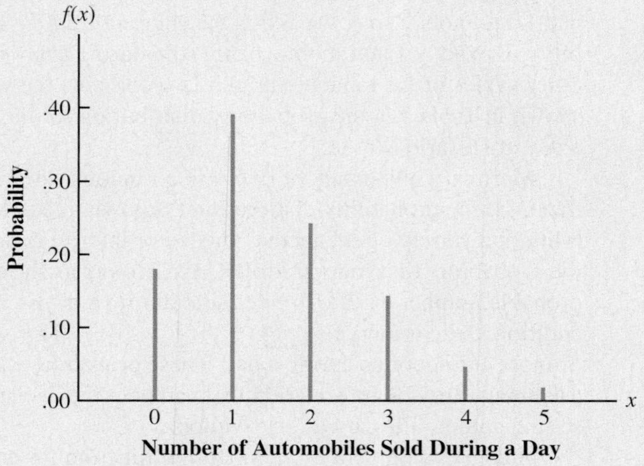

a discrete probability distribution given by a formula is the **discrete uniform probability distribution**. Its probability function is defined by equation (5.3).

DISCRETE UNIFORM PROBABILITY FUNCTION

$$f(x) = 1/n \tag{5.3}$$

where

n = the number of values the random variable may assume

For example, suppose that for the experiment of rolling a die we define the random variable x to be the number of dots on the upward face. For this experiment, $n = 6$ values are possible for the random variable; $x = 1, 2, 3, 4, 5, 6$. Thus, the probability function for this discrete uniform random variable is

$$f(x) = 1/6 \qquad x = 1, 2, 3, 4, 5, 6$$

The possible values of the random variable and the associated probabilities are shown.

x	$f(x)$
1	1/6
2	1/6
3	1/6
4	1/6
5	1/6
6	1/6

As another example, consider the random variable x with the following discrete probability distribution.

x	$f(x)$
1	1/10
2	2/10
3	3/10
4	4/10

This probability distribution can be defined by the formula

$$f(x) = \frac{x}{10} \qquad \text{for } x = 1, 2, 3, \text{ or } 4$$

Evaluating $f(x)$ for a given value of the random variable will provide the associated probability. For example, using the preceding probability function, we see that $f(2) = 2/10$ provides the probability that the random variable assumes a value of 2.

The more widely used discrete probability distributions generally are specified by formulas. Three important cases are the binomial, Poisson, and hypergeometric distributions; these distributions are discussed later in the chapter.

Exercises

Methods

SELF test

7. The probability distribution for the random variable x follows.

x	$f(x)$
20	.20
25	.15
30	.25
35	.40

   a. Is this probability distribution valid? Explain.
   b. What is the probability that $x = 30$?
   c. What is the probability that x is less than or equal to 25?
   d. What is the probability that x is greater than 30?

Applications

SELF test

8. The following data were collected by counting the number of operating rooms in use at Tampa General Hospital over a 20-day period: On three of the days only one operating room was used, on five of the days two were used, on eight of the days three were used, and on four days all four of the hospital's operating rooms were used.
   a. Use the relative frequency approach to construct a probability distribution for the number of operating rooms in use on any given day.
   b. Draw a graph of the probability distribution.
   c. Show that your probability distribution satisfies the required conditions for a valid discrete probability distribution.

9. Nationally, 38% of fourth-graders cannot read an age-appropriate book. The following data show the number of children, by age, identified as learning disabled under special education. Most of these children have reading problems that should be identified and corrected before third grade. Current federal law prohibits most children from receiving extra help from special education programs until they fall behind by approximately two years' worth of learning, and that typically means third grade or later (*USA Today,* September 6, 2001).

Age	Number of Children
6	37,369
7	87,436
8	160,840
9	239,719
10	286,719
11	306,533
12	310,787
13	302,604
14	289,168

Suppose that we want to select a sample of children identified as learning disabled under special education for a program designed to improve reading ability. Let x be a random variable indicating the age of one randomly selected child.

a. Use the data to develop a probability distribution for x. Specify the values for the random variable and the corresponding values for the probability function $f(x)$.
b. Draw a graph of the probability distribution.
c. Show that the probability distribution satisfies equations (5.1) and (5.2).

10. Table 5.4 shows the percent frequency distributions of job satisfaction scores for a sample of information systems (IS) senior executives and IS middle managers. The scores range from a low of 1 (very dissatisfied) to a high of 5 (very satisfied).

TABLE 5.4 PERCENT FREQUENCY DISTRIBUTION OF JOB SATISFACTION SCORES FOR INFORMATION SYSTEMS EXECUTIVES AND MIDDLE MANAGERS

Job Satisfaction Score	IS Senior Executives (%)	IS Middle Managers (%)
1	5	4
2	9	10
3	3	12
4	42	46
5	41	28

a. Develop a probability distribution for the job satisfaction score of a senior executive.
b. Develop a probability distribution for the job satisfaction score of a middle manager.
c. What is the probability a senior executive will report a job satisfaction score of 4 or 5?
d. What is the probability a middle manager is very satisfied?
e. Compare the overall job satisfaction of senior executives and middle managers.

11. A technician services mailing machines at companies in the Phoenix area. Depending on the type of malfunction, the service call can take 1, 2, 3, or 4 hours. The different types of malfunctions occur at about the same frequency.

a. Develop a probability distribution for the duration of a service call.
b. Draw a graph of the probability distribution.
c. Show that your probability distribution satisfies the conditions required for a discrete probability function.
d. What is the probability a service call will take three hours?
e. A service call has just come in, but the type of malfunction is unknown. It is 3:00 P.M. and service technicians usually get off at 5:00 P.M. What is the probability the service technician will have to work overtime to fix the machine today?

12. The director of admissions at Lakeville Community College subjectively assessed a probability distribution for x, the number of entering students, as follows.

x	$f(x)$
1000	.15
1100	.20
1200	.30
1300	.25
1400	.10

a. Is this probability distribution valid? Explain.
b. What is the probability of 1200 or fewer entering students?

13. A psychologist determined that the number of sessions required to obtain the trust of a new patient is either 1, 2, or 3. Let x be a random variable indicating the number of sessions required to gain the patient's trust. The following probability function has been proposed.

$$f(x) = \frac{x}{6} \qquad \text{for } x = 1, 2, \text{ or } 3$$

a. Is this probability function valid? Explain.
b. What is the probability that it takes exactly 2 sessions to gain the patient's trust?
c. What is the probability that it takes at least 2 sessions to gain the patient's trust?

14. The following table is a partial probability distribution for the MRA Company's projected profits (x = profit in $1000s) for the first year of operation (the negative value denotes a loss).

x	$f(x)$
−100	.10
0	.20
50	.30
100	.25
150	.10
200	

a. What is the proper value for $f(200)$? What is your interpretation of this value?
b. What is the probability that MRA will be profitable?
c. What is the probability that MRA will make at least $100,000?

5.3 Expected Value and Variance

Expected Value

The **expected value**, or mean, of a random variable is a measure of the central location for the random variable. The formula for the expected value of a discrete random variable x follows.

The expected value is a weighted average of the values the random variable may assume. The weights are the probabilities.

EXPECTED VALUE OF A DISCRETE RANDOM VARIABLE

$$E(x) = \mu = \Sigma x f(x) \tag{5.4}$$

Both the notations $E(x)$ and μ are used to denote the expected value of a random variable.

Equation (5.4) shows that to compute the expected value of a discrete random variable, we must multiply each value of the random variable by the corresponding probability $f(x)$ and then add the resulting products. Using the DiCarlo Motors automobile sales example from Section 5.2, we show the calculation of the expected value for the number of automobiles sold during a day in Table 5.5. The sum of the entries in the $xf(x)$ column shows that the expected value is 1.50 automobiles per day. We therefore know that although sales of 0, 1, 2, 3, 4, or 5 automobiles are possible on any one day, over time DiCarlo can anticipate selling an average of 1.50 automobiles per day. Assuming 30 days of operation during a month, we can use the expected value of 1.50 to forecast average monthly sales of 30(1.50) = 45 automobiles.

The expected value does not have to be a value the random variable can assume.

Variance

Even though the expected value provides the mean value for the random variable, we often need a measure of variability, or dispersion. Just as we used the variance in Chapter 3 to summarize the variability in data, we now use **variance** to summarize the variability in the values of a random variable. The formula for the variance of a discrete random variable follows.

The variance is a weighted average of the squared deviations of a random variable from its mean. The weights are the probabilities.

VARIANCE OF A DISCRETE RANDOM VARIABLE

$$\text{Var}(x) = \sigma^2 = \Sigma(x - \mu)^2 f(x) \tag{5.5}$$

TABLE 5.5 CALCULATION OF THE EXPECTED VALUE FOR THE NUMBER OF AUTOMOBILES SOLD DURING A DAY AT DICARLO MOTORS

x	$f(x)$	$xf(x)$
0	.18	0(.18) = .00
1	.39	1(.39) = .39
2	.24	2(.24) = .48
3	.14	3(.14) = .42
4	.04	4(.04) = .16
5	.01	5(.01) = .05
		1.50

$E(x) = \mu = \Sigma x f(x)$

TABLE 5.6 CALCULATION OF THE VARIANCE FOR THE NUMBER OF AUTOMOBILES SOLD DURING A DAY AT DICARLO MOTORS

x	$x - \mu$	$(x - \mu)^2$	$f(x)$	$(x - \mu)^2 f(x)$
0	$0 - 1.50 = -1.50$	2.25	.18	$2.25(.18) = .4050$
1	$1 - 1.50 = -.50$	.25	.39	$.25(.39) = .0975$
2	$2 - 1.50 = .50$	.25	.24	$.25(.24) = .0600$
3	$3 - 1.50 = 1.50$	2.25	.14	$2.25(.14) = .3150$
4	$4 - 1.50 = 2.50$	6.25	.04	$6.25(.04) = .2500$
5	$5 - 1.50 = 3.50$	12.25	.01	$12.25(.01) = .1225$
				1.2500

$\sigma^2 = \Sigma(x - \mu)^2 f(x)$

As equation (5.5) shows, an essential part of the variance formula is the deviation, $x - \mu$, which measures how far a particular value of the random variable is from the expected value, or mean, μ. In computing the variance of a random variable, the deviations are squared and then weighted by the corresponding value of the probability function. The sum of these weighted squared deviations for all values of the random variable is referred to as the *variance*. The notations Var(x) and σ^2 are both used to denote the variance of a random variable.

The calculation of the variance for the probability distribution of the number of automobiles sold during a day at DiCarlo Motors is summarized in Table 5.6. We see that the variance is 1.25. The **standard deviation**, σ, is defined as the positive square root of the variance. Thus, the standard deviation for the number of automobiles sold during a day is

$$\sigma = \sqrt{1.25} = 1.118$$

The standard deviation is measured in the same units as the random variable ($\sigma = 1.118$ automobiles) and therefore is often preferred in describing the variability of a random variable. The variance σ^2 is measured in squared units and is thus more difficult to interpret.

Exercises

Methods

15. The following table provides a probability distribution for the random variable x.

x	$f(x)$
3	.25
6	.50
9	.25

a. Compute $E(x)$, the expected value of x.
b. Compute σ^2, the variance of x.
c. Compute σ, the standard deviation of x.

SELF test

16. The following table provides a probability distribution for the random variable y.

y	$f(y)$
2	.20
4	.30
7	.40
8	.10

a. Compute $E(y)$.
b. Compute Var(y) and σ.

Applications

17. A volunteer ambulance service handles 0 to 5 service calls on any given day. The probability distribution for the number of service calls is as follows.

Number of Service Calls	Probability	Number of Service Calls	Probability
0	.10	3	.20
1	.15	4	.15
2	.30	5	.10

a. What is the expected number of service calls?
b. What is the variance in the number of service calls? What is the standard deviation?

SELF test

18. The American Housing Survey reported the following data on the number of bedrooms in owner-occupied and renter-occupied houses in central cities (www.census.gov, March 31, 2003).

	Number of Houses (1000s)	
Bedrooms	**Renter-Occupied**	**Owner-Occupied**
0	547	23
1	5012	541
2	6100	3832
3	2644	8690
4 or more	557	3783

a. Define a random variable x = number of bedrooms in renter-occupied houses and develop a probability distribution for the random variable. (Let $x = 4$ represent 4 or more bedrooms.)
b. Compute the expected value and variance for the number of bedrooms in renter-occupied houses.
c. Define a random variable y = number of bedrooms in owner-occupied houses and develop a probability distribution for the random variable. (Let $y = 4$ represent 4 or more bedrooms.)
d. Compute the expected value and variance for the number of bedrooms in owner-occupied houses.
e. What observations can you make from a comparison of the number of bedrooms in renter-occupied versus owner-occupied homes?

19. The National Basketball Association (NBA) records a variety of statistics for each team. Two of these statistics are the percentage of field goals made by the team and the percentage of three-point shots made by the team. For a portion of the 2004 season, the shooting records of the 29 teams in the NBA showed the probability of scoring two points by making

a field goal was .44, and the probability of scoring three points by making a three-point shot was .34 (www.nba.com, January 3, 2004).

a. What is the expected value of a two-point shot for these teams?
b. What is the expected value of a three-point shot for these teams?
c. If the probability of making a two-point shot is greater than the probability of making a three-point shot, why do coaches allow some players to shoot the three-point shot if they have the opportunity? Use expected value to explain your answer.

20. The probability distribution for damage claims paid by the Newton Automobile Insurance Company on collision insurance follows.

Payment ($)	Probability
0	.85
500	.04
1000	.04
3000	.03
5000	.02
8000	.01
10000	.01

a. Use the expected collision payment to determine the collision insurance premium that would enable the company to break even.
b. The insurance company charges an annual rate of $520 for the collision coverage. What is the expected value of the collision policy for a policyholder? (*Hint:* It is the expected payments from the company minus the cost of coverage.) Why does the policyholder purchase a collision policy with this expected value?

21. The following probability distributions of job satisfaction scores for a sample of information systems (IS) senior executives and IS middle managers range from a low of 1 (very dissatisfied) to a high of 5 (very satisfied).

	Probability	
Job Satisfaction Score	**IS Senior Executives**	**IS Middle Managers**
1	.05	.04
2	.09	.10
3	.03	.12
4	.42	.46
5	.41	.28

a. What is the expected value of the job satisfaction score for senior executives?
b. What is the expected value of the job satisfaction score for middle managers?
c. Compute the variance of job satisfaction scores for executives and middle managers.
d. Compute the standard deviation of job satisfaction scores for both probability distributions.
e. Compare the overall job satisfaction of senior executives and middle managers.

22. The demand for a product of Carolina Industries varies greatly from month to month. The probability distribution in the following table, based on the past two years of data, shows the company's monthly demand.

Unit Demand	Probability
300	.20
400	.30
500	.35
600	.15

a. If the company bases monthly orders on the expected value of the monthly demand, what should Carolina's monthly order quantity be for this product?
b. Assume that each unit demanded generates \$70 in revenue and that each unit ordered costs \$50. How much will the company gain or lose in a month if it places an order based on your answer to part (a) and the actual demand for the item is 300 units?

23. The 2002 New York City Housing and Vacancy Survey showed a total of 59,324 rent-controlled housing units and 236,263 rent-stabilized units built in 1947 or later. For these rental units, the probability distributions for the number of persons living in the unit are given (www.census.gov, January 12, 2004).

Number of Persons	Rent-Controlled	Rent-Stabilized
1	.61	.41
2	.27	.30
3	.07	.14
4	.04	.11
5	.01	.03
6	.00	.01

a. What is the expected value of the number of persons living in each type of unit?
b. What is the variance of the number of persons living in each type of unit?
c. Make some comparisons between the number of persons living in rent-controlled units and the number of persons living in rent-stabilized units.

24. The J. R. Ryland Computer Company is considering a plant expansion to enable the company to begin production of a new computer product. The company's president must determine whether to make the expansion a medium- or large-scale project. Demand for the new product is uncertain, which for planning purposes may be low demand, medium demand, or high demand. The probability estimates for demand are .20, .50, and .30, respectively. Letting x and y indicate the annual profit in thousands of dollars, the firm's planners developed the following profit forecasts for the medium- and large-scale expansion projects.

		Medium-Scale Expansion Profit		Large-Scale Expansion Profit	
		x	$f(x)$	y	$f(y)$
Demand	Low	50	.20	0	.20
	Medium	150	.50	100	.50
	High	200	.30	300	.30

a. Compute the expected value for the profit associated with the two expansion alternatives. Which decision is preferred for the objective of maximizing the expected profit?
b. Compute the variance for the profit associated with the two expansion alternatives. Which decision is preferred for the objective of minimizing the risk or uncertainty?

5.4 Binomial Probability Distribution

The binomial probability distribution is a discrete probability distribution that provides many applications. It is associated with a multiple-step experiment that we call the binomial experiment.

A Binomial Experiment

A **binomial experiment** exhibits the following four properties.

PROPERTIES OF A BINOMIAL EXPERIMENT

1. The experiment consists of a sequence of n identical trials.
2. Two outcomes are possible on each trial. We refer to one outcome as a *success* and the other outcome as a *failure.*
3. The probability of a success, denoted by p, does not change from trial to trial. Consequently, the probability of a failure, denoted by $1 - p$, does not change from trial to trial.
4. The trials are independent.

Jakob Bernoulli (1654–1705), the first of the Bernoulli family of Swiss mathematicians, published a treatise on probability that contained the theory of permutations and combinations, as well as the binomial theorem.

If properties 2, 3, and 4 are present, we say the trials are generated by a Bernoulli process. If, in addition, property 1 is present, we say we have a binomial experiment. Figure 5.2 depicts one possible sequence of successes and failures for a binomial experiment involving eight trials.

In a binomial experiment, our interest is in the *number of successes occurring in the n trials*. If we let x denote the number of successes occurring in the n trials, we see that x can assume the values of $0, 1, 2, 3, \ldots, n$. Because the number of values is finite, x is a *discrete* random variable. The probability distribution associated with this random variable is called the **binomial probability distribution**. For example, consider the experiment of tossing a coin five times and on each toss observing whether the coin lands with a head or a tail on its upward face. Suppose we want to count the number of heads appearing over the five tosses. Does this experiment show the properties of a binomial experiment? What is the random variable of interest? Note that:

1. The experiment consists of five identical trials; each trial involves the tossing of one coin.
2. Two outcomes are possible for each trial: a head or a tail. We can designate head a success and tail a failure.
3. The probability of a head and the probability of a tail are the same for each trial, with $p = .5$ and $1 - p = .5$.
4. The trials or tosses are independent because the outcome on any one trial is not affected by what happens on other trials or tosses.

FIGURE 5.2 ONE POSSIBLE SEQUENCE OF SUCCESSES AND FAILURES FOR AN EIGHT-TRIAL BINOMIAL EXPERIMENT

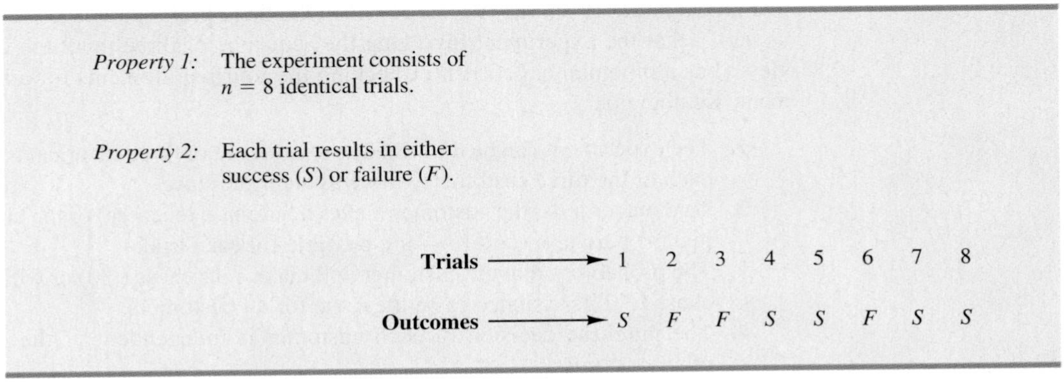

Thus, the properties of a binomial experiment are satisfied. The random variable of interest is $x =$ the number of heads appearing in the five trials. In this case, x can assume the values of 0, 1, 2, 3, 4, or 5.

As another example, consider an insurance salesperson who visits 10 randomly selected families. The outcome associated with each visit is classified as a success if the family purchases an insurance policy and a failure if the family does not. From past experience, the salesperson knows the probability that a randomly selected family will purchase an insurance policy is .10. Checking the properties of a binomial experiment, we observe that:

1. The experiment consists of 10 identical trials; each trial involves contacting one family.
2. Two outcomes are possible on each trial: the family purchases a policy (success) or the family does not purchase a policy (failure).
3. The probabilities of a purchase and a nonpurchase are assumed to be the same for each sales call, with $p = .10$ and $1 - p = .90$.
4. The trials are independent because the families are randomly selected.

Because the four assumptions are satisfied, this example is a binomial experiment. The random variable of interest is the number of sales obtained in contacting the 10 families. In this case, x can assume the values of 0, 1, 2, 3, 4, 5, 6, 7, 8, 9, and 10.

Property 3 of the binomial experiment is called the *stationarity assumption* and is sometimes confused with property 4, independence of trials. To see how they differ, consider again the case of the salesperson calling on families to sell insurance policies. If, as the day wore on, the salesperson got tired and lost enthusiasm, the probability of success (selling a policy) might drop to .05, for example, by the tenth call. In such a case, property 3 (stationarity) would not be satisfied, and we would not have a binomial experiment. Even if property 4 held—that is, the purchase decisions of each family were made independently—it would not be a binomial experiment if property 3 was not satisfied.

In applications involving binomial experiments, a special mathematical formula, called the *binomial probability function,* can be used to compute the probability of x successes in the n trials. Using probability concepts introduced in Chapter 4, we will show in the context of an illustrative problem how the formula can be developed.

Martin Clothing Store Problem

Let us consider the purchase decisions of the next three customers who enter the Martin Clothing Store. On the basis of past experience, the store manager estimates the probability that any one customer will make a purchase is .30. What is the probability that two of the next three customers will make a purchase?

Using a tree diagram (Figure 5.3), we can see that the experiment of observing the three customers each making a purchase decision has eight possible outcomes. Using S to denote success (a purchase) and F to denote failure (no purchase), we are interested in experimental outcomes involving two successes in the three trials (purchase decisions). Next, let us verify that the experiment involving the sequence of three purchase decisions can be viewed as a binomial experiment. Checking the four requirements for a binomial experiment, we note that:

1. The experiment can be described as a sequence of three identical trials, one trial for each of the three customers who will enter the store.
2. Two outcomes—the customer makes a purchase (success) or the customer does not make a purchase (failure)—are possible for each trial.
3. The probability that the customer will make a purchase (.30) or will not make a purchase (.70) is assumed to be the same for all customers.
4. The purchase decision of each customer is independent of the decisions of the other customers.

FIGURE 5.3 TREE DIAGRAM FOR THE MARTIN CLOTHING STORE PROBLEM

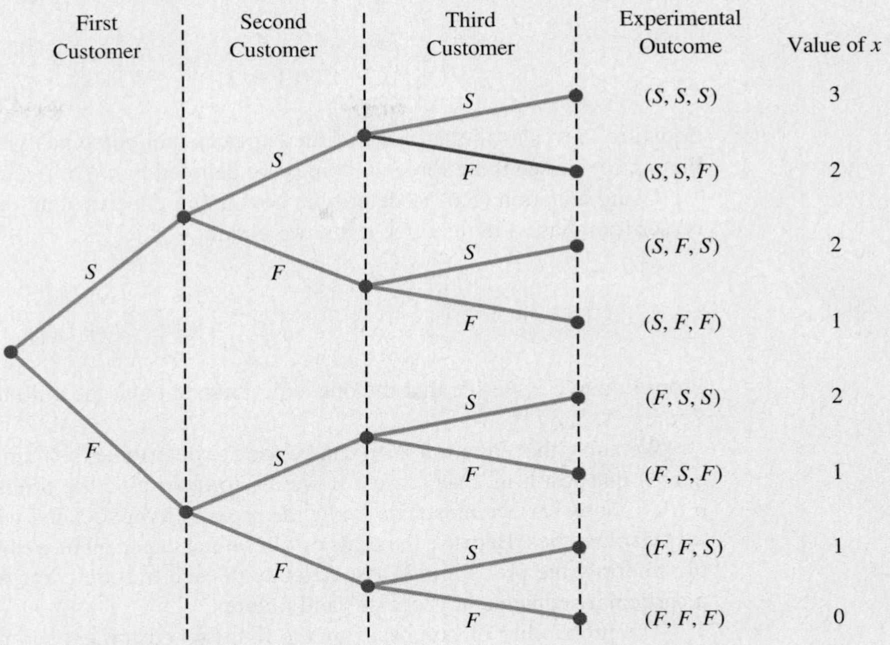

S = Purchase
F = No purchase
x = Number of customers making a purchase

Hence, the properties of a binomial experiment are present.

The number of experimental outcomes resulting in exactly x successes in n trials can be computed using the following formula.*

NUMBER OF EXPERIMENTAL OUTCOMES PROVIDING EXACTLY x SUCCESSES IN n TRIALS

$$\binom{n}{x} = \frac{n!}{x!(n-x)!} \tag{5.6}$$

where

$$n! = n(n-1)(n-2)\cdots(2)(1)$$

and, by definition,

$$0! = 1$$

Now let us return to the Martin Clothing Store experiment involving three customer purchase decisions. Equation (5.6) can be used to determine the number of experimental

*This formula, introduced in Chapter 4, determines the number of combinations of n objects selected x at a time. For the binomial experiment, this combinatorial formula provides the number of experimental outcomes (sequences of n trials) resulting in x successes.

outcomes involving two purchases; that is, the number of ways of obtaining $x = 2$ successes in the $n = 3$ trials. From equation (5.6) we have

$$\binom{n}{x} = \binom{3}{2} = \frac{3!}{2!(3-2)!} = \frac{(3)(2)(1)}{(2)(1)(1)} = \frac{6}{2} = 3$$

Equation (5.6) shows that three of the experimental outcomes yield two successes. From Figure 5.3 we see these three outcomes are denoted by (S, S, F), (S, F, S), and (F, S, S).

Using equation (5.6) to determine how many experimental outcomes have three successes (purchases) in the three trials, we obtain

$$\binom{n}{x} = \binom{3}{3} = \frac{3!}{3!(3-3)!} = \frac{3!}{3!0!} = \frac{(3)(2)(1)}{3(2)(1)(1)} = \frac{6}{6} = 1$$

From Figure 5.3 we see that the one experimental outcome with three successes is identified by (S, S, S).

We know that equation (5.6) can be used to determine the number of experimental outcomes that result in x successes. If we are to determine the probability of x successes in n trials, however, we must also know the probability associated with each of these experimental outcomes. Because the trials of a binomial experiment are independent, we can simply multiply the probabilities associated with each trial outcome to find the probability of a particular sequence of successes and failures.

The probability of purchases by the first two customers and no purchase by the third customer, denoted (S, S, F), is given by

$$pp(1 - p)$$

With a .30 probability of a purchase on any one trial, the probability of a purchase on the first two trials and no purchase on the third is given by

$$(.30)(.30)(.70) = (.30)^2(.70) = .063$$

Two other experimental outcomes also result in two successes and one failure. The probabilities for all three experimental outcomes involving two successes follow.

Trial Outcomes				
1st Customer	**2nd Customer**	**3rd Customer**	**Experimental Outcome**	**Probability of Experimental Outcome**
Purchase	Purchase	No purchase	(S, S, F)	$pp(1 - p) = p^2(1 - p)$ $= (.30)^2(.70) = .063$
Purchase	No purchase	Purchase	(S, F, S)	$p(1 - p)p = p^2(1 - p)$ $= (.30)^2(.70) = .063$
No purchase	Purchase	Purchase	(F, S, S)	$(1 - p)pp = p^2(1 - p)$ $= (.30)^2(.70) = .063$

Observe that all three experimental outcomes with two successes have exactly the same probability. This observation holds in general. In any binomial experiment, all sequences of trial outcomes yielding x successes in n trials have the *same probability* of occurrence. The probability of each sequence of trials yielding x successes in n trials follows.

$$\text{Probability of a particular sequence of trial outcomes with } x \text{ successes in } n \text{ trials} = p^x(1-p)^{(n-x)} \tag{5.7}$$

For the Martin Clothing Store, this formula shows that any experimental outcome with two successes has a probability of $p^2(1-p)^{(3-2)} = p^2(1-p)^1 = (.30)^2(.70)^1 = .063$.

Because equation (5.6) shows the number of outcomes in a binomial experiment with x successes and equation (5.7) gives the probability for each sequence involving x successes, we combine equations (5.6) and (5.7) to obtain the following **binomial probability function**.

BINOMIAL PROBABILITY FUNCTION

$$f(x) = \binom{n}{x} p^x(1-p)^{(n-x)} \tag{5.8}$$

where

$$f(x) = \text{the probability of } x \text{ successes in } n \text{ trials}$$
$$n = \text{the number of trials}$$
$$\binom{n}{x} = \frac{n!}{x!(n-x)!}$$
$$p = \text{the probability of a success on any one trial}$$
$$1 - p = \text{the probability of a failure on any one trial}$$

In the Martin Clothing Store example, let us compute the probability that no customer makes a purchase, exactly one customer makes a purchase, exactly two customers make a purchase, and all three customers make a purchase. The calculations are summarized in Table 5.7, which gives the probability distribution of the number of customers making a purchase. Figure 5.4 is a graph of this probability distribution.

The binomial probability function can be applied to *any* binomial experiment. If we are satisfied that a situation demonstrates the properties of a binomial experiment and if we know the values of n and p, we can use equation (5.8) to compute the probability of x successes in the n trials.

TABLE 5.7 PROBABILITY DISTRIBUTION FOR THE NUMBER OF CUSTOMERS MAKING A PURCHASE

x	$f(x)$
0	$\frac{3!}{0!3!}(.30)^0(.70)^3 = .343$
1	$\frac{3!}{1!2!}(.30)^1(.70)^2 = .441$
2	$\frac{3!}{2!1!}(.30)^2(.70)^1 = .189$
3	$\frac{3!}{3!0!}(.30)^3(.70)^0 = .027$
	1.000

FIGURE 5.4 GRAPHICAL REPRESENTATION OF THE PROBABILITY DISTRIBUTION FOR THE NUMBER OF CUSTOMERS MAKING A PURCHASE

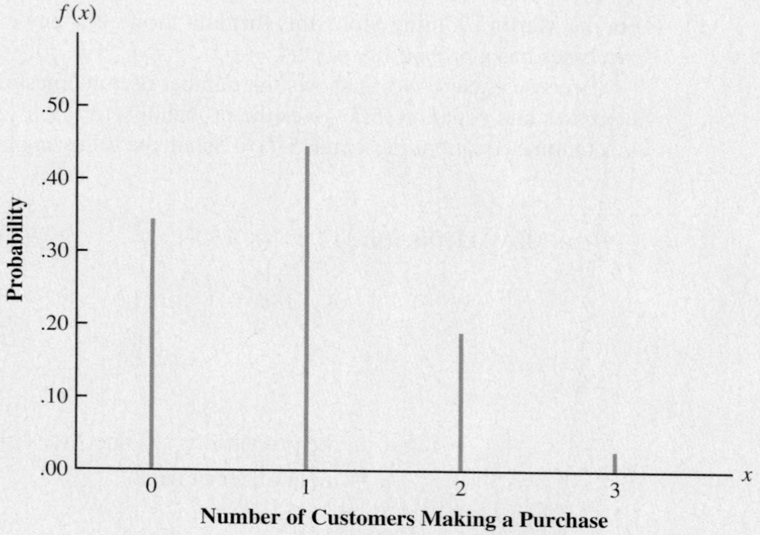

If we consider variations of the Martin experiment, such as 10 customers rather than three entering the store, the binomial probability function given by equation (5.8) is still applicable. Suppose we have a binomial experiment with $n = 10$, $x = 4$, and $p = .30$. The probability of making exactly four sales to 10 customers entering the store is

$$f(4) = \frac{10!}{4!6!}(.30)^4(.70)^6 = .2001$$

Using Tables of Binomial Probabilities

Tables have been developed that give the probability of x successes in n trials for a binomial experiment. The tables are generally easy to use and quicker than equation (5.8). Table 5 of Appendix B provides such a table of binomial probabilities. A portion of this table appears in Table 5.8. To use this table, we must specify the values of n, p, and x for the binomial experiment of interest. In the example at the top of Table 5.8, we see that the probability of $x = 3$ successes in a binomial experiment with $n = 10$ and $p = .40$ is .2150. You can use equation (5.8) to verify that you would obtain the same answer if you used the binomial probability function directly.

Now let us use Table 5.8 to verify the probability of four successes in 10 trials for the Martin Clothing Store problem. Note that the value of $f(4) = .2001$ can be read directly from the table of binomial probabilities, with $n = 10$, $x = 4$, and $p = .30$.

With modern calculators, these tables are almost unnecessary. It is easy to evaluate equation (5.8) directly.

Even though the tables of binomial probabilities are relatively easy to use, it is impossible to have tables that show all possible values of n and p that might be encountered in a binomial experiment. However, with today's calculators, using equation (5.8) to calculate the desired probability is not difficult, especially if the number of trials is not large. In the exercises, you should practice using equation (5.8) to compute the binomial probabilities unless the problem specifically requests that you use the binomial probability table.

TABLE 5.8 SELECTED VALUES FROM THE BINOMIAL PROBABILITY TABLE
EXAMPLE: $n = 10, x = 3, p = .40; f(3) = .2150$

						p					
n	*x*	.05	.10	.15	.20	.25	.30	.35	.40	.45	.50
9	0	.6302	.3874	.2316	.1342	.0751	.0404	.0207	.0101	.0046	.0020
	1	.2985	.3874	.3679	.3020	.2253	.1556	.1004	.0605	.0339	.0176
	2	.0629	.1722	.2597	.3020	.3003	.2668	.2162	.1612	.1110	.0703
	3	.0077	.0446	.1069	.1762	.2336	.2668	.2716	.2508	.2119	.1641
	4	.0006	.0074	.0283	.0661	.1168	.1715	.2194	.2508	.2600	.2461
	5	.0000	.0008	.0050	.0165	.0389	.0735	.1181	.1672	.2128	.2461
	6	.0000	.0001	.0006	.0028	.0087	.0210	.0424	.0743	.1160	.1641
	7	.0000	.0000	.0000	.0003	.0012	.0039	.0098	.0212	.0407	.0703
	8	.0000	.0000	.0000	.0000	.0001	.0004	.0013	.0035	.0083	.0176
	9	.0000	.0000	.0000	.0000	.0000	.0000	.0001	.0003	.0008	.0020
10	0	.5987	.3487	.1969	.1074	.0563	.0282	.0135	.0060	.0025	.0010
	1	.3151	.3874	.3474	.2684	.1877	.1211	.0725	.0403	.0207	.0098
	2	.0746	.1937	.2759	.3020	.2816	.2335	.1757	.1209	.0763	.0439
	3	.0105	.0574	.1298	.2013	.2503	.2668	.2522	**.2150**	.1665	.1172
	4	.0010	.0112	.0401	.0881	.1460	.2001	.2377	.2508	.2384	.2051
	5	.0001	.0015	.0085	.0264	.0584	.1029	.1536	.2007	.2340	.2461
	6	.0000	.0001	.0012	.0055	.0162	.0368	.0689	.1115	.1596	.2051
	7	.0000	.0000	.0001	.0008	.0031	.0090	.0212	.0425	.0746	.1172
	8	.0000	.0000	.0000	.0001	.0004	.0014	.0043	.0106	.0229	.0439
	9	.0000	.0000	.0000	.0000	.0000	.0001	.0005	.0016	.0042	.0098
	10	.0000	.0000	.0000	.0000	.0000	.0000	.0000	.0001	.0003	.0010

Statistical software packages such as Minitab and spreadsheet packages such as Excel also provide a capability for computing binomial probabilities. Consider the Martin Clothing Store example with $n = 10$ and $p = .30$. Figure 5.5 shows the binomial probabilities generated by Minitab for all possible values of x. Note that these values are the same as those found in the $p = .30$ column of Table 5.8. Appendix 5.1 gives the step-by-step procedure for using Minitab to generate the output in Figure 5.5. Appendix 5.2 describes how Excel can be used to compute binomial probabilities.

Expected Value and Variance for the Binomial Distribution

In Section 5.3 we provided formulas for computing the expected value and variance of a discrete random variable. In the special case where the random variable has a binomial distribution with a known number of trials n and a known probability of success p, the general formulas for the expected value and variance can be simplified. The results follow.

EXPECTED VALUE AND VARIANCE FOR THE BINOMIAL DISTRIBUTION

$$E(x) = \mu = np \qquad (5.9)$$

$$\text{Var}(x) = \sigma^2 = np(1 - p) \qquad (5.10)$$

FIGURE 5.5 MINITAB OUTPUT SHOWING BINOMIAL PROBABILITIES FOR THE MARTIN CLOTHING STORE PROBLEM

x	P(X = x)
0.00	0.0282
1.00	0.1211
2.00	0.2335
3.00	0.2668
4.00	0.2001
5.00	0.1029
6.00	0.0368
7.00	0.0090
8.00	0.0014
9.00	0.0001
10.00	0.0000

For the Martin Clothing Store problem with three customers, we can use equation (5.9) to compute the expected number of customers who will make a purchase.

$$E(x) = np = 3(.30) = .9$$

Suppose that for the next month the Martin Clothing Store forecasts 1000 customers will enter the store. What is the expected number of customers who will make a purchase? The answer is $\mu = np = (1000)(.3) = 300$. Thus, to increase the expected number of purchases, Martin's must induce more customers to enter the store and/or somehow increase the probability that any individual customer will make a purchase after entering.

For the Martin Clothing Store problem with three customers, we see that the variance and standard deviation for the number of customers who will make a purchase are

$$\sigma^2 = np(1 - p) = 3(.3)(.7) = .63$$
$$\sigma = \sqrt{.63} = .79$$

For the next 1000 customers entering the store, the variance and standard deviation for the number of customers who will make a purchase are

$$\sigma^2 = np(1 - p) = 1000(.3)(.7) = 210$$
$$\sigma = \sqrt{210} = 14.49$$

NOTES AND COMMENTS

1. The binomial tables in Appendix B show values of p only up to and including $p = .50$. It would appear that such tables cannot be used when the probability of success exceeds $p = .50$. However, they can be used by noting that the probability of $n - x$ failures is also the probability of x successes. When the probability of success is greater than $p = .50$, one can compute the probability of $n - x$ failures instead. The probability of failure, $1 - p$, will be less than .50 when $p > .50$.

2. Some sources present binomial tables in a cumulative form. In using such tables, one must subtract to find the probability of x successes in n trials. For example, $f(2) = P(x \leq 2) - P(x \leq 1)$. Our tables provide these probabilities directly. To compute cumulative probabilities using our tables, one simply sums the individual probabilities. For example, to compute $P(x \leq 2)$ using our tables, we sum $f(0) + f(1) + f(2)$.

Exercises

Methods

SELF test

25. Consider a binomial experiment with two trials and $p = .4$.
    a. Draw a tree diagram for this experiment (see Figure 5.3).
    b. Compute the probability of one success, $f(1)$.
    c. Compute $f(0)$.
    d. Compute $f(2)$.
    e. Compute the probability of at least one success.
    f. Compute the expected value, variance, and standard deviation.

26. Consider a binomial experiment with $n = 10$ and $p = .10$.
    a. Compute $f(0)$.
    b. Compute $f(2)$.
    c. Compute $P(x \leq 2)$.
    d. Compute $P(x \geq 1)$.
    e. Compute $E(x)$.
    f. Compute $\text{Var}(x)$ and σ.

27. Consider a binomial experiment with $n = 20$ and $p = .70$.
    a. Compute $f(12)$.
    b. Compute $f(16)$.
    c. Compute $P(x \geq 16)$.
    d. Compute $P(x \leq 15)$.
    e. Compute $E(x)$.
    f. Compute $\text{Var}(x)$ and σ.

Applications

28. A Harris Interactive survey for InterContinental Hotels & Resorts asked respondents, "When traveling internationally, do you generally venture out on your own to experience culture, or stick with your tour group and itineraries?" The survey found that 23% of the respondents stick with their tour group (*USA Today,* January 21, 2004).
    a. In a sample of six international travelers, what is the probability that two will stick with their tour group?
    b. In a sample of six international travelers, what is the probability that at least two will stick with their tour group?
    c. In a sample of 10 international travelers, what is the probability that none will stick with the tour group?

29. In San Francisco, 30% of workers take public transportation daily (*USA Today,* December 21, 2005).
    a. In a sample of 10 workers, what is the probability that exactly three workers take public transportation daily?
    b. In a sample of 10 workers, what is the probability that at least three workers take public transportation daily?

SELF test

30. When a new machine is functioning properly, only 3% of the items produced are defective. Assume that we will randomly select two parts produced on the machine and that we are interested in the number of defective parts found.
    a. Describe the conditions under which this situation would be a binomial experiment.
    b. Draw a tree diagram similar to Figure 5.3 showing this problem as a two-trial experiment.
    c. How many experimental outcomes result in exactly one defect being found?
    d. Compute the probabilities associated with finding no defects, exactly one defect, and two defects.

31. Nine percent of undergraduate students carry credit card balances greater than \$7000 (*Reader's Digest,* July 2002). Suppose 10 undergraduate students are selected randomly to be interviewed about credit card usage.
    a. Is the selection of 10 students a binomial experiment? Explain.
    b. What is the probability that two of the students will have a credit card balance greater than \$7000?
    c. What is the probability that none will have a credit card balance greater than \$7000?
    d. What is the probability that at least three will have a credit card balance greater than \$7000?
32. Military radar and missile detection systems are designed to warn a country of an enemy attack. A reliability question is whether a detection system will be able to identify an attack and issue a warning. Assume that a particular detection system has a .90 probability of detecting a missile attack. Use the binomial probability distribution to answer the following questions.
    a. What is the probability that a single detection system will detect an attack?
    b. If two detection systems are installed in the same area and operate independently, what is the probability that at least one of the systems will detect the attack?
    c. If three systems are installed, what is the probability that at least one of the systems will detect the attack?
    d. Would you recommend that multiple detection systems be used? Explain.
33. Fifty percent of Americans believed the country was in a recession, even though technically the economy had not shown two straight quarters of negative growth (*BusinessWeek,* July 30, 2001). For a sample of 20 Americans, make the following calculations.
    a. Compute the probability that exactly 12 people believed the country was in a recession.
    b. Compute the probability that no more than five people believed the country was in a recession.
    c. How many people would you expect to say the country was in a recession?
    d. Compute the variance and standard deviation of the number of people who believed the country was in a recession.
34. The Census Bureau's Current Population Survey shows 28% of individuals, ages 25 and older, have completed four years of college (*The New York Times Almanac,* 2006). For a sample of 15 individuals, ages 25 and older, answer the following questions:
    a. What is the probability four will have completed four years of college?
    b. What is the probability three or more will have completed four years of college?
35. A university found that 20% of its students withdraw without completing the introductory statistics course. Assume that 20 students registered for the course.
    a. Compute the probability that two or fewer will withdraw.
    b. Compute the probability that exactly four will withdraw.
    c. Compute the probability that more than three will withdraw.
    d. Compute the expected number of withdrawals.
36. For the special case of a binomial random variable, we stated that the variance could be computed using the formula $\sigma^2 = np(1 - p)$. For the Martin Clothing Store problem with $n = 3$ and $p = .3$ we found $\sigma^2 = np(1 - p) = 3(.3)(.7) = .63$. Use the general definition of variance for a discrete random variable, equation (5.5), and the probabilities in Table 5.7 to verify that the variance is in fact .63.
37. Twenty-three percent of automobiles are not covered by insurance (CNN, February 23, 2006). On a particular weekend, 35 automobiles are involved in traffic accidents.
    a. What is the expected number of these automobiles that are not covered by insurance?
    b. What is the variance and standard deviation?

5.5 Poisson Probability Distribution

In this section we consider a discrete random variable that is often useful in estimating the number of occurrences over a specified interval of time or space. For example, the random variable of interest might be the number of arrivals at a car wash in one hour, the number

The Poisson probability distribution is often used to model random arrivals in waiting line situations.

of repairs needed in 10 miles of highway, or the number of leaks in 100 miles of pipeline. If the following two properties are satisfied, the number of occurrences is a random variable described by the **Poisson probability distribution**.

PROPERTIES OF A POISSON EXPERIMENT

1. The probability of an occurrence is the same for any two intervals of equal length.
2. The occurrence or nonoccurrence in any interval is independent of the occurrence or nonoccurrence in any other interval.

The **Poisson probability function** is defined by equation (5.11).

POISSON PROBABILITY FUNCTION

$$f(x) = \frac{\mu^x e^{-\mu}}{x!} \tag{5.11}$$

where

$f(x)$ = the probability of x occurrences in an interval
μ = expected value or mean number of occurrences in an interval
e = 2.71828

Siméon Poisson taught mathematics at the Ecole Polytechnique in Paris from 1802 to 1808. In 1837, he published a work entitled, "Researches on the Probability of Criminal and Civil Verdicts," which includes a discussion of what later became known as the Poisson distribution.

Before we consider a specific example to see how the Poisson distribution can be applied, note that the number of occurrences, x, has no upper limit. It is a discrete random variable that may assume an infinite sequence of values ($x = 0, 1, 2, \ldots$).

An Example Involving Time Intervals

Bell Labs used the Poisson distribution to model the arrival of phone calls.

Suppose that we are interested in the number of arrivals at the drive-up teller window of a bank during a 15-minute period on weekday mornings. If we can assume that the probability of a car arriving is the same for any two time periods of equal length and that the arrival or nonarrival of a car in any time period is independent of the arrival or nonarrival in any other time period, the Poisson probability function is applicable. Suppose these assumptions are satisfied and an analysis of historical data shows that the average number of cars arriving in a 15-minute period of time is 10; in this case, the following probability function applies.

$$f(x) = \frac{10^x e^{-10}}{x!}$$

The random variable here is x = number of cars arriving in any 15-minute period.

If management wanted to know the probability of exactly five arrivals in 15 minutes, we would set $x = 5$ and thus obtain

$$\text{Probability of exactly 5 arrivals in 15 minutes} = f(5) = \frac{10^5 e^{-10}}{5!} = .0378$$

Although this probability was determined by evaluating the probability function with $\mu = 10$ and $x = 5$, it is often easier to refer to a table for the Poisson distribution. The table provides probabilities for specific values of x and μ. We included such a table as Table 7 of Appendix B. For convenience, we reproduced a portion of this table as Table 5.9. Note that to use the table of Poisson probabilities, we need know only the values of x and μ. From Table 5.9

TABLE 5.9 SELECTED VALUES FROM THE POISSON PROBABILITY TABLES
EXAMPLE: $\mu = 10, x = 5; f(5) = .0378$

	μ									
x	**9.1**	**9.2**	**9.3**	**9.4**	**9.5**	**9.6**	**9.7**	**9.8**	**9.9**	**10**
0	.0001	.0001	.0001	.0001	.0001	.0001	.0001	.0001	.0001	.0000
1	.0010	.0009	.0009	.0008	.0007	.0007	.0006	.0005	.0005	.0005
2	.0046	.0043	.0040	.0037	.0034	.0031	.0029	.0027	.0025	.0023
3	.0140	.0131	.0123	.0115	.0107	.0100	.0093	.0087	.0081	.0076
4	.0319	.0302	.0285	.0269	.0254	.0240	.0226	.0213	.0201	.0189
5	.0581	.0555	.0530	.0506	.0483	.0460	.0439	.0418	.0398	**.0378**
6	.0881	.0851	.0822	.0793	.0764	.0736	.0709	.0682	.0656	.0631
7	.1145	.1118	.1091	.1064	.1037	.1010	.0982	.0955	.0928	.0901
8	.1302	.1286	.1269	.1251	.1232	.1212	.1191	.1170	.1148	.1126
9	.1317	.1315	.1311	.1306	.1300	.1293	.1284	.1274	.1263	.1251
10	.1198	.1210	.1219	.1228	.1235	.1241	.1245	.1249	.1250	.1251
11	.0991	.1012	.1031	.1049	.1067	.1083	.1098	.1112	.1125	.1137
12	.0752	.0776	.0799	.0822	.0844	.0866	.0888	.0908	.0928	.0948
13	.0526	.0549	.0572	.0594	.0617	.0640	.0662	.0685	.0707	.0729
14	.0342	.0361	.0380	.0399	.0419	.0439	.0459	.0479	.0500	.0521
15	.0208	.0221	.0235	.0250	.0265	.0281	.0297	.0313	.0330	.0347
16	.0118	.0127	.0137	.0147	.0157	.0168	.0180	.0192	.0204	.0217
17	.0063	.0069	.0075	.0081	.0088	.0095	.0103	.0111	.0119	.0128
18	.0032	.0035	.0039	.0042	.0046	.0051	.0055	.0060	.0065	.0071
19	.0015	.0017	.0019	.0021	.0023	.0026	.0028	.0031	.0034	.0037
20	.0007	.0008	.0009	.0010	.0011	.0012	.0014	.0015	.0017	.0019
21	.0003	.0003	.0004	.0004	.0005	.0006	.0006	.0007	.0008	.0009
22	.0001	.0001	.0002	.0002	.0002	.0002	.0003	.0003	.0004	.0004
23	.0000	.0001	.0001	.0001	.0001	.0001	.0001	.0001	.0002	.0002
24	.0000	.0000	.0000	.0000	.0000	.0000	.0000	.0001	.0001	.0001

we see that the probability of five arrivals in a 15-minute period is found by locating the value in the row of the table corresponding to $x = 5$ and the column of the table corresponding to $\mu = 10$. Hence, we obtain $f(5) = .0378$.

A property of the Poisson distribution is that the mean and variance are equal.

In the preceding example, the mean of the Poisson distribution is $\mu = 10$ arrivals per 15-minute period. A property of the Poisson distribution is that the mean of the distribution and the variance of the distribution are *equal.* Thus, the variance for the number of arrivals during 15-minute periods is $\sigma^2 = 10$. The standard deviation is $\sigma = \sqrt{10} = 3.16$.

Our illustration involves a 15-minute period, but other time periods can be used. Suppose we want to compute the probability of one arrival in a 3-minute period. Because 10 is the expected number of arrivals in a 15-minute period, we see that $10/15 = 2/3$ is the expected number of arrivals in a 1-minute period and that $(2/3)(3 \text{ minutes}) = 2$ is the expected number of arrivals in a 3-minute period. Thus, the probability of x arrivals in a 3-minute time period with $\mu = 2$ is given by the following Poisson probability function.

$$f(x) = \frac{2^x e^{-2}}{x!}$$

The probability of one arrival in a 3-minute period is calculated as follows:

$$\text{Probability of exactly} \atop \text{1 arrival in 3 minutes} = f(1) = \frac{2^1 e^{-2}}{1!} = .2707$$

Earlier we computed the probability of five arrivals in a 15-minute period; it was .0378. Note that the probability of one arrival in a three-minute period (.2707) is not the same. When computing a Poisson probability for a different time interval, we must first convert the mean arrival rate to the time period of interest and then compute the probability.

An Example Involving Length or Distance Intervals

Let us illustrate an application not involving time intervals in which the Poisson distribution is useful. Suppose we are concerned with the occurrence of major defects in a highway one month after resurfacing. We will assume that the probability of a defect is the same for any two highway intervals of equal length and that the occurrence or nonoccurrence of a defect in any one interval is independent of the occurrence or nonoccurrence of a defect in any other interval. Hence, the Poisson distribution can be applied.

Suppose we learn that major defects one month after resurfacing occur at the average rate of two per mile. Let us find the probability of no major defects in a particular three-mile section of the highway. Because we are interested in an interval with a length of three miles, $\mu = (2 \text{ defects/mile})(3 \text{ miles}) = 6$ represents the expected number of major defects over the three-mile section of highway. Using equation (5.11), the probability of no major defects is $f(0) = 6^0 e^{-6}/0! = .0025$. Thus, it is unlikely that no major defects will occur in the three-mile section. In fact, this example indicates a $1 - .0025 = .9975$ probability of at least one major defect in the three-mile highway section.

Exercises

Methods

38. Consider a Poisson distribution with $\mu = 3$.
    a. Write the appropriate Poisson probability function.
    b. Compute $f(2)$.
    c. Compute $f(1)$.
    d. Compute $P(x \geq 2)$.

SELF test

39. Consider a Poisson distribution with a mean of two occurrences per time period.
    a. Write the appropriate Poisson probability function.
    b. What is the expected number of occurrences in three time periods?
    c. Write the appropriate Poisson probability function to determine the probability of x occurrences in three time periods.
    d. Compute the probability of two occurrences in one time period.
    e. Compute the probability of six occurrences in three time periods.
    f. Compute the probability of five occurrences in two time periods.

Applications

40. Phone calls arrive at the rate of 48 per hour at the reservation desk for Regional Airways.
    a. Compute the probability of receiving three calls in a 5-minute interval of time.
    b. Compute the probability of receiving exactly 10 calls in 15 minutes.
    c. Suppose no calls are currently on hold. If the agent takes 5 minutes to complete the current call, how many callers do you expect to be waiting by that time? What is the probability that none will be waiting?
    d. If no calls are currently being processed, what is the probability that the agent can take 3 minutes for personal time without being interrupted by a call?

41. During the period of time that a local university takes phone-in registrations, calls come in at the rate of one every two minutes.
    a. What is the expected number of calls in one hour?
    b. What is the probability of three calls in five minutes?
    c. What is the probability of no calls in a five-minute period?

SELF test

42. More than 50 million guests stay at bed and breakfasts (B&Bs) each year. The Web site for the Bed and Breakfast Inns of North America (www.bestinns.net), which averages approximately seven visitors per minute, enables many B&Bs to attract guests (*Time,* September 2001).
    a. Compute the probability of no Web site visitors in a one-minute period.
    b. Compute the probability of two or more Web site visitors in a one-minute period.
    c. Compute the probability of one or more Web site visitors in a 30-second period.
    d. Compute the probability of five or more Web site visitors in a one-minute period.

43. Airline passengers arrive randomly and independently at the passenger-screening facility at a major international airport. The mean arrival rate is 10 passengers per minute.
    a. Compute the probability of no arrivals in a one-minute period.
    b. Compute the probability that three or fewer passengers arrive in a one-minute period.
    c. Compute the probability of no arrivals in a 15-second period.
    d. Compute the probability of at least one arrival in a 15-second period.

44. An average of 15 aircraft accidents occur each year (*The World Almanac and Book of Facts,* 2004).
    a. Compute the mean number of aircraft accidents per month.
    b. Compute the probability of no accidents during a month.
    c. Compute the probability of exactly one accident during a month.
    d. Compute the probability of more than one accident during a month.

45. The National Safety Council (NSC) estimates that off-the-job accidents cost U.S. businesses almost $200 billion annually in lost productivity (National Safety Council, March 2006). Based on NSC estimates, companies with 50 employees are expected to average three employee off-the-job accidents per year. Answer the following questions for companies with 50 employees.
    a. What is the probability of no off-the-job accidents during a one-year period?
    b. What is the probability of at least two off-the-job accidents during a one-year period?
    c. What is the expected number of off-the-job accidents during six months?
    d. What is the probability of no off-the-job accidents during the next six months?

5.6 Hypergeometric Probability Distribution

The **hypergeometric probability distribution** is closely related to the binomial distribution. The two probability distributions differ in two key ways. With the hypergeometric distribution, the trials are not independent; and the probability of success changes from trial to trial.

In the usual notation for the hypergeometric distribution, r denotes the number of elements in the population of size N labeled success, and $N - r$ denotes the number of elements in the population labeled failure. The **hypergeometric probability function** is used to compute the probability that in a random selection of n elements, selected without replacement, we obtain x elements labeled success and $n - x$ elements labeled failure. For this outcome to occur, we must obtain x successes from the r successes in the population and $n - x$ failures from the $N - r$ failures. The following hypergeometric probability function provides $f(x)$, the probability of obtaining x successes in a sample of size n.

HYPERGEOMETRIC PROBABILITY FUNCTION

$$f(x) = \frac{\binom{r}{x}\binom{N-r}{n-x}}{\binom{N}{n}} \quad \text{for } 0 \le x \le r \tag{5.12}$$

where

$f(x)$ = probability of x successes in n trials
n = number of trials
N = number of elements in the population
r = number of elements in the population labeled success

Note that $\binom{N}{n}$ represents the number of ways a sample of size n can be selected from a population of size N; $\binom{r}{x}$ represents the number of ways that x successes can be selected from a total of r successes in the population; and $\binom{N-r}{n-x}$ represents the number of ways that $n - x$ failures can be selected from a total of $N - r$ failures in the population.

To illustrate the computations involved in using equation (5.12), let us consider the following quality control application. Electric fuses produced by Ontario Electric are packaged in boxes of 12 units each. Suppose an inspector randomly selects three of the 12 fuses in a box for testing. If the box contains exactly five defective fuses, what is the probability that the inspector will find exactly one of the three fuses defective? In this application, $n = 3$ and $N = 12$. With $r = 5$ defective fuses in the box the probability of finding $x = 1$ defective fuse is

$$f(1) = \frac{\binom{5}{1}\binom{7}{2}}{\binom{12}{3}} = \frac{\left(\frac{5!}{1!4!}\right)\left(\frac{7!}{2!5!}\right)}{\left(\frac{12!}{3!9!}\right)} = \frac{(5)(21)}{220} = .4773$$

Now suppose that we wanted to know the probability of finding *at least* 1 defective fuse. The easiest way to answer this question is to first compute the probability that the inspector does not find any defective fuses. The probability of $x = 0$ is

$$f(0) = \frac{\binom{5}{0}\binom{7}{3}}{\binom{12}{3}} = \frac{\left(\frac{5!}{0!5!}\right)\left(\frac{7!}{3!4!}\right)}{\left(\frac{12!}{3!9!}\right)} = \frac{(1)(35)}{220} = .1591$$

With a probability of zero defective fuses $f(0) = .1591$, we conclude that the probability of finding at least one defective fuse must be $1 - .1591 = .8409$. Thus, there is a reasonably high probability that the inspector will find at least 1 defective fuse.

The mean and variance of a hypergeometric distribution are as follows.

$$E(x) = \mu = n\left(\frac{r}{N}\right) \tag{5.13}$$

$$\text{Var}(x) = \sigma^2 = n\left(\frac{r}{N}\right)\left(1 - \frac{r}{N}\right)\left(\frac{N-n}{N-1}\right) \tag{5.14}$$

In the preceding example $n = 3$, $r = 5$, and $N = 12$. Thus, the mean and variance for the number of defective fuses is

$$\mu = n\left(\frac{r}{N}\right) = 3\left(\frac{5}{12}\right) = 1.25$$

$$\sigma^2 = n\left(\frac{r}{N}\right)\left(1 - \frac{r}{N}\right)\left(\frac{N-n}{N-1}\right) = 3\left(\frac{5}{12}\right)\left(1 - \frac{5}{12}\right)\left(\frac{12-3}{12-1}\right) = .60$$

The standard deviation is $\sigma = \sqrt{.60} = .77$.

NOTES AND COMMENTS

Consider a hypergeometric distribution with n trials. Let $p = (r/N)$ denote the probability of a success on the first trial. If the population size is large, the term $(N - n)/(N - 1)$ in equation (5.14) approaches 1. As a result, the expected value and variance can be written $E(x) = np$ and $\text{Var}(x) = np(1 - p)$. Note that these expressions are the same as the expressions used to compute the expected value and variance of a binomial distribution, as in equations (5.9) and (5.10). When the population size is large, a hypergeometric distribution can be approximated by a binomial distribution with n trials and a probability of success $p = (r/N)$.

Exercises

Methods

SELF test

46. Suppose $N = 10$ and $r = 3$. Compute the hypergeometric probabilities for the following values of n and x.
    a. $n = 4$, $x = 1$.
    b. $n = 2$, $x = 2$.
    c. $n = 2$, $x = 0$.
    d. $n = 4$, $x = 2$.
47. Suppose $N = 15$ and $r = 4$. What is the probability of $x = 3$ for $n = 10$?

Applications

48. In a survey conducted by the Gallup Organization, respondents were asked, "What is your favorite sport to watch?" Football and basketball ranked number one and two in terms of preference (www.gallup.com, January 3, 2004). Assume that in a group of 10 individuals, seven preferred football and three preferred basketball. A random sample of three of these individuals is selected.
    a. What is the probability that exactly two preferred football?
    b. What is the probability that the majority (either two or three) preferred football?
49. Blackjack, or twenty-one as it is frequently called, is a popular gambling game played in Las Vegas casinos. A player is dealt two cards. Face cards (jacks, queens, and kings) and tens have a point value of 10. Aces have a point value of 1 or 11. A 52-card deck contains 16 cards with a point value of 10 (jacks, queens, kings, and tens) and four aces.

a. What is the probability that both cards dealt are aces or 10-point cards?
b. What is the probability that both of the cards are aces?
c. What is the probability that both of the cards have a point value of 10?
d. A blackjack is a 10-point card and an ace for a value of 21. Use your answers to parts (a), (b), and (c) to determine the probability that a player is dealt blackjack. (*Hint:* Part (d) is not a hypergeometric problem. Develop your own logical relationship as to how the hypergeometric probabilities from parts (a), (b), and (c) can be combined to answer this question.)

SELF test

50. Axline Computers manufactures personal computers at two plants, one in Texas and the other in Hawaii. The Texas plant has 40 employees; the Hawaii plant has 20. A random sample of 10 employees is to be asked to fill out a benefits questionnaire.
 a. What is the probability that none of the employees in the sample work at the plant in Hawaii?
 b. What is the probability that one of the employees in the sample works at the plant in Hawaii?
 c. What is the probability that two or more of the employees in the sample work at the plant in Hawaii?
 d. What is the probability that nine of the employees in the sample work at the plant in Texas?

51. The *2003 Zagat Restaurant Survey* provides food, decor, and service ratings for some of the top restaurants across the United States. For 15 top-ranking restaurants located in Boston, the average price of a dinner, including one drink and tip, was $48.60. You are leaving for a business trip to Boston and will eat dinner at three of these restaurants. Your company will reimburse you for a maximum of $50 per dinner. Business associates familiar with these restaurants have told you that the meal cost at one-third of these restaurants will exceed $50. Suppose that you randomly select three of these restaurants for dinner.
 a. What is the probability that none of the meals will exceed the cost covered by your company?
 b. What is the probability that one of the meals will exceed the cost covered by your company?
 c. What is the probability that two of the meals will exceed the cost covered by your company?
 d. What is the probability that all three of the meals will exceed the cost covered by your company?

52. A shipment of 10 items has two defective and eight nondefective items. In the inspection of the shipment, a sample of items will be selected and tested. If a defective item is found, the shipment of 10 items will be rejected.
 a. If a sample of three items is selected, what is the probability that the shipment will be rejected?
 b. If a sample of four items is selected, what is the probability that the shipment will be rejected?
 c. If a sample of five items is selected, what is the probability that the shipment will be rejected?
 d. If management would like a .90 probability of rejecting a shipment with two defective and eight nondefective items, how large a sample would you recommend?

Summary

A random variable provides a numerical description of the outcome of an experiment. The probability distribution for a random variable describes how the probabilities are distributed over the values the random variable can assume. For any discrete random variable x, the probability distribution is defined by a probability function, denoted by $f(x)$, which provides the probability associated with each value of the random variable. Once the probability function is defined, we can compute the expected value, variance, and standard deviation for the random variable.

The binomial distribution can be used to determine the probability of x successes in n trials whenever the experiment has the following properties:

1. The experiment consists of a sequence of n identical trials.
2. Two outcomes are possible on each trial, one called success and the other failure.
3. The probability of a success p does not change from trial to trial. Consequently, the probability of failure, $1 - p$, does not change from trial to trial.
4. The trials are independent.

When the four properties hold, the binomial probability function can be used to determine the probability of obtaining x successes in n trials. Formulas were also presented for the mean and variance of the binomial distribution.

The Poisson distribution is used when it is desirable to determine the probability of obtaining x occurrences over an interval of time or space. The following assumptions are necessary for the Poisson distribution to be applicable.

1. The probability of an occurrence of the event is the same for any two intervals of equal length.
2. The occurrence or nonoccurrence of the event in any interval is independent of the occurrence or nonoccurrence of the event in any other interval.

A third discrete probability distribution, the hypergeometric, was introduced in Section 5.6. Like the binomial, it is used to compute the probability of x successes in n trials. But, in contrast to the binomial, the probability of success changes from trial to trial.

Glossary

Random variable A numerical description of the outcome of an experiment.
Discrete random variable A random variable that may assume either a finite number of values or an infinite sequence of values.
Continuous random variable A random variable that may assume any numerical value in an interval or collection of intervals.
Probability distribution A description of how the probabilities are distributed over the values of the random variable.
Probability function A function, denoted by $f(x)$, that provides the probability that x assumes a particular value for a discrete random variable.
Discrete uniform probability distribution A probability distribution for which each possible value of the random variable has the same probability.
Expected value A measure of the central location of a random variable.
Variance A measure of the variability, or dispersion, of a random variable.
Standard deviation The positive square root of the variance.
Binomial experiment An experiment having the four properties stated at the beginning of Section 5.4.
Binomial probability distribution A probability distribution showing the probability of x successes in n trials of a binomial experiment.
Binomial probability function The function used to compute binomial probabilities.
Poisson probability distribution A probability distribution showing the probability of x occurrences of an event over a specified interval of time or space.
Poisson probability function The function used to compute Poisson probabilities.
Hypergeometric probability distribution A probability distribution showing the probability of x successes in n trials from a population with r successes and $N - r$ failures.
Hypergeometric probability function The function used to compute hypergeometric probabilities.

Key Formulas

Discrete Uniform Probability Function

$$f(x) = 1/n \tag{5.3}$$

Expected Value of a Discrete Random Variable

$$E(x) = \mu = \Sigma x f(x) \tag{5.4}$$

Variance of a Discrete Random Variable

$$\text{Var}(x) = \sigma^2 = \Sigma(x - \mu)^2 f(x) \tag{5.5}$$

Number of Experimental Outcomes Providing Exactly *x* Successes in *n* Trials

$$\binom{n}{x} = \frac{n!}{x!(n-x)!} \tag{5.6}$$

Binomial Probability Function

$$f(x) = \binom{n}{x} p^x (1 - p)^{(n-x)} \tag{5.8}$$

Expected Value for the Binomial Distribution

$$E(x) = \mu = np \tag{5.9}$$

Variance for the Binomial Distribution

$$\text{Var}(x) = \sigma^2 = np(1 - p) \tag{5.10}$$

Poisson Probability Function

$$f(x) = \frac{\mu^x e^{-\mu}}{x!} \tag{5.11}$$

Hypergeometric Probability Function

$$f(x) = \frac{\binom{r}{x}\binom{N-r}{n-x}}{\binom{N}{n}} \quad \text{for } 0 \le x \le r \tag{5.12}$$

Expected Value for the Hypergeometric Distribution

$$E(x) = \mu = n\left(\frac{r}{N}\right) \tag{5.13}$$

Variance for the Hypergeometric Distribution

$$\text{Var}(x) = \sigma^2 = n\left(\frac{r}{N}\right)\left(1 - \frac{r}{N}\right)\left(\frac{N-n}{N-1}\right) \tag{5.14}$$

Supplementary Exercises

53. The *Barron's* Big Money Poll asked 131 investment managers across the United States about their short-term investment outlook (*Barron's,* October 28, 2002). Their responses showed 4% were very bullish, 39% were bullish, 29% were neutral, 21% were bearish, and 7% were very bearish. Let x be the random variable reflecting the level of optimism about the market. Set $x = 5$ for very bullish down through $x = 1$ for very bearish.
    a. Develop a probability distribution for the level of optimism of investment managers.
    b. Compute the expected value for the level of optimism.
    c. Compute the variance and standard deviation for the level of optimism.
    d. Comment on what your results imply about the level of optimism and its variability.

54. The American Association of Individual Investors publishes an annual guide to the top mutual funds (*The Individual Investor's Guide to the Top Mutual Funds,* 22e, American Association of Individual Investors, 2003). Table 5.10 contains their ratings of the total risk for 29 categories of mutual funds.
    a. Let $x = 1$ for low risk up through $x = 5$ for high risk, and develop a probability distribution for level of risk.
    b. What are the expected value and variance for total risk?
    c. It turns out that 11 of the fund categories were bond funds. For the bond funds, seven categories were rated low and four were rated below average. Compare the total risk of the bond funds with the 18 categories of stock funds.

TABLE 5.10 RISK RATING FOR 29 CATEGORIES OF MUTUAL FUNDS

Total Risk	Number of Fund Categories
Low	7
Below Average	6
Average	3
Above Average	6
High	7

55. The budgeting process for a midwestern college resulted in expense forecasts for the coming year (in $ millions) of $9, $10, $11, $12, and $13. Because the actual expenses are unknown, the following respective probabilities are assigned: .3, .2, .25, .05, and .2.
    a. Show the probability distribution for the expense forecast.
    b. What is the expected value of the expense forecast for the coming year?
    c. What is the variance of the expense forecast for the coming year?
    d. If income projections for the year are estimated at $12 million, comment on the financial position of the college.

56. A survey conducted by the Bureau of Transportation Statistics (BTS) showed that the average commuter spends about 26 minutes on a one-way door-to-door trip from home to work. In addition, 5% of commuters reported a one-way commute of more than one hour (www.bts.gov, January 12, 2004).
    a. If 20 commuters are surveyed on a particular day, what is the probability that three will report a one-way commute of more than one hour?
    b. If 20 commuters are surveyed on a particular day, what is the probability that none will report a one-way commute of more than one hour?

c. If a company has 2000 employees, what is the expected number of employees that have a one-way commute of more than one hour?
d. If a company has 2000 employees, what is the variance and standard deviation of the number of employees that have a one-way commute of more than one hour?

57. A company is planning to interview Internet users to learn how its proposed Web site will be received by different age groups. According to the Census Bureau, 40% of individuals ages 18 to 54 and 12% of individuals age 55 and older use the Internet (*Statistical Abstract of the United States,* 2000).
a. How many people from the 18–54 age group must be contacted to find an expected number of at least 10 Internet users?
b. How many people from the age group 55 and older must be contacted to find an expected number of at least 10 Internet users?
c. If you contact the number of 18- to 54-year-old people suggested in part (a), what is the standard deviation of the number who will be Internet users?
d. If you contact the number of people age 55 and older suggested in part (b), what is the standard deviation of the number who will be Internet users?

58. Many companies use a quality control technique called acceptance sampling to monitor incoming shipments of parts, raw materials, and so on. In the electronics industry, component parts are commonly shipped from suppliers in large lots. Inspection of a sample of n components can be viewed as the n trials of a binomial experiment. The outcome for each component tested (trial) will be that the component is classified as good or defective. Reynolds Electronics accepts a lot from a particular supplier if the defective components in the lot do not exceed 1%. Suppose a random sample of five items from a recent shipment is tested.
a. Assume that 1% of the shipment is defective. Compute the probability that no items in the sample are defective.
b. Assume that 1% of the shipment is defective. Compute the probability that exactly one item in the sample is defective.
c. What is the probability of observing one or more defective items in the sample if 1% of the shipment is defective?
d. Would you feel comfortable accepting the shipment if one item was found to be defective? Why or why not?

59. The unemployment rate is 4.1% (*Barron's,* September 4, 2000). Assume that 100 employable people are selected randomly.
a. What is the expected number of people who are unemployed?
b. What are the variance and standard deviation of the number of people who are unemployed?

60. A poll conducted by Zogby International showed that of those Americans who said music plays a "very important" role in their lives, 30% said their local radio stations "always" play the kind of music they like (www.zogby.com, January 12, 2004). Suppose a sample of 800 people who say music plays an important role in their lives is taken.
a. How many would you expect to say that their local radio stations always play the kind of music they like?
b. What is the standard deviation of the number of respondents who think their local radio stations always play the kind of music they like?
c. What is the standard deviation of the number of respondents who do not think their local radio stations always play the kind of music they like?

61. Cars arrive at a car wash randomly and independently; the probability of an arrival is the same for any two time intervals of equal length. The mean arrival rate is 15 cars per hour. What is the probability that 20 or more cars will arrive during any given hour of operation?

62. A new automated production process averages 1.5 breakdowns per day. Because of the cost associated with a breakdown, management is concerned about the possibility of having

three or more breakdowns during a day. Assume that breakdowns occur randomly, that the probability of a breakdown is the same for any two time intervals of equal length, and that breakdowns in one period are independent of breakdowns in other periods. What is the probability of having three or more breakdowns during a day?

63. A regional director responsible for business development in the state of Pennsylvania is concerned about the number of small business failures. If the mean number of small business failures per month is 10, what is the probability that exactly four small businesses will fail during a given month? Assume that the probability of a failure is the same for any two months and that the occurrence or nonoccurrence of a failure in any month is independent of failures in any other month.

64. Customer arrivals at a bank are random and independent; the probability of an arrival in any one-minute period is the same as the probability of an arrival in any other one-minute period. Answer the following questions, assuming a mean arrival rate of three customers per minute.
   a. What is the probability of exactly three arrivals in a one-minute period?
   b. What is the probability of at least three arrivals in a one-minute period?

65. A deck of playing cards contains 52 cards, four of which are aces. What is the probability that the deal of a five-card hand provides:
   a. A pair of aces?
   b. Exactly one ace?
   c. No aces?
   d. At least one ace?

66. Through the week ending September 16, 2001, Tiger Woods was the leading money winner on the PGA Tour, with total earnings of $5,517,777. Of the top 10 money winners, seven players used a Titleist brand golf ball (www.pgatour.com). Suppose that we randomly select two of the top 10 money winners.
   a. What is the probability that exactly one uses a Titleist golf ball?
   b. What is the probability that both use Titleist golf balls?
   c. What is the probability that neither uses a Titleist golf ball?

Appendix 5.1 Discrete Probability Distributions with Minitab

Statistical packages such as Minitab offer a relatively easy and efficient procedure for computing binomial probabilities. In this appendix, we show the step-by-step procedure for determining the binomial probabilities for the Martin Clothing Store problem in Section 5.4. Recall that the desired binomial probabilities are based on $n = 10$ and $p = .30$. Before beginning the Minitab routine, the user must enter the desired values of the random variable x into a column of the worksheet. We entered the values 0, 1, 2, . . . , 10 in column 1 (see Figure 5.5) to generate the entire binomial probability distribution. The Minitab steps to obtain the desired binomial probabilities follow.

Step 1. Select the **Calc** menu
Step 2. Choose **Probability Distributions**
Step 3. Choose **Binomial**
Step 4. When the Binomial Distribution dialog box appears:
Select **Probability**
Enter 10 in the **Number of trials** box
Enter .3 in the **Probability of success** box
Enter C1 in the **Input column** box
Click **OK**

The Minitab output with the binomial probabilities will appear as shown in Figure 5.5.

Minitab provides Poisson and hypergeometric probabilities in a similar manner. For instance, to compute Poisson probabilities the only differences are in step 3, where the **Poisson** option would be selected, and step 4, where the **Mean** would be entered rather than the number of trials and the probability of success.

Appendix 5.2 Discrete Probability Distributions with Excel

Excel provides functions for computing probabilities for the binomial, Poisson, and hypergeometric distributions introduced in this chapter. The Excel function for computing binomial probabilities is BINOMDIST. It has four arguments: x (the number of successes), n (the number of trials), p (the probability of success), and cumulative. FALSE is used for the fourth argument (cumulative) if we want the probability of x successes, and TRUE is used for the fourth argument if we want the cumulative probability of x or fewer successes. Here we show how to compute the probabilities of 0 through 10 successes for the Martin Clothing Store problem in Section 5.4 (see Figure 5.5).

As we describe the worksheet development refer to Figure 5.6; the formula worksheet is set in the background, and the value worksheet appears in the foreground. We entered

FIGURE 5.6 EXCEL WORKSHEET FOR COMPUTING BINOMIAL PROBABILITIES

	A	B	C	D
1	**Number of Trials (n)**	10		
2	**Probability of Success (p)**	0.3		
3				
4		x	$f(x)$	
5		0	=BINOMDIST(B5,$B$1,$B$2,FALSE)	
6		1	=BINOMDIST(B6,$B$1,$B$2,FALSE)	
7		2	=BINOMDIST(B7,$B$1,$B$2,FALSE)	
8		3	=BINOMDIST(B8,$B$1,$B$2,FALSE)	
9		4	=BINOMDIST(B9,$B$1,$B$2,FALSE)	
10		5	=BINOMDIST(B10,$B$1,$B$2,FALSE)	
11		6	=BINOMDIST(B11,$B$1,$B$2,FALSE)	
12		7	=BINOMDIST(B12,$B$1,$B$2,FALSE)	
13		8	=BINOMDIST(B13,$B$1,$B$2,FALSE)	
14		9	=BINOMDIST(B14,$B$1,$B$2,FALSE)	
15		10	=BINOMDIST(B15,$B$1,$B$2,FALSE)	
16				

	A	B	C	D
1	**Number of Trials (n)**	10		
2	**Probability of Success (p)**	0.3		
3				
4		x	$f(x)$	
5		0	0.0282	
6		1	0.1211	
7		2	0.2335	
8		3	0.2668	
9		4	0.2001	
10		5	0.1029	
11		6	0.0368	
12		7	0.0090	
13		8	0.0014	
14		9	0.0001	
15		10	0.0000	
16				

the number of trials (10) into cell B1, the probability of success into cell B2, and the values for the random variable into cells B5:B15. The following steps will generate the desired probabilities:

Step 1. Use the BINOMDIST function to compute the probability of $x = 0$ by entering the following formula into cell C5:

=BINOMDIST(B5,$B$1,$B$2,FALSE)

Step 2. Copy the formula in cell C5 into cells C6:C15.

The value worksheet in Figure 5.6 shows that the probabilities obtained are the same as in Figure 5.5. Poisson and hypergeometric probabilities can be computed in a similar fashion. The POISSON and HYPGEOMDIST functions are used. Excel's Insert Function tool can help the user in entering the proper arguments for these functions (see Appendix 2.2).

CHAPTER 6

Continuous Probability Distributions

CONTENTS

STATISTICS *in* PRACTICE

PROCTER & GAMBLE*
CINCINNATI, OHIO

Procter & Gamble (P&G) produces and markets such products as detergents, disposable diapers, over-the-counter pharmaceuticals, dentifrices, bar soaps, mouthwashes, and paper towels. Worldwide, it has the leading brand in more categories than any other consumer products company. Since its merger with Gillette, P&G also produces and markets razors, blades, and many other personal care products.

As a leader in the application of statistical methods in decision making, P&G employs people with diverse academic backgrounds: engineering, statistics, operations research, and business. The major quantitative technologies for which these people provide support are probabilistic decision and risk analysis, advanced simulation, quality improvement, and quantitative methods (e.g., linear programming, regression analysis, probability analysis).

The Industrial Chemicals Division of P&G is a major supplier of fatty alcohols derived from natural substances such as coconut oil and from petroleum-based derivatives. The division wanted to know the economic risks and opportunities of expanding its fatty-alcohol production facilities, so it called in P&G's experts in probabilistic decision and risk analysis to help. After structuring and modeling the problem, they determined that the key to profitability was the cost difference between the petroleum- and coconut-based raw materials. Future costs were unknown, but the analysts were able to approximate them with the following continuous random variables.

x = the coconut oil price per pound of fatty alcohol

and

y = the petroleum raw material price per pound of fatty alcohol

Because the key to profitability was the difference between these two random variables, a third random variable, $d = x - y$, was used in the analysis. Experts were interviewed to determine the probability distributions for x and y. In turn, this information was used to develop a probability distribution for the difference in prices d. This continuous probability distribution showed a .90 probability that the price difference would be \$.0655 or less and a .50 probability that the price difference would be \$.035 or less. In addition, there was only a .10 probability that the price difference would be \$.0045 or less.†

Some of Procter & Gamble's many well-known products. © AFP/Getty Images.

The Industrial Chemicals Division thought that being able to quantify the impact of raw material price differences was key to reaching a consensus. The probabilities obtained were used in a sensitivity analysis of the raw material price difference. The analysis yielded sufficient insight to form the basis for a recommendation to management.

The use of continuous random variables and their probability distributions was helpful to P&G in analyzing the economic risks associated with its fatty-alcohol production. In this chapter, you will gain an understanding of continuous random variables and their probability distributions, including one of the most important probability distributions in statistics, the normal distribution.

*The authors are indebted to Joel Kahn of Procter & Gamble for providing this Statistics in Practice.

†The price differences stated here have been modified to protect proprietary data.

In the preceding chapter we discussed discrete random variables and their probability distributions. In this chapter we turn to the study of continuous random variables. Specifically, we discuss three continuous probability distributions: the uniform, the normal, and the exponential.

A fundamental difference separates discrete and continuous random variables in terms of how probabilities are computed. For a discrete random variable, the probability function $f(x)$ provides the probability that the random variable assumes a particular value. With continuous random variables, the counterpart of the probability function is the **probability density function**, also denoted by $f(x)$. The difference is that the probability density function does not directly provide probabilities. However, the area under the graph of $f(x)$ corresponding to a given interval does provide the probability that the continuous random variable x assumes a value in that interval. So when we compute probabilities for continuous random variables we are computing the probability that the random variable assumes any value in an interval.

Because the area under the graph of $f(x)$ at any particular point is zero, one of the implications of the definition of probability for continuous random variables is that the probability of any particular value of the random variable is zero. In Section 6.1 we demonstrate these concepts for a continuous random variable that has a uniform distribution.

Much of the chapter is devoted to describing and showing applications of the normal distribution. The normal distribution is of major importance because of its wide applicability and its extensive use in statistical inference. The chapter closes with a discussion of the exponential distribution. The exponential distribution is useful in applications involving such factors as waiting times and service times.

6.1 Uniform Probability Distribution

Whenever the probability is proportional to the length of the interval, the random variable is uniformly distributed.

Consider the random variable x representing the flight time of an airplane traveling from Chicago to New York. Suppose the flight time can be any value in the interval from 120 minutes to 140 minutes. Because the random variable x can assume any value in that interval, x is a continuous rather than a discrete random variable. Let us assume that sufficient actual flight data are available to conclude that the probability of a flight time within any 1-minute interval is the same as the probability of a flight time within any other 1-minute interval contained in the larger interval from 120 to 140 minutes. With every 1-minute interval being equally likely, the random variable x is said to have a **uniform probability distribution**. The probability density function, which defines the uniform distribution for the flight-time random variable, is

$$f(x) = \begin{cases} 1/20 & \text{for } 120 \leq x \leq 140 \\ 0 & \text{elsewhere} \end{cases}$$

Figure 6.1 is a graph of this probability density function. In general, the uniform probability density function for a random variable x is defined by the following formula.

UNIFORM PROBABILITY DENSITY FUNCTION

$$f(x) = \begin{cases} \dfrac{1}{b - a} & \text{for } a \leq x \leq b \\ 0 & \text{elsewhere} \end{cases} \quad \textbf{(6.1)}$$

For the flight-time random variable, $a = 120$ and $b = 140$.

FIGURE 6.1 UNIFORM PROBABILITY DISTRIBUTION FOR FLIGHT TIME

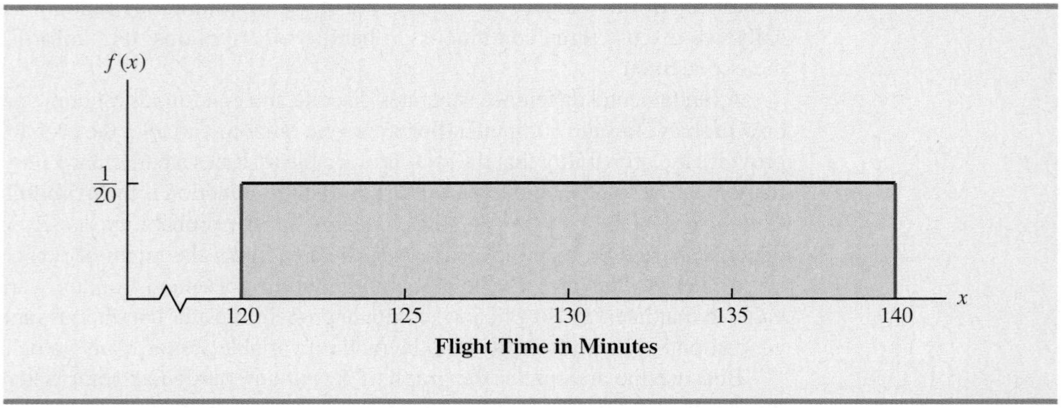

As noted in the introduction, for a continuous random variable, we consider probability only in terms of the likelihood that a random variable assumes a value within a specified interval. In the flight time example, an acceptable probability question is: What is the probability that the flight time is between 120 and 130 minutes? That is, what is $P(120 \leq x \leq 130)$? Because the flight time must be between 120 and 140 minutes and because the probability is described as being uniform over this interval, we feel comfortable saying $P(120 \leq x \leq 130) = .50$. In the following subsection we show that this probability can be computed as the area under the graph of $f(x)$ from 120 to 130 (see Figure 6.2).

Area as a Measure of Probability

Let us make an observation about the graph in Figure 6.2. Consider the area under the graph of $f(x)$ in the interval from 120 to 130. The area is rectangular, and the area of a rectangle is simply the width multiplied by the height. With the width of the interval equal to $130 - 120 = 10$ and the height equal to the value of the probability density function $f(x) = 1/20$, we have area = width $\times$ height $= 10(1/20) = 10/20 = .50$.

FIGURE 6.2 AREA PROVIDES PROBABILITY OF A FLIGHT TIME BETWEEN 120 AND 130 MINUTES

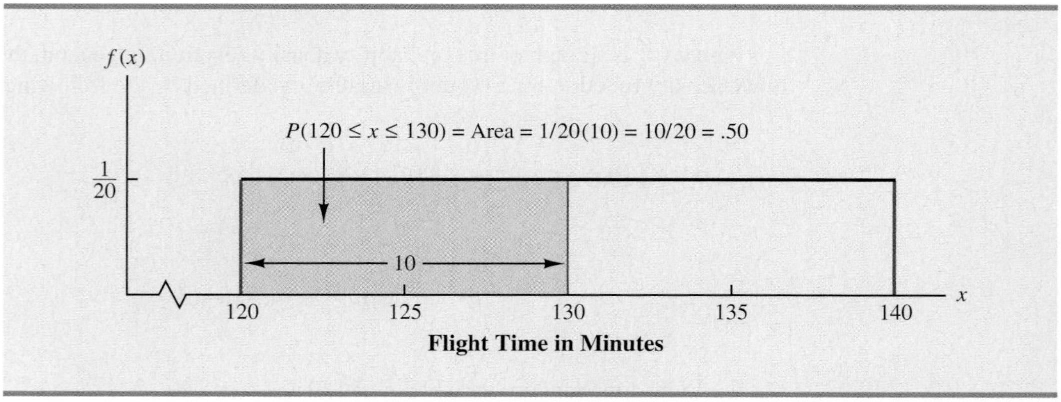

What observation can you make about the area under the graph of $f(x)$ and probability? They are identical! Indeed, this observation is valid for all continuous random variables. Once a probability density function $f(x)$ is identified, the probability that x takes a value between some lower value x_1 and some higher value x_2 can be found by computing the area under the graph of $f(x)$ over the interval from x_1 to x_2.

Given the uniform distribution for flight time and using the interpretation of area as probability, we can answer any number of probability questions about flight times. For example, what is the probability of a flight time between 128 and 136 minutes? The width of the interval is $136 - 128 = 8$. With the uniform height of $f(x) = 1/20$, we see that $P(128 \le x \le 136) = 8(1/20) = .40$.

Note that $P(120 \le x \le 140) = 20(1/20) = 1$; that is, the total area under the graph of $f(x)$ is equal to 1. This property holds for all continuous probability distributions and is the analog of the condition that the sum of the probabilities must equal 1 for a discrete probability function. For a continuous probability density function, we must also require that $f(x) \ge 0$ for all values of x. This requirement is the analog of the requirement that $f(x) \ge 0$ for discrete probability functions.

Two major differences stand out between the treatment of continuous random variables and the treatment of their discrete counterparts.

1. We no longer talk about the probability of the random variable assuming a particular value. Instead, we talk about the probability of the random variable assuming a value within some given interval.
2. The probability of a continuous random variable assuming a value within some given interval from x_1 to x_2 is defined to be the area under the graph of the probability density function between x_1 and x_2. Because a single point is an interval of zero width, this implies that the probability of a continuous random variable assuming any particular value exactly is zero. It also means that the probability of a continuous random variable assuming a value in any interval is the same whether or not the endpoints are included.

To see that the probability of any single point is 0, refer to Figure 6.2 and compute the probability of a single point, say, $x = 125$. $P(x = 125) = P(125 \le x \le 125) = 0(1/20) = 0$.

The calculation of the expected value and variance for a continuous random variable is analogous to that for a discrete random variable. However, because the computational procedure involves integral calculus, we leave the derivation of the appropriate formulas to more advanced texts.

For the uniform continuous probability distribution introduced in this section, the formulas for the expected value and variance are

$$E(x) = \frac{a + b}{2}$$

$$\text{Var}(x) = \frac{(b - a)^2}{12}$$

In these formulas, a is the smallest value and b is the largest value that the random variable may assume.

Applying these formulas to the uniform distribution for flight times from Chicago to New York, we obtain

$$E(x) = \frac{(120 + 140)}{2} = 130$$

$$\text{Var}(x) = \frac{(140 - 120)^2}{12} = 33.33$$

The standard deviation of flight times can be found by taking the square root of the variance. Thus, $\sigma = 5.77$ minutes.

NOTES AND COMMENTS

To see more clearly why the height of a probability density function is not a probability, think about a random variable with the following uniform probability distribution.

$$f(x) = \begin{cases} 2 & \text{for } 0 \le x \le .5 \\ 0 & \text{elsewhere} \end{cases}$$

The height of the probability density function, $f(x)$, is 2 for values of x between 0 and .5. However, we know probabilities can never be greater than 1. Thus, we see that $f(x)$ cannot be interpreted as the probability of x.

Exercises

Methods

SELF test

1. The random variable x is known to be uniformly distributed between 1.0 and 1.5.
   a. Show the graph of the probability density function.
   b. Compute $P(x = 1.25)$.
   c. Compute $P(1.0 \le x \le 1.25)$.
   d. Compute $P(1.20 < x < 1.5)$.
2. The random variable x is known to be uniformly distributed between 10 and 20.
   a. Show the graph of the probability density function.
   b. Compute $P(x < 15)$.
   c. Compute $P(12 \le x \le 18)$.
   d. Compute $E(x)$.
   e. Compute $\text{Var}(x)$.

Applications

3. Delta Airlines quotes a flight time of 2 hours, 5 minutes for its flights from Cincinnati to Tampa. Suppose we believe that actual flight times are uniformly distributed between 2 hours and 2 hours, 20 minutes.
   a. Show the graph of the probability density function for flight time.
   b. What is the probability that the flight will be no more than 5 minutes late?
   c. What is the probability that the flight will be more than 10 minutes late?
   d. What is the expected flight time?

SELF test

4. Most computer languages include a function that can be used to generate random numbers. In Excel, the RAND function can be used to generate random numbers between 0 and 1. If we let x denote a random number generated using RAND, then x is a continuous random variable with the following probability density function.

$$f(x) = \begin{cases} 1 & \text{for } 0 \le x \le 1 \\ 0 & \text{elsewhere} \end{cases}$$

   a. Graph the probability density function.
   b. What is the probability of generating a random number between .25 and .75?
   c. What is the probability of generating a random number with a value less than or equal to .30?
   d. What is the probability of generating a random number with a value greater than .60?
   e. Generate 50 random numbers by entering =RAND() into 50 cells of an Excel worksheet.
   f. Compute the mean and standard deviation for the random numbers in part (e).

5. The driving distance for the top 100 golfers on the PGA tour is between 284.7 and 310.6 yards (*Golfweek,* March 29, 2003). Assume that the driving distance for these golfers is uniformly distributed over this interval.
   a. Give a mathematical expression for the probability density function of driving distance.
   b. What is the probability the driving distance for one of these golfers is less than 290 yards?
   c. What is the probability the driving distance for one of these golfers is at least 300 yards?
   d. What is the probability the driving distance for one of these golfers is between 290 and 305 yards?
   e. How many of these golfers drive the ball at least 290 yards?
6. The label on a bottle of liquid detergent shows the contents to be 12 ounces per bottle. The production operation fills the bottle uniformly according to the following probability density function.

$$f(x) = \begin{cases} 8 & \text{for } 11.975 \le x \le 12.100 \\ 0 & \text{elsewhere} \end{cases}$$

   a. What is the probability that a bottle will be filled with between 12 and 12.05 ounces?
   b. What is the probability that a bottle will be filled with 12.02 or more ounces?
   c. Quality control accepts a bottle that is filled to within .02 ounces of the number of ounces shown on the container label. What is the probability that a bottle of this liquid detergent will fail to meet the quality control standard?
7. Suppose we are interested in bidding on a piece of land and we know one other bidder is interested.* The seller announced that the highest bid in excess of \$10,000 will be accepted. Assume that the competitor's bid x is a random variable that is uniformly distributed between \$10,000 and \$15,000.
   a. Suppose you bid \$12,000. What is the probability that your bid will be accepted?
   b. Suppose you bid \$14,000. What is the probability that your bid will be accepted?
   c. What amount should you bid to maximize the probability that you get the property?
   d. Suppose you know someone who is willing to pay you \$16,000 for the property. Would you consider bidding less than the amount in part (c)? Why or why not?

6.2 Normal Probability Distribution

Abraham de Moivre, a French mathematician, published The Doctrine of Chances *in 1733. He derived the normal distribution.*

The most important probability distribution for describing a continuous random variable is the **normal probability distribution**. The normal distribution has been used in a wide variety of practical applications in which the random variables are heights and weights of people, test scores, scientific measurements, amounts of rainfall, and other similar values. It is also widely used in statistical inference, which is the major topic of the remainder of this book. In such applications, the normal distribution provides a description of the likely results obtained through sampling.

Normal Curve

The form, or shape, of the normal distribution is illustrated by the bell-shaped normal curve in Figure 6.3. The probability density function that defines the bell-shaped curve of the normal distribution follows.

*This exercise is based on a problem suggested to us by Professor Roger Myerson of Northwestern University.

FIGURE 6.3 BELL-SHAPED CURVE FOR THE NORMAL DISTRIBUTION

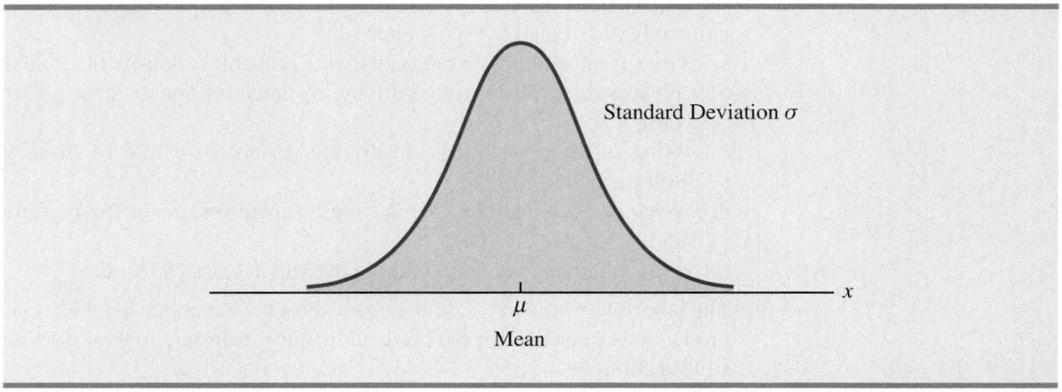

NORMAL PROBABILITY DENSITY FUNCTION

$$f(x) = \frac{1}{\sigma\sqrt{2\pi}} e^{-(x-\mu)^2/2\sigma^2} \tag{6.2}$$

where

μ = mean
σ = standard deviation
π = 3.14159
e = 2.71828

We make several observations about the characteristics of the normal distribution.

The normal curve has two parameters, μ and σ. They determine the location and shape of the normal distribution.

1. The entire family of normal distributions is differentiated by two parameters: the mean μ and the standard deviation σ.
2. The highest point on the normal curve is at the mean, which is also the median and mode of the distribution.
3. The mean of the distribution can be any numerical value: negative, zero, or positive. Three normal distributions with the same standard deviation but three different means (−10, 0, and 20) are shown here.

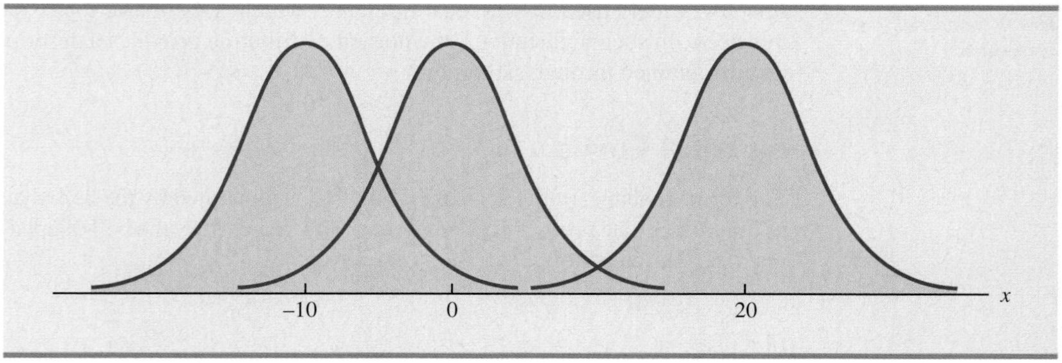

4. The normal distribution is symmetric, with the shape of the normal curve to the left of the mean a mirror image of the shape of the normal curve to the right of the mean. The tails of the normal curve extend to infinity in both directions and theoretically never touch the horizontal axis. Because it is symmetric, the normal distribution is not skewed; its skewness measure is zero.
5. The standard deviation determines how flat and wide the normal curve is. Larger values of the standard deviation result in wider, flatter curves, showing more variability in the data. Two normal distributions with the same mean but with different standard deviations are shown here.

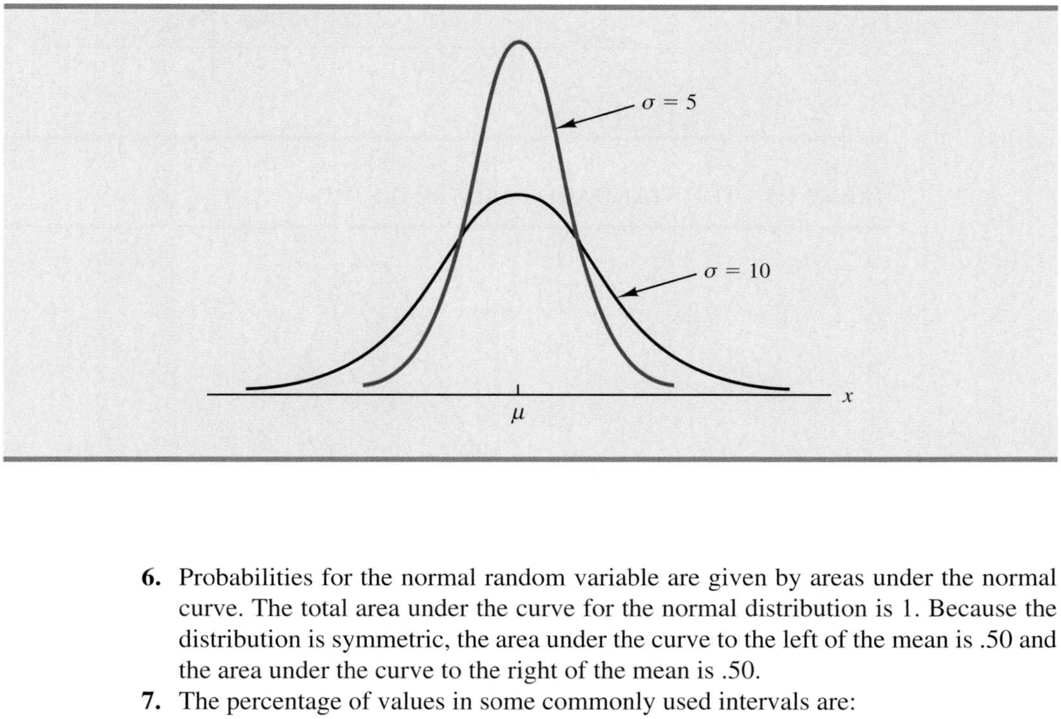

6. Probabilities for the normal random variable are given by areas under the normal curve. The total area under the curve for the normal distribution is 1. Because the distribution is symmetric, the area under the curve to the left of the mean is .50 and the area under the curve to the right of the mean is .50.
7. The percentage of values in some commonly used intervals are:
   a. 68.3% of the values of a normal random variable are within plus or minus one standard deviation of its mean.
   b. 95.4% of the values of a normal random variable are within plus or minus two standard deviations of its mean.
   c. 99.7% of the values of a normal random variable are within plus or minus three standard deviations of its mean.

These percentages are the basis for the empirical rule introduced in Section 3.3.

Figure 6.4 shows properties (a), (b), and (c) graphically.

Standard Normal Probability Distribution

A random variable that has a normal distribution with a mean of zero and a standard deviation of one is said to have a **standard normal probability distribution**. The letter z is commonly used to designate this particular normal random variable. Figure 6.5 is the graph of the standard normal distribution. It has the same general appearance as other normal distributions, but with the special properties of $\mu = 0$ and $\sigma = 1$.

FIGURE 6.4 AREAS UNDER THE CURVE FOR ANY NORMAL DISTRIBUTION

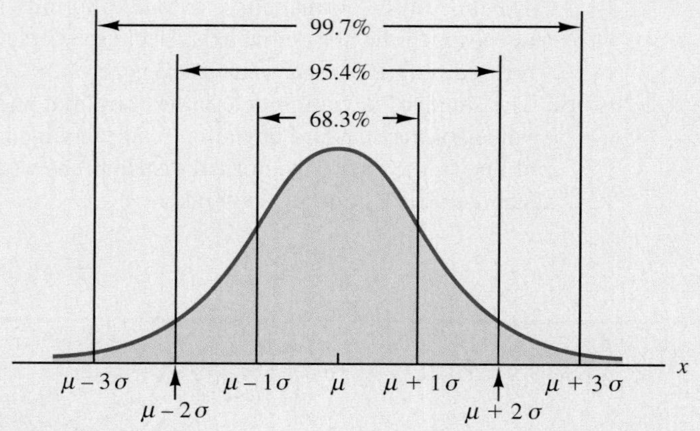

FIGURE 6.5 THE STANDARD NORMAL DISTRIBUTION

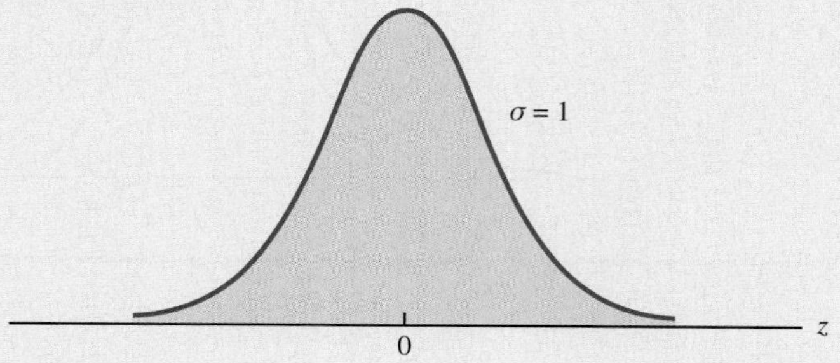

Because $\mu = 0$ and $\sigma = 1$, the formula for the standard normal probability density function is a simpler version of equation (6.2).

STANDARD NORMAL DENSITY FUNCTION

$$f(z) = \frac{1}{\sqrt{2\pi}} e^{-z^2/2}$$

For the normal probability density function, the height of the normal curve varies and more advanced mathematics is required to compute the areas that represent probability.

As with other continuous random variables, probability calculations with any normal distribution are made by computing areas under the graph of the probability density function. Thus, to find the probability that a normal random variable is within any specific interval, we must compute the area under the normal curve over that interval.

For the standard normal distribution, areas under the normal curve have been computed and are available in tables that can be used to compute probabilities. Such a table appears on the two pages inside the front cover of the text. The table on the left-hand page contains areas, or cumulative probabilities, for z values less than or equal to the mean of zero. The table on the right-hand page contains areas, or cumulative probabilities, for z values greater than or equal to the mean of zero.

The three types of probabilities we need to compute include (1) the probability that the standard normal random variable z will be less than or equal to a given value; (2) the probability that z will be between two given values; and (3) the probability that z will be greater than or equal to a given value. To see how the cumulative probability table for the standard normal distribution can be used to compute these three types of probabilities, let us consider some examples.

Because the standard normal random variable is continuous, $P(z \leq 1.00) = P(z < 1.00)$.

We start by showing how to compute the probability that z is less than or equal to 1.00; that is, $P(z \leq 1.00)$. This cumulative probability is the area under the normal curve to the left of $z = 1.00$ in the following graph.

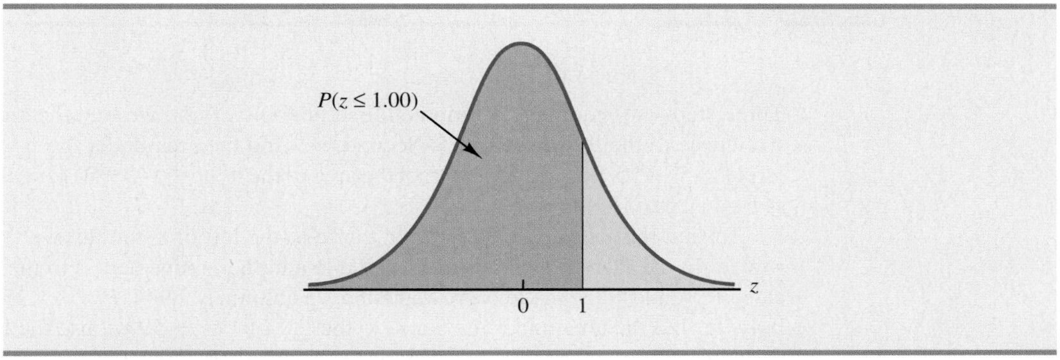

Refer to the right-hand page of the standard normal probability table inside the front cover of the text. The cumulative probability corresponding to $z = 1.00$ is the table value located at the intersection of the row labeled 1.0 and the column labeled .00. First we find 1.0 in the left column of the table and then find .00 in the top row of the table. By looking in the body of the table, we find that the 1.0 row and the .00 column intersect at the value of .8413; thus, $P(z \leq 1.00) = .8413$. The following excerpt from the probability table shows these steps.

z	**.00**	**.01**	**.02**
.			
.			
.			
.9	.8159	.8186	.8212
1.0	**.8413**	.8438	.8461
1.1	.8643	.8665	.8686
1.2	.8849	.8869	.8888
.			
.			
.			

$P(z \leq 1.00)$

To illustrate the second type of probability calculation we show how to compute the probability that z is in the interval between $-.50$ and 1.25; that is, $P(-.50 \leq z \leq 1.25)$. The following graph shows this area, or probability.

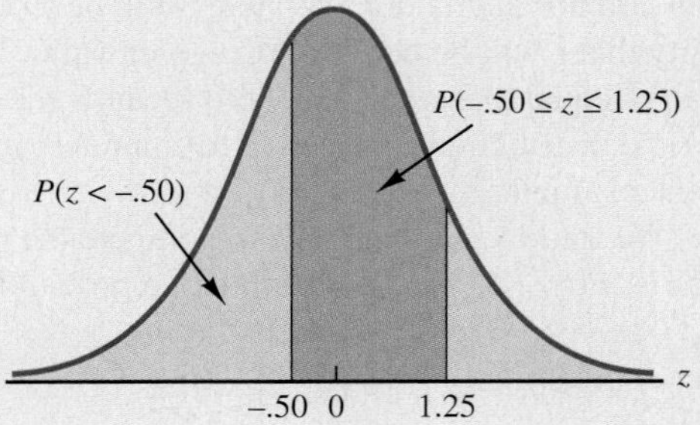

Three steps are required to compute this probability. First, we find the area under the normal curve to the left of $z = 1.25$. Second, we find the area under the normal curve to the left of $z = -.50$. Finally, we subtract the area to the left of $z = -.50$ from the area to the left of $z = 1.25$ to find $P(-.50 \le z \le 1.25)$.

To find the area under the normal curve to the left of $z = 1.25$, we first locate the 1.2 row in the standard normal probability table and then move across to the .05 column. Because the table value in the 1.2 row and the .05 column is .8944, $P(z \le 1.25) = .8944$. Similarly, to find the area under the curve to the left of $z = -.50$ we use the left-hand page of the table to locate the table value in the $-.5$ row and the .00 column; with a table value of .3085, $P(z \le -.50) = .3085$. Thus, $P(-.50 \le z \le 1.25) = P(z \le 1.25) - P(z \le -.50) = .8944 - .3085 = .5859$.

Let us consider another example of computing the probability that z is in the interval between two given values. Often it is of interest to compute the probability that a normal random variable assumes a value within a certain number of standard deviations of the mean. Suppose we want to compute the probability that the standard normal random variable is within one standard deviation of the mean; that is, $P(-1.00 \le z \le 1.00)$. To compute this probability we must find the area under the curve between -1.00 and 1.00. Earlier we found that $P(z \le 1.00) = .8413$. Referring again to the table inside the front cover of the book, we find that the area under the curve to the left of $z = -1.00$ is .1587, so $P(z \le -1.00) = .1587$. Therefore, $P(-1.00 \le z \le 1.00) = P(z \le 1.00) - P(z \le -1.00) = .8413 - .1587 = .6826$. This probability is shown graphically in the following figure.

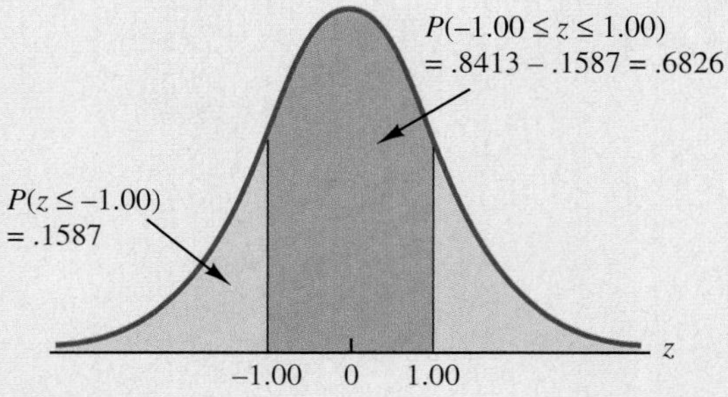

To illustrate how to make the third type of probability computation, suppose we want to compute the probability of obtaining a z value of at least 1.58; that is, $P(z \geq 1.58)$. The value in the $z = 1.5$ row and the .08 column of the cumulative normal table is .9429; thus, $P(z < 1.58) = .9429$. However, because the total area under the normal curve is 1, $P(z \geq 1.58) = 1 - .9429 = .0571$. This probability is shown in the following figure.

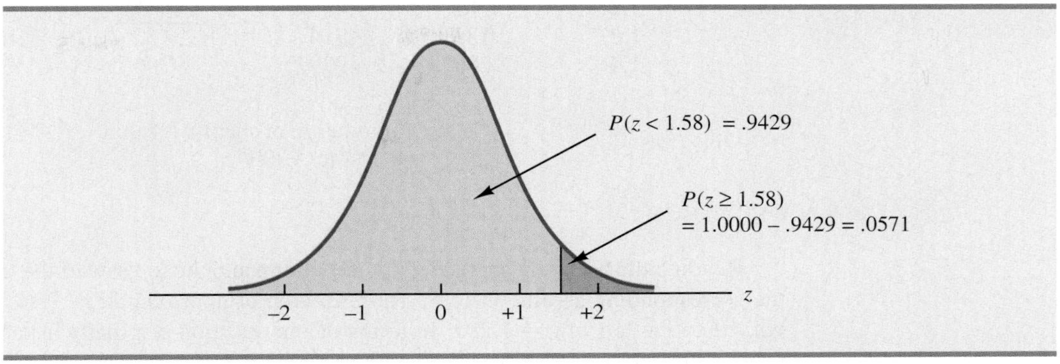

In the preceding illustrations, we showed how to compute probabilities given specified z values. In some situations, we are given a probability and are interested in working backward to find the corresponding z value. Suppose we want to find a z value such that the probability of obtaining a larger z value is .10. The following figure shows this situation graphically.

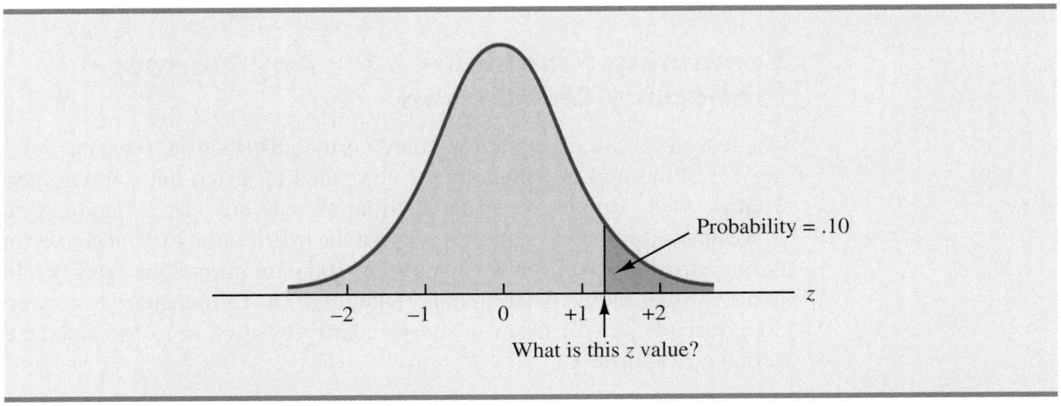

Given a probability, we can use the standard normal table in an inverse fashion to find the corresponding z value.

This problem is the inverse of those in the preceding examples. Previously, we specified the z value of interest and then found the corresponding probability, or area. In this example, we are given the probability, or area, and asked to find the corresponding z value. To do so, we use the standard normal probability table somewhat differently.

Recall that the standard normal probability table gives the area under the curve to the left of a particular z value. We have been given the information that the area in the upper tail of the curve is .10. Hence, the area under the curve to the left of the unknown z value must equal .9000. Scanning the body of the table, we find .8997 is the cumulative probability value closest to .9000. The section of the table providing this result follows.

z	.06	.07	.08	.09
.				
.				
.				
1.0	.8554	.8577	.8599	.8621
1.1	.8770	.8790	.8810	.8830
1.2	.8962	.8980	.8997	.9015
1.3	.9131	.9147	.9162	.9177
1.4	.9279	.9292	.9306	.9319
.				
.				
.				

Cumulative probability value closest to .9000

Reading the z value from the left-most column and the top row of the table, we find that the corresponding z value is 1.28. Thus, an area of approximately .9000 (actually .8997) will be to the left of $z = 1.28$.* In terms of the question originally asked, there is an approximately .10 probability of a z value larger than 1.28.

The examples illustrate that the table of cumulative probabilities for the standard normal probability distribution can be used to find probabilities associated with values of the standard normal random variable z. Two types of questions can be asked. The first type of question specifies a value, or values, for z and asks us to use the table to determine the corresponding areas or probabilities. The second type of question provides an area, or probability, and asks us to use the table to determine the corresponding z value. Thus, we need to be flexible in using the standard normal probability table to answer the desired probability question. In most cases, sketching a graph of the standard normal probability distribution and shading the appropriate area will help to visualize the situation and aid in determining the correct answer.

Computing Probabilities for Any Normal Probability Distribution

The reason for discussing the standard normal distribution so extensively is that probabilities for all normal distributions are computed by using the standard normal distribution. That is, when we have a normal distribution with any mean μ and any standard deviation σ, we answer probability questions about the distribution by first converting to the standard normal distribution. Then we can use the standard normal probability table and the appropriate z values to find the desired probabilities. The formula used to convert any normal random variable x with mean μ and standard deviation σ to the standard normal random variable z follows.

The formula for the standard normal random variable is similar to the formula we introduced in Chapter 3 for computing z-scores for a data set.

CONVERTING TO THE STANDARD NORMAL RANDOM VARIABLE

$$z = \frac{x - \mu}{\sigma} \tag{6.3}$$

*We could use interpolation in the body of the table to get a better approximation of the z value that corresponds to an area of .9000. Doing so to provide one more decimal place of accuracy would yield a z value of 1.282. However, in most practical situations, sufficient accuracy is obtained by simply using the table value closest to the desired probability.

A value of x equal to its mean μ results in $z = (\mu - \mu)/\sigma = 0$. Thus, we see that a value of x equal to its mean μ corresponds to $z = 0$. Now suppose that x is one standard deviation above its mean; that is, $x = \mu + \sigma$. Applying equation (6.3), we see that the corresponding z value is $z = [(\mu + \sigma) - \mu]/\sigma = \sigma/\sigma = 1$. Thus, an x value that is one standard deviation above its mean corresponds to $z = 1$. In other words, *we can interpret z as the number of standard deviations that the normal random variable x is from its mean μ.*

To see how this conversion enables us to compute probabilities for any normal distribution, suppose we have a normal distribution with $\mu = 10$ and $\sigma = 2$. What is the probability that the random variable x is between 10 and 14? Using equation (6.3), we see that at $x = 10$, $z = (x - \mu)/\sigma = (10 - 10)/2 = 0$ and that at $x = 14$, $z = (14 - 10)/2 = 4/2 = 2$. Thus, the answer to our question about the probability of x being between 10 and 14 is given by the equivalent probability that z is between 0 and 2 for the standard normal distribution. In other words, the probability that we are seeking is the probability that the random variable x is between its mean and two standard deviations above the mean. Using $z = 2.00$ and the standard normal probability table inside the front cover of the text, we see that $P(z \le 2) = .9772$. Because $P(z \le 0) = .5000$, we can compute $P(.00 \le z \le 2.00) = P(z \le 2) - P(z \le 0) = .9772 - .5000 = .4772$. Hence the probability that x is between 10 and 14 is .4772.

Grear Tire Company Problem

We turn now to an application of the normal probability distribution. Suppose the Grear Tire Company developed a new steel-belted radial tire to be sold through a national chain of discount stores. Because the tire is a new product, Grear's managers believe that the mileage guarantee offered with the tire will be an important factor in the acceptance of the product. Before finalizing the tire mileage guarantee policy, Grear's managers want probability information about x = number of miles the tires will last.

From actual road tests with the tires, Grear's engineering group estimated that the mean tire mileage is $\mu = 36{,}500$ miles and that the standard deviation is $\sigma = 5000$. In addition, the data collected indicate that a normal distribution is a reasonable assumption. What percentage of the tires can be expected to last more than 40,000 miles? In other words, what is the probability that the tire mileage, x, will exceed 40,000? This question can be answered by finding the area of the darkly shaded region in Figure 6.6.

FIGURE 6.6 GREAR TIRE COMPANY MILEAGE DISTRIBUTION

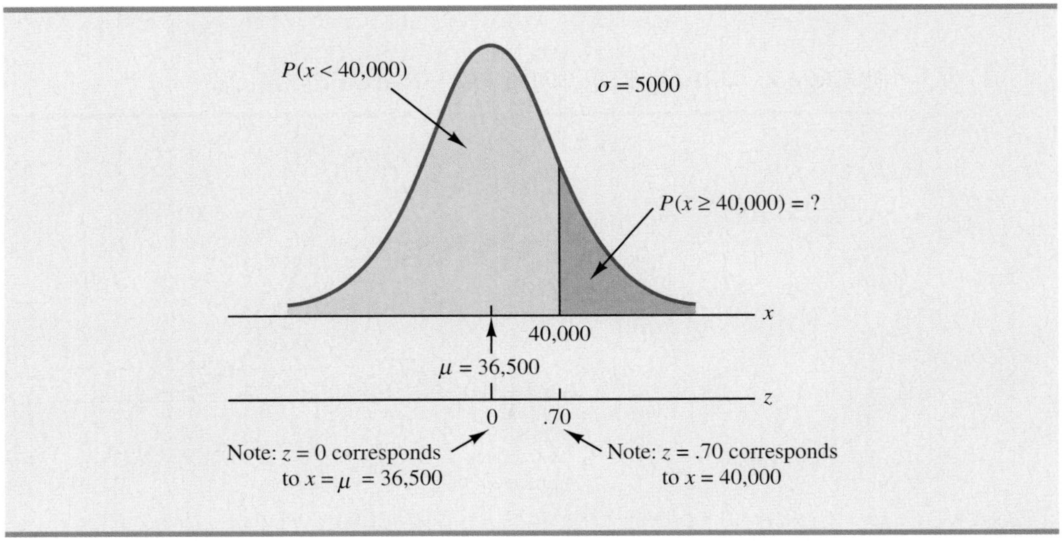

At $x = 40{,}000$, we have

$$z = \frac{x - \mu}{\sigma} = \frac{40{,}000 - 36{,}500}{5000} = \frac{3500}{5000} = .70$$

Refer now to the bottom of Figure 6.6. We see that a value of $x = 40{,}000$ on the Grear Tire normal distribution corresponds to a value of $z = .70$ on the standard normal distribution. Using the standard normal probability table, we see that the area under the standard normal curve to the left of $z = .70$ is .7580. Thus, $1.000 - .7580 = .2420$ is the probability that z will exceed .70 and hence x will exceed 40,000. We can conclude that about 24.2% of the tires will exceed 40,000 in mileage.

Let us now assume that Grear is considering a guarantee that will provide a discount on replacement tires if the original tires do not provide the guaranteed mileage. What should the guarantee mileage be if Grear wants no more than 10% of the tires to be eligible for the discount guarantee? This question is interpreted graphically in Figure 6.7.

According to Figure 6.7, the area under the curve to the left of the unknown guarantee mileage must be .10. So, we must first find the z-value that cuts off an area of .10 in the left tail of a standard normal distribution. Using the standard normal probability table, we see that $z = -1.28$ cuts off an area of .10 in the lower tail. Hence, $z = -1.28$ is the value of the standard normal random variable corresponding to the desired mileage guarantee on the Grear Tire normal distribution. To find the value of x corresponding to $z = -1.28$, we have

The guarantee mileage we need to find is 1.28 standard deviations below the mean. Thus, $x = \mu - 1.28\sigma$.

$$z = \frac{x - \mu}{\sigma} = -1.28$$
$$x - \mu = -1.28\sigma$$
$$x = \mu - 1.28\sigma$$

With $\mu = 36{,}500$ and $\sigma = 5000$,

$$x = 36{,}500 - 1.28(5000) = 30{,}100$$

With the guarantee set at 30,000 miles, the actual percentage eligible for the guarantee will be 9.68%.

Thus, a guarantee of 30,100 miles will meet the requirement that approximately 10% of the tires will be eligible for the guarantee. Perhaps, with this information, the firm will set its tire mileage guarantee at 30,000 miles.

FIGURE 6.7 GREAR'S DISCOUNT GUARANTEE

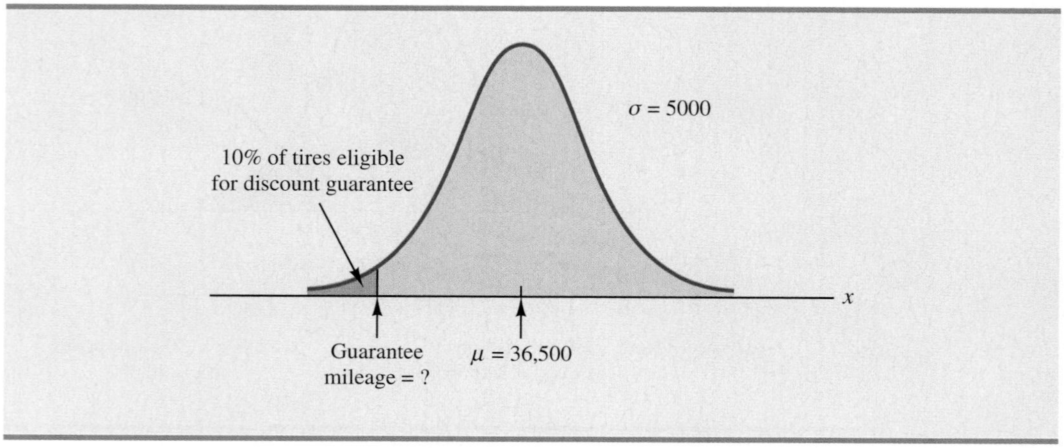

Again, we see the important role that probability distributions play in providing decision-making information. Namely, once a probability distribution is established for a particular application, it can be used to obtain probability information about the problem. Probability does not make a decision recommendation directly, but it provides information that helps the decision maker better understand the risks and uncertainties associated with the problem. Ultimately, this information may assist the decision maker in reaching a good decision.

EXERCISES

Methods

8. Using Figure 6.4 as a guide, sketch a normal curve for a random variable x that has a mean of $\mu = 100$ and a standard deviation of $\sigma = 10$. Label the horizontal axis with values of 70, 80, 90, 100, 110, 120, and 130.

9. A random variable is normally distributed with a mean of $\mu = 50$ and a standard deviation of $\sigma = 5$.
   a. Sketch a normal curve for the probability density function. Label the horizontal axis with values of 35, 40, 45, 50, 55, 60, and 65. Figure 6.4 shows that the normal curve almost touches the horizontal axis at three standard deviations below and at three standard deviations above the mean (in this case at 35 and 65).
   b. What is the probability the random variable will assume a value between 45 and 55?
   c. What is the probability the random variable will assume a value between 40 and 60?

10. Draw a graph for the standard normal distribution. Label the horizontal axis at values of $-3, -2, -1, 0, 1, 2$, and 3. Then use the table of probabilities for the standard normal distribution inside the front cover of the text to compute the following probabilities.
    a. $P(z \leq 1.5)$
    b. $P(z \leq 1)$
    c. $P(1 \leq z \leq 1.5)$
    d. $P(0 < z < 2.5)$

11. Given that z is a standard normal random variable, compute the following probabilities.
    a. $P(z \leq -1.0)$
    b. $P(z \geq -1)$
    c. $P(z \geq -1.5)$
    d. $P(-2.5 \leq z)$
    e. $P(-3 < z \leq 0)$

12. Given that z is a standard normal random variable, compute the following probabilities.
    a. $P(0 \leq z \leq .83)$
    b. $P(-1.57 \leq z \leq 0)$
    c. $P(z > .44)$
    d. $P(z \geq -.23)$
    e. $P(z < 1.20)$
    f. $P(z \leq -.71)$

SELF test

13. Given that z is a standard normal random variable, compute the following probabilities.
    a. $P(-1.98 \leq z \leq .49)$
    b. $P(.52 \leq z \leq 1.22)$
    c. $P(-1.75 \leq z \leq -1.04)$

14. Given that z is a standard normal random variable, find z for each situation.
    a. The area to the left of z is .9750.
    b. The area between 0 and z is .4750.
    c. The area to the left of z is .7291.
    d. The area to the right of z is .1314.
    e. The area to the left of z is .6700.
    f. The area to the right of z is .3300.

SELF test

15. Given that z is a standard normal random variable, find z for each situation.
   a. The area to the left of z is .2119.
   b. The area between $-z$ and z is .9030.
   c. The area between $-z$ and z is .2052.
   d. The area to the left of z is .9948.
   e. The area to the right of z is .6915.
16. Given that z is a standard normal random variable, find z for each situation.
   a. The area to the right of z is .01.
   b. The area to the right of z is .025.
   c. The area to the right of z is .05.
   d. The area to the right of z is .10.

Applications

17. For borrowers with good credit scores, the mean debt for revolving and installment accounts is $15,015 (*BusinessWeek,* March 20, 2006). Assume the standard deviation is $3540 and that debt amounts are normally distributed.
   a. What is the probability that the debt for a randomly selected borrower with good credit is more than $18,000?
   b. What is the probability that the debt for a randomly selected borrower with good credit is less than $10,000?
   c. What is the probability that the debt for a randomly selected borrower with good credit is between $12,000 and $18,000?
   d. What is the probability that the debt for a randomly selected borrower with good credit is no more than $14,000?

SELF test

18. The average stock price for companies making up the S&P 500 is $30, and the standard deviation is $8.20 (*BusinessWeek,* Special Annual Issue, Spring 2003). Assume the stock prices are normally distributed.
   a. What is the probability a company will have a stock price of at least $40?
   b. What is the probability a company will have a stock price no higher than $20?
   c. How high does a stock price have to be to put a company in the top 10%?
19. The average amount of precipitation in Dallas, Texas, during the month of April is 3.5 inches (*The World Almanac,* 2000). Assume that a normal distribution applies and that the standard deviation is .8 inches.
   a. What percentage of the time does the amount of rainfall in April exceed 5 inches?
   b. What percentage of the time is the amount of rainfall in April less than 3 inches?
   c. A month is classified as extremely wet if the amount of rainfall is in the upper 10% for that month. How much precipitation must fall in April for it to be classified as extremely wet?
20. In January 2003, the American worker spent an average of 77 hours logged on to the Internet while at work (CNBC, March 15, 2003). Assume the population mean is 77 hours, the times are normally distributed, and that the standard deviation is 20 hours.
   a. What is the probability that in January 2003 a randomly selected worker spent fewer than 50 hours logged on to the Internet?
   b. What percentage of workers spent more than 100 hours in January 2003 logged on to the Internet?
   c. A person is classified as a heavy user if he or she is in the upper 20% of usage. In January 2003, how many hours did a worker have to be logged on to the Internet to be considered a heavy user?
21. A person must score in the upper 2% of the population on an IQ test to qualify for membership in Mensa, the international high-IQ society (*U.S. Airways Attaché,* September 2000). If IQ scores are normally distributed with a mean of 100 and a standard deviation of 15, what score must a person have to qualify for Mensa?

22. The mean hourly pay rate for financial managers in the East North Central region is \$32.62, and the standard deviation is \$2.32 (Bureau of Labor Statistics, September 2005). Assume that pay rates are normally distributed.
    a. What is the probability a financial manager earns between \$30 and \$35 per hour?
    b. How high must the hourly rate be to put a financial manager in the top 10% with respect to pay?
    c. For a randomly selected financial manager, what is the probability the manager earned less than \$28 per hour?

23. The time needed to complete a final examination in a particular college course is normally distributed with a mean of 80 minutes and a standard deviation of 10 minutes. Answer the following questions.
    a. What is the probability of completing the exam in one hour or less?
    b. What is the probability that a student will complete the exam in more than 60 minutes but less than 75 minutes?
    c. Assume that the class has 60 students and that the examination period is 90 minutes in length. How many students do you expect will be unable to complete the exam in the allotted time?

CD file
Volume

24. Trading volume on the New York Stock Exchange is heaviest during the first half hour (early morning) and last half hour (late afternoon) of the trading day. The early morning trading volumes (millions of shares) for 13 days in January and February are shown here (*Barron's,* January 23, 2006; February 13, 2006; and February 27, 2006).

214	163	265	194	180
202	198	212	201	
174	171	211	211	

The probability distribution of trading volume is approximately normal.
    a. Compute the mean and standard deviation to use as estimates of the population mean and standard deviation.
    b. What is the probability that, on a randomly selected day, the early morning trading volume will be less than 180 million shares?
    c. What is the probability that, on a randomly selected day, the early morning trading volume will exceed 230 million shares?
    d. How many shares would have to be traded for the early morning trading volume on a particular day to be among the busiest 5% of days?

25. According to the Sleep Foundation, the average night's sleep is 6.8 hours (*Fortune,* March 20, 2006). Assume the standard deviation is .6 hours and that the probability distribution is normal.
    a. What is the probability that a randomly selected person sleeps more than 8 hours?
    b. What is the probability that a randomly selected person sleeps 6 hours or less?
    c. Doctors suggest getting between 7 and 9 hours of sleep each night. What percentage of the population gets this much sleep?

6.3 Normal Approximation of Binomial Probabilities

In Section 5.4 we presented the discrete binomial distribution. Recall that a binomial experiment consists of a sequence of n identical independent trials with each trial having two possible outcomes, a success or a failure. The probability of a success on a trial is the same for all trials and is denoted by p. The binomial random variable is the number of successes in the n trials, and probability questions pertain to the probability of x successes in the n trials.

FIGURE 6.8 NORMAL APPROXIMATION TO A BINOMIAL PROBABILITY DISTRIBUTION WITH $n = 100$ AND $p = .10$ SHOWING THE PROBABILITY OF 12 ERRORS

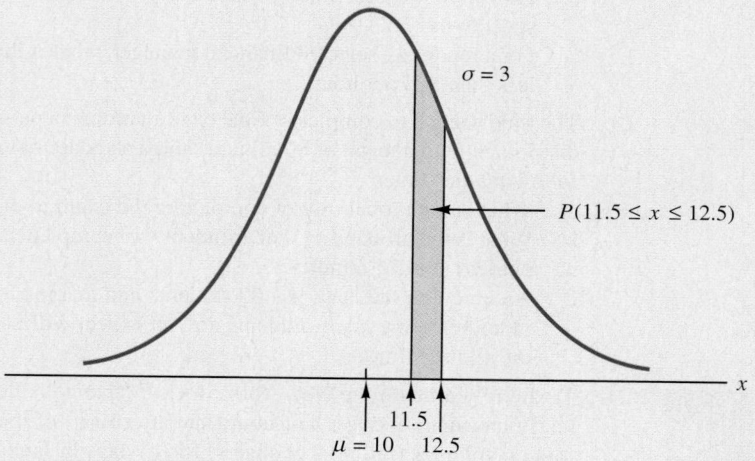

When the number of trials becomes large, evaluating the binomial probability function by hand or with a calculator is difficult. In cases where $np \geq 5$, and $n(1 - p) \geq 5$, the normal distribution provides an easy-to-use approximation of binomial probabilities. When using the normal approximation to the binomial, we set $\mu = np$ and $\sigma = \sqrt{np(1 - p)}$ in the definition of the normal curve.

Let us illustrate the normal approximation to the binomial by supposing that a particular company has a history of making errors in 10% of its invoices. A sample of 100 invoices has been taken, and we want to compute the probability that 12 invoices contain errors. That is, we want to find the binomial probability of 12 successes in 100 trials. In applying the normal approximation in this case, we set $\mu = np = (100)(.1) = 10$ and $\sigma = \sqrt{np(1 - p)} = \sqrt{(100)(.1)(.9)} = 3$. A normal distribution with $\mu = 10$ and $\sigma = 3$ is shown in Figure 6.8.

Recall that, with a continuous probability distribution, probabilities are computed as areas under the probability density function. As a result, the probability of any single value for the random variable is zero. Thus to approximate the binomial probability of 12 successes, we compute the area under the corresponding normal curve between 11.5 and 12.5. The .5 that we add and subtract from 12 is called a **continuity correction factor**. It is introduced because a continuous distribution is being used to approximate a discrete distribution. Thus, $P(x = 12)$ for the *discrete* binomial distribution is approximated by $P(11.5 \leq x \leq 12.5)$ for the *continuous* normal distribution.

Converting to the standard normal distribution to compute $P(11.5 \leq x \leq 12.5)$, we have

$$z = \frac{x - \mu}{\sigma} = \frac{12.5 - 10.0}{3} = .83 \quad \text{at } x = 12.5$$

and

$$z = \frac{x - \mu}{\sigma} = \frac{11.5 - 10.0}{3} = .50 \quad \text{at } x = 11.5$$

FIGURE 6.9 NORMAL APPROXIMATION TO A BINOMIAL PROBABILITY DISTRIBUTION WITH $n = 100$ AND $p = .10$ SHOWING THE PROBABILITY OF 13 OR FEWER ERRORS

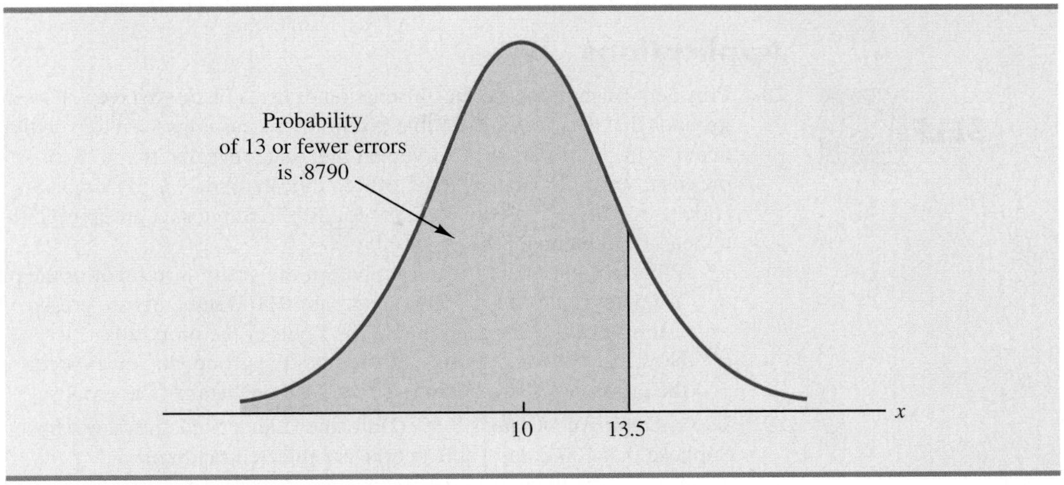

Using the standard normal probability table, we find that the area under the curve (in Figure 6.8) to the left of 12.5 is .7967. Similarly, the area under the curve to the left of 11.5 is .6915. Therefore, the area between 11.5 and 12.5 is .7967 − .6915 = .1052. The normal approximation to the probability of 12 successes in 100 trials is .1052.

For another illustration, suppose we want to compute the probability of 13 or fewer errors in the sample of 100 invoices. Figure 6.9 shows the area under the normal curve that approximates this probability. Note that the use of the continuity correction factor results in the value of 13.5 being used to compute the desired probability. The z value corresponding to $x = 13.5$ is

$$z = \frac{13.5 - 10.0}{3.0} = 1.17$$

The standard normal probability table shows that the area under the standard normal curve to the left of $z = 1.17$ is .8790. The area under the normal curve approximating the probability of 13 or fewer errors is given by the shaded portion of the graph in Figure 6.9.

Exercises

Methods

SELF test

26. A binomial probability distribution has $p = .20$ and $n = 100$.
    a. What are the mean and standard deviation?
    b. Is this situation one in which binomial probabilities can be approximated by the normal probability distribution? Explain.
    c. What is the probability of exactly 24 successes?
    d. What is the probability of 18 to 22 successes?
    e. What is the probability of 15 or fewer successes?
27. Assume a binomial probability distribution has $p = .60$ and $n = 200$.
    a. What are the mean and standard deviation?
    b. Is this situation one in which binomial probabilities can be approximated by the normal probability distribution? Explain.

c. What is the probability of 100 to 110 successes?
d. What is the probability of 130 or more successes?
e. What is the advantage of using the normal probability distribution to approximate the binomial probabilities? Use part (d) to explain the advantage.

Applications

SELF test

28. President Bush proposed the elimination of taxes on dividends paid to shareholders on the grounds that they result in double taxation. The earnings used to pay dividends are already taxed to the corporation. A survey on this issue revealed that 47% of Americans favor the proposal. By political party, 64% of Republicans and 29% of Democrats favor the proposal (*Investor's Business Daily,* January 13, 2003). Suppose a group of 250 Americans gather to hear a speech about the proposal.
    a. What is the probability at least half of the group is in favor of the proposal?
    b. You later find out 150 Republicans and 100 Democrats are present. Now what is your estimate of the expected number in favor of the proposal?
    c. Now that you know the composition of the group, do you expect a speaker in favor of the proposal will be better received than one against the proposal?
29. The unemployment rate is 5.8% (Bureau of Labor Statistics, www.bls.gov, April 3, 2003). Suppose that 100 employable people are selected randomly.
    a. What is the expected number who are unemployed?
    b. What are the variance and standard deviation of the number who are unemployed?
    c. What is the probability that exactly six are unemployed?
    d. What is the probability that at least four are unemployed?
30. When you sign up for a credit card, do you read the contract carefully? In a FindLaw.com survey, individuals were asked, "How closely do you read a contract for a credit card?" (*USA Today,* October 16, 2003). The findings were that 44% read every word, 33% read enough to understand the contract, 11% just glance at it, and 4% don't read it at all.
    a. For a sample of 500 people, how many would you expect to say that they read every word of a credit card contract?
    b. For a sample of 500 people, what is the probability that 200 or fewer will say they read every word of a credit card contract?
    c. For a sample of 500 people, what is the probability that at least 15 say they don't read credit card contracts?
31. A Myrtle Beach resort hotel has 120 rooms. In the spring months, hotel room occupancy is approximately 75%.
    a. What is the probability that at least half of the rooms are occupied on a given day?
    b. What is the probability that 100 or more rooms are occupied on a given day?
    c. What is the probability that 80 or fewer rooms are occupied on a given day?

6.4 Exponential Probability Distribution

The **exponential probability distribution** may be used for random variables such as the time between arrivals at a car wash, the time required to load a truck, the distance between major defects in a highway, and so on. The exponential probability density function follows.

EXPONENTIAL PROBABILITY DENSITY FUNCTION

$$f(x) = \frac{1}{\mu} e^{-x/\mu} \qquad \text{for } x \geq 0, \mu > 0 \tag{6.4}$$

where μ = expected value or mean

FIGURE 6.10 EXPONENTIAL DISTRIBUTION FOR THE SCHIPS LOADING DOCK EXAMPLE

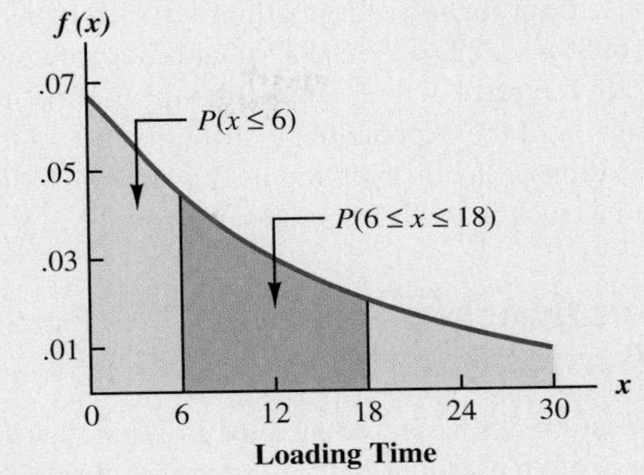

As an example of the exponential distribution, suppose that x represents the loading time for a truck at the Schips loading dock and follows such a distribution. If the mean, or average, loading time is 15 minutes ($\mu = 15$), the appropriate probability density function for x is

$$f(x) = \frac{1}{15} e^{-x/15}$$

Figure 6.10 is the graph of this probability density function.

Computing Probabilities for the Exponential Distribution

In waiting line applications, the exponential distribution is often used for service time.

As with any continuous probability distribution, the area under the curve corresponding to an interval provides the probability that the random variable assumes a value in that interval. In the Schips loading dock example, the probability that loading a truck will take 6 minutes or less $P(x \leq 6)$ is defined to be the area under the curve in Figure 6.10 from $x = 0$ to $x = 6$. Similarly, the probability that the loading time will be 18 minutes or less $P(x \leq 18)$ is the area under the curve from $x = 0$ to $x = 18$. Note also that the probability that the loading time will be between 6 minutes and 18 minutes $P(6 \leq x \leq 18)$ is given by the area under the curve from $x = 6$ to $x = 18$.

To compute exponential probabilities such as those just described, we use the following formula. It provides the cumulative probability of obtaining a value for the exponential random variable of less than or equal to some specific value denoted by x_0.

EXPONENTIAL DISTRIBUTION: CUMULATIVE PROBABILITIES

$$P(x \leq x_0) = 1 - e^{-x_0/\mu} \qquad \textbf{(6.5)}$$

For the Schips loading dock example, x = loading time in minutes and μ = 15 minutes. Using equation (6.5)

$$P(x \leq x_0) = 1 - e^{-x_0/15}$$

Hence, the probability that loading a truck will take 6 minutes or less is

$$P(x \leq 6) = 1 - e^{-6/15} = .3297$$

Using equation (6.5), we calculate the probability of loading a truck in 18 minutes or less.

$$P(x \leq 18) = 1 - e^{-18/15} = .6988$$

Thus, the probability that loading a truck will take between 6 minutes and 18 minutes is equal to $.6988 - .3297 = .3691$. Probabilities for any other interval can be computed similarly.

A property of the exponential distribution is that the mean and standard deviation are equal.

In the preceding example, the mean time it takes to load a truck is $\mu = 15$ minutes. A property of the exponential distribution is that the mean of the distribution and the standard deviation of the distribution are *equal.* Thus, the standard deviation for the time it takes to load a truck is $\sigma = 15$ minutes. The variance is $\sigma^2 = (15)^2 = 225$.

Relationship Between the Poisson and Exponential Distributions

In Section 5.5 we introduced the Poisson distribution as a discrete probability distribution that is often useful in examining the number of occurrences of an event over a specified interval of time or space. Recall that the Poisson probability function is

$$f(x) = \frac{\mu^x e^{-\mu}}{x!}$$

where

μ = expected value or mean number of occurrences over a specified interval

If arrivals follow a Poisson distribution, the time between arrivals must follow an exponential distribution.

The continuous exponential probability distribution is related to the discrete Poisson distribution. If the Poisson distribution provides an appropriate description of the number of occurrences per interval, the exponential distribution provides a description of the length of the interval between occurrences.

To illustrate this relationship, suppose the number of cars that arrive at a car wash during one hour is described by a Poisson probability distribution with a mean of 10 cars per hour. The Poisson probability function that gives the probability of x arrivals per hour is

$$f(x) = \frac{10^x e^{-10}}{x!}$$

Because the average number of arrivals is 10 cars per hour, the average time between cars arriving is

$$\frac{1 \text{ hour}}{10 \text{ cars}} = .1 \text{ hour/car}$$

Thus, the corresponding exponential distribution that describes the time between the arrivals has a mean of $\mu = .1$ hour per car; as a result, the appropriate exponential probability density function is

$$f(x) = \frac{1}{.1} e^{-x/.1} = 10e^{-10x}$$

NOTES AND COMMENTS

As we can see in Figure 6.10, the exponential distribution is skewed to the right. Indeed, the skewness measure for exponential distributions is 2. The exponential distribution gives us a good idea what a skewed distribution looks like.

Exercises

Methods

32. Consider the following exponential probability density function.

$$f(x) = \frac{1}{8} e^{-x/8} \qquad \text{for } x \geq 0$$

a. Find $P(x \leq 6)$.
b. Find $P(x \leq 4)$.
c. Find $P(x \geq 6)$.
d. Find $P(4 \leq x \leq 6)$.

SELF test

33. Consider the following exponential probability density function.

$$f(x) = \frac{1}{3} e^{-x/3} \qquad \text{for } x \geq 0$$

a. Write the formula for $P(x \leq x_0)$.
b. Find $P(x \leq 2)$.
c. Find $P(x \geq 3)$.
d. Find $P(x \leq 5)$.
e. Find $P(2 \leq x \leq 5)$.

Applications

34. The time required to pass through security screening at the airport can be annoying to travelers. The mean wait time during peak periods at Cincinnati/Northern Kentucky International Airport is 12.1 minutes (*The Cincinnati Enquirer,* February 2, 2006). Assume the time to pass through security screening follows an exponential distribution.
a. What is the probability it will take less than 10 minutes to pass through security screening during a peak period?
b. What is the probability it will take more than 20 minutes to pass through security screening during a peak period?
c. What is the probability it will take between 10 and 20 minutes to pass through security screening during a peak period?
d. It is 8:00 A.M. (a peak period) and you just entered the security line. To catch your plane you must be at the gate within 30 minutes. If it takes 12 minutes from the time you clear security until you reach your gate, what is the probability you will miss your flight?

SELF test

35. The time between arrivals of vehicles at a particular intersection follows an exponential probability distribution with a mean of 12 seconds.
a. Sketch this exponential probability distribution.
b. What is the probability that the arrival time between vehicles is 12 seconds or less?

c. What is the probability that the arrival time between vehicles is 6 seconds or less?
d. What is the probability of 30 or more seconds between vehicle arrivals?

36. The lifetime (hours) of an electronic device is a random variable with the following exponential probability density function.

$$f(x) = \frac{1}{50} e^{-x/50} \qquad \text{for } x \geq 0$$

a. What is the mean lifetime of the device?
b. What is the probability that the device will fail in the first 25 hours of operation?
c. What is the probability that the device will operate 100 or more hours before failure?

37. Sparagowski & Associates conducted a study of service times at the drive-up window of fast-food restaurants. The average service time at McDonald's restaurants was 2.78 minutes (*The Cincinnati Enquirer,* July 9, 2000). Service times such as these frequently follow an exponential distribution.
a. What is the probability that a customer's service time is less than 2 minutes?
b. What is the probability that a customer's service time is more than 5 minutes?
c. What is the probability that a customer's service time is more than 2.78 minutes?

38. Do interruptions while you are working reduce your productivity? According to a University of California–Irvine study, businesspeople are interrupted at the rate of approximately 5½ times per hour (*Fortune,* March 20, 2006). Suppose the number of interruptions follows a Poisson probability distribution.
a. Show the probability distribution for the time between interruptions.
b. What is the probability a businessperson will have no interruptions during a 15-minute period?
c. What is the probability that the next interruption will occur within 10 minutes for a particular businessperson?

Summary

This chapter extended the discussion of probability distributions to the case of continuous random variables. The major conceptual difference between discrete and continuous probability distributions involves the method of computing probabilities. With discrete distributions, the probability function $f(x)$ provides the probability that the random variable x assumes various values. With continuous distributions, the probability density function $f(x)$ does not provide probability values directly. Instead, probabilities are given by areas under the curve or graph of the probability density function $f(x)$. Because the area under the curve above a single point is zero, we observe that the probability of any particular value is zero for a continuous random variable.

Three continuous probability distributions—the uniform, normal, and exponential distributions—were treated in detail. The normal distribution is used widely in statistical inference and will be used extensively throughout the remainder of the text.

Glossary

Probability density function A function used to compute probabilities for a continuous random variable. The area under the graph of a probability density function over an interval represents probability.

Uniform probability distribution A continuous probability distribution for which the probability that the random variable will assume a value in any interval is the same for each interval of equal length.

Normal probability distribution A continuous probability distribution. Its probability density function is bell-shaped and determined by its mean μ and standard deviation σ.

Standard normal probability distribution A normal distribution with a mean of zero and a standard deviation of one.

Continuity correction factor A value of .5 that is added to or subtracted from a value of x when the continuous normal distribution is used to approximate the discrete binomial distribution.

Exponential probability distribution A continuous probability distribution that is useful in computing probabilities for the time it takes to complete a task.

Key Formulas

Uniform Probability Density Function

$$f(x) = \begin{cases} \dfrac{1}{b - a} & \text{for } a \leq x \leq b \\ 0 & \text{elsewhere} \end{cases} \tag{6.1}$$

Normal Probability Density Function

$$f(x) = \frac{1}{\sigma\sqrt{2\pi}} e^{-(x-\mu)^2/2\sigma^2} \tag{6.2}$$

Converting to the Standard Normal Random Variable

$$z = \frac{x - \mu}{\sigma} \tag{6.3}$$

Exponential Probability Density Function

$$f(x) = \frac{1}{\mu} e^{-x/\mu} \quad \text{for } x \geq 0, \mu > 0 \tag{6.4}$$

Exponential Distribution: Cumulative Probabilities

$$P(x \leq x_0) = 1 - e^{-x_0/\mu} \tag{6.5}$$

Supplementary Exercises

39. A business executive, transferred from Chicago to Atlanta, needs to sell her house in Chicago quickly. The executive's employer has offered to buy the house for $210,000, but the offer expires at the end of the week. The executive does not currently have a better offer, but can afford to leave the house on the market for another month. From conversations with her realtor, the executive believes the price she will get by leaving the house on the market for another month is uniformly distributed between $200,000 and $225,000.
    a. If she leaves the house on the market for another month, what is the mathematical expression for the probability density function of the sales price?
    b. If she leaves it on the market for another month, what is the probability she will get at least $215,000 for the house?
    c. If she leaves it on the market for another month, what is the probability she will get less than $210,000?
    d. Should the executive leave the house on the market for another month? Why or why not?

40. The U.S. Bureau of Labor Statistics reports that the average annual expenditure on food and drink for all families is \$5700 (*Money,* December 2003). Assume that annual expenditure on food and drink is normally distributed and that the standard deviation is \$1500.
    a. What is the range of expenditures of the 10% of families with the lowest annual spending on food and drink?
    b. What percentage of families spend more than \$7000 annually on food and drink?
    c. What is the range of expenditures for the 5% of families with the highest annual spending on food and drink?

41. Motorola used the normal distribution to determine the probability of defects and the number of defects expected in a production process. Assume a production process produces items with a mean weight of 10 ounces. Calculate the probability of a defect and the expected number of defects for a 1000-unit production run in the following situations.
    a. The process standard deviation is .15, and the process control is set at plus or minus one standard deviation. Units with weights less than 9.85 or greater than 10.15 ounces will be classified as defects.
    b. Through process design improvements, the process standard deviation can be reduced to .05. Assume the process control remains the same, with weights less than 9.85 or greater than 10.15 ounces being classified as defects.
    c. What is the advantage of reducing process variation, thereby causing process control limits to be at a greater number of standard deviations from the mean?

42. The average annual amount American households spend for daily transportation is \$6312 (*Money,* August 2001). Assume that the amount spent is normally distributed.
    a. Suppose you learn that 5% of American households spend less than \$1000 for daily transportation. What is the standard deviation of the amount spent?
    b. What is the probability that a household spends between \$4000 and \$6000?
    c. What is the range of spending for the 3% of households with the highest daily transportation cost?

43. *Condé Nast Traveler* publishes a Gold List of the top hotels all over the world. The Broadmoor Hotel in Colorado Springs contains 700 rooms and is on the 2004 Gold List (*Condé Nast Traveler,* January 2004). Suppose Broadmoor's marketing group forecasts a mean demand of 670 rooms for the coming weekend. Assume that demand for the upcoming weekend is normally distributed with a standard deviation of 30.
    a. What is the probability all the hotel's rooms will be rented?
    b. What is the probability 50 or more rooms will not be rented?
    c. Would you recommend the hotel consider offering a promotion to increase demand? What considerations would be important?

44. Ward Doering Auto Sales is considering offering a special service contract that will cover the total cost of any service work required on leased vehicles. From experience, the company manager estimates that yearly service costs are approximately normally distributed, with a mean of \$150 and a standard deviation of \$25.
    a. If the company offers the service contract to customers for a yearly charge of \$200, what is the probability that any one customer's service costs will exceed the contract price of \$200?
    b. What is Ward's expected profit per service contract?

45. Is lack of sleep causing traffic fatalities? A study conducted under the auspices of the National Highway Traffic Safety Administration found that the average number of fatal crashes caused by drowsy drivers each year was 1550 (*BusinessWeek,* January 26, 2004). Assume the annual number of fatal crashes per year is normally distributed with a standard deviation of 300.
    a. What is the probability of fewer than 1000 fatal crashes in a year?
    b. What is the probability the number of fatal crashes will be between 1000 and 2000 for a year?
    c. For a year to be in the upper 5% with respect to the number of fatal crashes, how many fatal crashes would have to occur?

46. Assume that the test scores from a college admissions test are normally distributed, with a mean of 450 and a standard deviation of 100.
    a. What percentage of the people taking the test score between 400 and 500?
    b. Suppose someone receives a score of 630. What percentage of the people taking the test score better? What percentage score worse?
    c. If a particular university will not admit anyone scoring below 480, what percentage of the persons taking the test would be acceptable to the university?

47. According to *Advertising Age,* the average base salary for women working as copywriters in advertising firms is higher than the average base salary for men. The average base salary for women is \$67,000 and the average base salary for men is \$65,500 (*Working Woman,* July/August 2000). Assume salaries are normally distributed and that the standard deviation is \$7000 for both men and women.
    a. What is the probability of a woman receiving a salary in excess of \$75,000?
    b. What is the probability of a man receiving a salary in excess of \$75,000?
    c. What is the probability of a woman receiving a salary below \$50,000?
    d. How much would a woman have to make to have a higher salary than 99% of her male counterparts?

48. A machine fills containers with a particular product. The standard deviation of filling weights is known from past data to be .6 ounce. If only 2% of the containers hold less than 18 ounces, what is the mean filling weight for the machine? That is, what must μ equal? Assume the filling weights have a normal distribution.

49. Consider a multiple-choice examination with 50 questions. Each question has four possible answers. Assume that a student who has done the homework and attended lectures has a 75% probability of answering any question correctly.
    a. A student must answer 43 or more questions correctly to obtain a grade of A. What percentage of the students who have done their homework and attended lectures will obtain a grade of A on this multiple-choice examination?
    b. A student who answers 35 to 39 questions correctly will receive a grade of C. What percentage of students who have done their homework and attended lectures will obtain a grade of C on this multiple-choice examination?
    c. A student must answer 30 or more questions correctly to pass the examination. What percentage of the students who have done their homework and attended lectures will pass the examination?
    d. Assume that a student has not attended class and has not done the homework for the course. Furthermore, assume that the student will simply guess at the answer to each question. What is the probability that this student will answer 30 or more questions correctly and pass the examination?

50. A blackjack player at a Las Vegas casino learned that the house will provide a free room if play is for four hours at an average bet of \$50. The player's strategy provides a probability of .49 of winning on any one hand, and the player knows that there are 60 hands per hour. Suppose the player plays for four hours at a bet of \$50 per hand.
    a. What is the player's expected payoff?
    b. What is the probability the player loses \$1000 or more?
    c. What is the probability the player wins?
    d. Suppose the player starts with \$1500. What is the probability of going broke?

51. The time in minutes for which a student uses a computer terminal at the computer center of a major university follows an exponential probability distribution with a mean of 36 minutes. Assume a student arrives at the terminal just as another student is beginning to work on the terminal.
    a. What is the probability that the wait for the second student will be 15 minutes or less?
    b. What is the probability that the wait for the second student will be between 15 and 45 minutes?
    c. What is the probability that the second student will have to wait an hour or more?

52. The Web site for the Bed and Breakfast Inns of North America (www.cimarron.net) gets approximately seven visitors per minute (*Time,* September 2001). Suppose the number of Web site visitors per minute follows a Poisson probability distribution.
    a. What is the mean time between visits to the Web site?
    b. Show the exponential probability density function for the time between Web site visits.
    c. What is the probability no one will access the Web site in a 1-minute period?
    d. What is the probability no one will access the Web site in a 12-second period?

53. The average travel time to work for New York City residents is 36.5 minutes (*Time Almanac,* 2001).
    a. Assume the exponential probability distribution is applicable and show the probability density function for the travel time to work for a typical New Yorker.
    b. What is the probability it will take a typical New Yorker between 20 and 40 minutes to travel to work?
    c. What is the probability it will take a typical New Yorker more than 40 minutes to travel to work?

54. The time (in minutes) between telephone calls at an insurance claims office has the following exponential probability distribution.

$$f(x) = .50e^{-.50x} \qquad \text{for } x \geq 0$$

    a. What is the mean time between telephone calls?
    b. What is the probability of having 30 seconds or less between telephone calls?
    c. What is the probability of having 1 minute or less between telephone calls?
    d. What is the probability of having 5 or more minutes without a telephone call?

Case Problem Specialty Toys

Specialty Toys, Inc., sells a variety of new and innovative children's toys. Management learned that the preholiday season is the best time to introduce a new toy, because many families use this time to look for new ideas for December holiday gifts. When Specialty discovers a new toy with good market potential, it chooses an October market entry date.

In order to get toys in its stores by October, Specialty places one-time orders with its manufacturers in June or July of each year. Demand for children's toys can be highly volatile. If a new toy catches on, a sense of shortage in the marketplace often increases the demand to high levels and large profits can be realized. However, new toys can also flop, leaving Specialty stuck with high levels of inventory that must be sold at reduced prices. The most important question the company faces is deciding how many units of a new toy should be purchased to meet anticipated sales demand. If too few are purchased, sales will be lost; if too many are purchased, profits will be reduced because of low prices realized in clearance sales.

For the coming season, Specialty plans to introduce a new product called Weather Teddy. This variation of a talking teddy bear is made by a company in Taiwan. When a child presses Teddy's hand, the bear begins to talk. A built-in barometer selects one of five responses that predict the weather conditions. The responses range from "It looks to be a very nice day! Have fun" to "I think it may rain today. Don't forget your umbrella." Tests with the product show that, even though it is not a perfect weather predictor, its predictions are surprisingly good. Several of Specialty's managers claimed Teddy gave predictions of the weather that were as good as many local television weather forecasters.

As with other products, Specialty faces the decision of how many Weather Teddy units to order for the coming holiday season. Members of the management team suggested order quantities of 15,000, 18,000, 24,000, or 28,000 units. The wide range of order quantities suggested indicates considerable disagreement concerning the market potential. The product management team asks you for an analysis of the stock-out probabilities for various order quantities, an estimate of the profit potential, and to help make an order quantity recommendation. Specialty expects to sell Weather Teddy for $24 based on a cost of

\$16 per unit. If inventory remains after the holiday season, Specialty will sell all surplus inventory for \$5 per unit. After reviewing the sales history of similar products, Specialty's senior sales forecaster predicted an expected demand of 20,000 units with a .95 probability that demand would be between 10,000 units and 30,000 units.

Managerial Report

Prepare a managerial report that addresses the following issues and recommends an order quantity for the Weather Teddy product.

1. Use the sales forecaster's prediction to describe a normal probability distribution that can be used to approximate the demand distribution. Sketch the distribution and show its mean and standard deviation.
2. Compute the probability of a stock-out for the order quantities suggested by members of the management team.
3. Compute the projected profit for the order quantities suggested by the management team under three scenarios: worst case in which sales = 10,000 units, most likely case in which sales = 20,000 units, and best case in which sales = 30,000 units.
4. One of Specialty's managers felt that the profit potential was so great that the order quantity should have a 70% chance of meeting demand and only a 30% chance of any stock-outs. What quantity would be ordered under this policy, and what is the projected profit under the three sales scenarios?
5. Provide your own recommendation for an order quantity and note the associated profit projections. Provide a rationale for your recommendation.

Appendix 6.1 Continuous Probability Distributions with Minitab

Let us demonstrate the Minitab procedure for computing continuous probabilities by referring to the Grear Tire Company problem where tire mileage was described by a normal distribution with $\mu = 36{,}500$ and $\sigma = 5000$. One question asked was: What is the probability that the tire mileage will exceed 40,000 miles?

For continuous probability distributions, Minitab gives a cumulative probability; that is, Minitab gives the probability that the random variable will assume a value less than or equal to a specified constant. For the Grear tire mileage question, Minitab can be used to determine the cumulative probability that the tire mileage will be less than or equal to 40,000 miles. (The specified constant in this case is 40,000.) After obtaining the cumulative probability from Minitab, we must subtract it from 1 to determine the probability that the tire mileage will exceed 40,000 miles.

Prior to using Minitab to compute a probability, one must enter the specified constant into a column of the worksheet. For the Grear tire mileage question we entered the specified constant of 40,000 into column C1 of the Minitab worksheet. The steps in using Minitab to compute the cumulative probability of the normal random variable assuming a value less than or equal to 40,000 follow.

Step 1. Select the **Calc** menu
Step 2. Choose **Probability Distributions**
Step 3. Choose **Normal**
Step 4. When the Normal Distribution dialog box appears:
Select **Cumulative probability**
Enter 36500 in the **Mean** box
Enter 5000 in the **Standard deviation** box
Enter C1 in the **Input column** box (the column containing 40,000)
Click **OK**

After the user clicks **OK,** Minitab prints the cumulative probability that the normal random variable assumes a value less than or equal to 40,000. Minitab shows that this probability is .7580. Because we are interested in the probability that the tire mileage will be greater than 40,000, the desired probability is 1 − .7580 = .2420.

A second question in the Grear Tire Company problem was: What mileage guarantee should Grear set to ensure that no more than 10% of the tires qualify for the guarantee? Here we are given a probability and want to find the corresponding value for the random variable. Minitab uses an inverse calculation routine to find the value of the random variable associated with a given cumulative probability. First, we must enter the cumulative probability into a column of the Minitab worksheet (say, C1). In this case, the desired cumulative probability is .10. Then, the first three steps of the Minitab procedure are as already listed. In step 4, we select **Inverse cumulative probability** instead of **Cumulative probability** and complete the remaining parts of the step. Minitab then displays the mileage guarantee of 30,092 miles.

Minitab is capable of computing probabilities for other continuous probability distributions, including the exponential probability distribution. To compute exponential probabilities, follow the procedure shown previously for the normal probability distribution and choose the **Exponential** option in step 3. Step 4 is as shown, with the exception that entering the standard deviation is not required. Output for cumulative probabilities and inverse cumulative probabilities is identical to that described for the normal probability distribution.

Appendix 6.2 Continuous Probability Distributions with Excel

Excel provides the capability for computing probabilities for several continuous probability distributions, including the normal and exponential probability distributions. In this appendix, we describe how Excel can be used to compute probabilities for any normal distribution. The procedures for the exponential and other continuous distributions are similar to the one we describe for the normal distribution.

Let us return to the Grear Tire Company problem where the tire mileage was described by a normal distribution with $\mu = 36{,}500$ and $\sigma = 5000$. Assume we are interested in the probability that tire mileage will exceed 40,000 miles.

Excel's NORMDIST function provides cumulative probabilities for a normal distribution. The general form of the function is NORMDIST (x, μ, σ, cumulative). For the fourth argument, TRUE is specified if a cumulative probability is desired. Thus, to compute the cumulative probability that the tire mileage will be less than or equal to 40,000 miles we would enter the following formula into any cell of an Excel worksheet:

=NORMDIST(40000,36500,5000,TRUE)

At this point, .7580 will appear in the cell where the formula was entered, indicating that the probability of tire mileage being less than or equal to 40,000 miles is .7580. Therefore, the probability that tire mileage will exceed 40,000 miles is 1 − .7580 = .2420.

Excel's NORMINV function uses an inverse computation to find the x value corresponding to a given cumulative probability. For instance, suppose we want to find the guaranteed mileage Grear should offer so that no more than 10% of the tires will be eligible for the guarantee. We would enter the following formula into any cell of an Excel worksheet:

=NORMINV(.1,36500,5000)

At this point, 30092 will appear in the cell where the formula was entered, indicating that the probability of a tire lasting 30,092 miles or less is .10.

The Excel function for computing exponential probabilities is EXPONDIST. Using it is straightforward. But if one needs help specifying the proper values for the arguments, Excel's Insert Function tool can be used (see Appendix E).

CHAPTER 7

Sampling and Sampling Distributions

CONTENTS

STATISTICS *in* PRACTICE

MEADWESTVACO CORPORATION*
STAMFORD, CONNECTICUT

MeadWestvaco Corporation, a leading producer of packaging, coated and specialty papers, consumer and office products, and specialty chemicals, employs more than 30,000 people. It operates worldwide in 29 countries and serves customers located in approximately 100 countries. MeadWestvaco holds a leading position in paper production, with an annual capacity of 1.8 million tons. The company's products include textbook paper, glossy magazine paper, beverage packaging systems, and office products. MeadWestvaco's internal consulting group uses sampling to provide a variety of information that enables the company to obtain significant productivity benefits and remain competitive.

For example, MeadWestvaco maintains large woodland holdings, which supply the trees, or raw material, for many of the company's products. Managers need reliable and accurate information about the timberlands and forests to evaluate the company's ability to meet its future raw material needs. What is the present volume in the forests? What is the past growth of the forests? What is the projected future growth of the forests? With answers to these important questions MeadWestvaco's managers can develop plans for the future, including long-term planting and harvesting schedules for the trees.

How does MeadWestvaco obtain the information it needs about its vast forest holdings? Data collected from sample plots throughout the forests are the basis for learning about the population of trees owned by the company. To identify the sample plots, the timberland holdings are first divided into three sections based on location and types of trees. Using maps and random numbers, MeadWestvaco analysts identify random samples of 1/5- to 1/7-acre plots in each section of the forest.

Random sampling of its forest holdings enables MeadWestvaco Corporation to meet future raw material needs. © Walter Hodges/Corbis.

MeadWestvaco foresters collect data from these sample plots to learn about the forest population.

Foresters throughout the organization participate in the field data collection process. Periodically, two-person teams gather information on each tree in every sample plot. The sample data are entered into the company's continuous forest inventory (CFI) computer system. Reports from the CFI system include a number of frequency distribution summaries containing statistics on types of trees, present forest volume, past forest growth rates, and projected future forest growth and volume. Sampling and the associated statistical summaries of the sample data provide the reports essential for the effective management of MeadWestvaco's forests and timberlands.

In this chapter you will learn about simple random sampling and the sample selection process. In addition, you will learn how statistics such as the sample mean and sample proportion are used to estimate the population mean and population proportion. The important concept of a sampling distribution is also introduced.

*The authors are indebted to Dr. Edward P. Winkofsky for providing this Statistics in Practice.

In Chapter 1, we defined a *population* and a *sample*. The definitions are restated here.

1. A *population* is the set of all the elements of interest in a study.
2. A *sample* is a subset of the population.

Numerical characteristics of a population, such as the mean and standard deviation, are called **parameters**. A primary purpose of statistical inference is to develop estimates and test hypotheses about population parameters using information contained in a sample.

Let us begin by citing two situations in which samples provide estimates of population parameters.

1. A tire manufacturer developed a new tire designed to provide an increase in mileage over the firm's current line of tires. To estimate the mean number of miles provided by the new tires, the manufacturer selected a sample of 120 new tires for testing. The test results provided a sample mean of 36,500 miles. Hence, an estimate of the mean tire mileage for the population of new tires was 36,500 miles.
2. Members of a political party were considering supporting a particular candidate for election to the U.S. Senate, and party leaders wanted an estimate of the proportion of registered voters favoring the candidate. The time and cost associated with contacting every individual in the population of registered voters were prohibitive. Hence, a sample of 400 registered voters was selected and 160 of the 400 voters indicated a preference for the candidate. An estimate of the proportion of the population of registered voters favoring the candidate was 160/400 = .40.

These two examples illustrate some of the reasons why samples are used. Note that in the tire mileage example, collecting the data on tire life involves wearing out each tire tested. Clearly it is not feasible to test every tire in the population; a sample is the only realistic way to obtain the desired tire mileage data. In the example involving the election, contacting every registered voter in the population is theoretically possible, but the time and cost in doing so are prohibitive; thus, a sample of registered voters is preferred.

A sample mean provides an estimate of a population mean, and a sample proportion provides an estimate of a population proportion. With estimates such as these, some estimation error can be expected. This chapter provides the basis for determining how large that error might be.

It is important to realize that sample results provide only *estimates* of the values of the population characteristics. We do not expect the sample mean of 36,500 miles to exactly equal the mean mileage for all tires in the population, nor do we expect exactly .40, or 40%, of the population of registered voters to favor the candidate. The reason is simply that the sample contains only a portion of the population. With proper sampling methods, the sample results will provide "good" estimates of the population parameters. But how good can we expect the sample results to be? Fortunately, statistical procedures are available for answering this question.

In this chapter we show how simple random sampling can be used to select a sample from a population. We then show how data obtained from a simple random sample can be used to compute estimates of a population mean, a population standard deviation, and a population proportion. In addition, we introduce the important concept of a sampling distribution. As we show, knowledge of the appropriate sampling distribution is what enables us to make statements about how close the sample estimates are to the corresponding population parameters. The last section discusses some alternatives to simple random sampling that are often employed in practice.

7.1 The Electronics Associates Sampling Problem

The director of personnel for Electronics Associates, Inc. (EAI), has been assigned the task of developing a profile of the company's 2500 managers. The characteristics to be identified include the mean annual salary for the managers and the proportion of managers having completed the company's management training program.

CD file EAI

Using the 2500 managers as the population for this study, we can find the annual salary and the training program status for each individual by referring to the firm's personnel records. The data file containing this information for all 2500 managers in the population is on the CD that accompanies the text.

Using the EAI data and the formulas presented in Chapter 3, we compute the population mean and the population standard deviation for the annual salary data.

$$\text{Population mean: } \mu = \$51{,}800$$
$$\text{Population standard deviation: } \sigma = \$4000$$

The data for the training program status show that 1500 of the 2500 managers completed the training program. Letting p denote the proportion of the population that completed the training program, we see that $p = 1500/2500 = .60$. The population mean annual salary ($\mu = \$51,800$), the population standard deviation of annual salary ($\sigma = \$4000$), and the population proportion that completed the training program ($p = .60$) are parameters of the population of EAI managers.

Often the cost of collecting information from a sample is substantially less than from a population, especially when personal interviews must be conducted to collect the information.

Now, suppose that the necessary information on all the EAI managers was not readily available in the company's database. The question we now consider is how the firm's director of personnel can obtain estimates of the population parameters by using a sample of managers rather than all 2500 managers in the population. Suppose that a sample of 30 managers will be used. Clearly, the time and the cost of developing a profile would be substantially less for 30 managers than for the entire population. If the personnel director could be assured that a sample of 30 managers would provide adequate information about the population of 2500 managers, working with a sample would be preferable to working with the entire population. Let us explore the possibility of using a sample for the EAI study by first considering how we can identify a sample of 30 managers.

7.2 Simple Random Sampling

Several methods can be used to select a sample from a population; one of the most common is **simple random sampling**. The definition of a simple random sample and the process of selecting a simple random sample depend on whether the population is *finite* or *infinite*. Because the EAI sampling problem involves a finite population of 2500 managers, we first consider sampling from a finite population.

Sampling from a Finite Population

A simple random sample of size n from a finite population of size N is defined as follows.

SIMPLE RANDOM SAMPLE (FINITE POPULATION)

A simple random sample of size n from a finite population of size N is a sample selected such that each possible sample of size n has the same probability of being selected.

One procedure for selecting a simple random sample from a finite population is to choose the elements for the sample one at a time in such a way that, at each step, each of the elements remaining in the population has the same probability of being selected. Sampling n elements in this way will satisfy the definition of a simple random sample from a finite population.

Computer-generated random numbers can also be used to implement the random sample selection process. Excel provides a function for generating random numbers in its worksheets.

The random numbers in the table are shown in groups of five for readability.

To select a simple random sample from the finite population of EAI managers, we first assign each manager a number. For example, we can assign the managers the numbers 1 to 2500 in the order that their names appear in the EAI personnel file. Next, we refer to the table of random numbers shown in Table 7.1. Using the first row of the table, each digit, 6, 3, 2, . . . , is a random digit having an equal chance of occurring. Because the largest number in the population list of EAI managers, 2500, has four digits, we will select random numbers from the table in sets or groups of four digits. Even though we may start the selection of random numbers anywhere in the table and move systematically in a direction of our choice, we will use the first row of Table 7.1 and move from left to right. The first 7 four-digit random numbers are

6327 1599 8671 7445 1102 1514 1807

Because the numbers in the table are random, these four-digit numbers are equally likely.

TABLE 7.1 RANDOM NUMBERS

63271	59986	71744	51102	15141	80714	58683	93108	13554	79945
88547	09896	95436	79115	08303	01041	20030	63754	08459	28364
55957	57243	83865	09911	19761	66535	40102	26646	60147	15702
46276	87453	44790	67122	45573	84358	21625	16999	13385	22782
55363	07449	34835	15290	76616	67191	12777	21861	68689	03263
69393	92785	49902	58447	42048	30378	87618	26933	40640	16281
13186	29431	88190	04588	38733	81290	89541	70290	40113	08243
17726	28652	56836	78351	47327	18518	92222	55201	27340	10493
36520	64465	05550	30157	82242	29520	69753	72602	23756	54935
81628	36100	39254	56835	37636	02421	98063	89641	64953	99337
84649	48968	75215	75498	49539	74240	03466	49292	36401	45525
63291	11618	12613	75055	43915	26488	41116	64531	56827	30825
70502	53225	03655	05915	37140	57051	48393	91322	25653	06543
06426	24771	59935	49801	11082	66762	94477	02494	88215	27191
20711	55609	29430	70165	45406	78484	31639	52009	18873	96927
41990	70538	77191	25860	55204	73417	83920	69468	74972	38712
72452	36618	76298	26678	89334	33938	95567	29380	75906	91807
37042	40318	57099	10528	09925	89773	41335	96244	29002	46453
53766	52875	15987	46962	67342	77592	57651	95508	80033	69828
90585	58955	53122	16025	84299	53310	67380	84249	25348	04332
32001	96293	37203	64516	51530	37069	40261	61374	05815	06714
62606	64324	46354	72157	67248	20135	49804	09226	64419	29457
10078	28073	85389	50324	14500	15562	64165	06125	71353	77669
91561	46145	24177	15294	10061	98124	75732	00815	83452	97355
13091	98112	53959	79607	52244	63303	10413	63839	74762	50289

We can now use these four-digit random numbers to give each manager in the population an equal chance of being included in the random sample. The first number, 6327, is greater than 2500. It does not correspond to one of the numbered managers in the population, and hence is discarded. The second number, 1599, is between 1 and 2500. Thus the first manager selected for the random sample is number 1599 on the list of EAI managers. Continuing this process, we ignore the numbers 8671 and 7445 before identifying managers number 1102, 1514, and 1807 to be included in the random sample. This process continues until the simple random sample of 30 EAI managers has been obtained.

In implementing this simple random sample selection process, it is possible that a random number used previously may appear again in the table before the sample of 30 EAI managers has been selected. Because we do not want to select a manager more than one time, any previously used random numbers are ignored because the corresponding manager is already included in the sample. Selecting a sample in this manner is referred to as **sampling without replacement**. If we selected a sample such that previously used random numbers are acceptable and specific managers could be included in the sample two or more times, we would be **sampling with replacement**. Sampling with replacement is a valid way of identifying a simple random sample. However, sampling without replacement is the sampling procedure used most often. When we refer to simple random sampling, we will assume that the sampling is without replacement.

In practice, a population being studied is usually considered infinite if it involves an ongoing process that makes listing or counting every element in the population impossible.

Sampling from an Infinite Population

In some situations, the population is either infinite or so large that for practical purposes it must be treated as infinite. For example, suppose that a fast-food restaurant would like to obtain a profile of its customers by selecting a simple random sample of customers and asking each customer to complete a short questionnaire. In such situations, the ongoing process of customer visits to the restaurant can be viewed as coming from an infinite population. The definition of a simple random sample from an infinite population follows.

SIMPLE RANDOM SAMPLE (INFINITE POPULATION)

A simple random sample from an infinite population is a sample selected such that the following conditions are satisfied.

1. Each element selected comes from the population.
2. Each element is selected independently.

For infinite populations, a sample selection procedure must be specially devised for each situation to select the items independently and thus avoid a selection bias that gives higher selection probabilities to certain types of elements.

For the example of selecting a simple random sample of customers at a fast-food restaurant, the first requirement is satisfied by any customer who comes into the restaurant. The second requirement is satisfied by selecting customers independently. The purpose of the second requirement is to prevent selection bias. Selection bias would occur if, for instance, five consecutive customers selected were all friends who arrived together. We might expect these customers to exhibit similar profiles. Selection bias can be avoided by ensuring that the selection of a particular customer does not influence the selection of any other customer. In other words, the customers must be selected independently.

McDonald's, the fast-food restaurant leader, implemented a simple random sampling procedure for just such a situation. The sampling procedure was based on the fact that some customers presented discount coupons. Whenever a customer presented a discount coupon, the next customer served was asked to complete a customer profile questionnaire. Because arriving customers presented discount coupons randomly, and independently, this sampling plan ensured that customers were selected independently. Thus, the two requirements for a simple random sample from an infinite population were satisfied.

Infinite populations are often associated with an ongoing process that operates continuously over time. For example, parts being manufactured on a production line, transactions occurring at a bank, telephone calls arriving at a technical support center, and customers entering stores may all be viewed as coming from an infinite population. In such cases, a creative sampling procedure ensures that no selection bias occurs and that the sample elements are selected independently.

NOTES AND COMMENTS

1. The number of different simple random samples of size n that can be selected from a finite population of size N is

$$\frac{N!}{n!(N-n)!}$$

In this formula, $N!$ and $n!$ are the factorial formulas discussed in Chapter 4. For the EAI problem with $N = 2500$ and $n = 30$, this expression can be used to show that approximately 2.75×10^{69} different simple random samples of 30 EAI managers can be obtained.

2. Computer software packages can be used to select a random sample. In the chapter appendixes, we show how Minitab and Excel can be used to select a simple random sample from a finite population.

Exercises

Methods

SELF test

1. Consider a finite population with five elements labeled A, B, C, D, and E. Ten possible simple random samples of size 2 can be selected.
   a. List the 10 samples beginning with AB, AC, and so on.
   b. Using simple random sampling, what is the probability that each sample of size 2 is selected?
   c. Assume random number 1 corresponds to A, random number 2 corresponds to B, and so on. List the simple random sample of size 2 that will be selected by using the random digits 8 0 5 7 5 3 2.
2. Assume a finite population has 350 elements. Using the last three digits of each of the following five-digit random numbers (e.g.; 601, 022, 448, . . .), determine the first four elements that will be selected for the simple random sample.

   98601 73022 83448 02147 34229 27553 84147 93289 14209

Applications

SELF test

3. *Fortune* publishes data on sales, profits, assets, stockholders' equity, market value, and earnings per share for the 500 largest U.S. industrial corporations (*Fortune* 500, 2003). Assume that you want to select a simple random sample of 10 corporations from the *Fortune* 500 list. Use the last three digits in column 9 of Table 7.1, beginning with 554. Read down the column and identify the numbers of the 10 corporations that would be selected.
4. The 10 most active stocks on the New York Stock Exchange on March 6, 2006, are shown here (*The Wall Street Journal,* March 7, 2006).

AT&T	Lucent	Nortel	Qwest	Bell South
Pfizer	Texas Instruments	Gen. Elect.	iShrMSJpn	LSI Logic

   Exchange authorities decided to investigate trading practices using a sample of three of these stocks.
   a. Beginning with the first random digit in column 6 of Table 7.1, read down the column to select a simple random sample of three stocks for the exchange authorities.
   b. Using the information in the first Note and Comment, determine how many different simple random samples of size 3 can be selected from the list of 10 stocks.
5. A student government organization is interested in estimating the proportion of students who favor a mandatory "pass-fail" grading policy for elective courses. A list of names and addresses of the 645 students enrolled during the current quarter is available from the registrar's office. Using three-digit random numbers in row 10 of Table 7.1 and moving across the row from left to right, identify the first 10 students who would be selected using simple random sampling. The three-digit random numbers begin with 816, 283, and 610.
6. The *County and City Data Book,* published by the Census Bureau, lists information on 3139 counties throughout the United States. Assume that a national study will collect data from 30 randomly selected counties. Use four-digit random numbers from the last column of Table 7.1 to identify the numbers corresponding to the first five counties selected for the sample. Ignore the first digits and begin with the four-digit random numbers 9945, 8364, 5702, and so on.

7. Assume that we want to identify a simple random sample of 12 of the 372 doctors practicing in a particular city. The doctors' names are available from a local medical organization. Use the eighth column of five-digit random numbers in Table 7.1 to identify the 12 doctors for the sample. Ignore the first two random digits in each five-digit grouping of the random numbers. This process begins with random number 108 and proceeds down the column of random numbers.

8. The following list provides the NCAA top 25 football teams for the 2002 season (*NCAA News,* January 4, 2003). Use the ninth column of the random numbers in Table 7.1, beginning with 13554, to select a simple random sample of six football teams. Begin with team 13 and use the first two digits in each row of the ninth column for your selection process. Which six football teams are selected for the simple random sample?

1. Ohio State	14. Virginia Tech
2. Miami	15. Penn State
3. Georgia	16. Auburn
4. Southern California	17. Notre Dame
5. Oklahoma	18. Pittsburgh
6. Kansas State	19. Marshall
7. Texas	20. West Virginia
8. Iowa	21. Colorado
9. Michigan	22. TCU
10. Washington State	23. Florida State
11. North Carolina State	24. Florida
12. Boise State	25. Virginia
13. Maryland	

9. *The Wall Street Journal* provides the net asset value, the year-to-date percent return, and the three-year percent return for 555 mutual funds (*The Wall Street Journal,* April 25, 2003). Assume that a simple random sample of 12 of the 555 mutual funds will be selected for a follow-up study on the size and performance of mutual funds. Use the fourth column of the random numbers in Table 7.1, beginning with 51102, to select the simple random sample of 12 mutual funds. Begin with mutual fund 102 and use the *last* three digits in each row of the fourth column for your selection process. What are the numbers of the 12 mutual funds in the simple random sample?

10. Indicate whether the following populations should be considered finite or infinite.
    a. All registered voters in the state of California.
    b. All television sets that could be produced by the Allentown, Pennsylvania, plant of the TV-M Company.
    c. All orders that could be processed by a mail-order firm.
    d. All emergency telephone calls that could come into a local police station.
    e. All components that Fibercon, Inc., produced on the second shift on May 17.

7.3 Point Estimation

Now that we have described how to select a simple random sample, let us return to the EAI problem. A simple random sample of 30 managers and the corresponding data on annual salary and management training program participation are as shown in Table 7.2. The notation x_1, x_2, and so on is used to denote the annual salary of the first manager in the sample, the annual salary of the second manager in the sample, and so on. Participation in the management training program is indicated by Yes in the management training program column.

To estimate the value of a population parameter, we compute a corresponding characteristic of the sample, referred to as a **sample statistic**. For example, to estimate the population mean μ and the population standard deviation σ for the annual salary of EAI

TABLE 7.2 ANNUAL SALARY AND TRAINING PROGRAM STATUS FOR A SIMPLE RANDOM SAMPLE OF 30 EAI MANAGERS

Annual Salary ($)	Management Training Program	Annual Salary ($)	Management Training Program
$x_1 = 49{,}094.30$	Yes	$x_{16} = 51{,}766.00$	Yes
$x_2 = 53{,}263.90$	Yes	$x_{17} = 52{,}541.30$	No
$x_3 = 49{,}643.50$	Yes	$x_{18} = 44{,}980.00$	Yes
$x_4 = 49{,}894.90$	Yes	$x_{19} = 51{,}932.60$	Yes
$x_5 = 47{,}621.60$	No	$x_{20} = 52{,}973.00$	Yes
$x_6 = 55{,}924.00$	Yes	$x_{21} = 45{,}120.90$	Yes
$x_7 = 49{,}092.30$	Yes	$x_{22} = 51{,}753.00$	Yes
$x_8 = 51{,}404.40$	Yes	$x_{23} = 54{,}391.80$	No
$x_9 = 50{,}957.70$	Yes	$x_{24} = 50{,}164.20$	No
$x_{10} = 55{,}109.70$	Yes	$x_{25} = 52{,}973.60$	No
$x_{11} = 45{,}922.60$	Yes	$x_{26} = 50{,}241.30$	No
$x_{12} = 57{,}268.40$	No	$x_{27} = 52{,}793.90$	No
$x_{13} = 55{,}688.80$	Yes	$x_{28} = 50{,}979.40$	Yes
$x_{14} = 51{,}564.70$	No	$x_{29} = 55{,}860.90$	Yes
$x_{15} = 56{,}188.20$	No	$x_{30} = 57{,}309.10$	No

managers, we use the data in Table 7.2 to calculate the corresponding sample statistics: the sample mean $\bar{x}$ and the sample standard deviation s. Using the formulas for a sample mean and a sample standard deviation presented in Chapter 3, the sample mean is

$$\bar{x} = \frac{\Sigma x_i}{n} = \frac{1{,}554{,}420}{30} = \$51{,}814$$

and the sample standard deviation is

$$s = \sqrt{\frac{\Sigma(x_i - \bar{x})^2}{n - 1}} = \sqrt{\frac{325{,}009{,}260}{29}} = \$3348$$

To estimate p, the proportion of managers in the population who completed the management training program, we use the corresponding sample proportion $\bar{p}$. Let x denote the number of managers in the sample who completed the management training program. The data in Table 7.2 show that $x = 19$. Thus, with a sample size of $n = 30$, the sample proportion is

$$\bar{p} = \frac{x}{n} = \frac{19}{30} = .63$$

By making the preceding computations, we perform the statistical procedure called *point estimation.* We refer to the sample mean $\bar{x}$ as the **point estimator** of the population mean μ, the sample standard deviation s as the point estimator of the population standard deviation σ, and the sample proportion $\bar{p}$ as the point estimator of the population proportion p. The numerical value obtained for $\bar{x}$, s, or $\bar{p}$ is called the **point estimate**. Thus, for the simple random sample of 30 EAI managers shown in Table 7.2, \$51,814 is the point estimate of μ, \$3348 is the point estimate of σ, and .63 is the point estimate of p. Table 7.3 summarizes the sample results and compares the point estimates to the actual values of the population parameters.

TABLE 7.3 SUMMARY OF POINT ESTIMATES OBTAINED FROM A SIMPLE RANDOM SAMPLE OF 30 EAI MANAGERS

Population Parameter	Parameter Value	Point Estimator	Point Estimate
μ = Population mean annual salary	\$51,800	$\bar{x}$ = Sample mean annual salary	\$51,814
σ = Population standard deviation for annual salary	\$4000	s = Sample standard deviation for annual salary	\$3348
p = Population proportion having completed the management training program	.60	$\bar{p}$ = Sample proportion having completed the management training program	.63

As evident from Table 7.3, the point estimates differ somewhat from the corresponding population parameters. This difference is to be expected because a sample, and not a census of the entire population, is being used to develop the point estimates. In the next chapter, we will show how to construct an interval estimate in order to provide information about how close the point estimate is to the population parameter.

Exercises

Methods

SELF test

11. The following data are from a simple random sample.

5 8 10 7 10 14

a. What is the point estimate of the population mean?
b. What is the point estimate of the population standard deviation?

12. A survey question for a sample of 150 individuals yielded 75 Yes responses, 55 No responses, and 20 No Opinions.
a. What is the point estimate of the proportion in the population who respond Yes?
b. What is the point estimate of the proportion in the population who respond No?

Applications

SELF test

13. A simple random sample of 5 months of sales data provided the following information:

Month:	1	2	3	4	5
Units Sold:	94	100	85	94	92

a. Develop a point estimate of the population mean number of units sold per month.
b. Develop a point estimate of the population standard deviation.

CD file
MutualFund

14. *BusinessWeek* published information on 283 equity mutual funds (*BusinessWeek,* January 26, 2004). A sample of 40 of those funds is contained in the data set MutualFund. Use the data set to answer the following questions.
a. Develop a point estimate of the proportion of the *BusinessWeek* equity funds that are load funds.
b. Develop a point estimate of the proportion of funds that are classified as high risk.
c. Develop a point estimate of the proportion of funds that have a below-average risk rating.

15. Many drugs used to treat cancer are expensive. *BusinessWeek* reported on the cost per treatment of Herceptin, a drug used to treat breast cancer (*BusinessWeek,* January 30, 2006).

Typical treatment costs (in dollars) for Herceptin are provided by a simple random sample of 10 patients.

4376	5578	2717	4920	4495
4798	6446	4119	4237	3814

a. Develop a point estimate of the mean cost per treatment with Herceptin.
b. Develop a point estimate of the standard deviation of the cost per treatment with Herceptin.

16. A sample of 50 *Fortune* 500 companies (*Fortune,* April 14, 2003) showed 5 were based in New York, 6 in California, 2 in Minnesota, and 1 in Wisconsin.
 a. Develop an estimate of the proportion of *Fortune* 500 companies based in New York.
 b. Develop an estimate of the number of *Fortune* 500 companies based in Minnesota.
 c. Develop an estimate of the proportion of *Fortune* 500 companies that are not based in these four states.
17. The American Association of Individual Investors (AAII) polls its subscribers on a weekly basis to determine the number who are bullish, bearish, or neutral on the short-term prospects for the stock market. Their findings for the week ending March 2, 2006, are consistent with the following sample results (www.aaii.com).

 Bullish 409 Neutral 299 Bearish 291

 Develop a point estimate of the following population parameters.
 a. The proportion of all AAII subscribers who are bullish on the stock market.
 b. The proportion of all AAII subscribers who are neutral on the stock market.
 c. The proportion of all AAII subscribers who are bearish on the stock market.

7.4 Introduction to Sampling Distributions

In the preceding section we said that the sample mean $\bar{x}$ is the point estimator of the population mean μ, and the sample proportion $\bar{p}$ is the point estimator of the population proportion p. For the simple random sample of 30 EAI managers shown in Table 7.2, the point estimate of μ is $\bar{x} = \$51,814$ and the point estimate of p is $\bar{p} = .63$. Suppose we select another simple random sample of 30 EAI managers and obtain the following point estimates:

$$\text{Sample mean: } \bar{x} = \$52,670$$
$$\text{Sample proportion: } \bar{p} = .70$$

Note that different values of $\bar{x}$ and $\bar{p}$ were obtained. Indeed, a second simple random sample of 30 EAI managers cannot be expected to provide the same point estimates as the first sample.

Now, suppose we repeat the process of selecting a simple random sample of 30 EAI managers over and over again, each time computing the values of $\bar{x}$ and $\bar{p}$. Table 7.4 contains a portion of the results obtained for 500 simple random samples, and Table 7.5 shows the frequency and relative frequency distributions for the 500 $\bar{x}$ values. Figure 7.1 shows the relative frequency histogram for the $\bar{x}$ values.

The ability to understand the material in subsequent chapters depends heavily on the ability to understand and use the sampling distributions presented in this chapter.

In Chapter 5 we defined a random variable as a numerical description of the outcome of an experiment. If we consider the process of selecting a simple random sample as an experiment, the sample mean $\bar{x}$ is the numerical description of the outcome of the experiment. Thus, the sample mean $\bar{x}$ is a random variable. As a result, just like other random variables, $\bar{x}$ has a mean or expected value, a standard deviation, and a probability distribution.

TABLE 7.4 VALUES OF $\bar{x}$ AND $\bar{p}$ FROM 500 SIMPLE RANDOM SAMPLES OF 30 EAI MANAGERS

Sample Number	Sample Mean ($\bar{x}$)	Sample Proportion ($\bar{p}$)
1	51,814	.63
2	52,670	.70
3	51,780	.67
4	51,588	.53
.	.	.
.	.	.
.	.	.
500	51,752	.50

Because the various possible values of $\bar{x}$ are the result of different simple random samples, the probability distribution of $\bar{x}$ is called the **sampling distribution** of $\bar{x}$. Knowledge of this sampling distribution and its properties will enable us to make probability statements about how close the sample mean $\bar{x}$ is to the population mean μ.

Let us return to Figure 7.1. We would need to enumerate every possible sample of 30 managers and compute each sample mean to completely determine the sampling distribution of $\bar{x}$. However, the histogram of 500 $\bar{x}$ values gives an approximation of this sampling distribution. From the approximation we observe the bell-shaped appearance of the distribution. We note that the largest concentration of the $\bar{x}$ values and the mean of the 500 $\bar{x}$ values is near the population mean $\mu = \$51,800$. We will describe the properties of the sampling distribution of $\bar{x}$ more fully in the next section.

The 500 values of the sample proportion $\bar{p}$ are summarized by the relative frequency histogram in Figure 7.2. As in the case of $\bar{x}$, $\bar{p}$ is a random variable. If every possible sample of size 30 were selected from the population and if a value of $\bar{p}$ were computed for each sample, the resulting probability distribution would be the sampling distribution of $\bar{p}$. The relative frequency histogram of the 500 sample values in Figure 7.2 provides a general idea of the appearance of the sampling distribution of $\bar{p}$.

In practice, we select only one simple random sample from the population. We repeated the sampling process 500 times in this section simply to illustrate that many different samples

TABLE 7.5 FREQUENCY DISTRIBUTION OF $\bar{x}$ FROM 500 SIMPLE RANDOM SAMPLES OF 30 EAI MANAGERS

Mean Annual Salary ($)	Frequency	Relative Frequency
49,500.00–49,999.99	2	.004
50,000.00–50,499.99	16	.032
50,500.00–50,999.99	52	.104
51,000.00–51,499.99	101	.202
51,500.00–51,999.99	133	.266
52,000.00–52,499.99	110	.220
52,500.00–52,999.99	54	.108
53,000.00–53,499.99	26	.052
53,500.00–53,999.99	6	.012
Totals	500	1.000

FIGURE 7.1 RELATIVE FREQUENCY HISTOGRAM OF $\bar{x}$ VALUES FROM 500 SIMPLE RANDOM SAMPLES OF SIZE 30 EACH

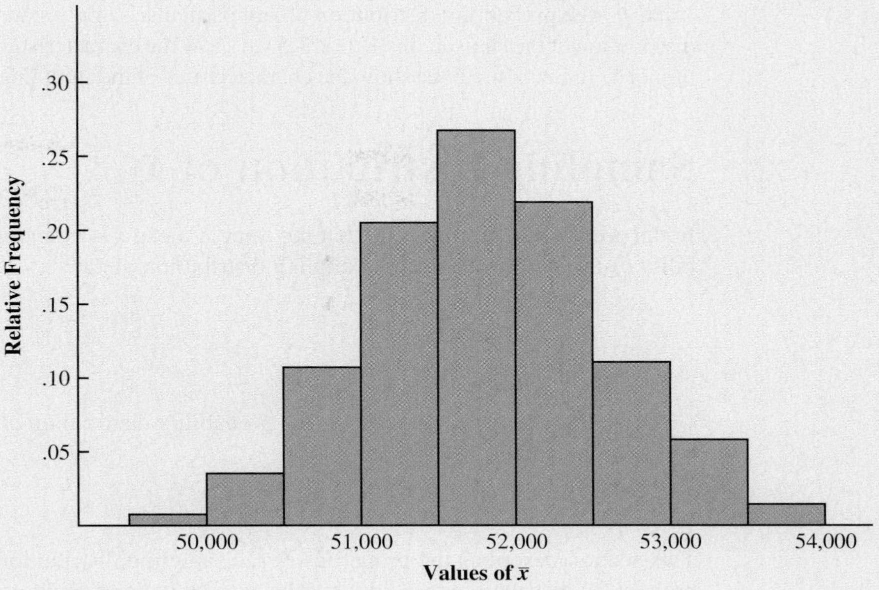

FIGURE 7.2 RELATIVE FREQUENCY HISTOGRAM OF $\bar{p}$ VALUES FROM 500 SIMPLE RANDOM SAMPLES OF SIZE 30 EACH

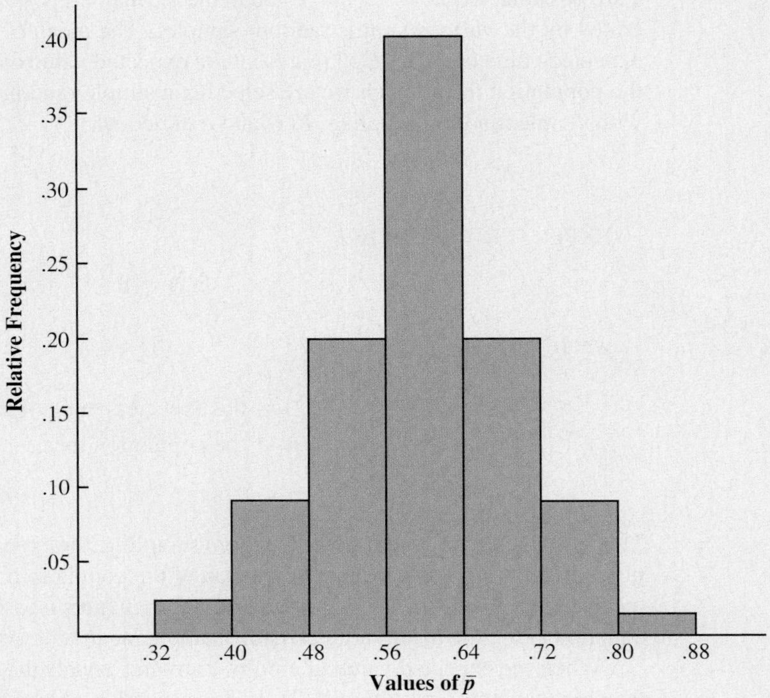

are possible and that the different samples generate a variety of values for the sample statistics $\bar{x}$ and $\bar{p}$. The probability distribution of any particular sample statistic is called the sampling distribution of the statistic. In Section 7.5 we show the characteristics of the sampling distribution of $\bar{x}$. In Section 7.6 we show the characteristics of the sampling distribution of $\bar{p}$.

7.5 Sampling Distribution of $\bar{x}$

In the previous section we said that the sample mean $\bar{x}$ is a random variable and its probability distribution is called the sampling distribution of $\bar{x}$.

SAMPLING DISTRIBUTION OF $\bar{x}$

The sampling distribution of $\bar{x}$ is the probability distribution of all possible values of the sample mean $\bar{x}$.

This section describes the properties of the sampling distribution of $\bar{x}$. Just as with other probability distributions we studied, the sampling distribution of $\bar{x}$ has an expected value or mean, a standard deviation, and a characteristic shape or form. Let us begin by considering the mean of all possible $\bar{x}$ values, which is referred to as the expected value of $\bar{x}$.

Expected Value of $\bar{x}$

In the EAI sampling problem we saw that different simple random samples result in a variety of values for the sample mean $\bar{x}$. Because many different values of the random variable $\bar{x}$ are possible, we are often interested in the mean of all possible values of $\bar{x}$ that can be generated by the various simple random samples. The mean of the $\bar{x}$ random variable is the expected value of $\bar{x}$. Let $E(\bar{x})$ represent the expected value of $\bar{x}$ and μ represent the mean of the population from which we are selecting a simple random sample. It can be shown that with simple random sampling, $E(\bar{x})$ and μ are equal.

The expected value of $\bar{x}$ equals the mean of the population from which the sample is selected.

EXPECTED VALUE OF $\bar{x}$

$$E(\bar{x}) = \mu \tag{7.1}$$

where

$E(\bar{x})$ = the expected value of $\bar{x}$
μ = the population mean

This result shows that with simple random sampling, the expected value or mean of the sampling distribution of $\bar{x}$ is equal to the mean of the population. In Section 7.1 we saw that the mean annual salary for the population of EAI managers is μ = \$51,800. Thus, according to equation (7.1), the mean of all possible sample means for the EAI study is also \$51,800.

When the expected value of a point estimator equals the population parameter, we say the point estimator is **unbiased**. Thus, equation (7.1) shows that $\bar{x}$ is an unbiased estimator of the population mean μ.

Standard Deviation of $\bar{x}$

Let us define the standard deviation of the sampling distribution of $\bar{x}$. We will use the following notation.

$$\sigma_{\bar{x}} = \text{the standard deviation of } \bar{x}$$
$$\sigma = \text{the standard deviation of the population}$$
$$n = \text{the sample size}$$
$$N = \text{the population size}$$

It can be shown that with simple random sampling, the standard deviation of $\bar{x}$ depends on whether the population is finite or infinite. The two formulas for the standard deviation of $\bar{x}$ follow.

STANDARD DEVIATION OF $\bar{x}$

Finite Population | *Infinite Population*

$$\sigma_{\bar{x}} = \sqrt{\frac{N-n}{N-1}}\left(\frac{\sigma}{\sqrt{n}}\right) \qquad \sigma_{\bar{x}} = \frac{\sigma}{\sqrt{n}} \tag{7.2}$$

In comparing the two formulas in (7.2), we see that the factor $\sqrt{(N-n)/(N-1)}$ is required for the finite population case but not for the infinite population case. This factor is commonly referred to as the **finite population correction factor**. In many practical sampling situations, we find that the population involved, although finite, is "large," whereas the sample size is relatively "small." In such cases the finite population correction factor $\sqrt{(N-n)/(N-1)}$ is close to 1. As a result, the difference between the values of the standard deviation of $\bar{x}$ for the finite and infinite population cases becomes negligible. Then, $\sigma_{\bar{x}} = \sigma/\sqrt{n}$ becomes a good approximation to the standard deviation of $\bar{x}$ even though the population is finite. This observation leads to the following general guideline, or rule of thumb, for computing the standard deviation of $\bar{x}$.

USE THE FOLLOWING EXPRESSION TO COMPUTE THE STANDARD DEVIATION OF $\bar{x}$

$$\sigma_{\bar{x}} = \frac{\sigma}{\sqrt{n}} \tag{7.3}$$

whenever

1. The population is infinite; or
2. The population is finite *and* the sample size is less than or equal to 5% of the population size; that is, $n/N \leq .05$.

Problem 21 shows that when $n/N \leq .05$, the finite population correction factor has little effect on the value of $\sigma_{\bar{x}}$.

In cases where $n/N > .05$, the finite population version of formula (7.2) should be used in the computation of $\sigma_{\bar{x}}$. Unless otherwise noted, throughout the text we will assume that the population size is "large," $n/N \leq .05$, and expression (7.3) can be used to compute $\sigma_{\bar{x}}$.

The term standard error is used throughout statistical inference to refer to the standard deviation of a point estimator.

To compute $\sigma_{\bar{x}}$, we need to know σ, the standard deviation of the population. To further emphasize the difference between $\sigma_{\bar{x}}$ and σ, we refer to the standard deviation of $\bar{x}$, $\sigma_{\bar{x}}$, as the **standard error** of the mean. In general, the term *standard error* refers to the standard deviation of a point estimator. Later we will see that the value of the standard error of the mean is helpful in determining how far the sample mean may be from the population mean. Let us now return to the EAI example and compute the standard error of the mean associated with simple random samples of 30 EAI managers.

In Section 7.1 we saw that the standard deviation of annual salary for the population of 2500 EAI managers is $\sigma = 4000$. In this case, the population is finite, with $N = 2500$. However, with a sample size of 30, we have $n/N = 30/2500 = .012$. Because the sample size is less than 5% of the population size, we can ignore the finite population correction factor and use equation (7.3) to compute the standard error.

$$\sigma_{\bar{x}} = \frac{\sigma}{\sqrt{n}} = \frac{4000}{\sqrt{30}} = 730.3$$

Form of the Sampling Distribution of $\bar{x}$

The preceding results concerning the expected value and standard deviation for the sampling distribution of $\bar{x}$ are applicable for any population. The final step in identifying the characteristics of the sampling distribution of $\bar{x}$ is to determine the form or shape of the sampling distribution. We will consider two cases: (1) the population has a normal distribution; and (2) the population does not have a normal distribution.

Population has a normal distribution. In many situations it is reasonable to assume that the population from which we are selecting a simple random sample has a normal, or nearly normal, distribution. When the population has a normal distribution, the sampling distribution of $\bar{x}$ is normally distributed for any sample size.

Population does not have a normal distribution. When the population from which we are selecting a simple random sample does not have a normal distribution, the **central limit theorem** is helpful in identifying the shape of the sampling distribution of $\bar{x}$. A statement of the central limit theorem as it applies to the sampling distribution of $\bar{x}$ follows.

CENTRAL LIMIT THEOREM

In selecting simple random samples of size n from a population, the sampling distribution of the sample mean $\bar{x}$ can be approximated by a *normal distribution* as the sample size becomes large.

Figure 7.3 shows how the central limit theorem works for three different populations; each column refers to one of the populations. The top panel of the figure shows that none of the populations are normally distributed. Population I follows a uniform distribution. Population II is often called the rabbit-eared distribution. It is symmetric, but the more likely values fall in the tails of the distribution. Population III is shaped like the exponential distribution; it is skewed to the right.

The bottom three panels of Figure 7.3 show the shape of the sampling distribution for samples of size $n = 2$, $n = 5$, and $n = 30$. When the sample size is 2, we see that the shape of each sampling distribution is different from the shape of the corresponding population distribution. For samples of size 5, we see that the shapes of the sampling distributions for populations I and II begin to look similar to the shape of a normal distribution. Even though the shape of the sampling distribution for population III begins to look similar to the shape

FIGURE 7.3 ILLUSTRATION OF THE CENTRAL LIMIT THEOREM FOR THREE POPULATIONS

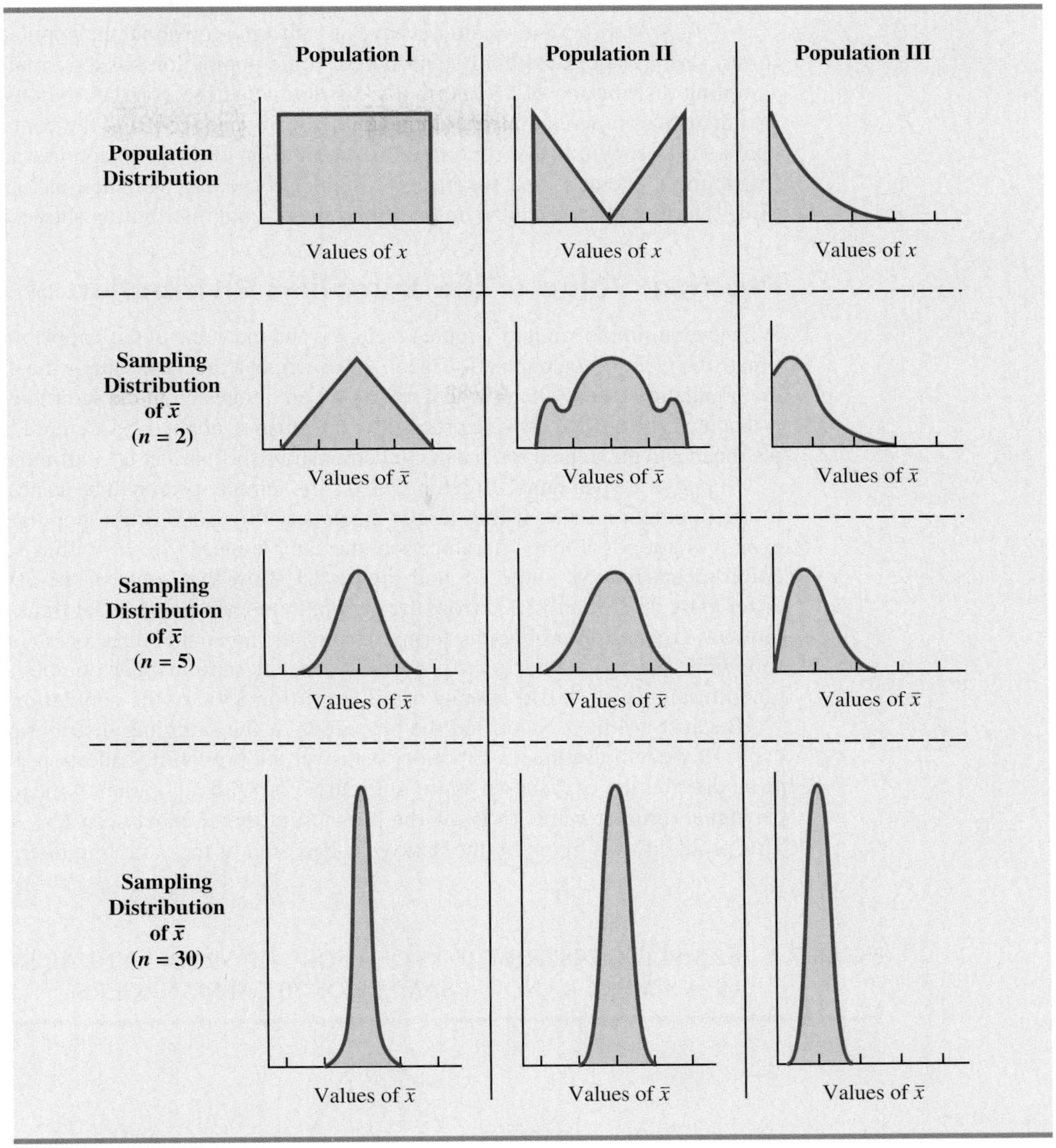

of a normal distribution, some skewness to the right is still present. Finally, for samples of size 30, the shapes of each of the three sampling distributions are approximately normal.

From a practitioner standpoint, we often want to know how large the sample size needs to be before the central limit theorem applies and we can assume that the shape of the sampling distribution is approximately normal. Statistical researchers have investigated this question by studying the sampling distribution of $\bar{x}$ for a variety of populations and a variety of sample sizes. General statistical practice is to assume that, for most applications, the sampling distribution of $\bar{x}$ can be approximated by a normal distribution whenever the sample is size 30 or more. In cases where the population is highly skewed or outliers are present, samples of size 50 may be needed. Finally, if the population is discrete, the sample size needed for a normal approximation often depends on the population proportion. We say more about this issue when we discuss the sampling distribution of $\bar{p}$ in Section 7.6.

Sampling Distribution of $\bar{x}$ for the EAI Problem

Let us return to the EAI problem where we previously showed that $E(\bar{x}) = \$51,800$ and $\sigma_{\bar{x}} = 730.3$. At this point, we do not have any information about the population distribution; it may or may not be normally distributed. If the population has a normal distribution, the sampling distribution of $\bar{x}$ is normally distributed. If the population does not have a normal distribution, the simple random sample of 30 managers and the central limit theorem enable us to conclude that the sampling distribution of $\bar{x}$ can be approximated by a normal distribution. In either case, we are comfortable proceeding with the conclusion that the sampling distribution of $\bar{x}$ can be described by the normal distribution shown in Figure 7.4.

Practical Value of the Sampling Distribution of $\bar{x}$

Whenever a simple random sample is selected and the value of the sample mean is used to estimate the value of the population mean μ, we cannot expect the sample mean to exactly equal the population mean. The practical reason we are interested in the sampling distribution of $\bar{x}$ is that it can be used to provide probability information about the difference between the sample mean and the population mean. To demonstrate this use, let us return to the EAI problem.

Suppose the personnel director believes the sample mean will be an acceptable estimate of the population mean if the sample mean is within \$500 of the population mean. However, it is not possible to guarantee that the sample mean will be within \$500 of the population mean. Indeed, Table 7.5 and Figure 7.1 show that some of the 500 sample means differed by more than \$2000 from the population mean. So we must think of the personnel director's request in probability terms. That is, the personnel director is concerned with the following question: What is the probability that the sample mean computed using a simple random sample of 30 EAI managers will be within \$500 of the population mean?

Because we have identified the properties of the sampling distribution of $\bar{x}$ (see Figure 7.4), we will use this distribution to answer the probability question. Refer to the sampling distribution of $\bar{x}$ shown again in Figure 7.5. With a population mean of \$51,800, the personnel director wants to know the probability that $\bar{x}$ is between \$51,300 and \$52,300. This probability is given by the darkly shaded area of the sampling distribution shown in

FIGURE 7.4 SAMPLING DISTRIBUTION OF $\bar{x}$ FOR THE MEAN ANNUAL SALARY OF A SIMPLE RANDOM SAMPLE OF 30 EAI MANAGERS

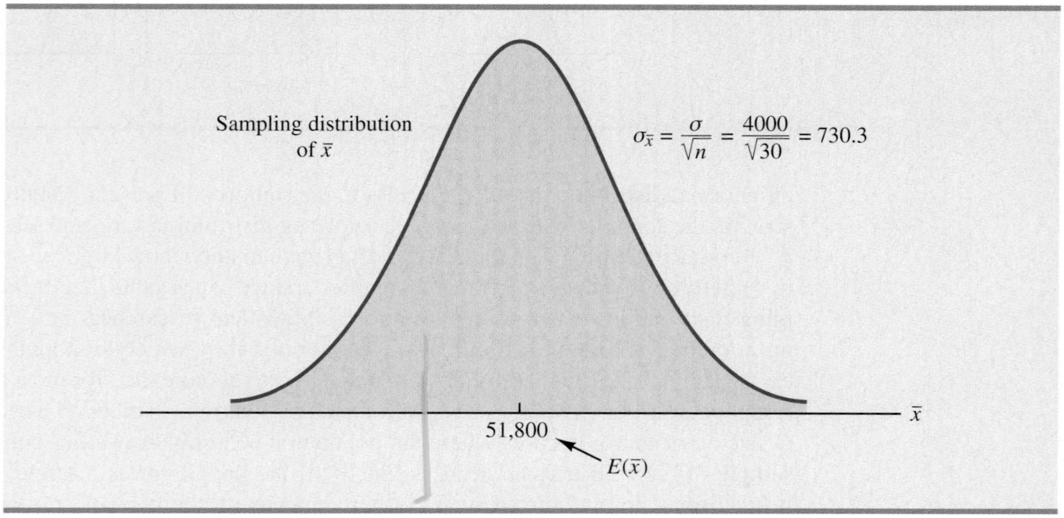

FIGURE 7.5 PROBABILITY OF A SAMPLE MEAN BEING WITHIN $500 OF THE POPULATION MEAN FOR A SIMPLE RANDOM SAMPLE OF 30 EAI MANAGERS

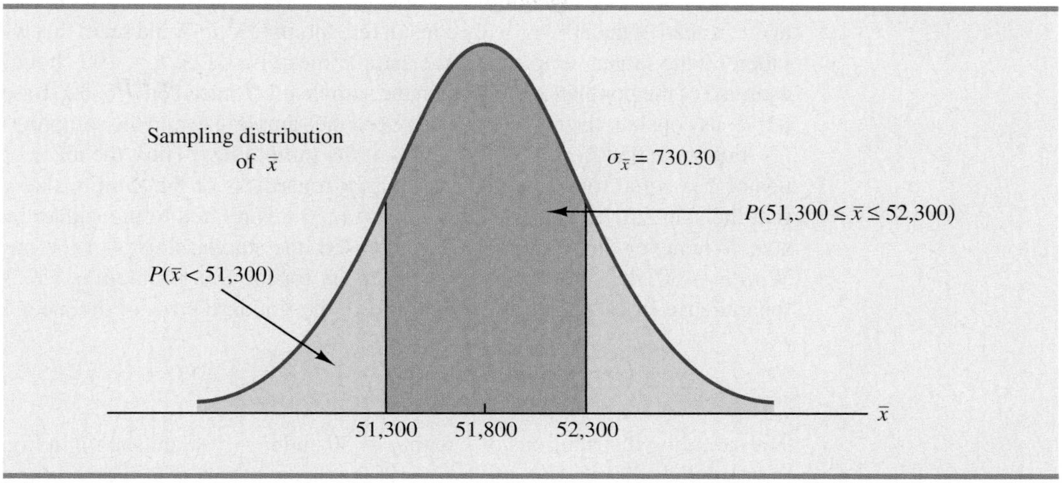

Figure 7.5. Because the sampling distribution is normally distributed, with mean 51,800 and standard error of the mean 730.3, we can use the standard normal probability table to find the area or probability.

We first calculate the z value at the upper endpoint of the interval (52,300) and use the table to find the area under the curve to the left of that point (left tail area). Then we compute the z value at the lower endpoint of the interval (51,300) and use the table to find the area under the curve to the left of that point (another left tail area). Subtracting the second tail area from the first gives us the desired probability.

At $\bar{x} = 52{,}300$, we have

$$z = \frac{52{,}300 - 51{,}800}{730.30} = .68$$

Referring to the standard normal probability table, we find a cumulative probability (area to the left of $z = .68$) of .7517.

At $\bar{x} = 51{,}300$, we have

$$z = \frac{51{,}300 - 51{,}800}{730.30} = -.68$$

The area under the curve to the left of $z = -.68$ is .2483. Therefore, $P(51{,}300 \leq \bar{x} \leq 52{,}300) = P(z \leq .68) - P(z < -.68) = .7517 - .2483 = .5034$.

The sampling distribution of $\bar{x}$ can be used to provide probability information about how close the sample mean $\bar{x}$ is to the population mean μ.

The preceding computations show that a simple random sample of 30 EAI managers has a .5034 probability of providing a sample mean $\bar{x}$ that is within $500 of the population mean. Thus, there is a $1 - .5034 = .4966$ probability that the difference between $\bar{x}$ and $\mu = \$51{,}800$ will be more than $500. In other words, a simple random sample of 30 EAI managers has roughly a 50/50 chance of providing a sample mean within the allowable $500. Perhaps a larger sample size should be considered. Let us explore this possibility by considering the relationship between the sample size and the sampling distribution of $\bar{x}$.

Relationship Between the Sample Size and the Sampling Distribution of $\bar{x}$

Suppose that in the EAI sampling problem we select a simple random sample of 100 EAI managers instead of the 30 originally considered. Intuitively, it would seem that with more data provided by the larger sample size, the sample mean based on $n = 100$ should provide a better estimate of the population mean than the sample mean based on $n = 30$. To see how much better, let us consider the relationship between the sample size and the sampling distribution of $\bar{x}$.

First note that $E(\bar{x}) = \mu$ regardless of the sample size. Thus, the mean of all possible values of $\bar{x}$ is equal to the population mean μ regardless of the sample size n. However, note that the standard error of the mean, $\sigma_{\bar{x}} = \sigma/\sqrt{n}$, is related to the square root of the sample size. Whenever the sample size is increased, the standard error of the mean $\sigma_{\bar{x}}$ decreases. With $n = 30$, the standard error of the mean for the EAI problem is 730.3. However, with the increase in the sample size to $n = 100$, the standard error of the mean is decreased to

$$\sigma_{\bar{x}} = \frac{\sigma}{\sqrt{n}} = \frac{4000}{\sqrt{100}} = 400$$

The sampling distributions of $\bar{x}$ with $n = 30$ and $n = 100$ are shown in Figure 7.6. Because the sampling distribution with $n = 100$ has a smaller standard error, the values of $\bar{x}$ have less variation and tend to be closer to the population mean than the values of $\bar{x}$ with $n = 30$.

We can use the sampling distribution of $\bar{x}$ for the case with $n = 100$ to compute the probability that a simple random sample of 100 EAI managers will provide a sample mean that is within \$500 of the population mean. Because the sampling distribution is normal, with mean 51,800 and standard error of the mean 400, we can use the standard normal probability table to find the area or probability.

At $\bar{x} = 52{,}300$ (see Figure 7.7), we have

$$z = \frac{52{,}300 - 51{,}800}{400} = 1.25$$

FIGURE 7.6 A COMPARISON OF THE SAMPLING DISTRIBUTIONS OF $\bar{x}$ FOR SIMPLE RANDOM SAMPLES OF $n = 30$ AND $n = 100$ EAI MANAGERS

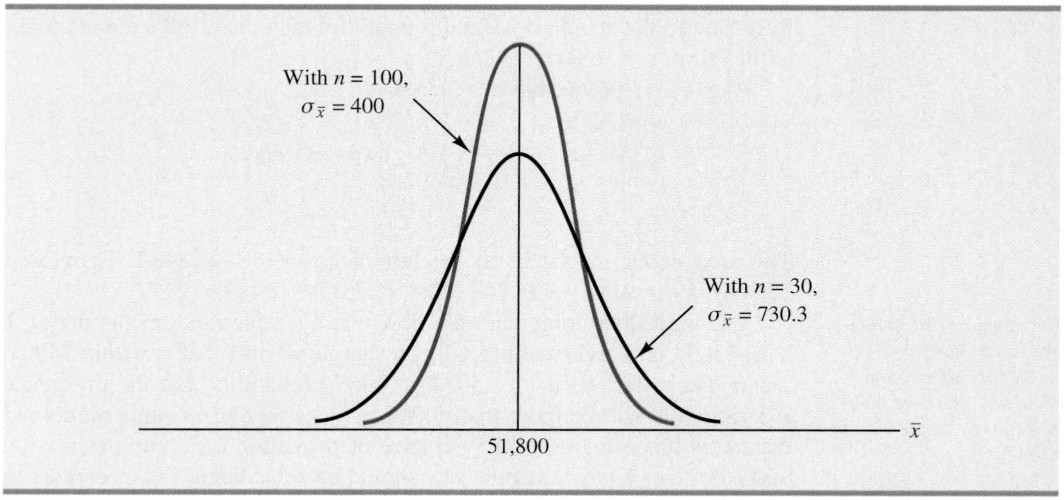

FIGURE 7.7 PROBABILITY OF A SAMPLE MEAN BEING WITHIN $500 OF THE POPULATION MEAN FOR A SIMPLE RANDOM SAMPLE OF 100 EAI MANAGERS

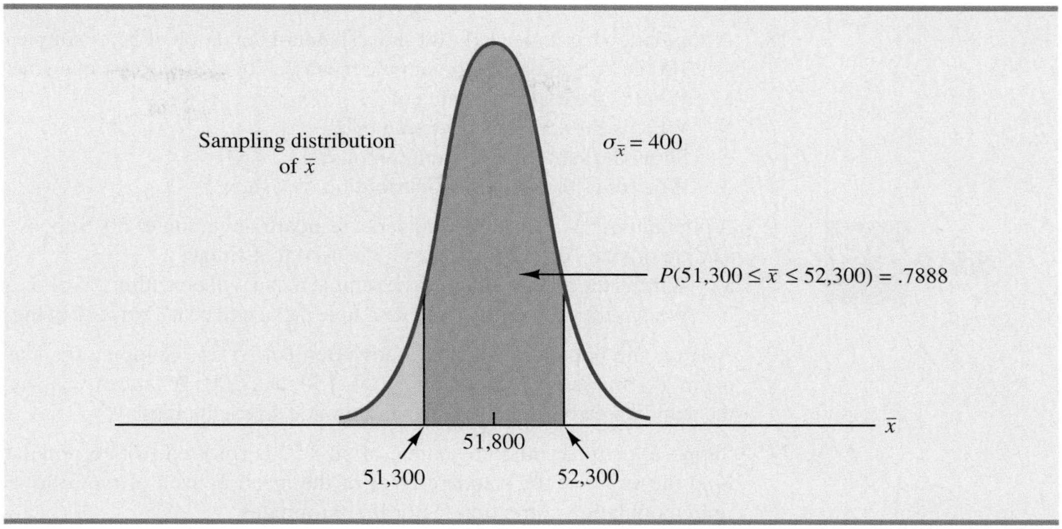

Referring to the standard normal probability table, we find a cumulative probability corresponding to $z = 1.25$ of .8944.

At $\bar{x} = 51{,}300$, we have

$$z = \frac{51{,}300 - 51{,}800}{400} = -1.25$$

The cumulative probability corresponding to $z = -1.25$ is .1056. Therefore, $P(51{,}300 \le \bar{x} \le 52{,}300) = P(z \le 1.25) - P(z \le -1.25) = .8944 - .1056 = .7888$. Thus, by increasing the sample size from 30 to 100 EAI managers, we increase the probability of obtaining a sample mean within $500 of the population mean from .5034 to .7888.

The important point in this discussion is that as the sample size is increased, the standard error of the mean decreases. As a result, the larger sample size provides a higher probability that the sample mean is within a specified distance of the population mean.

NOTES AND COMMENTS

1. In presenting the sampling distribution of $\bar{x}$ for the EAI problem, we took advantage of the fact that the population mean $\mu = 51{,}800$ and the population standard deviation $\sigma = 4000$ were known. However, usually the values of the population mean μ and the population standard deviation σ that are needed to determine the sampling distribution of $\bar{x}$ will be unknown. In Chapter 8 we will show how the sample mean $\bar{x}$ and the sample standard deviation s are used when μ and σ are unknown.
2. The theoretical proof of the central limit theorem requires independent observations in the sample. This condition is met for infinite populations and for finite populations where sampling is done with replacement. Although the central limit theorem does not directly address sampling without replacement from finite populations, general statistical practice applies the findings of the central limit theorem when the population size is large.

Exercises

Methods

18. A population has a mean of 200 and a standard deviation of 50. A simple random sample of size 100 will be taken and the sample mean $\bar{x}$ will be used to estimate the population mean.
    a. What is the expected value of $\bar{x}$?
    b. What is the standard deviation of $\bar{x}$?
    c. Show the sampling distribution of $\bar{x}$.
    d. What does the sampling distribution of $\bar{x}$ show?

SELF test

19. A population has a mean of 200 and a standard deviation of 50. Suppose a simple random sample of size 100 is selected and $\bar{x}$ is used to estimate μ.
    a. What is the probability that the sample mean will be within ± 5 of the population mean?
    b. What is the probability that the sample mean will be within ± 10 of the population mean?

20. Assume the population standard deviation is $\sigma = 25$. Compute the standard error of the mean, $\sigma_{\bar{x}}$, for sample sizes of 50, 100, 150, and 200. What can you say about the size of the standard error of the mean as the sample size is increased?

21. Suppose a simple random sample of size 50 is selected from a population with $\sigma = 10$. Find the value of the standard error of the mean in each of the following cases (use the finite population correction factor if appropriate).
    a. The population size is infinite.
    b. The population size is $N = 50{,}000$.
    c. The population size is $N = 5000$.
    d. The population size is $N = 500$.

Applications

22. Refer to the EAI sampling problem. Suppose a simple random sample of 60 managers is used.
    a. Sketch the sampling distribution of $\bar{x}$ when simple random samples of size 60 are used.
    b. What happens to the sampling distribution of $\bar{x}$ if simple random samples of size 120 are used?
    c. What general statement can you make about what happens to the sampling distribution of $\bar{x}$ as the sample size is increased? Does this generalization seem logical? Explain.

SELF test

23. In the EAI sampling problem (see Figure 7.5), we showed that for $n = 30$, there was .5034 probability of obtaining a sample mean within $\pm\$500$ of the population mean.
    a. What is the probability that $\bar{x}$ is within \$500 of the population mean if a sample of size 60 is used?
    b. Answer part (a) for a sample of size 120.

24. The mean tuition cost at state universities throughout the United States is \$4260 per year (*St. Petersburg Times,* December 11, 2002). Use this value as the population mean and assume that the population standard deviation is $\sigma = \$900$. Suppose that a random sample of 50 state universities will be selected.
    a. Show the sampling distribution of $\bar{x}$ where $\bar{x}$ is the sample mean tuition cost for the 50 state universities.
    b. What is the probability that the simple random sample will provide a sample mean within \$250 of the population mean?
    c. What is the probability that the simple random sample will provide a sample mean within \$100 of the population mean?

25. The College Board American College Testing Program reported a population mean SAT score of $\mu = 1020$ (*The World Almanac 2003*). Assume that the population standard deviation is $\sigma = 100$.

a. What is the probability that a random sample of 75 students will provide a sample mean SAT score within 10 of the population mean?

b. What is the probability a random sample of 75 students will provide a sample mean SAT score within 20 of the population mean?

26. The mean annual cost of automobile insurance is \$939 (*CNBC,* February 23, 2006). Assume that the standard deviation is $\sigma = \$245$.

a. What is the probability that a simple random sample of automobile insurance policies will have a sample mean within \$25 of the population mean for each of the following sample sizes: 30, 50, 100, and 400?

b. What is the advantage of a larger sample size when attempting to estimate the population mean?

27. *BusinessWeek* conducted a survey of graduates from 30 top MBA programs (*BusinessWeek,* September 22, 2003). On the basis of the survey, assume that the mean annual salary for male and female graduates 10 years after graduation is \$168,000 and \$117,000, respectively. Assume the standard deviation for the male graduates is \$40,000, and for the female graduates it is \$25,000.

a. What is the probability that a simple random sample of 40 male graduates will provide a sample mean within \$10,000 of the population mean, \$168,000?

b. What is the probability that a simple random sample of 40 female graduates will provide a sample mean within \$10,000 of the population mean, \$117,000?

c. In which of the preceding two cases, part (a) or part (b), do we have a higher probability of obtaining a sample estimate within \$10,000 of the population mean? Why?

d. What is the probability that a simple random sample of 100 male graduates will provide a sample mean more than \$4000 below the population mean?

28. The average score for male golfers is 95 and the average score for female golfers is 106 (*Golf Digest,* April 2006). Use these values as the population means for men and women and assume that the population standard deviation is $\sigma = 14$ strokes for both. A simple random sample of 30 male golfers and another simple random sample of 45 female golfers will be taken.

a. Show the sampling distribution of $\bar{x}$ for male golfers.

b. What is the probability that the sample mean is within 3 strokes of the population mean for the sample of male golfers?

c. What is the probability that the sample mean is within 3 strokes of the population mean for the sample of female golfers?

d. In which case, part (b) or part (c), is the probability of obtaining a sample mean within 3 strokes of the population mean higher? Why?

29. The average price of a gallon of unleaded regular gasoline was reported to be \$2.34 in northern Kentucky (*The Cincinnati Enquirer,* January 21, 2006). Use this price as the population mean, and assume the population standard deviation is \$.20.

a. What is the probability that the mean price for a sample of 30 service stations is within \$.03 of the population mean?

b. What is the probability that the mean price for a sample of 50 service stations is within \$.03 of the population mean?

c. What is the probability that the mean price for a sample of 100 service stations is within \$.03 of the population mean?

d. Which, if any, of the sample sizes in parts (a), (b), and (c) would you recommend to have at least a .95 probability that the sample mean is within \$.03 of the population mean?

30. To estimate the mean age for a population of 4000 employees, a simple random sample of 40 employees is selected.

a. Would you use the finite population correction factor in calculating the standard error of the mean? Explain.

b. If the population standard deviation is $\sigma = 8.2$ years, compute the standard error both with and without the finite population correction factor. What is the rationale for ignoring the finite population correction factor whenever $n/N \leq .05$?
c. What is the probability that the sample mean age of the employees will be within ± 2 years of the population mean age?

7.6 Sampling Distribution of $\bar{p}$

The sample proportion $\bar{p}$ is the point estimator of the population proportion p. The formula for computing the sample proportion is

$$\bar{p} = \frac{x}{n}$$

where

x = the number of elements in the sample that possess the characteristic of interest
n = sample size

As noted in Section 7.4, the sample proportion $\bar{p}$ is a random variable and its probability distribution is called the sampling distribution of $\bar{p}$.

SAMPLING DISTRIBUTION OF $\bar{p}$

The sampling distribution of $\bar{p}$ is the probability distribution of all possible values of the sample proportion $\bar{p}$.

To determine how close the sample proportion $\bar{p}$ is to the population proportion p, we need to understand the properties of the sampling distribution of $\bar{p}$: the expected value of $\bar{p}$, the standard deviation of $\bar{p}$, and the shape or form of the sampling distribution of $\bar{p}$.

Expected Value of $\bar{p}$

The expected value of $\bar{p}$, the mean of all possible values of $\bar{p}$, is equal to the population proportion p.

EXPECTED VALUE OF $\bar{p}$

$$E(\bar{p}) = p \tag{7.4}$$

where

$E(\bar{p})$ = the expected value of $\bar{p}$
p = the population proportion

Because $E(\bar{p}) = p$, $\bar{p}$ is an unbiased estimator of p. Recall from Section 7.1 we noted that $p = .60$ for the EAI population, where p is the proportion of the population of managers who participated in the company's management training program. Thus, the expected value of $\bar{p}$ for the EAI sampling problem is .60.

Standard Deviation of $\bar{p}$

Just as we found for the standard deviation of $\bar{x}$, the standard deviation of $\bar{p}$ depends on whether the population is finite or infinite. The two formulas for computing the standard deviation of $\bar{p}$ follow.

STANDARD DEVIATION OF $\bar{p}$

Finite Population | *Infinite Population*

$$\sigma_{\bar{p}} = \sqrt{\frac{N-n}{N-1}}\sqrt{\frac{p(1-p)}{n}} \qquad \sigma_{\bar{p}} = \sqrt{\frac{p(1-p)}{n}} \tag{7.5}$$

Comparing the two formulas in (7.5), we see that the only difference is the use of the finite population correction factor $\sqrt{(N-n)/(N-1)}$.

As was the case with the sample mean $\bar{x}$, the difference between the expressions for the finite population and the infinite population becomes negligible if the size of the finite population is large in comparison to the sample size. We follow the same rule of thumb that we recommended for the sample mean. That is, if the population is finite with $n/N \leq .05$, we will use $\sigma_{\bar{p}} = \sqrt{p(1-p)/n}$. However, if the population is finite with $n/N > .05$, the finite population correction factor should be used. Again, unless specifically noted, throughout the text we will assume that the population size is large in relation to the sample size and thus the finite population correction factor is unnecessary.

In Section 7.5 we used standard error of the mean to refer to the standard deviation of $\bar{x}$. We stated that in general the term standard error refers to the standard deviation of a point estimator. Thus, for proportions we use *standard error of the proportion* to refer to the standard deviation of $\bar{p}$. Let us now return to the EAI example and compute the standard error of the proportion associated with simple random samples of 30 EAI managers.

For the EAI study we know that the population proportion of managers who participated in the management training program is $p = .60$. With $n/N = 30/2500 = .012$, we can ignore the finite population correction factor when we compute the standard error of the proportion. For the simple random sample of 30 managers, $\sigma_{\bar{p}}$ is

$$\sigma_{\bar{p}} = \sqrt{\frac{p(1-p)}{n}} = \sqrt{\frac{.60(1-.60)}{30}} = .0894$$

Form of the Sampling Distribution of $\bar{p}$

Now that we know the mean and standard deviation of the sampling distribution of $\bar{p}$, the final step is to determine the form or shape of the sampling distribution. The sample proportion is $\bar{p} = x/n$. For a simple random sample from a large population, the value of x is a binomial random variable indicating the number of elements in the sample with the characteristic of interest. Because n is a constant, the probability of x/n is the same as the binomial probability of x, which means that the sampling distribution of $\bar{p}$ is also a discrete probability distribution and that the probability for each value of x/n is the same as the probability of x.

In Chapter 6 we also showed that a binomial distribution can be approximated by a normal distribution whenever the sample size is large enough to satisfy the following two conditions:

$$np \geq 5 \quad \text{and} \quad n(1 - p) \geq 5$$

Assuming these two conditions are satisfied, the probability distribution of x in the sample proportion, $\bar{p} = x/n$, can be approximated by a normal distribution. And because n is a constant, the sampling distribution of $\bar{p}$ can also be approximated by a normal distribution. This approximation is stated as follows:

> The sampling distribution of $\bar{p}$ can be approximated by a normal distribution whenever $np \geq 5$ and $n(1 - p) \geq 5$.

In practical applications, when an estimate of a population proportion is desired, we find that sample sizes are almost always large enough to permit the use of a normal approximation for the sampling distribution of $\bar{p}$.

Recall that for the EAI sampling problem we know that the population proportion of managers who participated in the training program is $p = .60$. With a simple random sample of size 30, we have $np = 30(.60) = 18$ and $n(1 - p) = 30(.40) = 12$. Thus, the sampling distribution of $\bar{p}$ can be approximated by a normal distribution shown in Figure 7.8.

Practical Value of the Sampling Distribution of $\bar{p}$

The practical value of the sampling distribution of $\bar{p}$ is that it can be used to provide probability information about the difference between the sample proportion and the population proportion. For instance, suppose that in the EAI problem the personnel director wants to know the probability of obtaining a value of $\bar{p}$ that is within .05 of the population proportion of EAI managers who participated in the training program. That is, what is the probability of obtaining a sample with a sample proportion $\bar{p}$ between .55 and .65? The darkly

FIGURE 7.8 SAMPLING DISTRIBUTION OF $\bar{p}$ FOR THE PROPORTION OF EAI MANAGERS WHO PARTICIPATED IN THE MANAGEMENT TRAINING PROGRAM

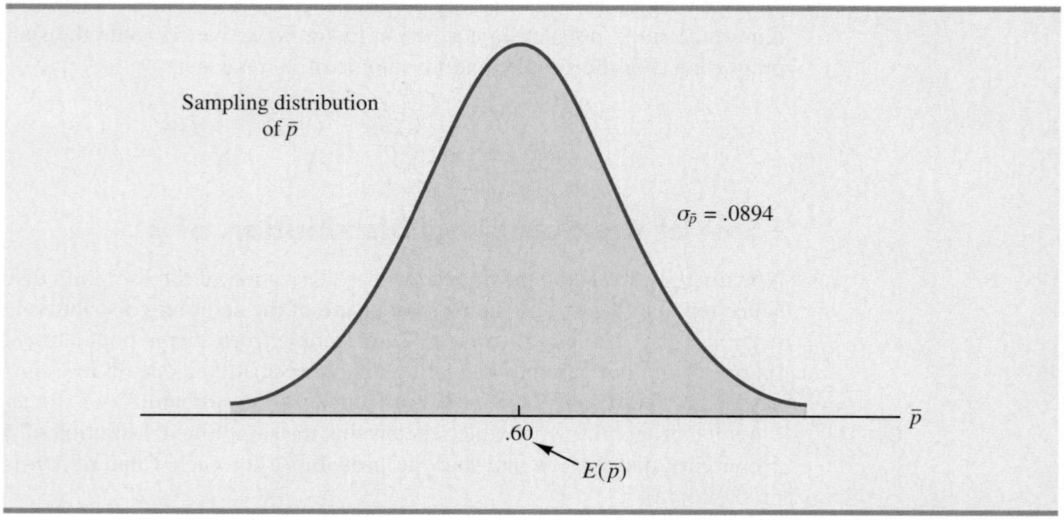

FIGURE 7.9 PROBABILITY OF OBTAINING $\bar{p}$ BETWEEN .55 AND .65

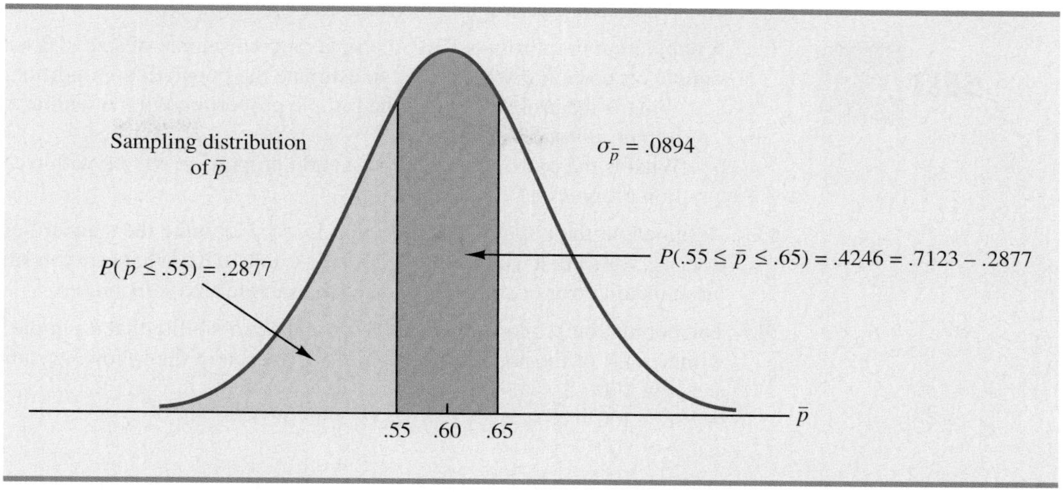

shaded area in Figure 7.9 shows this probability. Using the fact that the sampling distribution of $\bar{p}$ can be approximated by a normal distribution with a mean of .60 and a standard error of the proportion of $\sigma_{\bar{p}} = .0894$, we find that the standard normal random variable corresponding to $\bar{p} = .65$ has a value of $z = (.65 - .60)/.0894 = .56$. Referring to the standard normal probability table, we see that the cumulative probability corresponding to $z = .56$ is .7123. Similarly at $\bar{p} = .55$, we find $z = (.55 - .60)/.0894 = -.56$. From the standard normal probability table, we find the cumulative probability corresponding to $z = -.56$ is .2877. Thus, the probability of selecting a sample that provides a sample proportion $\bar{p}$ within .05 of the population proportion p is given by $.7123 - .2877 = .4246$.

If we consider increasing the sample size to $n = 100$, the standard error of the proportion becomes

$$\sigma_{\bar{p}} = \sqrt{\frac{.60(1 - .60)}{100}} = .049$$

With a sample size of 100 EAI managers, the probability of the sample proportion having a value within .05 of the population proportion can now be computed. Because the sampling distribution is approximately normal, with mean .60 and standard deviation .049, we can use the standard normal probability table to find the area or probability. At $\bar{p} = .65$, we have $z = (.65 - .60)/.049 = 1.02$. Referring to the standard normal probability table, we see that the cumulative probability corresponding to $z = 1.02$ is .8461. Similarly, at $\bar{p} = .55$, we have $z = (.55 - .60)/.049 = -1.02$. We find the cumulative probability corresponding to $z = -1.02$ is .1539. Thus, if the sample size is increased from 30 to 100, the probability that the sample proportion $\bar{p}$ is within .05 of the population proportion p will increase to $.8461 - .1539 = .6922$.

Exercises

Methods

31. A simple random sample of size 100 is selected from a population with $p = .40$.
    a. What is the expected value of $\bar{p}$?
    b. What is the standard error of $\bar{p}$?

c. Show the sampling distribution of $\bar{p}$.
d. What does the sampling distribution of $\bar{p}$ show?

SELF test

32. A population proportion is .40. A simple random sample of size 200 will be taken and the sample proportion $\bar{p}$ will be used to estimate the population proportion.
    a. What is the probability that the sample proportion will be within $\pm.03$ of the population proportion?
    b. What is the probability that the sample proportion will be within $\pm.05$ of the population proportion?
33. Assume that the population proportion is .55. Compute the standard error of the proportion, $\sigma_{\bar{p}}$, for sample sizes of 100, 200, 500, and 1000. What can you say about the size of the standard error of the proportion as the sample size is increased?
34. The population proportion is .30. What is the probability that a sample proportion will be within $\pm.04$ of the population proportion for each of the following sample sizes?
    a. $n = 100$
    b. $n = 200$
    c. $n = 500$
    d. $n = 1000$
    e. What is the advantage of a larger sample size?

Applications

SELF test

35. The president of Doerman Distributors, Inc., believes that 30% of the firm's orders come from first-time customers. A simple random sample of 100 orders will be used to estimate the proportion of first-time customers.
    a. Assume that the president is correct and $p = .30$. What is the sampling distribution of $\bar{p}$ for this study?
    b. What is the probability that the sample proportion $\bar{p}$ will be between .20 and .40?
    c. What is the probability that the sample proportion will be between .25 and .35?
36. *The Cincinnati Enquirer* reported that, in the United States, 66% of adults and 87% of youths ages 12 to 17 use the Internet (*The Cincinnati Enquirer,* February 7, 2006). Use the reported numbers as the population proportions and assume that samples of 300 adults and 300 youths will be used to learn about attitudes toward Internet security.
    a. Show the sampling distribution of $\bar{p}$ where $\bar{p}$ is the sample proportion of adults using the Internet.
    b. What is the probability that the sample proportion of adults using the Internet will be within $\pm.04$ of the population proportion?
    c. What is the probability that the sample proportion of youths using the Internet will be within $\pm.04$ of the population proportion?
    d. Is the probability different in parts (b) and (c)? If so, why?
    e. Answer part (b) for a sample of size 600. Is the probability smaller? Why?
37. *Time*/CNN voter polls monitored public opinion for the presidential candidates during the 2000 presidential election campaign. One *Time*/CNN poll conducted by Yankelovich Partners, Inc., used a sample of 589 likely voters (*Time,* June 26, 2000). Assume the population proportion for a presidential candidate is $p = .50$. Let $\bar{p}$ be the sample proportion of likely voters favoring the presidential candidate.
    a. Show the sampling distribution of $\bar{p}$.
    b. What is the probability the *Time*/CNN poll will provide a sample proportion within $\pm.04$ of the population proportion?
    c. What is the probability the *Time*/CNN poll will provide a sample proportion within $\pm.03$ of the population proportion?
    d. What is the probability the *Time*/CNN poll will provide a sample proportion within $\pm.02$ of the population proportion?

38. Roper ASW conducted a survey to learn about American adults' attitudes toward money and happiness (*Money,* October 2003). Fifty-six percent of the respondents said they balance their checkbook at least once a month.
    a. Suppose a sample of 400 American adults were taken. Show the sampling distribution of the proportion of adults who balance their checkbook at least once a month.
    b. What is the probability that the sample proportion will be within $\pm.02$ of the population proportion?
    c. What is the probability that the sample proportion will be within $\pm.04$ of the population proportion?

39. The *Democrat and Chronicle* reported that 25% of the flights arriving at the San Diego airport during the first five months of 2001 were late (*Democrat and Chronicle,* July 23, 2001). Assume the population proportion is $p = .25$.
    a. Show the sampling distribution of $\bar{p}$, the proportion of late flights in a sample of 1000 flights.
    b. What is the probability that the sample proportion will be within $\pm.03$ of the population proportion if a sample of size 1000 is selected?
    c. Answer part (b) for a sample of 500 flights.

40. The Grocery Manufacturers of America reported that 76% of consumers read the ingredients listed on a product's label. Assume the population proportion is $p = .76$ and a sample of 400 consumers is selected from the population.
    a. Show the sampling distribution of the sample proportion $\bar{p}$ where $\bar{p}$ is the proportion of the sampled consumers who read the ingredients listed on a product's label.
    b. What is the probability that the sample proportion will be within $\pm.03$ of the population proportion?
    c. Answer part (b) for a sample of 750 consumers.

41. The Food Marketing Institute shows that 17% of households spend more than \$100 per week on groceries. Assume the population proportion is $p = .17$ and a simple random sample of 800 households will be selected from the population.
    a. Show the sampling distribution of $\bar{p}$, the sample proportion of households spending more than \$100 per week on groceries.
    b. What is the probability that the sample proportion will be within $\pm.02$ of the population proportion?
    c. Answer part (b) for a sample of 1600 households.

7.7 Properties of Point Estimators

In this chapter we showed how sample statistics such as a sample mean $\bar{x}$, a sample standard deviation s, and a sample proportion $\bar{p}$ can be used as point estimators of their corresponding population parameters μ, σ, and p. It is intuitively appealing that each of these sample statistics is the point estimator of its corresponding population parameter. However, before using a sample statistic as a point estimator, statisticians check to see whether the sample statistic demonstrates certain properties associated with good point estimators. In this section we discuss the properties of good point estimators: unbiased, efficiency, and consistency.

Because several different sample statistics can be used as point estimators of different population parameters, we use the following general notation in this section.

$$\theta = \text{the population parameter of interest}$$
$$\hat{\theta} = \text{the sample statistic or point estimator of } \theta$$

The notation θ is the Greek letter theta, and the notation $\hat{\theta}$ is pronounced "theta-hat." In general, θ represents any population parameter such as a population mean, population standard deviation, population proportion, and so on; $\hat{\theta}$ represents the corresponding sample statistic such as the sample mean, sample standard deviation, and sample proportion.

Unbiased

If the expected value of the sample statistic is equal to the population parameter being estimated, the sample statistic is said to be an *unbiased estimator* of the population parameter.

UNBIASED

The sample statistic $\hat{\theta}$ is an unbiased estimator of the population parameter θ if

$$E(\hat{\theta}) = \theta$$

where

$$E(\hat{\theta}) = \text{the expected value of the sample statistic } \hat{\theta}$$

Hence, the expected value, or mean, of all possible values of an unbiased sample statistic is equal to the population parameter being estimated.

Figure 7.10 shows the cases of unbiased and biased point estimators. In the illustration showing the unbiased estimator, the mean of the sampling distribution is equal to the value of the population parameter. The estimation errors balance out in this case, because sometimes the value of the point estimator $\hat{\theta}$ may be less than θ and other times it may be greater than θ. In the case of a biased estimator, the mean of the sampling distribution is less than or greater than the value of the population parameter. In the illustration in Panel B of Figure 7.10, $E(\hat{\theta})$ is greater than θ; thus, the sample statistic has a high probability of overestimating the value of the population parameter. The amount of the bias is shown in the figure.

FIGURE 7.10 EXAMPLES OF UNBIASED AND BIASED POINT ESTIMATORS

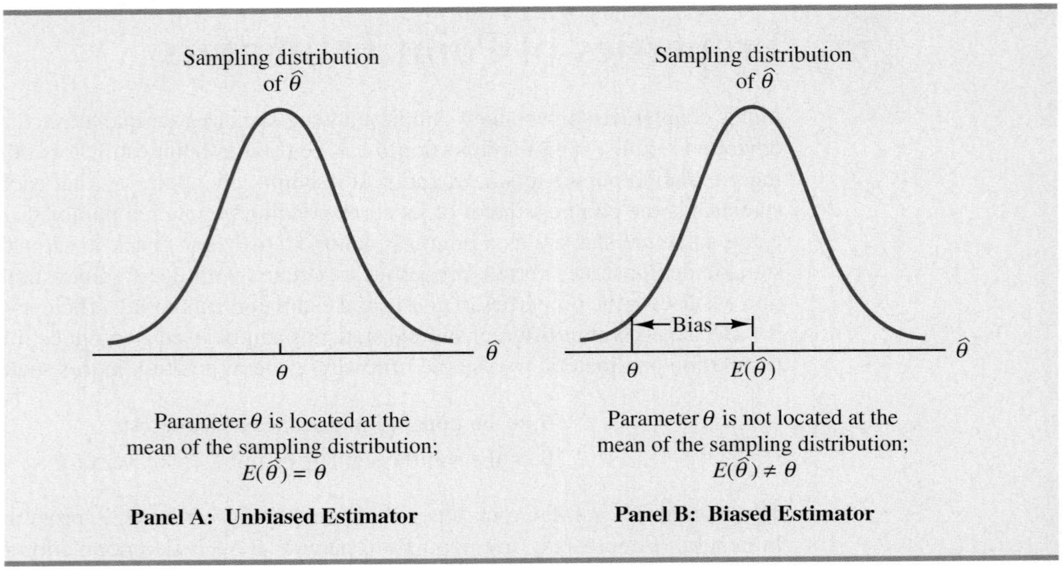

In discussing the sampling distributions of the sample mean and the sample proportion, we stated that $E(\bar{x}) = \mu$ and $E(\bar{p}) = p$. Thus, both $\bar{x}$ and $\bar{p}$ are unbiased estimators of their corresponding population parameters μ and p.

In the case of the sample standard deviation s and the sample variance s^2, it can be shown that $E(s^2) = \sigma^2$. Thus, we conclude that the sample variance s^2 is an unbiased estimator of the population variance σ^2. In fact, when we first presented the formulas for the sample variance and the sample standard deviation in Chapter 3, $n - 1$ rather than n was used in the denominator. The reason for using $n - 1$ rather than n is to make the sample variance an unbiased estimator of the population variance.

Efficiency

Assume that a simple random sample of n elements can be used to provide two unbiased point estimators of the same population parameter. In this situation, we would prefer to use the point estimator with the smaller standard error, because it tends to provide estimates closer to the population parameter. The point estimator with the smaller standard error is said to have greater **relative efficiency** than the other.

Figure 7.11 shows the sampling distributions of two unbiased point estimators, $\hat{\theta}_1$ and $\hat{\theta}_2$. Note that the standard error of $\hat{\theta}_1$ is less than the standard error of $\hat{\theta}_2$; thus, values of $\hat{\theta}_1$ have a greater chance of being close to the parameter θ than do values of $\hat{\theta}_2$. Because the standard error of point estimator $\hat{\theta}_1$ is less than the standard error of point estimator $\hat{\theta}_2$, $\hat{\theta}_1$ is relatively more efficient than $\hat{\theta}_2$ and is the preferred point estimator.

When sampling from a normal population, the standard error of the sample mean is less than the standard error of the sample median. Thus, the sample mean is more efficient than the sample median.

Consistency

A third property associated with good point estimators is **consistency**. Loosely speaking, a point estimator is consistent if the values of the point estimator tend to become closer to the population parameter as the sample size becomes larger. In other words, a large sample size tends to provide a better point estimate than a small sample size. Note that for the sample mean $\bar{x}$, we showed that the standard error of $\bar{x}$ is given by $\sigma_{\bar{x}} = \sigma/\sqrt{n}$. Because $\sigma_{\bar{x}}$ is related to the sample size such that larger sample sizes provide smaller

FIGURE 7.11 SAMPLING DISTRIBUTIONS OF TWO UNBIASED POINT ESTIMATORS

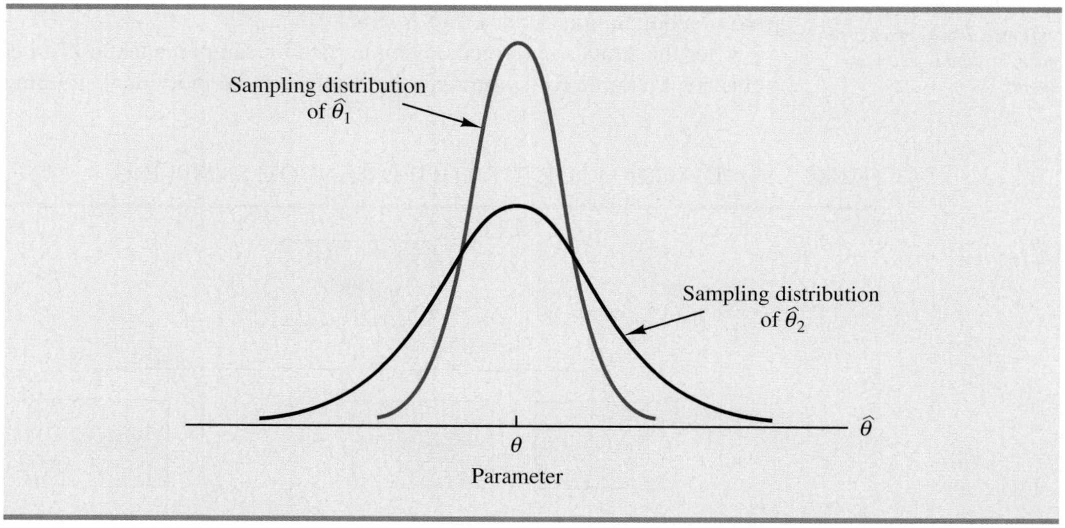

values for $\sigma_{\bar{x}}$, we conclude that a larger sample size tends to provide point estimates closer to the population mean μ. In this sense, we can say that the sample mean $\bar{x}$ is a consistent estimator of the population mean μ. Using a similar rationale, we can also conclude that the sample proportion $\bar{p}$ is a consistent estimator of the population proportion p.

NOTES AND COMMENTS

In Chapter 3 we stated that the mean and the median are two measures of central location. In this chapter we discussed only the mean. The reason is that in sampling from a normal population, where the population mean and population median are identical, the standard error of the median is approximately 25% larger than the standard error of the mean. Recall that in the EAI problem where $n = 30$, the standard error of the mean is $\sigma_{\bar{x}} = 730.3$. The standard error of the median for this problem would be $1.25 \times (730.3) = 913$. As a result, the sample mean is more efficient and will have a higher probability of being within a specified distance of the population mean.

7.8 Other Sampling Methods

This section provides a brief introduction to sampling methods other than simple random sampling.

We described the simple random sampling procedure and discussed the properties of the sampling distributions of $\bar{x}$ and $\bar{p}$ when simple random sampling is used. However, simple random sampling is not the only sampling method available. Such methods as stratified random sampling, cluster sampling, and systematic sampling provide advantages over simple random sampling in some situations. In this section we briefly introduce these alternative sampling methods. A more in-depth treatment is provided in Chapter 22, which is located on the CD that accompanies the text.

Stratified Random Sampling

Stratified random sampling works best when the variance among elements in each stratum is relatively small.

In **stratified random sampling**, the elements in the population are first divided into groups called *strata,* such that each element in the population belongs to one and only one stratum. The basis for forming the strata, such as department, location, age, industry type, and so on, is at the discretion of the designer of the sample. However, the best results are obtained when the elements within each stratum are as much alike as possible. Figure 7.12 is a diagram of a population divided into H strata.

After the strata are formed, a simple random sample is taken from each stratum. Formulas are available for combining the results for the individual stratum samples into one

FIGURE 7.12 DIAGRAM FOR STRATIFIED RANDOM SAMPLING

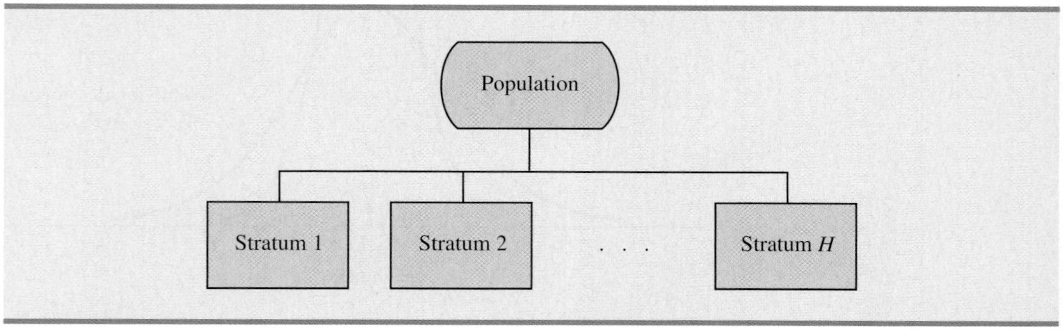

FIGURE 7.13 DIAGRAM FOR CLUSTER SAMPLING

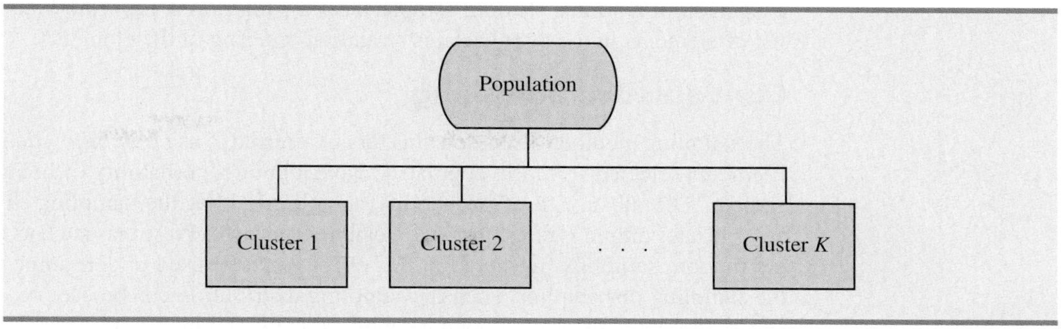

estimate of the population parameter of interest. The value of stratified random sampling depends on how homogeneous the elements are within the strata. If elements within strata are alike, the strata will have low variances. Thus relatively small sample sizes can be used to obtain good estimates of the strata characteristics. If strata are homogeneous, the stratified random sampling procedure provides results just as precise as those of simple random sampling by using a smaller total sample size.

Cluster Sampling

Cluster sampling works best when each cluster provides a small-scale representation of the population.

In **cluster sampling**, the elements in the population are first divided into separate groups called *clusters*. Each element of the population belongs to one and only one cluster (see Figure 7.13). A simple random sample of the clusters is then taken. All elements within each sampled cluster form the sample. Cluster sampling tends to provide the best results when the elements within the clusters are not alike. In the ideal case, each cluster is a representative small-scale version of the entire population. The value of cluster sampling depends on how representative each cluster is of the entire population. If all clusters are alike in this regard, sampling a small number of clusters will provide good estimates of the population parameters.

One of the primary applications of cluster sampling is area sampling, where clusters are city blocks or other well-defined areas. Cluster sampling generally requires a larger total sample size than either simple random sampling or stratified random sampling. However, it can result in cost savings because of the fact that when an interviewer is sent to a sampled cluster (e.g., a city-block location), many sample observations can be obtained in a relatively short time. Hence, a larger sample size may be obtainable with a significantly lower total cost.

Systematic Sampling

In some sampling situations, especially those with large populations, it is time-consuming to select a simple random sample by first finding a random number and then counting or searching through the list of the population until the corresponding element is found. An alternative to simple random sampling is **systematic sampling**. For example, if a sample size of 50 is desired from a population containing 5000 elements, we will sample one element for every $5000/50 = 100$ elements in the population. A systematic sample for this case involves selecting randomly one of the first 100 elements from the population list. Other sample elements are identified by starting with the first sampled element and then selecting every 100th element that follows in the population list. In effect, the sample of 50 is identified by moving systematically through the population and identifying every 100th element after the first randomly selected element. The sample of 50 usually will be easier to identify in this way than it would be if simple random sampling were used. Because the first element selected is a random choice, a systematic sample is usually assumed to have the properties of a simple random sample. This assumption is especially applicable when the list of elements in the population is a random ordering of the elements.

Convenience Sampling

The sampling methods discussed thus far are referred to as *probability sampling* techniques. Elements selected from the population have a known probability of being included in the sample. The advantage of probability sampling is that the sampling distribution of the appropriate sample statistic generally can be identified. Formulas such as the ones for simple random sampling presented in this chapter can be used to determine the properties of the sampling distribution. Then the sampling distribution can be used to make probability statements about the error associated with using the sample results to make inferences about the population.

Convenience sampling is a *nonprobability sampling* technique. As the name implies, the sample is identified primarily by convenience. Elements are included in the sample without prespecified or known probabilities of being selected. For example, a professor conducting research at a university may use student volunteers to constitute a sample simply because they are readily available and will participate as subjects for little or no cost. Similarly, an inspector may sample a shipment of oranges by selecting oranges haphazardly from among several crates. Labeling each orange and using a probability method of sampling would be impractical. Samples such as wildlife captures and volunteer panels for consumer research are also convenience samples.

Convenience samples have the advantage of relatively easy sample selection and data collection; however, it is impossible to evaluate the "goodness" of the sample in terms of its representativeness of the population. A convenience sample may provide good results or it may not; no statistically justified procedure allows a probability analysis and inference about the quality of the sample results. Sometimes researchers apply statistical methods designed for probability samples to a convenience sample, arguing that the convenience sample can be treated as though it were a probability sample. However, this argument cannot be supported, and we should be cautious in interpreting the results of convenience samples that are used to make inferences about populations.

Judgment Sampling

One additional nonprobability sampling technique is **judgment sampling**. In this approach, the person most knowledgeable on the subject of the study selects elements of the population that he or she feels are most representative of the population. Often this method is a relatively easy way of selecting a sample. For example, a reporter may sample two or three senators, judging that those senators reflect the general opinion of all senators. However, the quality of the sample results depends on the judgment of the person selecting the sample. Again, great caution is warranted in drawing conclusions based on judgment samples used to make inferences about populations.

NOTES AND COMMENTS

We recommend using probability sampling methods: simple random sampling, stratified random sampling, cluster sampling, or systematic sampling. For these methods, formulas are available for evaluating the "goodness" of the sample results in terms of the closeness of the results to the population parameters being estimated. An evaluation of the goodness cannot be made with convenience or judgment sampling. Thus, great care should be used in interpreting the results based on nonprobability sampling methods.

Summary

In this chapter we presented the concepts of simple random sampling and sampling distributions. We demonstrated how a simple random sample can be selected and how the data collected for the sample can be used to develop point estimates of population parameters. Because different simple random samples provide different values for the point estimators, point estimators such as $\bar{x}$ and $\bar{p}$ are random variables. The probability distribution of such a random variable is called a sampling distribution. In particular, we described the sampling distributions of the sample mean $\bar{x}$ and the sample proportion $\bar{p}$.

In considering the characteristics of the sampling distributions of $\bar{x}$ and $\bar{p}$, we stated that $E(\bar{x}) = \mu$ and $E(\bar{p}) = p$. After developing the standard deviation or standard error formulas for these estimators, we described the conditions necessary for the sampling distributions of $\bar{x}$ and $\bar{p}$ to follow a normal distribution. Other sampling methods including stratified random sampling, cluster sampling, systematic sampling, convenience sampling, and judgment sampling were discussed.

Glossary

Parameter A numerical characteristic of a population, such as a population mean μ, a population standard deviation σ, a population proportion p, and so on.

Simple random sampling Finite population: a sample selected such that each possible sample of size n has the same probability of being selected. Infinite population: a sample selected such that each element comes from the same population and the elements are selected independently.

Sampling without replacement Once an element has been included in the sample, it is removed from the population and cannot be selected a second time.

Sampling with replacement Once an element has been included in the sample, it is returned to the population. A previously selected element can be selected again and therefore may appear in the sample more than once.

Sample statistic A sample characteristic, such as a sample mean $\bar{x}$, a sample standard deviation s, a sample proportion $\bar{p}$, and so on. The value of the sample statistic is used to estimate the value of the corresponding population parameter.

Point estimator The sample statistic, such as $\bar{x}$, s, or $\bar{p}$, that provides the point estimate of the population parameter.

Point estimate The value of a point estimator used in a particular instance as an estimate of a population parameter.

Sampling distribution A probability distribution consisting of all possible values of a sample statistic.

Unbiased A property of a point estimator that is present when the expected value of the point estimator is equal to the population parameter it estimates.

Finite population correction factor The term $\sqrt{(N - n)/(N - 1)}$ that is used in the formulas for $\sigma_{\bar{x}}$ and $\sigma_{\bar{p}}$ whenever a finite population, rather than an infinite population, is being sampled. The generally accepted rule of thumb is to ignore the finite population correction factor whenever $n/N \leq .05$.

Standard error The standard deviation of a point estimator.

Central limit theorem A theorem that enables one to use the normal probability distribution to approximate the sampling distribution of $\bar{x}$ whenever the sample size is large.

Relative efficiency Given two unbiased point estimators of the same population parameter, the point estimator with the smaller standard error is more efficient.

Consistency A property of a point estimator that is present whenever larger sample sizes tend to provide point estimates closer to the population parameter.

Stratified random sampling A probability sampling method in which the population is first divided into strata and a simple random sample is then taken from each stratum.

Cluster sampling A probability sampling method in which the population is first divided into clusters and then a simple random sample of the clusters is taken.

Systematic sampling A probability sampling method in which we randomly select one of the first k elements and then select every kth element thereafter.

Convenience sampling A nonprobability method of sampling whereby elements are selected for the sample on the basis of convenience.

Judgment sampling A nonprobability method of sampling whereby elements are selected for the sample based on the judgment of the person doing the study.

Key Formulas

Expected Value of $\bar{x}$

$$E(\bar{x}) = \mu \tag{7.1}$$

Standard Deviation of $\bar{x}$ (Standard Error)

Finite Population / *Infinite Population*

$$\sigma_{\bar{x}} = \sqrt{\frac{N-n}{N-1}}\left(\frac{\sigma}{\sqrt{n}}\right) \qquad \sigma_{\bar{x}} = \frac{\sigma}{\sqrt{n}} \tag{7.2}$$

Expected Value of $\bar{p}$

$$E(\bar{p}) = p \tag{7.4}$$

Standard Deviation of $\bar{p}$ (Standard Error)

Finite Population / *Infinite Population*

$$\sigma_{\bar{p}} = \sqrt{\frac{N-n}{N-1}}\sqrt{\frac{p(1-p)}{n}} \qquad \sigma_{\bar{p}} = \sqrt{\frac{p(1-p)}{n}} \tag{7.5}$$

Supplementary Exercises

42. *BusinessWeek*'s Corporate Scoreboard provides quarterly data on sales, profits, net income, return on equity, price/earnings ratio, and earnings per share for 899 companies (*BusinessWeek,* August 14, 2000). The companies can be numbered 1 to 899 in the order they appear on the Corporate Scoreboard list. Begin at the bottom of the second column of random digits in Table 7.1. Ignoring the first two digits in each group and using three-digit random numbers beginning with 112, read *up* the column to identify the number (from 1 to 899) of the first eight companies to be included in a simple random sample.

43. Americans have become increasingly concerned about the rising cost of Medicare. In 1990, the average annual Medicare spending per enrollee was \$3267; in 2003, the average annual Medicare spending per enrollee was \$6883 (*Money,* Fall 2003). Suppose you hired a consulting firm to take a sample of fifty 2003 Medicare enrollees to further investigate the nature of expenditures. Assume the population standard deviation for 2003 was \$2000.
    a. Show the sampling distribution of the mean amount of Medicare spending for a sample of fifty 2003 enrollees.
    b. What is the probability the sample mean will be within $\pm$\$300 of the population mean?
    c. What is the probability the sample mean will be greater than \$7500? If the consulting firm tells you the sample mean for the Medicare enrollees they interviewed was \$7500, would you question whether they followed correct simple random sampling procedures? Why or why not?

44. *BusinessWeek* surveyed MBA alumni 10 years after graduation (*BusinessWeek,* September 22, 2003). One finding was that alumni spend an average of \$115.50 per week eating out socially. You have been asked to conduct a follow-up study by taking a sample of 40 of these MBA alumni. Assume the population standard deviation is \$35.
    a. Show the sampling distribution of $\bar{x}$, the sample mean weekly expenditure for the 40 MBA alumni.
    b. What is the probability the sample mean will be within \$10 of the population mean?
    c. Suppose you find a sample mean of \$100. What is the probability of finding a sample mean of \$100 or less? Would you consider this sample to be an unusually low spending group of alumni? Why or why not?

45. The mean television viewing time for Americans is 15 hours per week (*Money,* November 2003). Suppose a sample of 60 Americans is taken to further investigate viewing habits. Assume the population standard deviation for weekly viewing time is $\sigma = 4$ hours.
    a. What is the probability the sample mean will be within 1 hour of the population mean?
    b. What is the probability the sample mean will be within 45 minutes of the population mean?

46. The average annual salary for federal government employees in Indiana is \$41,979 (*The World Almanac,* 2001). Use this figure as the population mean and assume the population standard deviation is $\sigma =$ \$5000. Suppose that a random sample of 50 federal government employees will be selected from the population.
    a. What is the value of the standard error of the mean?
    b. What is the probability that the sample mean will be more than \$41,979?
    c. What is the probability the sample mean will be within \$1000 of the population mean?
    d. How would the probability in part (c) change if the sample size were increased to 100?

47. Three firms carry inventories that differ in size. Firm A's inventory contains 2000 items, firm B's inventory contains 5000 items, and firm C's inventory contains 10,000 items. The population standard deviation for the cost of the items in each firm's inventory is $\sigma = 144$. A statistical consultant recommends that each firm take a sample of 50 items from its inventory to provide statistically valid estimates of the average cost per item. Managers of the small firm state that because it has the smallest population, it should be able to make the estimate from a much smaller sample than that required by the larger firms. However, the consultant states that to obtain the same standard error and thus the same precision in the sample results, all firms should use the same sample size regardless of population size.
    a. Using the finite population correction factor, compute the standard error for each of the three firms given a sample of size 50.
    b. What is the probability that for each firm the sample mean $\bar{x}$ will be within ± 25 of the population mean μ?

48. A researcher reports survey results by stating that the standard error of the mean is 20. The population standard deviation is 500.
    a. How large was the sample used in this survey?
    b. What is the probability that the point estimate was within ±25 of the population mean?

49. A production process is checked periodically by a quality control inspector. The inspector selects simple random samples of 30 finished products and computes the sample mean product weights $\bar{x}$. If test results over a long period of time show that 5% of the $\bar{x}$ values are over 2.1 pounds and 5% are under 1.9 pounds, what are the mean and the standard deviation for the population of products produced with this process?

50. About 28% of private companies are owned by women (*The Cincinnati Enquirer,* January 26, 2006). Answer the following questions based on a sample of 240 private companies.
    a. Show the sampling distribution of $\bar{p}$, the sample proportion of companies that are owned by women.
    b. What is the probability the sample proportion will be within ±.04 of the population proportion?
    c. What is the probability the sample proportion will be within ±.02 of the population proportion?

51. A market research firm conducts telephone surveys with a 40% historical response rate. What is the probability that in a new sample of 400 telephone numbers, at least 150 individuals will cooperate and respond to the questions? In other words, what is the probability that the sample proportion will be at least 150/400 = .375?

52. Advertisers contract with Internet service providers and search engines to place ads on Web sites. They pay a fee based on the number of potential customers who click on their ad. Unfortunately, click fraud—the practice of someone clicking on an ad solely for the purpose of driving up advertising revenue—has become a problem. Forty percent of advertisers claim they have been a victim of click fraud (*BusinessWeek,* March 13, 2006). Suppose a simple random sample of 380 advertisers will be taken to learn more about how they are affected by this practice.
    a. What is the probability that the sample proportion will be within ±.04 of the population proportion experiencing click fraud?
    b. What is the probability that the sample proportion will be greater than .45?

53. The proportion of individuals insured by the All-Driver Automobile Insurance Company who received at least one traffic ticket during a five-year period is .15.
    a. Show the sampling distribution of $\bar{p}$ if a random sample of 150 insured individuals is used to estimate the proportion having received at least one ticket.
    b. What is the probability that the sample proportion will be within ±.03 of the population proportion?

54. Lori Jeffrey is a successful sales representative for a major publisher of college textbooks. Historically, Lori obtains a book adoption on 25% of her sales calls. Viewing her sales calls for one month as a sample of all possible sales calls, assume that a statistical analysis of the data yields a standard error of the proportion of .0625.
    a. How large was the sample used in this analysis? That is, how many sales calls did Lori make during the month?
    b. Let $\bar{p}$ indicate the sample proportion of book adoptions obtained during the month. Show the sampling distribution of $\bar{p}$.
    c. Using the sampling distribution of $\bar{p}$, compute the probability that Lori will obtain book adoptions on 30% or more of her sales calls during a one-month period.

Appendix 7.1 The Expected Value and Standard Deviation of $\bar{x}$

In this appendix we present the mathematical basis for the expressions for $E(\bar{x})$, the expected value of $\bar{x}$ as given by equation (7.1), and $\sigma_{\bar{x}}$, the standard deviation of $\bar{x}$ as given by equation (7.2).

Expected Value of $\bar{x}$

Assume a population with mean μ and variance σ^2. A simple random sample of size n is selected with individual observations denoted $x_1, x_2, \ldots, x_n$. A sample mean $\bar{x}$ is computed as follows.

$$\bar{x} = \frac{\Sigma x_i}{n}$$

With repeated simple random samples of size n, $\bar{x}$ is a random variable that assumes different numerical values depending on the specific n items selected. The expected value of the random variable $\bar{x}$ is the mean of all possible $\bar{x}$ values.

$$\begin{aligned}\text{Mean of } \bar{x} = E(\bar{x}) &= E\left(\frac{\Sigma x_i}{n}\right)\\ &= \frac{1}{n}[E(x_1 + x_2 + \cdots + x_n)]\\ &= \frac{1}{n}[E(x_1) + E(x_2) + \cdots + E(x_n)]\end{aligned}$$

For any x_i we have $E(x_i) = \mu$; therefore we can write

$$\begin{aligned}E(\bar{x}) &= \frac{1}{n}(\mu + \mu + \cdots + \mu)\\ &= \frac{1}{n}(n\mu) = \mu\end{aligned}$$

This result shows that the mean of all possible $\bar{x}$ values is the same as the population mean μ. That is, $E(\bar{x}) = \mu$.

Standard Deviation of $\bar{x}$

Again assume a population with mean μ, variance σ^2, and a sample mean given by

$$\bar{x} = \frac{\Sigma x_i}{n}$$

With repeated simple random samples of size n, we know that $\bar{x}$ is a random variable that takes different numerical values depending on the specific n items selected. What follows is the derivation of the expression for the standard deviation of the $\bar{x}$ values, $\sigma_{\bar{x}}$, for the case of an infinite population. The derivation of the expression for $\sigma_{\bar{x}}$ for a finite population when sampling is done without replacement is more difficult and is beyond the scope of this text.

Returning to the infinite population case, recall that a simple random sample from an infinite population consists of observations $x_1, x_2, \ldots, x_n$ that are independent. The following two expressions are general formulas for the variance of random variables.

$$\text{Var}(ax) = a^2\,\text{Var}(x)$$

where a is a constant and x is a random variable, and

$$\text{Var}(x + y) = \text{Var}(x) + \text{Var}(y)$$

where x and y are *independent* random variables. Using the two preceding equations, we can develop the expression for the variance of the random variable $\bar{x}$ as follows.

$$\text{Var}(\bar{x}) = \text{Var}\left(\frac{\Sigma x_i}{n}\right) = \text{Var}\left(\frac{1}{n}\Sigma x_i\right)$$

Then, with $1/n$ a constant, we have

$$\begin{aligned}\text{Var}(\bar{x}) &= \left(\frac{1}{n}\right)^2 \text{Var}(\Sigma x_i)\\ &= \left(\frac{1}{n}\right)^2 \text{Var}(x_1 + x_2 + \cdots + x_n)\end{aligned}$$

In the infinite population case, the random variables $x_1, x_2, \ldots, x_n$ are independent, which enables us to write

$$\text{Var}(\bar{x}) = \left(\frac{1}{n}\right)^2 [\text{Var}(x_1) + \text{Var}(x_2) + \cdots + \text{Var}(x_n)]$$

For any x_i, we have $\text{Var}(x_i) = \sigma^2$; therefore we have

$$\text{Var}(\bar{x}) = \left(\frac{1}{n}\right)^2 (\sigma^2 + \sigma^2 + \cdots + \sigma^2)$$

With n values of σ^2 in this expression, we have

$$\text{Var}(\bar{x}) = \left(\frac{1}{n}\right)^2 (n\sigma^2) = \frac{\sigma^2}{n}$$

Taking the square root provides the formula for the standard deviation of $\bar{x}$.

$$\sigma_{\bar{x}} = \sqrt{\text{Var}(\bar{x})} = \frac{\sigma}{\sqrt{n}}$$

Appendix 7.2 Random Sampling with Minitab

If a list of the elements in a population is available in a Minitab file, Minitab can be used to select a simple random sample. For example, a list of the top 100 metropolitan areas in the United States and Canada is provided in column 1 of the data set MetAreas

TABLE 7.6 OVERALL RATING FOR THE FIRST 10 METROPOLITAN AREAS IN THE DATA SET METAREAS

Metropolitan Area	Rating
Albany, NY	64.18
Albuquerque, NM	66.16
Appleton, WI	60.56
Atlanta, GA	69.97
Austin, TX	71.48
Baltimore, MD	69.75
Birmingham, AL	69.59
Boise City, ID	68.36
Boston, MA	68.99
Buffalo, NY	66.10

CD file
MetAreas

(*Places Rated Almanac—The Millennium Edition 2000*). Column 2 contains the overall rating of each metropolitan area. The first 10 metropolitan areas in the data set and their corresponding ratings are shown in Table 7.6.

Suppose that you would like to select a simple random sample of 30 metropolitan areas in order to do an in-depth study of the cost of living in the United States and Canada. The following steps can be used to select the sample.

Step 1. Select the **Calc** pull-down menu
Step 2. Choose **Random Data**
Step 3. Choose **Sample From Columns**
Step 4. When the Sample From Columns dialog box appears:
Enter 30 in the **Sample** box
Enter C1 C2 in the box below
Enter C3 C4 in the **Store samples in** box
Step 5. Click **OK**

The random sample of 30 metropolitan areas appears in columns C3 and C4.

Appendix 7.3 Random Sampling with Excel

If a list of the elements in a population is available in an Excel file, Excel can be used to select a simple random sample. For example, a list of the top 100 metropolitan areas in the United States and Canada is provided in column A of the data set MetAreas (*Places Rated Almanac—The Millennium Edition 2000*). Column B contains the overall rating of each metropolitan area. The first 10 metropolitan areas in the data set and their corresponding ratings are shown in Table 7.6. Assume that you would like to select a simple random sample of 30 metropolitan areas in order to do an in-depth study of the cost of living in the United States and Canada.

The rows of any Excel data set can be placed in a random order by adding an extra column to the data set and filling the column with random numbers using the =RAND() function. Then, using Excel's sort ascending capability on the random number column, the rows of the data set will be reordered randomly. The random sample of size n appears in the first n rows of the reordered data set.

In the MetAreas data set, labels are in row 1 and the 100 metropolitan areas are in rows 2 to 101. The following steps can be used to select a simple random sample of 30 metropolitan areas.

Step 1. Enter =RAND() in cell C2
Step 2. Copy cell C2 to cells C3:C101
Step 3. Select any cell in Column C
Step 4. Click the **Sort Ascending** button on the tool bar

The random sample of 30 metropolitan areas appears in rows 2 to 31 of the reordered data set. The random numbers in column C are no longer necessary and can be deleted if desired.

CHAPTER 8

Interval Estimation

CONTENTS

STATISTICS *in* PRACTICE

FOOD LION*
SALISBURY, NORTH CAROLINA

Founded in 1957 as Food Town, Food Lion is one of the largest supermarket chains in the United States, with 1200 stores in 11 Southeastern and Mid-Atlantic states. The company sells more than 24,000 different products and offers nationally and regionally advertised brand-name merchandise, as well as a growing number of high-quality private label products manufactured especially for Food Lion. The company maintains its low price leadership and quality assurance through operating efficiencies such as standard store formats, innovative warehouse design, energy-efficient facilities, and data synchronization with suppliers. Food Lion looks to a future of continued innovation, growth, price leadership, and service to its customers.

The Food Lion store in the Cambridge Shopping Center, Charlotte, North Carolina. © Courtesy of Food Lion.

Being in an inventory-intense business, Food Lion made the decision to adopt the LIFO (last-in, first-out) method of inventory valuation. This method matches current costs against current revenues, which minimizes the effect of radical price changes on profit and loss results. In addition, the LIFO method reduces net income thereby reducing income taxes during periods of inflation.

Food Lion establishes a LIFO index for each of seven inventory pools: Grocery, Paper/Household, Pet Supplies, Health & Beauty Aids, Dairy, Cigarette/Tobacco, and Beer/Wine. For example, a LIFO index of 1.008 for the Grocery pool would indicate that the company's grocery inventory value at current costs reflects a 0.8% increase due to inflation over the most recent one-year period.

A LIFO index for each inventory pool requires that the year-end inventory count for each product be valued at the current year-end cost and at the preceding year-end cost. To avoid excessive time and expense associated with counting the inventory in all 1200 store locations, Food Lion selects a random sample of 50 stores. Year-end physical inventories are taken in each of the sample stores. The current-year and preceding-year costs for each item are then used to construct the required LIFO indexes for each inventory pool.

For a recent year, the sample estimate of the LIFO index for the Health & Beauty Aids inventory pool was 1.015. Using a 95% confidence level, Food Lion computed a margin of error of .006 for the sample estimate. Thus, the interval from 1.009 to 1.021 provided a 95% confidence interval estimate of the population LIFO index. This level of precision was judged to be very good.

In this chapter you will learn how to compute the margin of error associated with sample estimates. You will also learn how to use this information to construct and interpret interval estimates of a population mean and a population proportion.

*The authors are indebted to Keith Cunningham, Tax Director, and Bobby Harkey, Staff Tax Accountant, at Food Lion for providing this Statistics in Practice.

In Chapter 7, we stated that a point estimator is a sample statistic used to estimate a population parameter. For instance, the sample mean $\bar{x}$ is a point estimator of the population mean μ and the sample proportion $\bar{p}$ is a point estimator of the population proportion p. Because a point estimator cannot be expected to provide the exact value of the population parameter, an **interval estimate** is often computed by adding and subtracting a value, called the **margin of error**, to the point estimate. The general form of an interval estimate is as follows:

$$\text{Point estimate} \pm \text{Margin of error}$$

The purpose of an interval estimate is to provide information about how close the point estimate, provided by the sample, is to the value of the population parameter.

In this chapter we show how to compute interval estimates of a population mean μ and a population proportion p. The general form of an interval estimate of a population mean is

$$\bar{x} \pm \text{Margin of error}$$

Similarly, the general form of an interval estimate of a population proportion is

$$\bar{p} \pm \text{Margin of error}$$

The sampling distributions of $\bar{x}$ and $\bar{p}$ play key roles in computing these interval estimates.

8.1 Population Mean: σ Known

In order to develop an interval estimate of a population mean, either the population standard deviation σ or the sample standard deviation s must be used to compute the margin of error. In most applications σ is not known, and s is used to compute the margin of error. In some applications, however, large amounts of relevant historical data are available and can be used to estimate the population standard deviation prior to sampling. Also, in quality control applications where a process is assumed to be operating correctly, or "in control," it is appropriate to treat the population standard deviation as known. We refer to such cases as the ***σ* known** case. In this section we introduce an example in which it is reasonable to treat σ as known and show how to construct an interval estimate for this case.

Each week Lloyd's Department Store selects a simple random sample of 100 customers in order to learn about the amount spent per shopping trip. With x representing the amount spent per shopping trip, the sample mean $\bar{x}$ provides a point estimate of μ, the mean amount spent per shopping trip for the population of all Lloyd's customers. Lloyd's has been using the weekly survey for several years. Based on the historical data, Lloyd's now assumes a known value of $\sigma = \$20$ for the population standard deviation. The historical data also indicate that the population follows a normal distribution.

CD file
Lloyd's

During the most recent week, Lloyd's surveyed 100 customers ($n = 100$) and obtained a sample mean of $\bar{x} = \$82$. The sample mean amount spent provides a point estimate of the population mean amount spent per shopping trip, μ. In the discussion that follows, we show how to compute the margin of error for this estimate and develop an interval estimate of the population mean.

Margin of Error and the Interval Estimate

In Chapter 7 we showed that the sampling distribution of $\bar{x}$ can be used to compute the probability that $\bar{x}$ will be within a given distance of μ. In the Lloyd's example, the historical data show that the population of amounts spent is normally distributed with a standard deviation of $\sigma = 20$. So, using what we learned in Chapter 7, we can conclude that the sampling distribution of $\bar{x}$ follows a normal distribution with a standard error of $\sigma_{\bar{x}} = \sigma/\sqrt{n} = 20/\sqrt{100} = 2$. This sampling distribution is shown in Figure 8.1.* Because

*We use the fact that the population of amounts spent has a normal distribution to conclude that the sampling distribution of $\bar{x}$ has a normal distribution. If the population did not have a normal distribution, we could rely on the central limit theorem and the sample size of $n = 100$ to conclude that the sampling distribution of $\bar{x}$ is approximately normal. In either case, the sampling distribution of $\bar{x}$ would appear as shown in Figure 8.1.

FIGURE 8.1 SAMPLING DISTRIBUTION OF THE SAMPLE MEAN AMOUNT SPENT FROM SIMPLE RANDOM SAMPLES OF 100 CUSTOMERS

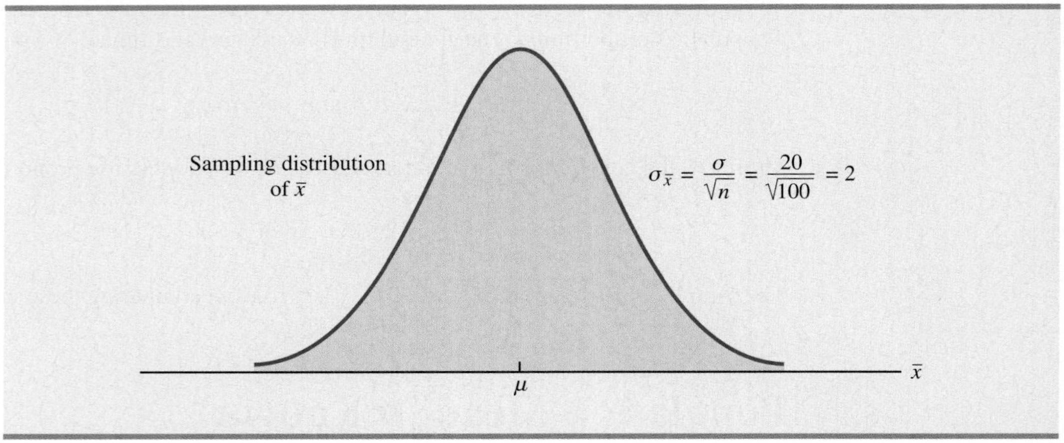

the sampling distribution shows how values of $\bar{x}$ are distributed around the population mean μ, the sampling distribution of $\bar{x}$ provides information about the possible differences between $\bar{x}$ and μ.

Using the standard normal probability table, we find that 95% of the values of any normally distributed random variable are within ± 1.96 standard deviations of the mean. Thus, when the sampling distribution of $\bar{x}$ is normally distributed, 95% of the $\bar{x}$ values must be within $\pm 1.96\sigma_{\bar{x}}$ of the mean μ. In the Lloyd's example we know that the sampling distribution of $\bar{x}$ is normally distributed with a standard error of $\sigma_{\bar{x}} = 2$. Because $\pm 1.96\sigma_{\bar{x}} = 1.96(2) = 3.92$, we can conclude that 95% of all $\bar{x}$ values obtained using a sample size of $n = 100$ will be within ± 3.92 of the population mean μ. See Figure 8.2.

FIGURE 8.2 SAMPLING DISTRIBUTION OF $\bar{x}$ SHOWING THE LOCATION OF SAMPLE MEANS THAT ARE WITHIN 3.92 OF μ

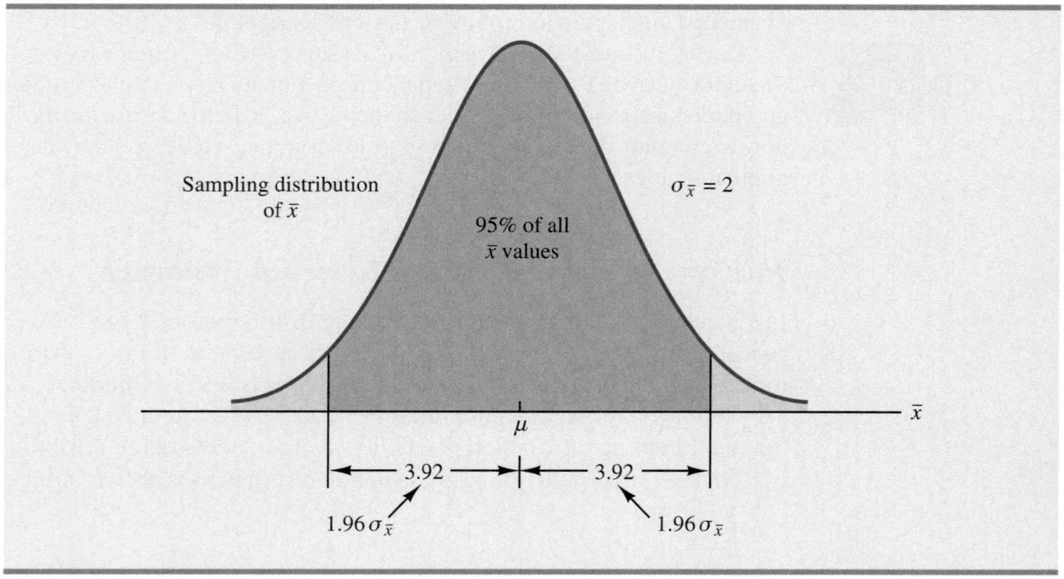

In the introduction to this chapter we said that the general form of an interval estimate of the population mean μ is $\bar{x} \pm$ margin of error. For the Lloyd's example, suppose we set the margin of error equal to 3.92 and compute the interval estimate of μ using $\bar{x} \pm 3.92$. To provide an interpretation for this interval estimate, let us consider the values of $\bar{x}$ that could be obtained if we took three *different* simple random samples, each consisting of 100 Lloyd's customers. The first sample mean might turn out to have the value shown as $\bar{x}_1$ in Figure 8.3. In this case, Figure 8.3 shows that the interval formed by subtracting 3.92 from $\bar{x}_1$ and adding 3.92 to $\bar{x}_1$ includes the population mean μ. Now consider what happens if the second sample mean turns out to have the value shown as $\bar{x}_2$ in Figure 8.3. Although this sample mean differs from the first sample mean, we see that the interval formed by subtracting 3.92 from $\bar{x}_2$ and adding 3.92 to $\bar{x}_2$ also includes the population mean μ. However, consider what happens if the third sample mean turns out to have the value shown as $\bar{x}_3$ in Figure 8.3. In this case, the interval formed by subtracting 3.92 from $\bar{x}_3$ and adding 3.92 to $\bar{x}_3$ does not include the population mean μ. Because $\bar{x}_3$ falls in the upper tail of the sampling distribution and is farther than 3.92 from μ, subtracting and adding 3.92 to $\bar{x}_3$ forms an interval that does not include μ.

Any sample mean $\bar{x}$ that is within the darkly shaded region of Figure 8.3 will provide an interval that contains the population mean μ. Because 95% of all possible sample means are in the darkly shaded region, 95% of all intervals formed by subtracting 3.92 from $\bar{x}$ and adding 3.92 to $\bar{x}$ will include the population mean μ.

Recall that during the most recent week, the quality assurance team at Lloyd's surveyed 100 customers and obtained a sample mean amount spent of $\bar{x} = 82$. Using $\bar{x} \pm 3.92$ to

FIGURE 8.3 INTERVALS FORMED FROM SELECTED SAMPLE MEANS AT LOCATIONS $\bar{x}_1$, $\bar{x}_2$, AND $\bar{x}_3$

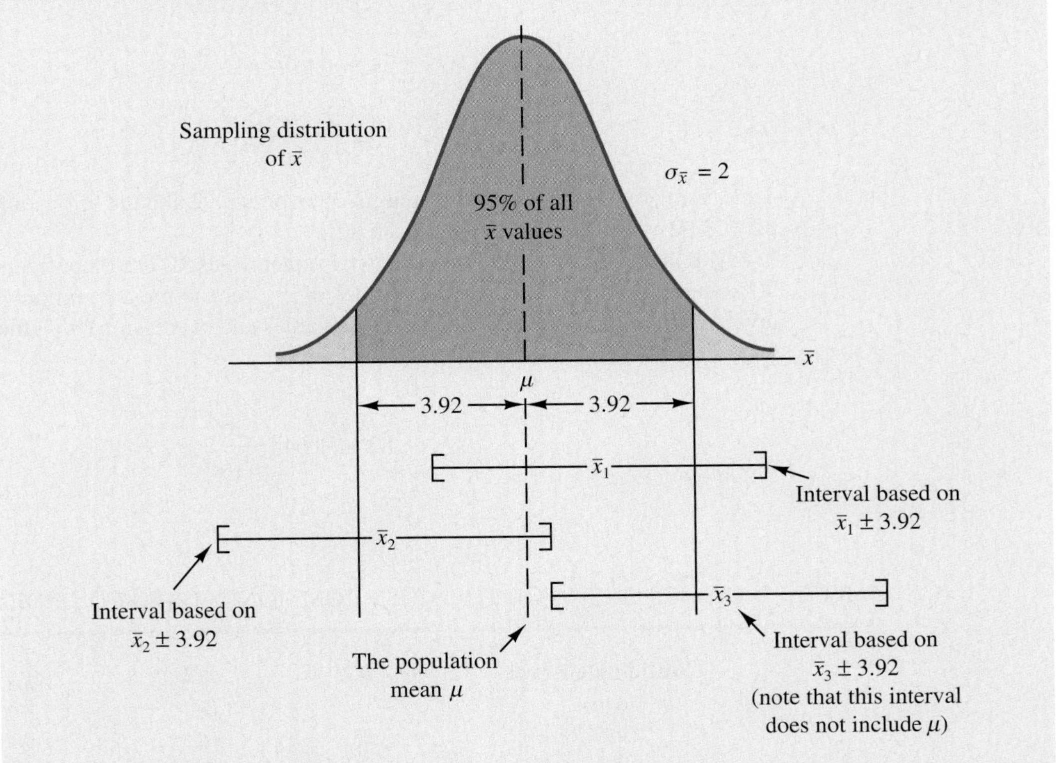

This discussion provides insight as to why the interval is called a 95% confidence interval.

construct the interval estimate, we obtain 82 ± 3.92. Thus, the specific interval estimate of μ based on the data from the most recent week is $82 - 3.92 = 78.08$ to $82 + 3.92 = 85.92$. Because 95% of all the intervals constructed using $\bar{x} \pm 3.92$ will contain the population mean, we say that we are 95% confident that the interval 78.08 to 85.92 includes the population mean μ. We say that this interval has been established at the 95% **confidence level**. The value .95 is referred to as the **confidence coefficient**, and the interval 78.08 to 85.92 is called the 95% **confidence interval**.

With the margin of error given by $z_{\alpha/2}(\sigma/\sqrt{n})$, the general form of an interval estimate of a population mean for the σ known case follows.

INTERVAL ESTIMATE OF A POPULATION MEAN: σ KNOWN

$$\bar{x} \pm z_{\alpha/2}\frac{\sigma}{\sqrt{n}} \tag{8.1}$$

where $(1 - \alpha)$ is the confidence coefficient and $z_{\alpha/2}$ is the z value providing an area of $\alpha/2$ in the upper tail of the standard normal probability distribution.

Let us use expression (8.1) to construct a 95% confidence interval for the Lloyd's example. For a 95% confidence interval, the confidence coefficient is $(1 - \alpha) = .95$ and thus, $\alpha = .05$. Using the standard normal probability table, an area of $\alpha/2 = .05/2 = .025$ in the upper tail provides $z_{.025} = 1.96$. With the Lloyd's sample mean $\bar{x} = 82$, $\sigma = 20$, and a sample size $n = 100$, we obtain

$$82 \pm 1.96\frac{20}{\sqrt{100}}$$

$$82 \pm 3.92$$

Thus, using expression (8.1), the margin of error is 3.92 and the 95% confidence interval is $82 - 3.92 = 78.08$ to $82 + 3.92 = 85.92$.

Although a 95% confidence level is frequently used, other confidence levels such as 90% and 99% may be considered. Values of $z_{\alpha/2}$ for the most commonly used confidence levels are shown in Table 8.1. Using these values and expression (8.1), the 90% confidence interval for the Lloyd's example is

$$82 \pm 1.645\frac{20}{\sqrt{100}}$$

$$82 \pm 3.29$$

TABLE 8.1 VALUES OF $z_{\alpha/2}$ FOR THE MOST COMMONLY USED CONFIDENCE LEVELS

Confidence Level	α	$\alpha/2$	$z_{\alpha/2}$
90%	.10	.05	1.645
95%	.05	.025	1.960
99%	.01	.005	2.576

Thus, at 90% confidence, the margin of error is 3.29 and the confidence interval is $82 - 3.29 = 78.71$ to $82 + 3.29 = 85.29$. Similarly, the 99% confidence interval is

$$82 \pm 2.576 \frac{20}{\sqrt{100}}$$
$$82 \pm 5.15$$

Thus, at 99% confidence, the margin of error is 5.15 and the confidence interval is $82 - 5.15 = 76.85$ to $82 + 5.15 = 87.15$.

Comparing the results for the 90%, 95%, and 99% confidence levels, we see that in order to have a higher degree of confidence, the margin of error and thus the width of the confidence interval must be larger.

Practical Advice

If the population follows a normal distribution, the confidence interval provided by expression (8.1) is exact. In other words, if expression (8.1) were used repeatedly to generate 95% confidence intervals, exactly 95% of the intervals generated would contain the population mean. If the population does not follow a normal distribution, the confidence interval provided by expression (8.1) will be approximate. In this case, the quality of the approximation depends on both the distribution of the population and the sample size.

In most applications, a sample size of $n \geq 30$ is adequate when using expression (8.1) to develop an interval estimate of a population mean. If the population is not normally distributed, but is roughly symmetric, sample sizes as small as 15 can be expected to provide good approximate confidence intervals. With smaller sample sizes, expression (8.1) should only be used if the analyst believes, or is willing to assume, that the population distribution is at least approximately normal.

NOTES AND COMMENTS

1. The interval estimation procedure discussed in this section is based on the assumption that the population standard deviation σ is known. By σ known we mean that historical data or other information are available that permit us to obtain a good estimate of the population standard deviation prior to taking the sample that will be used to develop an estimate of the population mean. So technically we don't mean that σ is actually known with certainty. We just mean that we obtained a good estimate of the standard deviation prior to sampling and thus we won't be using the same sample to estimate both the population mean and the population standard deviation.
2. The sample size n appears in the denominator of the interval estimation expression (8.1). Thus, if a particular sample size provides too wide an interval to be of any practical use, we may want to consider increasing the sample size. With n in the denominator, a larger sample size will provide a smaller margin of error, a narrower interval, and greater precision. The procedure for determining the size of a simple random sample necessary to obtain a desired precision is discussed in Section 8.3.

Exercises

Methods

1. A simple random sample of 40 items resulted in a sample mean of 25. The population standard deviation is $\sigma = 5$.
   a. What is the standard error of the mean, $\sigma_{\bar{x}}$?
   b. At 95% confidence, what is the margin of error?

SELF test

2. A simple random sample of 50 items from a population with $\sigma = 6$ resulted in a sample mean of 32.
   a. Provide a 90% confidence interval for the population mean.
   b. Provide a 95% confidence interval for the population mean.
   c. Provide a 99% confidence interval for the population mean.

3. A simple random sample of 60 items resulted in a sample mean of 80. The population standard deviation is $\sigma = 15$.
   a. Compute the 95% confidence interval for the population mean.
   b. Assume that the same sample mean was obtained from a sample of 120 items. Provide a 95% confidence interval for the population mean.
   c. What is the effect of a larger sample size on the interval estimate?

4. A 95% confidence interval for a population mean was reported to be 152 to 160. If $\sigma = 15$, what sample size was used in this study?

Applications

SELF test

5. In an effort to estimate the mean amount spent per customer for dinner at a major Atlanta restaurant, data were collected for a sample of 49 customers. Assume a population standard deviation of \$5.
   a. At 95% confidence, what is the margin of error?
   b. If the sample mean is \$24.80, what is the 95% confidence interval for the population mean?

CD file
Nielsen

6. Nielsen Media Research conducted a study of household television viewing times during the 8 P.M. to 11 P.M. time period. The data contained in the CD file named Nielsen are consistent with the findings reported (*The World Almanac,* 2003). Based upon past studies the population standard deviation is assumed known with $\sigma = 3.5$ hours. Develop a 95% confidence interval estimate of the mean television viewing time per week during the 8 P.M. to 11 P.M. time period.

7. A survey of small businesses with Web sites found that the average amount spent on a site was \$11,500 per year (*Fortune,* March 5, 2001). Given a sample of 60 businesses and a population standard deviation of $\sigma = \$4000$, what is the margin of error? Use 95% confidence. What would you recommend if the study required a margin of error of \$500?

8. The National Quality Research Center at the University of Michigan provides a quarterly measure of consumer opinions about products and services (*The Wall Street Journal,* February 18, 2003). A survey of 10 restaurants in the Fast Food/Pizza group showed a sample mean customer satisfaction index of 71. Past data indicate that the population standard deviation of the index has been relatively stable with $\sigma = 5$.
   a. What assumption should the researcher be willing to make if a margin of error is desired?
   b. Using 95% confidence, what is the margin of error?
   c. What is the margin of error if 99% confidence is desired?

9. The undergraduate grade point average (GPA) for students admitted to the top graduate business schools was 3.37 (*Best Graduate Schools, U.S. News and World Report,* 2001). Assume this estimate was based on a sample of 120 students admitted to the top schools. Using past years' data, the population standard deviation can be assumed known with $\sigma = .28$. What is the 95% confidence interval estimate of the mean undergraduate GPA for students admitted to the top graduate business schools?

10. *Playbill* magazine reported that the mean annual household income of its readers is \$119,155 (*Playbill,* January 2006). Assume this estimate of the mean annual household income is based on a sample of 80 households, and based on past studies, the population standard deviation is known to be $\sigma = \$30,000$.

a. Develop a 90% confidence interval estimate of the population mean.
b. Develop a 95% confidence interval estimate of the population mean.
c. Develop a 99% confidence interval estimate of the population mean.
d. Discuss what happens to the width of the confidence interval as the confidence level is increased. Does this result seem reasonable? Explain.

8.2 Population Mean: σ Unknown

When developing an interval estimate of a population mean we usually do not have a good estimate of the population standard deviation either. In these cases, we must use the same sample to estimate μ and σ. This situation represents the **σ unknown** case. When s is used to estimate σ, the margin of error and the interval estimate for the population mean are based on a probability distribution known as the ***t* distribution**. Although the mathematical development of the t distribution is based on the assumption of a normal distribution for the population we are sampling from, research shows that the t distribution can be successfully applied in many situations where the population deviates significantly from normal. Later in this section we provide guidelines for using the t distribution if the population is not normally distributed.

William Sealy Gosset, writing under the name "Student," is the founder of the t distribution. Gosset, an Oxford graduate in mathematics, worked for the Guinness Brewery in Dublin, Ireland. He developed the t distribution while working on small-scale materials and temperature experiments.

The t distribution is a family of similar probability distributions, with a specific t distribution depending on a parameter known as the **degrees of freedom**. The t distribution with one degree of freedom is unique, as is the t distribution with two degrees of freedom, with three degrees of freedom, and so on. As the number of degrees of freedom increases, the difference between the t distribution and the standard normal distribution becomes smaller and smaller. Figure 8.4 shows t distributions with 10 and 20 degrees of freedom and their relationship to the standard normal probability distribution. Note that a t distribution with more degrees of freedom exhibits less variability and more

FIGURE 8.4 COMPARISON OF THE STANDARD NORMAL DISTRIBUTION WITH t DISTRIBUTIONS HAVING 10 AND 20 DEGREES OF FREEDOM

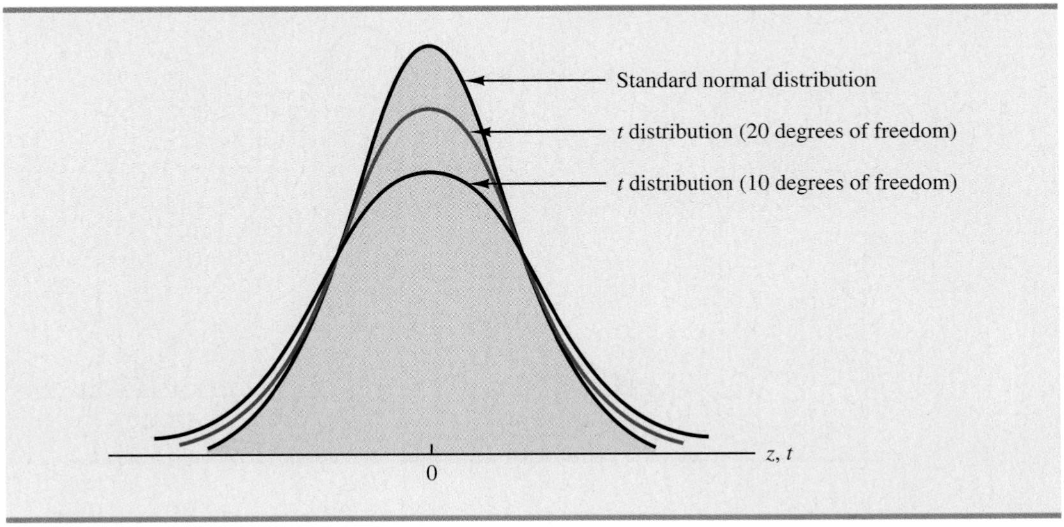

closely resembles the standard normal distribution. Note also that the mean of the t distribution is zero.

We place a subscript on t to indicate the area in the upper tail of the t distribution. For example, just as we used $z_{.025}$ to indicate the z value providing a .025 area in the upper tail of a standard normal distribution, we will use $t_{.025}$ to indicate a .025 area in the upper tail of a t distribution. In general, we will use the notation $t_{\alpha/2}$ to represent a t value with an area of $\alpha/2$ in the upper tail of the t distribution. See Figure 8.5.

As the degrees of freedom increase, the t distribution approaches the standard normal distribution.

Table 2 in Appendix B contains a table for the t distribution. A portion of this table is shown in Table 8.2. Each row in the table corresponds to a separate t distribution with the degrees of freedom shown. For example, for a t distribution with 9 degrees of freedom, $t_{.025} = 2.262$. Similarly, for a t distribution with 60 degrees of freedom, $t_{.025} = 2.000$. As the degrees of freedom continue to increase, $t_{.025}$ approaches $z_{.025} = 1.96$. In fact, the standard normal distribution z values can be found in the infinite degrees of freedom row (labeled ∞) of the t distribution table. If the degrees of freedom exceed 100, the infinite degrees of freedom row can be used to approximate the actual t value; in other words, for more than 100 degrees of freedom, the standard normal z value provides a good approximation to the t value.

Margin of Error and the Interval Estimate

In Section 8.1 we showed that an interval estimate of a population mean for the σ known case is

$$\bar{x} \pm z_{\alpha/2}\frac{\sigma}{\sqrt{n}}$$

To compute an interval estimate of μ for the σ unknown case, the sample standard deviation s is used to estimate σ, and $z_{\alpha/2}$ is replaced by the t distribution value $t_{\alpha/2}$. The margin

FIGURE 8.5 t DISTRIBUTION WITH $\alpha/2$ AREA OR PROBABILITY IN THE UPPER TAIL

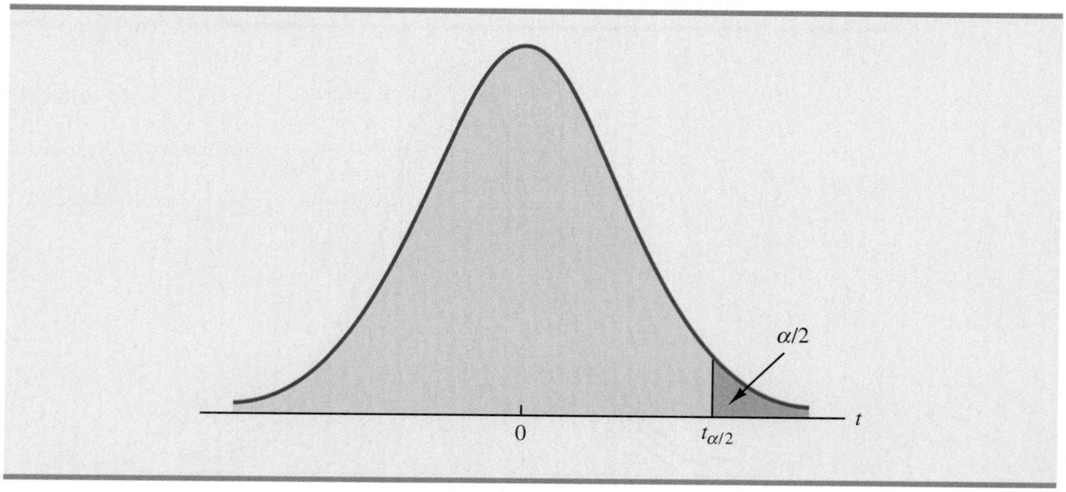

TABLE 8.2 SELECTED VALUES FROM THE *t* DISTRIBUTION TABLE*

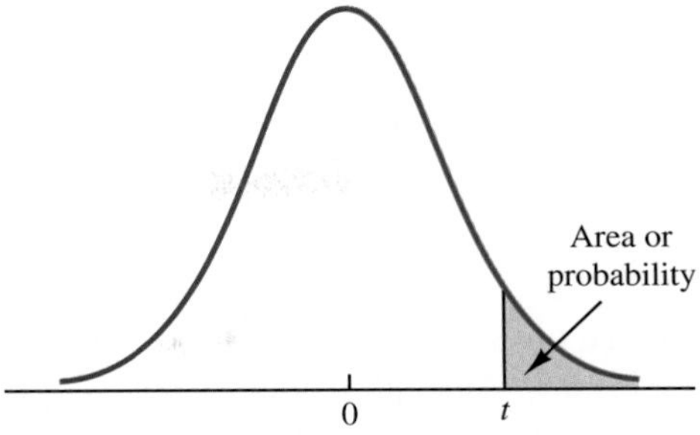

Degrees of Freedom	Area in Upper Tail .20	.10	.05	.025	.01	.005
1	1.376	3.078	6.314	12.706	31.821	63.656
2	1.061	1.886	2.920	4.303	6.965	9.925
3	.978	1.638	2.353	3.182	4.541	5.841
4	.941	1.533	2.132	2.776	3.747	4.604
5	.920	1.476	2.015	2.571	3.365	4.032
6	.906	1.440	1.943	2.447	3.143	3.707
7	.896	1.415	1.895	2.365	2.998	3.499
8	.889	1.397	1.860	2.306	2.896	3.355
9	.883	1.383	1.833	2.262	2.821	3.250
⋮	⋮	⋮	⋮	⋮	⋮	⋮
60	.848	1.296	1.671	2.000	2.390	2.660
61	.848	1.296	1.670	2.000	2.389	2.659
62	.847	1.295	1.670	1.999	2.388	2.657
63	.847	1.295	1.669	1.998	2.387	2.656
64	.847	1.295	1.669	1.998	2.386	2.655
65	.847	1.295	1.669	1.997	2.385	2.654
66	.847	1.295	1.668	1.997	2.384	2.652
67	.847	1.294	1.668	1.996	2.383	2.651
68	.847	1.294	1.668	1.995	2.382	2.650
69	.847	1.294	1.667	1.995	2.382	2.649
⋮	⋮	⋮	⋮	⋮	⋮	⋮
90	.846	1.291	1.662	1.987	2.368	2.632
91	.846	1.291	1.662	1.986	2.368	2.631
92	.846	1.291	1.662	1.986	2.368	2.630
93	.846	1.291	1.661	1.986	2.367	2.630
94	.845	1.291	1.661	1.986	2.367	2.629
95	.845	1.291	1.661	1.985	2.366	2.629
96	.845	1.290	1.661	1.985	2.366	2.628
97	.845	1.290	1.661	1.985	2.365	2.627
98	.845	1.290	1.661	1.984	2.365	2.627
99	.845	1.290	1.660	1.984	2.364	2.626
100	.845	1.290	1.660	1.984	2.364	2.626
∞	.842	1.282	1.645	1.960	2.326	2.576

Note: A more extensive table is provided as Table 2 of Appendix B.

of error is then given by $t_{\alpha/2} s/\sqrt{n}$. With this margin of error, the general expression for an interval estimate of a population mean when σ is unknown follows.

INTERVAL ESTIMATE OF A POPULATION MEAN: σ UNKNOWN

$$\bar{x} \pm t_{\alpha/2} \frac{s}{\sqrt{n}} \tag{8.2}$$

where s is the sample standard deviation, $(1 - \alpha)$ is the confidence coefficient, and $t_{\alpha/2}$ is the t value providing an area of $\alpha/2$ in the upper tail of the t distribution with $n - 1$ degrees of freedom.

The reason the number of degrees of freedom associated with the t value in expression (8.2) is $n - 1$ concerns the use of s as an estimate of the population standard deviation σ. The expression for the sample standard deviation is

$$s = \sqrt{\frac{\Sigma(x_i - \bar{x})^2}{n - 1}}$$

Degrees of freedom refer to the number of independent pieces of information that go into the computation of $\Sigma(x_i - \bar{x})^2$. The n pieces of information involved in computing $\Sigma(x_i - \bar{x})^2$ are as follows: $x_1 - \bar{x}, x_2 - \bar{x}, \ldots, x_n - \bar{x}$. In Section 3.2 we indicated that $\Sigma(x_i - \bar{x}) = 0$ for any data set. Thus, only $n - 1$ of the $x_i - \bar{x}$ values are independent; that is, if we know $n - 1$ of the values, the remaining value can be determined exactly by using the condition that the sum of the $x_i - \bar{x}$ values must be 0. Thus, $n - 1$ is the number of degrees of freedom associated with $\Sigma(x_i - \bar{x})^2$ and hence the number of degrees of freedom for the t distribution in expression (8.2).

To illustrate the interval estimation procedure for the σ unknown case, we will consider a study designed to estimate the mean credit card debt for the population of U.S. households. A sample of $n = 70$ households provided the credit card balances shown in Table 8.3. For this situation, no previous estimate of the population standard deviation σ is available. Thus, the sample data must be used to estimate both the population mean and the population standard deviation. Using the data in Table 8.3, we compute the sample mean $\bar{x} = \$9312$ and the

TABLE 8.3 CREDIT CARD BALANCES FOR A SAMPLE OF 70 HOUSEHOLDS

CD file
NewBalance

9430	14661	7159	9071	9691	11032
7535	12195	8137	3603	11448	6525
4078	10544	9467	16804	8279	5239
5604	13659	12595	13479	5649	6195
5179	7061	7917	14044	11298	12584
4416	6245	11346	6817	4353	15415
10676	13021	12806	6845	3467	15917
1627	9719	4972	10493	6191	12591
10112	2200	11356	615	12851	9743
6567	10746	7117	13627	5337	10324
13627	12744	9465	12557	8372	
18719	5742	19263	6232	7445	

sample standard deviation $s = \$4007$. With 95% confidence and $n - 1 = 69$ degrees of freedom, Table 8.2 can be used to obtain the appropriate value for $t_{.025}$. We want the t value in the row with 69 degrees of freedom, and the column corresponding to .025 in the upper tail. The value shown is $t_{.025} = 1.995$.

We use expression (8.2) to compute an interval estimate of the population mean credit card balance.

$$9312 \pm 1.995 \frac{4007}{\sqrt{70}}$$

$$9312 \pm 955$$

The point estimate of the population mean is \$9312, the margin of error is \$955, and the 95% confidence interval is $9312 - 955 = \$8357$ to $9312 + 955 = \$10{,}267$. Thus, we are 95% confident that the mean credit card balance for the population of all households is between \$8357 and \$10,267.

The procedures used by Minitab and Excel to develop confidence intervals for a population mean are described in Appendixes 8.1 and 8.2. For the household credit card balances study, the results of the Minitab interval estimation procedure are shown in Figure 8.6. The sample of 70 households provides a sample mean credit card balance of \$9312, a sample standard deviation of \$4007, and (after rounding) an estimate of the standard error of the mean of \$479, and a 95% confidence interval of \$8357 to \$10,267.

Practical Advice

If the population follows a normal distribution, the confidence interval provided by expression (8.2) is exact and can be used for any sample size. If the population does not follow a normal distribution, the confidence interval provided by expression (8.2) will be approximate. In this case, the quality of the approximation depends on both the distribution of the population and the sample size.

Larger sample sizes are needed if the distribution of the population is highly skewed or includes outliers.

In most applications, a sample size of $n \geq 30$ is adequate when using expression (8.2) to develop an interval estimate of a population mean. However, if the population distribution is highly skewed or contains outliers, most statisticians would recommend increasing the sample size to 50 or more. If the population is not normally distributed but is roughly symmetric, sample sizes as small as 15 can be expected to provide good approximate confidence intervals. With smaller sample sizes, expression (8.2) should only be used if the analyst believes, or is willing to assume, that the population distribution is at least approximately normal.

Using a Small Sample

In the following example we develop an interval estimate for a population mean when the sample size is small. As we already noted, an understanding of the distribution of the population becomes a factor in deciding whether the interval estimation procedure provides acceptable results.

Scheer Industries is considering a new computer-assisted program to train maintenance employees to do machine repairs. In order to fully evaluate the program, the director of

FIGURE 8.6 MINITAB CONFIDENCE INTERVAL FOR THE CREDIT CARD BALANCE SURVEY

```
Variable      N      Mean     StDev   SE Mean            95% CI
NewBalance   70   9312.00   4007.00    478.93   (8356.56, 10267.44)
```

TABLE 8.4 TRAINING TIME IN DAYS FOR A SAMPLE OF 20 SCHEER INDUSTRIES EMPLOYEES

52	59	54	42
44	50	42	48
55	54	60	55
44	62	62	57
45	46	43	56

CD file
Scheer

manufacturing requested an estimate of the population mean time required for maintenance employees to complete the computer-assisted training.

A sample of 20 employees is selected, with each employee in the sample completing the training program. Data on the training time in days for the 20 employees are shown in Table 8.4. A histogram of the sample data appears in Figure 8.7. What can we say about the distribution of the population based on this histogram? First, the sample data do not support the conclusion that the distribution of the population is normal, yet we do not see any evidence of skewness or outliers. Therefore, using the guidelines in the previous subsection, we conclude that an interval estimate based on the t distribution appears acceptable for the sample of 20 employees.

We continue by computing the sample mean and sample standard deviation as follows.

$$\bar{x} = \frac{\Sigma x_i}{n} = \frac{1030}{20} = 51.5 \text{ days}$$

$$s = \sqrt{\frac{\Sigma(x_i - \bar{x})^2}{n - 1}} = \sqrt{\frac{889}{20 - 1}} = 6.84 \text{ days}$$

FIGURE 8.7 HISTOGRAM OF TRAINING TIMES FOR THE SCHEER INDUSTRIES SAMPLE

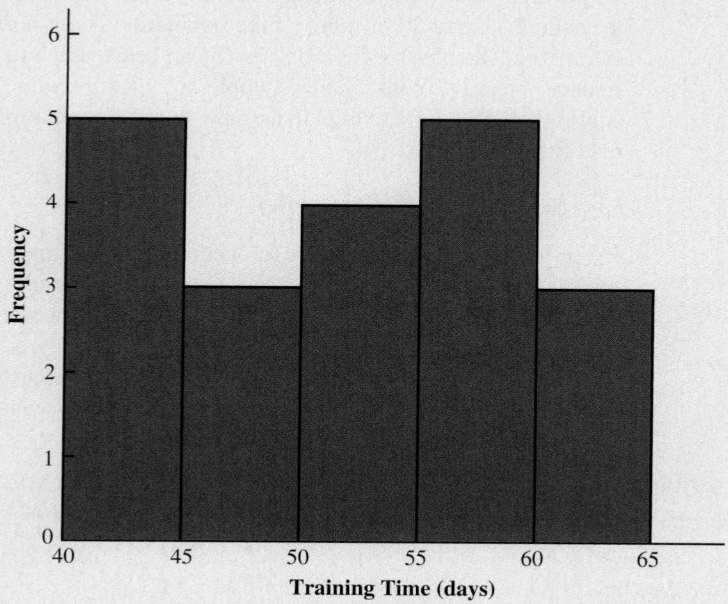

For a 95% confidence interval, we use Table 2 of Appendix B and $n - 1 = 19$ degrees of freedom to obtain $t_{.025} = 2.093$. Expression (8.2) provides the interval estimate of the population mean.

$$51.5 \pm 2.093\left(\frac{6.84}{\sqrt{20}}\right)$$

$$51.5 \pm 3.2$$

The point estimate of the population mean is 51.5 days. The margin of error is 3.2 days and the 95% confidence interval is $51.5 - 3.2 = 48.3$ days to $51.5 + 3.2 = 54.7$ days.

Using a histogram of the sample data to learn about the distribution of a population is not always conclusive, but in many cases it provides the only information available. The histogram, along with judgment on the part of the analyst, can often be used to decide whether expression (8.2) can be used to develop the interval estimate.

Summary of Interval Estimation Procedures

We provided two approaches to developing an interval estimate of a population mean. For the σ known case, σ and the standard normal distribution are used in expression (8.1) to compute the margin of error and to develop the interval estimate. For the σ unknown case, the sample standard deviation s and the t distribution are used in expression (8.2) to compute the margin of error and to develop the interval estimate.

A summary of the interval estimation procedures for the two cases is shown in Figure 8.8. In most applications, a sample size of $n \geq 30$ is adequate. If the population has a normal or approximately normal distribution, however, smaller sample sizes may be used. For the σ unknown case a sample size of $n \geq 50$ is recommended if the population distribution is believed to be highly skewed or has outliers.

FIGURE 8.8 SUMMARY OF INTERVAL ESTIMATION PROCEDURES FOR A POPULATION MEAN

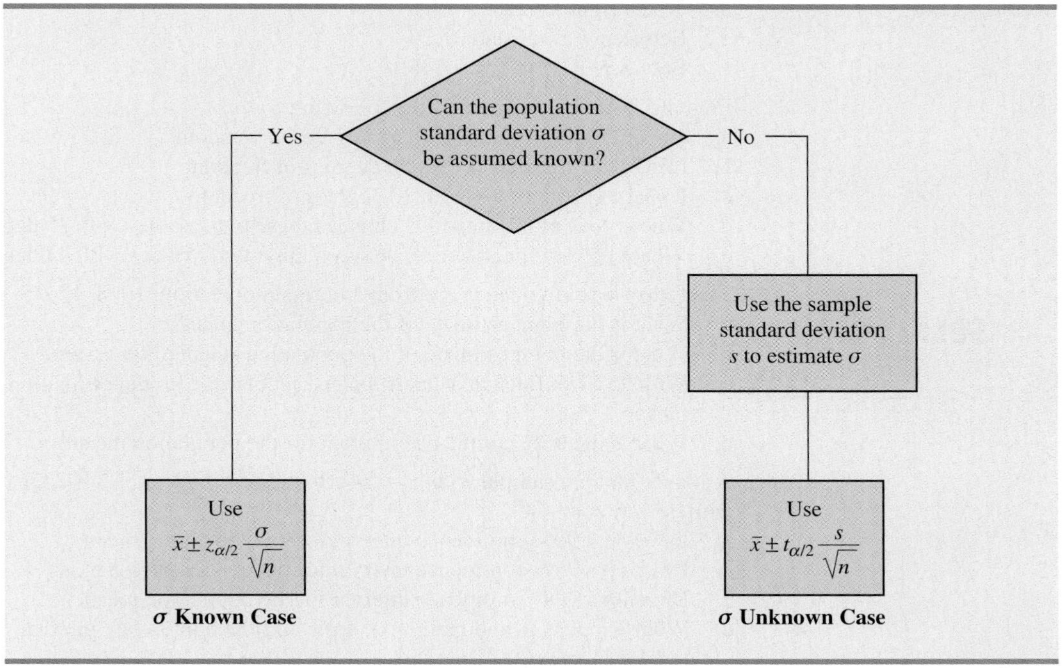

NOTES AND COMMENTS

1. When σ is known, the margin of error, $z_{\alpha/2}(\sigma/\sqrt{n})$, is fixed and is the same for all samples of size n. When σ is unknown, the margin of error, $t_{\alpha/2}(s/\sqrt{n})$, varies from sample to sample. This variation occurs because the sample standard deviation s varies depending upon the sample selected. A large value for s provides a larger margin of error, while a small value for s provides a smaller margin of error.
2. What happens to confidence interval estimates when the population is skewed? Consider a population that is skewed to the right with large data values stretching the distribution to the right. When such skewness exists, the sample mean $\bar{x}$ and the sample standard deviation s are positively correlated. Larger values of s tend to be associated with larger values of $\bar{x}$. Thus, when $\bar{x}$ is larger than the population mean, s tends to be larger than σ. This skewness causes the margin of error, $t_{\alpha/2}(s/\sqrt{n})$, to be larger than it would be with σ known. The confidence interval with the larger margin of error tends to include the population mean μ more often than it would if the true value of σ were used. But when $\bar{x}$ is smaller than the population mean, the correlation between $\bar{x}$ and s causes the margin of error to be small. In this case, the confidence interval with the smaller margin of error tends to miss the population mean more than it would if we knew σ and used it. For this reason, we recommend using larger sample sizes with highly skewed population distributions.

Exercises

Methods

11. For a t distribution with 16 degrees of freedom, find the area, or probability, in each region.
    a. To the right of 2.120
    b. To the left of 1.337
    c. To the left of -1.746
    d. To the right of 2.583
    e. Between -2.120 and 2.120
    f. Between -1.746 and 1.746
12. Find the t value(s) for each of the following cases.
    a. Upper tail area of .025 with 12 degrees of freedom
    b. Lower tail area of .05 with 50 degrees of freedom
    c. Upper tail area of .01 with 30 degrees of freedom
    d. Where 90% of the area falls between these two t values with 25 degrees of freedom
    e. Where 95% of the area falls between these two t values with 45 degrees of freedom

SELF test

13. The following sample data are from a normal population: 10, 8, 12, 15, 13, 11, 6, 5.
    a. What is the point estimate of the population mean?
    b. What is the point estimate of the population standard deviation?
    c. With 95% confidence, what is the margin of error for the estimation of the population mean?
    d. What is the 95% confidence interval for the population mean?
14. A simple random sample with $n = 54$ provided a sample mean of 22.5 and a sample standard deviation of 4.4.
    a. Develop a 90% confidence interval for the population mean.
    b. Develop a 95% confidence interval for the population mean.
    c. Develop a 99% confidence interval for the population mean.
    d. What happens to the margin of error and the confidence interval as the confidence level is increased?

Applications

SELF test

15. Sales personnel for Skillings Distributors submit weekly reports listing the customer contacts made during the week. A sample of 65 weekly reports showed a sample mean of 19.5 customer contacts per week. The sample standard deviation was 5.2. Provide 90% and 95% confidence intervals for the population mean number of weekly customer contacts for the sales personnel.

16. The mean number of hours of flying time for pilots at Continental Airlines is 49 hours per month (*The Wall Street Journal,* February 25, 2003). Assume that this mean was based on actual flying times for a sample of 100 Continental pilots and that the sample standard deviation was 8.5 hours.
    a. At 95% confidence, what is the margin of error?
    b. What is the 95% confidence interval estimate of the population mean flying time for the pilots?
    c. The mean number of hours of flying time for pilots at United Airlines is 36 hours per month. Use your results from part (b) to discuss differences between the flying times for the pilots at the two airlines. *The Wall Street Journal* reported United Airlines as having the highest labor cost among all airlines. Does the information in this exercise provide insight as to why United Airlines might expect higher labor costs?

17. The International Air Transport Association surveys business travelers to develop quality ratings for transatlantic gateway airports. The maximum possible rating is 10. Suppose a simple random sample of 50 business travelers is selected and each traveler is asked to provide a rating for the Miami International Airport. The ratings obtained from the sample of 50 business travelers follow.

CD file

Miami

6	4	6	8	7	7	6	3	3	8	10	4	8
7	8	7	5	9	5	8	4	3	8	5	5	4
4	4	8	4	5	6	2	5	9	9	8	4	8
9	9	5	9	7	8	3	10	8	9	6		

Develop a 95% confidence interval estimate of the population mean rating for Miami.

CD file

FastFood

18. Thirty fast-food restaurants including Wendy's, McDonald's, and Burger King were visited during the summer of 2000 (*The Cincinnati Enquirer,* July 9, 2000). During each visit, the customer went to the drive-through and ordered a basic meal such as a "combo" meal or a sandwich, fries, and shake. The time between pulling up to the menu board and receiving the filled order was recorded. The times in minutes for the 30 visits are as follows:

0.9	1.0	1.2	2.2	1.9	3.6	2.8	5.2	1.8	2.1
6.8	1.3	3.0	4.5	2.8	2.3	2.7	5.7	4.8	3.5
2.6	3.3	5.0	4.0	7.2	9.1	2.8	3.6	7.3	9.0

    a. Provide a point estimate of the population mean drive-through time at fast-food restaurants.
    b. At 95% confidence, what is the margin of error?
    c. What is the 95% confidence interval estimate of the population mean?
    d. Discuss skewness that may be present in this population. What suggestion would you make for a repeat of this study?

19. A National Retail Foundation survey found households intended to spend an average of $649 during the December holiday season (*The Wall Street Journal,* December 2, 2002). Assume that the survey included 600 households and that the sample standard deviation was $175.
    a. With 95% confidence, what is the margin of error?
    b. What is the 95% confidence interval estimate of the population mean?
    c. The prior year, the population mean expenditure per household was $632. Discuss the change in holiday season expenditures over the one-year period.

CD file
Program

20. Is your favorite TV program often interrupted by advertising? CNBC presented statistics on the average number of programming minutes in a half-hour sitcom (CNBC, February 23, 2006). The following data (in minutes) are representative of their findings.

21.06	22.24	20.62
21.66	21.23	23.86
23.82	20.30	21.52
21.52	21.91	23.14
20.02	22.20	21.20
22.37	22.19	22.34
23.36	23.44	

Assume the population is approximately normal. Provide a point estimate and a 95% confidence interval for the mean number of programming minutes during a half-hour television sitcom.

CD file
Alcohol

21. Consumption of alcoholic beverages by young women of drinking age has been increasing in the United Kingdom, the United States, and Europe (*The Wall Street Journal,* February 15, 2006). Data (annual consumption in liters) consistent with the findings reported in *The Wall Street Journal* article are shown for a sample of 20 European young women.

266	82	199	174	97
170	222	115	130	169
164	102	113	171	0
93	0	93	110	130

Assuming the population is roughly symmetric, construct a 95% confidence interval for the mean annual consumption of alcoholic beverages by European young women.

22. The first few weeks of 2004 were good for the stock market. A sample of 25 large open-end funds showed the following year-to-date returns through January 16, 2004 (*Barron's,* January 19, 2004).

CD file
OpenEndFunds

7.0	3.2	1.4	5.4	8.5
2.5	2.5	1.9	5.4	1.6
1.0	2.1	8.5	4.3	6.2
1.5	1.2	2.7	3.8	2.0
1.2	2.6	4.0	2.6	0.6

a. What is the point estimate of the population mean year-to-date return for large open-end funds?

b. Given that the population has a normal distribution, develop a 95% confidence interval for the population mean year-to-date return for open-end funds.

8.3 Determining the Sample Size

If a desired margin of error is selected prior to sampling, the procedures in this section can be used to determine the sample size necessary to satisfy the margin of error requirement.

In providing practical advice in the two preceding sections, we commented on the role of the sample size in providing good approximate confidence intervals when the population is not normally distributed. In this section, we focus on another aspect of the sample size issue. We describe how to choose a sample size large enough to provide a desired margin of error. To understand how this process is done, we return to the σ known case presented in Section 8.1. Using expression (8.1), the interval estimate is

$$\bar{x} \pm z_{\alpha/2}\frac{\sigma}{\sqrt{n}}$$

The quantity $z_{\alpha/2}(\sigma/\sqrt{n})$ is the margin of error. Thus, we see that $z_{\alpha/2}$, the population standard deviation σ, and the sample size n combine to determine the margin of error. Once we select a confidence coefficient $1 - \alpha$, $z_{\alpha/2}$ can be determined. Then, if we have a value for σ, we can determine the sample size n needed to provide any desired margin of error. Development of the formula used to compute the required sample size n follows.

Let E = the desired margin of error:

$$E = z_{\alpha/2} \frac{\sigma}{\sqrt{n}}$$

Solving for $\sqrt{n}$, we have

$$\sqrt{n} = \frac{z_{\alpha/2}\sigma}{E}$$

Squaring both sides of this equation, we obtain the following expression for the sample size.

Equation (8.3) can be used to provide a good sample size recommendation. However, judgment on the part of the analyst should be used to determine whether the final sample size should be adjusted upward.

SAMPLE SIZE FOR AN INTERVAL ESTIMATE OF A POPULATION MEAN

$$n = \frac{(z_{\alpha/2})^2\sigma^2}{E^2} \qquad \textbf{(8.3)}$$

This sample size provides the desired margin of error at the chosen confidence level.

In equation (8.3) E is the margin of error that the user is willing to accept, and the value of $z_{\alpha/2}$ follows directly from the confidence level to be used in developing the interval estimate. Although user preference must be considered, 95% confidence is the most frequently chosen value ($z_{.025} = 1.96$).

Finally, use of equation (8.3) requires a value for the population standard deviation σ. However, even if σ is unknown, we can use equation (8.3) provided we have a preliminary or *planning value* for σ. In practice, one of the following procedures can be chosen.

A planning value for the population standard deviation σ must be specified before the sample size can be determined. Three methods of obtaining a planning value for σ are discussed here.

1. Use the estimate of the population standard deviation computed from data of previous studies as the planning value for σ.
2. Use a pilot study to select a preliminary sample. The sample standard deviation from the preliminary sample can be used as the planning value for σ.
3. Use judgment or a "best guess" for the value of σ. For example, we might begin by estimating the largest and smallest data values in the population. The difference between the largest and smallest values provides an estimate of the range for the data. Finally, the range divided by 4 is often suggested as a rough approximation of the standard deviation and thus an acceptable planning value for σ.

Let us demonstrate the use of equation (8.3) to determine the sample size by considering the following example. A previous study that investigated the cost of renting automobiles in the United States found a mean cost of approximately $55 per day for renting a midsize automobile. Suppose that the organization that conducted this study would like to conduct a new study in order to estimate the population mean daily rental cost for a midsize automobile in the United States. In designing the new study, the project director specifies that the population mean daily rental cost be estimated with a margin of error of $2 and a 95% level of confidence.

The project director specified a desired margin of error of $E = 2$, and the 95% level of confidence indicates $z_{.025} = 1.96$. Thus, we only need a planning value for the population standard deviation σ in order to compute the required sample size. At this point, an analyst

Equation (8.3) provides the minimum sample size needed to satisfy the desired margin of error requirement. If the computed sample size is not an integer, rounding up to the next integer value will provide a margin of error slightly smaller than required.

reviewed the sample data from the previous study and found that the sample standard deviation for the daily rental cost was \$9.65. Using 9.65 as the planning value for σ, we obtain

$$n = \frac{(z_{\alpha/2})^2\sigma^2}{E^2} = \frac{(1.96)^2(9.65)^2}{2^2} = 89.43$$

Thus, the sample size for the new study needs to be at least 89.43 midsize automobile rentals in order to satisfy the project director's \$2 margin-of-error requirement. In cases where the computed n is not an integer, we round up to the next integer value; hence, the recommended sample size is 90 midsize automobile rentals.

Exercises

Methods

23. How large a sample should be selected to provide a 95% confidence interval with a margin of error of 10? Assume that the population standard deviation is 40.

SELF test

24. The range for a set of data is estimated to be 36.
    a. What is the planning value for the population standard deviation?
    b. At 95% confidence, how large a sample would provide a margin of error of 3?
    c. At 95% confidence, how large a sample would provide a margin of error of 2?

Applications

SELF test

25. Refer to the Scheer Industries example in Section 8.2. Use 6.84 days as a planning value for the population standard deviation.
    a. Assuming 95% confidence, what sample size would be required to obtain a margin of error of 1.5 days?
    b. If the precision statement was made with 90% confidence, what sample size would be required to obtain a margin of error of 2 days?

26. The average cost of a gallon of unleaded gasoline in Greater Cincinnati was reported to be \$2.41 (*The Cincinnati Enquirer*, February 3, 2006). During periods of rapidly changing prices, the newspaper samples service stations and prepares reports on gasoline prices frequently. Assume the standard deviation is \$.15 for the price of a gallon of unleaded regular gasoline, and recommend the appropriate sample size for the newspaper to use if they wish to report a margin of error at 95% confidence.
    a. Suppose the desired margin of error is \$.07.
    b. Suppose the desired margin of error is \$.05.
    c. Suppose the desired margin of error is \$.03.

27. Annual starting salaries for college graduates with degrees in business administration are generally expected to be between \$30,000 and \$45,000. Assume that a 95% confidence interval estimate of the population mean annual starting salary is desired. What is the planning value for the population standard deviation? How large a sample should be taken if the desired margin of error is
    a. \$500?
    b. \$200?
    c. \$100?
    d. Would you recommend trying to obtain the \$100 margin of error? Explain.

28. Smith Travel Research provides information on the one-night cost of hotel rooms throughout the United States (*USA Today*, July 8, 2002). Use \$2 as the desired margin of error and \$22.50 as the planning value for the population standard deviation to find the sample size recommended in (a), (b), and (c).
    a. A 90% confidence interval estimate of the population mean cost of hotel rooms.
    b. A 95% confidence interval estimate of the population mean cost of hotel rooms.

c. A 99% confidence interval estimate of the population mean cost of hotel rooms.
d. When the desired margin of error is fixed, what happens to the sample size as the confidence level is increased? Would you recommend a 99% confidence level be used by Smith Travel Research? Discuss.

29. The travel-to-work time for residents of the 15 largest cities in the United States is reported in the *2003 Information Please Almanac.* Suppose that a preliminary simple random sample of residents of San Francisco is used to develop a planning value of 6.25 minutes for the population standard deviation.
  a. If we want to estimate the population mean travel-to-work time for San Francisco residents with a margin of error of 2 minutes, what sample size should be used? Assume 95% confidence.
  b. If we want to estimate the population mean travel-to-work time for San Francisco residents with a margin of error of 1 minute, what sample size should be used? Assume 95% confidence.

30. During the first quarter of 2003, the price/earnings (P/E) ratio for stocks listed on the New York Stock Exchange generally ranged from 5 to 60 (*The Wall Street Journal,* March 7, 2003). Assume that we want to estimate the population mean P/E ratio for all stocks listed on the exchange. How many stocks should be included in the sample if we want a margin of error of 3? Use 95% confidence.

8.4 Population Proportion

In the introduction to this chapter we said that the general form of an interval estimate of a population proportion p is

$$\bar{p} \pm \text{Margin of error}$$

The sampling distribution of $\bar{p}$ plays a key role in computing the margin of error for this interval estimate.

In Chapter 7 we said that the sampling distribution of $\bar{p}$ can be approximated by a normal distribution whenever $np \geq 5$ and $n(1 - p) \geq 5$. Figure 8.9 shows the normal approximation

FIGURE 8.9 NORMAL APPROXIMATION OF THE SAMPLING DISTRIBUTION OF $\bar{p}$

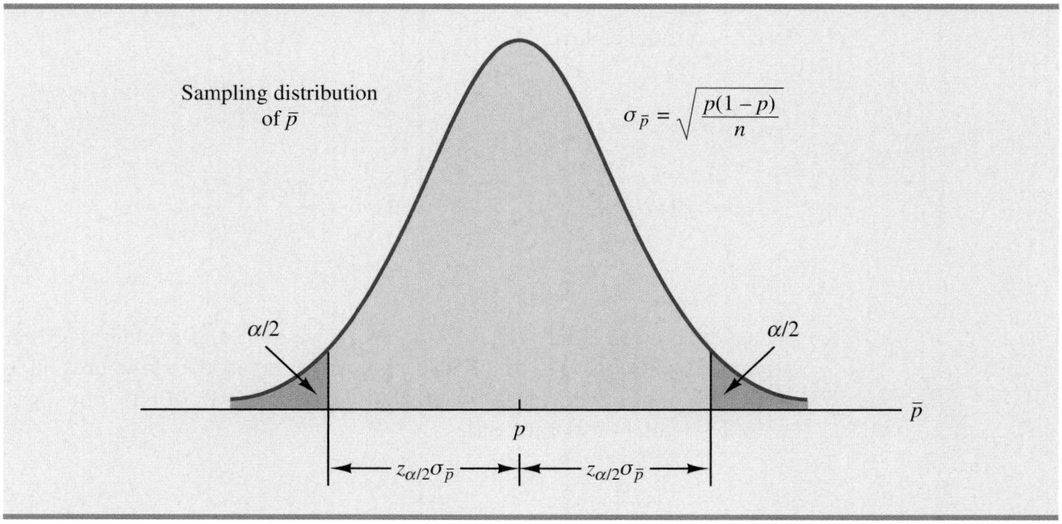

of the sampling distribution of $\bar{p}$. The mean of the sampling distribution of $\bar{p}$ is the population proportion p, and the standard error of $\bar{p}$ is

$$\sigma_{\bar{p}} = \sqrt{\frac{p(1-p)}{n}} \tag{8.4}$$

Because the sampling distribution of $\bar{p}$ is normally distributed, if we choose $z_{\alpha/2}\sigma_{\bar{p}}$ as the margin of error in an interval estimate of a population proportion, we know that $100(1-\alpha)\%$ of the intervals generated will contain the true population proportion. But $\sigma_{\bar{p}}$ cannot be used directly in the computation of the margin of error because p will not be known; p is what we are trying to estimate. So $\bar{p}$ is substituted for p and the margin of error for an interval estimate of a population proportion is given by

$$\text{Margin of error} = z_{\alpha/2}\sqrt{\frac{\bar{p}(1-\bar{p})}{n}} \tag{8.5}$$

With this margin of error, the general expression for an interval estimate of a population proportion is as follows.

When developing confidence intervals for proportions, the quantity $z_{\alpha/2}\sqrt{\bar{p}(1-\bar{p})/n}$ provides the margin of error.

INTERVAL ESTIMATE OF A POPULATION PROPORTION

$$\bar{p} \pm z_{\alpha/2}\sqrt{\frac{\bar{p}(1-\bar{p})}{n}} \tag{8.6}$$

where $1-\alpha$ is the confidence coefficient and $z_{\alpha/2}$ is the z value providing an area of $\alpha/2$ in the upper tail of the standard normal distribution.

CD file
TeeTimes

The following example illustrates the computation of the margin of error and interval estimate for a population proportion. A national survey of 900 women golfers was conducted to learn how women golfers view their treatment at golf courses in the United States. The survey found that 396 of the women golfers were satisfied with the availability of tee times. Thus, the point estimate of the proportion of the population of women golfers who are satisfied with the availability of tee times is 396/900 = .44. Using expression (8.6) and a 95% confidence level,

$$\bar{p} \pm z_{\alpha/2}\sqrt{\frac{\bar{p}(1-\bar{p})}{n}}$$

$$.44 \pm 1.96\sqrt{\frac{.44(1-.44)}{900}}$$

$$.44 \pm .0324$$

Thus, the margin of error is .0324 and the 95% confidence interval estimate of the population proportion is .4076 to .4724. Using percentages, the survey results enable us to state with 95% confidence that between 40.76% and 47.24% of all women golfers are satisfied with the availability of tee times.

Determining the Sample Size

Let us consider the question of how large the sample size should be to obtain an estimate of a population proportion at a specified level of precision. The rationale for the sample size determination in developing interval estimates of p is similar to the rationale used in Section 8.3 to determine the sample size for estimating a population mean.

Previously in this section we said that the margin of error associated with an interval estimate of a population proportion is $z_{\alpha/2}\sqrt{\bar{p}(1 - \bar{p})/n}$. The margin of error is based on the value of $z_{\alpha/2}$, the sample proportion $\bar{p}$, and the sample size n. Larger sample sizes provide a smaller margin of error and better precision.

Let E denote the desired margin of error.

$$E = z_{\alpha/2}\sqrt{\frac{\bar{p}(1 - \bar{p})}{n}}$$

Solving this equation for n provides a formula for the sample size that will provide a margin of error of size E.

$$n = \frac{(z_{\alpha/2})^2\bar{p}(1 - \bar{p})}{E^2}$$

Note, however, that we cannot use this formula to compute the sample size that will provide the desired margin of error because $\bar{p}$ will not be known until after we select the sample. What we need, then, is a planning value for $\bar{p}$ that can be used to make the computation. Using p^* to denote the planning value for $\bar{p}$, the following formula can be used to compute the sample size that will provide a margin of error of size E.

SAMPLE SIZE FOR AN INTERVAL ESTIMATE OF A POPULATION PROPORTION

$$n = \frac{(z_{\alpha/2})^2 p^*(1 - p^*)}{E^2} \qquad \textbf{(8.7)}$$

In practice, the planning value p^* can be chosen by one of the following procedures.

1. Use the sample proportion from a previous sample of the same or similar units.
2. Use a pilot study to select a preliminary sample. The sample proportion from this sample can be used as the planning value, p^*.
3. Use judgment or a "best guess" for the value of p^*.
4. If none of the preceding alternatives apply, use a planning value of $p^* = .50$.

Let us return to the survey of women golfers and assume that the company is interested in conducting a new survey to estimate the current proportion of the population of women golfers who are satisfied with the availability of tee times. How large should the sample be if the survey director wants to estimate the population proportion with a margin of error of .025 at 95% confidence? With $E = .025$ and $z_{\alpha/2} = 1.96$, we need a planning value p^* to answer the sample size question. Using the previous survey result of $\bar{p} = .44$ as the planning value p^*, equation (8.7) shows that

$$n = \frac{(z_{\alpha/2})^2 p^*(1 - p^*)}{E^2} = \frac{(1.96)^2(.44)(1 - .44)}{(.025)^2} = 1514.5$$

TABLE 8.5 SOME POSSIBLE VALUES FOR $p^*(1 - p^*)$

p^*	$p^*(1 - p^*)$	
.10	(.10)(.90) = .09	
.30	(.30)(.70) = .21	
.40	(.40)(.60) = .24	
.50	(.50)(.50) = .25	← Largest value for $p^*(1 - p^*)$
.60	(.60)(.40) = .24	
.70	(.70)(.30) = .21	
.90	(.90)(.10) = .09	

Thus, the sample size must be at least 1514.5 women golfers to satisfy the margin of error requirement. Rounding up to the next integer value indicates that a sample of 1515 women golfers is recommended to satisfy the margin of error requirement.

The fourth alternative suggested for selecting a planning value p^* is to use $p^* = .50$. This value of p^* is frequently used when no other information is available. To understand why, note that the numerator of equation (8.7) shows that the sample size is proportional to the quantity $p^*(1 - p^*)$. A larger value for the quantity $p^*(1 - p^*)$ will result in a larger sample size. Table 8.5 gives some possible values of $p^*(1 - p^*)$. Note that the largest value of $p^*(1 - p^*)$ occurs when $p^* = .50$. Thus, in case of any uncertainty about an appropriate planning value, we know that $p^* = .50$ will provide the largest sample size recommendation. In effect, we play it safe by recommending the largest necessary sample size. If the sample proportion turns out to be different from the .50 planning value, the margin of error will be smaller than anticipated. Thus, in using $p^* = .50$, we guarantee that the sample size will be sufficient to obtain the desired margin of error.

In the survey of women golfers example, a planning value of $p^* = .50$ would have provided the sample size

$$n = \frac{(z_{\alpha/2})^2 p^*(1 - p^*)}{E^2} = \frac{(1.96)^2(.50)(1 - .50)}{(.025)^2} = 1536.6$$

Thus, a slightly larger sample size of 1537 women golfers would be recommended.

NOTES AND COMMENTS

The desired margin of error for estimating a population proportion is almost always .10 or less. In national public opinion polls conducted by organizations such as Gallup and Harris, a .03 or .04 margin of error is common. With such margins of error, equation (8.7) will almost always provide a sample size that is large enough to satisfy the requirements of $np \geq 5$ and $n(1 - p) \geq 5$ for using a normal distribution as an approximation for the sampling distribution of $\bar{x}$.

Exercises

Methods

SELF test

31. A simple random sample of 400 individuals provides 100 Yes responses.
    a. What is the point estimate of the proportion of the population that would provide Yes responses?
    b. What is your estimate of the standard error of the proportion, $\sigma_{\bar{p}}$?
    c. Compute the 95% confidence interval for the population proportion.

32. A simple random sample of 800 elements generates a sample proportion $\bar{p} = .70$.
    a. Provide a 90% confidence interval for the population proportion.
    b. Provide a 95% confidence interval for the population proportion.

33. In a survey, the planning value for the population proportion is $p^* = .35$. How large a sample should be taken to provide a 95% confidence interval with a margin of error of .05?

34. At 95% confidence, how large a sample should be taken to obtain a margin of error of .03 for the estimation of a population proportion? Assume that past data are not available for developing a planning value for p^*.

Applications

SELF test

35. A survey of 611 office workers investigated telephone answering practices, including how often each office worker was able to answer incoming telephone calls and how often incoming telephone calls went directly to voice mail (*USA Today,* April 21, 2002). A total of 281 office workers indicated that they never need voice mail and are able to take every telephone call.
    a. What is the point estimate of the proportion of the population of office workers who are able to take every telephone call?
    b. At 90% confidence, what is the margin of error?
    c. What is the 90% confidence interval for the proportion of the population of office workers who are able to take every telephone call?

36. According to statistics reported on CNBC, a surprising number of motor vehicles are not covered by insurance (CNBC, February 23, 2006). Sample results, consistent with the CNBC report, showed 46 of 200 vehicles were not covered by insurance.
    a. What is the point estimate of the proportion of vehicles not covered by insurance?
    b. Develop a 95% confidence interval for the population proportion.

CD file

JobSatisfaction

37. Towers Perrin, a New York human resources consulting firm, conducted a survey of 1100 employees at medium-sized and large companies to determine how dissatisfied employees were with their jobs (*The Wall Street Journal,* January 29, 2003). Representative data are shown in the file JobSatisfaction. A response of Yes indicates the employee strongly disliked the current work experience.
    a. What is the point estimate of the proportion of the population of employees who strongly dislike their current work experience?
    b. At 95% confidence, what is the margin of error?
    c. What is the 95% confidence interval for the proportion of the population of employees who strongly dislike their current work experience?
    d. Towers Perrin estimates that it costs employers one-third of an hourly employee's annual salary to find a successor and as much as 1.5 times the annual salary to find a successor for a highly compensated employee. What message did this survey send to employers?

38. According to Thomson Financial, through January 25, 2006, the majority of companies reporting profits had beaten estimates (*BusinessWeek,* February 6, 2006). A sample of 162 companies showed 104 beat estimates, 29 matched estimates, and 29 fell short.
    a. What is the point estimate of the proportion that fell short of estimates?
    b. Determine the margin of error and provide a 95% confidence interval for the proportion that beat estimates.
    c. How large a sample is needed if the desired margin of error is .05?

SELF test

39. The percentage of people not covered by health care insurance in 2003 was 15.6% (*Statistical Abstract of the United States*, 2006). A congressional committee has been charged with conducting a sample survey to obtain more current information.
    a. What sample size would you recommend if the committee's goal is to estimate the current proportion of individuals without health care insurance with a margin of error of .03? Use a 95% confidence level.
    b. Repeat part (a) using a 99% confidence level.

40. The professional baseball home run record of 61 home runs in a season was held for 37 years by Roger Maris of the New York Yankees. However, between 1998 and 2001, three players—Mark McGwire, Sammy Sosa, and Barry Bonds—broke the standard set by Maris, with Bonds holding the current record of 73 home runs in a single season. With the long-standing home run record being broken and with many other new offensive records being set, suspicion arose that baseball players might be using illegal muscle-building drugs called steroids. A *USA Today*/CNN/Gallup poll found that 86% of baseball fans think professional baseball players should be tested for steroids (*USA Today,* July 8, 2002). If 650 baseball fans were included in the sample, compute the margin of error and the 95% confidence interval for the population proportion of baseball fans who think professional baseball players should be tested for steroids.

41. America's young people are heavy Internet users; 87% of Americans ages 12 to 17 are Internet users (*The Cincinnati Enquirer,* February 7, 2006). MySpace was voted the most popular Web site by 9% in a sample survey of Internet users in this age group. Suppose 1400 youths participated in the survey. What is the margin of error, and what is the interval estimate of the population proportion for which MySpace is the most popular Web site? Use a 95% confidence level.

42. A *USA Today*/CNN/Gallup poll for the presidential campaign sampled 491 potential voters in June (*USA Today,* June 9, 2000). A primary purpose of the poll was to obtain an estimate of the proportion of potential voters who favor each candidate. Assume a planning value of $p^* = .50$ and a 95% confidence level.
   a. For $p^* = .50$, what was the planned margin of error for the June poll?
   b. Closer to the November election, better precision and smaller margins of error are desired. Assume the following margins of error are requested for surveys to be conducted during the presidential campaign. Compute the recommended sample size for each survey.

Survey	**Margin of Error**
September	.04
October	.03
Early November	.02
Pre-Election Day	.01

43. A Phoenix Wealth Management/Harris Interactive survey of 1500 individuals with net worth of \$1 million or more provided a variety of statistics on wealthy people (*BusinessWeek,* September 22, 2003). The previous three-year period had been bad for the stock market, which motivated some of the questions asked.
   a. The survey reported that 53% of the respondents lost 25% or more of their portfolio value over the past three years. Develop a 95% confidence interval for the proportion of wealthy people who lost 25% or more of their portfolio value over the past three years.
   b. The survey reported that 31% of the respondents feel they have to save more for retirement to make up for what they lost. Develop a 95% confidence interval for the population proportion.
   c. Five percent of the respondents gave \$25,000 or more to charity over the previous year. Develop a 95% confidence interval for the proportion who gave \$25,000 or more to charity.
   d. Compare the margin of error for the interval estimates in parts (a), (b), and (c). How is the margin of error related to $\bar{p}$? When the same sample is being used to estimate a variety of proportions, which of the proportions should be used to choose the planning value p^*? Why do you think $p^* = .50$ is often used in these cases?

Summary

In this chapter we presented methods for developing interval estimates of a population mean and a population proportion. A point estimator may or may not provide a good estimate of a population parameter. The use of an interval estimate provides a measure of the precision of an estimate. Both the interval estimate of the population mean and the population proportion are of the form: point estimate ± margin of error.

We presented interval estimates for a population mean for two cases. In the σ known case, historical data or other information is used to develop an estimate of σ prior to taking a sample. Analysis of new sample data then proceeds based on the assumption that σ is known. In the σ unknown case, the sample data are used to estimate both the population mean and the population standard deviation. The final choice of which interval estimation procedure to use depends upon the analyst's understanding of which method provides the best estimate of σ.

In the σ known case, the interval estimation procedure is based on the assumed value of σ and the use of the standard normal distribution. In the σ unknown case, the interval estimation procedure uses the sample standard deviation s and the t distribution. In both cases the quality of the interval estimates obtained depends on the distribution of the population and the sample size. If the population is normally distributed the interval estimates will be exact in both cases, even for small sample sizes. If the population is not normally distributed, the interval estimates obtained will be approximate. Larger sample sizes will provide better approximations, but the more highly skewed the population is, the larger the sample size needs to be to obtain a good approximation. Practical advice about the sample size necessary to obtain good approximations was included in Sections 8.1 and 8.2. In most cases a sample of size 30 or more will provide good approximate confidence intervals.

The general form of the interval estimate for a population proportion is $\bar{p}$ ± margin of error. In practice the sample sizes used for interval estimates of a population proportion are generally large. Thus, the interval estimation procedure is based on the standard normal distribution.

Often a desired margin of error is specified prior to developing a sampling plan. We showed how to choose a sample size large enough to provide the desired precision.

Glossary

Interval estimate An estimate of a population parameter that provides an interval believed to contain the value of the parameter. For the interval estimates in this chapter, it has the form: point estimate ± margin of error.

Margin of error The ± value added to and subtracted from a point estimate in order to develop an interval estimate of a population parameter.

σ known The case when historical data or other information provides a good value for the population standard deviation prior to taking a sample. The interval estimation procedure uses this known value of σ in computing the margin of error.

Confidence level The confidence associated with an interval estimate. For example, if an interval estimation procedure provides intervals such that 95% of the intervals formed using the procedure will include the population parameter, the interval estimate is said to be constructed at the 95% confidence level.

Confidence coefficient The confidence level expressed as a decimal value. For example, .95 is the confidence coefficient for a 95% confidence level.

Confidence interval Another name for an interval estimate.

σ unknown The more common case when no good basis exists for estimating the population standard deviation prior to taking the sample. The interval estimation procedure uses the sample standard deviation s in computing the margin of error.

***t* distribution** A family of probability distributions that can be used to develop an interval estimate of a population mean whenever the population standard deviation σ is unknown and is estimated by the sample standard deviation s.

Degrees of freedom A parameter of the t distribution. When the t distribution is used in the computation of an interval estimate of a population mean, the appropriate t distribution has $n - 1$ degrees of freedom, where n is the size of the simple random sample.

Key Formulas

Interval Estimate of a Population Mean: σ Known

$$\bar{x} \pm z_{\alpha/2} \frac{\sigma}{\sqrt{n}} \tag{8.1}$$

Interval Estimate of a Population Mean: σ Unknown

$$\bar{x} \pm t_{\alpha/2} \frac{s}{\sqrt{n}} \tag{8.2}$$

Sample Size for an Interval Estimate of a Population Mean

$$n = \frac{(z_{\alpha/2})^2 \sigma^2}{E^2} \tag{8.3}$$

Interval Estimate of a Population Proportion

$$\bar{p} \pm z_{\alpha/2} \sqrt{\frac{\bar{p}(1 - \bar{p})}{n}} \tag{8.6}$$

Sample Size for an Interval Estimate of a Population Proportion

$$n = \frac{(z_{\alpha/2})^2 p^*(1 - p^*)}{E^2} \tag{8.7}$$

Supplementary Exercises

44. A sample survey of 54 discount brokers showed that the mean price charged for a trade of 100 shares at \$50 per share was \$33.77 (*AAII Journal,* February 2006). The survey is conducted annually. With the historical data available, assume a known population standard deviation of \$15.
    a. Using the sample data, what is the margin of error associated with a 95% confidence interval?
    b. Develop a 95% confidence interval for the mean price charged by discount brokers for a trade of 100 shares at \$50 per share.
45. A survey conducted by the American Automobile Association showed that a family of four spends an average of \$215.60 per day while on vacation. Suppose a sample of 64 families of four vacationing at Niagara Falls resulted in a sample mean of \$252.45 per day and a sample standard deviation of \$74.50.
    a. Develop a 95% confidence interval estimate of the mean amount spent per day by a family of four visiting Niagara Falls.
    b. Based on the confidence interval from part (a), does it appear that the population mean amount spent per day by families visiting Niagara Falls differs from the mean reported by the American Automobile Association? Explain.
46. The motion picture *Harry Potter and the Sorcerer's Stone* shattered the box office debut record previously held by *The Lost World: Jurassic Park* (*The Wall Street Journal,* November 19, 2001). A sample of 100 movie theaters showed that the mean three-day weekend gross was \$25,467 per theater. The sample standard deviation was \$4980.
    a. What is the margin of error for this study? Use 95% confidence.
    b. What is the 95% confidence interval estimate for the population mean weekend gross per theater?
    c. *The Lost World* took in \$72.1 million in its first three-day weekend. *Harry Potter and the Sorcerer's Stone* was shown in 3672 theaters. What is an estimate of the total *Harry Potter and the Sorcerer's Stone* took in during its first three-day weekend?
    d. An Associated Press article claimed *Harry Potter* "shattered" the box office debut record held by *The Lost World.* Do your results agree with this claim?

47. Many stock market observers say that when the P/E ratio for stocks gets over 20 the market is overvalued. The P/E ratio is the stock price divided by the most recent 12 months of earnings. Suppose you are interested in seeing whether the current market is overvalued and would also like to know what proportion of companies pay dividends. A random sample of 30 companies listed on the New York Stock Exchange (NYSE) is provided (*Barron's,* January 19, 2004).

CD file NYSEStocks

Company	Dividend	P/E Ratio	Company	Dividend	P/E Ratio
Albertsons	Yes	14	NY Times A	Yes	25
BRE Prop	Yes	18	Omnicare	Yes	25
CityNtl	Yes	16	PallCp	Yes	23
DelMonte	No	21	PubSvcEnt	Yes	11
EnrgzHldg	No	20	SensientTch	Yes	11
Ford Motor	Yes	22	SmtProp	Yes	12
Gildan A	No	12	TJX Cos	Yes	21
HudsnUtdBcp	Yes	13	Thomson	Yes	30
IBM	Yes	22	USB Hldg	Yes	12
JeffPilot	Yes	16	US Restr	Yes	26
KingswayFin	No	6	Varian Med	No	41
Libbey	Yes	13	Visx	No	72
MasoniteIntl	No	15	Waste Mgt	No	23
Motorola	Yes	68	Wiley A	Yes	21
Ntl City	Yes	10	Yum Brands	No	18

a. What is a point estimate of the P/E ratio for the population of stocks listed on the New York Stock Exchange? Develop a 95% confidence interval.
b. Based on your answer to part (a), do you believe that the market is overvalued?
c. What is a point estimate of the proportion of companies on the NYSE that pay dividends? Is the sample size large enough to justify using the normal distribution to construct a confidence interval for this proportion? Why or why not?

CD file Flights

48. US Airways conducted a number of studies that indicated a substantial savings could be obtained by encouraging Dividend Miles frequent flyer customers to redeem miles and schedule award flights online (*US Airways Attaché,* February 2003). One study collected data on the amount of time required to redeem miles and schedule an award flight over the telephone. A sample showing the time in minutes required for each of 150 award flights scheduled by telephone is contained in the data set Flights. Use Minitab or Excel to help answer the following questions.
a. What is the sample mean number of minutes required to schedule an award flight by telephone?
b. What is the 95% confidence interval for the population mean time to schedule an award flight by telephone?
c. Assume a telephone ticket agent works 7.5 hours per day. How many award flights can one ticket agent be expected to handle a day?
d. Discuss why this information supported US Airways' plans to use an online system to reduce costs.

CD file ActTemps

49. A survey by Accountemps asked a sample of 200 executives to provide data on the number of minutes per day office workers waste trying to locate mislabeled, misfiled, or misplaced items. Data consistent with this survey are contained in the data set ActTemps.
a. Use ActTemps to develop a point estimate of the number of minutes per day office workers waste trying to locate mislabeled, misfiled, or misplaced items.
b. What is the sample standard deviation?
c. What is the 95% confidence interval for the mean number of minutes wasted per day?

50. Mileage tests are conducted for a particular model of automobile. If a 98% confidence interval with a margin of error of 1 mile per gallon is desired, how many automobiles should be used in the test? Assume that preliminary mileage tests indicate the standard deviation is 2.6 miles per gallon.

51. In developing patient appointment schedules, a medical center wants to estimate the mean time that a staff member spends with each patient. How large a sample should be taken if the desired margin of error is two minutes at a 95% level of confidence? How large a sample should be taken for a 99% level of confidence? Use a planning value for the population standard deviation of eight minutes.

52. Annual salary plus bonus data for chief executive officers are presented in the *BusinessWeek* Annual Pay Survey. A preliminary sample showed that the standard deviation is \$675 with data provided in thousands of dollars. How many chief executive officers should be in a sample if we want to estimate the population mean annual salary plus bonus with a margin of error of \$100,000? (*Note:* The desired margin of error would be $E = 100$ if the data are in thousands of dollars.) Use 95% confidence.

53. The National Center for Education Statistics reported that 47% of college students work to pay for tuition and living expenses. Assume that a sample of 450 college students was used in the study.
    a. Provide a 95% confidence interval for the population proportion of college students who work to pay for tuition and living expenses.
    b. Provide a 99% confidence interval for the population proportion of college students who work to pay for tuition and living expenses.
    c. What happens to the margin of error as the confidence is increased from 95% to 99%?

54. A *USA Today*/CNN/Gallup survey of 369 working parents found 200 who said they spend too little time with their children because of work commitments.
    a. What is the point estimate of the proportion of the population of working parents who feel they spend too little time with their children because of work commitments?
    b. At 95% confidence, what is the margin of error?
    c. What is the 95% confidence interval estimate of the population proportion of working parents who feel they spend too little time with their children because of work commitments?

55. Which would be hardest for you to give up: Your computer or your television? In a recent survey of 1677 U.S. Internet users, 74% of the young tech elite (average age of 22) say their computer would be very hard to give up (*PC Magazine,* February 3, 2004). Only 48% say their television would be very hard to give up.
    a. Develop a 95% confidence interval for the proportion of the young tech elite that would find it very hard to give up their computer.
    b. Develop a 99% confidence interval for the proportion of the young tech elite that would find it very hard to give up their television.
    c. In which case, part (a) or part (b), is the margin of error larger? Explain why.

56. Cincinnati/Northern Kentucky International Airport had the second highest on-time arrival rate for 2005 among the nation's busiest airports (*The Cincinnati Enquirer,* February 3, 2006). Assume the findings were based on 455 on-time arrivals out of a sample of 550 flights.
    a. Develop a point estimate of the on-time arrival rate (proportion of flights arriving on time) for the airport.
    b. Construct a 95% confidence interval for the on-time arrival rate of the population of all flights at the airport during 2005.

57. The *2003 Statistical Abstract of the United States* reported the percentage of people 18 years of age and older who smoke. Suppose that a study designed to collect new data on smokers and nonsmokers uses a preliminary estimate of the proportion who smoke of .30.
    a. How large a sample should be taken to estimate the proportion of smokers in the population with a margin of error of .02? Use 95% confidence.
    b. Assume that the study uses your sample size recommendation in part (a) and finds 520 smokers. What is the point estimate of the proportion of smokers in the population?
    c. What is the 95% confidence interval for the proportion of smokers in the population?

58. A well-known bank credit card firm wishes to estimate the proportion of credit card holders who carry a nonzero balance at the end of the month and incur an interest charge. Assume that the desired margin of error is .03 at 98% confidence.
    a. How large a sample should be selected if it is anticipated that roughly 70% of the firm's card holders carry a nonzero balance at the end of the month?
    b. How large a sample should be selected if no planning value for the proportion could be specified?

59. In a survey, 200 people were asked to identify their major source of news information; 110 stated that their major source was television news.
    a. Construct a 95% confidence interval for the proportion of people in the population who consider television their major source of news information.
    b. How large a sample would be necessary to estimate the population proportion with a margin of error of .05 at 95% confidence?

60. Although airline schedules and cost are important factors for business travelers when choosing an airline carrier, a *USA Today* survey found that business travelers list an airline's frequent flyer program as the most important factor. From a sample of $n = 1993$ business travelers who responded to the survey, 618 listed a frequent flyer program as the most important factor.
    a. What is the point estimate of the proportion of the population of business travelers who believe a frequent flyer program is the most important factor when choosing an airline carrier?
    b. Develop a 95% confidence interval estimate of the population proportion.
    c. How large a sample would be required to report the margin of error of .01 at 95% confidence? Would you recommend that *USA Today* attempt to provide this degree of precision? Why or why not?

Case Problem 1 Young Professional Magazine

Young Professional magazine was developed for a target audience of recent college graduates who are in their first 10 years in a business/professional career. In its two years of publication, the magazine has been fairly successful. Now the publisher is interested in expanding the magazine's advertising base. Potential advertisers continually ask about the demographics and interests of subscribers to *Young Professional*. To collect this information, the magazine commissioned a survey to develop a profile of its subscribers. The survey results will be used to help the magazine choose articles of interest and provide advertisers with a profile of subscribers. As a new employee of the magazine, you have been asked to help analyze the survey results.

Some of the survey questions follow:

CD file
Professional

1. What is your age?
2. Are you: Male________ Female__________
3. Do you plan to make any real estate purchases in the next two years? Yes______ No______
4. What is the approximate total value of financial investments, exclusive of your home, owned by you or members of your household?
5. How many stock/bond/mutual fund transactions have you made in the past year?
6. Do you have broadband access to the Internet at home? Yes______ No______
7. Please indicate your total household income last year.
8. Do you have children? Yes______ No______

The file entitled Professional contains the responses to these questions. Table 8.6 shows the portion of the file pertaining to the first five survey respondents. The entire file is on the CD accompanying the text.

TABLE 8.6 PARTIAL SURVEY RESULTS FOR *YOUNG PROFESSIONAL* MAGAZINE

Age	Gender	Real Estate Purchases	Value of Investments($)	Number of Transactions	Broadband Access	Household Income($)	Children
38	Female	No	12200	4	Yes	75200	Yes
30	Male	No	12400	4	Yes	70300	Yes
41	Female	No	26800	5	Yes	48200	No
28	Female	Yes	19600	6	No	95300	No
31	Female	Yes	15100	5	No	73300	Yes
⋮	⋮	⋮	⋮	⋮	⋮	⋮	⋮

Managerial Report

Prepare a managerial report summarizing the results of the survey. In addition to statistical summaries, discuss how the magazine might use these results to attract advertisers. You might also comment on how the survey results could be used by the magazine's editors to identify topics that would be of interest to readers. Your report should address the following issues, but do not limit your analysis to just these areas.

1. Develop appropriate descriptive statistics to summarize the data.
2. Develop 95% confidence intervals for the mean age and household income of subscribers.
3. Develop 95% confidence intervals for the proportion of subscribers who have broadband access at home and the proportion of subscribers who have children.
4. Would *Young Professional* be a good advertising outlet for online brokers? Justify your conclusion with statistical data.
5. Would this magazine be a good place to advertise for companies selling educational software and computer games for young children?
6. Comment on the types of articles you believe would be of interest to readers of *Young Professional*.

Case Problem 2 Gulf Real Estate Properties

Gulf Real Estate Properties, Inc., is a real estate firm located in southwest Florida. The company, which advertises itself as "expert in the real estate market," monitors condominium sales by collecting data on location, list price, sale price, and number of days it takes to sell each unit. Each condominium is classified as *Gulf View* if it is located directly on the Gulf of Mexico or *No Gulf View* if it is located on the bay or a golf course, near but not on the Gulf. Sample data from the Multiple Listing Service in Naples, Florida, provided recent sales data for 40 Gulf View condominiums and 18 No Gulf View condominiums.* Prices are in thousands of dollars. The data are shown in Table 8.7.

Managerial Report

1. Use appropriate descriptive statistics to summarize each of the three variables for the 40 Gulf View condominiums.
2. Use appropriate descriptive statistics to summarize each of the three variables for the 18 No Gulf View condominiums.
3. Compare your summary results. Discuss any specific statistical results that would help a real estate agent understand the condominium market.

*Data based on condominium sales reported in the Naples MLS (Coldwell Banker, June 2000).

TABLE 8.7 SALES DATA FOR GULF REAL ESTATE PROPERTIES

Gulf View Condominiums			No Gulf View Condominiums		
List Price	**Sale Price**	**Days to Sell**	**List Price**	**Sale Price**	**Days to Sell**
495.0	475.0	130	217.0	217.0	182
379.0	350.0	71	148.0	135.5	338
529.0	519.0	85	186.5	179.0	122
552.5	534.5	95	239.0	230.0	150
334.9	334.9	119	279.0	267.5	169
550.0	505.0	92	215.0	214.0	58
169.9	165.0	197	279.0	259.0	110
210.0	210.0	56	179.9	176.5	130
975.0	945.0	73	149.9	144.9	149
314.0	314.0	126	235.0	230.0	114
315.0	305.0	88	199.8	192.0	120
885.0	800.0	282	210.0	195.0	61
975.0	975.0	100	226.0	212.0	146
469.0	445.0	56	149.9	146.5	137
329.0	305.0	49	160.0	160.0	281
365.0	330.0	48	322.0	292.5	63
332.0	312.0	88	187.5	179.0	48
520.0	495.0	161	247.0	227.0	52
425.0	405.0	149			
675.0	669.0	142			
409.0	400.0	28			
649.0	649.0	29			
319.0	305.0	140			
425.0	410.0	85			
359.0	340.0	107			
469.0	449.0	72			
895.0	875.0	129			
439.0	430.0	160			
435.0	400.0	206			
235.0	227.0	91			
638.0	618.0	100			
629.0	600.0	97			
329.0	309.0	114			
595.0	555.0	45			
339.0	315.0	150			
215.0	200.0	48			
395.0	375.0	135			
449.0	425.0	53			
499.0	465.0	86			
439.0	428.5	158			

CD file
GulfProp

4. Develop a 95% confidence interval estimate of the population mean sales price and population mean number of days to sell for Gulf View condominiums. Interpret your results.
5. Develop a 95% confidence interval estimate of the population mean sales price and population mean number of days to sell for No Gulf View condominiums. Interpret your results.
6. Assume the branch manager requested estimates of the mean selling price of Gulf View condominiums with a margin of error of $40,000 and the mean selling price

of No Gulf View condominiums with a margin of error of \$15,000. Using 95% confidence, how large should the sample sizes be?

7. Gulf Real Estate Properties just signed contracts for two new listings: a Gulf View condominium with a list price of \$589,000 and a No Gulf View condominium with a list price of \$285,000. What is your estimate of the final selling price and number of days required to sell each of these units?

Case Problem 3 Metropolitan Research, Inc.

Metropolitan Research, Inc., a consumer research organization, conducts surveys designed to evaluate a wide variety of products and services available to consumers. In one particular study, Metropolitan looked at consumer satisfaction with the performance of automobiles produced by a major Detroit manufacturer. A questionnaire sent to owners of one of the manufacturer's full-sized cars revealed several complaints about early transmission problems. To learn more about the transmission failures, Metropolitan used a sample of actual transmission repairs provided by a transmission repair firm in the Detroit area. The following data show the actual number of miles driven for 50 vehicles at the time of transmission failure.

CD file
Auto

85,092	32,609	59,465	77,437	32,534	64,090	32,464	59,902
39,323	89,641	94,219	116,803	92,857	63,436	65,605	85,861
64,342	61,978	67,998	59,817	101,769	95,774	121,352	69,568
74,276	66,998	40,001	72,069	25,066	77,098	69,922	35,662
74,425	67,202	118,444	53,500	79,294	64,544	86,813	116,269
37,831	89,341	73,341	85,288	138,114	53,402	85,586	82,256
77,539	88,798						

Managerial Report

1. Use appropriate descriptive statistics to summarize the transmission failure data.
2. Develop a 95% confidence interval for the mean number of miles driven until transmission failure for the population of automobiles with transmission failure. Provide a managerial interpretation of the interval estimate.
3. Discuss the implication of your statistical findings in terms of the belief that some owners of the automobiles experienced early transmission failures.
4. How many repair records should be sampled if the research firm wants the population mean number of miles driven until transmission failure to be estimated with a margin of error of 5000 miles? Use 95% confidence.
5. What other information would you like to gather to evaluate the transmission failure problem more fully?

Appendix 8.1 Interval Estimation with Minitab

We describe the use of Minitab in constructing confidence intervals for a population mean and a population proportion.

Population Mean: σ Known

CD file
Lloyd's

We illustrate interval estimation using the Lloyd's example in Section 8.1. The amounts spent per shopping trip for the sample of 100 customers are in column C1 of a Minitab worksheet. The population standard deviation $\sigma = 20$ is assumed known. The following steps can be used to compute a 95% confidence interval estimate of the population mean.

Step 1. Select the **Stat** menu
Step 2. Choose **Basic Statistics**
Step 3. Choose **1-Sample Z**
Step 4. When the 1-Sample Z dialog box appears:
  Enter C1 in the **Samples in columns** box
  Enter 20 in the **Standard deviation** box
Step 5. Click **OK**

The Minitab default is a 95% confidence level. In order to specify a different confidence level such as 90%, add the following to step 4.

Select **Options**
When the 1-Sample Z-Options dialog box appears:
  Enter 90 in the **Confidence level** box
Click **OK**

Population Mean: σ Unknown

CD file
NewBalance

We illustrate interval estimation using the data in Table 8.2 showing the credit card balances for a sample of 70 households. The data are in column C1 of a Minitab worksheet. In this case the population standard deviation σ will be estimated by the sample standard deviation s. The following steps can be used to compute a 95% confidence interval estimate of the population mean.

Step 1. Select the **Stat** menu
Step 2. Choose **Basic Statistics**
Step 3. Choose **1-Sample t**
Step 4. When the 1-Sample t dialog box appears:
  Enter C1 in the **Samples in columns** box
Step 5. Click **OK**

The Minitab default is a 95% confidence level. In order to specify a different confidence level such as 90%, add the following to step 4.

Select **Options**
When the 1-Sample t-Options dialog box appears:
  Enter 90 in the **Confidence level** box
Click **OK**

Population Proportion

CD file
TeeTimes

We illustrate interval estimation using the survey data for women golfers presented in Section 8.4. The data are in column C1 of a Minitab worksheet. Individual responses are recorded as Yes if the golfer is satisfied with the availability of tee times and No otherwise. The following steps can be used to compute a 95% confidence interval estimate of the proportion of women golfers who are satisfied with the availability of tee times.

Step 1. Select the **Stat** menu
Step 2. Choose **Basic Statistics**
Step 3. Choose **1 Proportion**
Step 4. When the 1 Proportion dialog box appears:
  Enter C1 in the **Samples in columns** box
Step 5. Select **Options**
Step 6. When the 1 Proportion-Options dialog box appears:
  Select **Use test and interval based on normal distribution**
  Click **OK**
Step 7. Click **OK**

The Minitab default is a 95% confidence level. In order to specify a different confidence level such as 90%, enter 90 in the **Confidence Level** box when the 1 Proportion-Options dialog box appears in step 6.

Note: Minitab's 1 Proportion routine uses an alphabetical ordering of the responses and selects the *second response* for the population proportion of interest. In the women golfers example, Minitab used the alphabetical ordering No-Yes and then provided the confidence interval for the proportion of Yes responses. Because Yes was the response of interest, the Minitab output was fine. However, if Minitab's alphabetical ordering does not provide the response of interest, select any cell in the column and use the sequence: Editor > Column > Value Order. It will provide you with the option of entering a user-specified order, but you must list the response of interest second in the define-an-order box.

Appendix 8.2 Interval Estimation Using Excel

We describe the use of Excel in constructing confidence intervals for a population mean and a population proportion.

Population Mean: σ Known

CD file
Lloyd's

We illustrate interval estimation using the Lloyd's example in Section 8.1. The population standard deviation $\sigma = 20$ is assumed known. The amounts spent for the sample of 100 customers are in column A of an Excel worksheet. The following steps can be used to compute the margin of error for an estimate of the population mean. We begin by using Excel's Descriptive Statistics Tool described in Chapter 3.

Step 1. Select the **Tools** menu
Step 2. Choose **Data Analysis**
Step 3. Choose **Descriptive Statistics** from the list of Analysis Tools
Step 4. When the Descriptive Statistics dialog box appears:
Enter A1:A101 in the **Input Range** box
Select **Grouped by Columns**
Select **Labels in First Row**
Select **Output Range**
Enter C1 in the **Output Range** box
Select **Summary Statistics**
Click **OK**

The summary statistics will appear in columns C and D. Continue by computing the margin of error using Excel's Confidence function as follows:

Step 5. Select cell C16 and enter the label Margin of Error
Step 6. Select cell D16 and enter the Excel formula =CONFIDENCE(.05,20,100)

The three parameters of the Confidence function are

Alpha = 1 − confidence coefficient = 1 − .95 = .05
The population standard deviation = 20
The sample size = 100 (*Note:* This parameter appears as Count in cell D15.)

The point estimate of the population mean is in cell D3 and the margin of error is in cell D16. The point estimate (82) and the margin of error (3.92) allow the confidence interval for the population mean to be easily computed.

Population Mean: σ Unknown

CD file
NewBalance

We illustrate interval estimation using the data in Table 8.2, which show the credit card balances for a sample of 70 households. The data are in column A of an Excel worksheet. The following steps can be used to compute the point estimate and the margin of error for an interval estimate of a population mean. We will use Excel's Descriptive Statistics Tool described in Chapter 3.

Step 1. Select the **Tools** menu
Step 2. Choose **Data Analysis**
Step 3. Choose **Descriptive Statistics** from the list of Analysis Tools
Step 4. When the Descriptive Statistics dialog box appears:
Enter A1:A71 in the **Input Range** box
Select **Grouped by Columns**
Select **Labels in First Row**
Select **Output Range**
Enter C1 in the Output Range box
Select **Summary Statistics**
Select **Confidence Level for Mean**
Enter 95 in the Confidence Level for Mean box
Click **OK**

The summary statistics will appear in columns C and D. The point estimate of the population mean appears in cell D3. The margin of error, labeled "Confidence Level(95.0%)," appears in cell D16. The point estimate ($9312) and the margin of error ($955) allow the confidence interval for the population mean to be easily computed. The output from this Excel procedure is shown in Figure 8.10.

FIGURE 8.10 INTERVAL ESTIMATION OF THE POPULATION MEAN CREDIT CARD BALANCE USING EXCEL

	A	B	C	D	E	F
1	**NewBalance**		*NewBalance*			
2	9430					
3	7535		Mean	9312	Point Estimate	
4	4078		Standard Error	478.9281		
5	5604		Median	9466		
6	5179		Mode	13627		
7	4416		Standard Deviation	4007		
8	10676		Sample Variance	16056048		
9	1627		Kurtosis	−0.296		
10	10112		Skewness	0.18792		
11	6567		Range	18648		
12	13627		Minimum	615		
13	18719		Maximum	19263		
14	14661		Sum	651840		
15	12195		Count	70		
16	10544		Confidence Level(95.0%)	955.4354	Margin of Error	
17	13659					
70	9743					
71	10324					
71						

Note: Rows 18 to 69 are hidden.

Population Proportion

We illustrate interval estimation using the survey data for women golfers presented in Section 8.4. The data are in column A of an Excel worksheet. Individual responses are recorded as Yes if the golfer is satisfied with the availability of tee times and No otherwise. Excel does not offer a built-in routine to handle the estimation of a population proportion; however, it is relatively easy to develop an Excel template that can be used for this purpose. The template shown in Figure 8.11 provides the 95% confidence interval estimate of the proportion of women golfers who are satisfied with the availability of tee times. Note that the

CD file
Interval p

FIGURE 8.11 EXCEL TEMPLATE FOR INTERVAL ESTIMATION OF A POPULATION PROPORTION

	A	B	C	D	E
1	**Response**		**Interval Estimate of a Population Proportion**		
2	Yes				
3	No		**Sample Size**	=COUNTA(A2:A901)	
4	Yes		**Response of Interest**	Yes	
5	Yes		**Count for Response**	=COUNTIF(A2:A901,D4)	
6	No		**Sample Proportion**	=D5/D3	
7	No				
8	No		**Confidence Coefficient**	0.95	
9	Yes		***z* Value**	=NORMSINV(0.5+D8/2)	
10	Yes				
11	Yes		**Standard Error**	=SQRT(D6*(1-D6)/D3)	
12	No		**Margin of Error**	=D9*D11	
13	No				
14	Yes		**Point Estimate**	=D6	
15	No		**Lower Limit**	=D14-D12	
16	No		**Upper Limit**	=D14+D12	
17	Yes				
18	No				
901	Yes				
902					

	A	B	C	D	E	F	G
1	**Response**		**Interval Estimate of a Population Proportion**				
2	Yes						
3	No		**Sample Size**	900			
4	Yes		**Response of Interest**	Yes			
5	Yes		**Count for Response**	396			
6	No		**Sample Proportion**	0.4400			
7	No						
8	No		**Confidence Coefficient**	0.95			
9	Yes		***z* Value**	1.960			
10	Yes						
11	Yes		**Standard Error**	0.0165			
12	No		**Margin of Error**	0.0324			
13	No						
14	Yes		**Point Estimate**	0.4400			
15	No		**Lower Limit**	0.4076			
16	No		**Upper Limit**	0.4724			
17	Yes						
18	No						
901	Yes						
902							

Enter the response of interest (pointing to D4)

Enter the confidence coefficient (pointing to D8)

Note: Rows 19 to 900 are hidden.

background worksheet in Figure 8.11 shows the cell formulas that provide the interval estimation results shown in the foreground worksheet. The following steps are necessary to use the template for this data set.

Step 1. Enter the data range A2:A901 into the =COUNTA cell formula in cell D3
Step 2. Enter Yes as the response of interest in cell D4
Step 3. Enter the data range A2:A901 into the =COUNTIF cell formula in cell D5
Step 4. Enter .95 as the confidence coefficient in cell D8

The template automatically provides the confidence interval in cells D15 and D16.

This template can be used to compute the confidence interval for a population proportion for other applications. For instance, to compute the interval estimate for a new data set, enter the new sample data into column A of the worksheet and then make the changes to the four cells as shown. If the new sample data have already been summarized, the sample data do not have to be entered into the worksheet. In this case, enter the sample size into cell D3 and the sample proportion into cell D6; the worksheet template will then provide the confidence interval for the population proportion. The worksheet in Figure 8.11 is available in the file Interval p on the CD that accompanies this book.

CHAPTER 9

Hypothesis Tests

CONTENTS

STATISTICS *in* PRACTICE

JOHN MORRELL & COMPANY*
CINCINNATI, OHIO

John Morrell & Company, which began in England in 1827, is considered the oldest continuously operating meat manufacturer in the United States. It is a wholly owned and independently managed subsidiary of Smithfield Foods, Smithfield, Virginia. John Morrell & Company offers an extensive product line of processed meats and fresh pork to consumers under 13 regional brands including John Morrell, E-Z-Cut, Tobin's First Prize, Dinner Bell, Hunter, Kretschmar, Rath, Rodeo, Shenson, Farmers Hickory Brand, Iowa Quality, and Peyton's. Each regional brand enjoys high brand recognition and loyalty among consumers.

Market research at Morrell provides management with up-to-date information on the company's various products and how the products compare with competing brands of similar products. A recent study compared a Beef Pot Roast made by Morrell to similar beef products from two major competitors. In the three-product comparison test, a sample of consumers was used to indicate how the products rated in terms of taste, appearance, aroma, and overall preference.

One research question concerned whether the Beef Pot Roast made by Morrell was the preferred choice of more than 50% of the consumer population. Letting p indicate the population proportion preferring Morrell's product, the hypothesis test for the research question is as follows:

$$H_0: p \leq .50$$
$$H_a: p > .50$$

The null hypothesis H_0 indicates the preference for Morrell's product is less than or equal to 50%. If the sample data support rejecting H_0 in favor of the alternative hypothesis H_a, Morrell will draw the research conclusion that in a three-product comparison, their Beef Pot Roast is preferred by more than 50% of the consumer population.

*The authors are indebted to Marty Butler, vice president of Marketing, John Morrell, for providing this Statistics in Practice.

Fully-cooked entrees allow consumers to heat and serve in the same microwaveable tray. © Courtesy of John Morrell's Convenient Cuisine products.

In an independent taste test study using a sample of 224 consumers in Cincinnati, Milwaukee, and Los Angeles, 150 consumers selected the Beef Pot Roast made by Morrell as the preferred product. Using statistical hypothesis testing procedures, the null hypothesis H_0 was rejected. The study provided statistical evidence supporting H_a and the conclusion that the Morrell product is preferred by more than 50% of the consumer population.

The point estimate of the population proportion was $\bar{p} = 150/224 = .67$. Thus, the sample data provided support for a food magazine advertisement showing that in a three-product taste comparison, Beef Pot Roast made by Morrell was "preferred 2 to 1 over the competition."

In this chapter we will discuss how to formulate hypotheses and how to conduct tests like the one used by Morrell. Through the analysis of sample data, we will be able to determine whether a hypothesis should or should not be rejected.

In Chapters 7 and 8 we showed how a sample could be used to develop point and interval estimates of population parameters. In this chapter we continue the discussion of statistical inference by showing how hypothesis testing can be used to determine whether a statement about the value of a population parameter should or should not be rejected.

In hypothesis testing we begin by making a tentative assumption about a population parameter. This tentative assumption is called the **null hypothesis** and is denoted by H_0. We then define another hypothesis, called the **alternative hypothesis**, which is the opposite of what is stated in the null hypothesis. The alternative hypothesis is denoted by H_a.

The hypothesis testing procedure uses data from a sample to test the two competing statements indicated by H_0 and H_a.

This chapter shows how hypothesis tests can be conducted about a population mean and a population proportion. We begin by providing examples that illustrate approaches to developing null and alternative hypotheses.

9.1 Developing Null and Alternative Hypotheses

Learning to formulate hypotheses correctly will take practice. Expect some initial confusion over the proper choice for H_0 and H_a. The examples in this section show a variety of forms for H_0 and H_a depending upon the application.

In some applications it may not be obvious how the null and alternative hypotheses should be formulated. Care must be taken to structure the hypotheses appropriately so that the hypothesis testing conclusion provides the information the researcher or decision maker wants. Guidelines for establishing the null and alternative hypotheses will be given for three types of situations in which hypothesis testing procedures are commonly employed.

Testing Research Hypotheses

Consider a particular automobile model that currently attains an average fuel efficiency of 24 miles per gallon. A product research group developed a new fuel injection system specifically designed to increase the miles-per-gallon rating. To evaluate the new system, several will be manufactured, installed in automobiles, and subjected to research-controlled driving tests. Here the product research group is looking for evidence to conclude that the new system *increases* the mean miles-per-gallon rating. In this case, the research hypothesis is that the new fuel injection system will provide a mean miles-per-gallon rating exceeding 24; that is, $\mu > 24$. As a general guideline, a research hypothesis should be stated as the *alternative hypothesis.* Hence, the appropriate null and alternative hypotheses for the study are:

$$H_0: \mu \leq 24$$
$$H_a: \mu > 24$$

The conclusion that the research hypothesis is true is made if the sample data contradict the null hypothesis.

If the sample results indicate that H_0 cannot be rejected, researchers cannot conclude that the new fuel injection system is better. Perhaps more research and subsequent testing should be conducted. However, if the sample results indicate that H_0 can be rejected, researchers can make the inference that $H_a: \mu > 24$ is true. With this conclusion, the researchers gain the statistical support necessary to state that the new system increases the mean number of miles per gallon. Production with the new system should be considered.

In research studies such as these, the null and alternative hypotheses should be formulated so that the rejection of H_0 supports the research conclusion. The research hypothesis therefore should be expressed as the alternative hypothesis.

Testing the Validity of a Claim

As an illustration of testing the validity of a claim, consider the situation of a manufacturer of soft drinks who states that two-liter soft drink containers are filled with an average of at least 67.6 fluid ounces. A sample of two-liter containers will be selected, and the contents will be measured to test the manufacturer's claim. In this type of hypothesis testing situation, we generally assume that the manufacturer's claim is true unless the sample evidence is contradictory. Using this approach for the soft-drink example, we would state the null and alternative hypotheses as follows.

$$H_0: \mu \geq 67.6$$
$$H_a: \mu < 67.6$$

If the sample results indicate H_0 cannot be rejected, the manufacturer's claim will not be challenged. However, if the sample results indicate H_0 can be rejected, the inference will be made that H_a: $\mu < 67.6$ is true. With this conclusion, statistical evidence indicates that the manufacturer's claim is incorrect and that the soft-drink containers are being filled with a mean less than the claimed 67.6 ounces. Appropriate action against the manufacturer may be considered.

A manufacturer's claim is usually given the benefit of the doubt and stated as the null hypothesis. The conclusion that the claim is false can be made if the null hypothesis is rejected.

In any situation that involves testing the validity of a claim, the null hypothesis is generally based on the assumption that the claim is true. The alternative hypothesis is then formulated so that rejection of H_0 will provide statistical evidence that the stated assumption is incorrect. Action to correct the claim should be considered whenever H_0 is rejected.

Testing in Decision-Making Situations

In testing research hypotheses or testing the validity of a claim, action is taken if H_0 is rejected. In some instances, however, action must be taken both when H_0 cannot be rejected and when H_0 can be rejected. In general, this type of situation occurs when a decision maker must choose between two courses of action, one associated with the null hypothesis and another associated with the alternative hypothesis. For example, on the basis of a sample of parts from a shipment just received, a quality control inspector must decide whether to accept the shipment or to return the shipment to the supplier because it does not meet specifications. Assume that specifications for a particular part require a mean length of two inches per part. If the mean length is greater or less than the two-inch standard, the parts will cause quality problems in the assembly operation. In this case, the null and alternative hypotheses would be formulated as follows.

This type of hypothesis test is employed in the quality control procedure called lot-acceptance sampling.

$$H_0: \mu = 2$$
$$H_a: \mu \neq 2$$

If the sample results indicate H_0 cannot be rejected, the quality control inspector will have no reason to doubt that the shipment meets specifications, and the shipment will be accepted. However, if the sample results indicate H_0 should be rejected, the conclusion will be that the parts do not meet specifications. In this case, the quality control inspector will have sufficient evidence to return the shipment to the supplier. Thus, we see that for these types of situations, action is taken both when H_0 cannot be rejected and when H_0 can be rejected.

Summary of Forms for Null and Alternative Hypotheses

The hypothesis tests in this chapter involve two population parameters: the population mean and the population proportion. Depending on the situation, hypothesis tests about a population parameter may take one of three forms: two use inequalities in the null hypothesis; the third uses an equality in the null hypothesis. For hypothesis tests involving a population mean, we let μ_0 denote the hypothesized value and we must choose one of the following three forms for the hypothesis test.

The three possible forms of hypotheses H_0 and H_a are shown here. Note that the equality always *appears in the null hypothesis H_0.*

$$H_0: \mu \geq \mu_0 \qquad H_0: \mu \leq \mu_0 \qquad H_0: \mu = \mu_0$$
$$H_a: \mu < \mu_0 \qquad H_a: \mu > \mu_0 \qquad H_a: \mu \neq \mu_0$$

For reasons that will be clear later, the first two forms are called one-tailed tests. The third form is called a two-tailed test.

In many situations, the choice of H_0 and H_a is not obvious and judgment is necessary to select the proper form. However, as the preceding forms show, the equality part of the expression (either $\geq$, $\leq$, or $=$) *always* appears in the null hypothesis. In selecting the proper form of H_0 and H_a, keep in mind that the alternative hypothesis is often what the test is attempting to establish. Hence, asking whether the user is looking for evidence to support $\mu < \mu_0$, $\mu > \mu_0$, or $\mu \neq \mu_0$ will help determine H_a. The following exercises are designed to provide practice in choosing the proper form for a hypothesis test involving a population mean.

Exercises

1. The manager of the Danvers-Hilton Resort Hotel stated that the mean guest bill for a weekend is \$600 or less. A member of the hotel's accounting staff noticed that the total charges for guest bills have been increasing in recent months. The accountant will use a sample of weekend guest bills to test the manager's claim.
   a. Which form of the hypotheses should be used to test the manager's claim? Explain.

$$H_0: \mu \geq 600 \qquad H_0: \mu \leq 600 \qquad H_0: \mu = 600$$
$$H_a: \mu < 600 \qquad H_a: \mu > 600 \qquad H_a: \mu \neq 600$$

   b. What conclusion is appropriate when H_0 cannot be rejected?
   c. What conclusion is appropriate when H_0 can be rejected?

SELF test

2. The manager of an automobile dealership is considering a new bonus plan designed to increase sales volume. Currently, the mean sales volume is 14 automobiles per month. The manager wants to conduct a research study to see whether the new bonus plan increases sales volume. To collect data on the plan, a sample of sales personnel will be allowed to sell under the new bonus plan for a one-month period.
   a. Develop the null and alternative hypotheses most appropriate for this research situation.
   b. Comment on the conclusion when H_0 cannot be rejected.
   c. Comment on the conclusion when H_0 can be rejected.
3. A production line operation is designed to fill cartons with laundry detergent to a mean weight of 32 ounces. A sample of cartons is periodically selected and weighed to determine whether underfilling or overfilling is occurring. If the sample data lead to a conclusion of underfilling or overfilling, the production line will be shut down and adjusted to obtain proper filling.
   a. Formulate the null and alternative hypotheses that will help in deciding whether to shut down and adjust the production line.
   b. Comment on the conclusion and the decision when H_0 cannot be rejected.
   c. Comment on the conclusion and the decision when H_0 can be rejected.
4. Because of high production-changeover time and costs, a director of manufacturing must convince management that a proposed manufacturing method reduces costs before the new method can be implemented. The current production method operates with a mean cost of \$220 per hour. A research study will measure the cost of the new method over a sample production period.
   a. Develop the null and alternative hypotheses most appropriate for this study.
   b. Comment on the conclusion when H_0 cannot be rejected.
   c. Comment on the conclusion when H_0 can be rejected.

9.2 Type I and Type II Errors

The null and alternative hypotheses are competing statements about the population. Either the null hypothesis H_0 is true or the alternative hypothesis H_a is true, but not both. Ideally the hypothesis testing procedure should lead to the acceptance of H_0 when H_0 is true and the

TABLE 9.1 ERRORS AND CORRECT CONCLUSIONS IN HYPOTHESIS TESTING

		Population Condition	
		H_0 True	H_a True
Conclusion	Accept H_0	Correct Conclusion	Type II Error
	Reject H_0	Type I Error	Correct Conclusion

rejection of H_0 when H_a is true. Unfortunately, the correct conclusions are not always possible. Because hypothesis tests are based on sample information, we must allow for the possibility of errors. Table 9.1 illustrates the two kinds of errors that can be made in hypothesis testing.

The first row of Table 9.1 shows what can happen if the conclusion is to accept H_0. If H_0 is true, this conclusion is correct. However, if H_a is true, we make a **Type II error**; that is, we accept H_0 when it is false. The second row of Table 9.1 shows what can happen if the conclusion is to reject H_0. If H_0 is true, we make a **Type I error**; that is, we reject H_0 when it is true. However, if H_a is true, rejecting H_0 is correct.

Recall the hypothesis testing illustration discussed in Section 9.1 in which an automobile product research group developed a new fuel injection system designed to increase the miles-per-gallon rating of a particular automobile. With the current model obtaining an average of 24 miles per gallon, the hypothesis test was formulated as follows.

$$H_0: \mu \leq 24$$
$$H_a: \mu > 24$$

The alternative hypothesis, $H_a: \mu > 24$, indicates that the researchers are looking for sample evidence to support the conclusion that the population mean miles per gallon with the new fuel injection system is greater than 24.

In this application, the Type I error of rejecting H_0 when it is true corresponds to the researchers claiming that the new system improves the miles-per-gallon rating ($\mu > 24$) when in fact the new system is not any better than the current system. In contrast, the Type II error of accepting H_0 when it is false corresponds to the researchers concluding that the new system is not any better than the current system ($\mu \leq 24$) when in fact the new system improves miles-per-gallon performance.

For the miles-per-gallon rating hypothesis test, the null hypothesis is $H_0: \mu \leq 24$. Suppose the null hypothesis is true as an equality; that is, $\mu = 24$. The probability of making a Type I error when the null hypothesis is true as an equality is called the **level of significance**. Thus, for the miles-per-gallon rating hypothesis test, the level of significance is the probability of rejecting H_0: $\mu \leq 24$ when $\mu = 24$. Because of the importance of this concept, we now restate the definition of level of significance.

LEVEL OF SIGNIFICANCE

The level of significance is the probability of making a Type I error when the null hypothesis is true as an equality.

The Greek symbol α (alpha) is used to denote the level of significance, and common choices for α are .05 and .01.

In practice, the person responsible for the hypothesis test specifies the level of significance. By selecting α, that person is controlling the probability of making a Type I error. If the cost of making a Type I error is high, small values of α are preferred. If the cost of making a Type I error is not too high, larger values of α are typically used. Applications of hypothesis testing that only control for the Type I error are called *significance tests.* Many applications of hypothesis testing are of this type.

If the sample data are consistent with the null hypothesis H_0, we will follow the practice of concluding "do not reject H_0." This conclusion is preferred over "accept H_0," because the conclusion to accept H_0 puts us at risk of making a Type II error.

Although most applications of hypothesis testing control for the probability of making a Type I error, they do not always control for the probability of making a Type II error. Hence, if we decide to accept H_0, we cannot determine how confident we can be with that decision. Because of the uncertainty associated with making a Type II error when conducting significance tests, statisticians usually recommend that we use the statement "do not reject H_0" instead of "accept H_0." Using the statement "do not reject H_0" carries the recommendation to withhold both judgment and action. In effect, by not directly accepting H_0, the statistician avoids the risk of making a Type II error. Whenever the probability of making a Type II error has not been determined and controlled, we will not make the statement "accept H_0." In such cases, only two conclusions are possible: *do not reject* H_0 or *reject* H_0.

Although controlling for a Type II error in hypothesis testing is not common, it can be done. In Sections 9.7 and 9.8 we will illustrate procedures for determining and controlling the probability of making a Type II error. If proper controls have been established for this error, action based on the "accept H_0" conclusion can be appropriate.

NOTES AND COMMENTS

Walter Williams, syndicated columnist and professor of economics at George Mason University, points out that the possibility of making a Type I or a Type II error is always present in decision making (*The Cincinnati Enquirer,* August 14, 2005). He notes that the Food and Drug Administration runs the risk of making these errors in their drug approval process. With a Type I error, the FDA fails to approve a drug that is safe and effective. A Type II error means the FDA approves a drug that has unanticipated dangerous side effects. Regardless of the decision made, the possibility of making a costly error cannot be eliminated.

Exercises

SELF test

5. Nielsen reported that young men in the United States watch 56.2 minutes of prime-time TV daily (*The Wall Street Journal Europe,* November 18, 2003). A researcher believes that young men in Germany spend more time watching prime-time TV. A sample of German young men will be selected by the researcher and the time they spend watching TV in one day will be recorded. The sample results will be used to test the following null and alternative hypotheses.

$$H_0\text{: } \mu \leq 56.2$$
$$H_a\text{: } \mu > 56.2$$

   a. What is the Type I error in this situation? What are the consequences of making this error?
   b. What is the Type II error in this situation? What are the consequences of making this error?

6. The label on a 3-quart container of orange juice claims that the orange juice contains an average of 1 gram of fat or less. Answer the following questions for a hypothesis test that could be used to test the claim on the label.
   a. Develop the appropriate null and alternative hypotheses.

b. What is the Type I error in this situation? What are the consequences of making this error?
c. What is the Type II error in this situation? What are the consequences of making this error?

7. Carpetland salespersons average $8000 per week in sales. Steve Contois, the firm's vice president, proposes a compensation plan with new selling incentives. Steve hopes that the results of a trial selling period will enable him to conclude that the compensation plan increases the average sales per salesperson.
   a. Develop the appropriate null and alternative hypotheses.
   b. What is the Type I error in this situation? What are the consequences of making this error?
   c. What is the Type II error in this situation? What are the consequences of making this error?

8. Suppose a new production method will be implemented if a hypothesis test supports the conclusion that the new method reduces the mean operating cost per hour.
   a. State the appropriate null and alternative hypotheses if the mean cost for the current production method is $220 per hour.
   b. What is the Type I error in this situation? What are the consequences of making this error?
   c. What is the Type II error in this situation? What are the consequences of making this error?

9.3 Population Mean: σ Known

In Chapter 8 we said that the σ known case corresponds to applications in which historical data and/or other information is available that enable us to obtain a good estimate of the population standard deviation prior to sampling. In such cases the population standard deviation can, for all practical purposes, be considered known. In this section we show how to conduct a hypothesis test about a population mean for the σ known case.

The methods presented in this section are exact if the sample is selected from a population that is normally distributed. In cases where it is not reasonable to assume the population is normally distributed, these methods are still applicable if the sample size is large enough. We provide some practical advice concerning the population distribution and the sample size at the end of this section.

One-Tailed Test

One-tailed tests about a population mean take one of the following two forms.

Lower Tail Test	Upper Tail Test
$H_0\colon \mu \geq \mu_0$	$H_0\colon \mu \leq \mu_0$
$H_a\colon \mu < \mu_0$	$H_a\colon \mu > \mu_0$

Let us consider an example involving a lower tail test.

The Federal Trade Commission (FTC) periodically conducts statistical studies designed to test the claims that manufacturers make about their products. For example, the label on a large can of Hilltop Coffee states that the can contains 3 pounds of coffee. The FTC knows that Hilltop's production process cannot place exactly 3 pounds of coffee in each can, even if the mean filling weight for the population of all cans filled is 3 pounds per can. However, as long as the population mean filling weight is at least 3 pounds per can, the rights of consumers will be protected. Thus, the FTC interprets the label information on a large can of coffee as a claim by Hilltop that the population mean filling weight is at least 3 pounds per can. We will show how the FTC can check Hilltop's claim by conducting a lower tail hypothesis test.

The first step is to develop the null and alternative hypotheses for the test. If the population mean filling weight is at least 3 pounds per can, Hilltop's claim is correct. This establishes the null hypothesis for the test. However, if the population mean weight is less than 3 pounds per can, Hilltop's claim is incorrect. This establishes the alternative hypothesis. With μ denoting the population mean filling weight, the null and alternative hypotheses are as follows:

$$H_0: \mu \geq 3$$
$$H_a: \mu < 3$$

Note that the hypothesized value of the population mean is $\mu_0 = 3$.

If the sample data indicate that H_0 cannot be rejected, the statistical evidence does not support the conclusion that a label violation has occurred. Hence, no action should be taken against Hilltop. However, if the sample data indicate H_0 can be rejected, we will conclude that the alternative hypothesis, H_a: $\mu < 3$, is true. In this case a conclusion of underfilling and a charge of a label violation against Hilltop would be justified.

Suppose a sample of 36 cans of coffee is selected and the sample mean $\bar{x}$ is computed as an estimate of the population mean μ. If the value of the sample mean $\bar{x}$ is less than 3 pounds, the sample results will cast doubt on the null hypothesis. What we want to know is how much less than 3 pounds must $\bar{x}$ be before we would be willing to declare the difference significant and risk making a Type I error by falsely accusing Hilltop of a label violation. A key factor in addressing this issue is the value the decision maker selects for the level of significance.

As noted in the preceding section, the level of significance, denoted by α, is the probability of making a Type I error by rejecting H_0 when the null hypothesis is true as an equality. The decision maker must specify the level of significance. If the cost of making a Type I error is high, a small value should be chosen for the level of significance. If the cost is not high, a larger value is more appropriate. In the Hilltop Coffee study, the director of the FTC's testing program made the following statement: "If the company is meeting its weight specifications at $\mu = 3$, I do not want to take action against them. But, I am willing to risk a 1% chance of making such an error." From the director's statement, we set the level of significance for the hypothesis test at $\alpha = .01$. Thus, we must design the hypothesis test so that the probability of making a Type I error when $\mu = 3$ is .01.

For the Hilltop Coffee study, by developing the null and alternative hypotheses and specifying the level of significance for the test, we carry out the first two steps required in conducting every hypothesis test. We are now ready to perform the third step of hypothesis testing: collect the sample data and compute the value of what is called a test statistic.

Test Statistic. For the Hilltop Coffee study, previous FTC tests show that the population standard deviation can be assumed known with a value of $\sigma = .18$. In addition, these tests also show that the population of filling weights can be assumed to have a normal distribution. From the study of sampling distributions in Chapter 7 we know that if the population from which we are sampling is normally distributed, the sampling distribution of $\bar{x}$ will also be normally distributed. Thus, for the Hilltop Coffee study, the sampling distribution of $\bar{x}$ is normally distributed. With a known value of $\sigma = .18$ and a sample size of $n = 36$, Figure 9.1 shows the sampling distribution of $\bar{x}$ when the null hypothesis is true as an equality; that is, when $\mu = \mu_0 = 3$.* Note that the standard error of $\bar{x}$ is given by $\sigma_{\bar{x}} = \sigma/\sqrt{n} = .18/\sqrt{36} = .03$.

The standard error of $\bar{x}$ is the standard deviation of the sampling distribution of $\bar{x}$.

Because the sampling distribution of $\bar{x}$ is normally distributed, the sampling distribution of

$$z = \frac{\bar{x} - \mu_0}{\sigma_{\bar{x}}} = \frac{\bar{x} - 3}{.03}$$

*In constructing sampling distributions for hypothesis tests, it is assumed that H_0 is satisfied as an equality.

FIGURE 9.1 SAMPLING DISTRIBUTION OF $\bar{x}$ FOR THE HILLTOP COFFEE STUDY WHEN THE NULL HYPOTHESIS IS TRUE AS AN EQUALITY ($\mu = 3$)

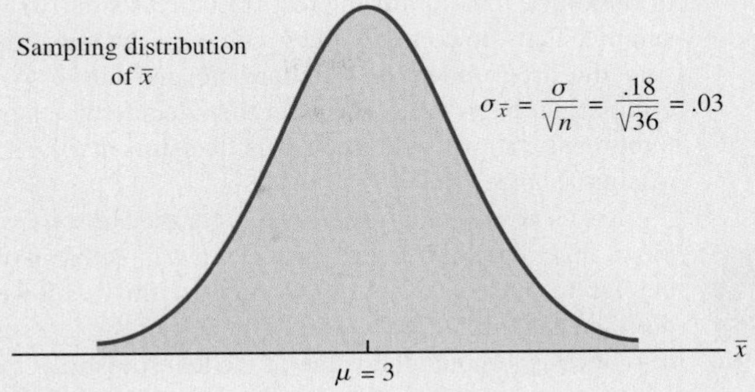

is a standard normal distribution. A value of $z = -1$ means that the value of $\bar{x}$ is one standard error below the hypothesized value of the mean, a value of $z = -2$ means that the value of $\bar{x}$ is two standard errors below the hypothesized value of the mean, and so on. We can use the standard normal probability table to find the lower tail probability corresponding to any z value. For instance, the lower tail area at $z = -3.00$ is .0013. Hence, the probability of obtaining a value of z that is three or more standard errors below the mean is .0013. As a result, the probability of obtaining a value of $\bar{x}$ that is 3 or more standard errors below the hypothesized population mean $\mu_0 = 3$ is also .0013. Such a result is unlikely if the null hypothesis is true.

For hypothesis tests about a population mean in the σ known case, we use the standard normal random variable z as a **test statistic** to determine whether $\bar{x}$ deviates from the hypothesized value of μ enough to justify rejecting the null hypothesis. With $\sigma_{\bar{x}} = \sigma/\sqrt{n}$, the test statistic is as follows.

TEST STATISTIC FOR HYPOTHESIS TESTS ABOUT A POPULATION MEAN: σ KNOWN

$$z = \frac{\bar{x} - \mu_0}{\sigma/\sqrt{n}} \tag{9.1}$$

The key question for a lower tail test is: How small must the test statistic z be before we choose to reject the null hypothesis? Two approaches can be used to answer this question: the p-value approach and the critical value approach.

p-value Approach. The p-value approach uses the value of the test statistic z to compute a probability called a ***p*-value**.

A small p-value indicates the value of the test statistic is unusual given the assumption that H_0 is true.

p-VALUE

A p-value is a probability that provides a measure of the evidence against the null hypothesis provided by the sample. Smaller p-values indicate more evidence against H_0.

The p-value is used to determine whether the null hypothesis should be rejected.

Let us see how the p-value is computed and used. The value of the test statistic is used to compute the p-value. The method used depends on whether the test is a lower tail, an upper tail, or a two-tailed test. For a lower tail test, the p-value is the probability of obtaining a value for the test statistic as small as or smaller than that provided by the sample. Thus, to compute the p-value for the lower tail test in the σ known case, we must find the area under the standard normal curve to the left of the test statistic. After computing the p-value, we must then decide whether it is small enough to reject the null hypothesis; as we will show, this decision involves comparing the p-value to the level of significance.

CD file Coffee

Let us now compute the p-value for the Hilltop Coffee lower tail test. Suppose the sample of 36 Hilltop coffee cans provides a sample mean of $\bar{x} = 2.92$ pounds. Is $\bar{x} = 2.92$ small enough to cause us to reject H_0? Because this is a lower tail test, the p-value is the area under the standard normal curve to the left of the test statistic. Using $\bar{x} = 2.92$, $\sigma = .18$, and $n = 36$, we compute the value of the test statistic z.

$$z = \frac{\bar{x} - \mu_0}{\sigma/\sqrt{n}} = \frac{2.92 - 3}{.18/\sqrt{36}} = -2.67$$

Thus, the p-value is the probability that the test statistic z is less than or equal to -2.67 (the area under the standard normal curve to the left of the test statistic).

Using the standard normal probability table, we find that the lower tail area at $z = -2.67$ is .0038. Figure 9.2 shows that $\bar{x} = 2.92$ corresponds to $z = -2.67$ and a p-value $= .0038$. This p-value indicates a small probability of obtaining a sample mean of $\bar{x} = 2.92$ (and a test statistic of -2.67) or smaller when sampling from a population with $\mu = 3$. This

FIGURE 9.2 p-VALUE FOR THE HILLTOP COFFEE STUDY WHEN $\bar{x} = 2.92$ AND $z = -2.67$

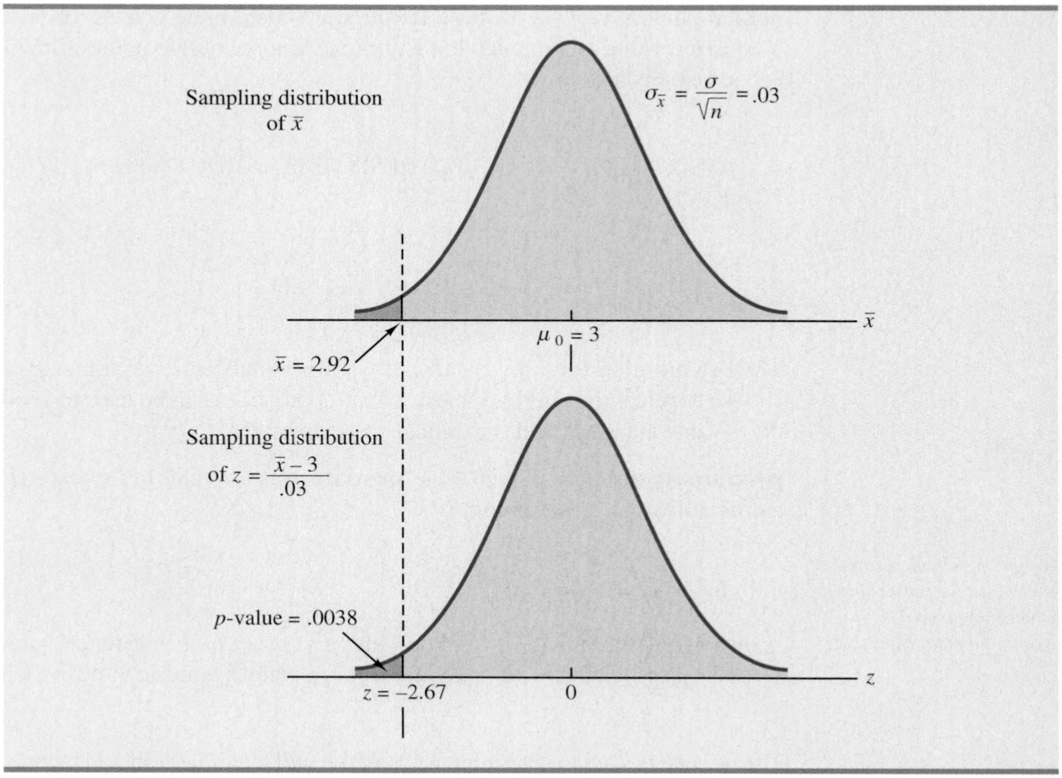

p-value does not provide much support for the null hypothesis, but is it small enough to cause us to reject H_0? The answer depends upon the level of significance for the test.

As noted previously, the director of the FTC's testing program selected a value of .01 for the level of significance. The selection of $\alpha = .01$ means that the director is willing to tolerate a probability of .01 of rejecting the null hypothesis when it is true as an equality ($\mu_0 = 3$). The sample of 36 coffee cans in the Hilltop Coffee study resulted in a p-value = .0038, which means that the probability of obtaining a value of $\bar{x} = 2.92$ or less when the null hypothesis is true as an equality is .0038. Because .0038 is less than or equal to $\alpha = .01$, we reject H_0. Therefore, we find sufficient statistical evidence to reject the null hypothesis at the .01 level of significance.

We can now state the general rule for determining whether the null hypothesis can be rejected when using the p-value approach. For a level of significance α, the rejection rule using the p-value approach is as follows:

REJECTION RULE USING p-VALUE

$$\text{Reject } H_0 \text{ if } p\text{-value} \leq \alpha$$

In the Hilltop Coffee test, the p-value of .0038 resulted in the rejection of the null hypothesis. Although the basis for making the rejection decision involves a comparison of the p-value to the level of significance specified by the FTC director, the observed p-value of .0038 means that we would reject H_0 for any value of $\alpha \geq .0038$. For this reason, the p-value is also called the *observed level of significance*.

Different decision makers may express different opinions concerning the cost of making a Type I error and may choose a different level of significance. By providing the p-value as part of the hypothesis testing results, another decision maker can compare the reported p-value to his or her own level of significance and possibly make a different decision with respect to rejecting H_0.

Critical Value Approach. The critical value approach requires that we first determine a value for the test statistic called the **critical value**. For a lower tail test, the critical value serves as a benchmark for determining whether the value of the test statistic is small enough to reject the null hypothesis. It is the value of the test statistic that corresponds to an area of α (the level of significance) in the lower tail of the sampling distribution of the test statistic. In other words, the critical value is the largest value of the test statistic that will result in the rejection of the null hypothesis. Let us return to the Hilltop Coffee example and see how this approach works.

In the σ known case, the sampling distribution for the test statistic z is a standard normal distribution. Therefore, the critical value is the value of the test statistic that corresponds to an area of $\alpha = .01$ in the lower tail of a standard normal distribution. Using the standard normal probability table, we find that $z = -2.33$ provides an area of .01 in the lower tail (see Figure 9.3). Thus, if the sample results in a value of the test statistic that is less than or equal to -2.33, the corresponding p-value will be less than or equal to .01; in this case, we should reject the null hypothesis. Hence, for the Hilltop Coffee study the critical value rejection rule for a level of significance of .01 is

$$\text{Reject } H_0 \text{ if } z \leq -2.33$$

In the Hilltop Coffee example, $\bar{x} = 2.92$ and the test statistic is $z = -2.67$. Because $z = -2.67 < -2.33$, we can reject H_0 and conclude that Hilltop Coffee is underfilling cans.

FIGURE 9.3 CRITICAL VALUE = −2.33 FOR THE HILLTOP COFFEE HYPOTHESIS TEST

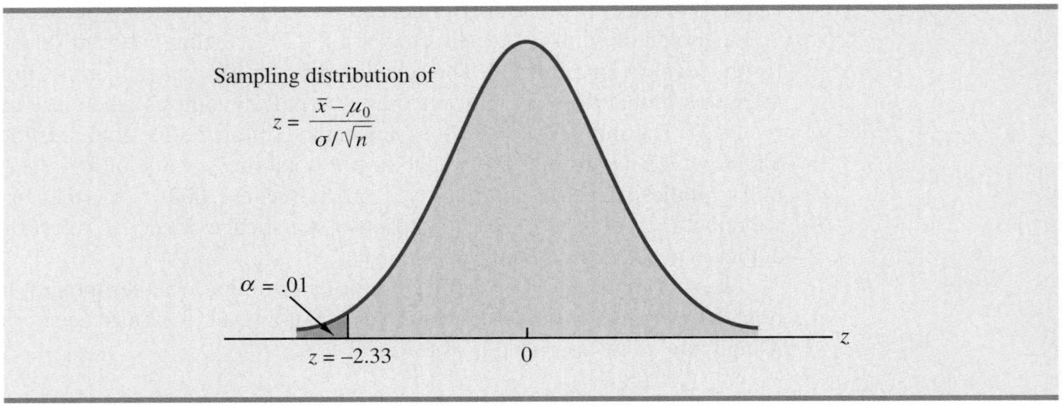

We can generalize the rejection rule for the critical value approach to handle any level of significance. The rejection rule for a lower tail test follows.

REJECTION RULE FOR A LOWER TAIL TEST: CRITICAL VALUE APPROACH

$$\text{Reject } H_0 \text{ if } z \leq -z_\alpha$$

where $-z_\alpha$ is the critical value; that is, the z value that provides an area of α in the lower tail of the standard normal distribution.

The p-value approach to hypothesis testing and the critical value approach will always lead to the same rejection decision; that is, whenever the p-value is less than or equal to α, the value of the test statistic will be less than or equal to the critical value. The advantage of the p-value approach is that the p-value tells us *how* significant the results are (the observed level of significance). If we use the critical value approach, we only know that the results are significant at the stated level of significance.

At the beginning of this section, we said that one-tailed tests about a population mean take one of the following two forms:

Lower Tail Test	Upper Tail Test
$H_0\colon\ \mu \geq \mu_0$	$H_0\colon\ \mu \leq \mu_0$
$H_a\colon\ \mu < \mu_0$	$H_a\colon\ \mu > \mu_0$

We used the Hilltop Coffee study to illustrate how to conduct a lower tail test. We can use the same general approach to conduct an upper tail test. The test statistic z is still computed using equation (9.1). But, for an upper tail test, the p-value is the probability of obtaining a value for the test statistic as large as or larger than that provided by the sample. Thus, to compute the p-value for the upper tail test in the σ known case, we must find the area under the standard normal curve to the right of the test statistic. Using the critical value approach causes us to reject the null hypothesis if the value of the test statistic is greater than or equal to the critical value z_α; in other words, we reject H_0 if $z \geq z_\alpha$.

Two-Tailed Test

In hypothesis testing, the general form for a **two-tailed test** about a population mean is as follows:

$$H_0: \mu = \mu_0$$
$$H_a: \mu \neq \mu_0$$

In this subsection we show how to conduct a two-tailed test about a population mean for the σ known case. As an illustration, we consider the hypothesis testing situation facing MaxFlight, Inc.

The U.S. Golf Association (USGA) establishes rules that manufacturers of golf equipment must meet if their products are to be acceptable for use in USGA events. MaxFlight uses a high-technology manufacturing process to produce golf balls with a mean driving distance of 295 yards. Sometimes, however, the process gets out of adjustment and produces golf balls with a mean driving distance different from 295 yards. When the mean distance falls below 295 yards, the company worries about losing sales because the golf balls do not provide as much distance as advertised. When the mean distance passes 295 yards, MaxFlight's golf balls may be rejected by the USGA for exceeding the overall distance standard concerning carry and roll.

MaxFlight's quality control program involves taking periodic samples of 50 golf balls to monitor the manufacturing process. For each sample, a hypothesis test is conducted to determine whether the process has fallen out of adjustment. Let us develop the null and alternative hypotheses. We begin by assuming that the process is functioning correctly; that is, the golf balls being produced have a mean distance of 295 yards. This assumption establishes the null hypothesis. The alternative hypothesis is that the mean distance is not equal to 295 yards. With a hypothesized value of $\mu_0 = 295$, the null and alternative hypotheses for the MaxFlight hypothesis test are as follows:

$$H_0: \mu = 295$$
$$H_a: \mu \neq 295$$

If the sample mean $\bar{x}$ is significantly less than 295 yards or significantly greater than 295 yards, we will reject H_0. In this case, corrective action will be taken to adjust the manufacturing process. On the other hand, if $\bar{x}$ does not deviate from the hypothesized mean $\mu_0 = 295$ by a significant amount, H_0 will not be rejected and no action will be taken to adjust the manufacturing process.

The quality control team selected $\alpha = .05$ as the level of significance for the test. Data from previous tests conducted when the process was known to be in adjustment show that the population standard deviation can be assumed known with a value of $\sigma = 12$. Thus, with a sample size of $n = 50$, the standard error of $\bar{x}$ is

$$\sigma_{\bar{x}} = \frac{\sigma}{\sqrt{n}} = \frac{12}{\sqrt{50}} = 1.7$$

Because the sample size is large, the central limit theorem (see Chapter 7) allows us to conclude that the sampling distribution of $\bar{x}$ can be approximated by a normal distribution. Figure 9.4 shows the sampling distribution of $\bar{x}$ for the MaxFlight hypothesis test with a hypothesized population mean of $\mu_0 = 295$.

CD file

GolfTest

Suppose that a sample of 50 golf balls is selected and that the sample mean is $\bar{x} = 297.6$ yards. This sample mean provides support for the conclusion that the population mean is larger than 295 yards. Is this value of $\bar{x}$ enough larger than 295 to cause us to reject H_0 at the .05 level of significance? In the previous section we described two approaches that can be used to answer this question: the p-value approach and the critical value approach.

FIGURE 9.4 SAMPLING DISTRIBUTION OF $\bar{x}$ FOR THE MAXFLIGHT HYPOTHESIS TEST

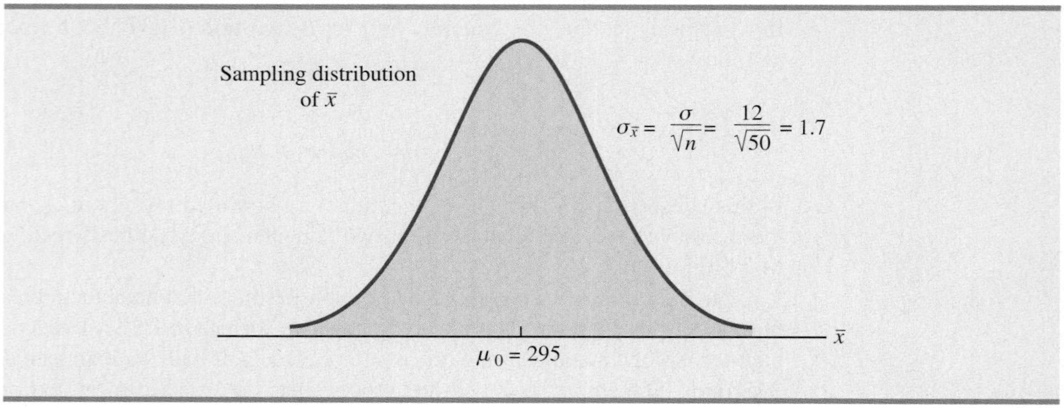

p-value Approach. Recall that the p-value is a probability used to determine whether the null hypothesis should be rejected. For a two-tailed test, values of the test statistic in *either* tail provide evidence against the null hypothesis. For a two-tailed test, the p-value is the probability of obtaining a value for the test statistic *as unlikely as or more unlikely than* that provided by the sample. Let us see how the p-value is computed for the MaxFlight hypothesis test.

First we compute the value of the test statistic. For the σ known case, the test statistic z is a standard normal random variable. Using equation (9.1) with $\bar{x} = 297.6$, the value of the test statistic is

$$z = \frac{\bar{x} - \mu_0}{\sigma/\sqrt{n}} = \frac{297.6 - 295}{12/\sqrt{50}} = 1.53$$

Now to compute the p-value we must find the probability of obtaining a value for the test statistic *at least as unlikely as* $z = 1.53$. Clearly values of $z \geq 1.53$ are *at least as unlikely.* But, because this is a two-tailed test, values of $z \leq -1.53$ are also *at least as unlikely as* the value of the test statistic provided by the sample. In Figure 9.5, we see that the two-tailed p-value in this case is given by $P(z \leq -1.53) + P(z \geq 1.53)$. Because the

FIGURE 9.5 p-VALUE FOR THE MAXFLIGHT HYPOTHESIS TEST

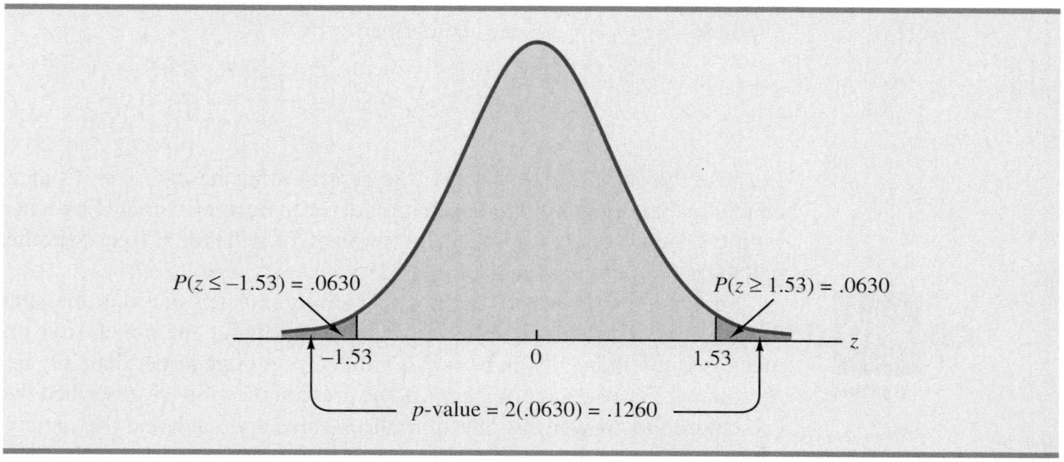

normal curve is symmetric, we can compute this probability by finding the area under the standard normal curve to the right of $z = 1.53$ and doubling it. The table for the standard normal distribution shows that the area to the left of $z = 1.53$ is .9370. Thus, the area under the standard normal curve to the right of the test statistic $z = 1.53$ is $1.0000 - .9370 = .0630$. Doubling this, we find the p-value for the MaxFlight two-tailed hypothesis test is p-value $= 2(.0630) = .1260$.

Next we compare the p-value to the level of significance to see whether the null hypothesis should be rejected. With a level of significance of $\alpha = .05$, we do not reject H_0 because the p-value $= .1260 > .05$. Because the null hypothesis is not rejected, no action will be taken to adjust the MaxFlight manufacturing process.

The computation of the p-value for a two-tailed test may seem a bit confusing as compared to the computation of the p-value for a one-tailed test. But it can be simplified by following three steps.

COMPUTATION OF p-VALUE FOR A TWO-TAILED TEST

1. Compute the value of the test statistic z.
2. If the value of the test statistic is in the upper tail ($z > 0$), find the area under the standard normal curve to the right of z. If the value of the test statistic is in the lower tail ($z < 0$), find the area under the standard normal curve to the left of z.
3. Double the tail area, or probability, obtained in step 2 to obtain the p-value.

Critical Value Approach. Before leaving this section, let us see how the test statistic z can be compared to a critical value to make the hypothesis testing decision for a two-tailed test. Figure 9.6 shows that the critical values for the test will occur in both the lower and upper tails of the standard normal distribution. With a level of significance of $\alpha = .05$, the area in each tail beyond the critical values is $\alpha/2 = .05/2 = .025$. Using the standard normal probability table, we find the critical values for the test statistic are $-z_{.025} = -1.96$ and $z_{.025} = 1.96$. Thus, using the critical value approach, the two-tailed rejection rule is

$$\text{Reject } H_0 \text{ if } z \leq -1.96 \text{ or if } z \geq 1.96$$

Because the value of the test statistic for the MaxFlight study is $z = 1.53$, the statistical evidence will not permit us to reject the null hypothesis at the .05 level of significance.

FIGURE 9.6 CRITICAL VALUES FOR THE MAXFLIGHT HYPOTHESIS TEST

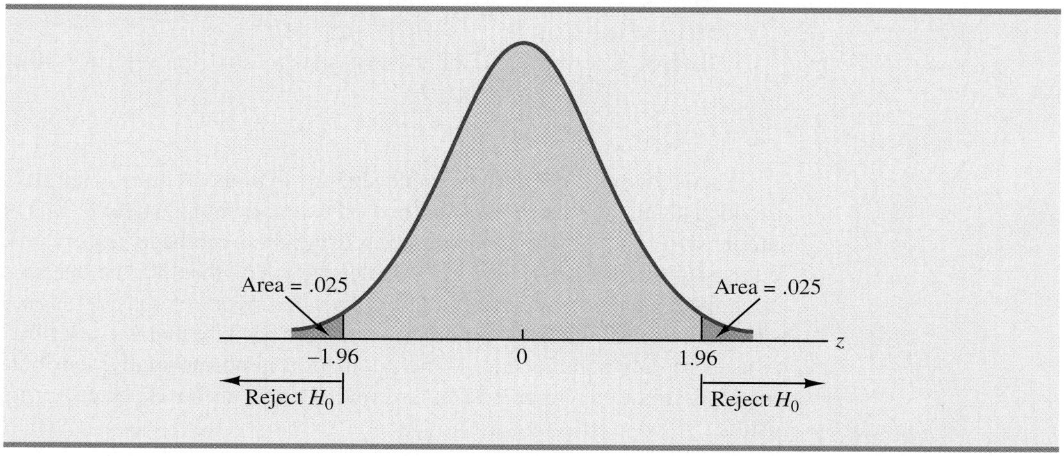

TABLE 9.2 SUMMARY OF HYPOTHESIS TESTS ABOUT A POPULATION MEAN: σ KNOWN CASE

	Lower Tail Test	**Upper Tail Test**	**Two-Tailed Test**
Hypotheses	$H_0: \mu \geq \mu_0$ $H_a: \mu < \mu_0$	$H_0: \mu \leq \mu_0$ $H_a: \mu > \mu_0$	$H_0: \mu = \mu_0$ $H_a: \mu \neq \mu_0$
Test Statistic	$z = \frac{\bar{x} - \mu_0}{\sigma/\sqrt{n}}$	$z = \frac{\bar{x} - \mu_0}{\sigma/\sqrt{n}}$	$z = \frac{\bar{x} - \mu_0}{\sigma/\sqrt{n}}$
Rejection Rule: *p*-Value Approach	Reject H_0 if p-value $\leq \alpha$	Reject H_0 if p-value $\leq \alpha$	Reject H_0 if p-value $\leq \alpha$
Rejection Rule: Critical Value Approach	Reject H_0 if $z \leq -z_\alpha$	Reject H_0 if $z \geq z_\alpha$	Reject H_0 if $z \leq -z_{\alpha/2}$ or if $z \geq z_{\alpha/2}$

Summary and Practical Advice

We presented examples of a lower tail test and a two-tailed test about a population mean. Based upon these examples, we can now summarize the hypothesis testing procedures about a population mean for the σ known case as shown in Table 9.2. Note that μ_0 is the hypothesized value of the population mean.

The hypothesis testing steps followed in the two examples presented in this section are common to every hypothesis test.

STEPS OF HYPOTHESIS TESTING

Step 1. Develop the null and alternative hypotheses.
Step 2. Specify the level of significance.
Step 3. Collect the sample data and compute the value of the test statistic.

p-Value Approach

Step 4. Use the value of the test statistic to compute the p-value.
Step 5. Reject H_0 if the p-value $\leq \alpha$.

Critical Value Approach

Step 4. Use the level of significance to determine the critical value and the rejection rule.
Step 5. Use the value of the test statistic and the rejection rule to determine whether to reject H_0.

Practical advice about the sample size for hypothesis tests is similar to the advice we provided about the sample size for interval estimation in Chapter 8. In most applications, a sample size of $n \geq 30$ is adequate when using the hypothesis testing procedure described in this section. In cases where the sample size is less than 30, the distribution of the population from which we are sampling becomes an important consideration. If the population is normally distributed, the hypothesis testing procedure that we described is exact and can be used for any sample size. If the population is not normally distributed but is at least roughly symmetric, sample sizes as small as 15 can be expected to provide acceptable results.

Relationship Between Interval Estimation and Hypothesis Testing

In Chapter 8 we showed how to develop a confidence interval estimate of a population mean. For the σ known case, the $(1 - \alpha)\%$ confidence interval estimate of a population mean is given by

$$\bar{x} \pm z_{\alpha/2} \frac{\sigma}{\sqrt{n}}$$

In this chapter, we showed that a two-tailed hypothesis test about a population mean takes the following form:

$$H_0: \mu = \mu_0$$
$$H_a: \mu \neq \mu_0$$

where μ_0 is the hypothesized value for the population mean.

Suppose that we follow the procedure described in Chapter 8 for constructing a $(1 - \alpha)\%$ confidence interval for the population mean. We know that $(1 - \alpha)\%$ of the confidence intervals generated will contain the population mean and $\alpha\%$ of the confidence intervals generated will not contain the population mean. Thus, if we reject H_0 whenever the confidence interval does not contain μ_0, we will be rejecting the null hypothesis when it is true $(\mu = \mu_0)$ with probability α. Recall that the level of significance is the probability of rejecting the null hypothesis when it is true. So constructing a $(1 - \alpha)\%$ confidence interval and rejecting H_0 whenever the interval does not contain μ_0 is equivalent to conducting a two-tailed hypothesis test with α as the level of significance. The procedure for using a confidence interval to conduct a two-tailed hypothesis test can now be summarized.

A CONFIDENCE INTERVAL APPROACH TO TESTING A HYPOTHESIS OF THE FORM

$$H_0: \mu = \mu_0$$
$$H_a: \mu \neq \mu_0$$

1. Select a simple random sample from the population and use the value of the sample mean $\bar{x}$ to develop the confidence interval for the population mean μ.

$$\bar{x} \pm z_{\alpha/2} \frac{\sigma}{\sqrt{n}}$$

2. If the confidence interval contains the hypothesized value μ_0, do not reject H_0. Otherwise, reject H_0.

For a two-tailed hypothesis test, the null hypothesis can be rejected if the confidence interval does not include μ_0.

Let us illustrate by conducting the MaxFlight hypothesis test using the confidence interval approach. The MaxFlight hypothesis test takes the following form:

$$H_0: \mu = 295$$
$$H_a: \mu \neq 295$$

To test this hypothesis with a level of significance of $\alpha = .05$, we sampled 50 golf balls and found a sample mean distance of $\bar{x} = 297.6$ yards. Recall that the population standard deviation is $\sigma = 12$. Using these results with $z_{.025} = 1.96$, we find that the 95% confidence interval estimate of the population mean is

$$\bar{x} \pm z_{.025}\frac{\sigma}{\sqrt{n}}$$

$$297.6 \pm 1.96\frac{12}{\sqrt{50}}$$

$$297.6 \pm 3.3$$

or

$$294.3 \text{ to } 300.9$$

This finding enables the quality control manager to conclude with 95% confidence that the mean distance for the population of golf balls is between 294.3 and 300.9 yards. Because the hypothesized value for the population mean, $\mu_0 = 295$, is in this interval, the hypothesis testing conclusion is that the null hypothesis, H_0: $\mu = 295$, cannot be rejected.

Note that this discussion and example pertain to two-tailed hypothesis tests about a population mean. However, the same confidence interval and two-tailed hypothesis testing relationship exists for other population parameters. The relationship can also be extended to one-tailed tests about population parameters. Doing so, however, requires the development of one-sided confidence intervals, which are rarely used in practice.

NOTES AND COMMENTS

We have shown how to use p-values. The smaller the p-value the greater the evidence against H_0 and the more the evidence in favor of H_a. Here are some guidelines statisticians suggest for interpreting small p-values.

- Less than .01—Overwhelming evidence to conclude H_a is true.
- Between .01 and .05—Strong evidence to conclude H_a is true.
- Between .05 and .10—Weak evidence to conclude H_a is true.
- Greater than .10—Insufficient evidence to conclude H_a is true.

Exercises

Note to Student: Some of the exercises that follow ask you to use the p-value approach and others ask you to use the critical value approach. Both methods will provide the same hypothesis testing conclusion. We provide exercises with both methods to give you practice using both. In later sections and in following chapters, we will generally emphasize the p-value approach as the preferred method, but you may select either based on personal preference.

Methods

9. Consider the following hypothesis test:

$$H_0: \mu \geq 20$$
$$H_a: \mu < 20$$

A sample of 50 provided a sample mean of 19.4. The population standard deviation is 2.

a. Compute the value of the test statistic.
b. What is the p-value?
c. Using $\alpha = .05$, what is your conclusion?
d. What is the rejection rule using the critical value? What is your conclusion?

SELF test

10. Consider the following hypothesis test:

$$H_0: \mu \leq 25$$
$$H_a: \mu > 25$$

A sample of 40 provided a sample mean of 26.4. The population standard deviation is 6.

a. Compute the value of the test statistic.
b. What is the p-value?
c. At $\alpha = .01$, what is your conclusion?
d. What is the rejection rule using the critical value? What is your conclusion?

SELF test

11. Consider the following hypothesis test:

$$H_0: \mu = 15$$
$$H_a: \mu \neq 15$$

A sample of 50 provided a sample mean of 14.15. The population standard deviation is 3.

a. Compute the value of the test statistic.
b. What is the p-value?
c. At $\alpha = .05$, what is your conclusion?
d. What is the rejection rule using the critical value? What is your conclusion?

12. Consider the following hypothesis test:

$$H_0: \mu \geq 80$$
$$H_a: \mu < 80$$

A sample of 100 is used and the population standard deviation is 12. Compute the p-value and state your conclusion for each of the following sample results. Use $\alpha = .01$.

a. $\bar{x} = 78.5$
b. $\bar{x} = 77$
c. $\bar{x} = 75.5$
d. $\bar{x} = 81$

13. Consider the following hypothesis test:

$$H_0: \mu \leq 50$$
$$H_a: \mu > 50$$

A sample of 60 is used and the population standard deviation is 8. Use the critical value approach to state your conclusion for each of the following sample results. Use $\alpha = .05$.

a. $\bar{x} = 52.5$
b. $\bar{x} = 51$
c. $\bar{x} = 51.8$

14. Consider the following hypothesis test:

$$H_0: \mu = 22$$
$$H_a: \mu \neq 22$$

A sample of 75 is used and the population standard deviation is 10. Compute the p-value and state your conclusion for each of the following sample results. Use $\alpha = .01$.

a. $\bar{x} = 23$
b. $\bar{x} = 25.1$
c. $\bar{x} = 20$

Applications

SELF test

15. Individuals filing federal income tax returns prior to March 31 received an average refund of $1056. Consider the population of "last-minute" filers who mail their tax return during the last five days of the income tax period (typically April 10 to April 15).
    a. A researcher suggests that a reason individuals wait until the last five days is that on average these individuals receive lower refunds than do early filers. Develop appropriate hypotheses such that rejection of H_0 will support the researcher's contention.
    b. For a sample of 400 individuals who filed a tax return between April 10 and 15, the sample mean refund was $910. Based on prior experience a population standard deviation of $\sigma = \$1600$ may be assumed. What is the p-value?
    c. At $\alpha = .05$, what is your conclusion?
    d. Repeat the preceding hypothesis test using the critical value approach.

CD file
RentalRates

16. Reis, Inc., a New York real estate research firm, tracks the cost of apartment rentals in the United States. In mid-2002, the nationwide mean apartment rental rate was $895 per month (*The Wall Street Journal,* July 8, 2002). Assume that, based on the historical quarterly surveys, a population standard deviation of $\sigma = \$225$ is reasonable. In a current study of apartment rental rates, a sample of 180 apartments nationwide provided the apartment rental rates shown in the CD file named RentalRates. Do the sample data enable Reis to conclude that the population mean apartment rental rate now exceeds the level reported in 2002?
    a. State the null and alternative hypotheses.
    b. What is the p-value?
    c. At $\alpha = .01$, what is your conclusion?
    d. What would you recommend Reis consider doing at this time?
17. Wall Street securities firms paid out record year-end bonuses of $125,500 per employee for 2005 (*Fortune,* February 6, 2006). Suppose we would like to take a sample of employees at the Jones & Ryan securities firm to see whether the mean year-end bonus is different from the reported mean of $125,500 for the population.
    a. State the null and alternative hypotheses you would use to test whether the year-end bonuses paid by Jones & Ryan were different from the population mean.
    b. Suppose a sample of 40 Jones & Ryan employees showed a sample mean year-end bonus of $118,000. Assume a population standard deviation of $\sigma = \$30{,}000$ and compute the p-value.
    c. With $\alpha = .05$ as the level of significance, what is your conclusion?
    d. Repeat the preceding hypothesis test using the critical value approach.
18. The average annual total return for U.S. Diversified Equity mutual funds from 1999 to 2003 was 4.1% (*Business Week,* January 26, 2004). A researcher would like to conduct a hypothesis test to see whether the returns for mid-cap growth funds over the same period are significantly different from the average for U.S. Diversified Equity funds.
    a. Formulate the hypotheses that can be used to determine whether the mean annual return for mid-cap growth funds differ from the mean for U.S. Diversified Equity funds.
    b. A sample of 40 mid-cap growth funds provides a mean return of $\bar{x} = 3.4\%$. Assume the population standard deviation for mid-cap growth funds is known from previous studies to be $\sigma = 2\%$. Use the sample results to compute the test statistic and p-value for the hypothesis test.
    c. At $\alpha = .05$, what is your conclusion?

19. In 2001, the U.S. Department of Labor reported the average hourly earnings for U.S. production workers to be \$14.32 per hour (*The World Almanac 2003*). A sample of 75 production workers during 2003 showed a sample mean of \$14.68 per hour. Assuming the population standard deviation $\sigma = \$1.45$, can we conclude that an increase occurred in the mean hourly earnings since 2001? Use $\alpha = .05$.

20. For the United States, the mean monthly Internet bill is \$32.79 per household (CNBC, January 18, 2006). A sample of 50 households in a southern state showed a sample mean of \$30.63. Use a population standard deviation of $\sigma = \$5.60$.
    a. Formulate hypotheses for a test to determine whether the sample data support the conclusion that the mean monthly Internet bill in the southern state is less than the national mean of \$32.79.
    b. What is the value of the test statistic?
    c. What is the p-value?
    d. At $\alpha = .01$, what is your conclusion?

CD file
Fowle

21. Fowle Marketing Research, Inc., bases charges to a client on the assumption that telephone surveys can be completed in a mean time of 15 minutes or less. If a longer mean survey time is necessary, a premium rate is charged. A sample of 35 surveys provided the survey times shown in the CD file named Fowle. Based upon past studies, the population standard deviation is assumed known with $\sigma = 4$ minutes. Is the premium rate justified?
    a. Formulate the null and alternative hypotheses for this application.
    b. Compute the value of the test statistic.
    c. What is the p-value?
    d. At $\alpha = .01$, what is your conclusion?

22. CCN and ActMedia provided a television channel targeted to individuals waiting in supermarket checkout lines. The channel showed news, short features, and advertisements. The length of the program was based on the assumption that the population mean time a shopper stands in a supermarket checkout line is 8 minutes. A sample of actual waiting times will be used to test this assumption and determine whether actual mean waiting time differs from this standard.
    a. Formulate the hypotheses for this application.
    b. A sample of 120 shoppers showed a sample mean waiting time of 8.5 minutes. Assume a population standard deviation $\sigma = 3.2$ minutes. What is the p-value?
    c. At $\alpha = .05$, what is your conclusion?
    d. Compute a 95% confidence interval for the population mean. Does it support your conclusion?

9.4 Population Mean: σ Unknown

In this section we describe how to conduct hypothesis tests about a population mean for the σ unknown case. Because the σ unknown case corresponds to situations in which an estimate of the population standard deviation cannot be developed prior to sampling, the sample must be used to develop an estimate of both μ and σ. Thus, to conduct a hypothesis test about a population mean for the σ unknown case, the sample mean $\bar{x}$ is used as an estimate of μ and the sample standard deviation s is used as an estimate of σ.

The steps of the hypothesis testing procedure for the σ unknown case are the same as those for the σ known case described in Section 9.3. But, with σ unknown, the computation of the test statistic and p-value is a bit different. Recall that for the σ known case, the sampling distribution of the test statistic has a standard normal distribution. For the σ unknown case, however, the sampling distribution of the test statistic follows the t distribution; it has slightly more variability because the sample is used to develop estimates of both μ and σ.

In Section 8.2 we showed that an interval estimate of a population mean for the σ unknown case is based on a probability distribution known as the t distribution. Hypothesis tests about a population mean for the σ unknown case are also based on the t distribution. For the σ unknown case, the test statistic has a t distribution with $n - 1$ degrees of freedom.

TEST STATISTIC FOR HYPOTHESIS TESTS ABOUT A POPULATION MEAN: σ UNKNOWN

$$t = \frac{\bar{x} - \mu_0}{s/\sqrt{n}} \tag{9.2}$$

In Chapter 8 we said that the t distribution is based on an assumption that the population from which we are sampling has a normal distribution. However, research shows that this assumption can be relaxed considerably when the sample size is large enough. We provide some practical advice concerning the population distribution and sample size at the end of the section.

One-Tailed Test

Let us consider an example of a one-tailed test about a population mean for the σ unknown case. A business travel magazine wants to classify transatlantic gateway airports according to the mean rating for the population of business travelers. A rating scale with a low score of 0 and a high score of 10 will be used, and airports with a population mean rating greater than 7 will be designated as superior service airports. The magazine staff surveyed a sample of 60 business travelers at each airport to obtain the ratings data. The sample for London's Heathrow Airport provided a sample mean rating of $\bar{x} = 7.25$ and a sample standard deviation of $s = 1.052$. Do the data indicate that Heathrow should be designated as a superior service airport?

CD file
AirRating

We want to develop a hypothesis test for which the decision to reject H_0 will lead to the conclusion that the population mean rating for the Heathrow Airport is *greater* than 7. Thus, an upper tail test with H_a: $\mu > 7$ is required. The null and alternative hypotheses for this upper tail test are as follows:

$$H_0: \mu \leq 7$$
$$H_a: \mu > 7$$

We will use $\alpha = .05$ as the level of significance for the test.

Using equation (9.2) with $\bar{x} = 7.25$, $\mu_0 = 7$, $s = 1.052$, and $n = 60$, the value of the test statistic is

$$t = \frac{\bar{x} - \mu_0}{s/\sqrt{n}} = \frac{7.25 - 7}{1.052/\sqrt{60}} = 1.84$$

The sampling distribution of t has $n - 1 = 60 - 1 = 59$ degrees of freedom. Because the test is an upper tail test, the p-value is the area under the curve of the t distribution to the right of $t = 1.84$.

The t distribution table provided in most textbooks will not contain sufficient detail to determine the exact p-value, such as the p-value corresponding to $t = 1.84$. For instance, using Table 2 in Appendix B, the t distribution with 59 degrees of freedom provides the following information.

Area in Upper Tail	.20	.10	.05	.025	.01	.005
t Value (59 df)	.848	1.296	1.671	2.001	2.391	2.662

$t = 1.84$

We see that $t = 1.84$ is between 1.671 and 2.001. Although the table does not provide the exact p-value, the values in the "Area in Upper Tail" row show that the p-value must be less than .05 and greater than .025. With a level of significance of $\alpha = .05$, this placement is all we need to know to make the decision to reject the null hypothesis and conclude that Heathrow should be classified as a superior service airport.

Appendix F shows how to compute p-values using Excel or Minitab.

Because it is cumbersome to use a t table to compute p-values, and only approximate values are obtained, we show how to compute the exact p-value using Excel or Minitab. The directions can be found in Appendix F at the end of this text. Using Excel or Minitab with $t = 1.84$ provides the upper tail p-value of .0354 for the Heathrow Airport hypothesis test. With $.0354 < .05$, we reject the null hypothesis and conclude that Heathrow should be classified as a superior service airport.

Two-Tailed Test

To illustrate how to conduct a two-tailed test about a population mean for the σ unknown case, let us consider the hypothesis testing situation facing Holiday Toys. The company manufactures and distributes its products through more than 1000 retail outlets. In planning production levels for the coming winter season, Holiday must decide how many units of each product to produce prior to knowing the actual demand at the retail level. For this year's most important new toy, Holiday's marketing director is expecting demand to average 40 units per retail outlet. Prior to making the final production decision based upon this estimate, Holiday decided to survey a sample of 25 retailers in order to develop more information about the demand for the new product. Each retailer was provided with information about the features of the new toy along with the cost and the suggested selling price. Then each retailer was asked to specify an anticipated order quantity.

With μ denoting the population mean order quantity per retail outlet, the sample data will be used to conduct the following two-tailed hypothesis test:

$$H_0: \mu = 40$$
$$H_a: \mu \neq 40$$

If H_0 cannot be rejected, Holiday will continue its production planning based on the marketing director's estimate that the population mean order quantity per retail outlet will be $\mu = 40$ units. However, if H_0 is rejected. Holiday will immediately reevaluate its production plan for the product. A two-tailed hypothesis test is used because Holiday wants to reevaluate the production plan if the population mean quantity per retail outlet is less than anticipated or greater than anticipated. Because no historical data are available (it's a new product), the population mean μ and the population standard deviation must both be estimated using $\bar{x}$ and s from the sample data.

CD file
Orders

The sample of 25 retailers provided a mean of $\bar{x} = 37.4$ and a standard deviation of $s = 11.79$ units. Before going ahead with the use of the t distribution, the analyst constructed a histogram of the sample data in order to check on the form of the population distribution. The histogram of the sample data showed no evidence of skewness or any extreme outliers, so the analyst concluded that the use of the t distribution with $n - 1 = 24$ degrees of freedom was appropriate. Using equation (9.2) with $\bar{x} = 37.4$, $\mu_0 = 40$, $s = 11.79$, and $n = 25$, the value of the test statistic is

$$t = \frac{\bar{x} - \mu_0}{s/\sqrt{n}} = \frac{37.4 - 40}{11.79/\sqrt{25}} = -1.10$$

Because we have a two-tailed test, the p-value is two times the area under the curve for the t distribution to the left of $t = -1.10$. Using Table 2 in Appendix B, the t distribution table for 24 degrees of freedom provides the following information.

Area in Upper Tail	**.20**	**.10**	**.05**	**.025**	**.01**	**.005**
***t* Value (24 df)**	.857	1.318	1.711	2.064	2.492	2.797

$t = 1.10$

The t distribution table only contains positive t values. Because the t distribution is symmetric, however, the area under the curve to the right of $t = 1.10$ is the same as the area under the curve to the left of $t = -1.10$. We see that $t = 1.10$ is between 0.857 and 1.318. From the "Area in Upper Tail" row, we see that the area in the tail to the right of $t = 1.10$ is between .20 and .10. When we double these amounts, we see that the p-value must be between .40 and .20. With a level of significance of $\alpha = .05$, we now know that the p-value is greater than α. Therefore, H_0 cannot be rejected. Sufficient evidence is not available to conclude that Holiday should change its production plan for the coming season.

Appendix F shows how the p-value for this test can be computed using Excel or Minitab. The p-value obtained is .2822. With a level of significance of $\alpha = .05$, we cannot reject H_0 because $.2822 > .05$.

The test statistic can also be compared to the critical value to make the two-tailed hypothesis testing decision. With $\alpha = .05$ and the t distribution with 24 degrees of freedom, $-t_{.025} = -2.064$ and $t_{.025} = 2.064$ are the critical values for the two-tailed test. The rejection rule using the test statistic is

$$\text{Reject } H_0 \text{ if } t \leq -2.064 \text{ or if } t \geq 2.064$$

Based on the test statistic $t = -1.10$, H_0 cannot be rejected. This result indicates that Holiday should continue its production planning for the coming season based on the expectation that $\mu = 40$.

Summary and Practical Advice

Table 9.3 provides a summary of the hypothesis testing procedures about a population mean for the σ unknown case. The key difference between these procedures and the ones for the σ known case is that s is used, instead of σ, in the computation of the test statistic. For this reason, the test statistic follows the t distribution.

The applicability of the hypothesis testing procedures of this section is dependent on the distribution of the population being sampled from and the sample size. When the population is normally distributed, the hypothesis tests described in this section provide exact results for any sample size. When the population is not normally distributed, the procedures are approximations. Nonetheless, we find that sample sizes of 30 or greater will provide good results in most cases. If the population is approximately normal, small sample sizes (e.g., $n < 15$) can provide acceptable results. If the population is highly skewed or contains outliers, sample sizes approaching 50 are recommended.

TABLE 9.3 SUMMARY OF HYPOTHESIS TESTS ABOUT A POPULATION MEAN: σ UNKNOWN CASE

	Lower Tail Test	Upper Tail Test	Two-Tailed Test
Hypotheses	$H_0: \mu \geq \mu_0$ $H_a: \mu < \mu_0$	$H_0: \mu \leq \mu_0$ $H_a: \mu > \mu_0$	$H_0: \mu = \mu_0$ $H_a: \mu \neq \mu_0$
Test Statistic	$t = \frac{\bar{x} - \mu_0}{s/\sqrt{n}}$	$t = \frac{\bar{x} - \mu_0}{s/\sqrt{n}}$	$t = \frac{\bar{x} - \mu_0}{s/\sqrt{n}}$
Rejection Rule: *p*-Value Approach	Reject H_0 if p-value $\leq \alpha$	Reject H_0 if p-value $\leq \alpha$	Reject H_0 if p-value $\leq \alpha$
Rejection Rule: Critical Value Approach	Reject H_0 if $t \leq -t_\alpha$	Reject H_0 if $t \geq t_\alpha$	Reject H_0 if $t \leq -t_{\alpha/2}$ or if $t \geq t_{\alpha/2}$

Exercises

Methods

23. Consider the following hypothesis test:

$$H_0: \mu \leq 12$$
$$H_a: \mu > 12$$

A sample of 25 provided a sample mean $\bar{x} = 14$ and a sample standard deviation $s = 4.32$.

a. Compute the value of the test statistic.
b. Use the t distribution table (Table 2 in Appendix B) to compute a range for the p-value.
c. At $\alpha = .05$, what is your conclusion?
d. What is the rejection rule using the critical value? What is your conclusion?

SELF test

24. Consider the following hypothesis test:

$$H_0: \mu = 18$$
$$H_a: \mu \neq 18$$

A sample of 48 provided a sample mean $\bar{x} = 17$ and a sample standard deviation $s = 4.5$.

a. Compute the value of the test statistic.
b. Use the t distribution table (Table 2 in Appendix B) to compute a range for the p-value.
c. At $\alpha = .05$, what is your conclusion?
d. What is the rejection rule using the critical value? What is your conclusion?

25. Consider the following hypothesis test:

$$H_0: \mu \geq 45$$
$$H_a: \mu < 45$$

A sample of 36 is used. Identify the p-value and state your conclusion for each of the following sample results. Use $\alpha = .01$.

a. $\bar{x} = 44$ and $s = 5.2$
b. $\bar{x} = 43$ and $s = 4.6$
c. $\bar{x} = 46$ and $s = 5.0$

26. Consider the following hypothesis test:

$$H_0: \mu = 100$$
$$H_a: \mu \neq 100$$

A sample of 65 is used. Identify the p-value and state your conclusion for each of the following sample results. Use $\alpha = .05$.

a. $\bar{x} = 103$ and $s = 11.5$
b. $\bar{x} = 96.5$ and $s = 11.0$
c. $\bar{x} = 102$ and $s = 10.5$

Applications

SELF test

27. The Employment and Training Administration reported the U.S. mean unemployment insurance benefit of $238 per week (*The World Almanac,* 2003). A researcher in the state of Virginia anticipated that sample data would show evidence that the mean weekly unemployment insurance benefit in Virginia was below the national level.
a. Develop appropriate hypotheses such that rejection of H_0 will support the researcher's contention.
b. For a sample of 100 individuals, the sample mean weekly unemployment insurance benefit was $231 with a sample standard deviation of $80. What is the p-value?
c. At $\alpha = .05$, what is your conclusion?
d. Repeat the preceding hypothesis test using the critical value approach.

28. The National Association of Professional Baseball Leagues, Inc., reported that attendance for 176 minor league baseball teams reached an all-time high during the 2001 season (*New York Times,* July 28, 2002). On a per-game basis, the mean attendance for minor league baseball was 3530 people per game. Midway through the 2002 season, the president of the association asked for an attendance report that would hopefully show that the mean attendance for 2002 was exceeding the 2001 level.
a. Formulate hypotheses that could be used determine whether the mean attendance per game in 2002 was greater than the previous year's level.
b. Assume that a sample of 92 minor league baseball games played during the first half of the 2002 season showed a mean attendance of 3740 people per game with a sample standard deviation of 810. What is the p-value?
c. At $\alpha = .01$, what is your conclusion?

CD file

Diamonds

29. The cost of a one-carat VS2 clarity, H color diamond from Diamond Source USA is $5600 (www.diasource.com, March 2003). A midwestern jeweler makes calls to contacts in the diamond district of New York City to see whether the mean price of diamonds there differs from $5600.
a. Formulate hypotheses that can be used to determine whether the mean price in New York City differs from $5600.
b. A sample of 25 New York City contacts provided the prices shown in the CD file named Diamonds. What is the p-value?
c. At $\alpha = .05$, can the null hypothesis be rejected? What is your conclusion?
d. Repeat the preceding hypothesis test using the critical value approach.

30. AOL Time Warner Inc.'s CNN has been the longtime ratings leader of cable television news. Nielsen Media Research indicated that the mean CNN viewing audience was 600,000 viewers per day during 2002 (*The Wall Street Journal,* March 10, 2003). Assume that for a sample of 40 days during the first half of 2003, the daily audience was 612,000 viewers with a sample standard deviation of 65,000 viewers.
a. What are the hypotheses if CNN management would like information on any change in the CNN viewing audience?
b. What is the p-value?
c. Select your own level of significance. What is your conclusion?
d. What recommendation would you make to CNN management in this application?

31. Raftelis Financial Consulting reported that the mean quarterly water bill in the United States is \$47.50 (*U.S. News & World Report,* August 12, 2002). Some water systems are operated by public utilities, whereas other water systems are operated by private companies. An economist pointed out that privatization does not equal competition and that monopoly powers provided to public utilities are now being transferred to private companies. The concern is that consumers end up paying higher-than-average rates for water provided by private companies. The water system for Atlanta, Georgia, is provided by a private company. A sample of 64 Atlanta consumers showed a mean quarterly water bill of \$51 with a sample standard deviation of \$12. At $\alpha = .05$, does the Atlanta sample support the conclusion that above-average rates exist for this private water system? What is your conclusion?

CD file
UsedCars

32. According to the National Automobile Dealers Association, the mean price for used cars is \$10,192. A manager of a Kansas City used car dealership reviewed a sample of 50 recent used car sales at the dealership in an attempt to determine whether the population mean price for used cars at this particular dealership differed from the national mean. The prices for the sample of 50 cars are shown in the CD file named Used Cars.
    a. Formulate the hypotheses that can be used to determine whether a difference exists in the mean price for used cars at the dealership.
    b. What is the p-value?
    c. At $\alpha = .05$, what is your conclusion?
33. Annual per capita consumption of milk is 21.6 gallons (*Statistical Abstract of the United States: 2006*). Being from the Midwest, you believe milk consumption is higher there and wish to support your opinion. A sample of 16 individuals from the midwestern town of Webster City showed a sample mean annual consumption of 24.1 gallons with a standard deviation of $s = 4.8$.
    a. Develop a hypothesis test that can be used to determine whether the mean annual consumption in Webster City is higher than the national mean.
    b. What is a point estimate of the difference between mean annual consumption in Webster City and the national mean?
    c. At $\alpha = .05$, test for a significant difference. What is your conclusion?
34. Joan's Nursery specializes in custom-designed landscaping for residential areas. The estimated labor cost associated with a particular landscaping proposal is based on the number of plantings of trees, shrubs, and so on to be used for the project. For cost-estimating purposes, managers use two hours of labor time for the planting of a medium-sized tree. Actual times from a sample of 10 plantings during the past month follow (times in hours).

1.7	1.5	2.6	2.2	2.4	2.3	2.6	3.0	1.4	2.3

    With a .05 level of significance, test to see whether the mean tree-planting time differs from two hours.
    a. State the null and alternative hypotheses.
    b. Compute the sample mean.
    c. Compute the sample standard deviation.
    d. What is the p-value?
    e. What is your conclusion?

9.5 Population Proportion

In this section we show how to conduct a hypothesis test about a population proportion p. Using p_0 to denote the hypothesized value for the population proportion, the three forms for a hypothesis test about a population proportion are as follows.

$$H_0: p \geq p_0 \qquad H_0: p \leq p_0 \qquad H_0: p = p_0$$
$$H_a: p < p_0 \qquad H_a: p > p_0 \qquad H_a: p \neq p_0$$

The first form is called a lower tail test, the second form is called an upper tail test, and the third form is called a two-tailed test.

Hypothesis tests about a population proportion are based on the difference between the sample proportion $\bar{p}$ and the hypothesized population proportion p_0. The methods used to conduct the hypothesis test are similar to those used for hypothesis tests about a population mean. The only difference is that we use the sample proportion and its standard error to compute the test statistic. The p-value approach or the critical value approach is then used to determine whether the null hypothesis should be rejected.

Let us consider an example involving a situation faced by Pine Creek golf course. Over the past year, 20% of the players at Pine Creek were women. In an effort to increase the proportion of women players, Pine Creek implemented a special promotion designed to attract women golfers. One month after the promotion was implemented, the course manager requested a statistical study to determine whether the proportion of women players at Pine Creek had increased. Because the objective of the study is to determine whether the proportion of women golfers increased, an upper tail test with H_a: $p > .20$ is appropriate. The null and alternative hypotheses for the Pine Creek hypothesis test are as follows:

$$H_0: p \leq .20$$
$$H_a: p > .20$$

If H_0 can be rejected, the test results will give statistical support for the conclusion that the proportion of women golfers increased and the promotion was beneficial. The course manager specified that a level of significance of $\alpha = .05$ be used in carrying out this hypothesis test.

The next step of the hypothesis testing procedure is to select a sample and compute the value of an appropriate test statistic. To show how this step is done for the Pine Creek upper tail test, we begin with a general discussion of how to compute the value of the test statistic for any form of a hypothesis test about a population proportion. The sampling distribution of $\bar{p}$, the point estimator of the population parameter p, is the basis for developing the test statistic.

When the null hypothesis is true as an equality, the expected value of $\bar{p}$ equals the hypothesized value p_0; that is, $E(\bar{p}) = p_0$. The standard error of $\bar{p}$ is given by

$$\sigma_{\bar{p}} = \sqrt{\frac{p_0(1 - p_0)}{n}}$$

In Chapter 7 we said that if $np \geq 5$ and $n(1 - p) \geq 5$, the sampling distribution of $\bar{p}$ can be approximated by a normal distribution.* Under these conditions, which usually apply in practice, the quantity

$$z = \frac{\bar{p} - p_0}{\sigma_{\bar{p}}} \tag{9.3}$$

has a standard normal probability distribution. With $\sigma_{\bar{p}} = \sqrt{p_0(1 - p_0)/n}$, the standard normal random variable z is the test statistic used to conduct hypothesis tests about a population proportion.

*In most applications involving hypothesis tests of a population proportion, sample sizes are large enough to use the normal approximation. The exact sampling distribution of $\bar{p}$ is discrete with the probability for each value of $\bar{p}$ given by the binomial distribution. So hypothesis testing is a bit more complicated for small samples when the normal approximation cannot be used.

TEST STATISTIC FOR HYPOTHESIS TESTS ABOUT A POPULATION PROPORTION

$$z = \frac{\bar{p} - p_0}{\sqrt{\frac{p_0(1 - p_0)}{n}}} \tag{9.4}$$

CD file
WomenGolf

We can now compute the test statistic for the Pine Creek hypothesis test. Suppose a random sample of 400 players was selected, and that 100 of the players were women. The proportion of women golfers in the sample is

$$\bar{p} = \frac{100}{400} = .25$$

Using equation (9.4), the value of the test statistic is

$$z = \frac{\bar{p} - p_0}{\sqrt{\frac{p_0(1 - p_0)}{n}}} = \frac{.25 - .20}{\sqrt{\frac{.20(1 - .20)}{400}}} = \frac{.05}{.02} = 2.50$$

Because the Pine Creek hypothesis test is an upper tail test, the p-value is the probability that z is greater than or equal to $z = 2.50$; that is, it is the area under the standard normal curve to the right of $z = 2.50$. Using the standard normal probability table, we find that the area to the left of $z = 2.50$ is .9938. Thus, the p-value for the Pine Creek test is $1.0000 - .9938 = .0062$. Figure 9.7 shows this p-value calculation.

Recall that the course manager specified a level of significance of $\alpha = .05$. A p-value $= .0062 < .05$ gives sufficient statistical evidence to reject H_0 at the .05 level of significance. Thus, the test provides statistical support for the conclusion that the special promotion increased the proportion of women players at the Pine Creek golf course.

The decision whether to reject the null hypothesis can also be made using the critical value approach. The critical value corresponding to an area of .05 in the upper tail of a normal probability distribution is $z_{.05} = 1.645$. Thus, the rejection rule using the critical value approach is to reject H_0 if $z \geq 1.645$. Because $z = 2.50 > 1.645$, H_0 is rejected.

Again, we see that the p-value approach and the critical value approach lead to the same hypothesis testing conclusion, but the p-value approach provides more information. With a

FIGURE 9.7 CALCULATION OF THE p-VALUE FOR THE PINE CREEK HYPOTHESIS TEST

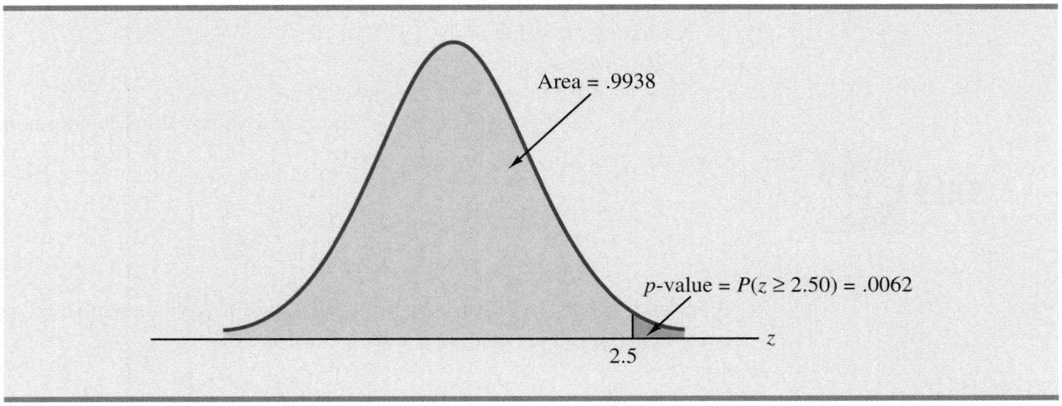

TABLE 9.4 SUMMARY OF HYPOTHESIS TESTS ABOUT A POPULATION PROPORTION

	Lower Tail Test	Upper Tail Test	Two-Tailed Test
Hypotheses	$H_0: p \geq p_0$ $H_a: p < p_0$	$H_0: p \leq p_0$ $H_a: p > p_0$	$H_0: p = p_0$ $H_a: p \neq p_0$
Test Statistic	$z = \dfrac{\bar{p} - p_0}{\sqrt{\dfrac{p_0(1-p_0)}{n}}}$	$z = \dfrac{\bar{p} - p_0}{\sqrt{\dfrac{p_0(1-p_0)}{n}}}$	$z = \dfrac{\bar{p} - p_0}{\sqrt{\dfrac{p_0(1-p_0)}{n}}}$
Rejection Rule: *p*-Value Approach	Reject H_0 if p-value $\leq \alpha$	Reject H_0 if p-value $\leq \alpha$	Reject H_0 if p-value $\leq \alpha$
Rejection Rule: Critical Value Approach	Reject H_0 if $z \leq -z_\alpha$	Reject H_0 if $z \geq z_\alpha$	Reject H_0 if $z \leq -z_{\alpha/2}$ or if $z \geq z_{\alpha/2}$

p-value $= .0062$, the null hypothesis would be rejected for any level of significance greater than or equal to .0062.

Summary

The procedure used to conduct a hypothesis test about a population proportion is similar to the procedure used to conduct a hypothesis test about a population mean. Although we only illustrated how to conduct a hypothesis test about a population proportion for an upper tail test, similar procedures can be used for lower tail and two-tailed tests. Table 9.4 provides a summary of the hypothesis tests about a population proportion. We assume that $np \geq 5$ and $n(1 - p) \geq 5$; thus the normal probability distribution can be used to approximate the sampling distribution of $\bar{p}$.

Exercises

Methods

35. Consider the following hypothesis test:

$$H_0: p = .20$$
$$H_a: p \neq .20$$

A sample of 400 provided a sample proportion $\bar{p} = .175$.

a. Compute the value of the test statistic.
b. What is the p-value?
c. At $\alpha = .05$, what is your conclusion?
d. What is the rejection rule using the critical value? What is your conclusion?

SELF test

36. Consider the following hypothesis test:

$$H_0: p \geq .75$$
$$H_a: p < .75$$

A sample of 300 items was selected. Compute the p-value and state your conclusion for each of the following sample results. Use $\alpha = .05$.

a. $\bar{p} = .68$
b. $\bar{p} = .72$
c. $\bar{p} = .70$
d. $\bar{p} = .77$

Applications

37. A study found that, in 2005, 12.5% of U.S. workers belonged to unions (*The Wall Street Journal,* January 21, 2006). Suppose a sample of 400 U.S. workers is collected in 2006 to determine whether union efforts to organize have increased union membership.
    a. Formulate the hypotheses that can be used to determine whether union membership increased in 2006.
    b. If the sample results show that 52 of the workers belonged to unions, what is the p-value for your hypothesis test?
    c. At $\alpha = .05$, what is your conclusion?

SELF test

38. A study by *Consumer Reports* showed that 64% of supermarket shoppers believe supermarket brands to be as good as national name brands. To investigate whether this result applies to its own product, the manufacturer of a national name-brand ketchup asked a sample of shoppers whether they believed that supermarket ketchup was as good as the national brand ketchup.
    a. Formulate the hypotheses that could be used to determine whether the percentage of supermarket shoppers who believe that the supermarket ketchup was as good as the national brand ketchup differed from 64%.
    b. If a sample of 100 shoppers showed 52 stating that the supermarket brand was as good as the national brand, what is the p-value?
    c. At $\alpha = .05$, what is your conclusion?
    d. Should the national brand ketchup manufacturer be pleased with this conclusion? Explain.

39. The National Center for Health Statistics released a report that stated 70% of adults do not exercise regularly (Associated Press, April 7, 2002). A researcher decided to conduct a study to see whether the claim made by the National Center for Health Statistics differed on a state-by-state basis.
    a. State the null and alternative hypotheses assuming the intent of the researcher is to identify states that differ from the 70% reported by the National Center for Health Statistics.
    b. At $\alpha = .05$, what is the research conclusion for the following states:

Wisconsin:	252 of 350 adults did not exercise regularly
California:	189 of 300 adults did not exercise regularly

40. Before the 2003 Super Bowl, ABC predicted that 22% of the Super Bowl audience would express an interest in seeing one of its forthcoming new television shows, including *8 Simple Rules, Are You Hot?,* and *Dragnet.* ABC ran commercials for these television shows during the Super Bowl. The day after the Super Bowl, Intermediate Advertising Group of New York sampled 1532 viewers who saw the commercials and found that 414 said that they would watch one of the ABC advertised television shows (*The Wall Street Journal,* January 30, 2003).
    a. What is the point estimate of the proportion of the audience that said they would watch the television shows after seeing the television commercials?
    b. At $\alpha = .05$, determine whether the intent to watch the ABC television shows significantly increased after seeing the television commercials. Formulate the appropriate hypotheses, compute the p-value, and state your conclusion.
    c. Why are such studies valuable to companies and advertising firms?

41. Speaking to a group of analysts in January 2006, a brokerage firm executive claimed that 70% of investors are currently confident of meeting their investment objectives. A UBS Investor Optimism Survey, conducted over the period January 2 to January 15, found that 67% of investors were confident of meeting their investment objectives (CNBC, January 20, 2006).
    a. Formulate the hypotheses that can be used to test the validity of the brokerage firm executive's claim.

b. Assume the UBS Investor Optimism Survey collected information from 300 investors. What is the p-value for the hypothesis test?
c. At $\alpha = .05$, should the executive's claim be rejected?

42. According to the Census Bureau's American Housing Survey, the primary reason people who move choose their new neighborhood is because the location is convenient to work (*USA Today,* December 24, 2002). Based on 1990 Census Bureau data, we know that 24% of the population of people who moved selected "location convenient to work" as the reason for selecting their new neighborhood. Assume a sample of 300 people who moved during 2003 found 93 did so to be closer to work. Do the sample data support the research conclusion that in 2003 more people are choosing where to live based on how close they will be to their work? What is the point estimate of the proportion of people who moved during 2003 that chose their new neighborhood because the location is convenient to work? What is your research conclusion? Use $\alpha = .05$.

CD file
Eagle

43. Eagle Outfitters is a chain of stores specializing in outdoor apparel and camping gear. They are considering a promotion that involves mailing discount coupons to all their credit card customers. This promotion will be considered a success if more than 10% of those receiving the coupons use them. Before going national with the promotion, coupons were sent to a sample of 100 credit card customers.
    a. Develop hypotheses that can be used to test whether the population proportion of those who will use the coupons is sufficient to go national.
    b. The file Eagle contains the sample data. Develop a point estimate of the population proportion.
    c. Use $\alpha = .05$ to conduct your hypothesis test. Should Eagle go national with the promotion?

CD file
Drowsy

44. In a cover story, *BusinessWeek* published information about sleep habits of Americans (*BusinessWeek,* January 26, 2004). The article noted that sleep deprivation causes a number of problems, including highway deaths. Fifty-one percent of adult drivers admit to driving while drowsy. A researcher hypothesized that this issue was an even bigger problem for night shift workers.
    a. Formulate the hypotheses that can be used to help determine whether more than 51% of the population of night shift workers admit to driving while drowsy.
    b. A sample of 500 night shift workers identified those who admitted to driving while drowsy. What is the sample proportion? What is the p-value?
    c. At $\alpha = .01$, what is your conclusion?

45. Many investors and financial analysts believe the Dow Jones Industrial Average (DJIA) provides a good barometer of the overall stock market. On January 31, 2006, 9 of the 30 stocks making up the DJIA increased in price (*The Wall Street Journal,* February 1, 2006). On the basis of this fact, a financial analyst claims we can assume that 30% of the stocks traded on the New York Stock Exchange (NYSE) went up the same day.
    a. Formulate null and alternative hypotheses to test the analyst's claim.
    b. A sample of 50 stocks traded on the NYSE that day showed that 24 went up. What is your point estimate of the population proportion of stocks that went up?
    c. Conduct your hypothesis test using $\alpha = .01$ as the level of significance. What is your conclusion?

9.6 Hypothesis Testing and Decision Making

In Section 9.1 we discussed three types of situations in which hypothesis testing is used:

1. Testing research hypotheses
2. Testing the validity of a claim
3. Testing in decision-making situations

In the first two situations, action is taken only when the null hypothesis H_0 is rejected and hence the alternative hypothesis H_a is concluded to be true. In the third situation—decision making—it is necessary to take action when the null hypothesis is not rejected as well as when it is rejected.

The hypothesis testing procedures presented thus far have limited applicability in a decision-making situation because it is not considered appropriate to accept H_0 and take action based on the conclusion that H_0 is true. The reason for not taking action when the test results indicate *do not reject* H_0 is that the decision to accept H_0 exposes the decision maker to the risk of making a Type II error; that is, accepting H_0 when it is false. With the hypothesis testing procedures described in the preceding sections, the probability of a Type I error is controlled by establishing a level of significance for the test. However, the probability of making the Type II error is not controlled.

Clearly, in certain decision-making situations the decision maker may want—and in some cases may be forced—to take action with both the conclusion *do not reject* H_0 and the conclusion *reject* H_0. A good illustration of this situation is lot-acceptance sampling, a topic we will discuss in more depth in Chapter 20. For example, a quality control manager must decide to accept a shipment of batteries from a supplier or to return the shipment because of poor quality. Assume that design specifications require batteries from the supplier to have a mean useful life of at least 120 hours. To evaluate the quality of an incoming shipment, a sample of 36 batteries will be selected and tested. On the basis of the sample, a decision must be made to accept the shipment of batteries or to return it to the supplier because of poor quality. Let μ denote the mean number of hours of useful life for batteries in the shipment. The null and alternative hypotheses about the population mean follow.

$$H_0\colon \mu \geq 120$$
$$H_a\colon \mu < 120$$

If H_0 is rejected, the alternative hypothesis is concluded to be true. This conclusion indicates that the appropriate action is to return the shipment to the supplier. However, if H_0 is not rejected, the decision maker must still determine what action should be taken. Thus, without directly concluding that H_0 is true, but merely by not rejecting it, the decision maker will have made the decision to accept the shipment as being of satisfactory quality.

In such decision-making situations, it is recommended that the hypothesis testing procedure be extended to control the probability of making a Type II error. Because a decision will be made and action taken when we do not reject H_0, knowledge of the probability of making a Type II error will be helpful. In Sections 9.7 and 9.8 we explain how to compute the probability of making a Type II error and how the sample size can be adjusted to help control the probability of making a Type II error.

9.7 Calculating the Probability of Type II Errors

In this section we show how to calculate the probability of making a Type II error for a hypothesis test about a population mean. We illustrate the procedure by using the lot-acceptance example described in Section 9.6. The null and alternative hypotheses about the mean number of hours of useful life for a shipment of batteries are $H_0\colon \mu \geq 120$ and $H_a\colon \mu < 120$. If H_0 is rejected, the decision will be to return the shipment to the supplier because the mean hours of useful life are less than the specified 120 hours. If H_0 is not rejected, the decision will be to accept the shipment.

Suppose a level of significance of $\alpha = .05$ is used to conduct the hypothesis test. The test statistic in the σ known case is

$$z = \frac{\bar{x} - \mu_0}{\sigma/\sqrt{n}} = \frac{\bar{x} - 120}{\sigma/\sqrt{n}}$$

Based on the critical value approach and $z_{.05} = 1.645$, the rejection rule for the lower tail test is

$$\text{Reject } H_0 \text{ if } z \leq -1.645$$

Suppose a sample of 36 batteries will be selected and based upon previous testing the population standard deviation can be assumed known with a value of $\sigma = 12$ hours. The rejection rule indicates that we will reject H_0 if

$$z = \frac{\bar{x} - 120}{12/\sqrt{36}} \leq -1.645$$

Solving for $\bar{x}$ in the preceding expression indicates that we will reject H_0 if

$$\bar{x} \leq 120 - 1.645\left(\frac{12}{\sqrt{36}}\right) = 116.71$$

Rejecting H_0 when $\bar{x} \leq 116.71$ means that we will make the decision to accept the shipment whenever

$$\bar{x} > 116.71$$

With this information, we are ready to compute probabilities associated with making a Type II error. First, recall that we make a Type II error whenever the true shipment mean is less than 120 hours and we make the decision to accept H_0: $\mu \geq 120$. Hence, to compute the probability of making a Type II error, we must select a value of μ less than 120 hours. For example, suppose the shipment is considered to be of poor quality if the batteries have a mean life of $\mu = 112$ hours. If $\mu = 112$ is really true, what is the probability of accepting H_0: $\mu \geq 120$ and hence committing a Type II error? Note that this probability is the probability that the sample mean $\bar{x}$ is greater than 116.71 when $\mu = 112$.

Figure 9.8 shows the sampling distribution of $\bar{x}$ when the mean is $\mu = 112$. The shaded area in the upper tail gives the probability of obtaining $\bar{x} > 116.71$. Using the standard normal distribution, we see that at $\bar{x} = 116.71$

$$z = \frac{\bar{x} - \mu}{\sigma/\sqrt{n}} = \frac{116.71 - 112}{12/\sqrt{36}} = 2.36$$

The standard normal probability table shows that with $z = 2.36$, the area in the upper tail is $1.0000 - .9909 = .0091$. Thus, .0091 is the probability of making a Type II error when $\mu = 112$. Denoting the probability of making a Type II error as β, we see that when $\mu = 112$, $\beta = .0091$. Therefore, we can conclude that if the mean of the population is 112 hours, the probability of making a Type II error is only .0091.

We can repeat these calculations for other values of μ less than 120. Doing so will show a different probability of making a Type II error for each value of μ. For example, suppose

FIGURE 9.8 PROBABILITY OF A TYPE II ERROR WHEN $\mu = 112$

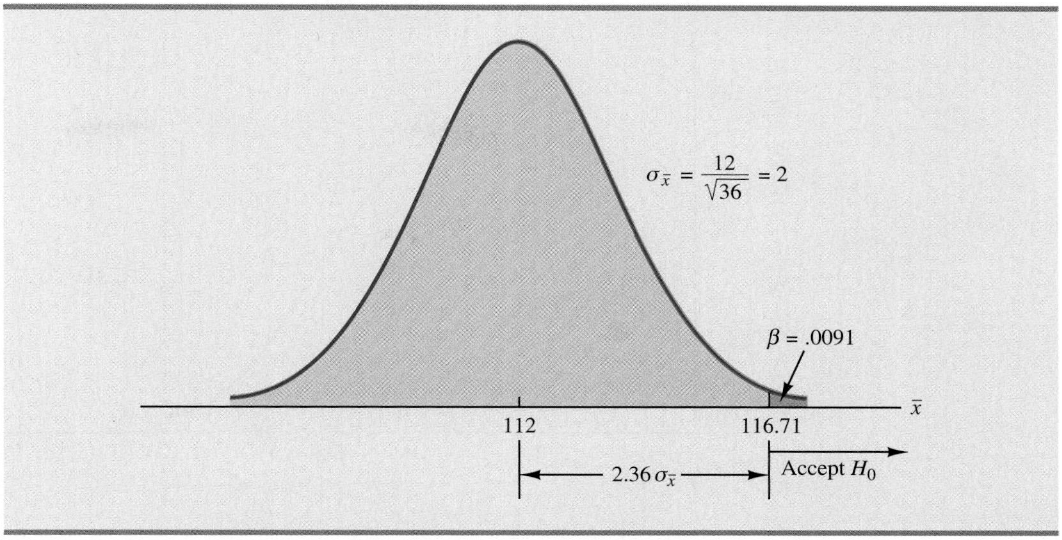

the shipment of batteries has a mean useful life of $\mu = 115$ hours. Because we will accept H_0 whenever $\bar{x} > 116.71$, the z value for $\mu = 115$ is given by

$$z = \frac{\bar{x} - \mu}{\sigma/\sqrt{n}} = \frac{116.71 - 115}{12/\sqrt{36}} = .86$$

From the standard normal probability table, we find that the area in the upper tail of the standard normal distribution for $z = .86$ is $1.0000 - .8051 = .1949$. Thus, the probability of making a Type II error is $\beta = .1949$ when the true mean is $\mu = 115$.

As Table 9.5 shows, the probability of a Type II error depends on the value of the population mean μ. For values of μ near μ_0, the probability of making the Type II error can be high.

In Table 9.5 we show the probability of making a Type II error for a variety of values of μ less than 120. Note that as μ increases toward 120, the probability of making a Type II error increases toward an upper bound of .95. However, as μ decreases to values farther below 120, the probability of making a Type II error diminishes. This pattern is what we should expect. When the true population mean μ is close to the null hypothesis value of $\mu = 120$, the probability is high that we will make a Type II error. However, when the true population mean μ is far below the null hypothesis value of $\mu = 120$, the probability is low that we will make a Type II error.

TABLE 9.5 PROBABILITY OF MAKING A TYPE II ERROR FOR THE LOT-ACCEPTANCE HYPOTHESIS TEST

Value of μ	$z = \frac{116.71 - \mu}{12/\sqrt{36}}$	**Probability of a Type II Error (β)**	**Power ($1 - \beta$)**
112	2.36	.0091	.9909
114	1.36	.0869	.9131
115	.86	.1949	.8051
116.71	.00	.5000	.5000
117	−.15	.5596	.4404
118	−.65	.7422	.2578
119.999	−1.645	.9500	.0500

FIGURE 9.9 POWER CURVE FOR THE LOT-ACCEPTANCE HYPOTHESIS TEST

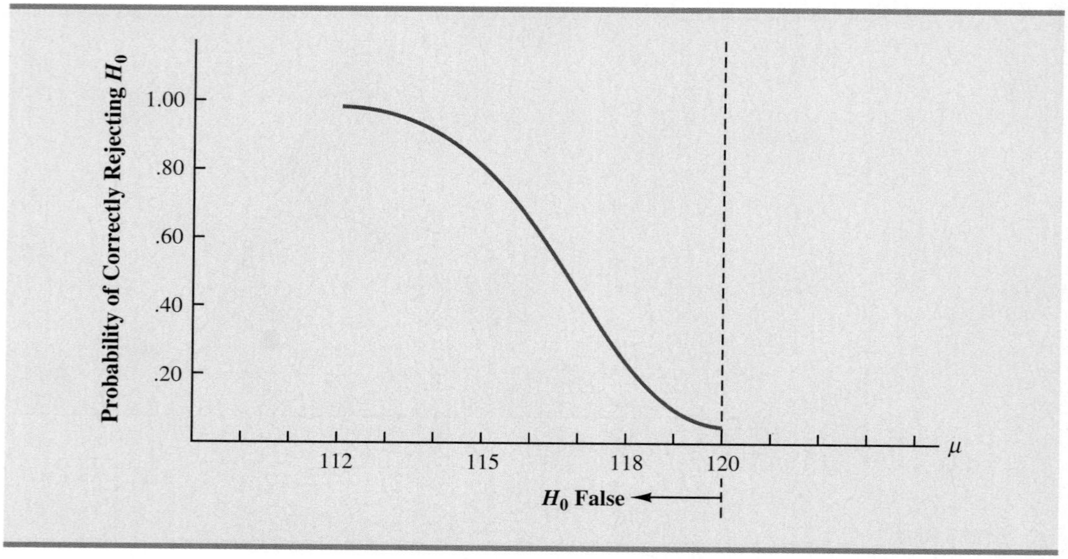

The probability of correctly rejecting H_0 when it is false is called the **power** of the test. For any particular value of μ, the power is $1 - \beta$; that is, the probability of correctly rejecting the null hypothesis is 1 minus the probability of making a Type II error. Values of power are also listed in Table 9.5. On the basis of these values, the power associated with each value of μ is shown graphically in Figure 9.9. Such a graph is called a **power curve**. Note that the power curve extends over the values of μ for which the null hypothesis is false. The height of the power curve at any value of μ indicates the probability of correctly rejecting H_0 when H_0 is false.*

In summary, the following step-by-step procedure can be used to compute the probability of making a Type II error in hypothesis tests about a population mean.

1. Formulate the null and alternative hypotheses.
2. Use the level of significance α and the critical value approach to determine the critical value and the rejection rule for the test.
3. Use the rejection rule to solve for the value of the sample mean corresponding to the critical value of the test statistic.
4. Use the results from step 3 to state the values of the sample mean that lead to the acceptance of H_0. These values define the acceptance region for the test.
5. Use the sampling distribution of $\bar{x}$ for a value of μ satisfying the alternative hypothesis, and the acceptance region from step 4, to compute the probability that the sample mean will be in the acceptance region. This probability is the probability of making a Type II error at the chosen value of μ.

Exercises

Methods

SELF test

46. Consider the following hypothesis test.

$$H_0: \mu \geq 10$$
$$H_a: \mu < 10$$

*Another graph, called the *operating characteristic curve,* is sometimes used to provide information about the probability of making a Type II error. The operating characteristic curve shows the probability of accepting H_0 and thus provides β for the values of μ where the null hypothesis is false. The probability of making a Type II error can be read directly from this graph.

The sample size is 120 and the population standard deviation is assumed known with $\sigma = 5$. Use $\alpha = .05$.

a. If the population mean is 9, what is the probability that the sample mean leads to the conclusion *do not reject* H_0?
b. What type of error would be made if the actual population mean is 9 and we conclude that H_0: $\mu \geq 10$ is true?
c. What is the probability of making a Type II error if the actual population mean is 8?

47. Consider the following hypothesis test.

$$H_0: \mu = 20$$
$$H_a: \mu \neq 20$$

A sample of 200 items will be taken and the population standard deviation is $\sigma = 10$. Use $\alpha = .05$. Compute the probability of making a Type II error if the population mean is:

a. $\mu = 18.0$
b. $\mu = 22.5$
c. $\mu = 21.0$

Applications

48. Fowle Marketing Research, Inc., bases charges to a client on the assumption that telephone surveys can be completed within 15 minutes or less. If more time is required, a premium rate is charged. With a sample of 35 surveys, a population standard deviation of 4 minutes, and a level of significance of .01, the sample mean will be used to test the null hypothesis H_0: $\mu \leq 15$.

a. What is your interpretation of the Type II error for this problem? What is its impact on the firm?
b. What is the probability of making a Type II error when the actual mean time is $\mu = 17$ minutes?
c. What is the probability of making a Type II error when the actual mean time is $\mu = 18$ minutes?
d. Sketch the general shape of the power curve for this test.

SELF test

49. A consumer research group is interested in testing an automobile manufacturer's claim that a new economy model will travel at least 25 miles per gallon of gasoline (H_0: $\mu \geq 25$).

a. With a .02 level of significance and a sample of 30 cars, what is the rejection rule based on the value of $\bar{x}$ for the test to determine whether the manufacturer's claim should be rejected? Assume that σ is 3 miles per gallon.
b. What is the probability of committing a Type II error if the actual mileage is 23 miles per gallon?
c. What is the probability of committing a Type II error if the actual mileage is 24 miles per gallon?
d. What is the probability of committing a Type II error if the actual mileage is 25.5 miles per gallon?

50. *Young Adult* magazine states the following hypotheses about the mean age of its subscribers.

$$H_0: \mu = 28$$
$$H_a: \mu \neq 28$$

a. What would it mean to make a Type II error in this situation?
b. The population standard deviation is assumed known at $\sigma = 6$ years and the sample size is 100. With $\alpha = .05$, what is the probability of accepting H_0 for μ equal to 26, 27, 29, and 30?
c. What is the power at $\mu = 26$? What does this result tell you?

51. A production line operation is tested for filling weight accuracy using the following hypotheses.

Hypothesis	Conclusion and Action
H_0: $\mu = 16$	Filling okay; keep running
H_a: $\mu \neq 16$	Filling off standard; stop and adjust machine

The sample size is 30 and the population standard deviation is $\sigma = .8$. Use $\alpha = .05$.

a. What would a Type II error mean in this situation?

b. What is the probability of making a Type II error when the machine is overfilling by .5 ounces?

c. What is the power of the statistical test when the machine is overfilling by .5 ounces?

d. Show the power curve for this hypothesis test. What information does it contain for the production manager?

52. Refer to Exercise 48. Assume the firm selects a sample of 50 surveys and repeat parts (b) and (c). What observation can you make about how increasing the sample size affects the probability of making a Type II error?

53. Sparr Investments, Inc., specializes in tax-deferred investment opportunities for its clients. Recently Sparr offered a payroll deduction investment program for the employees of a particular company. Sparr estimates that the employees are currently averaging \$100 or less per month in tax-deferred investments. A sample of 40 employees will be used to test Sparr's hypothesis about the current level of investment activity among the population of employees. Assume the employee monthly tax-deferred investment amounts have a standard deviation of \$75 and that a .05 level of significance will be used in the hypothesis test.

a. What is the Type II error in this situation?

b. What is the probability of the Type II error if the actual mean employee monthly investment is \$120?

c. What is the probability of the Type II error if the actual mean employee monthly investment is \$130?

d. Assume a sample size of 80 employees is used and repeat parts (b) and (c).

9.8 Determining the Sample Size for a Hypothesis Test About a Population Mean

Assume that a hypothesis test is to be conducted about the value of a population mean. The level of significance specified by the user determines the probability of making a Type I error for the test. By controlling the sample size, the user can also control the probability of making a Type II error. Let us show how a sample size can be determined for the following lower tail test about a population mean.

$$H_0: \mu \geq \mu_0$$
$$H_a: \mu < \mu_0$$

The upper panel of Figure 9.10 is the sampling distribution of $\bar{x}$ when H_0 is true with $\mu = \mu_0$. For a lower tail test, the critical value of the test statistic is denoted $-z_\alpha$. In the upper panel of the figure the vertical line, labeled c, is the corresponding value of $\bar{x}$. Note that, if we reject H_0 when $\bar{x} \leq c$, the probability of a Type I error will be α. With z_α representing the z value corresponding to an area of α in the upper tail of the standard normal distribution, we compute c using the following formula:

$$c = \mu_0 - z_\alpha \frac{\sigma}{\sqrt{n}} \qquad (9.5)$$

FIGURE 9.10 DETERMINING THE SAMPLE SIZE FOR SPECIFIED LEVELS OF THE TYPE I (α) AND TYPE II (β) ERRORS

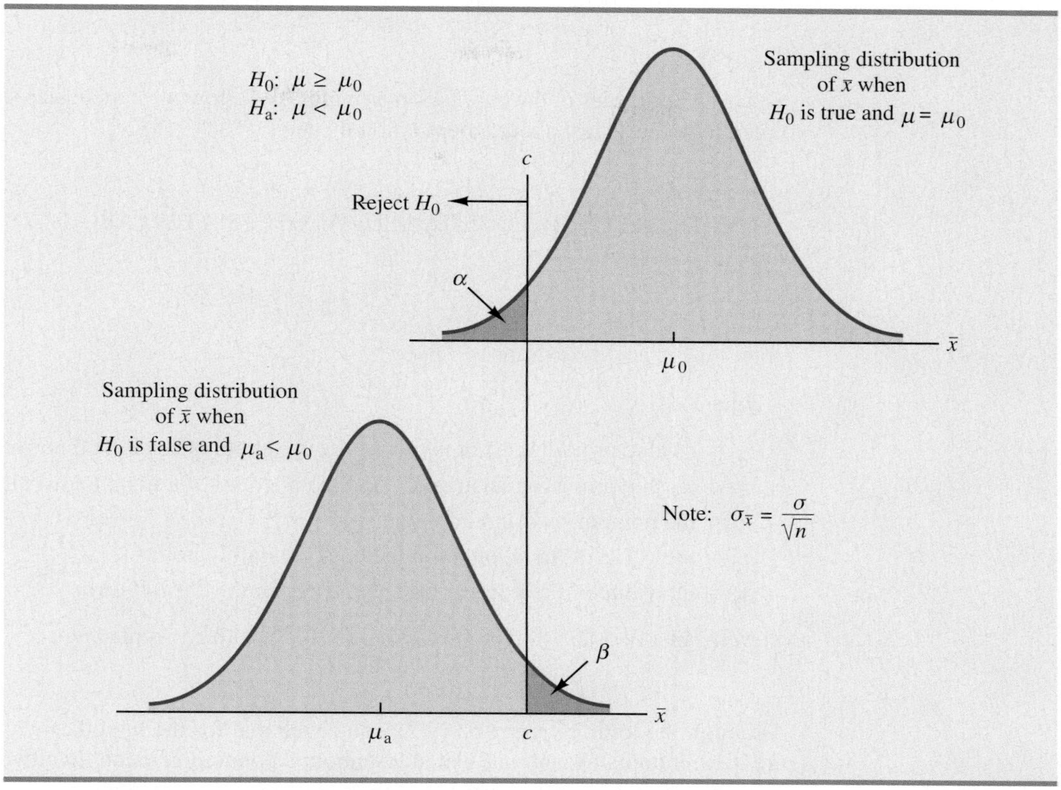

The lower panel of Figure 9.10 is the sampling distribution of $\bar{x}$ when the alternative hypothesis is true with $\mu = \mu_a < \mu_0$. The shaded region shows β, the probability of a Type II error that the decision maker will be exposed to if the null hypothesis is accepted when $\bar{x} > c$. With z_β representing the z value corresponding to an area of β in the upper tail of the standard normal distribution, we compute c using the following formula:

$$c = \mu_a + z_\beta \frac{\sigma}{\sqrt{n}} \tag{9.6}$$

Now what we want to do is to select a value for c so that when we reject H_0 and accept H_a, the probability of a Type I error is equal to the chosen value of α and the probability of a Type II error is equal to the chosen value of β. Therefore, both equations (9.5) and (9.6) must provide the same value for c, and the following equation must be true.

$$\mu_0 - z_\alpha \frac{\sigma}{\sqrt{n}} = \mu_a + z_\beta \frac{\sigma}{\sqrt{n}}$$

To determine the required sample size, we first solve for the $\sqrt{n}$ as follows.

$$\mu_0 - \mu_a = z_\alpha \frac{\sigma}{\sqrt{n}} + z_\beta \frac{\sigma}{\sqrt{n}}$$

$$\mu_0 - \mu_a = \frac{(z_\alpha + z_\beta)\sigma}{\sqrt{n}}$$

and

$$\sqrt{n} = \frac{(z_\alpha + z_\beta)\sigma}{(\mu_0 - \mu_a)}$$

Squaring both sides of the expression provides the following sample size formula for a one-tailed hypothesis test about a population mean.

SAMPLE SIZE FOR A ONE-TAILED HYPOTHESIS TEST ABOUT A POPULATION MEAN

$$n = \frac{(z_\alpha + z_\beta)^2\sigma^2}{(\mu_0 - \mu_a)^2} \tag{9.7}$$

where

z_α = z value providing an area of α in the upper tail of a standard normal distribution
z_β = z value providing an area of β in the upper tail of a standard normal distribution
σ = the population standard deviation
μ_0 = the value of the population mean in the null hypothesis
μ_a = the value of the population mean used for the Type II error

Note: In a two-tailed hypothesis test, use (9.7) with $z_{\alpha/2}$ replacing z_α.

Although the logic of equation (9.7) was developed for the hypothesis test shown in Figure 9.10, it holds for any one-tailed test about a population mean. In a two-tailed hypothesis test about a population mean, $z_{\alpha/2}$ is used instead of z_α in equation (9.7).

Let us return to the lot-acceptance example from Sections 9.6 and 9.7. The design specification for the shipment of batteries indicated a mean useful life of at least 120 hours for the batteries. Shipments were rejected if H_0: $\mu \geq 120$ was rejected. Let us assume that the quality control manager makes the following statements about the allowable probabilities for the Type I and Type II errors.

Type I error statement: If the mean life of the batteries in the shipment is $\mu = 120$, I am willing to risk an $\alpha = .05$ probability of rejecting the shipment.

Type II error statement: If the mean life of the batteries in the shipment is five hours under the specification (i.e., $\mu = 115$), I am willing to risk a $\beta = .10$ probability of accepting the shipment.

These statements are based on the judgment of the manager. Someone else might specify different restrictions on the probabilities. However, statements about the allowable probabilities of both errors must be made before the sample size can be determined.

In the example, $\alpha = .05$ and $\beta = .10$. Using the standard normal probability distribution, we have $z_{.05} = 1.645$ and $z_{.10} = 1.28$. From the statements about the error probabilities, we note that $\mu_0 = 120$ and $\mu_a = 115$. Finally, the population standard deviation was assumed known at $\sigma = 12$. By using equation (9.7), we find that the recommended sample size for the lot-acceptance example is

$$n = \frac{(1.645 + 1.28)^2(12)^2}{(120 - 115)^2} = 49.3$$

Rounding up, we recommend a sample size of 50.

Because both the Type I and Type II error probabilities have been controlled at allowable levels with $n = 50$, the quality control manager is now justified in using the *accept* H_0 and *reject* H_0 statements for the hypothesis test. The accompanying inferences are made with allowable probabilities of making Type I and Type II errors.

We can make three observations about the relationship among α, β, and the sample size n.

1. Once two of the three values are known, the other can be computed.
2. For a given level of significance α, increasing the sample size will reduce β.
3. For a given sample size, decreasing α will increase β, whereas increasing α will decrease β.

The third observation should be kept in mind when the probability of a Type II error is not being controlled. It suggests that one should not choose unnecessarily small values for the level of significance α. For a given sample size, choosing a smaller level of significance means more exposure to a Type II error. Inexperienced users of hypothesis testing often think that smaller values of α are always better. They are better if we are concerned only about making a Type I error. However, smaller values of α have the disadvantage of increasing the probability of making a Type II error.

Exercises

Methods

SELF test

54. Consider the following hypothesis test.

$$H_0: \mu \geq 10$$
$$H_a: \mu < 10$$

The sample size is 120 and the population standard deviation is 5. Use $\alpha = .05$. If the actual population mean is 9, the probability of a Type II error is .2912. Suppose the researcher wants to reduce the probability of a Type II error to .10 when the actual population mean is 9. What sample size is recommended?

55. Consider the following hypothesis test.

$$H_0: \mu = 20$$
$$H_a: \mu \neq 20$$

The population standard deviation is 10. Use $\alpha = .05$. How large a sample should be taken if the researcher is willing to accept a .05 probability of making a Type II error when the actual population mean is 22?

Applications

56. Suppose the project director for the Hilltop Coffee study (see Section 9.3) asked for a .10 probability of claiming that Hilltop was not in violation when it really was underfilling by 1 ounce ($\mu_a = 2.9375$ pounds). What sample size would have been recommended?

SELF test

57. A special industrial battery must have a life of at least 400 hours. A hypothesis test is to be conducted with a .02 level of significance. If the batteries from a particular production run have an actual mean use life of 385 hours, the production manager wants a sampling procedure that only 10% of the time would show erroneously that the batch is acceptable. What sample size is recommended for the hypothesis test? Use 30 hours as an estimate of the population standard deviation.

58. *Young Adult* magazine states the following hypotheses about the mean age of its subscribers.

$$H_0: \mu = 28$$
$$H_a: \mu \neq 28$$

If the manager conducting the test will permit a .15 probability of making a Type II error when the true mean age is 29, what sample size should be selected? Assume $\sigma = 6$ and a .05 level of significance.

59. An automobile mileage study tested the following hypotheses.

Hypothesis	**Conclusion**
$H_0: \mu \geq 25$ mpg	Manufacturer's claim supported
$H_a: \mu < 25$ mpg	Manufacturer's claim rejected; average mileage per gallon less than stated

For $\sigma = 3$ and a .02 level of significance, what sample size would be recommended if the researcher wants an 80% chance of detecting that μ is less than 25 miles per gallon when it is actually 24?

Summary

Hypothesis testing is a statistical procedure that uses sample data to determine whether a statement about the value of a population parameter should or should not be rejected. The hypotheses are two competing statements about a population parameter. One statement is called the null hypothesis (H_0), and the other statement is called the alternative hypothesis (H_a). In Section 9.1 we provided guidelines for developing hypotheses for three situations frequently encountered in practice.

Whenever historical data or other information provides a basis for assuming that the population standard deviation is known, the hypothesis testing procedure for the population mean is based on the standard normal distribution. Whenever σ is unknown, the sample standard deviation s is used to estimate σ and the hypothesis testing procedure is based on the t distribution. In both cases, the quality of results depends on both the form of the population distribution and the sample size. If the population has a normal distribution, both hypothesis testing procedures are applicable, even with small sample sizes. If the population is not normally distributed, larger sample sizes are needed. General guidelines about the sample size were provided in Sections 9.3 and 9.4. In the case of hypothesis tests about a population proportion, the hypothesis testing procedure uses a test statistic based on the standard normal distribution.

In all cases, the value of the test statistic can be used to compute a p-value for the test. A p-value is a probability used to determine whether the null hypothesis should be rejected. If the p-value is less than or equal to the level of significance α, the null hypothesis can be rejected.

Hypothesis testing conclusions can also be made by comparing the value of the test statistic to a critical value. For lower tail tests, the null hypothesis is rejected if the value of the test statistic is less than or equal to the critical value. For upper tail tests, the null hypothesis is rejected if the value of the test statistic is greater than or equal to the critical value. Two-tailed tests consist of two critical values: one in the lower tail of the sampling distribution and one in the upper tail. In this case, the null hypothesis is rejected if the value of the test statistic is less than or equal to the critical value in the lower tail or greater than or equal to the critical value in the upper tail.

Extensions of hypothesis testing procedures to include an analysis of the Type II error were also presented. In Section 9.7 we showed how to compute the probability of making a Type II error. In Section 9.8 we showed how to determine a sample size that will control for both the probability of making a Type I error and a Type II error.

Glossary

Null hypothesis The hypothesis tentatively assumed true in the hypothesis testing procedure.
Alternative hypothesis The hypothesis concluded to be true if the null hypothesis is rejected.
Type I error The error of rejecting H_0 when it is true.
Type II error The error of accepting H_0 when it is false.
Level of significance The probability of making a Type I error when the null hypothesis is true as an equality.
One-tailed test A hypothesis test in which rejection of the null hypothesis occurs for values of the test statistic in one tail of its sampling distribution.
Test statistic A statistic whose value helps determine whether a null hypothesis should be rejected.
***p*-value** A probability that provides a measure of the evidence against the null hypothesis given by the sample. Smaller p-values indicate more evidence against H_0. For a lower tail test, the p-value is the probability of obtaining a value for the test statistic as small as or smaller than that provided by the sample. For an upper tail test, the p-value is the probability of obtaining a value for the test statistic as large as or larger than that provided by the sample. For a two-tailed test, the p-value is the probability of obtaining a value for the test statistic at least as unlikely as or more unlikely than that provided by the sample.
Critical value A value that is compared with the test statistic to determine whether H_0 should be rejected.
Two-tailed test A hypothesis test in which rejection of the null hypothesis occurs for values of the test statistic in either tail of its sampling distribution.
Power The probability of correctly rejecting H_0 when it is false.
Power Curve A graph of the probability of rejecting H_0 for all possible values of the population parameter not satisfying the null hypothesis. The power curve provides the probability of correctly rejecting the null hypothesis.

Key Formulas

Test Statistic for Hypothesis Tests About a Population Mean: σ Known

$$z = \frac{\bar{x} - \mu_0}{\sigma/\sqrt{n}} \tag{9.1}$$

Test Statistic for Hypothesis Tests About a Population Mean: σ Unknown

$$t = \frac{\bar{x} - \mu_0}{s/\sqrt{n}} \tag{9.2}$$

Test Statistic for Hypothesis Tests About a Population Proportion

$$z = \frac{\bar{p} - p_0}{\sqrt{\dfrac{p_0(1 - p_0)}{n}}} \tag{9.4}$$

Sample Size for a One-Tailed Hypothesis Test About a Population Mean

$$n = \frac{(z_\alpha + z_\beta)^2\sigma^2}{(\mu_0 - \mu_a)^2} \tag{9.7}$$

In a two-tailed test, replace z_α with $z_{\alpha/2}$.

Supplementary Exercises

60. A production line operates with a mean filling weight of 16 ounces per container. Overfilling or underfilling presents a serious problem and when detected requires the operator to shut down the production line to readjust the filling mechanism. From past data, a population standard deviation $\sigma = .8$ ounces is assumed. A quality control inspector selects a sample of 30 items every hour and at that time makes the decision of whether to shut down the line for readjustment. The level of significance is $\alpha = .05$.
    a. State the hypothesis test for this quality control application.
    b. If a sample mean of $\bar{x} = 16.32$ ounces were found, what is the p-value? What action would you recommend?
    c. If a sample mean of $\bar{x} = 15.82$ ounces were found, what is the p-value? What action would you recommend?
    d. Use the critical value approach. What is the rejection rule for the preceding hypothesis testing procedure? Repeat parts (b) and (c). Do you reach the same conclusion?

61. At Western University the historical mean of scholarship examination scores for freshman applications is 900. A historical population standard deviation $\sigma = 180$ is assumed known. Each year, the assistant dean uses a sample of applications to determine whether the mean examination score for the new freshman applications has changed.
    a. State the hypotheses.
    b. What is the 95% confidence interval estimate of the population mean examination score if a sample of 200 applications provided a sample mean $\bar{x} = 935$?
    c. Use the confidence interval to conduct a hypothesis test. Using $\alpha = .05$, what is your conclusion?
    d. What is the p-value?

62. *Playbill* is a magazine distributed around the country to people attending musicals and other theatrical productions. The mean annual household income for the population of *Playbill* readers is \$119,155 (*Playbill,* January 2006). Assume the standard deviation is $\sigma = \$20{,}700$. A San Francisco civic group has asserted that the mean for theater goers in the Bay Area is higher. A sample of 60 theater attendees in the Bay Area showed a sample mean household income of \$126,100.
    a. Develop hypotheses that can be used to determine whether the sample data support the conclusion that theater attendees in the Bay Area have a higher mean household income than that for all *Playbill* readers.
    b. What is the p-value based on the sample of 60 theater attendees in the Bay Area?
    c. Use $\alpha = .01$ as the level of significance. What is your conclusion?

63. On Friday, Wall Street traders were anxiously awaiting the federal government's release of numbers on the January increase in nonfarm payrolls. The early consensus estimate among economists was for a growth of 250,000 new jobs (CNBC, February 3, 2006). However, a sample of 20 economists taken Thursday afternoon provided a sample mean of 266,000 with a sample standard deviation of 24,000. Financial analysts often call such a sample mean, based on late-breaking news, the *whisper number.* Treat the "consensus estimate" as the population mean. Conduct a hypothesis test to determine whether the whisper number justifies a conclusion of a statistically significant increase in the consensus estimate of economists. Use $\alpha = .01$ as the level of significance.

64. The College Board reported that the average number of freshman class applications to public colleges and universities is 6000 (*USA Today,* December 26, 2002). During a recent application/enrollment period, a sample of 32 colleges and universities showed that the sample mean number of freshman class applications was 5812 with a sample standard deviation of 1140. Do the data indicate a change in the mean number of applications? Use $\alpha = .05$.

65. An extensive study of the cost of health care in the United States presented data showing that the mean spending per Medicare enrollee in 2003 was \$6883 (*Money,* Fall 2003). To investigate differences across the country, a researcher took a sample of 40 Medicare

enrollees in Indianapolis. For the Indianapolis sample, the mean 2003 Medicare spending was \$5980 and the standard deviation was \$2518.

a. State the hypotheses that should be used if we would like to determine whether the mean annual Medicare spending in Indianapolis is lower than the national mean.
b. Use the preceding sample results to compute the test statistic and the p-value.
c. Use $\alpha = .05$. What is your conclusion?
d. Repeat the hypothesis test using the critical value approach.

66. The chamber of commerce of a Florida Gulf Coast community advertises that area residential property is available at a mean cost of \$125,000 or less per lot. Suppose a sample of 32 properties provided a sample mean of \$130,000 per lot and a sample standard deviation of \$12,500. Use a .05 level of significance to test the validity of the advertising claim.

CD file
Gasoline

67. The U.S. Energy Administration reported that the mean price for a gallon of regular gasoline in the United States was \$2.357 (U.S. Energy Administration, January 30, 2006). Data for a sample of regular gasoline prices at 50 service stations in the Lower Atlantic states are contained in the data file named Gasoline. Conduct a hypothesis test to determine whether the mean price for a gallon of gasoline in the Lower Atlantic states is different from the national mean. Use $\alpha = .05$ for the level of significance, and state your conclusion.

68. A study by the Center for Disease Control (CDC) found that 23.3% of adults are smokers and that roughly 70% of those who do smoke indicate that they want to quit (Associated Press, July 26, 2002). CDC reported that, of people who smoked at some point in their lives, 50% have been able to kick the habit. Part of the study suggested that the success rate for quitting rose by education level. Assume that a sample of 100 college graduates who smoked at some point in their lives showed that 64 had been able to successfully stop smoking.

a. State the hypotheses that can be used to determine whether the population of college graduates has a success rate higher than the overall population when it comes to breaking the smoking habit.
b. Given the sample data, what is the proportion of college graduates who, having smoked at some point in their lives, were able to stop smoking?
c. What is the p-value? At $\alpha = .01$, what is your hypothesis testing conclusion?

69. An airline promotion to business travelers is based on the assumption that two-thirds of business travelers use a laptop computer on overnight business trips.

a. State the hypotheses that can be used to test the assumption.
b. What is the sample proportion from an American Express sponsored survey that found 355 of 546 business travelers use a laptop computer on overnight business trips?
c. What is the p-value?
d. Use $\alpha = .05$. What is your conclusion?

70. Virtual call centers are staffed by individuals working out of their homes. Most home agents earn \$10 to \$15 per hour without benefits versus \$7 to \$9 per hour with benefits at a traditional call center (*BusinessWeek,* January 23, 2006). Regional Airways is considering employing home agents, but only if a level of customer satisfaction greater than 80% can be maintained. A test was conducted with home service agents. In a sample of 300 customers 252 reported that they were satisfied with service.

a. Develop hypotheses for a test to determine whether the sample data support the conclusion that customer service with home agents meets the Regional Airways criterion.
b. What is your point estimate of the percentage of satisfied customers?
c. What is the p-value provided by the sample data?
d. What is your hypothesis testing conclusion? Use $\alpha = .05$ as the level of significance.

71. During the 2004 election year, new polling results were reported daily. In an IBD/TIPP poll of 910 adults, 503 respondents reported that they were optimistic about the national outlook, and President Bush's leadership index jumped 4.7 points to 55.3 (*Investor's Business Daily,* January 14, 2004).

a. What is the sample proportion of respondents who are optimistic about the national outlook?

b. A campaign manager wants to claim that this poll indicates that the majority of adults are optimistic about the national outlook. Construct a hypothesis test so that rejection of the null hypothesis will permit the conclusion that the proportion optimistic is greater than 50%.

c. Use the polling data to compute the p-value for the hypothesis test in part (b). Explain to the manager what this p-value means about the level of significance of the results.

72. A radio station in Myrtle Beach announced that at least 90% of the hotels and motels would be full for the Memorial Day weekend. The station advised listeners to make reservations in advance if they planned to be in the resort over the weekend. On Saturday night a sample of 58 hotels and motels showed 49 with a no-vacancy sign and 9 with vacancies. What is your reaction to the radio station's claim after seeing the sample evidence? Use $\alpha = .05$ in making the statistical test. What is the p-value?

73. According to the federal government, 24% of workers covered by their company's health care plan were not required to contribute to the premium (*Statistical Abstract of the United States: 2006*). A recent study found that 81 out of 400 workers sampled were not required to contribute to their company's health care plan.

a. Develop hypotheses that can be used to test whether the percent of workers not required to contribute to their company's health care plan has declined.

b. What is a point estimate of the proportion receiving free company-sponsored health care insurance?

c. Has a statistically significant decline occurred in the proportion of workers receiving free company-sponsored health care insurance? Use $\alpha = .05$.

74. Shorney Construction Company bids on projects assuming that the mean idle time per worker is 72 or fewer minutes per day. A sample of 30 construction workers will be used to test this assumption. Assume that the population standard deviation is 20 minutes.

a. State the hypotheses to be tested.

b. What is the probability of making a Type II error when the population mean idle time is 80 minutes?

c. What is the probability of making a Type II error when the population mean idle time is 75 minutes?

d. What is the probability of making a Type II error when the population mean idle time is 70 minutes?

e. Sketch the power curve for this problem.

75. A federal funding program is available to low-income neighborhoods. To qualify for the funding, a neighborhood must have a mean household income of less than \$15,000 per year. Neighborhoods with mean annual household income of \$15,000 or more do not qualify. Funding decisions are based on a sample of residents in the neighborhood. A hypothesis test with a .02 level of significance is conducted. If the funding guidelines call for a maximum probability of .05 of not funding a neighborhood with a mean annual household income of \$14,000, what sample size should be used in the funding decision study? Use $\sigma = \$4000$ as a planning value.

76. H_0: $\mu = 120$ and H_a: $\mu \neq 120$ are used to test whether a bath soap production process is meeting the standard output of 120 bars per batch. Use a .05 level of significance for the test and a planning value of 5 for the standard deviation.

a. If the mean output drops to 117 bars per batch, the firm wants to have a 98% chance of concluding that the standard production output is not being met. How large a sample should be selected?

b. With your sample size from part (a), what is the probability of concluding that the process is operating satisfactorily for each of the following actual mean outputs: 117, 118, 119, 121, 122, and 123 bars per batch? That is, what is the probability of a Type II error in each case?

Case Problem 1 Quality Associates, Inc.

Quality Associates, Inc., a consulting firm, advises its clients about sampling and statistical procedures that can be used to control their manufacturing processes. In one particular application, a client gave Quality Associates a sample of 800 observations taken during a time in which that client's process was operating satisfactorily. The sample standard deviation for these data was .21; hence, with so much data, the population standard deviation was assumed to be .21. Quality Associates then suggested that random samples of size 30 be taken periodically to monitor the process on an ongoing basis. By analyzing the new samples, the client could quickly learn whether the process was operating satisfactorily. When the process was not operating satisfactorily, corrective action could be taken to eliminate the problem. The design specification indicated the mean for the process should be 12. The hypothesis test suggested by Quality Associates follows.

$$H_0\colon \mu = 12$$
$$H_a\colon \mu \neq 12$$

Corrective action will be taken any time H_0 is rejected.

The following samples were collected at hourly intervals during the first day of operation of the new statistical process control procedure. These data are available in the data set Quality.

CD file
Quality

Sample 1	Sample 2	Sample 3	Sample 4
11.55	11.62	11.91	12.02
11.62	11.69	11.36	12.02
11.52	11.59	11.75	12.05
11.75	11.82	11.95	12.18
11.90	11.97	12.14	12.11
11.64	11.71	11.72	12.07
11.80	11.87	11.61	12.05
12.03	12.10	11.85	11.64
11.94	12.01	12.16	12.39
11.92	11.99	11.91	11.65
12.13	12.20	12.12	12.11
12.09	12.16	11.61	11.90
11.93	12.00	12.21	12.22
12.21	12.28	11.56	11.88
12.32	12.39	11.95	12.03
11.93	12.00	12.01	12.35
11.85	11.92	12.06	12.09
11.76	11.83	11.76	11.77
12.16	12.23	11.82	12.20
11.77	11.84	12.12	11.79
12.00	12.07	11.60	12.30
12.04	12.11	11.95	12.27
11.98	12.05	11.96	12.29
12.30	12.37	12.22	12.47
12.18	12.25	11.75	12.03
11.97	12.04	11.96	12.17
12.17	12.24	11.95	11.94
11.85	11.92	11.89	11.97
12.30	12.37	11.88	12.23
12.15	12.22	11.93	12.25

Managerial Report

1. Conduct a hypothesis test for each sample at the .01 level of significance and determine what action, if any, should be taken. Provide the test statistic and p-value for each test.
2. Compute the standard deviation for each of the four samples. Does the assumption of .21 for the population standard deviation appear reasonable?
3. Compute limits for the sample mean $\bar{x}$ around $\mu = 12$ such that, as long as a new sample mean is within those limits, the process will be considered to be operating satisfactorily. If $\bar{x}$ exceeds the upper limit or if $\bar{x}$ is below the lower limit, corrective action will be taken. These limits are referred to as upper and lower control limits for quality control purposes.
4. Discuss the implications of changing the level of significance to a larger value. What mistake or error could increase if the level of significance is increased?

Case Problem 2 Unemployment Study

Each month the U.S. Bureau of Labor Statistics publishes a variety of unemployment statistics, including the number of individuals who are unemployed and the mean length of time the individuals have been unemployed. For November 1998, the Bureau of Labor Statistics reported that the national mean length of time of unemployment was 14.6 weeks.

The mayor of Philadelphia requested a study on the status of unemployment in the Philadelphia area. A sample of 50 unemployed residents of Philadelphia included data on their age and the number of weeks without a job. A portion of the data collected in November 1998 follows. The complete data set is available in the data file BLS.

CD file

BLS

Age	Weeks	Age	Weeks	Age	Weeks
56	22	22	11	25	12
35	19	48	6	25	1
22	7	48	22	59	33
57	37	25	5	49	26
40	18	40	20	33	13

Managerial Report

1. Use descriptive statistics to summarize the data.
2. Develop a 95% confidence interval estimate of the mean age of unemployed individuals in Philadelphia.
3. Conduct a hypothesis test to determine whether the mean duration of unemployment in Philadelphia is greater than the national mean duration of 14.6 weeks. Use a .01 level of significance. What is your conclusion?
4. Is there a relationship between the age of an unemployed individual and the number of weeks of unemployment? Explain.

Appendix 9.1 Hypothesis Testing with Minitab

We describe the use of Minitab to conduct hypothesis tests about a population mean and a population proportion.

Population Mean: σ Known

We illustrate using the MaxFlight golf ball distance example in Section 9.3. The data are in column C1 of a Minitab worksheet. The population standard deviation $\sigma = 12$ is assumed known and the level of significance is $\alpha = .05$. The following steps can be used to test the hypothesis H_0: $\mu = 295$ versus H_a: $\mu \neq 295$.

CD file
GolfTest

Step 1. Select the **Stat** menu
Step 2. Choose **Basic Statistics**
Step 3. Choose **1-Sample Z**
Step 4. When the 1-Sample Z dialog box appears:
Enter C1 in the **Samples in columns** box
Enter 12 in the **Standard deviation** box
Enter 295 in the **Test mean** box
Select **Options**
Step 5. When the 1-Sample Z-Options dialog box appears:
Enter 95 in the **Confidence level** box*
Select **not equal** in the **Alternative** box
Click **OK**
Step 6. Click **OK**

In addition to the hypothesis testing results, Minitab provides a 95% confidence interval for the population mean.

The procedure can be easily modified for a one-tailed hypothesis test by selecting the less than or greater than option in the **Alternative** box in step 5.

Population Mean: σ Unknown

CD file
AirRating

The ratings that 60 business travelers gave for Heathrow Airport are entered in column C1 of a Minitab worksheet. The level of significance for the test is $\alpha = .05$, and the population standard deviation σ will be estimated by the sample standard deviation s. The following steps can be used to test the hypothesis H_0: $\mu \leq 7$ against H_a: $\mu > 7$.

Step 1. Select the **Stat** menu
Step 2. Choose **Basic Statistics**
Step 3. Choose **1-Sample t**
Step 4. When the 1-Sample t dialog box appears:
Enter C1 in the **Samples in columns** box
Enter 7 in the **Test mean** box
Select **Options**
Step 5. When the 1-Sample t-options dialog box appears:
Enter 95 in the **Confidence level** box
Select **greater than** in the **Alternative** box
Click **OK**
Step 6. Click **OK**

The Heathrow Airport rating study involved a greater than alternative hypothesis. The preceding steps can be easily modified for other hypothesis tests by selecting the less than or not equal options in the **Alternative** box in step 5.

Population Proportion

CD file
WomenGolf

We illustrate using the Pine Creek golf course example in Section 9.5. The data with responses Female and Male are in column C1 of a Minitab worksheet. Minitab uses an alphabetical ordering of the responses and selects the *second response* for the population

*Minitab provides both hypothesis testing and interval estimation results simultaneously. The user may select any confidence level for the interval estimate of the population mean: 95% confidence is suggested here.

proportion of interest. In this example, Minitab uses the alphabetical ordering Female-Male to provide results for the population proportion of Male responses. Because Female is the response of interest, we change Minitab's ordering as follows: Select any cell in the column and use the sequence: Editor > Column > Value Order. Then choose the option of entering a user-specified order. Enter Male-Female in the **Define-an-order** box and click OK. Minitab's 1 Proportion routine will then provide the hypothesis test results for the population proportion of female golfers. We proceed as follows:

Step 1. Select the **Stat** menu
Step 2. Choose **Basic Statistics**
Step 3. Choose **1 Proportion**
Step 4. When the 1 Proportion dialog box appears:
Enter C1 in the **Samples in Columns** box
Select **Options**
Step 5. When the 1 Proportion-Options dialog box appears:
Enter 95 in the **Confidence level** box
Enter .20 in the **Test proportion** box
Select greater than in the **Alternative** box
Select **Use test and interval based on normal distribution**
Click **OK**
Step 6. Click **OK**

Appendix 9.2 Hypothesis Testing with Excel

Excel does not provide built-in routines for the hypothesis tests presented in this chapter. To handle these situations, we present Excel worksheets that we designed to test hypotheses about a population mean and a population proportion. The worksheets are easy to use and can be modified to handle any sample data. The worksheets are available on the CD that accompanies this book.

Population Mean: σ Known

We illustrate using the MaxFlight golf ball distance example in Section 9.3. The data are in column A of an Excel worksheet. The population standard deviation $\sigma = 12$ is assumed known and the level of significance is $\alpha = .05$. The following steps can be used to test the hypothesis H_0: $\mu = 295$ versus H_a: $\mu \neq 295$.

CD file
Hyp Sigma Known

Refer to Figure 9.11 as we describe the procedure. The worksheet in the background shows the cell formulas used to compute the results shown in the foreground worksheet. The data are entered into cells A2:A51. The following steps are necessary to use the template for this data set.

Step 1. Enter the data range A2:A51 into the =COUNT cell formula in cell D4
Step 2. Enter the data range A2:A51 into the =AVERAGE cell formula in cell D5
Step 3. Enter the population standard deviation $\sigma = 12$ into cell D6
Step 4. Enter the hypothesized value for the population mean 295 into cell D8

The remaining cell formulas automatically provide the standard error, the value of the test statistic z, and three p-values. Because the alternative hypothesis ($\mu_0 \neq 295$) indicates a two-tailed test, the p-value (Two Tail) in cell D15 is used to make the rejection decision. With p-value $= .1255 > \alpha = .05$, the null hypothesis cannot be rejected. The p-values in cells D13 or D14 would be used if the hypotheses involved a one-tailed test.

FIGURE 9.11 EXCEL WORKSHEET FOR HYPOTHESIS TESTS ABOUT A POPULATION MEAN WITH σ KNOWN

	A	B	C	D	E
1	Yards		Hypothesis Test About a Population Mean		
2	303		With σ Known		
3	282				
4	289		Sample Size	=COUNT(A2:A51)	
5	298		Sample Mean	=AVERAGE(A2:A51)	
6	283		Population Std. Deviation	12	
7	317				
8	297		Hypothesized Value	295	
9	308				
10	317		Standard Error	=D6/SQRT(D4)	
11	293		Test Statistic z	=(D5-D8)/D10	
12	284				
13	290		p-value (Lower Tail)	=NORMSDIST(D11)	
14	304		p-value (Upper Tail)	=1-D13	
15	290		p-value (Two Tail)	=2*MIN(D13,D14)	
16	311				
17	305				
49	303				
50	301				
51	292				
52					

	A	B	C	D	E
1	Yards		Hypothesis Test About a Population Mean		
2	303		With σ Known		
3	282				
4	289		Sample Size	50	
5	298		Sample Mean	297.6	
6	283		Population Std. Deviation	12	
7	317				
8	297		Hypothesized Value	295	
9	308				
10	317		Standard Error	1.70	
11	293		Test Statistic z	1.53	
12	284				
13	290		p-value (Lower Tail)	0.9372	
14	304		p-value (Upper Tail)	0.0628	
15	290		p-value (Two Tail)	0.1255	
16	311				
17	305				
49	303				
50	301				
51	292				
52					

Note: Rows 18 to 48 are hidden.

This template can be used to make hypothesis testing computations for other applications. For instance, to conduct a hypothesis test for a new data set, enter the new sample data into column A of the worksheet. Modify the formulas in cells D4 and D5 to correspond to the new data range. Enter the population standard deviation into cell D6 and the hypothesized value for the population mean into cell D8 to obtain the results. If the new sample data have already been summarized, the new sample data do not have to be entered into the worksheet. In this case, enter the sample size into cell D4, the sample mean into cell D5, the population standard deviation into cell D6, and the hypothesized value for the population mean into cell D8 to obtain the results. The worksheet in Figure 9.11 is available in the file Hyp Sigma Known on the CD that accompanies this book.

Population Mean: σ Unknown

We illustrate using the Heathrow Airport rating example in Section 9.4. The data are in column A of an Excel worksheet. The population standard deviation σ is unknown and will be estimated by the sample standard deviation s. The level of significance is $\alpha = .05$. The following steps can be used to test the hypothesis H_0: $\mu \leq 7$ versus H_a: $\mu > 7$.

CD file
Hyp Sigma Unknown

Refer to Figure 9.12 as we describe the procedure. The background worksheet shows the cell formulas used to compute the results shown in the foreground version of the worksheet. The data are entered into cells A2:A61. The following steps are necessary to use the template for this data set.

Step 1. Enter the data range A2:A61 into the =COUNT cell formula in cell D4
Step 2. Enter the data range A2:A61 into the =AVERAGE cell formula in cell D5
Step 3. Enter the data range A2:A61 into the =STDEV cell formula in cell D6
Step 4. Enter the hypothesized value for the population mean 7 into cell D8

The remaining cell formulas automatically provide the standard error, the value of the test statistic t, the number of degrees of freedom, and three p-values. Because the alternative hypothesis ($\mu > 7$) indicates an upper tail test, the p-value (Upper Tail) in cell D15 is used to make the decision. With p-value $= .0353 < \alpha = .05$, the null hypothesis is rejected. The p-values in cells D14 or D16 would be used if the hypotheses involved a lower tail test or a two-tailed test.

This template can be used to make hypothesis testing computations for other applications. For instance, to conduct a hypothesis test for a new data set, enter the new sample data into column A of the worksheet and modify the formulas in cells D4, D5, and D6 to correspond to the new data range. Enter the hypothesized value for the population mean into cell D8 to obtain the results. If the new sample data have already been summarized, the new sample data do not have to be entered into the worksheet. In this case, enter the sample size into cell D4, the sample mean into cell D5, the sample standard deviation into cell D6, and the hypothesized value for the population mean into cell D8 to obtain the results. The worksheet in Figure 9.12 is available in the file Hyp Sigma Unknown on the CD that accompanies this book.

Population Proportion

CD file
Hypothesis p

We illustrate using the Pine Creek golf course survey data presented in Section 9.5. The data of Male or Female golfer are in column A of an Excel worksheet. Refer to Figure 9.13 as we describe the procedure. The background worksheet shows the cell formulas used to compute the results shown in the foreground worksheet. The data are entered into cells A2:A401. The following steps can be used to test the hypothesis H_0: $p \leq .20$ versus H_a: $p > .20$.

Step 1. Enter the data range A2:A401 into the =COUNTA cell formula in cell D3
Step 2. Enter Female as the response of interest in cell D4
Step 3. Enter the data range A2:A401 into the =COUNTIF cell formula in cell D5
Step 4. Enter the hypothesized value for the population proportion .20 into cell D8

The remaining cell formulas automatically provide the standard error, the value of the test statistic z, and three p-values. Because the alternative hypothesis ($p_0 > .20$)

FIGURE 9.12 EXCEL WORKSHEET FOR HYPOTHESIS TESTS ABOUT A POPULATION MEAN WITH σ UNKNOWN

	A	B	C	D	E
1	Rating		Hypothesis Test About a Population Mean		
2	5		With σ Unknown		
3	7				
4	8		Sample Size	=COUNT(A2:A61)	
5	7		Sample Mean	=AVERAGE(A2:A61)	
6	8		Sample Std. Deviation	=STDEV(A2:A61)	
7	8				
8	8		Hypothesized Value	7	
9	7				
10	8		Standard Error	=D6/SQRT(D4)	
11	10		Test Statistic *t*	=(D5-D8)/D10	
12	6		Degrees of Freedom	=D4-1	
13	7				
14	8		*p*-value (Lower Tail)	=IF(D11<0,TDIST(-D11,D12,1),1-TDIST(D11,D12,1))	
15	8		*p*-value (Upper Tail)	=1-D14	
16	9		*p*-value (Two Tail)	=2*MIN(D14,D15)	
17	7				
59	7				
60	7				
61	8				
62					

	A	B	C	D	E
1	Rating		Hypothesis Test About a Population Mean		
2	5		With σ Unknown		
3	7				
4	8		Sample Size	60	
5	7		Sample Mean	7.25	
6	8		Sample Std. Deviation	1.05	
7	8				
8	8		Hypothesized Value	7	
9	7				
10	8		Standard Error	0.136	
11	10		Test Statistic *t*	1.841	
12	6		Degrees of Freedom	59	
13	7				
14	8		*p*-value (Lower Tail)	0.9647	
15	8		*p*-value (Upper Tail)	0.0353	
16	9		*p*-value (Two Tail)	0.0706	
17	7				
59	7				
60	7				
61	8				
62					

Note: Rows 18 to 58 are hidden.

indicates an upper tail test, the p-value (Upper Tail) in cell D14 is used to make the decision. With p-value $= .0062 < \alpha = .05$, the null hypothesis is rejected. The p-values in cells D13 or D15 would be used if the hypothesis involved a lower tail test or a two-tailed test.

This template can be used to make hypothesis testing computations for other applications. For instance, to conduct a hypothesis test for a new data set, enter the new sample data into column A of the worksheet. Modify the formulas in cells D3 and D5 to correspond to the new data range. Enter the response of interest into cell D4 and the hypothesized value for the population proportion into cell D8 to obtain the results. If the new sample data have

FIGURE 9.13 EXCEL WORKSHEET FOR HYPOTHESIS TESTS ABOUT A POPULATION PROPORTION

	A	B	C	D	E
1	**Golfer**		**Hypothesis Test About a Population Proportion**		
2	Female				
3	Male		**Sample Size**	=COUNTA(A2:A401)	
4	Female		**Response of Interest**	Female	
5	Male		**Count for Response**	=COUNTIF(A2:A401,D4)	
6	Male		**Sample Proportion**	=D5/D3	
7	Female				
8	Male		**Hypothesized Value**	0.20	
9	Male				
10	Female		**Standard Error**	=SQRT(D8*(1-D8)/D3)	
11	Male		**Test Statistic *z***	=(D6-D8)/D10	
12	Male				
13	Male		***p*-value (Lower Tail)**	=NORMSDIST(D11)	
14	Male		***p*-value (Upper Tail)**	=1-D13	
15	Male		***p*-value (Two Tail)**	=2*MIN(D13,D14)	
16	Female				
400	Male				
401	Male				
402					

	A	B	C	D	E
1	**Golfer**		**Hypothesis Test About a Population Proportion**		
2	Female				
3	Male		**Sample Size**	400	
4	Female		**Response of Interest**	Female	
5	Male		**Count for Response**	100	
6	Male		**Sample Proportion**	0.2500	
7	Female				
8	Male		**Hypothesized Value**	0.20	
9	Male				
10	Female		**Standard Error**	0.0200	
11	Male		**Test Statistic *z***	2.50	
12	Male				
13	Male		***p*-value (Lower Tail)**	0.9938	
14	Male		***p*-value (Upper Tail)**	0.0062	
15	Male		***p*-value (Two Tail)**	0.0124	
16	Female				
400	Male				
401	Male				
402					

Note: Rows 17 to 399 are hidden.

already been summarized, the new sample data do not have to be entered into the worksheet. In this case, enter the sample size into cell D3, the sample proportion into cell D6, and the hypothesized value for the population proportion into cell D8 to obtain the results. The worksheet in Figure 9.13 is available in the file Hypothesis p on the CD that accompanies this book.

CHAPTER 10

Statistical Inference About Means and Proportions with Two Populations

CONTENTS

STATISTICS *in* PRACTICE

U.S. FOOD AND DRUG ADMINISTRATION
WASHINGTON, D.C.

It is the responsibility of the U.S. Food and Drug Administration (FDA), through its Center for Drug Evaluation and Research (CDER), to ensure that drugs are safe and effective. But CDER does not do the actual testing of new drugs itself. It is the responsibility of the company seeking to market a new drug to test it and submit evidence that it is safe and effective. CDER statisticians and scientists then review the evidence submitted.

Companies seeking approval of a new drug conduct extensive statistical studies to support their application. The testing process in the pharmaceutical industry usually consists of three stages: (1) preclinical testing, (2) testing for long-term usage and safety, and (3) clinical efficacy testing. At each successive stage, the chance that a drug will pass the rigorous tests decreases; however, the cost of further testing increases dramatically. Industry surveys indicate that on average the research and development for one new drug costs $250 million and takes 12 years. Hence, it is important to eliminate unsuccessful new drugs in the early stages of the testing process, as well as to identify promising ones for further testing.

Statistics plays a major role in pharmaceutical research, where government regulations are stringent and rigorously enforced. In preclinical testing, a two- or three-population statistical study typically is used to determine whether a new drug should continue to be studied in the long-term usage and safety program. The populations may consist of the new drug, a control, and a standard drug. The preclinical testing process begins when a new drug is sent to the pharmacology group for evaluation of efficacy—the capacity of the drug to produce the desired effects. As part of the process, a statistician is asked to design an experiment that can be used to test the new drug. The design must specify the sample size and the statistical methods of analysis. In a two-population study, one sample is used to obtain data on the efficacy of the new drug (population 1) and a second sample is used to obtain data on the efficacy of a standard drug (population 2). Depending on the intended use, the new and standard drugs are tested in such disciplines as neurology, cardiology, and immunology. In most studies, the statistical method involves hypothesis testing for the difference between the means of the new drug population and the standard drug population. If a new drug lacks efficacy or produces undesirable effects in comparison with the standard drug, the new drug is rejected and withdrawn from further testing. Only new drugs that show promising comparisons with the standard drugs are forwarded to the long-term usage and safety testing program.

Statistical methods are used to test and develop new drugs. © Lester Lefkowitz/CORBIS.

Further data collection and multipopulation studies are conducted in the long-term usage and safety testing program and in the clinical testing programs. The FDA requires that statistical methods be defined prior to such testing to avoid data-related biases. In addition, to avoid human biases, some of the clinical trials are double or triple blind. That is, neither the subject nor the investigator knows what drug is administered to whom. If the new drug meets all requirements in relation to the standard drug, a new drug application (NDA) is filed with the FDA. The application is rigorously scrutinized by statisticians and scientists at the agency.

In this chapter you will learn how to construct interval estimates and make hypothesis tests about means and proportions with two populations. Techniques will be presented for analyzing independent random samples as well as matched samples.

In Chapters 8 and 9 we showed how to develop interval estimates and conduct hypothesis tests for situations involving a single population mean and a single population proportion. In this chapter we continue our discussion of statistical inference by showing how interval estimates and hypothesis tests can be developed for situations involving two populations when the difference between the two population means or the two population proportions is of prime importance. For example, we may want to develop an interval estimate of the difference between the mean starting salary for a population of men and the mean starting salary for a population of women or conduct a hypothesis test to determine whether any difference is present between the proportion of defective parts in a population of parts produced by supplier A and the proportion of defective parts in a population of parts produced by supplier B. We begin our discussion of statistical inference about two populations by showing how to develop interval estimates and conduct hypothesis tests about the difference between the means of two populations when the standard deviations of the two populations are assumed known.

10.1 Inferences About the Difference Between Two Population Means: σ_1 and σ_2 Known

Letting μ_1 denote the mean of population 1 and μ_2 denote the mean of population 2, we will focus on inferences about the difference between the means: $\mu_1 - \mu_2$. To make an inference about this difference, we select a simple random sample of n_1 units from population 1 and a second simple random sample of n_2 units from population 2. The two samples, taken separately and independently, are referred to as **independent simple random samples**. In this section, we assume that information is available such that the two population standard deviations, σ_1 and σ_2, can be assumed known prior to collecting the samples. We refer to this situation as the σ_1 and σ_2 known case. In the following example we show how to compute a margin of error and develop an interval estimate of the difference between the two population means when σ_1 and σ_2 are known.

Interval Estimation of $\mu_1 - \mu_2$

Greystone Department Stores, Inc., operates two stores in Buffalo, New York: one is in the inner city and the other is in a suburban shopping center. The regional manager noticed that products that sell well in one store do not always sell well in the other. The manager believes this situation may be attributable to differences in customer demographics at the two locations. Customers may differ in age, education, income, and so on. Suppose the manager asks us to investigate the difference between the mean ages of the customers who shop at the two stores.

Let us define population 1 as all customers who shop at the inner-city store and population 2 as all customers who shop at the suburban store.

μ_1 = mean of population 1 (i.e., the mean age of all customers who shop at the inner-city store)

μ_2 = mean of population 2 (i.e., the mean age of all customers who shop at the suburban store)

The difference between the two population means is $\mu_1 - \mu_2$.

To estimate $\mu_1 - \mu_2$, we will select a simple random sample of n_1 customers from population 1 and a simple random sample of n_2 customers from population 2. We then compute the two sample means.

$\bar{x}_1$ = sample mean age for the simple random sample of n_1 inner-city customers

$\bar{x}_2$ = sample mean age for the simple random sample of n_2 suburban customers

The point estimator of the difference between the two population means is the difference between the two sample means.

POINT ESTIMATOR OF THE DIFFERENCE BETWEEN TWO POPULATION MEANS

$$\bar{x}_1 - \bar{x}_2 \tag{10.1}$$

Figure 10.1 provides an overview of the process used to estimate the difference between two population means based on two independent simple random samples.

The standard error of $\bar{x}_1 - \bar{x}_2$ is the standard deviation of the sampling distribution of $\bar{x}_1 - \bar{x}_2$.

As with other point estimators, the point estimator $\bar{x}_1 - \bar{x}_2$ has a standard error that describes the variation in the sampling distribution of the estimator. With two independent simple random samples, the standard error of $\bar{x}_1 - \bar{x}_2$ is as follows:

STANDARD ERROR OF $\bar{x}_1 - \bar{x}_2$

$$\sigma_{\bar{x}_1 - \bar{x}_2} = \sqrt{\frac{\sigma_1^2}{n_1} + \frac{\sigma_2^2}{n_2}} \tag{10.2}$$

If both populations have a normal distribution, or if the sample sizes are large enough that the central limit theorem enables us to conclude that the sampling distributions of $\bar{x}_1$ and $\bar{x}_2$ can be approximated by a normal distribution, the sampling distribution of $\bar{x}_1 - \bar{x}_2$ will have a normal distribution with mean given by $\mu_1 - \mu_2$.

As we showed in Chapter 8, an interval estimate is given by a point estimate $\pm$ a margin of error. In the case of estimation of the difference between two population means, an interval estimate will take the following form:

$$\bar{x}_1 - \bar{x}_2 \pm \text{Margin of error}$$

FIGURE 10.1 ESTIMATING THE DIFFERENCE BETWEEN TWO POPULATION MEANS

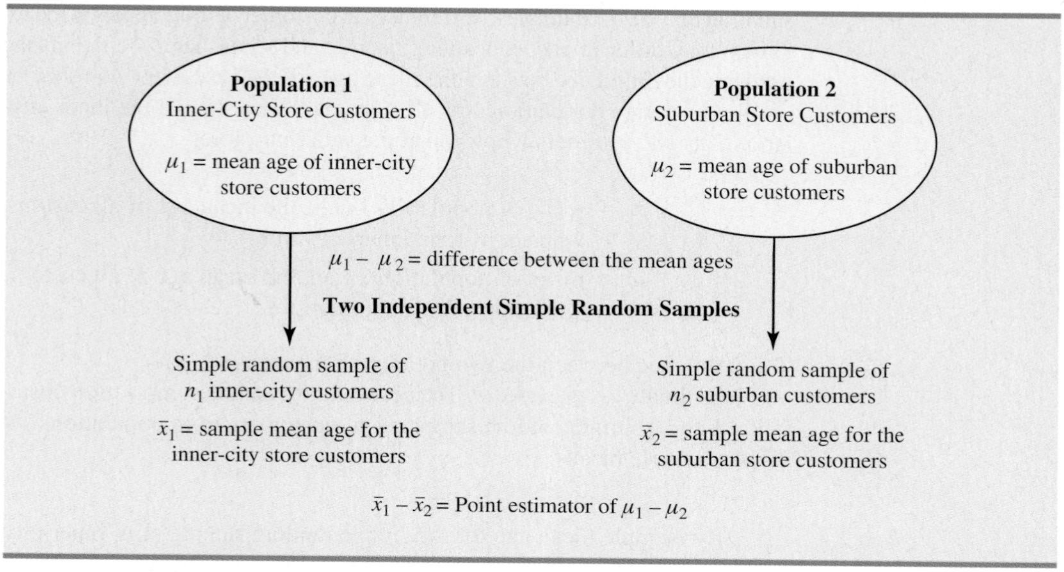

With the sampling distribution of $\bar{x}_1 - \bar{x}_2$ having a normal distribution, we can write the margin of error as follows:

The margin of error is given by multiplying the standard error by $z_{\alpha/2}$.

$$\text{Margin of error} = z_{\alpha/2}\sigma_{\bar{x}_1-\bar{x}_2} = z_{\alpha/2}\sqrt{\frac{\sigma_1^2}{n_1} + \frac{\sigma_2^2}{n_2}} \quad (10.3)$$

Thus the interval estimate of the difference between two population means is as follows:

INTERVAL ESTIMATE OF THE DIFFERENCE BETWEEN TWO POPULATION MEANS: σ_1 AND σ_2 KNOWN

$$\bar{x}_1 - \bar{x}_2 \pm z_{\alpha/2}\sqrt{\frac{\sigma_1^2}{n_1} + \frac{\sigma_2^2}{n_2}} \quad (10.4)$$

where $1 - \alpha$ is the confidence coefficient.

Let us return to the Greystone example. Based on data from previous customer demographic studies, the two population standard deviations are known with $\sigma_1 = 9$ years and $\sigma_2 = 10$ years. The data collected from the two independent simple random samples of Greystone customers provided the following results.

	Inner City Store	**Suburban Store**
Sample Size	$n_1 = 36$	$n_2 = 49$
Sample Mean	$\bar{x}_1 = 40$ years	$\bar{x}_2 = 35$ years

Using expression (10.1), we find that the point estimate of the difference between the mean ages of the two populations is $\bar{x}_1 - \bar{x}_2 = 40 - 35 = 5$ years. Thus, we estimate that the customers at the inner-city store have a mean age five years greater than the mean age of the suburban store customers. We can now use expression (10.4) to compute the margin of error and provide the interval estimate of $\mu_1 - \mu_2$. Using 95% confidence and $z_{\alpha/2} = z_{.025} = 1.96$, we have

$$\bar{x}_1 - \bar{x}_2 \pm z_{\alpha/2}\sqrt{\frac{\sigma_1^2}{n_1} + \frac{\sigma_2^2}{n_2}}$$

$$40 - 35 \pm 1.96\sqrt{\frac{9^2}{36} + \frac{10^2}{49}}$$

$$5 \pm 4.06$$

Thus, the margin of error is 4.06 years and the 95% confidence interval estimate of the difference between the two population means is $5 - 4.06 = .94$ years to $5 + 4.06 = 9.06$ years.

Hypothesis Tests About $\mu_1 - \mu_2$

Let us consider hypothesis tests about the difference between two population means. Using D_0 to denote the hypothesized difference between μ_1 and μ_2, the three forms for a hypothesis test are as follows:

$$H_0: \mu_1 - \mu_2 \geq D_0 \qquad H_0: \mu_1 - \mu_2 \leq D_0 \qquad H_0: \mu_1 - \mu_2 = D_0$$
$$H_a: \mu_1 - \mu_2 < D_0 \qquad H_a: \mu_1 - \mu_2 > D_0 \qquad H_a: \mu_1 - \mu_2 \neq D_0$$

In many applications, $D_0 = 0$. Using the two-tailed test as an example, when $D_0 = 0$ the null hypothesis is H_0: $\mu_1 - \mu_2 = 0$. In this case, the null hypothesis is that μ_1 and μ_2 are equal. Rejection of H_0 leads to the conclusion that H_a: $\mu_1 - \mu_2 \neq 0$ is true; that is, μ_1 and μ_2 are not equal.

The steps for conducting hypothesis tests presented in Chapter 9 are applicable here. We must choose a level of significance, compute the value of the test statistic and find the p-value to determine whether the null hypothesis should be rejected. With two independent simple random samples, we showed that the point estimator $\bar{x}_1 - \bar{x}_2$ has a standard error $\sigma_{\bar{x}_1 - \bar{x}_2}$ given by expression (10.2) and, when the sample sizes are large enough, the distribution of $\bar{x}_1 - \bar{x}_2$ can be described by a normal distribution. In this case, the test statistic for the difference between two population means when σ_1 and σ_2 are known is as follows.

TEST STATISTIC FOR HYPOTHESIS TESTS ABOUT $\mu_1 - \mu_2$: σ_1 AND σ_2 KNOWN

$$z = \frac{(\bar{x}_1 - \bar{x}_2) - D_0}{\sqrt{\dfrac{\sigma_1^2}{n_1} + \dfrac{\sigma_2^2}{n_2}}} \tag{10.5}$$

Let us demonstrate the use of this test statistic in the following hypothesis testing example.

As part of a study to evaluate differences in education quality between two training centers, a standardized examination is given to individuals who are trained at the centers. The difference between the mean examination scores is used to assess quality differences between the centers. The population means for the two centers are as follows.

μ_1 = the mean examination score for the population of individuals trained at center A

μ_2 = the mean examination score for the population of individuals trained at center B

We begin with the tentative assumption that no difference exists between the training quality provided at the two centers. Hence, in terms of the mean examination scores, the null hypothesis is that $\mu_1 - \mu_2 = 0$. If sample evidence leads to the rejection of this hypothesis, we will conclude that the mean examination scores differ for the two populations. This conclusion indicates a quality differential between the two centers and suggests that a follow-up study investigating the reason for the differential may be warranted. The null and alternative hypotheses for this two-tailed test are written as follows.

$$H_0: \mu_1 - \mu_2 = 0$$
$$H_a: \mu_1 - \mu_2 \neq 0$$

The standardized examination given previously in a variety of settings always resulted in an examination score standard deviation near 10 points. Thus, we will use this information to assume that the population standard deviations are known with $\sigma_1 = 10$ and $\sigma_2 = 10$. An $\alpha = .05$ level of significance is specified for the study.

CD file
ExamScores

Independent simple random samples of $n_1 = 30$ individuals from training center A and $n_2 = 40$ individuals from training center B are taken. The respective sample means are $\bar{x}_1 = 82$ and $\bar{x}_2 = 78$. Do these data suggest a significant difference between the population means at the two training centers? To help answer this question, we compute the test statistic using equation (10.5).

$$z = \frac{(\bar{x}_1 - \bar{x}_2) - D_0}{\sqrt{\frac{\sigma_1^2}{n_1} + \frac{\sigma_2^2}{n_2}}} = \frac{(82 - 78) - 0}{\sqrt{\frac{10^2}{30} + \frac{10^2}{40}}} = 1.66$$

Next let us compute the p-value for this two-tailed test. Because the test statistic z is in the upper tail, we first compute the area under the curve to the right of $z = 1.66$. Using the standard normal distribution table, the area to the left of $z = 1.66$ is .9515. Thus, the area in the upper tail of the distribution is $1.0000 - .9515 = .0485$. Because this test is a two-tailed test, we must double the tail area: p-value $= 2(.0485) = .0970$. Following the usual rule to reject H_0 if p-value $\leq \alpha$, we see that the p-value of .0970 does not allow us to reject H_0 at the .05 level of significance. The sample results do not provide sufficient evidence to conclude the training centers differ in quality.

In this chapter we will use the p-value approach to hypothesis testing as described in Chapter 9. However, if you prefer, the test statistic and the critical value rejection rule may be used. With $\alpha = .05$ and $z_{\alpha/2} = z_{.025} = 1.96$, the rejection rule employing the critical value approach would be reject H_0 if $z \leq -1.96$ or if $z \geq 1.96$. With $z = 1.66$, we reach the same do not reject H_0 conclusion.

In the preceding example, we demonstrated a two-tailed hypothesis test about the difference between two population means. Lower tail and upper tail tests can also be considered. These tests use the same test statistic as given in equation (10.5). The procedure for computing the p-value and the rejection rules for these one-tailed tests are the same as those presented in Chapter 9.

Practical Advice

In most applications of the interval estimation and hypothesis testing procedures presented in this section, random samples with $n_1 \geq 30$ and $n_2 \geq 30$ are adequate. In cases where either or both sample sizes are less than 30, the distributions of the populations become important considerations. In general, with smaller sample sizes, it is more important for the analyst to be satisfied that it is reasonable to assume that the distributions of the two populations are at least approximately normal.

Exercises

Methods

SELF test

1. The following results come from two independent random samples taken of two populations.

Sample 1	Sample 2
$n_1 = 50$	$n_2 = 35$
$\bar{x}_1 = 13.6$	$\bar{x}_2 = 11.6$
$\sigma_1 = 2.2$	$\sigma_2 = 3.0$

a. What is the point estimate of the difference between the two population means?
b. Provide a 90% confidence interval for the difference between the two population means.
c. Provide a 95% confidence interval for the difference between the two population means.

SELF test

2. Consider the following hypothesis test.

$$H_0\colon \mu_1 - \mu_2 \leq 0$$
$$H_a\colon \mu_1 - \mu_2 > 0$$

The following results are for two independent samples taken from the two populations.

Sample 1	Sample 2
$n_1 = 40$	$n_2 = 50$
$\bar{x}_1 = 25.2$	$\bar{x}_2 = 22.8$
$\sigma_1 = 5.2$	$\sigma_2 = 6.0$

a. What is the value of the test statistic?
b. What is the p-value?
c. With $\alpha = .05$, what is your hypothesis testing conclusion?

3. Consider the following hypothesis test.

$$H_0\colon \mu_1 - \mu_2 = 0$$
$$H_a\colon \mu_1 - \mu_2 \neq 0$$

The following results are for two independent samples taken from the two populations.

Sample 1	Sample 2
$n_1 = 80$	$n_2 = 70$
$\bar{x}_1 = 104$	$\bar{x}_2 = 106$
$\sigma_1 = 8.4$	$\sigma_2 = 7.6$

a. What is the value of the test statistic?
b. What is the p-value?
c. With $\alpha = .05$, what is your hypothesis testing conclusion?

Applications

4. Gasoline prices reached record high levels in 16 states during 2003 (*The Wall Street Journal*, March 7, 2003). Two of the affected states were California and Florida. The American Automobile Association reported a sample mean price of \$2.04 per gallon in California and a sample mean price of \$1.72 per gallon in Florida. Use a sample size of 40 for the California data and a sample size of 35 for the Florida data. Assume that prior studies indicate a population standard deviation of .10 in California and .08 in Florida are reasonable.
   a. What is a point estimate of the difference between the population mean prices per gallon in California and Florida?
   b. At 95% confidence, what is the margin of error?
   c. What is the 95% confidence interval estimate of the difference between the population mean prices per gallon in the two states?
5. The average expenditure on Valentine's Day was expected to be \$100.89 (*USA Today*, February 13, 2006). Do male and female consumers differ in the amounts they spend? The average expenditure in a sample survey of 40 male consumers was \$135.67, and the average expenditure in a sample survey of 30 female consumers was \$68.64. Based on past surveys, the standard deviation for male consumers is assumed to be \$35, and the standard deviation for female consumers is assumed to be \$20.

a. What is the point estimate of the difference between the population mean expenditure for males and the population mean expenditure for females?
b. At 99% confidence, what is the margin of error?
c. Develop a 99% confidence interval for the difference between the two population means.

6. The nation's 40,000 mortgage brokerages are some of the most profitable small businesses in the United States. These low-profile companies find loans for customers in exchange for commissions. Mortgage Bankers Association of America provides data on the average size of loans handled by mortgage brokerages (*The Wall Street Journal,* February 24, 2003). The CD file named Mortgage contains data from a sample of 250 loans made in 2001 and a sample of 270 loans made in 2002 that are consistent with these data. Based on historical loan data, the population standard deviations for the loan amounts can be assumed known at \$55,000 in 2002 and \$50,000 in 2001. Do the sample data indicate an increase in the mean loan amount between 2001 and 2002? Use $\alpha = .05$.

CD file
Mortgage

7. During the 2003 season, Major League Baseball took steps to speed up the play of baseball games in order to maintain fan interest (*CNN Headline News,* September 30, 2003). The following results come from a sample of 60 games played during the summer of 2002 and a sample of 50 games played during the summer of 2003. The sample mean shows the mean duration of the games included in each sample.

2002 Season	2003 Season
$n_1 = 60$	$n_2 = 50$
$\bar{x}_1 = 2$ hours, 52 minutes	$\bar{x}_2 = 2$ hours, 46 minutes

a. A research hypothesis was that the steps taken during the 2003 season would reduce the population mean duration of baseball games. Formulate the null and alternative hypotheses.
b. What is the point estimate of the reduction in the mean duration of games during the 2003 season?
c. Historical data indicate a population standard deviation of 12 minutes is a reasonable assumption for both years. Conduct the hypothesis test and report the p-value. At a .05 level of significance, what is your conclusion?
d. Provide a 95% confidence interval estimate of the reduction in the mean duration of games during the 2003 season.
e. What was the percentage reduction in the mean time of baseball games during the 2003 season? Should management be pleased with the results of the statistical analysis? Discuss. Should the length of baseball games continue to be an issue in future years? Explain.

8. Arnold Palmer and Tiger Woods are two of the best golfers to ever play the game. To show how these two golfers would compare if both were playing at the top of their game, the following sample data provide the results of 18-hole scores during a PGA tournament competition. Palmer's scores are from his 1960 season, while Woods' scores are from his 1999 season (*Golf Magazine,* February 2000).

Palmer, 1960	Woods, 1999
$n_1 = 112$	$n_2 = 84$
$\bar{x}_1 = 69.95$	$\bar{x}_2 = 69.56$

Use the sample results to test the hypothesis of no difference between the population mean 18-hole scores for the two golfers.
a. Assume a population standard deviation of 2.5 for both golfers. What is the value of the test statistic?
b. What is the p-value?
c. At $\alpha = .01$, what is your conclusion?

10.2 Inferences About the Difference Between Two Population Means: σ_1 and σ_2 Unknown

In this section we extend the discussion of inferences about the difference between two population means to the case when the two population standard deviations, σ_1 and σ_2, are unknown. In this case, we will use the sample standard deviations, s_1 and s_2, to estimate the unknown population standard deviations. When we use the sample standard deviations, the interval estimation and hypothesis testing procedures will be based on the t distribution rather than the standard normal distribution.

Interval Estimation of $\mu_1 - \mu_2$

In the following example we show how to compute a margin of error and develop an interval estimate of the difference between two population means when σ_1 and σ_2 are unknown. Clearwater National Bank is conducting a study designed to identify differences between checking account practices by customers at two of its branch banks. A simple random sample of 28 checking accounts is selected from the Cherry Grove Branch and an independent simple random sample of 22 checking accounts is selected from the Beechmont Branch. The current checking account balance is recorded for each of the checking accounts. A summary of the account balances follows:

CD file
CheckAcct

	Cherry Grove	Beechmont
Sample Size	$n_1 = 28$	$n_2 = 22$
Sample Mean	$\bar{x}_1 = \$1025$	$\bar{x}_2 = \$910$
Sample Standard Deviation	$s_1 = \$150$	$s_2 = \$125$

Clearwater National Bank would like to estimate the difference between the mean checking account balance maintained by the population of Cherry Grove customers and the population of Beechmont customers. Let us develop the margin of error and an interval estimate of the difference between these two population means.

In Section 10.1, we provided the following interval estimate for the case when the population standard deviations, σ_1 and σ_2, are known.

$$\bar{x}_1 - \bar{x}_2 \pm z_{\alpha/2}\sqrt{\frac{\sigma_1^2}{n_1} + \frac{\sigma_2^2}{n_2}}$$

When σ_1 and σ_2 are estimated by s_1 and s_2, the t distribution is used to make inferences about the difference between two population means.

With σ_1 and σ_2 unknown, we will use the sample standard deviations s_1 and s_2 to estimate σ_1 and σ_2 and replace $z_{\alpha/2}$ with $t_{\alpha/2}$. As a result, the interval estimate of the difference between two population means is given by the following expression:

INTERVAL ESTIMATE OF THE DIFFERENCE BETWEEN TWO POPULATION MEANS: σ_1 AND σ_2 UNKNOWN

$$\bar{x}_1 - \bar{x}_2 \pm t_{\alpha/2}\sqrt{\frac{s_1^2}{n_1} + \frac{s_2^2}{n_2}} \qquad \textbf{(10.6)}$$

where $1 - \alpha$ is the confidence coefficient.

In this expression, the use of the t distribution is an approximation, but it provides excellent results and is relatively easy to use. The only difficulty that we encounter in using expression (10.6) is determining the appropriate degrees of freedom for $t_{\alpha/2}$. Statistical software packages compute the appropriate degrees of freedom automatically. The formula used is as follows:

DEGREES OF FREEDOM: t DISTRIBUTION WITH TWO INDEPENDENT RANDOM SAMPLES

$$df = \frac{\left(\frac{s_1^2}{n_1} + \frac{s_2^2}{n_2}\right)^2}{\frac{1}{n_1 - 1}\left(\frac{s_1^2}{n_1}\right)^2 + \frac{1}{n_2 - 1}\left(\frac{s_2^2}{n_2}\right)^2} \tag{10.7}$$

Let us return to the Clearwater National Bank example and show how to use expression (10.6) to provide a 95% confidence interval estimate of the difference between the population mean checking account balances at the two branch banks. The sample data show $n_1 = 28$, $\bar{x}_1 = \$1025$, and $s_1 = \$150$ for the Cherry Grove branch, and $n_2 = 22$, $\bar{x}_2 = \$910$, and $s_2 = \$125$ for the Beechmont branch. The calculation for degrees of freedom for $t_{\alpha/2}$ is as follows:

$$df = \frac{\left(\frac{s_1^2}{n_1} + \frac{s_2^2}{n_2}\right)^2}{\frac{1}{n_1 - 1}\left(\frac{s_1^2}{n_1}\right)^2 + \frac{1}{n_2 - 1}\left(\frac{s_2^2}{n_2}\right)^2} = \frac{\left(\frac{150^2}{28} + \frac{125^2}{22}\right)^2}{\frac{1}{28 - 1}\left(\frac{150^2}{28}\right)^2 + \frac{1}{22 - 1}\left(\frac{125^2}{22}\right)^2} = 47.8$$

We round the noninteger degrees of freedom *down* to 47 to provide a larger t-value and a more conservative interval estimate. Using the t distribution table with 47 degrees of freedom, we find $t_{.025} = 2.012$. Using expression (10.6), we develop the 95% confidence interval estimate of the difference between the two population means as follows.

$$\bar{x}_1 - \bar{x}_2 \pm t_{.025}\sqrt{\frac{s_1^2}{n_1} + \frac{s_2^2}{n_2}}$$

$$1025 - 910 \pm 2.012\sqrt{\frac{150^2}{28} + \frac{125^2}{22}}$$

$$115 \pm 78$$

The point estimate of the difference between the population mean checking account balances at the two branches is \$115. The margin of error is \$78, and the 95% confidence interval estimate of the difference between the two population means is $115 - 78 = \$37$ to $115 + 78 = \$193$.

This suggestion should help if you are using equation (10.7) to calculate the degrees of freedom by hand.

The computation of the degrees of freedom (equation (10.7)) is cumbersome if you are doing the calculation by hand, but it is easily implemented with a computer software package. However, note that the expressions s_1^2/n_1 and s_2^2/n_2 appear in both expression (10.6) and equation (10.7). These values only need to be computed once in order to evaluate both (10.6) and (10.7).

Hypothesis Tests About $\mu_1 - \mu_2$

Let us now consider hypothesis tests about the difference between the means of two populations when the population standard deviations σ_1 and σ_2 are unknown. Letting D_0 denote the hypothesized difference between μ_1 and μ_2, Section 10.1 showed that the test statistic used for the case where σ_1 and σ_2 are known is as follows.

$$z = \frac{(\bar{x}_1 - \bar{x}_2) - D_0}{\sqrt{\dfrac{\sigma_1^2}{n_1} + \dfrac{\sigma_2^2}{n_2}}}$$

The test statistic, z, follows the standard normal distribution.

When σ_1 and σ_2 are unknown, we use s_1 as an estimator of σ_1 and s_2 as an estimator of σ_2. Substituting these sample standard deviations for σ_1 and σ_2 provides the following test statistic when σ_1 and σ_2 are unknown.

TEST STATISTIC FOR HYPOTHESIS TESTS ABOUT $\mu_1 - \mu_2$: σ_1 AND σ_2 UNKNOWN

$$t = \frac{(\bar{x}_1 - \bar{x}_2) - D_0}{\sqrt{\dfrac{s_1^2}{n_1} + \dfrac{s_2^2}{n_2}}} \tag{10.8}$$

The degrees of freedom for t are given by equation (10.7).

Let us demonstrate the use of this test statistic in the following hypothesis testing example.

Consider a new computer software package developed to help systems analysts reduce the time required to design, develop, and implement an information system. To evaluate the benefits of the new software package, a random sample of 24 systems analysts is selected. Each analyst is given specifications for a hypothetical information system. Then 12 of the analysts are instructed to produce the information system by using current technology. The other 12 analysts are trained in the use of the new software package and then instructed to use it to produce the information system.

This study involves two populations: a population of systems analysts using the current technology and a population of systems analysts using the new software package. In terms of the time required to complete the information system design project, the population means are as follow.

μ_1 = the mean project completion time for systems analysts using the current technology

μ_2 = the mean project completion time for systems analysts using the new software package

The researcher in charge of the new software evaluation project hopes to show that the new software package will provide a shorter mean project completion time. Thus, the researcher is looking for evidence to conclude that μ_2 is less than μ_1; in this case, the difference between the two population means, $\mu_1 - \mu_2$, will be greater than zero. The research hypothesis $\mu_1 - \mu_2 > 0$ is stated as the alternative hypothesis. Thus, the hypothesis test becomes

$$H_0: \mu_1 - \mu_2 \leq 0$$
$$H_a: \mu_1 - \mu_2 > 0$$

We will use $\alpha = .05$ as the level of significance.

TABLE 10.1 COMPLETION TIME DATA AND SUMMARY STATISTICS FOR THE SOFTWARE TESTING STUDY

CD file
SoftwareTest

	Current Technology	New Software
	300	274
	280	220
	344	308
	385	336
	372	198
	360	300
	288	315
	321	258
	376	318
	290	310
	301	332
	283	263
Summary Statistics		
Sample size	$n_1 = 12$	$n_2 = 12$
Sample mean	$\bar{x}_1 = 325$ hours	$\bar{x}_2 = 286$ hours
Sample standard deviation	$s_1 = 40$	$s_2 = 44$

Suppose that the 24 analysts complete the study with the results shown in Table 10.1. Using the test statistic in equation (10.8), we have

$$t = \frac{(\bar{x}_1 - \bar{x}_2) - D_0}{\sqrt{\dfrac{s_1^2}{n_1} + \dfrac{s_2^2}{n_2}}} = \frac{(325 - 286) - 0}{\sqrt{\dfrac{40^2}{12} + \dfrac{44^2}{12}}} = 2.27$$

Computing the degrees of freedom using equation (10.7), we have

$$df = \frac{\left(\dfrac{s_1^2}{n_1} + \dfrac{s_2^2}{n_2}\right)^2}{\dfrac{1}{n_1 - 1}\left(\dfrac{s_1^2}{n_1}\right)^2 + \dfrac{1}{n_2 - 1}\left(\dfrac{s_2^2}{n_2}\right)^2} = \frac{\left(\dfrac{40^2}{12} + \dfrac{44^2}{12}\right)^2}{\dfrac{1}{12 - 1}\left(\dfrac{40^2}{12}\right)^2 + \dfrac{1}{12 - 1}\left(\dfrac{44^2}{12}\right)^2} = 21.8$$

Rounding down, we will use a t distribution with 21 degrees of freedom. This row of the t distribution table is as follows:

Area in Upper Tail	**.20**	**.10**	**.05**	**.025**	**.01**	**.005**
***t* Value (21 df)**	0.859	1.323	1.721	2.080	2.518	2.831

$t = 2.27$

Using the t distribution table, we can only determine a range for the p-value. Use of Excel or Minitab shows the exact p-value = .017.

With an upper tail test, the p-value is the area in the upper tail to the right of $t = 2.27$. From the above results, we see that the p-value is between .025 and .01. Thus, the p-value is less than $\alpha = .05$ and H_0 is rejected. The sample results enable the researcher to conclude that $\mu_1 - \mu_2 > 0$, or $\mu_1 > \mu_2$. Thus, the research study supports the conclusion that the new software package provides a smaller population mean completion time.

FIGURE 10.2 MINITAB OUTPUT FOR THE HYPOTHESIS TEST OF THE CURRENT AND NEW SOFTWARE TECHNOLOGY

```
Two-sample T for Current vs New

            N      Mean     StDev    SE Mean
Current    12     325.0      40.0         12
New        12     286.0      44.0         13

Difference = mu Current - mu New
Estimate for difference:  39.0000
95% lower bound for difference = 9.4643
T-Test of difference = 0 (vs >):  T-Value = 2.27  P-Value = 0.017  DF = 21
```

Minitab or Excel can be used to analyze data for testing hypotheses about the difference between two population means. The Minitab output comparing the current and new software technology is shown in Figure 10.2. The last line of the output shows $t = 2.27$ and p-value $= .017$. Note that Minitab used equation (10.7) to compute 21 degrees of freedom for this analysis.

Practical Advice

Whenever possible, equal sample sizes, $n_1 = n_2$, are recommended.

The interval estimation and hypothesis testing procedures presented in this section are robust and can be used with relatively small sample sizes. In most applications, equal or nearly equal sample sizes such that the total sample size $n_1 + n_2$ is at least 20 can be expected to provide very good results even if the populations are not normal. Larger sample sizes are recommended if the distributions of the populations are highly skewed or contain outliers. Smaller sample sizes should only be used if the analyst is satisfied that the distributions of the populations are at least approximately normal.

NOTES AND COMMENTS

Another approach used to make inferences about the difference between two population means when σ_1 and σ_2 are unknown is based on the assumption that the two population standard deviations are *equal* ($\sigma_1 = \sigma_2 = \sigma$). Under this assumption, the two sample standard deviations are combined to provide the following *pooled sample variance:*

$$s_p^2 = \frac{(n_1 - 1)s_1^2 + (n_2 - 1)s_2^2}{n_1 + n_2 - 2}$$

The t test statistic becomes

$$t = \frac{(\bar{x}_1 - \bar{x}_2) - D_0}{s_p\sqrt{\dfrac{1}{n_1} + \dfrac{1}{n_2}}}$$

and has $n_1 + n_2 - 2$ degrees of freedom. At this point, the computation of the p-value and the interpretation of the sample results are identical to the procedures discussed earlier in this section.

A difficulty with this procedure is that the assumption that the two population standard deviations are equal is usually difficult to verify. Unequal population standard deviations are frequently encountered. Using the pooled procedure may not provide satisfactory results, especially if the sample sizes n_1 and n_2 are quite different.

The t procedure that we presented in this section does not require the assumption of equal population standard deviations and can be applied whether the population standard deviations are equal or not. It is a more general procedure and is recommended for most applications.

Exercises

Methods

SELF test

9. The following results are for independent random samples taken from two populations.

Sample 1	Sample 2
$n_1 = 20$	$n_2 = 30$
$\bar{x}_1 = 22.5$	$\bar{x}_2 = 20.1$
$s_1 = 2.5$	$s_2 = 4.8$

a. What is the point estimate of the difference between the two population means?
b. What is the degrees of freedom for the t distribution?
c. At 95% confidence, what is the margin of error?
d. What is the 95% confidence interval for the difference between the two population means?

SELF test

10. Consider the following hypothesis test.

$$H_0: \mu_1 - \mu_2 = 0$$
$$H_a: \mu_1 - \mu_2 \neq 0$$

The following results are from independent samples taken from two populations.

Sample 1	Sample 2
$n_1 = 35$	$n_2 = 40$
$\bar{x}_1 = 13.6$	$\bar{x}_2 = 10.1$
$s_1 = 5.2$	$s_2 = 8.5$

a. What is the value of the test statistic?
b. What is the degrees of freedom for the t distribution?
c. What is the p-value?
d. At $\alpha = .05$, what is your conclusion?

11. Consider the following data for two independent random samples taken from two normal populations.

Sample 1	10	7	13	7	9	8
Sample 2	8	7	8	4	6	9

a. Compute the two sample means.
b. Compute the two sample standard deviations.
c. What is the point estimate of the difference between the two population means?
d. What is the 90% confidence interval estimate of the difference between the two population means?

Applications

SELF test

12. The U.S. Department of Transportation provides the number of miles that residents of the 75 largest metropolitan areas travel per day in a car. Suppose that for a simple random sample of 50 Buffalo residents the mean is 22.5 miles a day and the standard deviation is

8.4 miles a day, and for an independent simple random sample of 40 Boston residents the mean is 18.6 miles a day and the standard deviation is 7.4 miles a day.

a. What is the point estimate of the difference between the mean number of miles that Buffalo residents travel per day and the mean number of miles that Boston residents travel per day?
b. What is the 95% confidence interval for the difference between the two population means?

CD file
Cargo

13. FedEx and United Parcel Service (UPS) are the world's two leading cargo carriers by volume and revenue (*The Wall Street Journal,* January 27, 2004). According to the Airports Council International, the Memphis International Airport (FedEx) and the Louisville International Airport (UPS) are two of the ten largest cargo airports in the world. The following random samples show the tons of cargo per day handled by these airports. Data are in thousands of tons.

Memphis					
9.1	15.1	8.8	10.0	7.5	10.5
8.3	9.1	6.0	5.8	12.1	9.3
Louisville					
4.7	5.0	4.2	3.3	5.5	
2.2	4.1	2.6	3.4	7.0	

a. Compute the sample mean and sample standard deviation for each airport.
b. What is the point estimate of the difference between the two population means? Interpret this value in terms of the higher-volume airport and a comparison of the volume difference between the two airports.
c. Develop a 95% confidence interval of the difference between the daily population means for the two airports.

14. Coastal areas of the United States including Cape Cod, the Outer Banks, the Carolinas, and the Gulf Coast had relatively high population growth rates during the 1990s. Data were collected on residents living in the coastal communities as well as on residents living in noncoastal areas throughout the United States (*USA Today,* July 21, 2000). Assume that the following sample results were obtained on the ages of individuals in the two populations:

Coastal Areas	Noncoastal Areas
$n_1 = 150$	$n_2 = 175$
$\bar{x}_1 = 39.3$ years	$\bar{x}_2 = 35.4$ years
$s_1 = 16.8$ years	$s_2 = 15.2$ years

Test the hypothesis of no difference between the two population means. Use $\alpha = .05$.

a. Formulate the null and alternative hypotheses.
b. What is the value of the test statistic?
c. What is the p-value?
d. What is your conclusion?

15. Injuries to Major League Baseball players have been increasing in recent years. For the period 1992 to 2001, league expansion caused Major League Baseball rosters to increase 15%. However, the number of players being put on the disabled list due to injury increased 32% over the same period (*USA Today,* July 8, 2002). A research question addressed whether Major League Baseball players being put on the disabled list are on the list longer in 2001 than players put on the disabled list a decade earlier.

a. Using the population mean number of days a player is on the disabled list, formulate null and alternative hypotheses that can be used to test the research question.

b. Assume that the following data apply:

	2001 Season	1992 Season
Sample size	$n_1 = 45$	$n_2 = 38$
Sample mean	$\bar{x}_1 = 60$ days	$\bar{x}_2 = 51$ days
Sample standard deviation	$s_1 = 18$ days	$s_2 = 15$ days

What is the point estimate of the difference between population mean number of days on the disabled list for 2001 compared to 1992? What is the percentage increase in the number of days on the disabled list?

c. Use $\alpha = .01$. What is your conclusion about the number of days on the disabled list? What is the p-value?

d. Do these data suggest that Major League Baseball should be concerned about the situation?

CD file
SATVerbal

16. The College Board provided comparisons of Scholastic Aptitude Test (SAT) scores based on the highest level of education attained by the test taker's parents. A research hypothesis was that students whose parents had attained a higher level of education would on average score higher on the SAT. During 2003, the overall mean SAT verbal score was 507 (*The World Almanac 2004*). SAT verbal scores for independent samples of students follow. The first sample shows the SAT verbal test scores for students whose parents are college graduates with a bachelor's degree. The second sample shows the SAT verbal test scores for students whose parents are high school graduates but do not have a college degree.

Student's Parents			
College Grads		High School Grads	
485	487	442	492
534	533	580	478
650	526	479	425
554	410	486	485
550	515	528	390
572	578	524	535
497	448		
592	469		

a. Formulate the hypotheses that can be used to determine whether the sample data support the hypothesis that students show a higher population mean verbal score on the SAT if their parents attained a higher level of education.

b. What is the point estimate of the difference between the means for the two populations?

c. Compute the p-value for the hypothesis test.

d. At $\alpha = .05$, what is your conclusion?

17. Periodically, Merrill Lynch customers are asked to evaluate Merrill Lynch financial consultants and services (2000 Merrill Lynch Client Satisfaction Survey). Higher ratings on the client satisfaction survey indicate better service, with 7 the maximum service rating. Independent samples of service ratings for two financial consultants are summarized here. Consultant A has 10 years of experience, whereas consultant B has 1 year of experience. Use $\alpha = .05$ and test to see whether the consultant with more experience has the higher population mean service rating.

Consultant A	Consultant B
$n_1 = 16$	$n_2 = 10$
$\bar{x}_1 = 6.82$	$\bar{x}_2 = 6.25$
$s_1 = .64$	$s_2 = .75$

a. State the null and alternative hypotheses.
b. Compute the value of the test statistic.
c. What is the p-value?
d. What is your conclusion?

CD file
SAT

18. Educational testing companies provide tutoring, classroom learning, and practice tests in an effort to help students perform better on tests such as the Scholastic Aptitude Test (SAT). The test preparation companies claim that their courses will improve SAT score performances by an average of 120 points (*The Wall Street Journal,* January 23, 2003). A researcher is uncertain of this claim and believes that 120 points may be an overstatement in an effort to encourage students to take the test preparation course. In an evaluation study of one test preparation service, the researcher collects SAT score data for 35 students who took the test preparation course and 48 students who did not take the course. The CD file named SAT contains the scores for this study.
    a. Formulate the hypotheses that can be used to test the researcher's belief that the improvement in SAT scores may be less than the stated average of 120 points.
    b. Using $\alpha = .05$, what is your conclusion?
    c. What is the point estimate of the improvement in the average SAT scores provided by the test preparation course? Provide a 95% confidence interval estimate of the improvement.
    d. What advice would you have for the researcher after seeing the confidence interval?

10.3 Inferences About the Difference Between Two Population Means: Matched Samples

Suppose employees at a manufacturing company can use two different methods to perform a production task. To maximize production output, the company wants to identify the method with the smaller population mean completion time. Let μ_1 denote the population mean completion time for production method 1 and μ_2 denote the population mean completion time for production method 2. With no preliminary indication of the preferred production method, we begin by tentatively assuming that the two production methods have the same population mean completion time. Thus, the null hypothesis is $H_0\colon \mu_1 - \mu_2 = 0$. If this hypothesis is rejected, we can conclude that the population mean completion times differ. In this case, the method providing the smaller mean completion time would be recommended. The null and alternative hypotheses are written as follows.

$$H_0\colon \mu_1 - \mu_2 = 0$$
$$H_a\colon \mu_1 - \mu_2 \neq 0$$

In choosing the sampling procedure that will be used to collect production time data and test the hypotheses, we consider two alternative designs. One is based on independent samples and the other is based on **matched samples.**

1. *Independent sample design:* A simple random sample of workers is selected and each worker in the sample uses method 1. A second independent simple random sample of workers is selected and each worker in this sample uses method 2. The

test of the difference between population means is based on the procedures in Section 10.2.

2. *Matched sample design:* One simple random sample of workers is selected. Each worker first uses one method and then uses the other method. The order of the two methods is assigned randomly to the workers, with some workers performing method 1 first and others performing method 2 first. Each worker provides a pair of data values, one value for method 1 and another value for method 2.

In the matched sample design the two production methods are tested under similar conditions (i.e., with the same workers); hence this design often leads to a smaller sampling error than the independent sample design. The primary reason is that in a matched sample design, variation between workers is eliminated because the same workers are used for both production methods.

Let us demonstrate the analysis of a matched sample design by assuming it is the method used to test the difference between population means for the two production methods. A random sample of six workers is used. The data on completion times for the six workers are given in Table 10.2. Note that each worker provides a pair of data values, one for each production method. Also note that the last column contains the difference in completion times d_i for each worker in the sample.

The key to the analysis of the matched sample design is to realize that we consider only the column of differences. Therefore, we have six data values (.6, −.2, .5, .3, .0, and .6) that will be used to analyze the difference between population means of the two production methods.

Let μ_d = the mean of the *difference* in values for the population of workers. With this notation, the null and alternative hypotheses are rewritten as follows.

$$H_0: \mu_d = 0$$
$$H_a: \mu_d \neq 0$$

If H_0 is rejected, we can conclude that the population mean completion times differ.

Other than the use of the d notation, the formulas for the sample mean and sample standard deviation are the same ones used previously in the text.

The d notation is a reminder that the matched sample provides *difference* data. The sample mean and sample standard deviation for the six difference values in Table 10.2 follow.

$$\bar{d} = \frac{\Sigma d_i}{n} = \frac{1.8}{6} = .30$$

$$s_d = \sqrt{\frac{\Sigma(d_i - \bar{d})^2}{n-1}} = \sqrt{\frac{.56}{5}} = .335$$

TABLE 10.2 TASK COMPLETION TIMES FOR A MATCHED SAMPLE DESIGN

CD file
Matched

Worker	Completion Time for Method 1 (minutes)	Completion Time for Method 2 (minutes)	Difference in Completion Times (d_i)
1	6.0	5.4	.6
2	5.0	5.2	−.2
3	7.0	6.5	.5
4	6.2	5.9	.3
5	6.0	6.0	.0
6	6.4	5.8	.6

It is not necessary to make the assumption that the population has a normal distribution if the sample size is large. Sample size guidelines for using the t distribution were presented in Chapters 8 and 9.

With the small sample of $n = 6$ workers, we need to make the assumption that the population of differences has a normal distribution. This assumption is necessary so that we may use the t distribution for hypothesis testing and interval estimation procedures. Based on this assumption, the following test statistic has a t distribution with $n - 1$ degrees of freedom.

TEST STATISTIC FOR HYPOTHESIS TESTS INVOLVING MATCHED SAMPLES

$$t = \frac{\bar{d} - \mu_d}{s_d/\sqrt{n}} \qquad \textbf{(10.9)}$$

Once the difference data are computed, the t distribution procedure for matched samples is the same as the one-population estimation and hypothesis testing procedures described in Chapters 8 and 9.

Let us use equation (10.9) to test the hypotheses H_0: $\mu_d = 0$ and H_a: $\mu_d \neq 0$, using $\alpha = .05$. Substituting the sample results $\bar{d} = .30$, $s_d = .335$, and $n = 6$ into equation (10.9), we compute the value of the test statistic.

$$t = \frac{\bar{d} - \mu_d}{s_d/\sqrt{n}} = \frac{.30 - 0}{.335/\sqrt{6}} = 2.20$$

Now let us compute the p-value for this two-tailed test. Because $t = 2.20 > 0$, the test statistic is in the upper tail of the t distribution. With $t = 2.20$, the area in the upper tail to the right of the test statistic can be found by using the t distribution table with degrees of freedom $= n - 1 = 6 - 1 = 5$. Information from the 5 degrees of freedom row of the t distribution table is as follows:

Area in Upper Tail	**.20**	**.10**	**.05**	**.025**	**.01**	**.005**
***t* Value (5 df)**	0.920	1.476	2.015	2.571	3.365	4.032

$t = 2.20$

Thus, we see that the area in the upper tail is between .05 and .025. Because this test is a two-tailed test, we double these values to conclude that the p-value is between .10 and .05. This p-value is greater than $\alpha = .05$. Thus, the null hypothesis H_0: $\mu_d = 0$ is not rejected. Using Excel or Minitab and the data in Table 10.2, we find the exact p-value $= .080$.

In addition we can obtain an interval estimate of the difference between the two population means by using the single population methodology of Chapter 8. At 95% confidence, the calculation follows.

$$\bar{d} \pm t_{.025}\frac{s_d}{\sqrt{n}}$$

$$.3 \pm 2.571\left(\frac{.335}{\sqrt{6}}\right)$$

$$.3 \pm .35$$

Thus, the margin of error is .35 and the 95% confidence interval for the difference between the population means of the two production methods is $-.05$ minutes to .65 minutes.

NOTES AND COMMENTS

1. In the example presented in this section, workers performed the production task with first one method and then the other method. This example illustrates a matched sample design in which each sampled element (worker) provides a pair of data values. It is also possible to use different but "similar" elements to provide the pair of data values. For example, a worker at one location could be matched with a similar worker at another location (similarity based on age, education, gender, experience, etc.). The pairs of workers would provide the difference data that could be used in the matched sample analysis.
2. A matched sample procedure for inferences about two population means generally provides better precision than the independent sample approach; therefore it is the recommended design. However, in some applications the matching cannot be achieved, or perhaps the time and cost associated with matching are excessive. In such cases, the independent sample design should be used.

Exercises

Methods

SELF test

19. Consider the following hypothesis test.

$$H_0: \mu_d \leq 0$$
$$H_a: \mu_d > 0$$

The following data are from matched samples taken from two populations.

Element	Population 1	Population 2
1	21	20
2	28	26
3	18	18
4	20	20
5	26	24

a. Compute the difference value for each element.
b. Compute $\bar{d}$.
c. Compute the standard deviation s_d.
d. Conduct a hypothesis test using $\alpha = .05$. What is your conclusion?

20. The following data are from matched samples taken from two populations.

Element	Population 1	Population 2
1	11	8
2	7	8
3	9	6
4	12	7
5	13	10
6	15	15
7	15	14

a. Compute the difference value for each element.
b. Compute $\bar{d}$.
c. Compute the standard deviation s_d.
d. What is the point estimate of the difference between the two population means?
e. Provide a 95% confidence interval for the difference between the two population means.

Applications

SELF test

21. A market research firm used a sample of individuals to rate the purchase potential of a particular product before and after the individuals saw a new television commercial about the product. The purchase potential ratings were based on a 0 to 10 scale, with higher values indicating a higher purchase potential. The null hypothesis stated that the mean rating "after" would be less than or equal to the mean rating "before." Rejection of this hypothesis would show that the commercial improved the mean purchase potential rating. Use $\alpha = .05$ and the following data to test the hypothesis and comment on the value of the commercial.

	Purchase Rating			Purchase Rating	
Individual	**After**	**Before**	**Individual**	**After**	**Before**
1	6	5	5	3	5
2	6	4	6	9	8
3	7	7	7	7	5
4	4	3	8	6	6

CD file
Earnings2005

22. Per-share earnings data comparing the current quarter's earnings with the previous quarter are in the CD file entitled Earnings 2005 (*The Wall Street Journal,* January 27, 2006). Provide a 95% confidence interval estimate of the difference between the population mean for the current quarter versus the previous quarter. Have earnings increased?

23. Bank of America's Consumer Spending Survey collected data on annual credit card charges in seven different categories of expenditures: transportation, groceries, dining out, household expenses, home furnishings, apparel, and entertainment (*U.S. Airways Attaché,* December 2003). Using data from a sample of 42 credit card accounts, assume that each account was used to identify the annual credit card charges for groceries (population 1) and the annual credit card charges for dining out (population 2). Using the difference data, the sample mean difference was $\bar{d} = \$850$, and the sample standard deviation was $s_d = \$1123$.
    a. Formulate the null and alternative hypotheses to test for no difference between the population mean credit card charges for groceries and the population mean credit card charges for dining out.
    b. Use a .05 level of significance. Can you conclude that the population means differ? What is the *p*-value?
    c. Which category, groceries or dining out, has a higher population mean annual credit card charge? What is the point estimate of the difference between the population means? What is the 95% confidence interval estimate of the difference between the population means?

CD file
AirFare

24. Airline travelers often choose which airport to fly from based on flight cost. Cost data (in dollars) for a sample of flights to eight cities from Dayton, Ohio, and Louisville, Kentucky, were collected to help determine which of the two airports was more costly to fly from (*The Cincinnati Enquirer,* February 19, 2006). A researcher argued that it is significantly more costly to fly out of Dayton than Louisville. Use the sample data to see whether they support the researcher's argument. Use $\alpha = .05$ as the level of significance.

Destination	Dayton	Louisville
Chicago-O'Hare	$319	$142
Grand Rapids, Michigan	192	213
Portland, Oregon	503	317
Atlanta	256	387
Seattle	339	317
South Bend, Indiana	379	167
Miami	268	273
Dallas–Ft. Worth	288	274

25. In recent years, a growing array of entertainment options competes for consumer time. By 2004, cable television and radio surpassed broadcast television, recorded music, and the daily newspaper to become the two entertainment media with the greatest usage (*The Wall Street Journal,* January 26, 2004). Researchers used a sample of 15 individuals and collected data on the hours per week spent watching cable television and hours per week spent listening to the radio.

CD file

TVRadio

Individual	Television	Radio	Individual	Television	Radio
1	22	25	9	21	21
2	8	10	10	23	23
3	25	29	11	14	15
4	22	19	12	14	18
5	12	13	13	14	17
6	26	28	14	16	15
7	22	23	15	24	23
8	19	21			

a. Use a .05 level of significance and test for a difference between the population mean usage for cable television and radio. What is the p-value?
b. What is the sample mean number of hours per week spent watching cable television? What is the sample mean number of hours per week spent listening to radio? Which medium has the greater usage?

26. StreetInsider.com reported 2002 earnings per share data for a sample of major companies (February 12, 2003). Prior to 2002, financial analysts predicted the 2002 earnings per share for these same companies (*Barron's,* September 10, 2001). Use the following data to comment on differences between actual and estimated earnings per share.

CD file

Earnings

Company	Actual	Predicted
AT&T	1.29	0.38
American Express	2.01	2.31
Citigroup	2.59	3.43
Coca-Cola	1.60	1.78
DuPont	1.84	2.18
ExxonMobil	2.72	2.19
General Electric	1.51	1.71
Johnson & Johnson	2.28	2.18
McDonald's	0.77	1.55
Wal-Mart	1.81	1.74

a. Use $\alpha = .05$ and test for any difference between the population mean actual and population mean estimated earnings per share. What is the p-value? What is your conclusion?
b. What is the point estimate of the difference between the two means? Did the analysts tend to underestimate or overestimate the earnings?
c. At 95% confidence, what is the margin of error for the estimate in part (b)? What would you recommend based on this information?

27. A manufacturer produces both a deluxe and a standard model of an automatic sander designed for home use. Selling prices obtained from a sample of retail outlets follow.

	Model Price ($)			Model Price ($)	
Retail Outlet	**Deluxe**	**Standard**	**Retail Outlet**	**Deluxe**	**Standard**
1	39	27	5	40	30
2	39	28	6	39	34
3	45	35	7	35	29
4	38	30			

a. The manufacturer's suggested retail prices for the two models show a $10 price differential. Use a .05 level of significance and test that the mean difference between the prices of the two models is $10.
b. What is the 95% confidence interval for the difference between the mean prices of the two models?

10.4 Inferences About the Difference Between Two Population Proportions

Letting p_1 denote the proportion for population 1 and p_2 denote the proportion for population 2, we next consider inferences about the difference between the two population proportions: $p_1 - p_2$. To make an inference about this difference, we will select two independent random samples consisting of n_1 units from population 1 and n_2 units from population 2.

Interval Estimation of $p_1 - p_2$

In the following example, we show how to compute a margin of error and develop an interval estimate of the difference between two population proportions.

A tax preparation firm is interested in comparing the quality of work at two of its regional offices. By randomly selecting samples of tax returns prepared at each office and verifying the sample returns' accuracy, the firm will be able to estimate the proportion of erroneous returns prepared at each office. Of particular interest is the difference between these proportions.

$$p_1 = \text{proportion of erroneous returns for population 1 (office 1)}$$
$$p_2 = \text{proportion of erroneous returns for population 2 (office 2)}$$
$$\bar{p}_1 = \text{sample proportion for a simple random sample from population 1}$$
$$\bar{p}_2 = \text{sample proportion for a simple random sample from population 2}$$

The difference between the two population proportions is given by $p_1 - p_2$. The point estimator of $p_1 - p_2$ is as follows.

POINT ESTIMATOR OF THE DIFFERENCE BETWEEN TWO POPULATION PROPORTIONS

$$\bar{p}_1 - \bar{p}_2 \tag{10.10}$$

Thus, the point estimator of the difference between two population proportions is the difference between the sample proportions of two independent simple random samples.

As with other point estimators, the point estimator $\bar{p}_1 - \bar{p}_2$ has a sampling distribution that reflects the possible values of $\bar{p}_1 - \bar{p}_2$ if we repeatedly took two independent random samples. The mean of this sampling distribution is $p_1 - p_2$ and the standard error of $\bar{p}_1 - \bar{p}_2$ is as follows:

STANDARD ERROR OF $\bar{p}_1 - \bar{p}_2$

$$\sigma_{\bar{p}_1 - \bar{p}_2} = \sqrt{\frac{p_1(1 - p_1)}{n_1} + \frac{p_2(1 - p_2)}{n_2}} \tag{10.11}$$

If the sample sizes are large enough that n_1p_1, $n_1(1 - p_1)$, n_2p_2, and $n_2(1 - p_2)$ are all greater than or equal to 5, the sampling distribution of $\bar{p}_1 - \bar{p}_2$ can be approximated by a normal distribution.

As we showed previously, an interval estimate is given by a point estimate $\pm$ a margin of error. In the estimation of the difference between two population proportions, an interval estimate will take the following form:

$$\bar{p}_1 - \bar{p}_2 \pm \text{Margin of error}$$

With the sampling distribution of $\bar{p}_1 - \bar{p}_2$ approximated by a normal distribution, we would like to use $z_{\alpha/2}\sigma_{\bar{p}_1 - \bar{p}_2}$ as the margin of error. However, $\sigma_{\bar{p}_1 - \bar{p}_2}$ given by equation (10.11) cannot be used directly because the two population proportions, p_1 and p_2, are unknown. Using the sample proportion $\bar{p}_1$ to estimate p_1 and the sample proportion $\bar{p}_2$ to estimate p_2, the margin of error is as follows.

$$\text{Margin of error} = z_{\alpha/2}\sqrt{\frac{\bar{p}_1(1 - \bar{p}_1)}{n_1} + \frac{\bar{p}_2(1 - \bar{p}_2)}{n_2}} \tag{10.12}$$

The general form of an interval estimate of the difference between two population proportions is as follows.

INTERVAL ESTIMATE OF THE DIFFERENCE BETWEEN TWO POPULATION PROPORTIONS

$$\bar{p}_1 - \bar{p}_2 \pm z_{\alpha/2}\sqrt{\frac{\bar{p}_1(1 - \bar{p}_1)}{n_1} + \frac{\bar{p}_2(1 - \bar{p}_2)}{n_2}} \tag{10.13}$$

where $1 - \alpha$ is the confidence coefficient.

Returning to the tax preparation example, we find that independent simple random samples from the two offices provide the following information.

Office 1	Office 2
$n_1 = 250$	$n_2 = 300$
Number of returns with errors = 35	Number of returns with errors = 27

CD file
TaxPrep

The sample proportions for the two offices follow.

$$\bar{p}_1 = \frac{35}{250} = .14$$

$$\bar{p}_2 = \frac{27}{300} = .09$$

The point estimate of the difference between the proportions of erroneous tax returns for the two populations is $\bar{p}_1 - \bar{p}_2 = .14 - .09 = .05$. Thus, we estimate that office 1 has a .05, or 5%, greater error rate than office 2.

Expression (10.13) can now be used to provide a margin of error and interval estimate of the difference between the two population proportions. Using a 90% confidence interval with $z_{\alpha/2} = z_{.05} = 1.645$, we have

$$\bar{p}_1 - \bar{p}_2 \pm z_{\alpha/2}\sqrt{\frac{\bar{p}_1(1 - \bar{p}_1)}{n_1} + \frac{\bar{p}_2(1 - \bar{p}_2)}{n_2}}$$

$$.14 - .09 \pm 1.645\sqrt{\frac{.14(1 - .14)}{250} + \frac{.09(1 - .09)}{300}}$$

$$.05 \pm .045$$

Thus, the margin of error is .045, and the 90% confidence interval is .005 to .095.

Hypothesis Tests About $p_1 - p_2$

Let us now consider hypothesis tests about the difference between the proportions of two populations. We focus on tests involving no difference between the two population proportions. In this case, the three forms for a hypothesis test are as follows:

All hypotheses considered use 0 as the difference of interest.

$$H_0\colon p_1 - p_2 \geq 0 \qquad H_0\colon p_1 - p_2 \leq 0 \qquad H_0\colon p_1 - p_2 = 0$$
$$H_a\colon p_1 - p_2 < 0 \qquad H_a\colon p_1 - p_2 > 0 \qquad H_a\colon p_1 - p_2 \neq 0$$

When we assume H_0 is true as an equality, we have $p_1 - p_2 = 0$, which is the same as saying that the population proportions are equal, $p_1 = p_2$.

We will base the test statistic on the sampling distribution of the point estimator $\bar{p}_1 - \bar{p}_2$. In equation (10.11), we showed that the standard error of $\bar{p}_1 - \bar{p}_2$ is given by

$$\sigma_{\bar{p}_1 - \bar{p}_2} = \sqrt{\frac{p_1(1 - p_1)}{n_1} + \frac{p_2(1 - p_2)}{n_2}}$$

Under the assumption H_0 is true as an equality, the population proportions are equal and $p_1 = p_2 = p$. In this case, $\sigma_{\bar{p}_1 - \bar{p}_2}$ becomes

STANDARD ERROR OF $\bar{p}_1 - \bar{p}_2$ WHEN $p_1 = p_2 = p$

$$\sigma_{\bar{p}_1 - \bar{p}_2} = \sqrt{\frac{p(1-p)}{n_1} + \frac{p(1-p)}{n_2}} = \sqrt{p(1-p)\left(\frac{1}{n_1} + \frac{1}{n_2}\right)} \tag{10.14}$$

With p unknown, we pool, or combine, the point estimators from the two samples ($\bar{p}_1$ and $\bar{p}_2$) to obtain a single point estimator of p as follows:

POOLED ESTIMATOR OF p WHEN $p_1 = p_2 = p$

$$\bar{p} = \frac{n_1\bar{p}_1 + n_2\bar{p}_2}{n_1 + n_2} \tag{10.15}$$

This **pooled estimator of p** is a weighted average of $\bar{p}_1$ and $\bar{p}_2$.

Substituting $\bar{p}$ for p in equation (10.14), we obtain an estimate of the standard error of $\bar{p}_1 - \bar{p}_2$. This estimate of the standard error is used in the test statistic. The general form of the test statistic for hypothesis tests about the difference between two population proportions is the point estimator divided by the estimate of $\sigma_{\bar{p}_1 - \bar{p}_2}$.

TEST STATISTIC FOR HYPOTHESIS TESTS ABOUT $p_1 - p_2$

$$z = \frac{(\bar{p}_1 - \bar{p}_2)}{\sqrt{\bar{p}(1-\bar{p})\left(\frac{1}{n_1} + \frac{1}{n_2}\right)}} \tag{10.16}$$

This test statistic applies to large sample situations where n_1p_1, $n_1(1 - p_1)$, n_2p_2, and $n_2(1 - p_2)$ are all greater than or equal to 5.

Let us return to the tax preparation firm example and assume that the firm wants to use a hypothesis test to determine whether the error proportions differ between the two offices. A two-tailed test is required. The null and alternative hypotheses are as follows:

$$H_0: p_1 - p_2 = 0$$
$$H_a: p_1 - p_2 \neq 0$$

If H_0 is rejected, the firm can conclude that the error rates at the two offices differ. We will use $\alpha = .10$ as the level of significance.

The sample data previously collected showed $\bar{p}_1 = .14$ for the $n_1 = 250$ returns sampled at office 1 and $\bar{p}_2 = .09$ for the $n_2 = 300$ returns sampled at office 2. We continue by computing the pooled estimate of p.

$$\bar{p} = \frac{n_1\bar{p}_1 + n_2\bar{p}_2}{n_1 + n_2} = \frac{250(.14) + 300(.09)}{250 + 300} = .1127$$

Using this pooled estimate and the difference between the sample proportions, the value of the test statistic is as follows.

$$z = \frac{(\bar{p}_1 - \bar{p}_2)}{\sqrt{\bar{p}(1 - \bar{p})\left(\frac{1}{n_1} + \frac{1}{n_2}\right)}} = \frac{(.14 - .09)}{\sqrt{.1127(1 - .1127)\left(\frac{1}{250} + \frac{1}{300}\right)}} = 1.85$$

In computing the p-value for this two-tailed test, we first note that $z = 1.85$ is in the upper tail of the standard normal distribution. Using $z = 1.85$ and the standard normal distribution table, we find the area in the upper tail is $1.0000 - .9678 = .0322$. Doubling this area for a two-tailed test, we find the p-value $= 2(.0322) = .0644$. With the p-value less than $\alpha = .10$, H_0 is rejected at the .10 level of significance. The firm can conclude that the error rates differ between the two offices. This hypothesis testing conclusion is consistent with the earlier interval estimation results that showed the interval estimate of the difference between the population error rates at the two offices to be .005 to .095, with Office 1 having the higher error rate.

Exercises

Methods

28. Consider the following results for independent samples taken from two populations.

Sample 1	Sample 2
$n_1 = 400$	$n_2 = 300$
$\bar{p}_1 = .48$	$\bar{p}_2 = .36$

a. What is the point estimate of the difference between the two population proportions?
b. Develop a 90% confidence interval for the difference between the two population proportions.
c. Develop a 95% confidence interval for the difference between the two population proportions.

SELF test

29. Consider the hypothesis test

$$H_0: p_1 - p_2 \le 0$$
$$H_a: p_1 - p_2 > 0$$

The following results are for independent samples taken from the two populations.

Sample 1	Sample 2
$n_1 = 200$	$n_2 = 300$
$\bar{p}_1 = .22$	$\bar{p}_2 = .16$

a. What is the p-value?
b. With $\alpha = .05$, what is your hypothesis testing conclusion?

Applications

SELF test

30. A *BusinessWeek*/Harris survey asked senior executives at large corporations their opinions about the economic outlook for the future. One question was "Do you think that there will be an increase in the number of full-time employees at your company over the next 12 months?" In the current survey, 220 of 400 executives answered yes, while in a previous year survey, 192 of 400 executives had answered yes. Provide a 95% confidence interval estimate for the difference between the proportions at the two points in time. What is your interpretation of the interval estimate?

31. In recent years, the number of people who use the Internet to obtain political news has grown. Often the political Web sites ask Internet users to register their opinions by participating in online surveys. Pew Research Center conducted a survey of its own to learn about the participation of Republicans and Democrats in online surveys (Associated Press, January 6, 2003). The following sample data apply.

Political Party	Sample Size	Participate in Online Surveys
Republican	250	115
Democrat	350	98

a. Compute the point estimate of the proportion of Republicans who indicate they would participate in online surveys. Compute the point estimate for the Democrats.
b. What is the point estimate of the difference between the two population proportions?
c. At 95% confidence, what is the margin of error?
d. Representatives of the scientific polling industry claim that the profusion of online surveys can confuse people about actual public opinion. Do you agree with this statement? Use the 95% confidence interval estimate of the difference between the Republican and Democrat population proportions to help justify your answer.

32. An American Automobile Association (AAA) study investigated the question of whether a man or a woman was more likely to stop and ask for directions (AAA, January 2006). The situation referred to in the study stated the following: "If you and your spouse are driving together and become lost, would you stop and ask for directions?" A sample representative of the data used by AAA showed 300 of 811 women said that they would stop and ask for directions, while 255 of 750 men said that they would stop and ask for directions.
a. The AAA research hypothesis was that women would be more likely to say that they would stop and ask for directions. Formulate the null and alternative hypotheses for this study.
b. What is the percentage of women who indicated that they would stop and ask for directions?
c. What is the percentage of men who indicated that they would stop and ask for directions?
d. At $\alpha = .05$, test the hypothesis. What is the p-value, and what conclusion would you expect AAA to draw from this study?

33. Slot machines are the favorite game at casinos throughout the United States (*Harrah's Survey 2002: Profile of the American Gambler*). The following sample data show the number of women and number of men who selected slot machines as their favorite game.

	Women	Men
Sample Size	320	250
Favorite Game—Slots	256	165

a. What is the point estimate of the proportion of women who say slots is their favorite game?
b. What is the point estimate of the proportion of men who say slots is their favorite game?
c. Provide a 95% confidence interval estimate of the difference between the proportion of women and proportion of men who say slots is their favorite game.

34. The Bureau of Transportation tracks the flight arrival performances of the 10 biggest airlines in the United States (*The Wall Street Journal,* March 4, 2003). Flights that arrive within 15 minutes of schedule are considered on time. Using sample data consistent with Bureau of Transportation statistics reported in January 2001 and January 2002, consider the following:

January 2001	A sample of 924 flights showed 742 on time.
January 2002	A sample of 841 flights showed 714 on time.

a. What is the point estimate of on-time flights in January 2001?
b. What is the point estimate of on-time flights in January 2002?
c. Let p_1 denote the population proportion of on-time flights in January 2001 and p_2 denote the population proportion of on-time flights in January 2002. State the hypotheses that could be tested to determine whether the major airlines improved on-time flight performance during the one-year period.
d. At $\alpha = .05$, what is your conclusion? What is the p-value?

35. In a test of the quality of two television commercials, each commercial was shown in a separate test area six times over a one-week period. The following week a telephone survey was conducted to identify individuals who had seen the commercials. Those individuals were asked to state the primary message in the commercials. The following results were recorded.

	Commercial A	Commercial B
Number Who Saw Commercial	150	200
Number Who Recalled Message	63	60

a. Use $\alpha = .05$ and test the hypothesis that there is no difference in the recall proportions for the two commercials.
b. Compute a 95% confidence interval for the difference between the recall proportions for the two populations.

36. During the 2003 Super Bowl, Miller Lite Beer's commercial referred to as "The Miller Lite Girls" ranked among the top three most effective advertisements aired during the Super Bowl (*USA Today,* December 29, 2003). The survey of advertising effectiveness, conducted by *USA Today*'s Ad Track poll, reported separate samples by respondent age group to learn about how the Super Bowl advertisement appealed to different age groups. The following sample data apply to the "The Miller Lite Girls" commercial.

Age Group	Sample Size	Liked the Ad a Lot
Under 30	100	49
30 to 49	150	54

a. Formulate a hypothesis test that can be used to determine whether the population proportions for the two age groups differ.

b. What is the point estimate of the difference between the two population proportions?
c. Conduct the hypothesis test and report the p-value. At $\alpha = .05$, what is your conclusion?
d. Discuss the appeal of the advertisements to the younger and the older age groups. Would the Miller Lite organization find the results of the *USA Today* Ad Track poll encouraging? Explain.

37. A 2003 *New York Times*/CBS News poll sampled 523 adults who were planning a vacation during the next six months and found that 141 were expecting to travel by airplane (*New York Times News Service,* March 2, 2003). A similar survey question in a May 1993 *New York Times*/CBS News poll found that of 477 adults who were planning a vacation in the next six months, 81 were expecting to travel by airplane.
a. State the hypotheses that can be used to determine whether a significant change occurred in the population proportion planning to travel by airplane over the 10-year period.
b. What is the sample proportion expecting to travel by airplane in 2003? In 1993?
c. Use $\alpha = .01$ and test for a significant difference. What is your conclusion?
d. Discuss reasons that might provide an explanation for this conclusion.

Summary

In this chapter we discussed procedures for developing interval estimates and conducting hypothesis tests involving two populations. First, we showed how to make inferences about the difference between two population means when independent simple random samples are selected. We first considered the case where the population standard deviations, σ_1 and σ_2, could be assumed known. The standard normal distribution z was used to develop the interval estimate and served as the test statistic for hypothesis tests. We then considered the case where the population standard deviations were unknown and estimated by the sample standard deviations s_1 and s_2. In this case, the t distribution was used to develop the interval estimate and served as the test statistic for hypothesis tests.

Inferences about the difference between two population means were then discussed for the matched sample design. In the matched sample design each element provides a pair of data values, one from each population. The difference between the paired data values is then used in the statistical analysis. The matched sample design is generally preferred to the independent sample design because the matched-sample procedure often improves the precision of the estimate.

Finally, interval estimation and hypothesis testing about the difference between two population proportions were discussed. Statistical procedures for analyzing the difference between two population proportions are similar to the procedures for analyzing the difference between two population means.

Glossary

Independent simple random samples Samples selected from two populations in such a way that the elements making up one sample are chosen independently of the elements making up the other sample.
Matched samples Samples in which each data value of one sample is matched with a corresponding data value of the other sample.
Pooled estimator of *p* An estimator of a population proportion obtained by computing a weighted average of the point estimators obtained from two independent samples.

Key Formulas

Point Estimator of the Difference Between Two Population Means

$$\bar{x}_1 - \bar{x}_2 \tag{10.1}$$

Standard Error of $\bar{x}_1 - \bar{x}_2$

$$\sigma_{\bar{x}_1 - \bar{x}_2} = \sqrt{\frac{\sigma_1^2}{n_1} + \frac{\sigma_2^2}{n_2}} \tag{10.2}$$

Interval Estimate of the Difference Between Two Population Means: σ_1 and σ_2 Known

$$\bar{x}_1 - \bar{x}_2 \pm z_{\alpha/2}\sqrt{\frac{\sigma_1^2}{n_1} + \frac{\sigma_2^2}{n_2}} \tag{10.4}$$

Test Statistic for Hypothesis Tests About $\mu_1 - \mu_2$: σ_1 and σ_2 Known

$$z = \frac{(\bar{x}_1 - \bar{x}_2) - D_0}{\sqrt{\frac{\sigma_1^2}{n_1} + \frac{\sigma_2^2}{n_2}}} \tag{10.5}$$

Interval Estimate of the Difference Between Two Population Means: σ_1 and σ_2 Unknown

$$\bar{x}_1 - \bar{x}_2 \pm t_{\alpha/2}\sqrt{\frac{s_1^2}{n_1} + \frac{s_2^2}{n_2}} \tag{10.6}$$

Degrees of Freedom: t Distribution with Two Independent Random Samples

$$df = \frac{\left(\frac{s_1^2}{n_1} + \frac{s_2^2}{n_2}\right)^2}{\frac{1}{n_1 - 1}\left(\frac{s_1^2}{n_1}\right)^2 + \frac{1}{n_2 - 1}\left(\frac{s_2^2}{n_2}\right)^2} \tag{10.7}$$

Test Statistic for Hypothesis Tests About $\mu_1 - \mu_2$: σ_1 and σ_2 Unknown

$$t = \frac{(\bar{x}_1 - \bar{x}_2) - D_0}{\sqrt{\frac{s_1^2}{n_1} + \frac{s_2^2}{n_2}}} \tag{10.8}$$

Test Statistic for Hypothesis Tests Involving Matched Samples

$$t = \frac{\bar{d} - \mu_d}{s_d/\sqrt{n}} \tag{10.9}$$

Point Estimator of the Difference Between Two Population Proportions

$$\bar{p}_1 - \bar{p}_2 \tag{10.10}$$

Standard Error of $\bar{p}_1 - \bar{p}_2$

$$\sigma_{\bar{p}_1 - \bar{p}_2} = \sqrt{\frac{p_1(1 - p_1)}{n_1} + \frac{p_2(1 - p_2)}{n_2}} \tag{10.11}$$

Interval Estimate of the Difference Between Two Population Proportions

$$\bar{p}_1 - \bar{p}_2 \pm z_{\alpha/2}\sqrt{\frac{\bar{p}_1(1 - \bar{p}_1)}{n_1} + \frac{\bar{p}_2(1 - \bar{p}_2)}{n_2}} \tag{10.13}$$

Standard Error of $\bar{p}_1 - \bar{p}_2$ When $p_1 = p_2 = p$

$$\sigma_{\bar{p}_1 - \bar{p}_2} = \sqrt{p(1 - p)\left(\frac{1}{n_1} + \frac{1}{n_2}\right)} \tag{10.14}$$

Pooled Estimator of p When $p_1 = p_2 = p$

$$\bar{p} = \frac{n_1\bar{p}_1 + n_2\bar{p}_2}{n_1 + n_2} \tag{10.15}$$

Test Statistic for Hypothesis Tests About $p_1 - p_2$

$$z = \frac{(\bar{p}_1 - \bar{p}_2)}{\sqrt{\bar{p}(1 - \bar{p})\left(\frac{1}{n_1} + \frac{1}{n_2}\right)}} \tag{10.16}$$

Supplementary Exercises

38. Safegate Foods, Inc., is redesigning the checkout lanes in its supermarkets throughout the country and is considering two designs. Tests on customer checkout times conducted at two stores where the two new systems have been installed result in the following summary of the data.

System A	System B
$n_1 = 120$	$n_2 = 100$
$\bar{x}_1 = 4.1$ minutes	$\bar{x}_2 = 3.4$ minutes
$\sigma_1 = 2.2$ minutes	$\sigma_2 = 1.5$ minutes

Test at the .05 level of significance to determine whether the population mean checkout times of the two systems differ. Which system is preferred?

39. Three-megapixel digital cameras are typically the lightest, most compact, and easiest to use. However, if you plan to enlarge or crop images, you will probably want to spend more for a higher-resolution model. The following shows sample prices of five-megapixel and three-megapixel digital cameras (*Consumer Reports Buying Guide*, 2004).

CD file
Digital

Five-Megapixel		Three-Megapixel	
Model	Price	Model	Price
Nikon 5700	890	Kodak DX4330	280
Olympus C-5050	620	Canon A70	290
Sony DCS-F717	730	Sony DSC P8	370
Olympus C-5050	480	Minolta XI	400
Minolta 7Hi	1060	Sony DSC P72	310
HP 935	450	Nikon 3100	340
Pentax 550	540	Panasonic DMC-LC33	270
Canon S50	500	Pentax S	380
Kyocera TVS	890		
Minolta F300	440		

a. Provide a point estimate of the difference between population mean prices for the two types of digital cameras. What observation can you make about the price of the higher-quality five-megapixel model?
b. Develop a 95% confidence interval estimate of the difference between the two population mean prices.

40. Mutual funds are classified as *load* or *no-load* funds. Load funds require an investor to pay an initial fee based on a percentage of the amount invested in the fund. The no-load funds do not require this initial fee. Some financial advisors argue that the load mutual funds may be worth the extra fee because these funds provide a higher mean rate of return than the no-load mutual funds. A sample of 30 load mutual funds and a sample of 30 no-load mutual funds were selected. Data were collected on the annual return for the funds over a five-year period. The data are contained in the data set Mutual. The data for the first five load and first five no-load mutual funds are as follows.

CD file
Mutual

Mutual Funds—Load	Return	Mutual Funds—No Load	Return
American National Growth	15.51	Amana Income Fund	13.24
Arch Small Cap Equity	14.57	Berger One Hundred	12.13
Bartlett Cap Basic	17.73	Columbia International Stock	12.17
Calvert World International	10.31	Dodge & Cox Balanced	16.06
Colonial Fund A	16.23	Evergreen Fund	17.61

a. Formulate H_0 and H_a such that rejection of H_0 leads to the conclusion that the load mutual funds have a higher mean annual return over the five-year period.
b. Use the 60 mutual funds in the data set Mutual to conduct the hypothesis test. What is the p-value? At $\alpha = .05$, what is your conclusion?

41. The National Association of Home Builders provided data on the cost of the most popular home remodeling projects. Sample data on cost in thousands of dollars for two types of remodeling projects are as follows.

Kitchen	Master Bedroom	Kitchen	Master Bedroom
25.2	18.0	23.0	17.8
17.4	22.9	19.7	24.6
22.8	26.4	16.9	21.0
21.9	24.8	21.8	
19.7	26.9	23.6	

a. Develop a point estimate of the difference between the population mean remodeling costs for the two types of projects.
b. Develop a 90% confidence interval for the difference between the two population means.

42. Typical prices of single-family homes in the state of Florida are shown for a sample of 15 metropolitan areas (*Naples Daily News,* February 23, 2003). Data are in thousands of dollars.

CD file
Florida

Metropolitan Area	January 2003	January 2002
Daytona Beach	117	96
Fort Lauderdale	207	169
Fort Myers	143	129
Fort Walton Beach	139	134
Gainesville	131	119
Jacksonville	128	119
Lakeland	91	85
Miami	193	165
Naples	263	233
Ocala	86	90
Orlando	134	121
Pensacola	111	105
Sarasota-Bradenton	168	141
Tallahassee	140	130
Tampa-St. Petersburg	139	129

a. Use a matched-sample analysis to develop a point estimate of the population mean one-year increase in the price of single-family homes in Florida.
b. Develop a 90% confidence interval estimate of the population mean one-year increase in the price of single-family homes in Florida.
c. What was the percentage increase over the one-year period?

43. Jupiter Media used a survey to determine how people use their free time. Watching television was the most popular activity selected by both men and women (*The Wall Street Journal,* January 26, 2004). The proportion of men and the proportion of women who selected watching television as their most popular leisure time activity can be estimated from the following sample data.

Gender	Sample Size	Watching Television
Men	800	248
Women	600	156

a. State the hypotheses that can be used to test for a difference between the proportion for the population of men and the proportion for the population of women who selected watching television as their most popular leisure time activity.
b. What is the sample proportion of men who selected watching television as their most popular leisure time activity? What is the sample proportion of women?
c. Conduct the hypothesis test and compute the p-value. At a .05 level of significance, what is your conclusion?
d. What is the margin of error and 95% confidence interval estimate of the difference between the population proportions?

44. A large automobile insurance company selected samples of single and married male policyholders and recorded the number who made an insurance claim over the preceding three-year period.

Single Policyholders	Married Policyholders
$n_1 = 400$	$n_2 = 900$
Number making claims = 76	Number making claims = 90

a. Use $\alpha = .05$. Test to determine whether the claim rates differ between single and married male policyholders.
b. Provide a 95% confidence interval for the difference between the proportions for the two populations.

45. Medical tests were conducted to learn about drug-resistant tuberculosis. Of 142 cases tested in New Jersey, 9 were found to be drug-resistant. Of 268 cases tested in Texas, 5 were found to be drug-resistant. Do these data suggest a statistically significant difference between the proportions of drug-resistant cases in the two states? Use a .02 level of significance. What is the p-value, and what is your conclusion?

46. In July 2001, the Harris Ad Track Research Service conducted a survey to evaluate the effectiveness of a major advertising campaign for Kodak cameras (*USA Today,* August 27, 2001). In a sample of 430 respondents, 163 thought the ads were very effective. In another sample of 285 respondents to other ad campaigns, 66 thought the ads were very effective.
   a. Estimate the proportion of respondents who thought the Kodak ads were very effective and the proportion of respondents who felt the other ads were very effective.
   b. Provide a 95% confidence interval for the difference in proportions.
   c. On the basis of your results in part (b), do you believe the Kodak advertising campaign is more effective than most advertising campaigns?

47. In June 2001, 38% of fund managers surveyed believed that the core inflation rate would be higher in one year. One month later a similar survey revealed that 22% of fund managers expected the core inflation rate to be higher in one year (*Global Research Highlights,* Merrill Lynch, July 20, 2001). Assume that the sample size was 200 in both the June and July surveys.
   a. Develop a point estimate of the difference between the June and July proportions of fund managers who felt the core inflation rate would be higher in one year.
   b. Develop hypotheses such that rejection of the null hypothesis allows us to conclude that inflation expectations diminished between June and July.
   c. Conduct a test of the hypotheses in part (b) using $\alpha = .01$. What is your conclusion?

Case Problem Par, Inc.

Par, Inc., is a major manufacturer of golf equipment. Management believes that Par's market share could be increased with the introduction of a cut-resistant, longer-lasting golf ball. Therefore, the research group at Par has been investigating a new golf ball coating designed to resist cuts and provide a more durable ball. The tests with the coating have been promising.

One of the researchers voiced concern about the effect of the new coating on driving distances. Par would like the new cut-resistant ball to offer driving distances comparable to those of the current-model golf ball. To compare the driving distances for the two balls, 40 balls of both the new and current models were subjected to distance tests. The testing was performed with a mechanical hitting machine so that any difference between the mean distances for the two models could be attributed to a difference in the two models. The results of the tests, with distances measured to the nearest yard, follow. These data are available on the CD that accompanies the text.

CD file

Golf

Model		Model		Model		Model	
Current	**New**	**Current**	**New**	**Current**	**New**	**Current**	**New**
264	277	270	272	263	274	281	283
261	269	287	259	264	266	274	250
267	263	289	264	284	262	273	253
272	266	280	280	263	271	263	260
258	262	272	274	260	260	275	270
283	251	275	281	283	281	267	263
258	262	265	276	255	250	279	261
266	289	260	269	272	263	274	255
259	286	278	268	266	278	276	263
270	264	275	262	268	264	262	279

Managerial Report

1. Formulate and present the rationale for a hypothesis test that Par could use to compare the driving distances of the current and new golf balls.
2. Analyze the data to provide the hypothesis testing conclusion. What is the p-value for your test? What is your recommendation for Par, Inc.?
3. Provide descriptive statistical summaries of the data for each model.
4. What is the 95% confidence interval for the population mean of each model, and what is the 95% confidence interval for the difference between the means of the two populations?
5. Do you see a need for larger sample sizes and more testing with the golf balls? Discuss.

Appendix 10.1 Inferences About Two Populations Using Minitab

We describe the use of Minitab to develop interval estimates and conduct hypothesis tests about the difference between two population means and the difference between two population proportions. Minitab provides both interval estimation and hypothesis testing results within the same module. Thus, the Minitab procedure is the same for both types of inferences. In the examples that follow, we will demonstrate interval estimation and hypothesis testing for the same two samples. We note that Minitab does not provide a routine for inferences about the difference between two population means when the population standard deviations σ_1 and σ_2 are known.

Difference Between Two Population Means: σ_1 and σ_2 Unknown

CD file

CheckAcct

We will use the data for the checking account balances example presented in Section 10.2. The checking account balances at the Cherry Grove branch are in column C1, and the checking account balances at the Beechmont branch are in column C2. In this example, we will use the Minitab 2-Sample t procedure to provide a 95% confidence interval estimate of the difference between population means for the checking account balances at the two branch banks. The output of the procedure also provides the p-value for the hypothesis test: H_0: $\mu_1 - \mu_2 = 0$ versus H_a: $\mu_1 - \mu_2 \neq 0$. The following steps are necessary to execute the procedure:

Step 1. Select the **Stat** menu
Step 2. Choose **Basic Statistics**
Step 3. Choose **2-Sample t**
Step 4. When the 2-Sample t (Test and Confidence Interval) dialog box appears:
Select **Samples in different columns**
Enter C1 in the **First** box
Enter C2 in the **Second** box
Select **Options**
Step 5. When the 2-Sample t - Options dialog box appears:
Enter 95 in the **Confidence level** box
Enter 0 in the **Test difference** box
Enter not equal in the **Alternative** box
Click **OK**
Step 6. Click **OK**

The 95% confidence interval estimate is \$37 to \$193, as described in Section 10.2. The p-value = .005 shows the null hypothesis of equal population means can be rejected at the $\alpha = .01$ level of significance. In other applications, step 5 may be modified to provide different confidence levels, different hypothesized values, and different forms of the hypotheses.

Difference Between Two Population Means with Matched Samples

CD file
Matched

We use the data on production times in Table 10.2 to illustrate the matched-sample procedure. The completion times for method 1 are entered into column C1 and the completion times for method 2 are entered into column C2. The Minitab steps for a matched sample are as follows:

Step 1. Select the **Stat** menu
Step 2. Choose **Basic Statistics**
Step 3. Choose **Paired t**
Step 4. When the Paired t (Test and Confidence Interval) dialog box appears:
Select **Samples in columns**
Enter C1 in the **First sample** box
Enter C2 in the **Second sample** box
Select **Options**
Step 5. When the Paired t - Options dialog box appears:
Enter 95 in the **Confidence level**
Enter 0 in the **Test mean** box
Enter not equal in the **Alternative** box
Click **OK**
Step 6. Click **OK**

The 95% confidence interval estimate is $-.05$ to .65, as described in Section 10.3. The p-value = .08 shows that the null hypothesis of no difference in completion times cannot be rejected at $\alpha = .05$. Step 5 may be modified to provide different confidence levels, different hypothesized values, and different forms of the hypothesis.

CD file
TaxPrep

Difference Between Two Population Proportions

We will use the data on tax preparation errors presented in Section 10.4. The sample results for 250 tax returns prepared at Office 1 are in column C1 and the sample results for 300 tax returns prepared at Office 2 are in column C2. Yes denotes an error was found in the tax return and No indicates no error was found. The procedure we describe provides both a 95% confidence interval estimate of the difference between the two population proportions and hypothesis testing results for H_0: $p_1 - p_2 = 0$ and H_a: $p_1 - p_2 \neq 0$.

Step 1. Select the **Stat** menu
Step 2. Choose **Basic Statistics**
Step 3. Choose **2 Proportions**
Step 4. When the 2 Proportions (Test and Confidence Interval) dialog box appears:
Select **Samples in different columns**
Enter C1 in the **First** box
Enter C2 in the **Second** box
Select **Options**
Step 5. When the 2 Proportions-Options dialog box appears:
Enter 90 in the **Confidence level** box
Enter 0 in the **Test difference** box
Enter not equal in the **Alternative** box
Select **Use pooled estimate of p for test**
Click **OK**
Step 6. Click **OK**

The 90% confidence interval estimate is .005 to .095, as described in Section 10.4. The p-value $= .065$ shows the null hypothesis of no difference in error rates can be rejected at $\alpha = .10$. Step 5 may be modified to provide different confidence levels, different hypothesized values, and different forms of the hypotheses.

In the tax preparation example, the data are qualitative. Yes and No are used to indicate whether an error is present. In modules involving proportions, Minitab calculates proportions for the response coming second in alphabetic order. Thus, in the tax preparation example, Minitab computes the proportion of Yes responses, which is the proportion we wanted.

If Minitab's alphabetical ordering does not compute the proportion for the response of interest, we can fix it. Select any cell in the data column, go to the Minitab menu bar, and select Editor > Column > Value Order. This sequence will provide the option of entering a user-specified order. Simply make sure that the response of interest is listed second in the define-an-order box. Minitab's 2 Proportion routine will then provide the confidence interval and hypothesis testing results for the population proportion of interest.

Finally, we note that Minitab's 2 Proportion routine uses a computational procedure different from the procedure described in the text. Thus, the Minitab output can be expected to provide slightly different interval estimates and slightly different p-values. However, results from the two methods should be close and are expected to provide the same interpretation and conclusion.

Appendix 10.2 Inferences About Two Populations Using Excel

We describe the use of Excel to conduct hypothesis tests about the difference between two population means.* We begin with inferences about the difference between the means of two populations when the population standard deviations σ_1 and σ_2 are known.

*Excel's data analysis tools provide hypothesis testing procedures for the difference between two population means. No routines are available for interval estimation of the difference between two population means nor for inferences about the difference between two population proportions.

Difference Between Two Population Means: σ_1 and σ_2 Known

CD file
ExamScores

We will use the examination scores for the two training centers discussed in Section 10.1. The label Center A is in cell A1 and the label Center B is in cell B1. The examination scores for Center A are in cells A2:A31 and examination scores for Center B are in cells B2:B41. The population standard deviations are assumed known with $\sigma_1 = 10$ and $\sigma_2 = 10$. The Excel routine will request the input of variances which are $\sigma_1^2 = 100$ and $\sigma_2^2 = 100$. The following steps can be used to conduct a hypothesis test about the difference between the two population means.

Step 1. Select the **Tools** menu
Step 2. Choose **Data Analysis**
Step 3. When the Data Analysis dialog box appears:
Choose **z-Test: Two Sample for Means**
Click **OK**
Step 4. When the z-Test: Two Sample for Means dialog box appears:
Enter A1:A31 in the **Variable 1 Range** box
Enter B1:B41 in the **Variable 2 Range** box
Enter 0 in the **Hypothesized Mean Difference** box
Enter 100 in the **Variable 1 Variance** box
Enter 100 in the **Variable 2 Variance** box
Select **Labels**
Enter .05 in the **Alpha** box
Select **Output Range** and enter C1 in the box
Click **OK**

The two-tailed p-value is denoted P($Z <= z$) two-tail. Its value of .0978 does not allow us to reject the null hypothesis at $\alpha = .05$.

Difference Between Two Population Means: σ_1 and σ_2 Unknown

CD file
SoftwareTest

We use the data for the software testing study in Table 10.1. The data are already entered into an Excel worksheet with the label Current in cell A1 and the label New in cell B1. The completion times for the current technology are in cells A2:A13, and the completion times for the new software are in cells B2:B13. The following steps can be used to conduct a hypothesis test about the difference between two population means with σ_1 and σ_2 unknown.

Step 1. Select **Tools** menu
Step 2. Choose **Data Analysis**
Step 3. When the Data Analysis dialog box appears:
Choose **t-Test: Two Sample Assuming Unequal Variances**
Click **OK**
Step 4. When the t-Test: Two Sample Assuming Unequal Variances dialog box appears:
Enter A1:A13 in the **Variable 1 Range** box
Enter B1:B13 in the **Variable 2 Range** box
Enter 0 in the **Hypothesized Mean Difference** box
Select **Labels**
Enter .05 in the **Alpha** box
Select **Output Range** and enter C1 in the box
Click **OK**

The appropriate p-value is denoted P(T <=t) one-tail. Its value of .017 allows us to reject the null hypothesis at $\alpha = .05$.

Difference Between Two Population Means with Matched Samples

CD file
Matched

We use the matched-sample completion times in Table 10.2 to illustrate. The data are entered into a worksheet with the label Method 1 in cell A1 and the label Method 2 in cell B1. The completion times for method 1 are in cells A2:A7 and the completion times for method 2 are in cells B2:B7. The Excel procedure uses the steps previously described for the *t*-Test except the user chooses the **t-Test: Paired Two Sample for Means** data analysis tool in step 3. The variable 1 range is A1:A7 and the variable 2 range is B1:B7.

The appropriate *p*-value is denoted P(T<=t) two-tail. Its value of .08 does not allow us to reject the null hypothesis at $\alpha = .05$.

CHAPTER 12

Tests of Goodness of Fit and Independence

CONTENTS

STATISTICS *in* PRACTICE

UNITED WAY*
ROCHESTER, NEW YORK

United Way of Greater Rochester is a nonprofit organization dedicated to improving the quality of life for all people in the seven counties it serves by meeting the community's most important human care needs.

The annual United Way/Red Cross fund-raising campaign, conducted each spring, funds hundreds of programs offered by more than 200 service providers. These providers meet a wide variety of human needs—physical, mental, and social—and serve people of all ages, backgrounds, and economic means.

Because of enormous volunteer involvement, United Way of Greater Rochester is able to hold its operating costs at just eight cents of every dollar raised.

The United Way of Greater Rochester decided to conduct a survey to learn more about community perceptions of charities. Focus-group interviews were held with professional, service, and general worker groups to get preliminary information on perceptions. The information obtained was then used to help develop the questionnaire for the survey. The questionnaire was pretested, modified, and distributed to 440 individuals; 323 completed questionnaires were obtained.

A variety of descriptive statistics, including frequency distributions and crosstabulations, were provided from the data collected. An important part of the analysis involved the use of contingency tables and chi-square tests of independence. One use of such statistical tests was to determine whether perceptions of administrative expenses were independent of occupation.

The hypotheses for the test of independence were:

H_0: Perception of United Way administrative expenses is independent of the occupation of the respondent.

United Way programs meet the needs of children as well as adults. © Ed Bock/CORBIS.

H_a: Perception of United Way administrative expenses is not independent of the occupation of the respondent.

Two questions in the survey provided the data for the statistical test. One question obtained data on perceptions of the percentage of funds going to administrative expenses (up to 10%, 11–20%, and 21% or more). The other question asked for the occupation of the respondent.

The chi-square test at a .05 level of significance led to rejection of the null hypothesis of independence and to the conclusion that perceptions of United Way's administrative expenses did vary by occupation. Actual administrative expenses were less than 9%, but 35% of the respondents perceived that administrative expenses were 21% or more. Hence, many had inaccurate perceptions of administrative costs. In this group, production-line, clerical, sales, and professional-technical employees had more inaccurate perceptions than other groups.

The community perceptions study helped United Way of Rochester to develop adjustments to its programs and fund-raising activities. In this chapter, you will learn how a statistical test of independence, such as that described here, is conducted.

*The authors are indebted to Dr. Philip R. Tyler, Marketing Consultant to the United Way, for providing this Statistics in Practice.

In Chapter 11 we showed how the chi-square distribution could be used in estimation and in hypothesis tests about a population variance. In Chapter 12, we introduce two additional hypothesis testing procedures, both based on the use of the chi-square distribution. Like other hypothesis testing procedures, these tests compare sample results with those that are expected when the null hypothesis is true. The conclusion of the hypothesis test is based on how "close" the sample results are to the expected results.

In the following section we introduce a goodness of fit test for a multinomial population. Later we discuss the test for independence using contingency tables and then show goodness of fit tests for the Poisson and normal distributions.

12.1 Goodness of Fit Test: A Multinomial Population

In this section we consider the case in which each element of a population is assigned to one and only one of several classes or categories. Such a population is a **multinomial population**. The multinomial distribution can be thought of as an extension of the binomial distribution to the case of three or more categories of outcomes. On each trial of a multinomial experiment, one and only one of the outcomes occurs. Each trial of the experiment is assumed to be independent, and the probabilities of the outcomes remain the same for each trial.

The assumptions for the multinomial experiment parallel those for the binomial experiment with the exception that the multinomial has three or more outcomes per trial.

As an example, consider the market share study being conducted by Scott Marketing Research. Over the past year market shares stabilized at 30% for company A, 50% for company B, and 20% for company C. Recently company C developed a "new and improved" product to replace its current entry in the market. Company C retained Scott Marketing Research to determine whether the new product will alter market shares.

In this case, the population of interest is a multinomial population; each customer is classified as buying from company A, company B, or company C. Thus, we have a multinomial population with three outcomes. Let us use the following notation for the proportions.

$$p_A = \text{market share for company A}$$
$$p_B = \text{market share for company B}$$
$$p_C = \text{market share for company C}$$

Scott Marketing Research will conduct a sample survey and compute the proportion preferring each company's product. A hypothesis test will then be conducted to see whether the new product caused a change in market shares. Assuming that company C's new product will not alter the market shares, the null and alternative hypotheses are stated as follows.

$$H_0\colon p_A = .30,\ p_B = .50,\ \text{and } p_C = .20$$
$$H_a\colon \text{The population proportions are not } p_A = .30,\ p_B = .50,\ \text{and } p_C = .20$$

If the sample results lead to the rejection of H_0, Scott Marketing Research will have evidence that the introduction of the new product affects market shares.

Let us assume that the market research firm has used a consumer panel of 200 customers for the study. Each individual was asked to specify a purchase preference among the three alternatives: company A's product, company B's product, and company C's new product. The 200 responses are summarized here.

The consumer panel of 200 customers in which each individual is asked to select one of three alternatives is equivalent to a multinomial experiment consisting of 200 trials.

Observed Frequency		
Company A's Product	**Company B's Product**	**Company C's New Product**
48	98	54

We now can perform a **goodness of fit test** that will determine whether the sample of 200 customer purchase preferences is consistent with the null hypothesis. The goodness of fit test is based on a comparison of the sample of *observed* results with the *expected* results under the assumption that the null hypothesis is true. Hence, the next step is to compute expected purchase preferences for the 200 customers under the assumption that $p_A = .30$, $p_B = .50$, and $p_C = .20$. Doing so provides the expected results.

Expected Frequency		
Company A's Product	**Company B's Product**	**Company C's New Product**
200(.30) = 60	200(.50) = 100	200(.20) = 40

Thus, we see that the expected frequency for each category is found by multiplying the sample size of 200 by the hypothesized proportion for the category.

The goodness of fit test now focuses on the differences between the observed frequencies and the expected frequencies. Large differences between observed and expected frequencies cast doubt on the assumption that the hypothesized proportions or market shares are correct. Whether the differences between the observed and expected frequencies are "large" or "small" is a question answered with the aid of the following test statistic.

TEST STATISTIC FOR GOODNESS OF FIT

$$\chi^2 = \sum_{i=1}^{k} \frac{(f_i - e_i)^2}{e_i} \tag{12.1}$$

where

f_i = observed frequency for category i
e_i = expected frequency for category i
k = the number of categories

Note: The test statistic has a chi-square distribution with $k - 1$ degrees of freedom provided that the expected frequencies are 5 *or more* for all categories.

Let us continue with the Scott Market Research example and use the sample data to test the hypothesis that the multinomial population retains the proportions $p_A = .30$, $p_B = .50$, and $p_C = .20$. We will use an $\alpha = .05$ level of significance. We proceed by using the observed and expected frequencies to compute the value of the test statistic. With the expected frequencies all 5 or more, the computation of the chi-square test statistic is shown in Table 12.1. Thus, we have $\chi^2 = 7.34$.

The test for goodness of fit is always a one-tailed test with the rejection occurring in the upper tail of the chi-square distribution.

We will reject the null hypothesis if the differences between the observed and expected frequencies are *large*. Large differences between the observed and expected frequencies will result in a large value for the test statistic. Thus the test of goodness of fit will always be an upper tail test. We can use the upper tail area for the test statistic and the p-value approach to determine whether the null hypothesis can be rejected. With $k - 1 = 3 - 1 = 2$ degrees of freedom, the chi-square table (Table 3 of Appendix B) provides the following:

An introduction to the chi-square distribution and the use of the chi-square table were presented in Section 11.1.

Area in Upper Tail	**.10**	**.05**	**.025**	**.01**	**.005**
χ^2 Value (2 *df*)	4.605	5.991	7.378	9.210	10.597

↑ $\chi^2 = 7.34$ (between 5.991 and 7.378)

TABLE 12.1 COMPUTATION OF THE CHI-SQUARE TEST STATISTIC FOR THE SCOTT MARKETING RESEARCH MARKET SHARE STUDY

Category	Hypothesized Proportion	Observed Frequency (f_i)	Expected Frequency (e_i)	Difference ($f_i - e_i$)	Squared Difference $(f_i - e_i)^2$	Squared Difference Divided by Expected Frequency $(f_i - e_i)^2/e_i$
Company A	.30	48	60	−12	144	2.40
Company B	.50	98	100	−2	4	0.04
Company C	.20	54	40	14	196	4.90
Total		200				$\chi^2 = 7.34$

The test statistic $\chi^2 = 7.34$ is between 5.991 and 7.378. Thus, the corresponding upper tail area or p-value must be between .05 and .025. With p-value $\leq \alpha = .05$, we reject H_0 and conclude that the introduction of the new product by company C will alter the current market share structure. Minitab or Excel procedures provided in Appendix F at the back of the book can be used to show $\chi^2 = 7.34$ provides a p-value $= .0255$.

Instead of using the p-value, we could use the critical value approach to draw the same conclusion. With $\alpha = .05$ and 2 degrees of freedom, the critical value for the test statistic is $\chi^2_{.05} = 5.991$. The upper tail rejection rule becomes

$$\text{Reject } H_0 \text{ if } \chi^2 \geq 5.991$$

With $7.34 > 5.991$, we reject H_0. The p-value approach and critical value approach provide the same hypothesis testing conclusion.

Although no further conclusions can be made as a result of the test, we can compare the observed and expected frequencies informally to obtain an idea of how the market share structure may change. Considering company C, we find that the observed frequency of 54 is larger than the expected frequency of 40. Because the expected frequency was based on current market shares, the larger observed frequency suggests that the new product will have a positive effect on company C's market share. Comparisons of the observed and expected frequencies for the other two companies indicate that company C's gain in market share will hurt company A more than company B.

Let us summarize the general steps that can be used to conduct a goodness of fit test for a hypothesized multinomial population distribution.

MULTINOMIAL DISTRIBUTION GOODNESS OF FIT TEST: A SUMMARY

1. State the null and alternative hypotheses.

   H_0: The population follows a multinomial distribution with specified probabilities for each of the k categories

   H_a: The population does not follow a multinomial distribution with the specified probabilities for each of the k categories

2. Select a random sample and record the observed frequencies f_i for each category.
3. Assume the null hypothesis is true and determine the expected frequency e_i in each category by multiplying the category probability by the sample size.

4. Compute the value of the test statistic.

$$\chi^2 = \sum_{i=1}^{k} \frac{(f_i - e_i)^2}{e_i}$$

5. Rejection rule:

p-value approach:	Reject H_0 if p-value $\leq \alpha$
Critical value approach:	Reject H_0 if $\chi^2 \geq \chi^2_\alpha$

where α is the level of significance for the test and there are $k - 1$ degrees of freedom.

Exercises

Methods

SELF test

1. Test the following hypotheses by using the χ^2 goodness of fit test.

$$H_0: p_A = .40, p_B = .40, \text{ and } p_C = .20$$
$$H_a: \text{The population proportions are not } p_A = .40, p_B = .40, \text{ and } p_C = .20$$

A sample of size 200 yielded 60 in category A, 120 in category B, and 20 in category C. Use $\alpha = .01$ and test to see whether the proportions are as stated in H_0.

a. Use the p-value approach.

b. Repeat the test using the critical value approach.

2. Suppose we have a multinomial population with four categories: A, B, C, and D. The null hypothesis is that the proportion of items is the same in every category. The null hypothesis is

$$H_0: p_A = p_B = p_C = p_D = .25$$

A sample of size 300 yielded the following results.

A: 85 B: 95 C: 50 D: 70

Use $\alpha = .05$ to determine whether H_0 should be rejected. What is the p-value?

Applications

SELF test

3. During the first 13 weeks of the television season, the Saturday evening 8:00 P.M. to 9:00 P.M. audience proportions were recorded as ABC 29%, CBS 28%, NBC 25%, and independents 18%. A sample of 300 homes two weeks after a Saturday night schedule revision yielded the following viewing audience data: ABC 95 homes, CBS 70 homes, NBC 89 homes, and independents 46 homes. Test with $\alpha = .05$ to determine whether the viewing audience proportions changed.

4. M&M/MARS, makers of M&M® Chocolate Candies, conducted a national poll in which more than 10 million people indicated their preference for a new color. The tally of this poll resulted in the replacement of tan-colored M&Ms with a new blue color. In the brochure "Colors," made available by M&M/MARS Consumer Affairs, the distribution of colors for the plain candies is as follows:

Brown	Yellow	Red	Orange	Green	Blue
30%	20%	20%	10%	10%	10%

In a follow-up study, samples of 1-pound bags were used to determine whether the reported percentages were indeed valid. The following results were obtained for one sample of 506 plain candies.

Brown	Yellow	Red	Orange	Green	Blue
177	135	79	41	36	38

Use $\alpha = .05$ to determine whether these data support the percentages reported by the company.

5. Where do women most often buy casual clothing? Data from the U.S. Shopper Database provided the following percentages for women shopping at each of the various outlets (*The Wall Street Journal,* January 28, 2004).

Outlet	Percentage	Outlet	Percentage
Wal-Mart	24	Kohl's	8
Traditional department stores	11	Mail order	12
JC Penney	8	Other	37

The other category included outlets such as Target, Kmart, and Sears as well as numerous smaller specialty outlets. No individual outlet in this group accounted for more than 5% of the women shoppers. A recent survey using a sample of 140 women shoppers in Atlanta, Georgia, found 42 Wal-Mart, 20 traditional department store, 8 JC Penney, 10 Kohl's, 21 mail order, and 39 other outlet shoppers. Does this sample suggest that women shoppers in Atlanta differ from the shopping preferences expressed in the U.S. Shopper Database? What is the p-value? Use $\alpha = .05$. What is your conclusion?

6. The American Bankers Association collects data on the use of credit cards, debit cards, personal checks, and cash when consumers pay for in-store purchases (*The Wall Street Journal,* December 16, 2003). In 1999, the following usages were reported.

In-Store Purchase	Percentage
Credit card	22
Debit card	21
Personal check	18
Cash	39

A sample taken in 2003 found that for 220 in-stores purchases, 46 used a credit card, 67 used a debit card, 33 used a personal check, and 74 used cash.

a. At $\alpha = .01$, can we conclude that a change occurred in how customers paid for in-store purchases over the four-year period from 1999 to 2003? What is the p-value?

b. Compute the percentage of use for each method of payment using the 2003 sample data. What appears to have been the major change or changes over the four-year period?

c. In 2003, what percentage of payments was made using plastic (credit card or debit card)?

7. *The Wall Street Journal's* Shareholder Scoreboard tracks the performance of 1000 major U.S. companies (*The Wall Street Journal,* March 10, 2003). The performance of each company is rated based on the annual total return, including stock price changes and the reinvestment of dividends. Ratings are assigned by dividing all 1000 companies into five groups from A (top 20%), B (next 20%), to E (bottom 20%). Shown here are the one-year ratings for a sample of 60 of the largest companies. Do the largest companies differ in performance from the performance of the 1000 companies in the Shareholder Scoreboard? Use $\alpha = .05$.

A	B	C	D	E
5	8	15	20	12

8. How well do airline companies serve their customers? A study showed the following customer ratings: 3% excellent, 28% good, 45% fair, and 24% poor (*BusinessWeek,* September 11, 2000). In a follow-up study of service by telephone companies, assume that a sample of 400 adults found the following customer ratings: 24 excellent, 124 good, 172 fair, and 80 poor. Is the distribution of the customer ratings for telephone companies different from the distribution of customer ratings for airline companies? Test with $\alpha = .01$. What is your conclusion?

12.2 Test of Independence

Another important application of the chi-square distribution involves using sample data to test for the independence of two variables. Let us illustrate the test of independence by considering the study conducted by the Alber's Brewery of Tucson, Arizona. Alber's manufactures and distributes three types of beer: light, regular, and dark. In an analysis of the market segments for the three beers, the firm's market research group raised the question of whether preferences for the three beers differ among male and female beer drinkers. If beer preference is independent of the gender of the beer drinker, one advertising campaign will be initiated for all of Alber's beers. However, if beer preference depends on the gender of the beer drinker, the firm will tailor its promotions to different target markets.

A test of independence addresses the question of whether the beer preference (light, regular, or dark) is independent of the gender of the beer drinker (male, female). The hypotheses for this test of independence are:

H_0: Beer preference is independent of the gender of the beer drinker

H_a: Beer preference is not independent of the gender of the beer drinker

Table 12.2 can be used to describe the situation being studied. After identification of the population as all male and female beer drinkers, a sample can be selected and each individual

TABLE 12.2 CONTINGENCY TABLE FOR BEER PREFERENCE AND GENDER OF BEER DRINKER

		Beer Preference		
		Light	**Regular**	**Dark**
Gender	**Male**	cell(1,1)	cell(1,2)	cell(1,3)
	Female	cell(2,1)	cell(2,2)	cell(2,3)

TABLE 12.3 SAMPLE RESULTS FOR BEER PREFERENCES OF MALE AND FEMALE BEER DRINKERS (OBSERVED FREQUENCIES)

		Beer Preference			
		Light	Regular	Dark	Total
Gender	Male	20	40	20	80
	Female	30	30	10	70
	Total	50	70	30	150

To test whether two variables are independent, one sample is selected and crosstabulation is used to summarize the data for the two variables simultaneously.

asked to state his or her preference for the three Alber's beers. Every individual in the sample will be classified in one of the six cells in the table. For example, an individual may be a male preferring regular beer (cell (1,2)), a female preferring light beer (cell (2,1)), a female preferring dark beer (cell (2,3)), and so on. Because we have listed all possible combinations of beer preference and gender or, in other words, listed all possible contingencies, Table 12.2 is called a **contingency table.** The test of independence uses the contingency table format and for that reason is sometimes referred to as a *contingency table test.*

Suppose a simple random sample of 150 beer drinkers is selected. After tasting each beer, the individuals in the sample are asked to state their preference or first choice. The crosstabulation in Table 12.3 summarizes the responses for the study. As we see, the data for the test of independence are collected in terms of counts or frequencies for each cell or category. Of the 150 individuals in the sample, 20 were men who favored light beer, 40 were men who favored regular beer, 20 were men who favored dark beer, and so on.

The data in Table 12.3 are the observed frequencies for the six classes or categories. If we can determine the expected frequencies under the assumption of independence between beer preference and gender of the beer drinker, we can use the chi-square distribution to determine whether there is a significant difference between observed and expected frequencies.

Expected frequencies for the cells of the contingency table are based on the following rationale. First we assume that the null hypothesis of independence between beer preference and gender of the beer drinker is true. Then we note that in the entire sample of 150 beer drinkers, a total of 50 prefer light beer, 70 prefer regular beer, and 30 prefer dark beer. In terms of fractions we conclude that $^{50}\!/_{150} = \frac{1}{3}$ of the beer drinkers prefer light beer, $^{70}\!/_{150} = \frac{7}{15}$ prefer regular beer, and $^{30}\!/_{150} = \frac{1}{5}$ prefer dark beer. If the *independence* assumption is valid, we argue that these fractions must be applicable to both male and female beer drinkers. Thus, under the assumption of independence, we would expect the sample of 80 male beer drinkers to show that $(\frac{1}{3})80 = 26.67$ prefer light beer, $(\frac{7}{15})80 = 37.33$ prefer regular beer, and $(\frac{1}{5})80 = 16$ prefer dark beer. Application of the same fractions to the 70 female beer drinkers provides the expected frequencies shown in Table 12.4.

Let e_{ij} denote the expected frequency for the contingency table category in row i and column j. With this notation, let us reconsider the expected frequency calculation for males

TABLE 12.4 EXPECTED FREQUENCIES IF BEER PREFERENCE IS INDEPENDENT OF THE GENDER OF THE BEER DRINKER

		Beer Preference			
		Light	Regular	Dark	Total
Gender	Male	26.67	37.33	16.00	80
	Female	23.33	32.67	14.00	70
	Total	50.00	70.00	30.00	150

(row $i = 1$) who prefer regular beer (column $j = 2$); that is, expected frequency e_{12}. Following the preceding argument for the computation of expected frequencies, we can show that

$$e_{12} = (7/15)80 = 37.33$$

This expression can be written slightly differently as

$$e_{12} = (7/15)80 = (70/150)80 = \frac{(80)(70)}{150} = 37.33$$

Note that 80 in the expression is the total number of males (row 1 total), 70 is the total number of individuals preferring regular beer (column 2 total), and 150 is the total sample size. Hence, we see that

$$e_{12} = \frac{(\text{Row 1 Total})(\text{Column 2 Total})}{\text{Sample Size}}$$

Generalization of the expression shows that the following formula provides the expected frequencies for a contingency table in the test of independence.

EXPECTED FREQUENCIES FOR CONTINGENCY TABLES UNDER THE ASSUMPTION OF INDEPENDENCE

$$e_{ij} = \frac{(\text{Row } i \text{ Total})(\text{Column } j \text{ Total})}{\text{Sample Size}} \tag{12.2}$$

Using the formula for male beer drinkers who prefer dark beer, we find an expected frequency of $e_{13} = (80)(30)/150 = 16.00$, as shown in Table 12.4. Use equation (12.2) to verify the other expected frequencies shown in Table 12.4.

The test procedure for comparing the observed frequencies of Table 12.3 with the expected frequencies of Table 12.4 is similar to the goodness of fit calculations made in Section 12.1. Specifically, the χ^2 value based on the observed and expected frequencies is computed as follows.

TEST STATISTIC FOR INDEPENDENCE

$$\chi^2 = \sum_i \sum_j \frac{(f_{ij} - e_{ij})^2}{e_{ij}} \tag{12.3}$$

where

f_{ij} = observed frequency for contingency table category in row i and column j
e_{ij} = expected frequency for contingency table category in row i and column j based on the assumption of independence

Note: With n rows and m columns in the contingency table, the test statistic has a chi-square distribution with $(n - 1)(m - 1)$ degrees of freedom provided that the expected frequencies are five or more for all categories.

TABLE 12.5 COMPUTATION OF THE CHI-SQUARE TEST STATISTIC FOR DETERMINING WHETHER BEER PREFERENCE IS INDEPENDENT OF THE GENDER OF THE BEER DRINKER

Gender	Beer Preference	Observed Frequency (f_{ij})	Expected Frequency (e_{ij})	Difference ($f_{ij} - e_{ij}$)	Squared Difference $(f_{ij} - e_{ij})^2$	Squared Difference Divided by Expected Frequency $(f_{ij} - e_{ij})^2/e_{ij}$
Male	Light	20	26.67	−6.67	44.44	1.67
Male	Regular	40	37.33	2.67	7.11	0.19
Male	Dark	20	16.00	4.00	16.00	1.00
Female	Light	30	23.33	6.67	44.44	1.90
Female	Regular	30	32.67	−2.67	7.11	0.22
Female	Dark	10	14.00	−4.00	16.00	1.14
	Total	150				$\chi^2 = 6.12$

The double summation in equation (12.3) is used to indicate that the calculation must be made for all the cells in the contingency table.

By reviewing the expected frequencies in Table 12.4, we see that the expected frequencies are five or more for each category. We therefore proceed with the computation of the chi-square test statistic. The calculations necessary to compute the chi-square test statistic for determining whether beer preference is independent of the gender of the beer drinker are shown in Table 12.5. We see that the value of the test statistic is $\chi^2 = 6.12$.

The number of degrees of freedom for the appropriate chi-square distribution is computed by multiplying the number of rows minus 1 by the number of columns minus 1. With two rows and three columns, we have $(2 - 1)(3 - 1) = 2$ degrees of freedom. Just like the test for goodness of fit, the test for independence rejects H_0 if the differences between observed and expected frequencies provide a large value for the test statistic. Thus the test for independence is also an upper tail test. Using the chi-square table (Table 3 in Appendix B), we find the following information for 2 degrees of freedom.

The test for independence is always a one-tailed test with the rejection region in the upper tail of the chi-square distribution.

Area in Upper Tail	.10	.05	.025	.01	.005
χ^2 Value (2 df)	4.605	5.991	7.378	9.210	10.597

$\chi^2 = 6.12$

The test statistic $\chi^2 = 6.12$ is between 5.991 and 7.378. Thus, the corresponding upper tail area or p-value is between .05 and .025. The Minitab or Excel procedures in Appendix F can be used to show p-value $= .0469$. With p-value $\leq \alpha = .05$, we reject the null hypothesis and conclude that beer preference is not independent of the gender of the beer drinker.

Computer software packages such as Minitab and Excel can be used to simplify the computations required for tests of independence. The input to these computer procedures is the contingency table of observed frequencies shown in Table 12.3. The software then computes the expected frequencies, the value of the χ^2 test statistic, and the p-value automatically. The Minitab and Excel procedures that can be used to conduct these tests of independence are presented in Appendixes 12.1 and 12.2. The Minitab output for the Alber's Brewery test of independence is shown in Figure 12.1.

Although no further conclusions can be made as a result of the test, we can compare the observed and expected frequencies informally to obtain an idea about the dependence between beer preference and gender. Refer to Tables 12.3 and 12.4. We see that male beer drinkers have higher observed than expected frequencies for both regular and dark beers,

FIGURE 12.1 MINITAB OUTPUT FOR THE ALBER'S BREWERY TEST OF INDEPENDENCE

```
Expected counts are printed below observed counts

         Light    Regular      Dark    Total
    1       20         40        20       80
         26.67      37.33     16.00

    2       30         30        10       70
         23.33      32.67     14.00

Total       50         70        30      150

DF = 2, P-Value = 0.047
```

whereas female beer drinkers have a higher observed than expected frequency only for light beer. These observations give us insight about the beer preference differences between male and female beer drinkers.

Let us summarize the steps in a contingency table test of independence.

TEST OF INDEPENDENCE: A SUMMARY

1. State the null and alternative hypotheses.

H_0: The column variable is independent of the row variable
H_a: The column variable is not independent of the row variable

2. Select a random sample and record the observed frequencies for each cell of the contingency table.
3. Use equation (12.2) to compute the expected frequency for each cell.
4. Use equation (12.3) to compute the value of the test statistic.
5. Rejection rule:

p-value approach:	Reject H_0 if p-value $\leq \alpha$
Critical value approach:	Reject H_0 if $\chi^2 \geq \chi^2_\alpha$

where α is the level of significance, with n rows and m columns providing $(n - 1)(m - 1)$ degrees of freedom.

NOTES AND COMMENTS

The test statistic for the chi-square tests in this chapter requires an expected frequency of five for each category. When a category has fewer than five, it is often appropriate to combine two adjacent categories to obtain an expected frequency of five or more in each category.

Exercises

Methods

SELF test

9. The following 2 × 3 contingency table contains observed frequencies for a sample of 200. Test for independence of the row and column variables using the χ^2 test with $\alpha = .05$.

	Column Variable		
Row Variable	**A**	**B**	**C**
P	20	44	50
Q	30	26	30

10. The following 3 × 3 contingency table contains observed frequencies for a sample of 240. Test for independence of the row and column variables using the χ^2 test with $\alpha = .05$.

	Column Variable		
Row Variable	**A**	**B**	**C**
P	20	30	20
Q	30	60	25
R	10	15	30

Applications

SELF test

11. One of the questions on the *BusinessWeek* Subscriber Study was, "In the past 12 months, when traveling for business, what type of airline ticket did you purchase most often?" The data obtained are shown in the following contingency table.

	Type of Flight	
Type of Ticket	**Domestic Flights**	**International Flights**
First class	29	22
Business/executive class	95	121
Full fare economy/coach class	518	135

Use $\alpha = .05$ and test for the independence of type of flight and type of ticket. What is your conclusion?

12. Visa Card USA studied how frequently consumers of various age groups use plastic cards (debit and credit cards) when making purchases (Associated Press, January 16, 2006). Sample data for 300 customers shows the use of plastic cards by four age groups.

	Age Group			
Payment	**18–24**	**25–34**	**35–44**	**45 and over**
Plastic	21	27	27	36
Cash or Check	21	36	42	90

a. Test for the independence between method of payment and age group. What is the *p*-value? Using $\alpha = .05$, what is your conclusion?
b. If method of payment and age group are not independent, what observation can you make about how different age groups use plastic to make purchases?
c. What implications does this study have for companies such as Visa, MasterCard, and Discover?

13. With double-digit annual percentage increases in the cost of health insurance, more and more workers are likely to lack health insurance coverage (*USA Today*, January 23, 2004). The following sample data provide a comparison of workers with and without health insurance coverage for small, medium, and large companies. For the purposes of this study,

small companies are companies that have fewer than 100 employees. Medium companies have 100 to 999 employees, and large companies have 1000 or more employees. Sample data are reported for 50 employees of small companies, 75 employees of medium companies, and 100 employees of large companies.

	Health Insurance		
Size of Company	**Yes**	**No**	**Total**
Small	36	14	50
Medium	65	10	75
Large	88	12	100

a. Conduct a test of independence to determine whether employee health insurance coverage is independent of the size of the company. Use $\alpha = .05$. What is the p-value, and what is your conclusion?

b. The *USA Today* article indicated employees of small companies are more likely to lack health insurance coverage. Use percentages based on the preceding data to support this conclusion.

14. A State of Washington's Public Interest Research Group (PIRG) study showed that 46% of full-time college students work 25 or more hours per week. The PIRG study provided data on the effects of working on grades (*USA Today,* April 17, 2002). A sample of 200 students included 90 who worked 1–15 hours per week, 60 who worked 16–24 hours per week, and 50 who worked 25–34 hours per week. The sample number of students indicating their work had a positive effect, no effect, or a negative effect on grades is as follows.

	Effect on Grades			
Hours Worked per Week	**Positive**	**None**	**Negative**	**Total**
1–15 hours	26	50	14	90
16–24 hours	16	27	17	60
25–34 hours	11	19	20	50

a. Conduct a test of independence to determine whether the effect on grades is independent of the hours worked per week. Use $\alpha = .05$. What is the p-value, and what is your conclusion?

b. Use row percentages to learn more about how working affects grades. What is your conclusion?

15. FlightStats, Inc., collects data on the number of flights scheduled and the number of flights flown at major airports throughout the United States. FlightStats data showed 56% of flights scheduled at Newark, La Guardia, and Kennedy airports were flown during a three-day snowstorm (*The Wall Street Journal,* February 21, 2006). All airlines say they always operate within set safety parameters—if conditions are too poor, they don't fly. The following data show a sample of 400 scheduled flights during the snowstorm.

	Airline				
Did It Fly?	**American**	**Continental**	**Delta**	**United**	**Total**
Yes	48	69	68	25	210
No	52	41	62	35	190

Use the chi-square test of independence with a .05 level of significance to analyze the data. What is your conclusion? Do you have a preference for which airline you would choose to fly during similar snowstorm conditions? Explain.

16. Businesses are increasingly placing orders online. The Performance Measurement Group collected data on the rates of correctly filled electronic orders by industry (*Investor's Business Daily,* May 8, 2000). Assume a sample of 700 electronic orders provided the following results.

	Industry			
Order	**Pharmaceutical**	**Consumer**	**Computers**	**Telecommunications**
Correct	207	136	151	178
Incorrect	3	4	9	12

a. Test a hypothesis to determine whether order fulfillment is independent of industry. Use $\alpha = .05$. What is your conclusion?
b. Which industry has the highest percentage of correctly filled orders?

17. The National Sleep Foundation used a survey to determine whether hours of sleeping per night are independent of age (*Newsweek,* January 19, 2004). The following show the hours of sleep on weeknights for a sample of individuals age 49 and younger and for a sample of individuals age 50 and older.

	Hours of Sleep				
Age	**Fewer than 6**	**6 to 6.9**	**7 to 7.9**	**8 or more**	**Total**
49 or younger	38	60	77	65	240
50 or older	36	57	75	92	260

a. Conduct a test of independence to determine whether the hours of sleep on weeknights are independent of age. Use $\alpha = .05$. What is the p-value, and what is your conclusion?
b. What is your estimate of the percentage of people who sleep fewer than 6 hours, 6 to 6.9 hours, 7 to 7.9 hours, and 8 or more hours on weeknights?

18. Samples taken in three cities, Anchorage, Atlanta, and Minneapolis, were used to learn about the percentage of married couples with both the husband and the wife in the workforce (*USA Today,* January 15, 2006). Analyze the following data to see whether both the husband and wife being in the workforce is independent of location. Use a .05 level of significance. What is your conclusion? What is the overall estimate of the percentage of married couples with both the husband and the wife in the workforce?

		Location	
In Workforce	**Anchorage**	**Atlanta**	**Minneapolis**
Both	57	70	63
Only One	33	50	90

19. On a syndicated television show the two hosts often create the impression that they strongly disagree about which movies are best. Each movie review is categorized as Pro

("thumbs up"), Con ("thumbs down"), or Mixed. The results of 160 movie ratings by the two hosts are shown here.

	Host B		
Host A	**Con**	**Mixed**	**Pro**
Con	24	8	13
Mixed	8	13	11
Pro	10	9	64

Use the chi-square test of independence with a .01 level of significance to analyze the data. What is your conclusion?

Experimental Design and Analysis of Variance

CONTENTS

STATISTICS *in* PRACTICE

BURKE MARKETING SERVICES, INC.*

CINCINNATI, OHIO

Burke Marketing Services, Inc., is one of the most experienced market research firms in the industry. Burke writes more proposals, on more projects, every day than any other market research company in the world. Supported by state-of-the-art technology, Burke offers a wide variety of research capabilities, providing answers to nearly any marketing question.

In one study, a firm retained Burke to evaluate potential new versions of a children's dry cereal. To maintain confidentiality, we refer to the cereal manufacturer as the Anon Company. The four key factors that Anon's product developers thought would enhance the taste of the cereal were the following:

1. Ratio of wheat to corn in the cereal flake
2. Type of sweetener: sugar, honey, or artificial
3. Presence or absence of flavor bits with a fruit taste
4. Short or long cooking time

Burke designed an experiment to determine what effects these four factors had on cereal taste. For example, one test cereal was made with a specified ratio of wheat to corn, sugar as the sweetener, flavor bits, and a short cooking time; another test cereal was made with a different ratio of wheat to corn and the other three factors the same, and so on. Groups of children then taste-tested the cereals and stated what they thought about the taste of each.

Burke uses taste tests to provide valuable statistical information on what customers want from a product. © JLP/Sylvia Torres/CORBIS.

Analysis of variance was the statistical method used to study the data obtained from the taste tests. The results of the analysis showed the following:

- The flake composition and sweetener type were highly influential in taste evaluation.
- The flavor bits actually detracted from the taste of the cereal.
- The cooking time had no effect on the taste.

This information helped Anon identify the factors that would lead to the best-tasting cereal.

The experimental design employed by Burke and the subsequent analysis of variance were helpful in making a product design recommendation. In this chapter, we will see how such procedures are carried out.

*The authors are indebted to Dr. Ronald Tatham of Burke Marketing Services for providing this Statistics in Practice.

In Chapter 1 we stated that statistical studies can be classified as either experimental or observational. In an experimental statistical study, an experiment is conducted to generate the data. An experiment begins with identifying a variable of interest. Then one or more other variables, thought to be related, are identified and controlled, and data are collected about how those variables influence the variable of interest.

In an observational study, data are usually obtained through sample surveys and not a controlled experiment. Good design principles are still employed, but the rigorous controls associated with an experimental statistical study are often not possible. For instance, in a study of the relationship between smoking and lung cancer the researcher cannot assign a smoking habit to subjects. The researcher is restricted to simply observing the effects of smoking on people who already smoke and the effects of not smoking on people who already do not smoke.

Sir Ronald Alymer Fisher (1890–1962) invented the branch of statistics known as experimental design. In addition to being accomplished in statistics, he was a noted scientist in the field of genetics.

In this chapter we introduce three types of experimental designs: a completely randomized design, a randomized block design, and a factorial experiment. For each design we show how a statistical procedure called analysis of variance (ANOVA) can be used to analyze the data available. ANOVA can also be used to analyze the data obtained through an observation study. For instance, we will see that the ANOVA procedure used for a completely randomized experimental design also works for testing the equality of three or more population means when data are obtained through an observational study. In the following chapters we will see that ANOVA plays a key role in analyzing the results of regression studies involving both experimental and observational data.

In the first section, we introduce the basic principles of an experimental study and show how they are employed in a completely randomized design. In the second section, we then show how ANOVA can be used to analyze the data from a completely randomized experimental design. In later sections we discuss multiple comparison procedures and two other widely used experimental designs, the randomized block design and the factorial experiment.

13.1 An Introduction to Experimental Design and Analysis of Variance

Cause-and-effect relationships can be difficult to establish in observational studies; such relationships are easier to establish in experimental studies.

As an example of an experimental statistical study, let us consider the problem facing Chemitech, Inc. Chemitech developed a new filtration system for municipal water supplies. The components for the new filtration system will be purchased from several suppliers, and Chemitech will assemble the components at its plant in Columbia, South Carolina. The industrial engineering group is responsible for determining the best assembly method for the new filtration system. After considering a variety of possible approaches, the group narrows the alternatives to three: method A, method B, and method C. These methods differ in the sequence of steps used to assemble the system. Managers at Chemitech want to determine which assembly method can produce the greatest number of filtration systems per week.

In the Chemitech experiment, assembly method is the independent variable or **factor**. Because three assembly methods correspond to this factor, we say that three treatments are associated with this experiment; each **treatment** corresponds to one of the three assembly methods. The Chemitech problem is an example of a **single-factor experiment**; it involves one qualitative factor (method of assembly). More complex experiments may consist of multiple factors; some factors may be qualitative and others may be quantitative.

The three assembly methods or treatments define the three populations of interest for the Chemitech experiment. One population is all Chemitech employees who use assembly method A, another is those who use method B, and the third is those who use method C. Note that for each population the dependent or **response variable** is the number of filtration systems assembled per week, and the primary statistical objective of the experiment is to determine whether the mean number of units produced per week is the same for all three populations (methods).

Randomization is the process of assigning the treatments to the experimental units at random. Prior to the work of Sir R. A. Fisher, treatments were assigned on a systematic or subjective basis.

Suppose a random sample of three employees is selected from all assembly workers at the Chemitech production facility. In experimental design terminology, the three randomly selected workers are the **experimental units**. The experimental design that we will use for the Chemitech problem is called a **completely randomized design**. This type of design requires that each of the three assembly methods or treatments be assigned randomly to one of the experimental units or workers. For example, method A might be randomly assigned to the second worker, method B to the first worker, and method C to the third worker. The concept of *randomization,* as illustrated in this example, is an important principle of all experimental designs.

FIGURE 13.1 COMPLETELY RANDOMIZED DESIGN FOR EVALUATING THE CHEMITECH ASSEMBLY METHOD EXPERIMENT

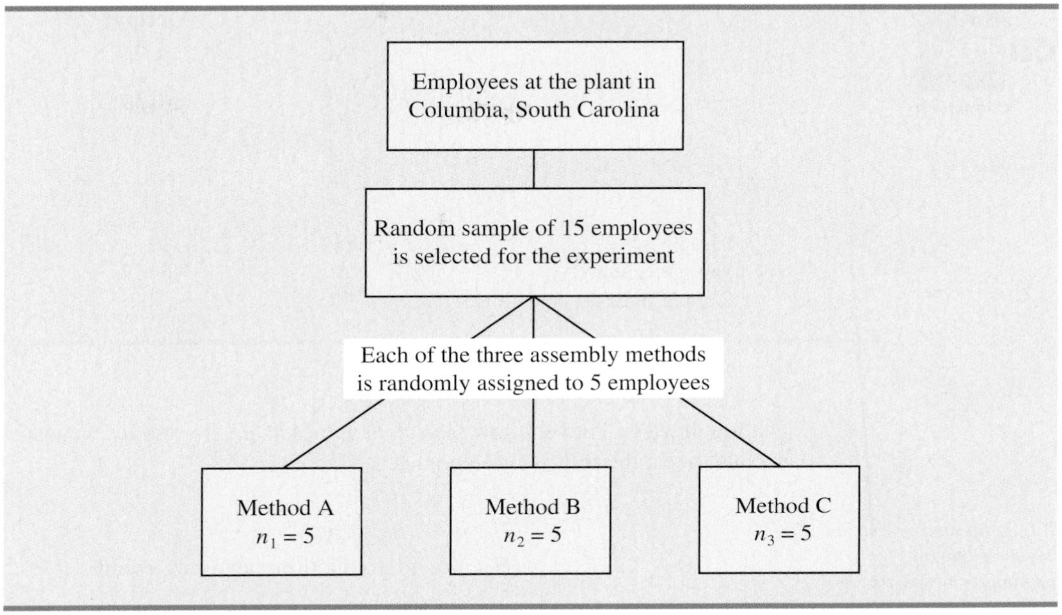

Note that this experiment would result in only one measurement or number of units assembled for each treatment. To obtain additional data for each assembly method, we must repeat or replicate the basic experimental process. Suppose, for example, that instead of selecting just three workers at random we selected 15 workers and then randomly assigned each of the three treatments to five of the workers. Because each method of assembly is assigned to five workers, we say that five replicates have been obtained. The process of *replication* is another important principle of experimental design. Figure 13.1 shows the completely randomized design for the Chemitech experiment.

Data Collection

Once we are satisfied with the experimental design, we proceed by collecting and analyzing the data. In the Chemitech case, the employees would be instructed in how to perform the assembly method assigned to them and then would begin assembling the new filtration systems using that method. After this assignment and training, the number of units assembled by each employee during one week is as shown in Table 13.1. The sample means, sample variances, and sample standard deviations for each assembly method are also provided. Thus, the sample mean number of units produced using method A is 62; the sample mean using method B is 66; and the sample mean using method C is 52. From these data, method B appears to result in higher production rates than either of the other methods.

The real issue is whether the three sample means observed are different enough for us to conclude that the means of the populations corresponding to the three methods of assembly are different. To write this question in statistical terms, we introduce the following notation.

μ_1 = mean number of units produced per week using method A
μ_2 = mean number of units produced per week using method B
μ_3 = mean number of units produced per week using method C

TABLE 13.1 NUMBER OF UNITS PRODUCED BY 15 WORKERS

CD file

Chemitech

	Method		
	A	B	C
	58	58	48
	64	69	57
	55	71	59
	66	64	47
	67	68	49
Sample mean	62	66	52
Sample variance	27.5	26.5	31.0
Sample standard deviation	5.244	5.148	5.568

Although we will never know the actual values of μ_1, μ_2, and μ_3, we want to use the sample means to test the following hypotheses.

If H_0 is rejected, we cannot conclude that all population means are different. Rejecting H_0 means that at least two population means have different values.

$$H_0\colon \mu_1 = \mu_2 = \mu_3$$
H_a: Not all population means are equal

As we will demonstrate shortly, analysis of variance (ANOVA) is the statistical procedure used to determine whether the observed differences in the three sample means are large enough to reject H_0.

Assumptions for Analysis of Variance

Three assumptions are required to use analysis of variance.

If the sample sizes are equal, analysis of variance is not sensitive to departures from the assumption of normally distributed populations.

1. **For each population, the response variable is normally distributed.** Implication: In the Chemitech experiment the number of units produced per week (response variable) must be normally distributed for each assembly method.
2. **The variance of the response variable, denoted σ^2, is the same for all of the populations.** Implication: In the Chemitech experiment, the variance of the number of units produced per week must be the same for each assembly method.
3. **The observations must be independent.** Implication: In the Chemitech experiment, the number of units produced per week for each employee must be independent of the number of units produced per week for any other employee.

Analysis of Variance: A Conceptual Overview

If the means for the three populations are equal, we would expect the three sample means to be close together. In fact, the closer the three sample means are to one another, the more evidence we have for the conclusion that the population means are equal. Alternatively, the more the sample means differ, the more evidence we have for the conclusion that the population means are not equal. In other words, if the variability among the sample means is "small," it supports H_0; if the variability among the sample means is "large," it supports H_a.

If the null hypothesis, H_0: $\mu_1 = \mu_2 = \mu_3$, is true, we can use the variability among the sample means to develop an estimate of σ^2. First, note that if the assumptions for analysis

FIGURE 13.2 SAMPLING DISTRIBUTION OF $\bar{x}$ GIVEN H_0 IS TRUE

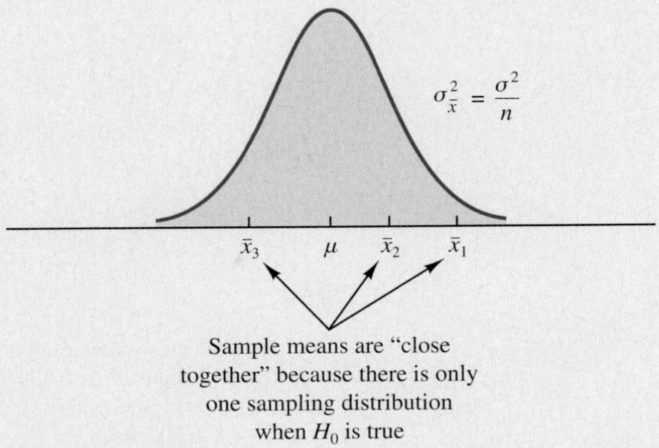

of variance are satisfied, each sample will have come from the same normal distribution with mean μ and variance σ^2. Recall from Chapter 7 that the sampling distribution of the sample mean $\bar{x}$ for a simple random sample of size n from a normal population will be normally distributed with mean μ and variance σ^2/n. Figure 13.2 illustrates such a sampling distribution.

Thus, if the null hypothesis is true, we can think of each of the three sample means, $\bar{x}_1 = 62$, $\bar{x}_2 = 66$, and $\bar{x}_3 = 52$ from Table 13.1, as values drawn at random from the sampling distribution shown in Figure 13.2. In this case, the mean and variance of the three $\bar{x}$ values can be used to estimate the mean and variance of the sampling distribution. When the sample sizes are equal, as in the Chemitech experiment, the best estimate of the mean of the sampling distribution of $\bar{x}$ is the mean or average of the sample means. Thus, in the Chemitech experiment, an estimate of the mean of the sampling distribution of $\bar{x}$ is $(62 + 66 + 52)/3 = 60$. We refer to this estimate as the *overall sample mean.* An estimate of the variance of the sampling distribution of $\bar{x}$, $\sigma_{\bar{x}}^2$, is provided by the variance of the three sample means.

$$s_{\bar{x}}^2 = \frac{(62 - 60)^2 + (66 - 60)^2 + (52 - 60)^2}{3 - 1} = \frac{104}{2} = 52$$

Because $\sigma_{\bar{x}}^2 = \sigma^2/n$, solving for σ^2 gives

$$\sigma^2 = n\sigma_{\bar{x}}^2$$

Hence,

$$\text{Estimate of } \sigma^2 = n\,(\text{Estimate of } \sigma_{\bar{x}}^2) = ns_{\bar{x}}^2 = 5(52) = 260$$

The result, $ns_{\bar{x}}^2 = 260$, is referred to as the *between-treatments* estimate of σ^2.

The between-treatments estimate of σ^2 is based on the assumption that the null hypothesis is true. In this case, each sample comes from the same population, and there is only

FIGURE 13.3 SAMPLING DISTRIBUTIONS OF $\bar{x}$ GIVEN H_0 IS FALSE

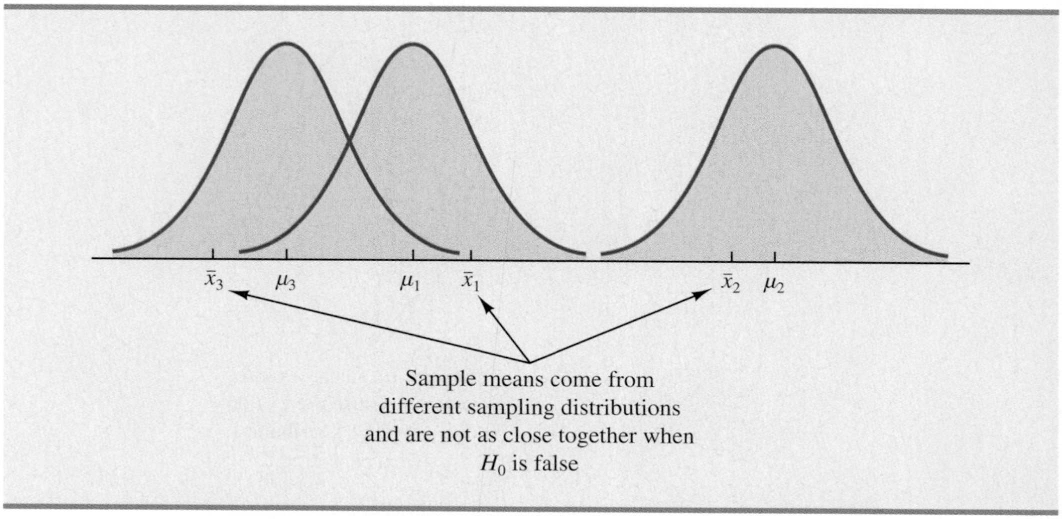

one sampling distribution of $\bar{x}$. To illustrate what happens when H_0 is false, suppose the population means all differ. Note that because the three samples are from normal populations with different means, they will result in three different sampling distributions. Figure 13.3 shows that in this case, the sample means are not as close together as they were when H_0 was true. Thus, $s_{\bar{x}}^2$ will be larger, causing the between-treatments estimate of σ^2 to be larger. In general, when the population means are not equal, the between-treatments estimate will overestimate the population variance σ^2.

The variation within each of the samples also has an effect on the conclusion we reach in analysis of variance. When a simple random sample is selected from each population, each of the sample variances provides an unbiased estimate of σ^2. Hence, we can combine or pool the individual estimates of σ^2 into one overall estimate. The estimate of σ^2 obtained in this way is called the *pooled* or *within-treatments* estimate of σ^2. Because each sample variance provides an estimate of σ^2 based only on the variation within each sample, the within-treatments estimate of σ^2 is not affected by whether the population means are equal. When the sample sizes are equal, the within-treatments estimate of σ^2 can be obtained by computing the average of the individual sample variances. For the Chemitech experiment we obtain

$$\text{Within-treatments estimate of } \sigma^2 = \frac{27.5 + 26.5 + 31.0}{3} = \frac{85}{3} = 28.33$$

In the Chemitech experiment, the between-treatments estimate of σ^2 (260) is much larger than the within-treatments estimate of σ^2 (28.33). In fact, the ratio of these two estimates is 260/28.33 = 9.18. Recall, however, that the between-treatments approach provides a good estimate of σ^2 only if the null hypothesis is true; if the null hypothesis is false, the between-treatments approach overestimates σ^2. The within-treatments approach provides a good estimate of σ^2 in either case. Thus, if the null hypothesis is true, the two estimates will be similar and their ratio will be close to 1. If the null hypothesis is false, the between-treatments estimate will be larger than the within-treatments estimate, and their ratio will be large. In the next section we will show how large this ratio must be to reject H_0.

In summary, the logic behind ANOVA is based on the development of two independent estimates of the common population variance σ^2. One estimate of σ^2 is based on the variability among the sample means themselves, and the other estimate of σ^2 is based on the variability of the data within each sample. By comparing these two estimates of σ^2, we will be able to determine whether the population means are equal.

NOTES AND COMMENTS

1. Randomization in experimental design is the analog of probability sampling in an observational study.
2. In many medical experiments, potential bias is eliminated by using a double-blind experimental design. With this design, neither the physician applying the treatment nor the subject knows which treatment is being applied. Many other types of experiments could benefit from this type of design.
3. In this section we provided a conceptual overview of how analysis of variance can be used to test for the equality of k population means for a completely randomized experimental design. We will see that the same procedure can also be used to test for the equality of k population means for an observational or nonexperimental study.
4. In Sections 10.1 and 10.2 we presented statistical methods for testing the hypothesis that the means of two populations are equal. ANOVA can also be used to test the hypothesis that the means of two populations are equal. In practice, however, analysis of variance is usually not used except when dealing with three or more population means.

13.2 Analysis of Variance and the Completely Randomized Design

In this section we show how analysis of variance can be used to test for the equality of k population means for a completely randomized design. The general form of the hypotheses tested is

$$H_0\colon \mu_1 = \mu_2 = \cdots = \mu_k$$
$$H_a\colon \text{Not all population means are equal}$$

where

$$\mu_j = \text{mean of the } j\text{th population}$$

We assume that a simple random sample of size n_j has been selected from each of the k populations or treatments. For the resulting sample data, let

$$\begin{aligned}
x_{ij} &= \text{value of observation } i \text{ for treatment } j \\
n_j &= \text{number of observations for treatment } j \\
\bar{x}_j &= \text{sample mean for treatment } j \\
s_j^2 &= \text{sample variance for treatment } j \\
s_j &= \text{sample standard deviation for treatment } j
\end{aligned}$$

The formulas for the sample mean and sample variance for treatment j are as follow.

$$\bar{x}_j = \frac{\sum_{i=1}^{n_j} x_{ij}}{n_j} \tag{13.1}$$

$$s_j^2 = \frac{\sum_{i=1}^{n_j} (x_{ij} - \bar{x}_j)^2}{n_j - 1} \tag{13.2}$$

The overall sample mean, denoted $\bar{\bar{x}}$, is the sum of all the observations divided by the total number of observations. That is,

$$\bar{\bar{x}} = \frac{\sum_{j=1}^{k}\sum_{i=1}^{n_j} x_{ij}}{n_T} \tag{13.3}$$

where

$$n_T = n_1 + n_2 + \cdots + n_k \tag{13.4}$$

If the size of each sample is n, $n_T = kn$; in this case equation (13.3) reduces to

$$\bar{\bar{x}} = \frac{\sum_{j=1}^{k}\sum_{i=1}^{n_j} x_{ij}}{kn} = \frac{\sum_{j=1}^{k}\sum_{i=1}^{n_j} x_{ij}/n}{k} = \frac{\sum_{j=1}^{k} \bar{x}_j}{k} \tag{13.5}$$

In other words, whenever the sample sizes are the same, the overall sample mean is just the average of the k sample means.

Because each sample in the Chemitech experiment consists of $n = 5$ observations, the overall sample mean can be computed by using equation (13.5). For the data in Table 13.1 we obtained the following result.

$$\bar{\bar{x}} = \frac{62 + 66 + 52}{3} = 60$$

If the null hypothesis is true ($\mu_1 = \mu_2 = \mu_3 = \mu$), the overall sample mean of 60 is the best estimate of the population mean μ.

Between-Treatments Estimate of Population Variance

In the preceding section, we introduced the concept of a between-treatments estimate of σ^2 and showed how to compute it when the sample sizes were equal. This estimate of σ^2 is called the *mean square due to treatments* and is denoted MSTR. The general formula for computing MSTR is

$$\text{MSTR} = \frac{\sum_{j=1}^{k} n_j(\bar{x}_j - \bar{\bar{x}})^2}{k - 1} \tag{13.6}$$

The numerator in equation (13.6) is called the *sum of squares due to treatments* and is denoted SSTR. The denominator, $k - 1$, represents the degrees of freedom associated with SSTR. Hence, the mean square due to treatments can be computed by the following formula.

MEAN SQUARE DUE TO TREATMENTS

$$\text{MSTR} = \frac{\text{SSTR}}{k - 1} \tag{13.7}$$

where

$$\text{SSTR} = \sum_{j=1}^{k} n_j(\bar{x}_j - \bar{\bar{x}})^2 \tag{13.8}$$

If H_0 is true, MSTR provides an unbiased estimate of σ^2. However, if the means of the k populations are not equal, MSTR is not an unbiased estimate of σ^2; in fact, in that case, MSTR should overestimate σ^2.

For the Chemitech data in Table 13.1, we obtain the following results.

$$\text{SSTR} = \sum_{j=1}^{k} n_j(\bar{x}_j - \bar{\bar{x}})^2 = 5(62 - 60)^2 + 5(66 - 60)^2 + 5(52 - 60)^2 = 520$$

$$\text{MSTR} = \frac{\text{SSTR}}{k - 1} = \frac{520}{2} = 260$$

Within-Treatments Estimate of Population Variance

Earlier, we introduced the concept of a within-treatments estimate of σ^2 and showed how to compute it when the sample sizes were equal. This estimate of σ^2 is called the *mean square due to error* and is denoted MSE. The general formula for computing MSE is

$$\text{MSE} = \frac{\sum_{j=1}^{k}(n_j - 1)s_j^2}{n_T - k} \tag{13.9}$$

The numerator in equation (13.9) is called the *sum of squares due to error* and is denoted SSE. The denominator of MSE is referred to as the degrees of freedom associated with SSE. Hence, the formula for MSE can also be stated as follows.

MEAN SQUARE DUE TO ERROR

$$\text{MSE} = \frac{\text{SSE}}{n_T - k} \tag{13.10}$$

where

$$\text{SSE} = \sum_{j=1}^{k}(n_j - 1)s_j^2 \tag{13.11}$$

Note that MSE is based on the variation within each of the treatments; it is not influenced by whether the null hypothesis is true. Thus, MSE always provides an unbiased estimate of σ^2.

For the Chemitech data in Table 13.1 we obtain the following results.

$$\text{SSE} = \sum_{j=1}^{k}(n_j - 1)s_j^2 = (5 - 1)27.5 + (5 - 1)26.5 + (5 - 1)31 = 340$$

$$\text{MSE} = \frac{\text{SSE}}{n_T - k} = \frac{340}{15 - 3} = \frac{340}{12} = 28.33$$

Comparing the Variance Estimates: The F Test

An introduction to the F distribution and the use of the F distribution table were presented in Section 11.2.

If the null hypothesis is true, MSTR and MSE provide two independent, unbiased estimates of σ^2. Based on the material covered in Chapter 11 we know that for normal populations, the sampling distribution of the ratio of two independent estimates of σ^2 follows an F distribution. Hence, if the null hypothesis is true and the ANOVA assumptions are valid, the sampling distribution of MSTR/MSE is an F distribution with numerator degrees of freedom equal to $k - 1$ and denominator degrees of freedom equal to $n_T - k$. In other words, if the null hypothesis is true, the value of MSTR/MSE should appear to have been selected from this F distribution.

However, if the null hypothesis is false, the value of MSTR/MSE will be inflated because MSTR overestimates σ^2. Hence, we will reject H_0 if the resulting value of MSTR/MSE appears to be too large to have been selected from an F distribution with $k - 1$ numerator degrees of freedom and $n_T - k$ denominator degrees of freedom. Because the decision to reject H_0 is based on the value of MSTR/MSE, the test statistic used to test for the equality of k population means is as follows.

TEST STATISTIC FOR THE EQUALITY OF k POPULATION MEANS

$$F = \frac{\text{MSTR}}{\text{MSE}} \tag{13.12}$$

The test statistic follows an F distribution with $k - 1$ degrees of freedom in the numerator and $n_T - k$ degrees of freedom in the denominator.

Let us return to the Chemitech experiment and use a level of significance $\alpha = .05$ to conduct the hypothesis test. The value of the test statistic is

$$F = \frac{\text{MSTR}}{\text{MSE}} = \frac{260}{28.33} = 9.18$$

The numerator degrees of freedom is $k - 1 = 3 - 1 = 2$ and the denominator degrees of freedom is $n_T - k = 15 - 3 = 12$. Because we will only reject the null hypothesis for large values of the test statistic, the p-value is the upper tail area of the F distribution to the right of the test statistic $F = 9.18$. Figure 13.4 shows the sampling distribution of F = MSTR/MSE, the value of the test statistic, and the upper tail area that is the p-value for the hypothesis test.

From Table 4 of Appendix B we find the following areas in the upper tail of an F distribution with 2 numerator degrees of freedom and 12 denominator degrees of freedom.

Area in Upper Tail	**.10**	**.05**	**.025**	**.01**
***F* Value ($df_1 = 2, df_2 = 12$)**	2.81	3.89	5.10	6.93

$F = 9.18$

FIGURE 13.4 COMPUTATION OF p-VALUE USING THE SAMPLING DISTRIBUTION OF MSTR/MSE

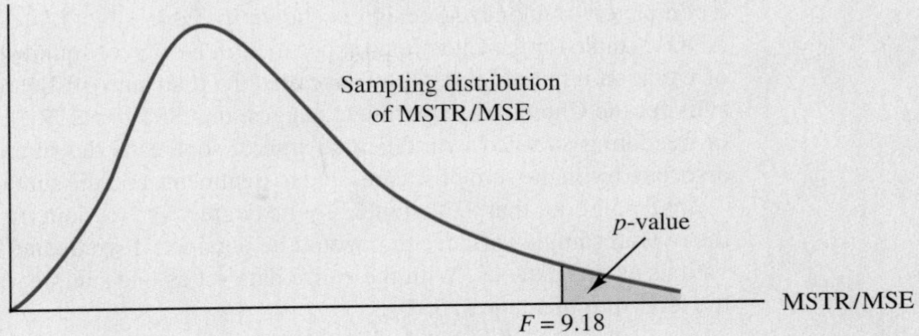

Appendix F shows how to compute p-values using Minitab or Excel.

Because $F = 9.18$ is greater than 6.93, the area in the upper tail at $F = 9.18$ is less than .01. Thus, the p-value is less than .01. Minitab or Excel can be used to show that the exact p-value is .004. With $p\text{-value} \leq \alpha = .05$, H_0 is rejected. The test provides sufficient evidence to conclude that the means of the three populations are not equal. In other words, analysis of variance supports the conclusion that the population mean number of units produced per week for the three assembly methods are not equal.

As with other hypothesis testing procedures, the critical value approach may also be used. With $\alpha = .05$, the critical F value occurs with an area of .05 in the upper tail of an F distribution with 2 and 12 degrees of freedom. From the F distribution table, we find $F_{.05} = 3.89$. Hence, the appropriate upper tail rejection rule for the Chemitech experiment is

$$\text{Reject } H_0 \text{ if } F \geq 3.89$$

With $F = 9.18$, we reject H_0 and conclude that the means of the three populations are not equal. A summary of the overall procedure for testing for the equality of k population means follows.

TEST FOR THE EQUALITY OF k POPULATION MEANS

$$H_0\colon \mu_1 = \mu_2 = \cdots = \mu_k$$
$$H_a\colon \text{Not all population means are equal}$$

TEST STATISTIC

$$F = \frac{\text{MSTR}}{\text{MSE}}$$

REJECTION RULE

p-value approach:	Reject H_0 if $p\text{-value} \leq \alpha$
Critical value approach:	Reject H_0 if $F \geq F_\alpha$

where the value of F_α is based on an F distribution with $k - 1$ numerator degrees of freedom and $n_T - k$ denominator degrees of freedom.

ANOVA Table

The results of the preceding calculations can be displayed conveniently in a table referred to as the analysis of variance or **ANOVA table**. The general form of the ANOVA table for a completely randomized design is shown in Table 13.2; Table 13.3 is the corresponding ANOVA table for the Chemitech experiment. The sum of squares associated with the source of variation referred to as "Total" is called the total sum of squares (SST). Note that the results for the Chemitech experiment suggest that SST = SSTR + SSE, and that the degrees of freedom associated with this total sum of squares is the sum of the degrees of freedom associated with the sum of squares due to treatments and the sum of squares due to error.

We point out that SST divided by its degrees of freedom $n_T - 1$ is nothing more than the overall sample variance that would be obtained if we treated the entire set of 15 observations as one data set. With the entire data set as one sample, the formula for computing the total sum of squares, SST, is

$$\text{SST} = \sum_{j=1}^{k}\sum_{i=1}^{n_j}(x_{ij} - \bar{\bar{x}})^2 \qquad \textbf{(13.13)}$$

It can be shown that the results we observed for the analysis of variance table for the Chemitech experiment also apply to other problems. That is,

$$\text{SST} = \text{SSTR} + \text{SSE} \qquad \textbf{(13.14)}$$

Analysis of variance can be thought of as a statistical procedure for partitioning the total sum of squares into separate components.

In other words, SST can be partitioned into two sums of squares: the sum of squares due to treatments and the sum of squares due to error. Note also that the degrees of freedom corresponding to SST, $n_T - 1$, can be partitioned into the degrees of freedom corresponding to SSTR, $k - 1$, and the degrees of freedom corresponding to SSE, $n_T - k$. The analysis of variance can be viewed as the process of **partitioning** the total sum of squares and the degrees of freedom into their corresponding sources: treatments and error. Dividing the sum of squares by the appropriate degrees of freedom provides the variance estimates, the F value, and the p-value used to test the hypothesis of equal population means.

TABLE 13.2 ANOVA TABLE FOR A COMPLETELY RANDOMIZED DESIGN

Source of Variation	Sum of Squares	Degrees of Freedom	Mean Square	F	p-value
Treatments	SSTR	$k - 1$	$\text{MSTR} = \dfrac{\text{SSTR}}{k - 1}$	$\dfrac{\text{MSTR}}{\text{MSE}}$	
Error	SSE	$n_T - k$	$\text{MSE} = \dfrac{\text{SSE}}{n_T - k}$		
Total	SST	$n_T - 1$			

TABLE 13.3 ANALYSIS OF VARIANCE TABLE FOR THE CHEMITECH EXPERIMENT

Source of Variation	Sum of Squares	Degrees of Freedom	Mean Square	F	p-value
Treatments	520	2	260.00	9.18	.004
Error	340	12	28.33		
Total	860	14			

FIGURE 13.5 MINITAB OUTPUT FOR THE CHEMITECH EXPERIMENT ANALYSIS OF VARIANCE

```
Source   DF      SS      MS      F      P
Factor    2   520.0   260.0   9.18  0.004
Error    12   340.0    28.3
Total    14   860.0

S = 5.323     R-Sq = 60.47%     R-Sq(adj) = 53.88%

                                Individual 95% CIs For Mean Based on
                                Pooled StDev
 Level   N    Mean   StDev    ---+---------+---------+---------+------
 A       5  62.000   5.244                 (-------*-------)
 B       5  66.000   4.148                           (------*-------)
 C       5  52.000   5.568    (------*-------)
                              ---+---------+---------+---------+------
Pooled StDev = 5.323            49.0      56.0      63.0      70.0
```

Computer Results for Analysis of Variance

Using statistical computer packages, analysis of variance computations with large sample sizes or a large number of populations can be performed easily. Appendixes 13.1 and 13.2 show the steps required to use Minitab and Excel to perform the analysis of variance computations. In Figure 13.5 we show output for the Chemitech experiment obtained using Minitab. The first part of the computer output contains the familiar ANOVA table format. Comparing Figure 13.5 with Table 13.3, we see that the same information is available, although some of the headings are slightly different. The heading Source is used for the source of variation column, Factor identifies the treatments row, and the sum of squares and degrees of freedom columns are interchanged.

Note that following the ANOVA table the computer output contains the respective sample sizes, the sample means, and the standard deviations. In addition, Minitab provides a figure that shows individual 95% confidence interval estimates of each population mean. In developing these confidence interval estimates, Minitab uses MSE as the estimate of σ^2. Thus, the square root of MSE provides the best estimate of the population standard deviation σ. This estimate of σ on the computer output is Pooled StDev; it is equal to 5.323. To provide an illustration of how these interval estimates are developed, we will compute a 95% confidence interval estimate of the population mean for method A.

From our study of interval estimation in Chapter 8, we know that the general form of an interval estimate of a population mean is

$$\bar{x} \pm t_{\alpha/2} \frac{s}{\sqrt{n}} \tag{13.15}$$

where s is the estimate of the population standard deviation σ. Because the best estimate of σ is provided by the Pooled StDev, we use a value of 5.323 for s in expression (13.15). The degrees of freedom for the t value is 12, the degrees of freedom associated with the error sum of squares. Hence, with $t_{.025} = 2.179$ we obtain

$$62 \pm 2.179 \frac{5.323}{\sqrt{5}} = 62 \pm 5.19$$

Thus, the individual 95% confidence interval for method A goes from 62 − 5.19 = 56.81 to 62 + 5.19 = 67.19. Because the sample sizes are equal for the Chemitech experiment, the individual confidence intervals for methods B and C are also constructed by adding and subtracting 5.19 from each sample mean. Thus, in the figure provided by Minitab we see that the widths of the confidence intervals are the same.

Testing for the Equality of *k* Population Means: An Observational Study

We have shown how analysis of variance can be used to test for the equality of *k* population means for a completely randomized experimental design. It is important to understand that ANOVA can also be used to test for the equality of three or more population means using data obtained from an observational study. As an example, let us consider the situation at National Computer Products, Inc. (NCP).

NCP manufactures printers and fax machines at plants located in Atlanta, Dallas, and Seattle. To measure how much employees at these plants know about quality management, a random sample of six employees was selected from each plant and the employees selected were given a quality awareness examination. The examination scores for these 18 employees are shown in Table 13.4. The sample means, sample variances, and sample standard deviations for each group are also provided. Managers want to use these data to test the hypothesis that the mean examination score is the same for all three plants.

We define population 1 as all employees at the Atlanta plant, population 2 as all employees at the Dallas plant, and population 3 as all employees at the Seattle plant. Let

$$\mu_1 = \text{mean examination score for population 1}$$
$$\mu_2 = \text{mean examination score for population 2}$$
$$\mu_3 = \text{mean examination score for population 3}$$

Although we will never know the actual values of μ_1, μ_2, and μ_3, we want to use the sample results to test the following hypotheses.

$$H_0\colon \mu_1 = \mu_2 = \mu_3$$
$$H_a\colon \text{Not all population means are equal}$$

Note that the hypothesis test for the NCP observational study is exactly the same as the hypothesis test for the Chemitech experiment. Indeed, the same analysis of variance

CD file

NCP

TABLE 13.4 EXAMINATION SCORES FOR 18 EMPLOYEES

	Plant 1 Atlanta	Plant 2 Dallas	Plant 3 Seattle
	85	71	59
	75	75	64
	82	73	62
	76	74	69
	71	69	75
	85	82	67
Sample mean	79	74	66
Sample variance	34	20	32
Sample standard deviation	5.83	4.47	5.66

Exercise 8 will ask you to analyze the NCP data using the analysis of variance procedure.

methodology we used to analyze the Chemitech experiment can also be used to analyze the data from the NCP observational study.

Even though the same ANOVA methodology is used for the analysis, it is worth noting how the NCP observational statistical study differs from the Chemitech experimental statistical study. The individuals who conducted the NCP study had no control over how the plants were assigned to individual employees. That is, the plants were already in operation and a particular employee worked at one of the three plants. All that NCP could do was to select a random sample of six employees from each plant and administer the quality awareness examination. To be classified as an experimental study, NCP would have had to be able to randomly select 18 employees and then assign the plants to each employee in a random fashion.

NOTES AND COMMENTS

1. The overall sample mean can also be computed as a weighted average of the k sample means.

$$\bar{\bar{x}} = \frac{n_1\bar{x}_1 + n_2\bar{x}_2 + \cdots + n_k\bar{x}_k}{n_T}$$

In problems where the sample means are provided, this formula is simpler than equation (13.3) for computing the overall mean.

2. If each sample consists of n observations, equation (13.6) can be written as

$$\text{MSTR} = \frac{n\sum_{j=1}^{k}(\bar{x}_j - \bar{\bar{x}})^2}{k-1} = n\left[\frac{\sum_{j=1}^{k}(\bar{x}_j - \bar{\bar{x}})^2}{k-1}\right] = ns_{\bar{x}}^2$$

Note that this result is the same as presented in Section 13.1 when we introduced the concept of the between-treatments estimate of σ^2. Equation (13.6) is simply a generalization of this result to the unequal sample-size case.

3. If each sample has n observations, $n_T = kn$; thus, $n_T - k = k(n-1)$, and equation (13.9) can be rewritten as

$$\text{MSE} = \frac{\sum_{j=1}^{k}(n-1)s_j^2}{k(n-1)} = \frac{(n-1)\sum_{j=1}^{k}s_j^2}{k(n-1)} = \frac{\sum_{j=1}^{k}s_j^2}{k}$$

In other words, if the sample sizes are the same, MSE is just the average of the k sample variances. Note that it is the same result we used in Section 13.1 when we introduced the concept of the within-treatments estimate of σ^2.

Exercises

Methods

SELF test

1. The following data are from a completely randomized design.

	Treatment		
	A	B	C
	162	142	126
	142	156	122
	165	124	138
	145	142	140
	148	136	150
	174	152	128
Sample mean	156	142	134
Sample variance	164.4	131.2	110.4

a. Compute the sum of squares between treatments.
b. Compute the mean square between treatments.

c. Compute the sum of squares due to error.
d. Compute the mean square due to error.
e. Set up the ANOVA table for this problem.
f. At the $\alpha = .05$ level of significance, test whether the means for the three treatments are equal.

2. In a completely randomized design, seven experimental units were used for each of the five levels of the factor. Complete the following ANOVA table.

Source of Variation	Sum of Squares	Degrees of Freedom	Mean Square	*F*	*p*-value
Treatments	300				
Error					
Total	460				

3. Refer to exercise 2.
   a. What hypotheses are implied in this problem?
   b. At the $\alpha = .05$ level of significance, can we reject the null hypothesis in part (a)? Explain.

4. In an experiment designed to test the output levels of three different treatments, the following results were obtained: SST = 400, SSTR = 150, $n_T = 19$. Set up the ANOVA table and test for any significant difference between the mean output levels of the three treatments. Use $\alpha = .05$.

5. In a completely randomized design, 12 experimental units were used for the first treatment, 15 for the second treatment, and 20 for the third treatment. Complete the following analysis of variance. At a .05 level of significance, is there a significant difference between the treatments?

Source of Variation	Sum of Squares	Degrees of Freedom	Mean Square	*F*	*p*-value
Treatments	1200				
Error					
Total	1800				

6. Develop the analysis of variance computations for the following completely randomized design. At $\alpha = .05$, is there a significant difference between the treatment means?

CD file
Exer6

	Treatment		
	A	B	C
	136	107	92
	120	114	82
	113	125	85
	107	104	101
	131	107	89
	114	109	117
	129	97	110
	102	114	120
		104	98
		89	106
$\bar{x}_j$	119	107	100
s_j^2	146.86	96.44	173.78

Applications

7. Three different methods for assembling a product were proposed by an industrial engineer. To investigate the number of units assembled correctly with each method, 30 employees were randomly selected and randomly assigned to the three proposed methods in such a way that each method was used by 10 workers. The number of units assembled correctly was recorded, and the analysis of variance procedure was applied to the resulting data set. The following results were obtained: SST = 10,800; SSTR = 4560.
   a. Set up the ANOVA table for this problem.
   b. Use $\alpha = .05$ to test for any significant difference in the means for the three assembly methods.

8. Refer to the NCP data in Table 13.4. Set up the ANOVA table and test for any significant difference in the mean examination score for the three plants. Use $\alpha = .05$.

9. To study the effect of temperature on yield in a chemical process, five batches were produced at each of three temperature levels. The results follow. Construct an analysis of variance table. Use a .05 level of significance to test whether the temperature level has an effect on the mean yield of the process.

	Temperature	
50°C	**60°C**	**70°C**
34	30	23
24	31	28
36	34	28
39	23	30
32	27	31

10. Auditors must make judgments about various aspects of an audit on the basis of their own direct experience, indirect experience, or a combination of the two. In a study, auditors were asked to make judgments about the frequency of errors to be found in an audit. The judgments by the auditors were then compared to the actual results. Suppose the following data were obtained from a similar study; lower scores indicate better judgments.

CD file

AudJudg

Direct	Indirect	Combination
17.0	16.6	25.2
18.5	22.2	24.0
15.8	20.5	21.5
18.2	18.3	26.8
20.2	24.2	27.5
16.0	19.8	25.8
13.3	21.2	24.2

Use $\alpha = .05$ to test to see whether the basis for the judgment affects the quality of the judgment. What is your conclusion?

11. Four different paints are advertised as having the same drying time. To check the manufacturer's claims, five samples were tested for each of the paints. The time in minutes until the paint was dry enough for a second coat to be applied was recorded. The following data were obtained.

CD file

Paint

Paint 1	Paint 2	Paint 3	Paint 4
128	144	133	150
137	133	143	142
135	142	137	135
124	146	136	140
141	130	131	153

At the $\alpha = .05$ level of significance, test to see whether the mean drying time is the same for each type of paint.

12. A well-known automotive magazine took three top-of-the-line midsize automobiles manufactured in the United States, test-drove them, and compared them on a variety of criteria. In the area of gasoline mileage performance, five automobiles of each brand were each test-driven 500 miles; the miles per gallon data obtained follow. Use $\alpha = .05$ to test whether there is a significant difference in the mean number of miles per gallon for the three types of automobiles.

	Automobile	
A	B	C
19	19	24
21	20	26
20	22	23
19	21	25
21	23	27

13.3 Multiple Comparison Procedures

When we use analysis of variance to test whether the means of k populations are equal, rejection of the null hypothesis allows us to conclude only that the population means are *not all equal.* In some cases we will want to go a step further and determine where the differences among means occur. The purpose of this section is to show how **multiple comparison procedures** can be used to conduct statistical comparisons between pairs of population means.

Fisher's LSD

Suppose that analysis of variance provides statistical evidence to reject the null hypothesis of equal population means. In this case, Fisher's least significant difference (LSD) procedure can be used to determine where the differences occur. To illustrate the use of Fisher's LSD procedure in making pairwise comparisons of population means, recall the Chemitech experiment introduced in Section 13.1. Using analysis of variance, we concluded that the mean number of units produced per week are not the same for the three assembly methods. In this case, the follow-up question is: We believe the assembly methods differ, but where do the differences occur? That is, do the means of populations 1 and 2 differ? Or those of populations 1 and 3? Or those of populations 2 and 3?

In Chapter 10 we presented a statistical procedure for testing the hypothesis that the means of two populations are equal. With a slight modification in how we estimate the population variance, Fisher's LSD procedure is based on the t test statistic presented for the two-population case. The following table summarizes Fisher's LSD procedure.

FISHER'S LSD PROCEDURE

$$H_0: \mu_i = \mu_j$$
$$H_a: \mu_i \neq \mu_j$$

TEST STATISTIC

$$t = \frac{\bar{x}_i - \bar{x}_j}{\sqrt{\text{MSE}\left(\frac{1}{n_i} + \frac{1}{n_j}\right)}} \tag{13.16}$$

REJECTION RULE

p-value approach: Reject H_0 if p-value $\leq \alpha$

Critical value approach: Reject H_0 if $t \leq -t_{\alpha/2}$ or $t \geq t_{\alpha/2}$

where the value of $t_{\alpha/2}$ is based on a t distribution with $n_T - k$ degrees of freedom.

Let us now apply this procedure to determine whether there is a significant difference between the means of population 1 (method A) and population 2 (method B) at the $\alpha = .05$ level of significance. Table 13.1 showed that the sample mean is 62 for method A and 66 for method B. Table 13.3 showed that the value of MSE is 28.33; it is the estimate of σ^2 and is based on 12 degrees of freedom. For the Chemitech data the value of the test statistic is

$$t = \frac{62 - 66}{\sqrt{28.33\left(\frac{1}{5} + \frac{1}{5}\right)}} = -1.19$$

Because we have a two-tailed test, the p-value is two times the area under the curve for the t distribution to the left of $t = -1.19$. Using Table 2 in Appendix B, the t distribution table for 12 degrees of freedom provides the following information.

Area in Upper Tail	**.20**	**.10**	**.05**	**.025**	**.01**	**.005**
***t* Value (12 *df*)**	.873	1.356	1.782	2.179	2.681	3.055

$t = 1.19$

Appendix F shows how to compute p-values using Excel or Minitab.

The t distribution table only contains positive t values. Because the t distribution is symmetric, however, we can find the area under the curve to the right of $t = 1.19$ and double it to find the p-value corresponding to $t = -1.19$. We see that $t = 1.19$ is between .20 and .10. Doubling these amounts, we see that the p-value must be between .40 and .20. Excel or Minitab can be used to show that the exact p-value is .2571. Because the p-value is greater than $\alpha = .05$, we cannot reject the null hypothesis. Hence, we cannot conclude that the population mean number of units produced per week for method A is different from the population mean for method B.

Many practitioners find it easier to determine how large the difference between the sample means must be to reject H_0. In this case the test statistic is $\bar{x}_i - \bar{x}_j$, and the test is conducted by the following procedure.

FISHER'S LSD PROCEDURE BASED ON THE TEST STATISTIC $\bar{x}_i - \bar{x}_j$

$$H_0: \mu_i = \mu_j$$
$$H_a: \mu_i \neq \mu_j$$

TEST STATISTIC

$$\bar{x}_i - \bar{x}_j$$

REJECTION RULE AT A LEVEL OF SIGNIFICANCE α

$$\text{Reject } H_0 \text{ if } |\bar{x}_i - \bar{x}_j| \geq \text{LSD}$$

where

$$\text{LSD} = t_{\alpha/2}\sqrt{\text{MSE}\left(\frac{1}{n_i} + \frac{1}{n_j}\right)} \tag{13.17}$$

For the Chemitech experiment the value of LSD is

$$\text{LSD} = 2.179\sqrt{28.33\left(\frac{1}{5} + \frac{1}{5}\right)} = 7.34$$

Note that when the sample sizes are equal, only one value for LSD is computed. In such cases we can simply compare the magnitude of the difference between any two sample means with the value of LSD. For example, the difference between the sample means for population 1 (method A) and population 3 (method C) is $62 - 52 = 10$. This difference is greater than LSD $= 7.34$, which means we can reject the null hypothesis that the population mean number of units produced per week for method A is equal to the population mean for method C. Similarly, with the difference between the sample means for populations 2 and 3 of $66 - 52 = 14 > 7.34$, we can also reject the hypothesis that the population mean for method B is equal to the population mean for method C. In effect, our conclusion is that methods A and B both differ from method C.

Fisher's LSD can also be used to develop a confidence interval estimate of the difference between the means of two populations. The general procedure follows.

CONFIDENCE INTERVAL ESTIMATE OF THE DIFFERENCE BETWEEN TWO POPULATION MEANS USING FISHER'S LSD PROCEDURE

$$\bar{x}_i - \bar{x}_j \pm \text{LSD} \tag{13.18}$$

where

$$\text{LSD} = t_{\alpha/2}\sqrt{\text{MSE}\left(\frac{1}{n_i} + \frac{1}{n_j}\right)} \tag{13.19}$$

and $t_{\alpha/2}$ is based on a t distribution with $n_T - k$ degrees of freedom.

If the confidence interval in expression (13.18) includes the value zero, we cannot reject the hypothesis that the two population means are equal. However, if the confidence interval does not include the value zero, we conclude that there is a difference between the population means. For the Chemitech experiment, recall that LSD = 7.34 (corresponding to $t_{.025} = 2.179$). Thus, a 95% confidence interval estimate of the difference between the means of populations 1 and 2 is $62 - 66 \pm 7.34 = -4 \pm 7.34 = -11.34$ to 3.34; because this interval includes zero, we cannot reject the hypothesis that the two population means are equal.

Type I Error Rates

We began the discussion of Fisher's LSD procedure with the premise that analysis of variance gave us statistical evidence to reject the null hypothesis of equal population means. We showed how Fisher's LSD procedure can be used in such cases to determine where the differences occur. Technically, it is referred to as a *protected* or *restricted* LSD test because it is employed only if we first find a significant F value by using analysis of variance. To see why this distinction is important in multiple comparison tests, we need to explain the difference between a *comparisonwise* Type I error rate and an *experimentwise* Type I error rate.

In the Chemitech experiment we used Fisher's LSD procedure to make three pairwise comparisons.

Test 1	**Test 2**	**Test 3**
$H_0: \mu_1 = \mu_2$	$H_0: \mu_1 = \mu_3$	$H_0: \mu_2 = \mu_3$
$H_a: \mu_1 \neq \mu_2$	$H_a: \mu_1 \neq \mu_3$	$H_a: \mu_2 \neq \mu_3$

In each case, we used a level of significance of $\alpha = .05$. Therefore, for each test, if the null hypothesis is true, the probability that we will make a Type I error is $\alpha = .05$; hence, the probability that we will not make a Type I error on each test is $1 - .05 = .95$. In discussing multiple comparison procedures we refer to this probability of a Type I error ($\alpha = .05$) as the **comparisonwise Type I error rate**; comparisonwise Type I error rates indicate the level of significance associated with a single pairwise comparison.

Let us now consider a slightly different question. What is the probability that in making three pairwise comparisons, we will commit a Type I error on at least one of the three tests? To answer this question, note that the probability that we will not make a Type I error on any of the three tests is $(.95)(.95)(.95) = .8574$.* Therefore, the probability of making at least one Type I error is $1 - .8574 = .1426$. Thus, when we use Fisher's LSD procedure to make all three pairwise comparisons, the Type I error rate associated with this approach is not .05, but actually .1426; we refer to this error rate as the *overall* or **experimentwise Type I error rate**. To avoid confusion, we denote the experimentwise Type I error rate as α_{EW}.

The experimentwise Type I error rate gets larger for problems with more populations. For example, a problem with five populations has 10 possible pairwise comparisons. If we tested all possible pairwise comparisons by using Fisher's LSD with a comparisonwise error rate of $\alpha = .05$, the experimentwise Type I error rate would be $1 - (1 - .05)^{10} = .40$. In such cases, practitioners look to alternatives that provide better control over the experimentwise error rate.

One alternative for controlling the overall experimentwise error rate, referred to as the Bonferroni adjustment, involves using a smaller comparisonwise error rate for each test. For example, if we want to test C pairwise comparisons and want the maximum probability

---

*The assumption is that the three tests are independent, and hence the joint probability of the three events can be obtained by simply multiplying the individual probabilities. In fact, the three tests are not independent because MSE is used in each test; therefore, the error involved is even greater than that shown.

of making a Type I error for the overall experiment to be α_{EW}, we simply use a comparisonwise error rate equal to α_{EW}/C. In the Chemitech experiment, if we want to use Fisher's LSD procedure to test all three pairwise comparisons with a maximum experimentwise error rate of $\alpha_{EW} = .05$, we set the comparisonwise error rate to be $\alpha = .05/3 = .017$. For a problem with five populations and 10 possible pairwise comparisons, the Bonferroni adjustment would suggest a comparisonwise error rate of $.05/10 = .005$. Recall from our discussion of hypothesis testing in Chapter 9 that for a fixed sample size, any decrease in the probability of making a Type I error will result in an increase in the probability of making a Type II error, which corresponds to accepting the hypothesis that the two population means are equal when in fact they are not equal. As a result, many practitioners are reluctant to perform individual tests with a low comparisonwise Type I error rate because of the increased risk of making a Type II error.

Several other procedures, such as Tukey's procedure and Duncan's multiple range test, have been developed to help in such situations. However, there is considerable controversy in the statistical community as to which procedure is "best." The truth is that no one procedure is best for all types of problems.

Exercises

Methods

SELF test

13. The following data are from a completely randomized design.

	Treatment A	Treatment B	Treatment C
	32	44	33
	30	43	36
	30	44	35
	26	46	36
	32	48	40
Sample mean	30	45	36
Sample variance	6.00	4.00	6.50

a. At the $\alpha = .05$ level of significance, can we reject the null hypothesis that the means of the three treatments are equal?

b. Use Fisher's LSD procedure to test whether there is a significant difference between the means for treatments A and B, treatments A and C, and treatments B and C. Use $\alpha = .05$.

c. Use Fisher's LSD procedure to develop a 95% confidence interval estimate of the difference between the means of treatments A and B.

14. The following data are from a completely randomized design. In the following calculations, use $\alpha = .05$.

	Treatment 1	Treatment 2	Treatment 3
	63	82	69
	47	72	54
	54	88	61
	40	66	48
$\bar{x}_j$	51	77	58
s_j^2	96.67	97.34	81.99

a. Use analysis of variance to test for a significant difference among the means of the three treatments.
b. Use Fisher's LSD procedure to determine which means are different.

Applications

SELF test

15. To test whether the mean time needed to mix a batch of material is the same for machines produced by three manufacturers, the Jacobs Chemical Company obtained the following data on the time (in minutes) needed to mix the material.

Manufacturer		
1	**2**	**3**
20	28	20
26	26	19
24	31	23
22	27	22

a. Use these data to test whether the population mean times for mixing a batch of material differ for the three manufacturers. Use $\alpha = .05$.
b. At the $\alpha = .05$ level of significance, use Fisher's LSD procedure to test for the equality of the means for manufacturers 1 and 3. What conclusion can you draw after carrying out this test?

SELF test

16. Refer to exercise 15. Use Fisher's LSD procedure to develop a 95% confidence interval estimate of the difference between the means for manufacturer 1 and manufacturer 2.
17. The following data are from an experiment designed to investigate the perception of corporate ethical values among individuals specializing in marketing (higher scores indicate higher ethical values).

Marketing Managers	Marketing Research	Advertising
6	5	6
5	5	7
4	4	6
5	4	5
6	5	6
4	4	6

a. Use $\alpha = .05$ to test for significant differences in perception among the three groups.
b. At the $\alpha = .05$ level of significance, we can conclude that there are differences in the perceptions for marketing managers, marketing research specialists, and advertising specialists. Use the procedures in this section to determine where the differences occur. Use $\alpha = .05$.

18. To test for any significant difference in the number of hours between breakdowns for four machines, the following data were obtained.

Machine 1	Machine 2	Machine 3	Machine 4
6.4	8.7	11.1	9.9
7.8	7.4	10.3	12.8
5.3	9.4	9.7	12.1
7.4	10.1	10.3	10.8
8.4	9.2	9.2	11.3
7.3	9.8	8.8	11.5

a. At the $\alpha = .05$ level of significance, what is the difference, if any, in the population mean times among the four machines?
b. Use Fisher's LSD procedure to test for the equality of the means for machines 2 and 4. Use a .05 level of significance.

19. Refer to exercise 18. Use the Bonferroni adjustment to test for a significant difference between all pairs of means. Assume that a maximum overall experimentwise error rate of .05 is desired.

20. *Condé Nast Traveler* conducts an annual survey in which readers rate their favorite cruise ships. Ratings are provided for small ships (carrying up to 500 passengers), medium ships (carrying more than 500 but less than 1500 passengers), and large ships (carrying a minimum of 1500 passengers). The following data show the service ratings for eight randomly selected small ships, eight randomly selected medium ships, and eight randomly selected large ships. All ships are rated on a 100-point scale, with higher values indicating better service (*Condé Nast Traveler*, February 2003).

CD file
Ships

Small Ships		Medium Ships		Large Ships	
Name	**Rating**	**Name**	**Rating**	**Name**	**Rating**
Hanseactic	90.5	Amsterdam	91.1	Century	89.2
Mississippi Queen	78.2	Crystal Symphony	98.9	Disney Wonder	90.2
Philae	92.3	Maasdam	94.2	Enchantment of the Seas	85.9
Royal Clipper	95.7	Noordam	84.3	Grand Princess	84.2
Seabourn Pride	94.1	Royal Princess	84.8	Infinity	90.2
Seabourn Spirit	100	Ryndam	89.2	Legend of the Seas	80.6
Silver Cloud	91.8	Statendam	86.4	Paradise	75.8
Silver Wind	95	Veendam	88.3	Sun Princess	82.3

a. Use $\alpha = .05$ to test for any significant difference in the mean service ratings among the three sizes of cruise ships.
b. Use the procedures in this section to determine where the differences occur. Use $\alpha = .05$.

13.4 Randomized Block Design

Thus far we have considered the completely randomized experimental design. Recall that to test for a difference among treatment means, we computed an F value by using the ratio

$$F = \frac{\text{MSTR}}{\text{MSE}} \tag{13.20}$$

A completely randomized design is useful when the experimental units are homogeneous. If the experimental units are heterogeneous, ***blocking*** *is often used to form homogeneous groups.*

A problem can arise whenever differences due to extraneous factors (ones not considered in the experiment) cause the MSE term in this ratio to become large. In such cases, the F value in equation (13.20) can become small, signaling no difference among treatment means when in fact such a difference exists.

In this section we present an experimental design known as a **randomized block design**. Its purpose is to control some of the extraneous sources of variation by removing such variation from the MSE term. This design tends to provide a better estimate of the true error variance and leads to a more powerful hypothesis test in terms of the ability to detect differences among treatment means. To illustrate, let us consider a stress study for air traffic controllers.

Air Traffic Controller Stress Test

A study measuring the fatigue and stress of air traffic controllers resulted in proposals for modification and redesign of the controller's work station. After consideration of several designs for the work station, three specific alternatives are selected as having the best potential for reducing controller stress. The key question is: To what extent do the three alternatives differ in terms of their effect on controller stress? To answer this question, we need to design an experiment that will provide measurements of air traffic controller stress under each alternative.

Experimental studies in business often involve experimental units that are highly heterogeneous; as a result, randomized block designs are often employed.

In a completely randomized design, a random sample of controllers would be assigned to each work station alternative. However, controllers are believed to differ substantially in their ability to handle stressful situations. What is high stress to one controller might be only moderate or even low stress to another. Hence, when considering the within-group source of variation (MSE), we must realize that this variation includes both random error and error due to individual controller differences. In fact, managers expected controller variability to be a major contributor to the MSE term.

Blocking in experimental design is similar to stratification in sampling.

One way to separate the effect of the individual differences is to use a randomized block design. Such a design will identify the variability stemming from individual controller differences and remove it from the MSE term. The randomized block design calls for a single sample of controllers. Each controller in the sample is tested with each of the three work station alternatives. In experimental design terminology, the work station is the *factor of interest* and the controllers are the *blocks*. The three treatments or populations associated with the work station factor correspond to the three work station alternatives. For simplicity, we refer to the work station alternatives as system A, system B, and system C.

The *randomized* aspect of the randomized block design is the random order in which the treatments (systems) are assigned to the controllers. If every controller were to test the three systems in the same order, any observed difference in systems might be due to the order of the test rather than to true differences in the systems.

To provide the necessary data, the three work station alternatives were installed at the Cleveland Control Center in Oberlin, Ohio. Six controllers were selected at random and assigned to operate each of the systems. A follow-up interview and a medical examination of each controller participating in the study provided a measure of the stress for each controller on each system. The data are reported in Table 13.5.

Table 13.6 is a summary of the stress data collected. In this table we include column totals (treatments) and row totals (blocks) as well as some sample means that will be helpful

TABLE 13.5 A RANDOMIZED BLOCK DESIGN FOR THE AIR TRAFFIC CONTROLLER STRESS TEST

CD file AirTraf

		Treatments		
		System A	**System B**	**System C**
Blocks	**Controller 1**	15	15	18
	Controller 2	14	14	14
	Controller 3	10	11	15
	Controller 4	13	12	17
	Controller 5	16	13	16
	Controller 6	13	13	13

TABLE 13.6 SUMMARY OF STRESS DATA FOR THE AIR TRAFFIC CONTROLLER STRESS TEST

		Treatments				
		System A	System B	System C	Row or Block Totals	Block Means
Blocks	Controller 1	15	15	18	48	$\bar{x}_{1\cdot} = 48/3 = 16.0$
	Controller 2	14	14	14	42	$\bar{x}_{2\cdot} = 42/3 = 14.0$
	Controller 3	10	11	15	36	$\bar{x}_{3\cdot} = 36/3 = 12.0$
	Controller 4	13	12	17	42	$\bar{x}_{4\cdot} = 42/3 = 14.0$
	Controller 5	16	13	16	45	$\bar{x}_{5\cdot} = 45/3 = 15.0$
	Controller 6	13	13	13	39	$\bar{x}_{6\cdot} = 39/3 = 13.0$
Column or Treatment Totals		81	78	93	252	$\bar{\bar{x}} = \frac{252}{18} = 14.0$
Treatment Means		$\bar{x}_{\cdot 1} = \frac{81}{6} = 13.5$	$\bar{x}_{\cdot 2} = \frac{78}{6} = 13.0$	$\bar{x}_{\cdot 3} = \frac{93}{6} = 15.5$		

in making the sum of squares computations for the ANOVA procedure. Because lower stress values are viewed as better, the sample data seem to favor system B with its mean stress rating of 13. However, the usual question remains: Do the sample results justify the conclusion that the population mean stress levels for the three systems differ? That is, are the differences statistically significant? An analysis of variance computation similar to the one performed for the completely randomized design can be used to answer this statistical question.

ANOVA Procedure

The ANOVA procedure for the randomized block design requires us to partition the sum of squares total (SST) into three groups: sum of squares due to treatments, sum of squares due to blocks, and sum of squares due to error. The formula for this partitioning follows.

$$\text{SST} = \text{SSTR} + \text{SSBL} + \text{SSE} \tag{13.21}$$

This sum of squares partition is summarized in the ANOVA table for the randomized block design as shown in Table 13.7. The notation used in the table is

$$k = \text{the number of treatments}$$
$$b = \text{the number of blocks}$$
$$n_T = \text{the total sample size } (n_T = kb)$$

Note that the ANOVA table also shows how the $n_T - 1$ total degrees of freedom are partitioned such that $k - 1$ degrees of freedom go to treatments, $b - 1$ go to blocks, and $(k - 1)(b - 1)$ go to the error term. The mean square column shows the sum of squares divided by the degrees of freedom, and F = MSTR/MSE is the F ratio used to test for a significant difference among the treatment means. The primary contribution of the randomized block design is that, by including blocks, we remove the individual controller differences from the MSE term and obtain a more powerful test for the stress differences in the three work station alternatives.

TABLE 13.7 ANOVA TABLE FOR THE RANDOMIZED BLOCK DESIGN WITH k TREATMENTS AND b BLOCKS

Source of Variation	Sum of Squares	Degrees of Freedom	Mean Square	F	p-value
Treatments	SSTR	$k - 1$	$\text{MSTR} = \dfrac{\text{SSTR}}{k-1}$	$\dfrac{\text{MSTR}}{\text{MSE}}$	
Blocks	SSBL	$b - 1$	$\text{MSBL} = \dfrac{\text{SSBL}}{b-1}$		
Error	SSE	$(k-1)(b-1)$	$\text{MSE} = \dfrac{\text{SSE}}{(k-1)(b-1)}$		
Total	SST	$n_T - 1$			

Computations and Conclusions

To compute the F statistic needed to test for a difference among treatment means with a randomized block design, we need to compute MSTR and MSE. To calculate these two mean squares, we must first compute SSTR and SSE; in doing so, we will also compute SSBL and SST. To simplify the presentation, we perform the calculations in four steps. In addition to k, b, and n_T as previously defined, the following notation is used.

x_{ij} = value of the observation corresponding to treatment j in block i
$\bar{x}_{\cdot j}$ = sample mean of the jth treatment
$\bar{x}_{i\cdot}$ = sample mean for the ith block
$\bar{\bar{x}}$ = overall sample mean

Step 1. Compute the total sum of squares (SST).

$$\text{SST} = \sum_{i=1}^{b}\sum_{j=1}^{k}(x_{ij} - \bar{\bar{x}})^2 \tag{13.22}$$

Step 2. Compute the sum of squares due to treatments (SSTR).

$$\text{SSTR} = b\sum_{j=1}^{k}(\bar{x}_{\cdot j} - \bar{\bar{x}})^2 \tag{13.23}$$

Step 3. Compute the sum of squares due to blocks (SSBL).

$$\text{SSBL} = k\sum_{i=1}^{b}(\bar{x}_{i\cdot} - \bar{\bar{x}})^2 \tag{13.24}$$

Step 4. Compute the sum of squares due to error (SSE).

$$\text{SSE} = \text{SST} - \text{SSTR} - \text{SSBL} \tag{13.25}$$

For the air traffic controller data in Table 13.6, these steps lead to the following sums of squares.

Step 1. $\text{SST} = (15 - 14)^2 + (15 - 14)^2 + (18 - 14)^2 + \cdots + (13 - 14)^2 = 70$

Step 2. $\text{SSTR} = 6[(13.5 - 14)^2 + (13.0 - 14)^2 + (15.5 - 14)^2] = 21$

Step 3. $\text{SSBL} = 3[(16 - 14)^2 + (14 - 14)^2 + (12 - 14)^2 + (14 - 14)^2 + (15 - 14)^2 + (13 - 14)^2] = 30$

Step 4. $\text{SSE} = 70 - 21 - 30 = 19$

TABLE 13.8 ANOVA TABLE FOR THE AIR TRAFFIC CONTROLLER STRESS TEST

Source of Variation	Sum of Squares	Degrees of Freedom	Mean Square	F	p-value
Treatments	21	2	10.5	10.5/1.9 = 5.53	.0241
Blocks	30	5	6.0		
Error	19	10	1.9		
Total	70	17			

These sums of squares divided by their degrees of freedom provide the corresponding mean square values shown in Table 13.8.

Let us use a level of significance $\alpha = .05$ to conduct the hypothesis test. The value of the test statistic is

$$F = \frac{\text{MSTR}}{\text{MSE}} = \frac{10.5}{1.9} = 5.53$$

The numerator degrees of freedom is $k - 1 = 3 - 1 = 2$ and the denominator degrees of freedom is $(k - 1)(b - 1) = (3 - 1)(6 - 1) = 10$. Because we will only reject the null hypothesis for large values of the test statistic, the p-value is the area under the F distribution to the right of $F = 5.53$. From Table 4 of Appendix B we find that with the degrees of freedom 2 and 10, $F = 5.53$ is between $F_{.025} = 5.46$ and $F_{.01} = 7.56$. As a result, the area in the upper tail, or the p-value, is between .01 and .025. Alternatively, we can use Excel or Minitab to show that the exact p-value for $F = 5.53$ is .0241. With p-value $\leq \alpha = .05$, we reject the null hypothesis H_0: $\mu_1 = \mu_2 = \mu_3$ and conclude that the population mean stress levels differ for the three work station alternatives.

Some general comments can be made about the randomized block design. The experimental design described in this section is a *complete* block design; the word "complete" indicates that each block is subjected to all k treatments. That is, all controllers (blocks) were tested with all three systems (treatments). Experimental designs in which some but not all treatments are applied to each block are referred to as *incomplete* block designs. A discussion of incomplete block designs is beyond the scope of this text.

Because each controller in the air traffic controller stress test was required to use all three systems, this approach guarantees a complete block design. In some cases, however, blocking is carried out with "similar" experimental units in each block. For example, assume that in a pretest of air traffic controllers, the population of controllers was divided into groups ranging from extremely high-stress individuals to extremely low-stress individuals. The blocking could still be accomplished by having three controllers from each of the stress classifications participate in the study. Each block would then consist of three controllers in the same stress group. The randomized aspect of the block design would be the random assignment of the three controllers in each block to the three systems.

Finally, note that the ANOVA table shown in Table 13.7 provides an F value to test for treatment effects but *not* for blocks. The reason is that the experiment was designed to test a single factor—work station design. The blocking based on individual stress differences was conducted to remove such variation from the MSE term. However, the study was not designed to test specifically for individual differences in stress.

Some analysts compute F = MSB/MSE and use that statistic to test for significance of the blocks. Then they use the result as a guide to whether the same type of blocking would be desired in future experiments. However, if individual stress difference is to be a factor in the study, a different experimental design should be used. A test of significance on blocks should not be performed as a basis for a conclusion about a second factor.

NOTES AND COMMENTS

The error degrees of freedom are less for a randomized block design than for a completely randomized design because $b - 1$ degrees of freedom are lost for the b blocks. If n is small, the potential effects due to blocks can be masked because of the loss of error degrees of freedom; for large n, the effects are minimized.

Exercises

Methods

SELF test

21. Consider the experimental results for the following randomized block design. Make the calculations necessary to set up the analysis of variance table.

		Treatments		
		A	**B**	**C**
Blocks	**1**	10	9	8
	2	12	6	5
	3	18	15	14
	4	20	18	18
	5	8	7	8

Use $\alpha = .05$ to test for any significant differences.

22. The following data were obtained for a randomized block design involving five treatments and three blocks: SST = 430, SSTR = 310, SSBL = 85. Set up the ANOVA table and test for any significant differences. Use $\alpha = .05$.

23. An experiment has been conducted for four treatments with eight blocks. Complete the following analysis of variance table.

Source of Variation	Sum of Squares	Degrees of Freedom	Mean Square	F
Treatments	900			
Blocks	400			
Error				
Total	1800			

Use $\alpha = .05$ to test for any significant differences.

Applications

24. An automobile dealer conducted a test to determine if the time in minutes needed to complete a minor engine tune-up depends on whether a computerized engine analyzer or an electronic analyzer is used. Because tune-up time varies among compact, intermediate, and full-sized cars, the three types of cars were used as blocks in the experiment. The data obtained follow.

		Analyzer	
		Computerized	**Electronic**
Car	**Compact**	50	42
	Intermediate	55	44
	Full-sized	63	46

Use α = .05 to test for any significant differences.

25. Prices for vitamins and other health supplements increased over the past several years, and the prices charged by different retail outlets often vary a great deal. The following data show the prices for 13 products at four retail outlets in Rochester, New York (*Democrat and Chronicle,* February 13, 2005).

CD file
Vitamins

Item	**CVS**	**Kmart**	**Rite-Aid**	**Wegmans**
Caltrate +D (600 mg/60 tablets)	8.49	5.99	7.99	5.99
Centrum (130 tablets)	9.49	9.47	9.89	7.97
Cod liver oil (100 gel tablets)	2.66	2.59	1.99	2.69
Fish oil (1,000 mg/60 tablets)	6.19	4.99	4.99	5.99
Flintstones Children's (60 tablets)	7.69	5.99	5.99	6.29
Folic acid (400 mcg/250 tablets)	2.19	2.49	3.74	2.69
One-a-Day Maximum (100 tablets)	8.99	7.49	6.99	6.99
One-a-Day Scooby (50 tablets)	7.49	5.99	6.49	5.47
Poly-Vi-Scl (drops, 50 ml)	9.99	8.49	9.99	8.37
Vitamin B-12 (100 mcg/100 tablets)	3.59	1.99	1.99	1.79
Vitamin C (500 mg/100 tablets)	2.99	2.49	1.99	2.39
Vitamin E (200 IU/100 tablets)	4.69	3.49	2.99	3.29
Zinc (50 mg/100 tablets)	2.66	2.59	3.99	2.79

Use α = .05 to test for any significant difference in the mean price for the four retail outlets.

26. An important factor in selecting software for word-processing and database management systems is the time required to learn how to use the system. To evaluate three file management systems, a firm designed a test involving five word-processing operators. Because operator variability was believed to be a significant factor, each of the five operators was trained on each of the three file management systems. The data obtained follow.

		System		
		A	**B**	**C**
Operator	**1**	16	16	24
	2	19	17	22
	3	14	13	19
	4	13	12	18
	5	18	17	22

Use α = .05 to test for any difference in the mean training time (in hours) for the three systems.

27. A study reported in the *Journal of the American Medical Association* investigated the cardiac demands of heavy snow shoveling. Ten healthy men underwent exercise testing with a treadmill and a cycle ergometer modified for arm cranking. The men then cleared two tracts of heavy, wet snow by using a lightweight plastic snow shovel and an electric snow thrower. Each subject's heart rate, blood pressure, oxygen uptake, and perceived exertion during snow removal were compared with the values obtained during treadmill and

arm-crank ergometer testing. Suppose the following table gives the heart rates in beats per minute for each of the 10 subjects.

CD file

Snow

Subject	Treadmill	Arm-Crank Ergometer	Snow Shovel	Snow Thrower
1	177	205	180	98
2	151	177	164	120
3	184	166	167	111
4	161	152	173	122
5	192	142	179	151
6	193	172	205	158
7	164	191	156	117
8	207	170	160	123
9	177	181	175	127
10	174	154	191	109

At the .05 level of significance, test for any significant differences.

13.5 Factorial Experiment

The experimental designs we have considered thus far enable us to draw statistical conclusions about one factor. However, in some experiments we want to draw conclusions about more than one variable or factor. A **factorial experiment** is an experimental design that allows simultaneous conclusions about two or more factors. The term *factorial* is used because the experimental conditions include all possible combinations of the factors. For example, for a levels of factor A and b levels of factor B, the experiment will involve collecting data on ab treatment combinations. In this section we will show the analysis for a two-factor factorial experiment. The basic approach can be extended to experiments involving more than two factors.

As an illustration of a two-factor factorial experiment, we will consider a study involving the Graduate Management Admissions Test (GMAT), a standardized test used by graduate schools of business to evaluate an applicant's ability to pursue a graduate program in that field. Scores on the GMAT range from 200 to 800, with higher scores implying higher aptitude.

In an attempt to improve students' performance on the GMAT exam, a major Texas university is considering offering the following three GMAT preparation programs.

1. A three-hour review session covering the types of questions generally asked on the GMAT.
2. A one-day program covering relevant exam material, along with the taking and grading of a sample exam.
3. An intensive 10-week course involving the identification of each student's weaknesses and the setting up of individualized programs for improvement.

Hence, one factor in this study is the GMAT preparation program, which has three treatments: three-hour review, one-day program, and 10-week course. Before selecting the preparation program to adopt, further study will be conducted to determine how the proposed programs affect GMAT scores.

The GMAT is usually taken by students from three colleges: the College of Business, the College of Engineering, and the College of Arts and Sciences. Therefore, a second factor of interest in the experiment is whether a student's undergraduate college affects the GMAT score. This second factor, undergraduate college, also has three treatments: business, engineering, and arts and sciences. The factorial design for this experiment with three treatments corresponding to factor A, the preparation program, and three treatments corresponding to

TABLE 13.9 NINE TREATMENT COMBINATIONS FOR THE TWO-FACTOR GMAT EXPERIMENT

		Factor B: College		
		Business	**Engineering**	**Arts and Sciences**
Factor A: Preparation Program	**Three-hour review**	1	2	3
	One-day program	4	5	6
	10-week course	7	8	9

factor B, the undergraduate college, will have a total of $3 \times 3 = 9$ treatment combinations. These treatment combinations or experimental conditions are summarized in Table 13.9.

Assume that a sample of two students will be selected corresponding to each of the nine treatment combinations shown in Table 13.9: two business students will take the three-hour review, two will take the one-day program, and two will take the 10-week course. In addition, two engineering students and two arts and sciences students will take each of the three preparation programs. In experimental design terminology, the sample size of two for each treatment combination indicates that we have two **replications**. Additional replications and a larger sample size could easily be used, but we elect to minimize the computational aspects for this illustration.

This experimental design requires that six students who plan to attend graduate school be randomly selected from *each* of the three undergraduate colleges. Then two students from each college should be assigned randomly to each preparation program, resulting in a total of 18 students being used in the study.

Let us assume that the randomly selected students participated in the preparation programs and then took the GMAT. The scores obtained are reported in Table 13.10.

The analysis of variance computations with the data in Table 13.10 will provide answers to the following questions.

- **Main effect (factor A):** Do the preparation programs differ in terms of effect on GMAT scores?
- **Main effect (factor B):** Do the undergraduate colleges differ in terms of effect on GMAT scores?
- **Interaction effect (factors A and B):** Do students in some colleges do better on one type of preparation program whereas others do better on a different type of preparation program?

The term **interaction** refers to a new effect that we can now study because we used a factorial experiment. If the interaction effect has a significant impact on the GMAT scores,

TABLE 13.10 GMAT SCORES FOR THE TWO-FACTOR EXPERIMENT

CD file GMAT

		Factor B: College		
		Business	**Engineering**	**Arts and Sciences**
Factor A: Preparation Program	**Three-hour review**	500	540	480
		580	460	400
	One-day program	460	560	420
		540	620	480
	10-week course	560	600	480
		600	580	410

TABLE 13.11 ANOVA TABLE FOR THE TWO-FACTOR FACTORIAL EXPERIMENT WITH r REPLICATIONS

Source of Variation	Sum of Squares	Degrees of Freedom	Mean Square	F	p-value
Factor A	SSA	$a - 1$	$\text{MSA} = \frac{\text{SSA}}{a - 1}$	$\frac{\text{MSA}}{\text{MSE}}$	
Factor B	SSB	$b - 1$	$\text{MSB} = \frac{\text{SSB}}{b - 1}$	$\frac{\text{MSB}}{\text{MSE}}$	
Interaction	SSAB	$(a - 1)(b - 1)$	$\text{MSAB} = \frac{\text{SSAB}}{(a - 1)(b - 1)}$	$\frac{\text{MSAB}}{\text{MSE}}$	
Error	SSE	$ab(r - 1)$	$\text{MSE} = \frac{\text{SSE}}{ab(r - 1)}$		
Total	SST	$n_T - 1$			

we can conclude that the effect of the type of preparation program depends on the undergraduate college.

ANOVA Procedure

The ANOVA procedure for the two-factor factorial experiment is similar to the completely randomized experiment and the randomized block experiment in that we again partition the sum of squares and the degrees of freedom into their respective sources. The formula for partitioning the sum of squares for the two-factor factorial experiments follows.

$$\text{SST} = \text{SSA} + \text{SSB} + \text{SSAB} + \text{SSE} \tag{13.26}$$

The partitioning of the sum of squares and degrees of freedom is summarized in Table 13.11. The following notation is used.

a = number of levels of factor A
b = number of levels of factor B
r = number of replications
n_T = total number of observations taken in the experiment; $n_T = abr$

Computations and Conclusions

To compute the F statistics needed to test for the significance of factor A, factor B, and interaction, we need to compute MSA, MSB, MSAB, and MSE. To calculate these four mean squares, we must first compute SSA, SSB, SSAB, and SSE; in doing so we will also compute SST. To simplify the presentation, we perform the calculations in five steps. In addition to a, b, r, and n_T as previously defined, the following notation is used.

x_{ijk} = observation corresponding to the kth replicate taken from treatment i of factor A and treatment j of factor B
$\bar{x}_{i\cdot}$ = sample mean for the observations in treatment i (factor A)
$\bar{x}_{\cdot j}$ = sample mean for the observations in treatment j (factor B)
$\bar{x}_{ij}$ = sample mean for the observations corresponding to the combination of treatment i (factor A) and treatment j (factor B)
$\bar{\bar{x}}$ = overall sample mean of all n_T observations

Step 1. Compute the total sum of squares.

$$\text{SST} = \sum_{i=1}^{a}\sum_{j=1}^{b}\sum_{k=1}^{r}(x_{ijk} - \bar{\bar{x}})^2 \tag{13.27}$$

Step 2. Compute the sum of squares for factor A.

$$\text{SSA} = br\sum_{i=1}^{a}(\bar{x}_{i\cdot} - \bar{\bar{x}})^2 \tag{13.28}$$

Step 3. Compute the sum of squares for factor B.

$$\text{SSB} = ar\sum_{j=1}^{b}(\bar{x}_{\cdot j} - \bar{\bar{x}})^2 \tag{13.29}$$

Step 4. Compute the sum of squares for interaction.

$$\text{SSAB} = r\sum_{i=1}^{a}\sum_{j=1}^{b}(\bar{x}_{ij} - \bar{x}_{i\cdot} - \bar{x}_{\cdot j} + \bar{\bar{x}})^2 \tag{13.30}$$

Step 5. Compute the sum of squares due to error.

$$\text{SSE} = \text{SST} - \text{SSA} - \text{SSB} - \text{SSAB} \tag{13.31}$$

Table 13.12 reports the data collected in the experiment and the various sums that will help us with the sum of squares computations. Using equations (13.27) through (13.31), we calculate the following sums of squares for the GMAT two-factor factorial experiment.

Step 1. $\text{SST} = (500 - 515)^2 + (580 - 515)^2 + (540 - 515)^2 + \cdots + (410 - 515)^2 = 82{,}450$

Step 2. $\text{SSA} = (3)(2)[(493.33 - 515)^2 + (513.33 - 515)^2 + (538.33 - 515)^2] = 6100$

Step 3. $\text{SSB} = (3)(2)[(540 - 515)^2 + (560 - 515)^2 + (445 - 515)^2] = 45{,}300$

Step 4. $\text{SSAB} = 2[(540 - 493.33 - 540 + 515)^2 + (500 - 493.33 - 560 + 515)^2 + \cdots + (445 - 538.33 - 445 + 515)^2] = 11{,}200$

Step 5. $\text{SSE} = 82{,}450 - 6100 - 45{,}300 - 11{,}200 = 19{,}850$

These sums of squares divided by their corresponding degrees of freedom provide the appropriate mean square values for testing the two main effects (preparation program and undergraduate college) and the interaction effect.

Let us use a level of significance $\alpha = .05$ to conduct the hypothesis tests for the two-factor GMAT study. Because of the computational effort involved in any modest- to large-size factorial experiment, the computer usually plays an important role in performing the analysis of variance computations and in the calculation of the p-values used to make the hypothesis testing decisions. Figure 13.6 shows the Minitab output for the analysis of variance for the GMAT two-factor factorial experiment. The p-value used to test for significant differences among the three preparation programs (factor A) is .299. Because the p-value = .299 is greater than $\alpha = .05$, there is no significant difference in the mean GMAT test scores for the three preparation programs. However, for the undergraduate college effect, the p-value = .005 is less than $\alpha = .05$; thus, there is a significant difference in the mean GMAT test scores among the three undergraduate colleges. Finally, because the p-value of .350 for

TABLE 13.12 GMAT SUMMARY DATA FOR THE TWO-FACTOR EXPERIMENT

		Factor B: College				
	Treatment combination totals	Business	Engineering	Arts and Sciences	Row Totals	Factor A Means
Factor A: Preparation Program	Three-hour review	500 580 1080	540 460 1000	480 400 880	2960	$\bar{x}_{1\cdot} = \frac{2960}{6} = 493.33$
		$\bar{x}_{11} = \frac{1080}{2} = 540$	$\bar{x}_{12} = \frac{1000}{2} = 500$	$\bar{x}_{13} = \frac{880}{2} = 440$		
	One-day program	460 540 1000	560 620 1180	420 480 900	3080	$\bar{x}_{2\cdot} = \frac{3080}{6} = 513.33$
		$\bar{x}_{21} = \frac{1000}{2} = 500$	$\bar{x}_{22} = \frac{1180}{2} = 590$	$\bar{x}_{23} = \frac{900}{2} = 450$		
	10-week course	560 600 1160	600 580 1180	480 410 890	3230	$\bar{x}_{3\cdot} = \frac{3230}{6} = 538.33$
		$\bar{x}_{31} = \frac{1160}{2} = 580$	$\bar{x}_{32} = \frac{1180}{2} = 590$	$\bar{x}_{33} = \frac{890}{2} = 445$		
	Column Totals	3240	3360	2670	9270 ← Overall total	
	Factor B Means	$\bar{x}_{\cdot 1} = \frac{3240}{6} = 540$	$\bar{x}_{\cdot 2} = \frac{3360}{6} = 560$	$\bar{x}_{\cdot 3} = \frac{2670}{6} = 445$	$\bar{\bar{x}} = \frac{9270}{18} = 515$	

FIGURE 13.6 MINITAB OUTPUT FOR THE GMAT TWO-FACTOR DESIGN

```
SOURCE          DF        SS        MS        F        P
Factor A         2      6100      3050     1.38    0.299
Factor B         2     45300     22650    10.27    0.005
Interaction      4     11200      2800     1.27    0.350
Error            9     19850      2206
Total           17     82450
```

the interaction effect is greater than $\alpha = .05$, there is no significant interaction effect. Therefore, the study provides no reason to believe that the three preparation programs differ in their ability to prepare students from the different colleges for the GMAT.

Undergraduate college was found to be a significant factor. Checking the calculations in Table 13.12, we see that the sample means are: business students $\bar{x}_{\cdot 1} = 540$, engineering students $\bar{x}_{\cdot 2} = 560$, and arts and sciences students $\bar{x}_{\cdot 3} = 445$. Tests on individual treatment means can be conducted; yet after reviewing the three sample means, we would anticipate no difference in preparation for business and engineering graduates. However, the arts and sciences students appear to be significantly less prepared for the GMAT than students in the other colleges. Perhaps this observation will lead the university to consider other options for assisting these students in preparing for graduate management admission tests.

Exercises

Methods

SELF test

28. A factorial experiment involving two levels of factor A and three levels of factor B resulted in the following data.

		Factor B		
		Level 1	Level 2	Level 3
Factor A	Level 1	135 165	90 66	75 93
	Level 2	125 95	127 105	120 136

Test for any significant main effects and any interaction. Use $\alpha = .05$.

29. The calculations for a factorial experiment involving four levels of factor A, three levels of factor B, and three replications resulted in the following data: SST = 280, SSA = 26, SSB = 23, SSAB = 175. Set up the ANOVA table and test for any significant main effects and any interaction effect. Use $\alpha = .05$.

Applications

30. A mail-order catalog firm designed a factorial experiment to test the effect of the size of a magazine advertisement and the advertisement design on the number of catalog requests received (data in thousands). Three advertising designs and two different-size advertisements were considered. The data obtained follow. Use the ANOVA procedure for

factorial designs to test for any significant effects due to type of design, size of advertisement, or interaction. Use $\alpha = .05$.

		Size of Advertisement	
		Small	Large
Design	A	8 12	12 8
	B	22 14	26 30
	C	10 18	18 14

31. An amusement park studied methods for decreasing the waiting time (minutes) for rides by loading and unloading riders more efficiently. Two alternative loading/unloading methods have been proposed. To account for potential differences due to the type of ride and the possible interaction between the method of loading and unloading and the type of ride, a factorial experiment was designed. Use the following data to test for any significant effect due to the loading and unloading method, the type of ride, and interaction. Use $\alpha = .05$.

	Type of Ride		
	Roller Coaster	Screaming Demon	Log Flume
Method 1	41 43	52 44	50 46
Method 2	49 51	50 46	48 44

32. The U.S. Bureau of Labor Statistics collects information on the earnings of men and women for different occupations. Suppose that a reporter for *The Tampa Tribune* wanted to investigate whether there were any differences between the weekly salaries of men and women employed as financial managers, computer programmers, and pharmacists. A sample of five men and women was selected from each of the three occupations, and the weekly salary for each individual in the sample was recorded. The data obtained follow.

CD file
Salaries

Weekly Salary ($)	Occupation	Gender
872	Financial Manager	Male
859	Financial Manager	Male
1028	Financial Manager	Male
1117	Financial Manager	Male
1019	Financial Manager	Male
519	Financial Manager	Female
702	Financial Manager	Female
805	Financial Manager	Female
558	Financial Manager	Female
591	Financial Manager	Female
747	Computer Programmer	Male
766	Computer Programmer	Male
901	Computer Programmer	Male
690	Computer Programmer	Male

(continued)

Weekly Salary ($)	Occupation	Gender
881	Computer Programmer	Male
884	Computer Programmer	Female
765	Computer Programmer	Female
685	Computer Programmer	Female
700	Computer Programmer	Female
671	Computer Programmer	Female
1105	Pharmacist	Male
1144	Pharmacist	Male
1085	Pharmacist	Male
903	Pharmacist	Male
998	Pharmacist	Male
813	Pharmacist	Female
985	Pharmacist	Female
1006	Pharmacist	Female
1034	Pharmacist	Female
817	Pharmacist	Female

At the $\alpha = .05$ level of significance, test for any significant effect due to occupation, gender, and interaction.

33. A study reported in *The Accounting Review* examined the separate and joint effects of two levels of time pressure (low and moderate) and three levels of knowledge (naive, declarative, and procedural) on key word selection behavior in tax research. Subjects were given a tax case containing a set of facts, a tax issue, and a key word index consisting of 1336 key words. They were asked to select the key words they believed would refer them to a tax authority relevant to resolving the tax case. Prior to the experiment, a group of tax experts determined that the text contained 19 relevant key words. Subjects in the naive group had little or no declarative or procedural knowledge, subjects in the declarative group had significant declarative knowledge but little or no procedural knowledge, and subjects in the procedural group had significant declarative knowledge and procedural knowledge. Declarative knowledge consists of knowledge of both the applicable tax rules and the technical terms used to describe such rules. Procedural knowledge is knowledge of the rules that guide the tax researcher's search for relevant key words. Subjects in the low time pressure situation were told they had 25 minutes to complete the problem, an amount of time which should be "more than adequate" to complete the case; subjects in the moderate time pressure situation were told they would have "only" 11 minutes to complete the case. Suppose 25 subjects were selected for each of the six treatment combinations and the sample means for each treatment combination are as follows (standard deviations are in parentheses).

		Knowledge		
		Naive	Declarative	Procedural
Time Pressure	Low	1.13 (1.12)	1.56 (1.33)	2.00 (1.54)
	Moderate	0.48 (0.80)	1.68 (1.36)	2.86 (1.80)

Use the ANOVA procedure to test for any significant differences due to time pressure, knowledge, and interaction. Use a .05 level of significance. Assume that the total sum of squares for this experiment is 327.50.

Summary

In this chapter we showed how analysis of variance can be used to test for differences among means of several populations or treatments. We introduced the completely randomized design, the randomized block design, and the two-factor factorial experiment. The completely randomized design and the randomized block design are used to draw conclusions about differences in the means of a single factor. The primary purpose of blocking in the randomized block design is to remove extraneous sources of variation from the error term. Such blocking provides a better estimate of the true error variance and a better test to determine whether the population or treatment means of the factor differ significantly.

We showed that the basis for the statistical tests used in analysis of variance and experimental design is the development of two independent estimates of the population variance σ^2. In the single-factor case, one estimator is based on the variation between the treatments; this estimator provides an unbiased estimate of σ^2 only if the means $\mu_1, \mu_2, \ldots, \mu_k$ are all equal. A second estimator of σ^2 is based on the variation of the observations within each sample; this estimator will always provide an unbiased estimate of σ^2. By computing the ratio of these two estimators (the F statistic) we developed a rejection rule for determining whether to reject the null hypothesis that the population or treatment means are equal. In all the experimental designs considered, the partitioning of the sum of squares and degrees of freedom into their various sources enabled us to compute the appropriate values for the analysis of variance calculations and tests. We also showed how Fisher's LSD procedure and the Bonferroni adjustment can be used to perform pairwise comparisons to determine which means are different.

Glossary

ANOVA table A table used to summarize the analysis of variance computations and results. It contains columns showing the source of variation, the sum of squares, the degrees of freedom, the mean square, and the F value(s).

Partitioning The process of allocating the total sum of squares and degrees of freedom to the various components.

Multiple comparison procedures Statistical procedures that can be used to conduct statistical comparisons between pairs of population means.

Comparisonwise Type I error rate The probability of a Type I error associated with a single pairwise comparison.

Experimentwise Type I error rate The probability of making a Type I error on at least one of several pairwise comparisons.

Factor Another word for the independent variable of interest.

Treatments Different levels of a factor.

Single-factor experiment An experiment involving only one factor with k populations or treatments.

Response variable Another word for the dependent variable of interest.

Experimental units The objects of interest in the experiment.

Completely randomized design An experimental design in which the treatments are randomly assigned to the experimental units.

Blocking The process of using the same or similar experimental units for all treatments. The purpose of blocking is to remove a source of variation from the error term and hence provide a more powerful test for a difference in population or treatment means.

Randomized block design An experimental design employing blocking.

Factorial experiment An experimental design that allows simultaneous conclusions about two or more factors.

Replications The number of times each experimental condition is repeated in an experiment.
Interaction The effect produced when the levels of one factor interact with the levels of another factor in influencing the response variable.

Key Formulas

Completely Randomized Design

Sample Mean for Treatment *j*

$$\bar{x}_j = \frac{\sum_{i=1}^{n_j} x_{ij}}{n_j} \tag{13.1}$$

Sample Variance for Treatment *j*

$$s_j^2 = \frac{\sum_{i=1}^{n_j} (x_{ij} - \bar{x}_j)^2}{n_j - 1} \tag{13.2}$$

Overall Sample Mean

$$\bar{\bar{x}} = \frac{\sum_{j=1}^{k} \sum_{i=1}^{n_j} x_{ij}}{n_T} \tag{13.3}$$

$$n_T = n_1 + n_2 + \cdots + n_k \tag{13.4}$$

Mean Square Due to Treatments

$$\text{MSTR} = \frac{\text{SSTR}}{k - 1} \tag{13.7}$$

Sum of Squares Due to Treatments

$$\text{SSTR} = \sum_{j=1}^{k} n_j(\bar{x}_j - \bar{\bar{x}})^2 \tag{13.8}$$

Mean Square Due to Error

$$\text{MSE} = \frac{\text{SSE}}{n_T - k} \tag{13.10}$$

Sum of Squares Due to Error

$$\text{SSE} = \sum_{j=1}^{k} (n_j - 1)s_j^2 \tag{13.11}$$

Test Statistic for the Equality of *k* Population Means

$$F = \frac{\text{MSTR}}{\text{MSE}} \tag{13.12}$$

Total Sum of Squares

$$\text{SST} = \sum_{j=1}^{k}\sum_{i=1}^{n_j}(x_{ij} - \bar{\bar{x}})^2 \tag{13.13}$$

Partitioning of Sum of Squares

$$\text{SST} = \text{SSTR} + \text{SSE} \tag{13.14}$$

Multiple Comparison Procedures

Test Statistic for Fisher's LSD Procedure

$$t = \frac{\bar{x}_i - \bar{x}_j}{\sqrt{\text{MSE}\left(\frac{1}{n_i} + \frac{1}{n_j}\right)}} \tag{13.16}$$

Fisher's LSD

$$\text{LSD} = t_{\alpha/2}\sqrt{\text{MSE}\left(\frac{1}{n_i} + \frac{1}{n_j}\right)} \tag{13.17}$$

Randomized Block Design

Total Sum of Squares

$$\text{SST} = \sum_{i=1}^{b}\sum_{j=1}^{k}(x_{ij} - \bar{\bar{x}})^2 \tag{13.22}$$

Sum of Squares Due to Treatments

$$\text{SSTR} = b\sum_{j=1}^{k}(\bar{x}_{.j} - \bar{\bar{x}})^2 \tag{13.23}$$

Sum of Squares Due to Blocks

$$\text{SSBL} = k\sum_{i=1}^{b}(\bar{x}_{i.} - \bar{\bar{x}})^2 \tag{13.24}$$

Sum of Squares Due to Error

$$\text{SSE} = \text{SST} - \text{SSTR} - \text{SSBL} \tag{13.25}$$

Factorial Experiment

Total Sum of Squares

$$\text{SST} = \sum_{i=1}^{a}\sum_{j=1}^{b}\sum_{k=1}^{r}(x_{ijk} - \bar{\bar{x}})^2 \tag{13.27}$$

Sum of Squares for Factor A

$$\text{SSA} = br\sum_{i=1}^{a}(\bar{x}_{i.} - \bar{\bar{x}})^2 \tag{13.28}$$

Sum of Squares for Factor B

$$\text{SSB} = ar\sum_{j=1}^{b}(\bar{x}_{\cdot j} - \bar{\bar{x}})^2 \tag{13.29}$$

Sum of Squares for Interaction

$$\text{SSAB} = r\sum_{i=1}^{a}\sum_{j=1}^{b}(\bar{x}_{ij} - \bar{x}_{i\cdot} - \bar{x}_{\cdot j} + \bar{\bar{x}})^2 \tag{13.30}$$

Sum of Squares for Error

$$\text{SSE} = \text{SST} - \text{SSA} - \text{SSB} - \text{SSAB} \tag{13.31}$$

Supplementary Exercises

34. In a completely randomized experimental design, three brands of paper towels were tested for their ability to absorb water. Equal-size towels were used, with four sections of towels tested per brand. The absorbency rating data follow. At a .05 level of significance, does there appear to be a difference in the ability of the brands to absorb water?

Brand		
x	y	z
91	99	83
100	96	88
88	94	89
89	99	76

35. A study reported in the *Journal of Small Business Management* concluded that self-employed individuals do not experience higher job satisfaction than individuals who are not self-employed. In this study, job satisfaction is measured using 18 items, each of which is rated using a Likert-type scale with 1–5 response options ranging from strong agreement to strong disagreement. A higher score on this scale indicates a higher degree of job satisfaction. The sum of the ratings for the 18 items, ranging from 18–90, is used as the measure of job satisfaction. Suppose that this approach was used to measure the job satisfaction for lawyers, physical therapists, cabinetmakers, and systems analysts. The results obtained for a sample of 10 individuals from each profession follow.

CD file
SatisJob

Lawyer	Physical Therapist	Cabinetmaker	Systems Analyst
44	55	54	44
42	78	65	73
74	80	79	71
42	86	69	60
53	60	79	64
50	59	64	66
45	62	59	41
48	52	78	55
64	55	84	76
38	50	60	62

At the $\alpha = .05$ level of significance, test for any difference in the job satisfaction among the four professions.

36. *Money* magazine reports percentage returns and expense ratios for stock and bond funds. The following data are the expense ratios for 10 midcap stock funds, 10 small-cap stock funds, 10 hybrid stock funds, and 10 specialty stock funds (*Money,* March 2003).

CD file Funds

Midcap	Small-Cap	Hybrid	Specialty
1.2	2.0	2.0	1.6
1.1	1.2	2.7	2.7
1.0	1.7	1.8	2.6
1.2	1.8	1.5	2.5
1.3	1.5	2.5	1.9
1.8	2.3	1.0	1.5
1.4	1.9	0.9	1.6
1.4	1.3	1.9	2.7
1.0	1.2	1.4	2.2
1.4	1.3	0.3	0.7

Use $\alpha = .05$ to test for any significant difference in the mean expense ratio among the four types of stock funds.

37. *Business 2.0*'s first annual employment survey provided data showing the typical annual salary for 97 different jobs. The following data show the annual salary for 30 different jobs in three fields: computer software and hardware, construction, and engineering (*Business 2.0,* March 2003).

CD file JobSalary

Computers		Construction		Engineering	
Job	**Salary**	**Job**	**Salary**	**Job**	**Salary**
Data Mgr.	94	Administrator	55	Aeronautical	75
Mfg. Mgr.	90	Architect	53	Agricultural	70
Programmer	63	Architect Mgr.	77	Chemical	88
Project Mgr.	84	Const. Mgr.	60	Civil	77
Software Dev.	73	Foreperson	41	Electrical	89
Sr. Design	75	Interior Design	54	Mechanical	85
Staff Systems	94	Landscape Architect	51	Mining	96
Systems Analyst	77	Sr. Estimator	64	Nuclear	105

Use $\alpha = .05$ to test for any significant difference in the mean annual salary among the three job fields.

38. Three different assembly methods have been proposed for a new product. A completely randomized experimental design was chosen to determine which assembly method results in the greatest number of parts produced per hour, and 30 workers were randomly selected and assigned to use one of the proposed methods. The number of units produced by each worker follows.

CD file Assembly

Method		
A	**B**	**C**
97	93	99
73	100	94
93	93	87
100	55	66
73	77	59
91	91	75
100	85	84
86	73	72
92	90	88
95	83	86

Use these data and test to see whether the mean number of parts produced is the same with each method. Use $\alpha = .05$.

39. In a study conducted to investigate browsing activity by shoppers, each shopper was initially classified as a nonbrowser, light browser, or heavy browser. For each shopper, the study obtained a measure to determine how comfortable the shopper was in a store. Higher scores indicated greater comfort. Suppose the following data were collected.

CD file
Browsing

Nonbrowser	Light Browser	Heavy Browser
4	5	5
5	6	7
6	5	5
3	4	7
3	7	4
4	4	6
5	6	5
4	5	7

a. Use $\alpha = .05$ to test for differences among comfort levels for the three types of browsers.
b. Use Fisher's LSD procedure to compare the comfort levels of nonbrowsers and light browsers. Use $\alpha = .05$. What is your conclusion?

40. A research firm tests the miles-per-gallon characteristics of three brands of gasoline. Because of different gasoline performance characteristics in different brands of automobiles, five brands of automobiles are selected and treated as blocks in the experiment; that is, each brand of automobile is tested with each type of gasoline. The results of the experiment (in miles per gallon) follow.

		Gasoline Brands		
		I	II	III
Automobiles	A	18	21	20
	B	24	26	27
	C	30	29	34
	D	22	25	24
	E	20	23	24

a. At $\alpha = .05$, is there a significant difference in the mean miles-per-gallon characteristics of the three brands of gasoline?
b. Analyze the experimental data using the ANOVA procedure for completely randomized designs. Compare your findings with those obtained in part (a). What is the advantage of attempting to remove the block effect?

41. Wegman's Food Markets and Tops Friendly Markets are the major grocery chains in the Rochester, New York, area. When Wal-Mart opened a Supercenter in one of the Rochester suburbs, experts predicted that Wal-Mart would undersell both local stores. The *Democrat and Chronicle* obtained the price data in the following table for a 15-item market basket (*Democrat and Chronicle,* March 17, 2002).

Item	Tops	Wal-Mart	Wegmans
Bananas (1 lb.)	0.49	0.48	0.49
Campbell's soup (10.75 oz.)	0.60	0.54	0.77
Chicken breasts (3 lbs.)	10.47	8.61	8.07
Colgate toothpaste (6.2 oz.)	1.99	2.40	1.97
Large eggs (1 dozen)	1.59	0.88	0.79
Heinz ketchup (36 oz.)	2.59	1.78	2.59
Jell-O (cherry, 3 oz.)	0.67	0.42	0.65
Jif peanut butter (18 oz.)	2.29	1.78	2.09
Milk (fat free, 1/2 gal.)	1.34	1.24	1.34
Oscar Meyer hotdogs (1 lb.)	3.29	1.50	3.39
Ragu pasta sauce (1 lb., 10 oz.)	2.09	1.50	1.25
Ritz crackers (1 lb.)	3.29	2.00	3.39
Tide detergent (liquid, 100 oz.)	6.79	5.24	5.99
Tropicana orange juice (1/2 gal.)	2.50	2.50	2.50
Twizzlers (strawberry, 1 lb.)	1.19	1.27	1.69

CD file

Grocery

At the .05 level of significance, test for any significant difference in the mean price for the 15-item shopping basket for the three stores.

42. The U.S. Department of Housing and Urban Development provides data that show the fair market monthly rent for metropolitan areas. The following data show the fair market monthly rent ($) in 2005 for 1-bedroom, 2-bedroom, and 3-bedroom apartments for five metropolitan areas (*The New York Times Almanac,* 2006).

	Boston	Miami	San Diego	San Jose	Washington
1 Bedroom	1077	775	975	1107	1045
2 Bedrooms	1266	929	1183	1313	1187
3 Bedrooms	1513	1204	1725	1889	1537

At the .05 level of significance, test whether the mean fair market monthly rent is the same for each metropolitan area.

43. A factorial experiment was designed to test for any significant differences in the time needed to perform English to foreign language translations with two computerized language translators. Because the type of language translated was also considered a significant factor, translations were made with both systems for three different languages: Spanish, French, and German. Use the following data for translation time in hours.

	Language		
	Spanish	**French**	**German**
System 1	8	10	12
	12	14	16
System 2	6	14	16
	10	16	22

Test for any significant differences due to language translator, type of language, and interaction. Use $\alpha = .05$.

44. A manufacturing company designed a factorial experiment to determine whether the number of defective parts produced by two machines differed and if the number of defective parts produced also depended on whether the raw material needed by each machine was

loaded manually or by an automatic feed system. The following data give the numbers of defective parts produced. Use $\alpha = .05$ to test for any significant effect due to machine, loading system, and interaction.

	Loading System	
	Manual	**Automatic**
Machine 1	30	30
	34	26
Machine 2	20	24
	22	28

Case Problem 1 Wentworth Medical Center

As part of a long-term study of individuals 65 years of age or older, sociologists and physicians at the Wentworth Medical Center in upstate New York investigated the relationship between geographic location and depression. A sample of 60 individuals, all in reasonably good health, was selected; 20 individuals were residents of Florida, 20 were residents of New York, and 20 were residents of North Carolina. Each of the individuals sampled was given a standardized test to measure depression. The data collected follow; higher test scores indicate higher levels of depression. These data are available on the data disk in the file Medical1.

A second part of the study considered the relationship between geographic location and depression for individuals 65 years of age or older who had a chronic health condition such as arthritis, hypertension, and/or heart ailment. A sample of 60 individuals with such conditions was identified. Again, 20 were residents of Florida, 20 were residents of New York, and 20 were residents of North Carolina. The levels of depression recorded for this study follow. These data are available on the CD accompanying the text in the file named Medical2.

CD file Medical1

CD file Medical2

Data from Medical1			Data from Medical2		
Florida	**New York**	**North Carolina**	**Florida**	**New York**	**North Carolina**
3	8	10	13	14	10
7	11	7	12	9	12
7	9	3	17	15	15
3	7	5	17	12	18
8	8	11	20	16	12
8	7	8	21	24	14
8	8	4	16	18	17
5	4	3	14	14	8
5	13	7	13	15	14
2	10	8	17	17	16
6	6	8	12	20	18
2	8	7	9	11	17
6	12	3	12	23	19
6	8	9	15	19	15
9	6	8	16	17	13
7	8	12	15	14	14
5	5	6	13	9	11
4	7	3	10	14	12
7	7	8	11	13	13
3	8	11	17	11	11

Managerial Report

1. Use descriptive statistics to summarize the data from the two studies. What are your preliminary observations about the depression scores?
2. Use analysis of variance on both data sets. State the hypotheses being tested in each case. What are your conclusions?
3. Use inferences about individual treatment means where appropriate. What are your conclusions?

Case Problem 2 Compensation for Sales Professionals

Suppose that a local chapter of sales professionals in the greater San Francisco area conducted a survey of its membership to study the relationship, if any, between the years of experience and salary for individuals employed in inside and outside sales positions. On the survey, respondents were asked to specify one of three levels of years of experience: low (1–10 years), medium (11–20 years), and high (21 or more years). A portion of the data obtained follow. The complete data set, consisting of 120 observations, is available on the CD accompanying the text in the file named SalesSalary.

CD file
SalesSalary

Observation	Salary $	Position	Experience
1	53938	Inside	Medium
2	52694	Inside	Medium
3	70515	Outside	Low
4	52031	Inside	Medium
5	62283	Outside	Low
6	57718	Inside	Low
7	79081	Outside	High
8	48621	Inside	Low
9	72835	Outside	High
10	54768	Inside	Medium
.	.	.	.
.	.	.	.
.	.	.	.
115	58080	Inside	High
116	78702	Outside	Medium
117	83131	Outside	Medium
118	57788	Inside	High
119	53070	Inside	Medium
120	60259	Outside	Low

Managerial Report

1. Use descriptive statistics to summarize the data.
2. Develop a 95% confidence interval estimate of the mean annual salary for all salespersons, regardless of years of experience and type of position.
3. Develop a 95% confidence interval estimate of the mean salary for inside salespersons.
4. Develop a 95% confidence interval estimate of the mean salary for outside salespersons.

5. Use analysis of variance to test for any significant differences due to position. Use a .05 level of significance, and for now, ignore the effect of years of experience.
6. Use analysis of variance to test for any significant differences due to years of experience. Use a .05 level of significance, and for now, ignore the effect of position.
7. At the .05 level of significance test for any significant differences due to position, years of experience, and interaction.

Appendix 13.1 Analysis of Variance with Minitab

Completely Randomized Design

In Section 13.2 we showed how analysis of variance could be used to test for the equality of k population means using data from a completely randomized design. To illustrate how Minitab can be used for this type of experimental design, we show how to test whether the mean number of units produced per week is the same for each assembly method in the Chemitech experiment introduced in Section 13.1. The sample data are entered into the first three columns of a Minitab worksheet; column 1 is labeled A, column 2 is labeled B, and column 3 is labeled C. The following steps produce the Minitab output in Figure 13.4.

CD file
Chemitech

Step 1. Select the **Stat** menu
Step 2. Choose **ANOVA**
Step 3. Choose **One-way (Unstacked)**
Step 4. When the One-way Analysis of Variance dialog box appears:
Enter C1-C3 in the **Responses (in separate columns)** box
Click **OK**

Randomized Block Design

In Section 13.4 we showed how analysis of variance could be used to test for the equality of k population means using data from a randomized block design. To illustrate how Minitab can be used for this type of experimental design, we show how to test whether the mean stress levels for air traffic controllers is the same for three work stations. The stress level scores shown in Table 13.5 are entered into column 1 of a Minitab worksheet. Coding the treatments as 1 for System A, 2 for System B, and 3 for System C, the coded values for the treatments are entered into column 2 of the worksheet. Finally, the corresponding number of each controller (1, 2, 3, 4, 5, 6) is entered into column 3. Thus, the values in the first row of the worksheet are 15, 1, 1; the values in row 2 are 15, 2, 1; the values in row 3 are 18, 3, 1; the values in row 4 are 14, 1, 2; and so on. The following steps produce the Minitab output corresponding to the ANOVA table shown in Table 13.8.

Step 1. Select the **Stat** menu
Step 2. Choose **ANOVA**
Step 3. Choose **Two-way**
Step 4. When the Two-way Analysis of Variance dialog box appears:
Enter C1 in the **Response** box
Enter C2 in the **Row factor** box
Enter C3 in the **Column factor** box
Select **Fit additive model**
Click **OK**

Factorial Experiment

In Section 13.5 we showed how analysis of variance could be used to test for the equality of k population means using data from a factorial experiment. To illustrate how Minitab can be used for this type of experimental design, we show how to analyze the data for the two-factor GMAT experiment introduced in that section. The GMAT scores shown in Table 13.11 are entered into column 1 of a Minitab worksheet; column 1 is labeled Score, column 2 is labeled Factor A, and column 3 is labeled Factor B. Coding the factor A preparation programs as 1 for the three-hour review, 2 for the one-day program, and 3 for the 10-week course, the coded values for factor A are entered into column 2 of the worksheet. Coding the factor B colleges as 1 for Business, 2 for Engineering, and 3 for Arts and Sciences, the coded values for factor B are entered into column 3. Thus, the values in the first row of the worksheet are 500, 1, 1; the values in row 2 are 580, 1, 1; the values in row 3 are 540, 1, 2; the values in row 4 are 460, 1, 2; and so on. The following steps produce the Minitab output corresponding to the ANOVA table shown in Figure 13.6.

Step 1. Select the **Stat** menu
Step 2. Choose **ANOVA**
Step 3. Choose **Two-way**
Step 4. When the Two-way Analysis of Variance dialog box appears:
Enter C1 in the **Response** box
Enter C2 in the **Row factor** box
Enter C3 in the **Column factor** box
Click **OK**

Appendix 13.2 Analysis of Variance with Excel

Completely Randomized Design

CD file
Chemitech

In Section 13.2 we showed how analysis of variance could be used to test for the equality of k population means using data from a completely randomized design. To illustrate how Excel can be used to test for the equality of k population means for this type of experimental design, we show how to test whether the mean number of units produced per week is the same for each assembly method in the Chemitech experiment introduced in Section 13.1. The sample data are entered into worksheet rows 2 to 6 of columns A, B, and C as shown in Figure 13.7. The following steps are used to obtain the output shown in cells A9:G23; the ANOVA portion of this output corresponds to the ANOVA table shown in Table 13.3.

Step 1. Select the **Tools** menu
Step 2. Choose **Data Analysis**
Step 3. Choose **Anova: Single Factor** from the list of Analysis Tools
Click **OK**
Step 4. When the Anova: Single Factor dialog box appears:
Enter A1:C6 in **Input Range** box
Select **Columns**
Select **Labels in First Row**
Select **Output Range** and enter A9 in the box
Click **OK**

FIGURE 13.7 EXCEL SOLUTION FOR THE CHEMITECH EXPERIMENT

	A	B	C	D	E	F	G	H
1	**Method A**	**Method B**	**Method C**					
2	58	58	48					
3	64	69	57					
4	55	71	59					
5	66	64	47					
6	67	68	49					
7								
8	Anova: Single Factor							
9								
10	SUMMARY							
11	*Groups*	*Count*	*Sum*	*Average*	*Variance*			
12	Method A	5	310	62	27.5			
13	Method B	5	330	66	26.5			
14	Method C	5	260	52	31			
15								
16								
17	ANOVA							
18	*Source of Variation*	*SS*	*df*	*MS*	*F*	*P-value*	*F crit*	
19	Between Groups	520	2	260	9.1765	0.0038	3.8853	
20	Within Groups	340	12	28.3333				
21								
22	Total	860	14					
23								
24								

Randomized Block Design

CD file

AirTraf

In Section 13.4 we showed how analysis of variance could be used to test for the equality of k population means using data from a randomized block design. To illustrate how Excel can be used for this type of experimental design, we show how to test whether the mean stress levels for air traffic controllers are the same for three work stations. The stress level scores shown in Table 13.5 are entered into worksheet rows 2 to 7 of columns B, C, and D as shown in Figure 13.8. The cells in rows 2 to 7 of column A contain the number of each controller (1, 2, 3, 4, 5, 6). The following steps produce the Excel output corresponding to the ANOVA table shown in Table 13.8.

Step 1. Select the **Tools** menu
Step 2. Choose **Data Analysis**
Step 3. Choose **Anova: Two-Factor Without Replication** from the list of Analysis Tools
Click **OK**
Step 4. When the Anova: Two-Factor Without Replication dialog box appears:
Enter A1:D7 in **Input Range** box
Select **Labels**
Select **Output Range** and enter A9 in the box
Click **OK**

Factorial Experiment

In Section 13.5 we showed how analysis of variance could be used to test for the equality of k population means using data from a factorial experiment. To illustrate how Excel

FIGURE 13.8 EXCEL SOLUTION FOR THE AIR TRAFFIC CONTROLLER STRESS TEST

	A	B	C	D	E	F	G	H
1	**Controller**	**System A**	**System B**	**System C**				
2	1	15	15	18				
3	2	14	14	14				
4	3	10	11	15				
5	4	13	12	17				
6	5	16	13	16				
7	6	13	13	13				
8								
9	Anova: Two-Factor Without Replication							
10								
11	*SUMMARY*	*Count*	*Sum*	*Average*	*Variance*			
12	1	3	48	16	3			
13	2	3	42	14	0			
14	3	3	36	12	7			
15	4	3	42	14	7			
16	5	3	45	15	3			
17	6	3	39	13	0			
18								
19	System A	6	81	13.5	4.3			
20	System B	6	78	13	2			
21	System C	6	93	15.5	3.5			
22								
23								
24	ANOVA							
25	*Source of Variation*	*SS*	*df*	*MS*	*F*	*P-value*	*F crit*	
26	Rows	30	5	6	3.16	0.0574	3.33	
27	Columns	21	2	10.5	5.53	0.0242	4.10	
28	Error	19	10	1.9				
29								
30	Total	70	17					
31								

CD file
GMAT

can be used for this type of experimental design, we show how to analyze the data for the two-factor GMAT experiment introduced in that section. The GMAT scores shown in Table 13.10 are entered into worksheet rows 2 to 7 of columns B, C, and D as shown in Figure 13.9. The following steps are used to obtain the output shown in cells A9:G44; the ANOVA portion of this output corresponds to the ANOVA table in Figure 13.6.

Step 1. Select the **Tools** menu
Step 2. Choose **Data Analysis**
Step 3. Choose **Anova: Two-Factor With Replication** from the list of Analysis Tools
Click **OK**
Step 4. When the Anova: Two-Factor With Replication dialog box appears:
Enter A1:D7 in **Input Range** box
Enter 2 in **Rows per sample** box
Select **Output Range** and enter A9 in the box
Click **OK**

FIGURE 13.9 EXCEL SOLUTION FOR THE TWO-FACTOR GMAT EXPERIMENT

	A	B	C	D	E	F	G	H
1		**Business**	**Engineering**	**Arts and Sciences**				
2	**3-hour review**	500	540	480				
3		580	460	400				
4	**1-day program**	460	560	420				
5		540	620	480				
6	**10-week course**	560	600	480				
7		600	580	410				
8								
9	Anova: Two-Factor With Replication							
10								
11	SUMMARY	Business	Engineering	Arts and Sciences	Total			
12	*3-hour review*							
13	Count	2	2	2	6			
14	Sum	1080	1000	880	2960			
15	Average	540	500	440	493.33333			
16	Variance	3200	3200	3200	3946.6667			
17								
18	*1-day program*							
19	Count	2	2	2	6			
20	Sum	1000	1180	900	3080			
21	Average	500	590	450	513.33333			
22	Variance	3200	1800	1800	5386.6667			
23								
24	*10-week course*							
25	Count	2	2	2	6			
26	Sum	1160	1180	890	3230			
27	Average	580	590	445	538.33333			
28	Variance	800	200	2450	5936.6667			
29								
30	*Total*							
31	Count	6	6	6				
32	Sum	3240	3360	2670				
33	Average	540	560	445				
34	Variance	2720	3200	1510				
35								
36								
37	ANOVA							
38	*Source of Variation*	*SS*	*df*	*MS*	*F*	*P-value*	*F crit*	
39	Sample	6100	2	3050	1.38	0.2994	4.26	
40	Columns	45300	2	22650	10.27	0.0048	4.26	
41	Interaction	11200	4	2800	1.27	0.3503	3.63	
42	Within	19850	9	2205.5556				
43								
44	Total	82450	17					
45								

CHAPTER 14

Simple Linear Regression

CONTENTS

STATISTICS *in* PRACTICE

ALLIANCE DATA SYSTEMS*
DALLAS, TEXAS

Alliance Data Systems (ADS) provides transaction processing, credit services, and marketing services for clients in the rapidly growing customer relationship management (CRM) industry. ADS clients are concentrated in four industries: retail, petroleum/convenience stores, utilities, and transportation. In 1983, Alliance began offering end-to-end credit processing services to the retail, petroleum, and casual dining industries; today they employ more than 6500 employees who provide services to clients around the world. Operating more than 140,000 point-of-sale terminals in the United States alone, ADS processes in excess of 2.5 billion transactions annually. The company ranks second in the United States in private label credit services by representing 49 private label programs with nearly 72 million cardholders. In 2001, ADS made an initial public offering and is now listed on the New York Stock Exchange.

As one of its marketing services, ADS designs direct mail campaigns and promotions. With its database containing information on the spending habits of more than 100 million consumers, ADS can target those consumers most likely to benefit from a direct mail promotion. The Analytical Development Group uses regression analysis to build models that measure and predict the responsiveness of consumers to direct market campaigns. Some regression models predict the probability of purchase for individuals receiving a promotion, and others predict the amount spent by those consumers making a purchase.

For one particular campaign, a retail store chain wanted to attract new customers. To predict the effect of the campaign, ADS analysts selected a sample from the consumer database, sent the sampled individuals promotional materials, and then collected transaction data on the consumers' response. Sample data were collected on the amount of purchase made by the consumers responding to the campaign, as well as a variety of consumer-specific variables thought to be useful in predicting sales. The consumer-specific variable that contributed most to predicting the amount purchased was the total amount of credit purchases at related stores over the past 39 months. ADS analysts developed an estimated regression equation relating the amount of purchase to the amount spent at related stores:

Alliance Data analysts discuss use of a regression model to predict sales for a direct marketing campaign. © Courtesy of Alliance Data Systems.

$$\hat{y} = 26.7 + 0.00205x$$

where

$$\hat{y} = \text{amount of purchase}$$
$$x = \text{amount spent at related stores}$$

Using this equation, we could predict that someone spending \$10,000 over the past 39 months at related stores would spend \$47.20 when responding to the direct mail promotion. In this chapter, you will learn how to develop this type of estimated regression equation.

The final model developed by ADS analysts also included several other variables that increased the predictive power of the preceding equation. Some of these variables included the absence/presence of a bank credit card, estimated income, and the average amount spent per trip at a selected store. In the following chapter, we will learn how such additional variables can be incorporated into a multiple regression model.

*The authors are indebted to Philip Clemance, Director of Analytical Development at Alliance Data Systems, for providing this Statistics in Practice.

Managerial decisions often are based on the relationship between two or more variables. For example, after considering the relationship between advertising expenditures and sales, a marketing manager might attempt to predict sales for a given level of advertising expenditures. In another case, a public utility might use the relationship between the daily high temperature and the demand for electricity to predict electricity usage on the basis of next month's anticipated daily high temperatures. Sometimes a manager will rely on intuition to judge how two variables are related. However, if data can be obtained, a statistical procedure called *regression analysis* can be used to develop an equation showing how the variables are related.

The statistical methods used in studying the relationship between two variables were first employed by Sir Francis Galton (1822–1911). Galton was interested in studying the relationship between a father's height and the son's height. Galton's disciple, Karl Pearson (1857–1936), analyzed the relationship between the father's height and the son's height for 1078 pairs of subjects.

In regression terminology, the variable being predicted is called the **dependent variable**. The variable or variables being used to predict the value of the dependent variable are called the **independent variables**. For example, in analyzing the effect of advertising expenditures on sales, a marketing manager's desire to predict sales would suggest making sales the dependent variable. Advertising expenditure would be the independent variable used to help predict sales. In statistical notation, y denotes the dependent variable and x denotes the independent variable.

In this chapter we consider the simplest type of regression analysis involving one independent variable and one dependent variable in which the relationship between the variables is approximated by a straight line. It is called **simple linear regression**. Regression analysis involving two or more independent variables is called multiple regression analysis; multiple regression and cases involving curvilinear relationships are covered in Chapters 15 and 16.

14.1 Simple Linear Regression Model

Armand's Pizza Parlors is a chain of Italian-food restaurants located in a five-state area. Armand's most successful locations are near college campuses. The managers believe that quarterly sales for these restaurants (denoted by y) are related positively to the size of the student population (denoted by x); that is, restaurants near campuses with a large student population tend to generate more sales than those located near campuses with a small student population. Using regression analysis, we can develop an equation showing how the dependent variable y is related to the independent variable x.

Regression Model and Regression Equation

In the Armand's Pizza Parlors example, the population consists of all the Armand's restaurants. For every restaurant in the population, there is a value of x (student population) and a corresponding value of y (quarterly sales). The equation that describes how y is related to x and an error term is called the **regression model**. The regression model used in simple linear regression follows.

SIMPLE LINEAR REGRESSION MODEL

$$y = \beta_0 + \beta_1 x + \epsilon \qquad \textbf{(14.1)}$$

β_0 and β_1 are referred to as the parameters of the model, and ϵ (the Greek letter epsilon) is a random variable referred to as the error term. The error term accounts for the variability in y that cannot be explained by the linear relationship between x and y.

The population of all Armand's restaurants can also be viewed as a collection of subpopulations, one for each distinct value of x. For example, one subpopulation consists of all Armand's restaurants located near college campuses with 8000 students; another subpopulation consists of all Armand's restaurants located near college campuses with 9000 students; and so on. Each subpopulation has a corresponding distribution of y values. Thus, a distribution of y values is associated with restaurants located near campuses with 8000 students; a distribution of y values is associated with restaurants located near campuses with 9000 students; and so on. Each distribution of y values has its own mean or expected value. The equation that describes how the expected value of y, denoted $E(y)$, is related to x is called the **regression equation**. The regression equation for simple linear regression follows.

SIMPLE LINEAR REGRESSION EQUATION

$$E(y) = \beta_0 + \beta_1 x \quad \textbf{(14.2)}$$

The graph of the simple linear regression equation is a straight line; β_0 is the y-intercept of the regression line, β_1 is the slope, and $E(y)$ is the mean or expected value of y for a given value of x.

Examples of possible regression lines are shown in Figure 14.1. The regression line in Panel A shows that the mean value of y is related positively to x, with larger values of $E(y)$ associated with larger values of x. The regression line in Panel B shows the mean value of y is related negatively to x, with smaller values of $E(y)$ associated with larger values of x. The regression line in Panel C shows the case in which the mean value of y is not related to x; that is, the mean value of y is the same for every value of x.

Estimated Regression Equation

If the values of the population parameters β_0 and β_1 were known, we could use equation (14.2) to compute the mean value of y for a given value of x. In practice, the parameter values are not known, and must be estimated using sample data. Sample statistics (denoted b_0 and b_1) are computed as estimates of the population parameters β_0 and β_1. Substituting the values of the sample statistics b_0 and b_1 for β_0 and β_1 in the regression equation, we obtain the

FIGURE 14.1 POSSIBLE REGRESSION LINES IN SIMPLE LINEAR REGRESSION

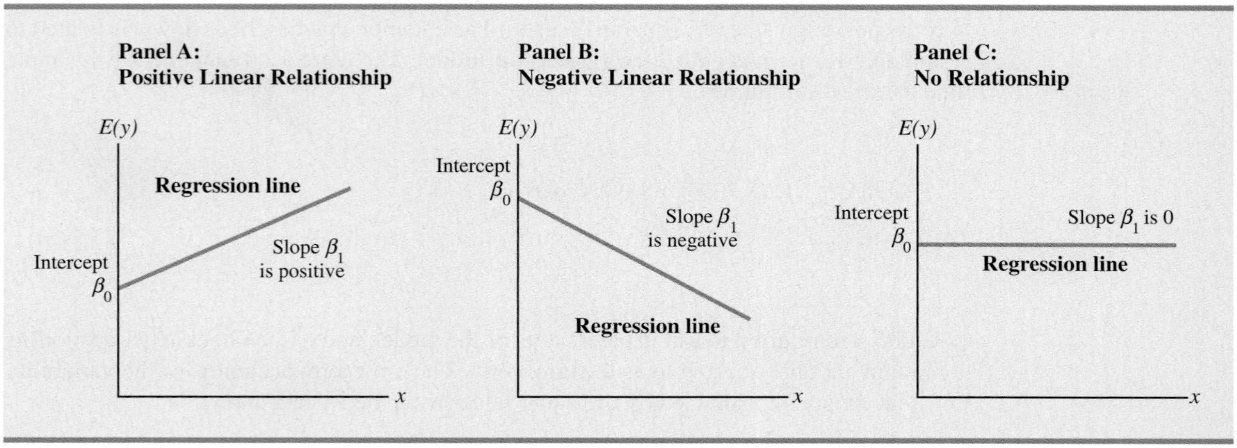

estimated regression equation. The estimated regression equation for simple linear regression follows.

ESTIMATED SIMPLE LINEAR REGRESSION EQUATION

$$\hat{y} = b_0 + b_1x \tag{14.3}$$

The graph of the estimated simple linear regression equation is called the *estimated regression line*; b_0 is the y intercept and b_1 is the slope. In the next section, we show how the least squares method can be used to compute the values of b_0 and b_1 in the estimated regression equation.

In general, $\hat{y}$ is the point estimator of $E(y)$, the mean value of y for a given value of x. Thus, to estimate the mean or expected value of quarterly sales for all restaurants located near campuses with 10,000 students, Armand's would substitute the value of 10,000 for x in equation (14.3). In some cases, however, Armand's may be more interested in predicting sales for one particular restaurant. For example, suppose Armand's would like to predict quarterly sales for the restaurant located near Talbot College, a school with 10,000 students. As it turns out, the best estimate of y for a given value of x is also provided by $\hat{y}$. Thus, to predict quarterly sales for the restaurant located near Talbot College, Armand's would also substitute the value of 10,000 for x in equation (14.3).

Because the value of $\hat{y}$ provides both a point estimate of $E(y)$ for a given value of x and a point estimate of an individual value of y for a given value of x, we will refer to $\hat{y}$ simply as the *estimated value of y*. Figure 14.2 provides a summary of the estimation process for simple linear regression.

The estimation of β_0 and β_1 is a statistical process much like the estimation of μ discussed in Chapter 7. β_0 and β_1 are the unknown parameters of interest, and b_0 and b_1 are the sample statistics used to estimate the parameters.

FIGURE 14.2 THE ESTIMATION PROCESS IN SIMPLE LINEAR REGRESSION

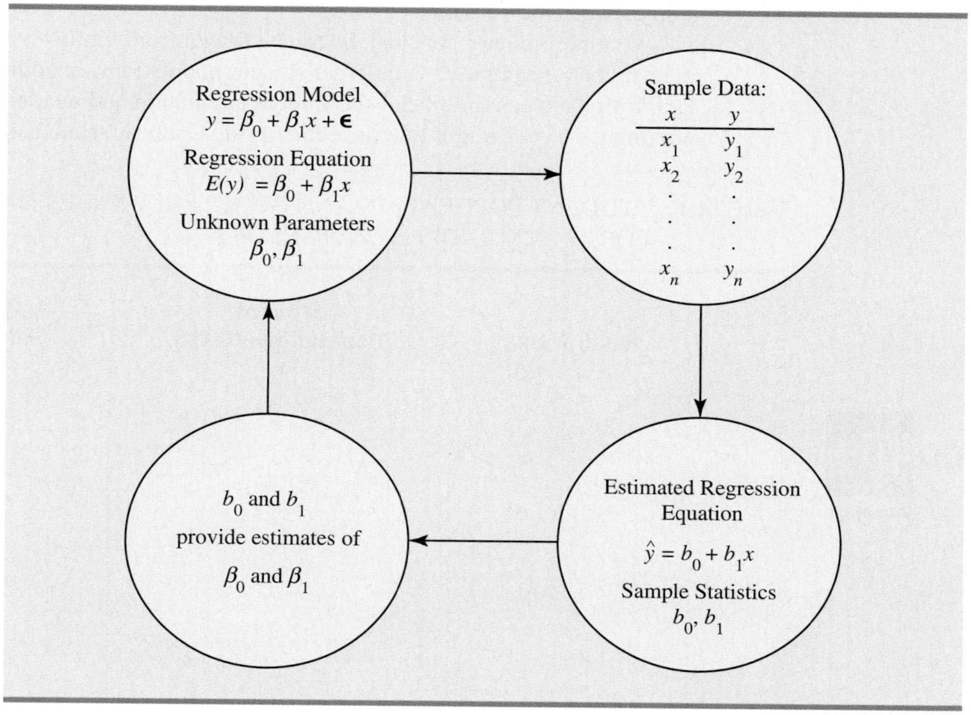

NOTES AND COMMENTS

1. Regression analysis cannot be interpreted as a procedure for establishing a cause-and-effect relationship between variables. It can only indicate how or to what extent variables are associated with each other. Any conclusions about cause and effect must be based upon the judgment of those individuals most knowledgeable about the application.

2. The regression equation in simple linear regression is $E(y) = \beta_0 + \beta_1 x$. More advanced texts in regression analysis often write the regression equation as $E(y|x) = \beta_0 + \beta_1 x$ to emphasize that the regression equation provides the mean value of y for a given value of x.

14.2 Least Squares Method

In simple linear regression, each observation consists of two values: one for the independent variable and one for the dependent variable.

The **least squares method** is a procedure for using sample data to find the estimated regression equation. To illustrate the least squares method, suppose data were collected from a sample of 10 Armand's Pizza Parlor restaurants located near college campuses. For the ith observation or restaurant in the sample, x_i is the size of the student population (in thousands) and y_i is the quarterly sales (in thousands of dollars). The values of x_i and y_i for the 10 restaurants in the sample are summarized in Table 14.1. We see that restaurant 1, with $x_1 = 2$ and $y_1 = 58$, is near a campus with 2000 students and has quarterly sales of $58,000. Restaurant 2, with $x_2 = 6$ and $y_2 = 105$, is near a campus with 6000 students and has quarterly sales of $105,000. The largest sales value is for restaurant 10, which is near a campus with 26,000 students and has quarterly sales of $202,000.

Figure 14.3 is a scatter diagram of the data in Table 14.1. Student population is shown on the horizontal axis and quarterly sales is shown on the vertical axis. **Scatter diagrams** for regression analysis are constructed with the independent variable x on the horizontal axis and the dependent variable y on the vertical axis. The scatter diagram enables us to observe the data graphically and to draw preliminary conclusions about the possible relationship between the variables.

What preliminary conclusions can be drawn from Figure 14.3? Quarterly sales appear to be higher at campuses with larger student populations. In addition, for these data the relationship between the size of the student population and quarterly sales appears to be approximated by a straight line; indeed, a positive linear relationship is indicated between x

TABLE 14.1 STUDENT POPULATION AND QUARTERLY SALES DATA FOR 10 ARMAND'S PIZZA PARLORS

CD file Armand's

Restaurant i	Student Population (1000s) x_i	Quarterly Sales ($1000s) y_i
1	2	58
2	6	105
3	8	88
4	8	118
5	12	117
6	16	137
7	20	157
8	20	169
9	22	149
10	26	202

FIGURE 14.3 SCATTER DIAGRAM OF STUDENT POPULATION AND QUARTERLY SALES FOR ARMAND'S PIZZA PARLORS

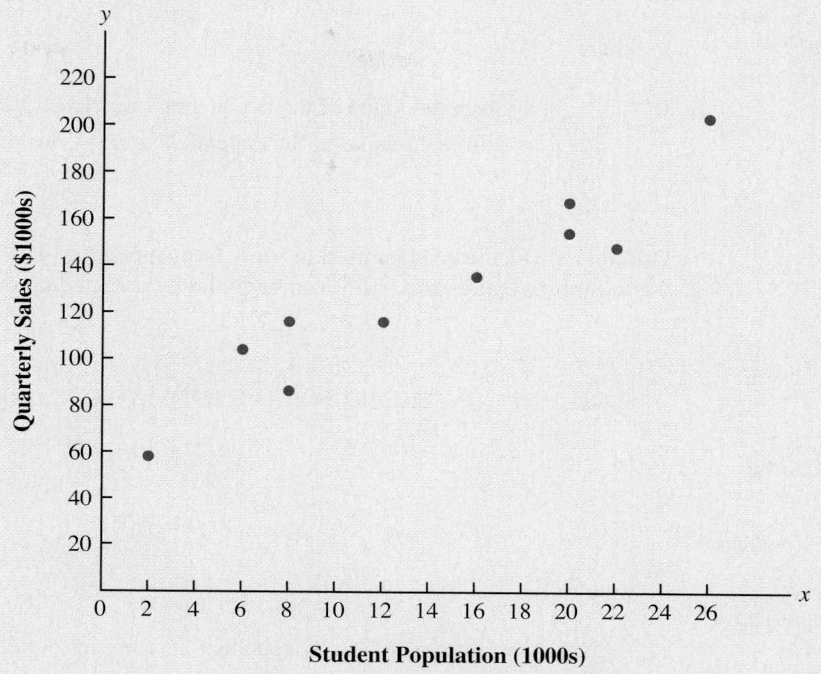

and y. We therefore choose the simple linear regression model to represent the relationship between quarterly sales and student population. Given that choice, our next task is to use the sample data in Table 14.1 to determine the values of b_0 and b_1 in the estimated simple linear regression equation. For the ith restaurant, the estimated regression equation provides

$$\hat{y}_i = b_0 + b_1 x_i \tag{14.4}$$

where

$\hat{y}_i$ = estimated value of quarterly sales ($1000s) for the ith restaurant
b_0 = the y intercept of the estimated regression line
b_1 = the slope of the estimated regression line
x_i = size of the student population (1000s) for the ith restaurant

With y_i denoting the observed (actual) sales for restaurant i and $\hat{y}_i$ in equation (14.4) representing the estimated value of sales for restaurant i, every restaurant in the sample will have an observed value of sales y_i and an estimated value of sales $\hat{y}_i$. For the estimated regression line to provide a good fit to the data, we want the differences between the observed sales values and the estimated sales values to be small.

The least squares method uses the sample data to provide the values of b_0 and b_1 that minimize the *sum of the squares of the deviations* between the observed values of the dependent variable y_i and the estimated values of the dependent variable. The criterion for the least squares method is given by expression (14.5).

Carl Friedrich Gauss (1777–1855) proposed the least squares method.

LEAST SQUARES CRITERION

$$\min \Sigma(y_i - \hat{y}_i)^2 \tag{14.5}$$

where

y_i = observed value of the dependent variable for the ith observation
$\hat{y}_i$ = estimated value of the dependent variable for the ith observation

Differential calculus can be used to show (see Appendix 14.1) that the values of b_0 and b_1 that minimize expression (14.5) can be found by using equations (14.6) and (14.7).

In computing b_1 with a calculator, carry as many significant digits as possible in the intermediate calculations. We recommend carrying at least four significant digits.

SLOPE AND y-INTERCEPT FOR THE ESTIMATED REGRESSION EQUATION*

$$b_1 = \frac{\Sigma(x_i - \bar{x})(y_i - \bar{y})}{\Sigma(x_i - \bar{x})^2} \tag{14.6}$$

$$b_0 = \bar{y} - b_1\bar{x} \tag{14.7}$$

where

x_i = value of the independent variable for the ith observation
y_i = value of the dependent variable for the ith observation
$\bar{x}$ = mean value for the independent variable
$\bar{y}$ = mean value for the dependent variable
n = total number of observations

Some of the calculations necessary to develop the least squares estimated regression equation for Armand's Pizza Parlors are shown in Table 14.2. With the sample of 10 restaurants, we have $n = 10$ observations. Because equations (14.6) and (14.7) require $\bar{x}$ and $\bar{y}$ we begin the calculations by computing $\bar{x}$ and $\bar{y}$.

$$\bar{x} = \frac{\Sigma x_i}{n} = \frac{140}{10} = 14$$

$$\bar{y} = \frac{\Sigma y_i}{n} = \frac{1300}{10} = 130$$

Using equations (14.6) and (14.7) and the information in Table 14.2, we can compute the slope and intercept of the estimated regression equation for Armand's Pizza Parlors. The calculation of the slope (b_1) proceeds as follows.

---

*An alternate formula for b_1 is

$$b_1 = \frac{\Sigma x_i y_i - (\Sigma x_i \Sigma y_i)/n}{\Sigma x_i^2 - (\Sigma x_i)^2/n}$$

This form of equation (14.6) is often recommended when using a calculator to compute b_1.

TABLE 14.2 CALCULATIONS FOR THE LEAST SQUARES ESTIMATED REGRESSION EQUATION FOR ARMAND PIZZA PARLORS

Restaurant i	x_i	y_i	$x_i - \bar{x}$	$y_i - \bar{y}$	$(x_i - \bar{x})(y_i - \bar{y})$	$(x_i - \bar{x})^2$
1	2	58	−12	−72	864	144
2	6	105	−8	−25	200	64
3	8	88	−6	−42	252	36
4	8	118	−6	−12	72	36
5	12	117	−2	−13	26	4
6	16	137	2	7	14	4
7	20	157	6	27	162	36
8	20	169	6	39	234	36
9	22	149	8	19	152	64
10	26	202	12	72	864	144
Totals	140	1300			2840	568
	Σx_i	Σy_i			$\Sigma(x_i - \bar{x})(y_i - \bar{y})$	$\Sigma(x_i - \bar{x})^2$

$$b_1 = \frac{\Sigma(x_i - \bar{x})(y_i - \bar{y})}{\Sigma(x_i - \bar{x})^2} = \frac{2840}{568} = 5$$

The calculation of the y intercept (b_0) follows.

$$b_0 = \bar{y} - b_1\bar{x} = 130 - 5(14) = 60$$

Thus, the estimated regression equation is

$$\hat{y} = 60 + 5x$$

Figure 14.4 shows the graph of this equation on the scatter diagram.

The slope of the estimated regression equation ($b_1 = 5$) is positive, implying that as student population increases, sales increase. In fact, we can conclude (based on sales measured in \$1000s and student population in 1000s) that an increase in the student population of 1000 is associated with an increase of \$5000 in expected sales; that is, quarterly sales are expected to increase by \$5 per student.

Using the estimated regression equation to make predictions outside the range of the values of the independent variable should be done with caution because outside that range we cannot be sure that the same relationship is valid.

If we believe the least squares estimated regression equation adequately describes the relationship between x and y, it would seem reasonable to use the estimated regression equation to predict the value of y for a given value of x. For example, if we wanted to predict quarterly sales for a restaurant to be located near a campus with 16,000 students, we would compute

$$\hat{y} = 60 + 5(16) = 140$$

Hence, we would predict quarterly sales of \$140,000 for this restaurant. In the following sections we will discuss methods for assessing the appropriateness of using the estimated regression equation for estimation and prediction.

FIGURE 14.4 GRAPH OF THE ESTIMATED REGRESSION EQUATION FOR ARMAND'S PIZZA PARLORS: $\hat{y} = 60 + 5x$

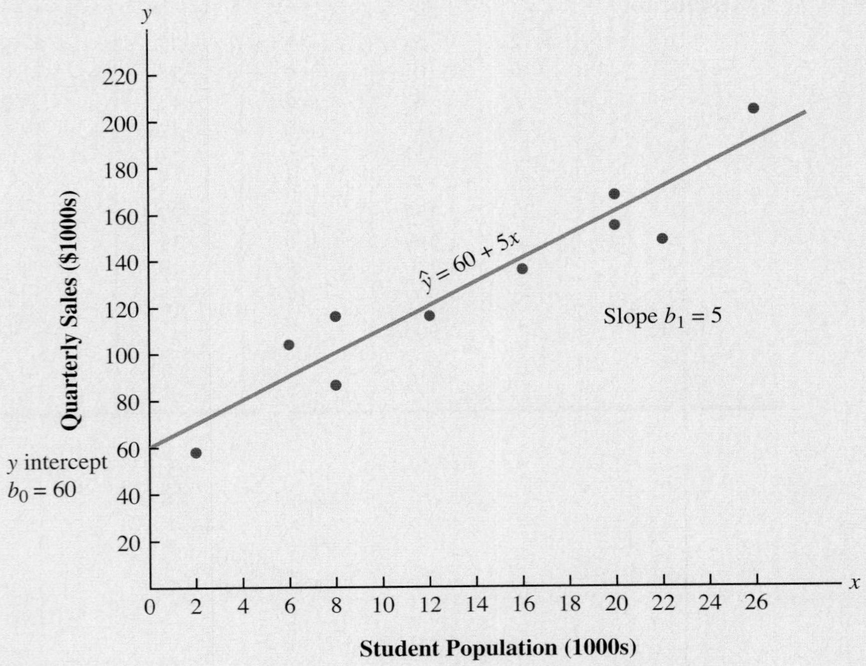

NOTES AND COMMENTS

The least squares method provides an estimated regression equation that minimizes the sum of squared deviations between the observed values of the dependent variable y_i and the estimated values of the dependent variable $\hat{y}_i$. This least squares criterion is used to choose the equation that provides the best fit. If some other criterion were used, such as minimizing the sum of the absolute deviations between y_i and $\hat{y}_i$, a different equation would be obtained. In practice, the least squares method is the most widely used.

Exercises

Methods

SELF test

1. Given are five observations for two variables, x and y.

x_i	1	2	3	4	5
y_i	3	7	5	11	14

   a. Develop a scatter diagram for these data.
   b. What does the scatter diagram developed in part (a) indicate about the relationship between the two variables?

c. Try to approximate the relationship between x and y by drawing a straight line through the data.
d. Develop the estimated regression equation by computing the values of b_0 and b_1 using equations (14.6) and (14.7).
e. Use the estimated regression equation to predict the value of y when $x = 4$.

2. Given are five observations for two variables, x and y.

x_i	3	12	6	20	14
y_i	55	40	55	10	15

a. Develop a scatter diagram for these data.
b. What does the scatter diagram developed in part (a) indicate about the relationship between the two variables?
c. Try to approximate the relationship between x and y by drawing a straight line through the data.
d. Develop the estimated regression equation by computing the values of b_0 and b_1 using equations (14.6) and (14.7).
e. Use the estimated regression equation to predict the value of y when $x = 10$.

3. Given are five observations collected in a regression study on two variables.

x_i	2	6	9	13	20
y_i	7	18	9	26	23

a. Develop a scatter diagram for these data.
b. Develop the estimated regression equation for these data.
c. Use the estimated regression equation to predict the value of y when $x = 4$.

Applications

SELF test

4. The following data were collected on the height (inches) and weight (pounds) of women swimmers.

Height	68	64	62	65	66
Weight	132	108	102	115	128

a. Develop a scatter diagram for these data with height as the independent variable.
b. What does the scatter diagram developed in part (a) indicate about the relationship between the two variables?
c. Try to approximate the relationship between height and weight by drawing a straight line through the data.
d. Develop the estimated regression equation by computing the values of b_0 and b_1.
e. If a swimmer's height is 63 inches, what would you estimate her weight to be?

5. Technological advances helped make inflatable paddlecraft suitable for backcountry use. These blow-up rubber boats, which can be rolled into a bundle not much bigger than a golf bag, are large enough to accommodate one or two paddlers and their camping gear. *Canoe & Kayak* magazine tested boats from nine manufacturers to determine how they would perform on a three-day wilderness paddling trip. One of the criteria in their evaluation was the baggage capacity of the boat, evaluated using a 4-point rating scale from 1 (lowest rating) to 4 (highest rating). The following data show the baggage capacity rating and the price of the boat (*Canoe & Kayak,* March 2003).

CD file
Boats

Boat	Baggage Capacity	Price ($)
S14	4	1595
Orinoco	4	1399
Outside Pro	4	1890
Explorer 380X	3	795
River XK2	2.5	600
Sea Tiger	4	1995
Maverik II	3	1205
Starlite 100	2	583
Fat Pack Cat	3	1048

a. Develop a scatter diagram for these data with baggage capacity rating as the independent variable.
b. What does the scatter diagram developed in part (a) indicate about the relationship between baggage capacity and price?
c. Draw a straight line through the data to approximate a linear relationship between baggage capacity and price.
d. Use the least squares method to develop the estimated regression equation.
e. Provide an interpretation for the slope of the estimated regression equation.
f. Predict the price for a boat with a baggage capacity rating of 3.

6. Wageweb conducts surveys of salary data and presents summaries on its Web site. Based on salary data as of October 1, 2002, Wageweb reported that the average annual salary for sales vice presidents was $142,111, with an average annual bonus of $15,432 (Wageweb.com, March 13, 2003). Assume the following data are a sample of the annual salary and bonus for 10 sales vice presidents. Data are in thousands of dollars.

CD file
VPSalary

Vice President	Salary	Bonus
1	135	12
2	115	14
3	146	16
4	167	19
5	165	22
6	176	24
7	98	7
8	136	17
9	163	18
10	119	11

a. Develop a scatter diagram for these data with salary as the independent variable.
b. What does the scatter diagram developed in part (a) indicate about the relationship between salary and bonus?
c. Use the least squares method to develop the estimated regression equation.
d. Provide an interpretation for the slope of the estimated regression equation.
e. Predict the bonus for a vice president with an annual salary of $120,000.

7. Would you expect more reliable cars to cost more? *Consumer Reports* rated 15 upscale sedans. Reliability was rated on a 5-point scale: poor (1), fair (2), good (3), very good (4), and excellent (5). The price and reliability rating for each of the 15 cars are shown (*Consumer Reports,* February 2004).

CD file
Cars

Make and Model	Reliability	Price ($)
Acura TL	4	33,150
BMW 330i	3	40,570
Lexus IS300	5	35,105
Lexus ES330	5	35,174
Mercedes-Benz C320	1	42,230
Lincoln LS Premium (V6)	3	38,225
Audi A4 3.0 Quattro	2	37,605
Cadillac CTS	1	37,695
Nissan Maxima 3.5 SE	4	34,390
Infiniti I35	5	33,845
Saab 9-3 Aero	3	36,910
Infiniti G35	4	34,695
Jaguar X-Type 3.0	1	37,995
Saab 9-5 Arc	3	36,955
Volvo S60 2.5T	3	33,890

a. Develop a scatter diagram for these data with the reliability rating as the independent variable.
b. Develop the least squares estimated regression equation.
c. Based upon your analysis, do you think more reliable cars cost more? Explain.
d. Estimate the price for an upscale sedan that has a good reliability rating.

8. Mountain bikes that cost less than $1000 now contain many of the high-quality components that until recently were only available on high-priced models. Today, even sub-$1000 models often offer supple suspensions, clipless pedals, and highly engineered frames. An interesting question is whether higher price still buys a higher level of handling, as measured by the bike's sidetrack capability. To measure sidetrack capability, *Outside Magazine* used a rating scale from 1 to 5, with 1 representing an average rating and 5 representing an excellent rating. The sidetrack capability and the price for 10 mountain bikes tested by *Outside Magazine* follow (*Outside Magazine Buyer's Guide,* 2001).

CD file
MtnBikes

Manufacturer and Model	Sidetrack Capability	Price ($)
Raleigh M80	1	600
Marin Bear Valley Feminina	1	649
GT Avalanche 2.0	2	799
Kona Jake the Snake	1	899
Schwinn Moab 2	3	950
Giant XTC NRS 3	4	1100
Fisher Paragon Genesisters	4	1149
Jamis Dakota XC	3	1300
Trek Fuel 90	5	1550
Specialized Stumpjumper M4	4	1625

a. Develop a scatter diagram for these data with sidetrack capability as the independent variable.
b. Does it appear that higher priced models have a higher level of handling? Explain.
c. Develop the least squares estimated regression equation.
d. What is the estimated price for a mountain bike if it has a sidetrack capability rating of 4?

9. A sales manager collected the following data on annual sales and years of experience.

CD file
Sales

Salesperson	Years of Experience	Annual Sales ($1000s)
1	1	80
2	3	97
3	4	92
4	4	102
5	6	103
6	8	111
7	10	119
8	10	123
9	11	117
10	13	136

a. Develop a scatter diagram for these data with years of experience as the independent variable.
b. Develop an estimated regression equation that can be used to predict annual sales given the years of experience.
c. Use the estimated regression equation to predict annual sales for a salesperson with 9 years of experience.

10. Bergans of Norway has been making outdoor gear since 1908. The following data show the temperature rating (F°) and the price ($) for 11 models of sleeping bags produced by Bergans (*Backpacker* 2006 Gear Guide).

CD file
SleepingBags

Model	Rating	Price
Ranger 3-Seasons	12	319
Ranger Spring	24	289
Ranger Winter	3	389
Rondane 3-Seasons	13	239
Rondane Summer	38	149
Rondane Winter	4	289
Senja Ice	5	359
Senja Snow	15	259
Senja Zero	25	229
Super Light	45	129
Tight & Light	25	199

a. Develop a scatter diagram for these data with temperature rating (F°) as the independent variable.
b. What does the scatter diagram developed in part (a) indicate about the relationship between temperature rating (F°) and price?
c. Use the least squares method to develop the estimated regression equation.
d. Predict the price for a sleeping bag with a temperature rating (F°) of 20.

11. Although delays at major airports are now less frequent, it helps to know which airports are likely to throw off your schedule. In addition, if your plane is late arriving at a particular airport where you must make a connection, how likely is it that the departure will be late and thus increase your chances of making the connection? The following data show the percentage of late arrivals and departures during August for 13 airports (*Business 2.0,* February 2002).

CD file
Airport

Airport	Late Arrivals (%)	Late Departures (%)
Atlanta	24	22
Charlotte	20	20
Chicago	30	29
Cincinnati	20	19
Dallas	20	22
Denver	23	23
Detroit	18	19
Houston	20	16
Minneapolis	18	18
Phoenix	21	22
Pittsburgh	25	22
Salt Lake City	18	17
St. Louis	16	16

a. Develop a scatter diagram for these data with the percentage of late arrivals as the independent variable.
b. What does the scatter diagram developed in part (a) indicate about the relationship between late arrivals and late departures?
c. Use the least squares method to develop the estimated regression equation.
d. Provide an interpretation for the slope of the estimated regression equation.
e. Suppose the percentage of late arrivals at the Philadelphia airport for August was 22%. What is an estimate of the percentage of late departures?

12. A personal watercraft (PWC) is a vessel propelled by water jets, designed to be operated by a person sitting, standing, or kneeling on the vessel. In the early 1970s, Kawasaki Motors Corp. U.S.A. introduced the JET SKI® watercraft, the first commercially successful PWC. Today, *jet ski* is commonly used as a generic term for personal watercraft. The following data show the weight (rounded to the nearest 10 lbs.) and the price (rounded to the nearest $50) for 10 three-seater personal watercraft (www.jetskinews.com, 2006).

CD file
JetSki

Make and Model	Weight (lbs.)	Price ($)
Honda AquaTrax F-12	750	9500
Honda AquaTrax F-12X	790	10500
Honda AquaTrax F-12X GPScape	800	11200
Kawasaki STX-12F Jetski	740	8500
Yamaha FX Cruiser Waverunner	830	10000
Yamaha FX High Output Waverunner	770	10000
Yamaha FX Waverunner	830	9300
Yamaha VX110 Deluxe Waverunner	720	7700
Yamaha VX110 Sport Waverunner	720	7000
Yamaha XLT1200 Waverunner	780	8500

a. Develop a scatter diagram for these data with weight as the independent variable.
b. What does the scatter diagram developed in part (a) indicate about the relationship between weight and price?
c. Use the least squares method to develop the estimated regression equation.
d. Predict the price for a three-seater PWC with a weight of 750 pounds.
e. The Honda AquaTrax F-12 weighs 750 pounds and has a price of $9500. Shouldn't the predicted price you developed in part (d) for a PWC with a weight of 750 pounds also be $9500?

f. The Kawasaki SX-R 800 Jetski has a seating capacity of one and weighs 350 pounds. Do you think the estimated regression equation developed in part (c) should be used to predict the price for this model?

13. To the Internal Revenue Service, the reasonableness of total itemized deductions depends on the taxpayer's adjusted gross income. Large deductions, which include charity and medical deductions, are more reasonable for taxpayers with large adjusted gross incomes. If a taxpayer claims larger than average itemized deductions for a given level of income, the chances of an IRS audit are increased. Data (in thousands of dollars) on adjusted gross income and the average or reasonable amount of itemized deductions follow.

Adjusted Gross Income ($1000s)	Reasonable Amount of Itemized Deductions ($1000s)
22	9.6
27	9.6
32	10.1
48	11.1
65	13.5
85	17.7
120	25.5

a. Develop a scatter diagram for these data with adjusted gross income as the independent variable.
b. Use the least squares method to develop the estimated regression equation.
c. Estimate a reasonable level of total itemized deductions for a taxpayer with an adjusted gross income of $52,500. If this taxpayer claimed itemized deductions of $20,400, would the IRS agent's request for an audit appear justified? Explain.

14. Starting salaries for accountants and auditors in Rochester, New York, trail those of many U.S. cities. The following data show the starting salary (in thousands of dollars) and the cost of living index for Rochester and nine other metropolitan areas (*Democrat and Chronicle,* September 1, 2002). The cost of living index, based on a city's food, housing, taxes, and other costs, ranges from 0 (most expensive) to 100 (least expensive).

CD file
Salaries

Metropolitan Area	Index	Salary ($1000s)
Oklahoma City	82.44	23.9
Tampa/St. Petersburg/Clearwater	79.89	24.5
Indianapolis	55.53	27.4
Buffalo/Niagara Falls	41.36	27.7
Atlanta	39.38	27.1
Rochester	28.05	25.6
Sacramento	25.50	28.7
Raleigh/Durham/Chapel Hill	13.32	26.7
San Diego	3.12	27.8
Honolulu	0.57	28.3

a. Develop a scatter diagram for these data with the cost of living index as the independent variable.
b. Develop the estimated regression equation relating the cost of living index to the starting salary.
c. Estimate the starting salary for a metropolitan area with a cost of living index of 50.

14.3 Coefficient of Determination

For the Armand's Pizza Parlors example, we developed the estimated regression equation $\hat{y} = 60 + 5x$ to approximate the linear relationship between the size of the student population x and quarterly sales y. A question now is: How well does the estimated regression equation fit the data? In this section, we show that the **coefficient of determination** provides a measure of the goodness of fit for the estimated regression equation.

For the ith observation, the difference between the observed value of the dependent variable, y_i, and the estimated value of the dependent variable, $\hat{y}_i$, is called the ***i*th residual**. The ith residual represents the error in using $\hat{y}_i$ to estimate y_i. Thus, for the ith observation, the residual is $y_i - \hat{y}_i$. The sum of squares of these residuals or errors is the quantity that is minimized by the least squares method. This quantity, also known as the *sum of squares due to error*, is denoted by SSE.

SUM OF SQUARES DUE TO ERROR

$$SSE = \Sigma(y_i - \hat{y}_i)^2 \tag{14.8}$$

The value of SSE is a measure of the error in using the estimated regression equation to estimate the values of the dependent variable in the sample.

In Table 14.3 we show the calculations required to compute the sum of squares due to error for the Armand's Pizza Parlors example. For instance, for restaurant 1 the values of the independent and dependent variables are $x_1 = 2$ and $y_1 = 58$. Using the estimated regression equation, we find that the estimated value of quarterly sales for restaurant 1 is $\hat{y}_1 = 60 + 5(2) = 70$. Thus, the error in using $\hat{y}_1$ to estimate y_1 for restaurant 1 is $y_1 - \hat{y}_1 = 58 - 70 = -12$. The squared error, $(-12)^2 = 144$, is shown in the last column of Table 14.3. After computing and squaring the residuals for each restaurant in the sample, we sum them to obtain SSE = 1530. Thus, SSE = 1530 measures the error in using the estimated regression equation $\hat{y} = 60 + 5x$ to predict sales.

Now suppose we are asked to develop an estimate of quarterly sales without knowledge of the size of the student population. Without knowledge of any related variables, we would

TABLE 14.3 CALCULATION OF SSE FOR ARMAND'S PIZZA PARLORS

Restaurant i	x_i = Student Population (1000s)	y_i = Quarterly Sales ($1000s)	Predicted Sales $\hat{y}_i = 60 + 5x_i$	Error $y_i - \hat{y}_i$	Squared Error $(y_i - \hat{y}_i)^2$
1	2	58	70	−12	144
2	6	105	90	15	225
3	8	88	100	−12	144
4	8	118	100	18	324
5	12	117	120	−3	9
6	16	137	140	−3	9
7	20	157	160	−3	9
8	20	169	160	9	81
9	22	149	170	−21	441
10	26	202	190	12	144
					SSE = 1530

TABLE 14.4 COMPUTATION OF THE TOTAL SUM OF SQUARES FOR ARMAND'S PIZZA PARLORS

Restaurant i	x_i = Student Population (1000s)	y_i = Quarterly Sales ($1000s)	Deviation $y_i - \bar{y}$	Squared Deviation $(y_i - \bar{y})^2$
1	2	58	−72	5,184
2	6	105	−25	625
3	8	88	−42	1,764
4	8	118	−12	144
5	12	117	−13	169
6	16	137	7	49
7	20	157	27	729
8	20	169	39	1,521
9	22	149	19	361
10	26	202	72	5,184
				SST = 15,730

use the sample mean as an estimate of quarterly sales at any given restaurant. Table 14.2 showed that for the sales data, $\Sigma y_i = 1300$. Hence, the mean value of quarterly sales for the sample of 10 Armand's restaurants is $\bar{y} = \Sigma y_i / n = 1300/10 = 130$. In Table 14.4 we show the sum of squared deviations obtained by using the sample mean $\bar{y} = 130$ to estimate the value of quarterly sales for each restaurant in the sample. For the ith restaurant in the sample, the difference $y_i - \bar{y}$ provides a measure of the error involved in using $\bar{y}$ to estimate sales. The corresponding sum of squares, called the *total sum of squares,* is denoted SST.

TOTAL SUM OF SQUARES

$$\text{SST} = \Sigma(y_i - \bar{y})^2 \tag{14.9}$$

The sum at the bottom of the last column in Table 14.4 is the total sum of squares for Armand's Pizza Parlors; it is SST = 15,730.

With SST = 15,730 and SSE = 1530, the estimated regression line provides a much better fit to the data than the line $y = \bar{y}$.

In Figure 14.5 we show the estimated regression line $\hat{y} = 60 + 5x$ and the line corresponding to $\bar{y} = 130$. Note that the points cluster more closely around the estimated regression line than they do about the line $\bar{y} = 130$. For example, for the 10th restaurant in the sample we see that the error is much larger when $\bar{y} = 130$ is used as an estimate of y_{10} than when $\hat{y}_{10} = 60 + 5(26) = 190$ is used. We can think of SST as a measure of how well the observations cluster about the $\bar{y}$ line and SSE as a measure of how well the observations cluster about the $\hat{y}$ line.

To measure how much the $\hat{y}$ values on the estimated regression line deviate from $\bar{y}$, another sum of squares is computed. This sum of squares, called the *sum of squares due to regression,* is denoted SSR.

SUM OF SQUARES DUE TO REGRESSION

$$\text{SSR} = \Sigma(\hat{y}_i - \bar{y})^2 \tag{14.10}$$

FIGURE 14.5 DEVIATIONS ABOUT THE ESTIMATED REGRESSION LINE AND THE LINE $y = \bar{y}$ FOR ARMAND'S PIZZA PARLORS

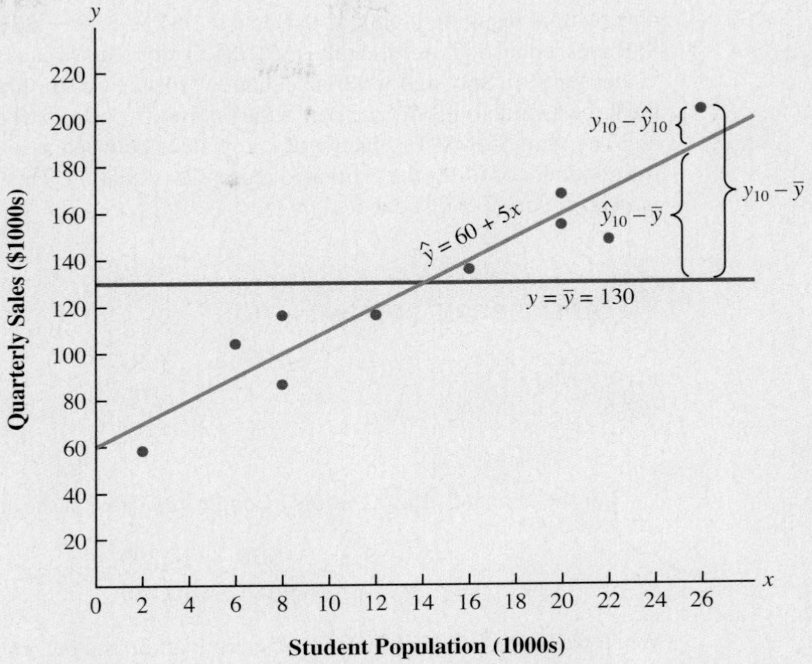

From the preceding discussion, we should expect that SST, SSR, and SSE are related. Indeed, the relationship among these three sums of squares provides one of the most important results in statistics.

SSR can be thought of as the explained portion of SST, and SSE can be thought of as the unexplained portion of SST.

RELATIONSHIP AMONG SST, SSR, AND SSE

$$\text{SST} = \text{SSR} + \text{SSE} \qquad (14.11)$$

where

$$\begin{aligned}\text{SST} &= \text{total sum of squares}\\ \text{SSR} &= \text{sum of squares due to regression}\\ \text{SSE} &= \text{sum of squares due to error}\end{aligned}$$

Equation (14.11) shows that the total sum of squares can be partitioned into two components, the sum of squares due to regression and the sum of squares due to error. Hence, if the values of any two of these sum of squares are known, the third sum of squares can be computed easily. For instance, in the Armand's Pizza Parlors example, we already know that SSE = 1530 and SST = 15,730; therefore, solving for SSR in equation (14.11), we find that the sum of squares due to regression is

$$\text{SSR} = \text{SST} - \text{SSE} = 15{,}730 - 1530 = 14{,}200$$

Now let us see how the three sums of squares, SST, SSR, and SSE, can be used to provide a measure of the goodness of fit for the estimated regression equation. The estimated regression equation would provide a perfect fit if every value of the dependent variable y_i happened to lie on the estimated regression line. In this case, $y_i - \hat{y}_i$ would be zero for each observation, resulting in SSE $= 0$. Because SST $=$ SSR $+$ SSE, we see that for a perfect fit SSR must equal SST, and the ratio (SSR/SST) must equal one. Poorer fits will result in larger values for SSE. Solving for SSE in equation (14.11), we see that SSE $=$ SST $-$ SSR. Hence, the largest value for SSE (and hence the poorest fit) occurs when SSR $= 0$ and SSE $=$ SST.

The ratio SSR/SST, which will take values between zero and one, is used to evaluate the goodness of fit for the estimated regression equation. This ratio is called the *coefficient of determination* and is denoted by r^2.

COEFFICIENT OF DETERMINATION

$$r^2 = \frac{\text{SSR}}{\text{SST}} \tag{14.12}$$

For the Armand's Pizza Parlors example, the value of the coefficient of determination is

$$r^2 = \frac{\text{SSR}}{\text{SST}} = \frac{14{,}200}{15{,}730} = .9027$$

When we express the coefficient of determination as a percentage, r^2 can be interpreted as the percentage of the total sum of squares that can be explained by using the estimated regression equation. For Armand's Pizza Parlors, we can conclude that 90.27% of the total sum of squares can be explained by using the estimated regression equation $\hat{y} = 60 + 5x$ to predict quarterly sales. In other words, 90.27% of the variability in sales can be explained by the linear relationship between the size of the student population and sales. We should be pleased to find such a good fit for the estimated regression equation.

Correlation Coefficient

In Chapter 3 we introduced the **correlation coefficient** as a descriptive measure of the strength of linear association between two variables, x and y. Values of the correlation coefficient are always between -1 and $+1$. A value of $+1$ indicates that the two variables x and y are perfectly related in a positive linear sense. That is, all data points are on a straight line that has a positive slope. A value of -1 indicates that x and y are perfectly related in a negative linear sense, with all data points on a straight line that has a negative slope. Values of the correlation coefficient close to zero indicate that x and y are not linearly related.

In Section 3.5 we presented the equation for computing the sample correlation coefficient. If a regression analysis has already been performed and the coefficient of determination r^2 computed, the sample correlation coefficient can be computed as follows.

SAMPLE CORRELATION COEFFICIENT

$$\begin{aligned} r_{xy} &= (\text{sign of } b_1)\sqrt{\text{Coefficient of determination}} \\ &= (\text{sign of } b_1)\sqrt{r^2} \end{aligned} \tag{14.13}$$

where

$$b_1 = \text{the slope of the estimated regression equation } \hat{y} = b_0 + b_1 x$$

The sign for the sample correlation coefficient is positive if the estimated regression equation has a positive slope ($b_1 > 0$) and negative if the estimated regression equation has a negative slope ($b_1 < 0$).

For the Armand's Pizza Parlor example, the value of the coefficient of determination corresponding to the estimated regression equation $\hat{y} = 60 + 5x$ is .9027. Because the slope of the estimated regression equation is positive, equation (14.13) shows that the sample correlation coefficient is $+\sqrt{.9027} = +.9501$. With a sample correlation coefficient of $r_{xy} = +.9501$, we would conclude that a strong positive linear association exists between x and y.

In the case of a linear relationship between two variables, both the coefficient of determination and the sample correlation coefficient provide measures of the strength of the relationship. The coefficient of determination provides a measure between zero and one, whereas the sample correlation coefficient provides a measure between -1 and $+1$. Although the sample correlation coefficient is restricted to a linear relationship between two variables, the coefficient of determination can be used for nonlinear relationships and for relationships that have two or more independent variables. Thus, the coefficient of determination provides a wider range of applicability.

NOTES AND COMMENTS

1. In developing the least squares estimated regression equation and computing the coefficient of determination, we made no probabilistic assumptions about the error term ϵ, and no statistical tests for significance of the relationship between x and y were conducted. Larger values of r^2 imply that the least squares line provides a better fit to the data; that is, the observations are more closely grouped about the least squares line. But, using only r^2, we can draw no conclusion about whether the relationship between x and y is statistically significant. Such a conclusion must be based on considerations that involve the sample size and the properties of the appropriate sampling distributions of the least squares estimators.
2. As a practical matter, for typical data found in the social sciences, values of r^2 as low as .25 are often considered useful. For data in the physical and life sciences, r^2 values of .60 or greater are often found; in fact, in some cases, r^2 values greater than .90 can be found. In business applications, r^2 values vary greatly, depending on the unique characteristics of each application.

Exercises

Methods

SELF test

15. The data from exercise 1 follow.

x_i	1	2	3	4	5
y_i	3	7	5	11	14

The estimated regression equation for these data is $\hat{y} = .20 + 2.60x$.

a. Compute SSE, SST, and SSR using equations (14.8), (14.9), and (14.10).
b. Compute the coefficient of determination r^2. Comment on the goodness of fit.
c. Compute the sample correlation coefficient.

16. The data from exercise 2 follow.

x_i	3	12	6	20	14
y_i	55	40	55	10	15

The estimated regression equation for these data is $\hat{y} = 68 - 3x$.

a. Compute SSE, SST, and SSR.
b. Compute the coefficient of determination r^2. Comment on the goodness of fit.
c. Compute the sample correlation coefficient.

17. The data from exercise 3 follow.

x_i	2	6	9	13	20
y_i	7	18	9	26	23

The estimated regression equation for these data is $\hat{y} = 7.6 + .9x$. What percentage of the total sum of squares can be accounted for by the estimated regression equation? What is the value of the sample correlation coefficient?

Applications

SELF test

18. The following data are the monthly salaries y and the grade point averages x for students who obtained a bachelor's degree in business administration with a major in information systems. The estimated regression equation for these data is $\hat{y} = 1790.5 + 581.1x$.

GPA	Monthly Salary ($)
2.6	3300
3.4	3600
3.6	4000
3.2	3500
3.5	3900
2.9	3600

a. Compute SST, SSR, and SSE.
b. Compute the coefficient of determination r^2. Comment on the goodness of fit.
c. What is the value of the sample correlation coefficient?

19. The data from exercise 7 follow.

CD file

Cars

Make and Model	x = Reliability	y = Price ($)
Acura TL	4	33,150
BMW 330i	3	40,570
Lexus IS300	5	35,105
Lexus ES330	5	35,174
Mercedes-Benz C320	1	42,230
Lincoln LS Premium (V6)	3	38,225
Audi A4 3.0 Quattro	2	37,605
Cadillac CTS	1	37,695
Nissan Maxima 3.5 SE	4	34,390
Infiniti I35	5	33,845
Saab 9-3 Aero	3	36,910
Infiniti G35	4	34,695
Jaguar X-Type 3.0	1	37,995
Saab 9-5 Arc	3	36,955
Volvo S60 2.5T	3	33,890

The estimated regression equation for these data is $\hat{y} = 40{,}639 - 1301.2x$. What percentage of the total sum of squares can be accounted for by the estimated regression equation? Comment on the goodness of fit. What is the sample correlation coefficient?

20. *Consumer Reports* provided extensive testing and ratings for more than 100 HDTVs. An overall score, based primarily on picture quality, was developed for each model. In general, a higher overall score indicates better performance. The following data show the price and overall score for the ten 42-inch plasma televisions (*Consumer Reports,* March 2006).

CD file
PlasmaTV

Brand	Price	Score
Dell	2800	62
Hisense	2800	53
Hitachi	2700	44
JVC	3500	50
LG	3300	54
Maxent	2000	39
Panasonic	4000	66
Phillips	3000	55
Proview	2500	34
Samsung	3000	39

a. Use these data to develop an estimated regression equation that could be used to estimate the overall score for a 42-inch plasma television given the price.
b. Compute r^2. Did the estimated regression equation provide a good fit?
c. Estimate the overall score for a 42-inch plasma television with a price of $3200.

21. An important application of regression analysis in accounting is in the estimation of cost. By collecting data on volume and cost and using the least squares method to develop an estimated regression equation relating volume and cost, an accountant can estimate the cost associated with a particular manufacturing volume. Consider the following sample of production volumes and total cost data for a manufacturing operation.

Production Volume (units)	Total Cost ($)
400	4000
450	5000
550	5400
600	5900
700	6400
750	7000

a. Use these data to develop an estimated regression equation that could be used to predict the total cost for a given production volume.
b. What is the variable cost per unit produced?
c. Compute the coefficient of determination. What percentage of the variation in total cost can be explained by production volume?
d. The company's production schedule shows 500 units must be produced next month. What is the estimated total cost for this operation?

22. *PC World* provided ratings for the top five small-office laser printers and five corporate laser printers (*PC World,* February 2003). The highest rated small-office laser printer was the Minolta-QMS PagePro 1250W, with an overall rating of 91. The highest rated corporate

laser printer, the Xerox Phaser 4400/N, had an overall rating of 83. The following data show the speed for plain text printing in pages per minute (ppm) and the price for each printer.

CD file

Printers

Name	Type	Speed (ppm)	Price ($)
Minolta-QMS PagePro 1250W	Small Office	12	199
Brother HL-1850	Small Office	10	499
Lexmark E320	Small Office	12.2	299
Minolta-QMS PagePro 1250E	Small Office	10.3	299
HP Laserjet 1200	Small Office	11.7	399
Xerox Phaser 4400/N	Corporate	17.8	1850
Brother HL-2460N	Corporate	16.1	1000
IBM Infoprint 1120n	Corporate	11.8	1387
Lexmark W812	Corporate	19.8	2089
Oki Data B8300n	Corporate	28.2	2200

a. Develop the estimated regression equation with speed as the independent variable.
b. Compute r^2. What percentage of the variation in price can be explained by the printing speed?
c. What is the sample correlation coefficient between speed and price? Does it reflect a strong or weak relationship between printing speed and cost?

14.4 Model Assumptions

In conducting a regression analysis, we begin by making an assumption about the appropriate model for the relationship between the dependent and independent variable(s). For the case of simple linear regression, the assumed regression model is

$$y = \beta_0 + \beta_1 x + \epsilon$$

Then the least squares method is used to develop values for b_0 and b_1, the estimates of the model parameters β_0 and β_1, respectively. The resulting estimated regression equation is

$$\hat{y} = b_0 + b_1 x$$

We saw that the value of the coefficient of determination (r^2) is a measure of the goodness of fit of the estimated regression equation. However, even with a large value of r^2, the estimated regression equation should not be used until further analysis of the appropriateness of the assumed model has been conducted. An important step in determining whether the assumed model is appropriate involves testing for the significance of the relationship. The tests of significance in regression analysis are based on the following assumptions about the error term ϵ.

ASSUMPTIONS ABOUT THE ERROR TERM ϵ IN THE REGRESSION MODEL

$$y = \beta_0 + \beta_1 x + \epsilon$$

1. The error term ϵ is a random variable with a mean or expected value of zero; that is, $E(\epsilon) = 0$.
Implication: β_0 and β_1 are constants, therefore $E(\beta_0) = \beta_0$ and $E(\beta_1) = \beta_1$; thus, for a given value of x, the expected value of y is

$$E(y) = \beta_0 + \beta_1 x \tag{14.14}$$

(continued)

As we indicated previously, equation (14.14) is referred to as the regression equation.

2. The variance of ϵ, denoted by σ^2, is the same for all values of x.
Implication: The variance of y about the regression line equals σ^2 and is the same for all values of x.
3. The values of ϵ are independent.
Implication: The value of ϵ for a particular value of x is not related to the value of ϵ for any other value of x; thus, the value of y for a particular value of x is not related to the value of y for any other value of x.
4. The error term ϵ is a normally distributed random variable.
Implication: Because y is a linear function of ϵ, y is also a normally distributed random variable.

Figure 14.6 illustrates the model assumptions and their implications; note that in this graphical interpretation, the value of $E(y)$ changes according to the specific value of x considered. However, regardless of the x value, the probability distribution of ϵ and hence the probability distributions of y are normally distributed, each with the same variance. The specific value of the error ϵ at any particular point depends on whether the actual value of y is greater than or less than $E(y)$.

At this point, we must keep in mind that we are also making an assumption or hypothesis about the form of the relationship between x and y. That is, we assume that a straight

FIGURE 14.6 ASSUMPTIONS FOR THE REGRESSION MODEL

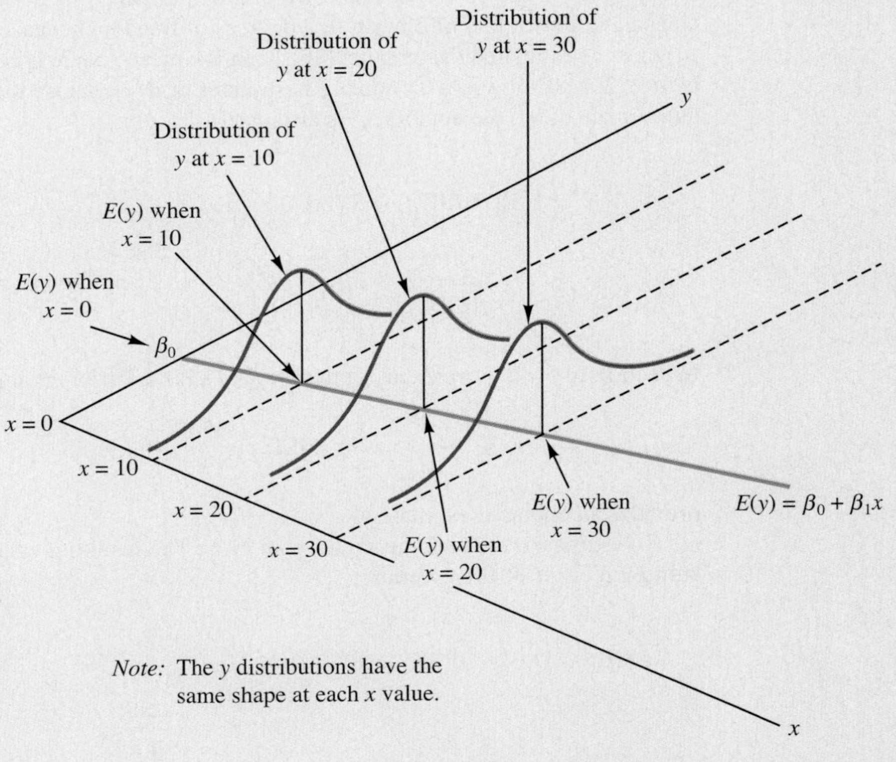

Note: The y distributions have the same shape at each x value.

line represented by $\beta_0 + \beta_1 x$ is the basis for the relationship between the variables. We must not lose sight of the fact that some other model, for instance $y = \beta_0 + \beta_1 x^2 + \epsilon$, may turn out to be a better model for the underlying relationship.

14.5 Testing for Significance

In a simple linear regression equation, the mean or expected value of y is a linear function of x: $E(y) = \beta_0 + \beta_1 x$. If the value of β_1 is zero, $E(y) = \beta_0 + (0)x = \beta_0$. In this case, the mean value of y does not depend on the value of x and hence we would conclude that x and y are not linearly related. Alternatively, if the value of β_1 is not equal to zero, we would conclude that the two variables are related. Thus, to test for a significant regression relationship, we must conduct a hypothesis test to determine whether the value of β_1 is zero. Two tests are commonly used. Both require an estimate of σ^2, the variance of ϵ in the regression model.

Estimate of σ^2

From the regression model and its assumptions we can conclude that σ^2, the variance of ϵ, also represents the variance of the y values about the regression line. Recall that the deviations of the y values about the estimated regression line are called residuals. Thus, SSE, the sum of squared residuals, is a measure of the variability of the actual observations about the estimated regression line. The **mean square error** (MSE) provides the estimate of σ^2; it is SSE divided by its degrees of freedom.

With $\hat{y}_i = b_0 + b_1 x_i$, SSE can be written as

$$\text{SSE} = \Sigma(y_i - \hat{y}_i)^2 = \Sigma(y_i - b_0 - b_1 x_i)^2$$

Every sum of squares is associated with a number called its degrees of freedom. Statisticians have shown that SSE has $n - 2$ degrees of freedom because two parameters (β_0 and β_1) must be estimated to compute SSE. Thus, the mean square is computed by dividing SSE by $n - 2$. MSE provides an unbiased estimator of σ^2. Because the value of MSE provides an estimate of σ^2, the notation s^2 is also used.

MEAN SQUARE ERROR (ESTIMATE OF σ^2)

$$s^2 = \text{MSE} = \frac{\text{SSE}}{n - 2} \tag{14.15}$$

In Section 14.3 we showed that for the Armand's Pizza Parlors example, SSE $= 1530$; hence,

$$s^2 = \text{MSE} = \frac{1530}{8} = 191.25$$

provides an unbiased estimate of σ^2.

To estimate σ we take the square root of s^2. The resulting value, s, is referred to as the **standard error of the estimate**.

STANDARD ERROR OF THE ESTIMATE

$$s = \sqrt{\text{MSE}} = \sqrt{\frac{\text{SSE}}{n - 2}} \tag{14.16}$$

For the Armand's Pizza Parlors example, $s = \sqrt{\text{MSE}} = \sqrt{191.25} = 13.829$. In the following discussion, we use the standard error of the estimate in the tests for a significant relationship between x and y.

t Test

The simple linear regression model is $y = \beta_0 + \beta_1 x + \epsilon$. If x and y are linearly related, we must have $\beta_1 \neq 0$. The purpose of the t test is to see whether we can conclude that $\beta_1 \neq 0$. We will use the sample data to test the following hypotheses about the parameter β_1.

$$H_0: \beta_1 = 0$$
$$H_a: \beta_1 \neq 0$$

If H_0 is rejected, we will conclude that $\beta_1 \neq 0$ and that a statistically significant relationship exists between the two variables. However, if H_0 cannot be rejected, we will have insufficient evidence to conclude that a significant relationship exists. The properties of the sampling distribution of b_1, the least squares estimator of β_1, provide the basis for the hypothesis test.

First, let us consider what would happen if we used a different random sample for the same regression study. For example, suppose that Armand's Pizza Parlors used the sales records of a different sample of 10 restaurants. A regression analysis of this new sample might result in an estimated regression equation similar to our previous estimated regression equation $\hat{y} = 60 + 5x$. However, it is doubtful that we would obtain exactly the same equation (with an intercept of exactly 60 and a slope of exactly 5). Indeed, b_0 and b_1, the least squares estimators, are sample statistics with their own sampling distributions. The properties of the sampling distribution of b_1 follow.

SAMPLING DISTRIBUTION OF b_1

Expected Value

$$E(b_1) = \beta_1$$

Standard Deviation

$$\sigma_{b_1} = \frac{\sigma}{\sqrt{\Sigma(x_i - \bar{x})^2}} \qquad \textbf{(14.17)}$$

Distribution Form

Normal

Note that the expected value of b_1 is equal to β_1, so b_1 is an unbiased estimator of β_1.

Because we do not know the value of σ, we develop an estimate of σ_{b_1}, denoted s_{b_1}, by estimating σ with s in equation (14.17). Thus, we obtain the following estimate of σ_{b_1}.

The standard deviation of b_1 is also referred to as the standard error of b_1. Thus, s_{b_1} provides an estimate of the standard error of b_1.

ESTIMATED STANDARD DEVIATION OF b_1

$$s_{b_1} = \frac{s}{\sqrt{\Sigma(x_i - \bar{x})^2}} \qquad \textbf{(14.18)}$$

For Armand's Pizza Parlors, $s = 13.829$. Hence, using $\Sigma(x_i - \bar{x})^2 = 568$ as shown in Table 14.2, we have

$$s_{b_1} = \frac{13.829}{\sqrt{568}} = .5803$$

as the estimated standard deviation of b_1.

The t test for a significant relationship is based on the fact that the test statistic

$$\frac{b_1 - \beta_1}{s_{b_1}}$$

follows a t distribution with $n - 2$ degrees of freedom. If the null hypothesis is true, then $\beta_1 = 0$ and $t = b_1/s_{b_1}$.

Let us conduct this test of significance for Armand's Pizza Parlors at the $\alpha = .01$ level of significance. The test statistic is

$$t = \frac{b_1}{s_{b_1}} = \frac{5}{.5803} = 8.62$$

Appendixes 14.3 and 14.4 show how Minitab and Excel can be used to compute the p-value.

The t distribution table shows that with $n - 2 = 10 - 2 = 8$ degrees of freedom, $t = 3.355$ provides an area of .005 in the upper tail. Thus, the area in the upper tail of the t distribution corresponding to the test statistic $t = 8.62$ must be less than .005. Because this test is a two-tailed test, we double this value to conclude that the p-value associated with $t = 8.62$ must be less than $2(.005) = .01$. Excel or Minitab show the p-value $= .000$. Because the p-value is less than $\alpha = .01$, we reject H_0 and conclude that β_1 is not equal to zero. This evidence is sufficient to conclude that a significant relationship exists between student population and quarterly sales. A summary of the t test for significance in simple linear regression follows.

***t* TEST FOR SIGNIFICANCE IN SIMPLE LINEAR REGRESSION**

$$H_0: \beta_1 = 0$$
$$H_a: \beta_1 \neq 0$$

TEST STATISTIC

$$t = \frac{b_1}{s_{b_1}} \tag{14.19}$$

REJECTION RULE

p-value approach: Reject H_0 if p-value $\leq \alpha$

Critical value approach: Reject H_0 if $t \leq -t_{\alpha/2}$ or if $t \geq t_{\alpha/2}$

where $t_{\alpha/2}$ is based on a t distribution with $n - 2$ degrees of freedom.

Confidence Interval for β_1

The form of a confidence interval for β_1 is as follows:

$$b_1 \pm t_{\alpha/2} s_{b_1}$$

The point estimator is b_1 and the margin of error is $t_{\alpha/2}s_{b_1}$. The confidence coefficient associated with this interval is $1 - \alpha$, and $t_{\alpha/2}$ is the t value providing an area of $\alpha/2$ in the upper tail of a t distribution with $n - 2$ degrees of freedom. For example, suppose that we wanted to develop a 99% confidence interval estimate of β_1 for Armand's Pizza Parlors. From Table 2 of Appendix B we find that the t value corresponding to $\alpha = .01$ and $n - 2 = 10 - 2 = 8$ degrees of freedom is $t_{.005} = 3.355$. Thus, the 99% confidence interval estimate of β_1 is

$$b_1 \pm t_{\alpha/2}s_{b_1} = 5 \pm 3.355(.5803) = 5 \pm 1.95$$

or 3.05 to 6.95.

In using the t test for significance, the hypotheses tested were

$$H_0: \beta_1 = 0$$
$$H_a: \beta_1 \neq 0$$

At the $\alpha = .01$ level of significance, we can use the 99% confidence interval as an alternative for drawing the hypothesis testing conclusion for the Armand's data. Because 0, the hypothesized value of β_1, is not included in the confidence interval (3.05 to 6.95), we can reject H_0 and conclude that a significant statistical relationship exists between the size of the student population and quarterly sales. In general, a confidence interval can be used to test any two-sided hypothesis about β_1. If the hypothesized value of β_1 is contained in the confidence interval, do not reject H_0. Otherwise, reject H_0.

F Test

An F test, based on the F probability distribution, can also be used to test for significance in regression. With only one independent variable, the F test will provide the same conclusion as the t test; that is, if the t test indicates $\beta_1 \neq 0$ and hence a significant relationship, the F test will also indicate a significant relationship. But with more than one independent variable, only the F test can be used to test for an overall significant relationship.

The logic behind the use of the F test for determining whether the regression relationship is statistically significant is based on the development of two independent estimates of σ^2. We explained how MSE provides an estimate of σ^2. If the null hypothesis H_0: $\beta_1 = 0$ is true, the sum of squares due to regression, SSR, divided by its degrees of freedom provides another independent estimate of σ^2. This estimate is called the *mean square due to regression,* or simply the *mean square regression,* and is denoted MSR. In general,

$$\text{MSR} = \frac{\text{SSR}}{\text{Regression degrees of freedom}}$$

For the models we consider in this text, the regression degrees of freedom is always equal to the number of independent variables in the model:

$$\text{MSR} = \frac{\text{SSR}}{\text{Number of independent variables}} \tag{14.20}$$

Because we consider only regression models with one independent variable in this chapter, we have MSR = SSR/1 = SSR. Hence, for Armand's Pizza Parlors, MSR = SSR = 14,200.

If the null hypothesis (H_0: $\beta_1 = 0$) is true, MSR and MSE are two independent estimates of σ^2 and the sampling distribution of MSR/MSE follows an F distribution with numerator degrees of freedom equal to one and denominator degrees of freedom equal to $n - 2$. Therefore, when $\beta_1 = 0$, the value of MSR/MSE should be close to one. However, if the null hypothesis is false ($\beta_1 \neq 0$), MSR will overestimate σ^2 and the value of MSR/MSE will be inflated; thus, large values of MSR/MSE lead to the rejection of H_0 and the conclusion that the relationship between x and y is statistically significant.

Let us conduct the F test for the Armand's Pizza Parlors example. The test statistic is

$$F = \frac{\text{MSR}}{\text{MSE}} = \frac{14{,}200}{191.25} = 74.25$$

The F test and the t test provide identical results for simple linear regression.

The F distribution table (Table 4 of Appendix B) shows that with one degree of freedom in the numerator and $n - 2 = 10 - 2 = 8$ degrees of freedom in the denominator, $F = 11.26$ provides an area of .01 in the upper tail. Thus, the area in the upper tail of the F distribution corresponding to the test statistic $F = 74.25$ must be less than .01. Thus, we conclude that the p-value must be less than .01. Excel or Minitab show the p-value $= .000$. Because the p-value is less than $\alpha = .01$, we reject H_0 and conclude that a significant relationship exists between the size of the student population and quarterly sales. A summary of the F test for significance in simple linear regression follows.

If H_0 is false, MSE *still provides an unbiased estimate of σ^2 and* MSR *overestimates σ^2. If H_0 is true, both* MSE *and* MSR *provide unbiased estimates of σ^2; in this case the value of* MSR/MSE *should be close to 1.*

F TEST FOR SIGNIFICANCE IN SIMPLE LINEAR REGRESSION

$$H_0\colon \beta_1 = 0$$
$$H_a\colon \beta_1 \neq 0$$

TEST STATISTIC

$$F = \frac{\text{MSR}}{\text{MSE}} \tag{14.21}$$

REJECTION RULE

p-value approach: Reject H_0 if p-value $\leq \alpha$

Critical value approach: Reject H_0 if $F \geq F_\alpha$

where F_α is based on an F distribution with 1 degree of freedom in the numerator and $n - 2$ degrees of freedom in the denominator.

In Chapter 13 we covered analysis of variance (ANOVA) and showed how an **ANOVA table** could be used to provide a convenient summary of the computational aspects of analysis of variance. A similar ANOVA table can be used to summarize the results of the F test for significance in regression. Table 14.5 is the general form of the ANOVA table for simple linear regression. Table 14.6 is the ANOVA table with the F test computations performed for Armand's Pizza Parlors. Regression, Error, and Total are the labels for the three sources of variation, with SSR, SSE, and SST appearing as the corresponding sum of squares in column 2. The degrees of freedom, 1 for SSR, $n - 2$ for SSE, and $n - 1$ for SST, are shown in column 3. Column 4 contains the values of MSR and MSE, column 5 contains the value of F = MSR/MSE, and column 6 contains the p-value corresponding to the F value in column 5. Almost all computer printouts of regression analysis include an ANOVA table summary of the F test for significance.

In every analysis of variance table the total sum of squares is the sum of the regression sum of squares and the error sum of squares; in addition, the total degrees of freedom is the sum of the regression degrees of freedom and the error degrees of freedom.

TABLE 14.5 GENERAL FORM OF THE ANOVA TABLE FOR SIMPLE LINEAR REGRESSION

Source of Variation	Sum of Squares	Degrees of Freedom	Mean Square	F	p-value
Regression	SSR	1	$\text{MSR} = \dfrac{\text{SSR}}{1}$	$F = \dfrac{\text{MSR}}{\text{MSE}}$	
Error	SSE	$n - 2$	$\text{MSE} = \dfrac{\text{SSE}}{n-2}$		
Total	SST	$n - 1$			

Some Cautions About the Interpretation of Significance Tests

Regression analysis, which can be used to identify how variables are associated with one another, cannot be used as evidence of a cause-and-effect relationship.

Rejecting the null hypothesis H_0: $\beta_1 = 0$ and concluding that the relationship between x and y is significant does not enable us to conclude that a cause-and-effect relationship is present between x and y. Concluding a cause-and-effect relationship is warranted only if the analyst can provide some type of theoretical justification that the relationship is in fact causal. In the Armand's Pizza Parlors example, we can conclude that there is a significant relationship between the size of the student population x and quarterly sales y; moreover, the estimated regression equation $\hat{y} = 60 + 5x$ provides the least squares estimate of the relationship. We cannot, however, conclude that changes in student population x *cause* changes in quarterly sales y just because we identified a statistically significant relationship. The appropriateness of such a cause-and-effect conclusion is left to supporting theoretical justification and to good judgment on the part of the analyst. Armand's managers felt that increases in the student population were a likely cause of increased quarterly sales. Thus, the result of the significance test enabled them to conclude that a cause-and-effect relationship was present.

In addition, just because we are able to reject H_0: $\beta_1 = 0$ and demonstrate statistical significance does not enable us to conclude that the relationship between x and y is linear. We can state only that x and y are related and that a linear relationship explains a significant portion of the variability in y over the range of values for x observed in the sample. Figure 14.7 illustrates this situation. The test for significance calls for the rejection of the null hypothesis H_0: $\beta_1 = 0$ and leads to the conclusion that x and y are significantly related, but the figure shows that the actual relationship between x and y is not linear. Although the

TABLE 14.6 ANOVA TABLE FOR THE ARMAND'S PIZZA PARLORS PROBLEM

Source of Variation	Sum of Squares	Degrees of Freedom	Mean Square	F	p-value
Regression	14,200	1	$\dfrac{14{,}200}{1} = 14{,}200$	$\dfrac{14{,}200}{191.25} = 74.25$	.000
Error	1,530	8	$\dfrac{1530}{8} = 191.25$		
Total	15,730	9			

FIGURE 14.7 EXAMPLE OF A LINEAR APPROXIMATION OF A NONLINEAR RELATIONSHIP

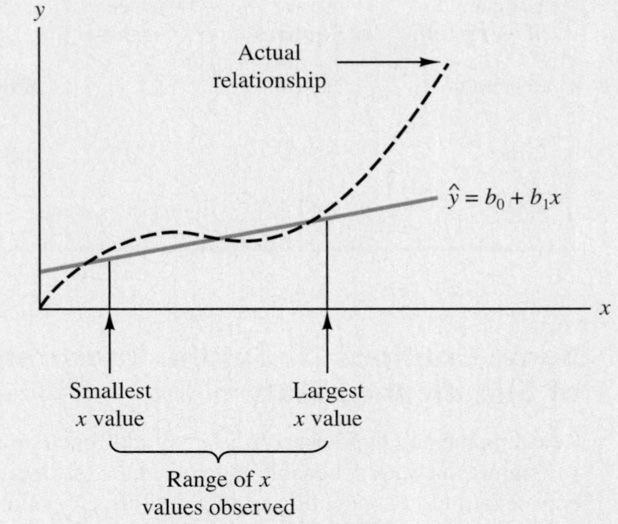

linear approximation provided by $\hat{y} = b_0 + b_1x$ is good over the range of x values observed in the sample, it becomes poor for x values outside that range.

Given a significant relationship, we should feel confident in using the estimated regression equation for predictions corresponding to x values within the range of the x values observed in the sample. For Armand's Pizza Parlors, this range corresponds to values of x between 2 and 26. Unless other reasons indicate that the model is valid beyond this range, predictions outside the range of the independent variable should be made with caution. For Armand's Pizza Parlors, because the regression relationship has been found significant at the .01 level, we should feel confident using it to predict sales for restaurants where the associated student population is between 2000 and 26,000.

NOTES AND COMMENTS

1. The assumptions made about the error term (Section 14.4) are what allow the tests of statistical significance in this section. The properties of the sampling distribution of b_1 and the subsequent t and F tests follow directly from these assumptions.
2. Do not confuse statistical significance with practical significance. With very large sample sizes, statistically significant results can be obtained for small values of b_1; in such cases, one must exercise care in concluding that the relationship has practical significance.
3. A test of significance for a linear relationship between x and y can also be performed by using the sample correlation coefficient r_{xy}. With ρ_{xy} denoting the population correlation coefficient, the hypotheses are as follows.

$$H_0: \rho_{xy} = 0$$
$$H_a: \rho_{xy} \neq 0$$

A significant relationship can be concluded if H_0 is rejected. The details of this test are provided in Appendix 14.2. However, the t and F tests presented previously in this section give the same result as the test for significance using the correlation coefficient. Conducting a test for significance using the correlation coefficient therefore is not necessary if a t or F test has already been conducted.

Exercises

Methods

SELF test

23. The data from exercise 1 follow.

x_i	1	2	3	4	5
y_i	3	7	5	11	14

a. Compute the mean square error using equation (14.15).
b. Compute the standard error of the estimate using equation (14.16).
c. Compute the estimated standard deviation of b_1 using equation (14.18).
d. Use the t test to test the following hypotheses ($\alpha = .05$):

$$H_0: \beta_1 = 0$$
$$H_a: \beta_1 \neq 0$$

e. Use the F test to test the hypotheses in part (d) at a .05 level of significance. Present the results in the analysis of variance table format.

24. The data from exercise 2 follow.

x_i	3	12	6	20	14
y_i	55	40	55	10	15

a. Compute the mean square error using equation (14.15).
b. Compute the standard error of the estimate using equation (14.16).
c. Compute the estimated standard deviation of b_1 using equation (14.18).
d. Use the t test to test the following hypotheses ($\alpha = .05$):

$$H_0: \beta_1 = 0$$
$$H_a: \beta_1 \neq 0$$

e. Use the F test to test the hypotheses in part (d) at a .05 level of significance. Present the results in the analysis of variance table format.

25. The data from exercise 3 follow.

x_i	2	6	9	13	20
y_i	7	18	9	26	23

a. What is the value of the standard error of the estimate?
b. Test for a significant relationship by using the t test. Use $\alpha = .05$.
c. Use the F test to test for a significant relationship. Use $\alpha = .05$. What is your conclusion?

Applications

SELF test

26. In exercise 18 the data on grade point average and monthly salary were as follows.

GPA	Monthly Salary ($)	GPA	Monthly Salary ($)
2.6	3300	3.2	3500
3.4	3600	3.5	3900
3.6	4000	2.9	3600

a. Does the t test indicate a significant relationship between grade point average and monthly salary? What is your conclusion? Use $\alpha = .05$.
b. Test for a significant relationship using the F test. What is your conclusion? Use $\alpha = .05$.
c. Show the ANOVA table.

27. *Outside Magazine* tested 10 different models of day hikers and backpacking boots. The following data show the upper support and price for each model tested. Upper support was measured using a rating from 1 to 5, with a rating of 1 denoting average upper support and a rating of 5 denoting excellent upper support (*Outside Magazine Buyer's Guide,* 2001).

CD file
Boots

Manufacturer and Model	Upper Support	Price ($)
Salomon Super Raid	2	120
Merrell Chameleon Prime	3	125
Teva Challenger	3	130
Vasque Fusion GTX	3	135
Boreal Maigmo	3	150
L.L. Bean GTX Super Guide	5	189
Lowa Kibo	5	190
Asolo AFX 520 GTX	4	195
Raichle Mt. Trail GTX	4	200
Scarpa Delta SL M3	5	220

a. Use these data to develop an estimated regression equation to estimate the price of a day hiker and backpacking boot given the upper support rating.
b. At the .05 level of significance, determine whether upper support and price are related.
c. Would you feel comfortable using the estimated regression equation developed in part (a) to estimate the price for a day hiker or backpacking boot given the upper support rating?
d. Estimate the price for a day hiker with an upper support rating of 4.

28. In exercise 10, data on x = temperature rating (F°) and y = price ($) for 11 sleeping bags manufactured by Bergans of Norway provided the estimated regression equation $\hat{y} = 359.2668 - 5.2772x$. At the .05 level of significance, test whether temperature rating and price are related. Show the ANOVA table. What is your conclusion?

29. Refer to exercise 21, where data on production volume and cost were used to develop an estimated regression equation relating production volume and cost for a particular manufacturing operation. Use $\alpha = .05$ to test whether the production volume is significantly related to the total cost. Show the ANOVA table. What is your conclusion?

30. Refer to exercise 22, where the following data were used to determine whether the price of a printer is related to the speed for plain text printing (*PC World,* February 2003).

CD file
Printers

Name	Type	Speed (ppm)	Price ($)
Minolta-QMS PagePro 1250W	Small Office	12	199
Brother HL-1850	Small Office	10	499
Lexmark E320	Small Office	12.2	299
Minolta-QMS PagePro 1250E	Small Office	10.3	299
HP Laserjet 1200	Small Office	11.7	399
Xerox Phaser 4400/N	Corporate	17.8	1850
Brother HL-2460N	Corporate	16.1	1000

(continued)

Name	Type	Speed (ppm)	Price ($)
IBM Infoprint 1120n	Corporate	11.8	1387
Lexmark W812	Corporate	19.8	2089
Oki Data B8300n	Corporate	28.2	2200

Does the evidence indicate a significant relationship between printing speed and price? Conduct the appropriate statistical test and state your conclusion. Use $\alpha = .05$.

31. In exercise 20, data on x = price ($) and y = overall score for ten 42-inch plasma televisions tested by *Consumer Reports* provided the estimated regression equation $\hat{y} = 12.0169 + .0127x$. For these data SSE = 540.04 and SST = 982.40. Use the F test to determine whether the price for a 42-inch plasma television and the overall score are related at the .05 level of significance.

14.6 Using the Estimated Regression Equation for Estimation and Prediction

When using the simple linear regression model we are making an assumption about the relationship between x and y. We then use the least squares method to obtain the estimated simple linear regression equation. If a significant relationship exists between x and y, and the coefficient of determination shows that the fit is good, the estimated regression equation should be useful for estimation and prediction.

Point Estimation

In the Armand's Pizza Parlors example, the estimated regression equation $\hat{y} = 60 + 5x$ provides an estimate of the relationship between the size of the student population x and quarterly sales y. We can use the estimated regression equation to develop a point estimate of the mean value of y for a particular value of x or to predict an individual value of y corresponding to a given value of x. For instance, suppose Armand's managers want a point estimate of the mean quarterly sales for all restaurants located near college campuses with 10,000 students. Using the estimated regression equation $\hat{y} = 60 + 5x$, we see that for $x = 10$ (or 10,000 students), $\hat{y} = 60 + 5(10) = 110$. Thus, a point estimate of the mean quarterly sales for all restaurants located near campuses with 10,000 students is $110,000.

Now suppose Armand's managers want to predict sales for an individual restaurant located near Talbot College, a school with 10,000 students. In this case we are not interested in the mean value for all restaurants located near campuses with 10,000 students; we are just interested in predicting quarterly sales for one individual restaurant. As it turns out, the point estimate for an individual value of y is the same as the point estimate for the mean value of y. Hence, we would predict quarterly sales of $\hat{y} = 60 + 5(10) = 110$ or $110,000 for this one restaurant.

Interval Estimation

Confidence intervals and prediction intervals show the precision of the regression results. Narrower intervals provide a higher degree of precision.

Point estimates do not provide any information about the precision associated with an estimate. For that we must develop interval estimates much like those in Chapters 8, 10, and 11. The first type of interval estimate, a **confidence interval**, is an interval estimate of the *mean value of* y for a given value of x. The second type of interval estimate, a **prediction interval**, is used whenever we want an interval estimate of an *individual value of* y for a given value of x. The point estimate of the mean value of y is the same as the point estimate of an individual value of y. But, the interval estimates we obtain for the two cases are different. The margin of error is larger for a prediction interval.

Confidence Interval for the Mean Value of y

The estimated regression equation provides a point estimate of the mean value of y for a given value of x. In developing the confidence interval, we will use the following notation.

x_p = the particular or given value of the independent variable x

y_p = the value of the dependent variable y corresponding to the given x_p

$E(y_p)$ = the mean or expected value of the dependent variable y corresponding to the given x_p

$\hat{y}_p = b_0 + b_1 x_p$ = the point estimate of $E(y_p)$ when $x = x_p$

Using this notation to estimate the mean sales for all Armand's restaurants located near a campus with 10,000 students, we have $x_p = 10$, and $E(y_p)$ denotes the unknown mean value of sales for all restaurants where $x_p = 10$. The point estimate of $E(y_p)$ is provided by $\hat{y}_p = 60 + 5(10) = 110$.

In general, we cannot expect $\hat{y}_p$ to equal $E(y_p)$ exactly. If we want to make an inference about how close $\hat{y}_p$ is to the true mean value $E(y_p)$, we will have to estimate the variance of $\hat{y}_p$. The formula for estimating the variance of $\hat{y}_p$ given x_p, denoted by $s^2_{\hat{y}_p}$, is

$$s^2_{\hat{y}_p} = s^2\left[\frac{1}{n} + \frac{(x_p - \bar{x})^2}{\Sigma(x_i - \bar{x})^2}\right] \tag{14.22}$$

The estimate of the standard deviation of $\hat{y}_p$ is given by the square root of equation (14.22).

$$s_{\hat{y}_p} = s\sqrt{\frac{1}{n} + \frac{(x_p - \bar{x})^2}{\Sigma(x_i - \bar{x})^2}} \tag{14.23}$$

The computational results for Armand's Pizza Parlors in Section 14.5 provided $s = 13.829$. With $x_p = 10$, $\bar{x} = 14$, and $\Sigma(x_i - \bar{x})^2 = 568$, we can use equation (14.23) to obtain

$$s_{\hat{y}_p} = 13.829\sqrt{\frac{1}{10} + \frac{(10 - 14)^2}{568}}$$

$$= 13.829\sqrt{.1282} = 4.95$$

The general expression for a confidence interval follows.

The margin of error associated with this internal estimate is $t_{\alpha/2} s_{\hat{y}_p}$.

CONFIDENCE INTERVAL FOR $E(y_p)$

$$\hat{y}_p \pm t_{\alpha/2} s_{\hat{y}_p} \tag{14.24}$$

where the confidence coefficient is $1 - \alpha$ and $t_{\alpha/2}$ is based on a t distribution with $n - 2$ degrees of freedom.

Using expression (14.24) to develop a 95% confidence interval of the mean quarterly sales for all Armand's restaurants located near campuses with 10,000 students, we need the value of t for $\alpha/2 = .025$ and $n - 2 = 10 - 2 = 8$ degrees of freedom. Using Table 2 of Appendix B, we have $t_{.025} = 2.306$. Thus, with $\hat{y}_p = 110$ and a margin of error of $t_{\alpha/2} s_{\hat{y}_p} = 2.306(4.95) = 11.415$, the 95% confidence interval estimate is

$$110 \pm 11.415$$

FIGURE 14.8 CONFIDENCE INTERVALS FOR THE MEAN SALES y AT GIVEN VALUES OF STUDENT POPULATION x

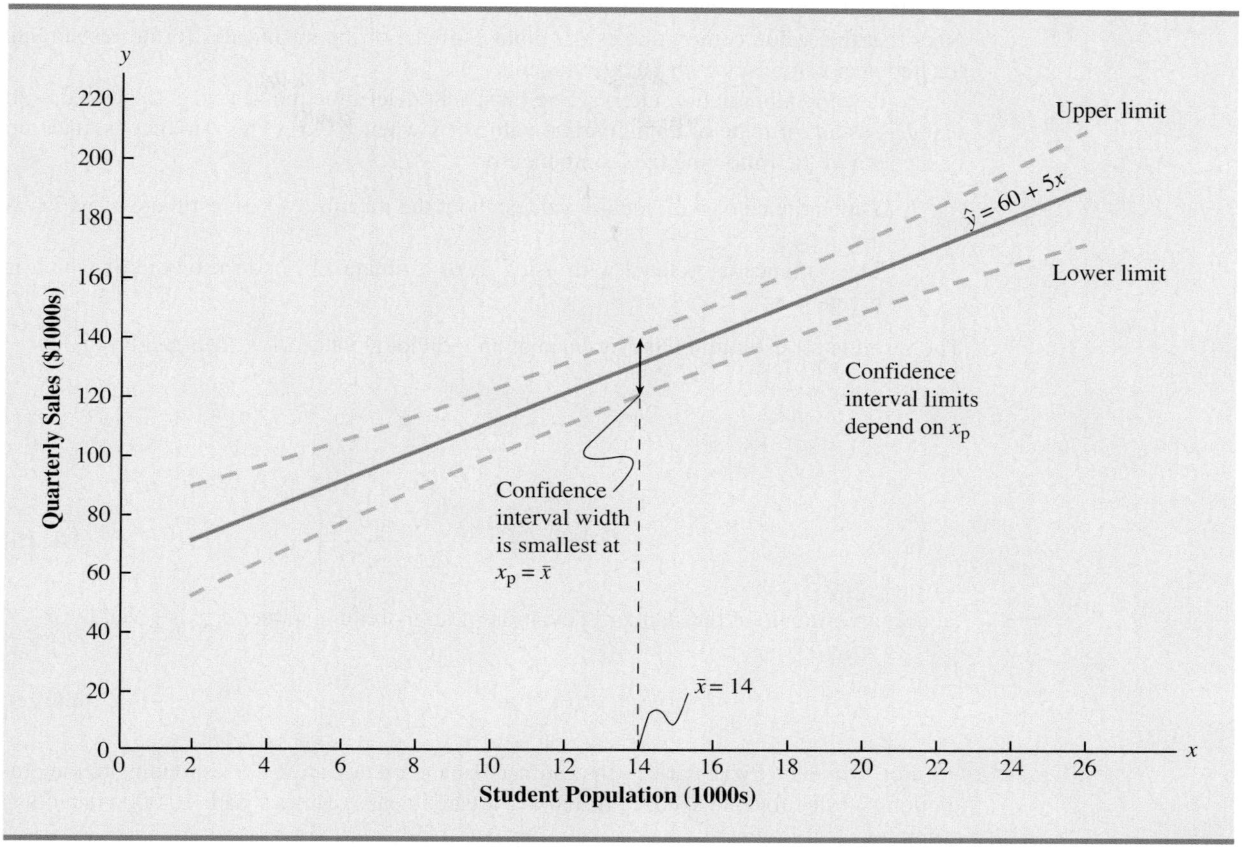

In dollars, the 95% confidence interval for the mean quarterly sales of all restaurants near campuses with 10,000 students is \$110,000 ± \$11,415. Therefore, the 95% confidence interval for the mean quarterly sales when the student population is 10,000 is \$98,585 to \$121,415.

Note that the estimated standard deviation of $\hat{y}_p$ given by equation (14.23) is smallest when $x_p = \bar{x}$ and the quantity $x_p - \bar{x} = 0$. In this case, the estimated standard deviation of $\hat{y}_p$ becomes

$$s_{\hat{y}_p} = s\sqrt{\frac{1}{n} + \frac{(\bar{x} - \bar{x})^2}{\Sigma(x_i - \bar{x})^2}} = s\sqrt{\frac{1}{n}}$$

This result implies that we can make the best or most precise estimate of the mean value of y whenever $x_p = \bar{x}$. In fact, the further x_p is from $\bar{x}$ the larger $x_p - \bar{x}$ becomes. As a result, confidence intervals for the mean value of y will become wider as x_p deviates more from $\bar{x}$. This pattern is shown graphically in Figure 14.8.

Prediction Interval for an Individual Value of y

Suppose that instead of estimating the mean value of sales for all Armand's restaurants located near campuses with 10,000 students, we want to estimate the sales for an individual restaurant located near Talbot College, a school with 10,000 students. As noted previously, the point estimate of y_p, the value of y corresponding to the given x_p, is provided by the estimated regression equation $\hat{y}_p = b_0 + b_1x_p$. For the restaurant at Talbot College, we have $x_p = 10$ and a corresponding predicted quarterly sales of $\hat{y}_p = 60 + 5(10) = 110$, or \$110,000. Note that this value is the same as the point estimate of the mean sales for all restaurants located near campuses with 10,000 students.

To develop a prediction interval, we must first determine the variance associated with using $\hat{y}_p$ as an estimate of an individual value of y when $x = x_p$. This variance is made up of the sum of the following two components.

1. The variance of individual y values about the mean $E(y_p)$, an estimate of which is given by s^2
2. The variance associated with using $\hat{y}_p$ to estimate $E(y_p)$, an estimate of which is given by $s^2_{\hat{y}_p}$

The formula for estimating the variance of an individual value of y_p, denoted by s^2_{ind}, is

$$\begin{aligned} s^2_{\text{ind}} &= s^2 + s^2_{\hat{y}_p} \\ &= s^2 + s^2\left[\frac{1}{n} + \frac{(x_p - \bar{x})^2}{\Sigma(x_i - \bar{x})^2}\right] \\ &= s^2\left[1 + \frac{1}{n} + \frac{(x_p - \bar{x})^2}{\Sigma(x_i - \bar{x})^2}\right] \end{aligned} \tag{14.25}$$

Hence, an estimate of the standard deviation of an individual value of y_p is given by

$$s_{\text{ind}} = s\sqrt{1 + \frac{1}{n} + \frac{(x_p - \bar{x})^2}{\Sigma(x_i - \bar{x})^2}} \tag{14.26}$$

For Armand's Pizza Parlors, the estimated standard deviation corresponding to the prediction of sales for one specific restaurant located near a campus with 10,000 students is computed as follows.

$$\begin{aligned} s_{\text{ind}} &= 13.829\sqrt{1 + \frac{1}{10} + \frac{(10 - 14)^2}{568}} \\ &= 13.829\sqrt{1.1282} \\ &= 14.69 \end{aligned}$$

The general expression for a prediction interval follows.

The margin of error associated with this interval estimate is $t_{\alpha/2}s_{\text{ind}}$.

PREDICTION INTERVAL FOR y_p

$$\hat{y}_p \pm t_{\alpha/2}s_{\text{ind}} \tag{14.27}$$

where the confidence coefficient is $1 - \alpha$ and $t_{\alpha/2}$ is based on a t distribution with $n - 2$ degrees of freedom.

The 95% prediction interval for quarterly sales at Armand's Talbot College restaurant can be found by using $t_{.025} = 2.306$ and $s_{\text{ind}} = 14.69$. Thus, with $\hat{y}_p = 110$ and a margin of error of $t_{\alpha/2}s_{\text{ind}} = 2.306(14.69) = 33.875$, the 95% prediction interval is

$$110 \pm 33.875$$

FIGURE 14.9 CONFIDENCE AND PREDICTION INTERVALS FOR SALES y AT GIVEN VALUES OF STUDENT POPULATION x

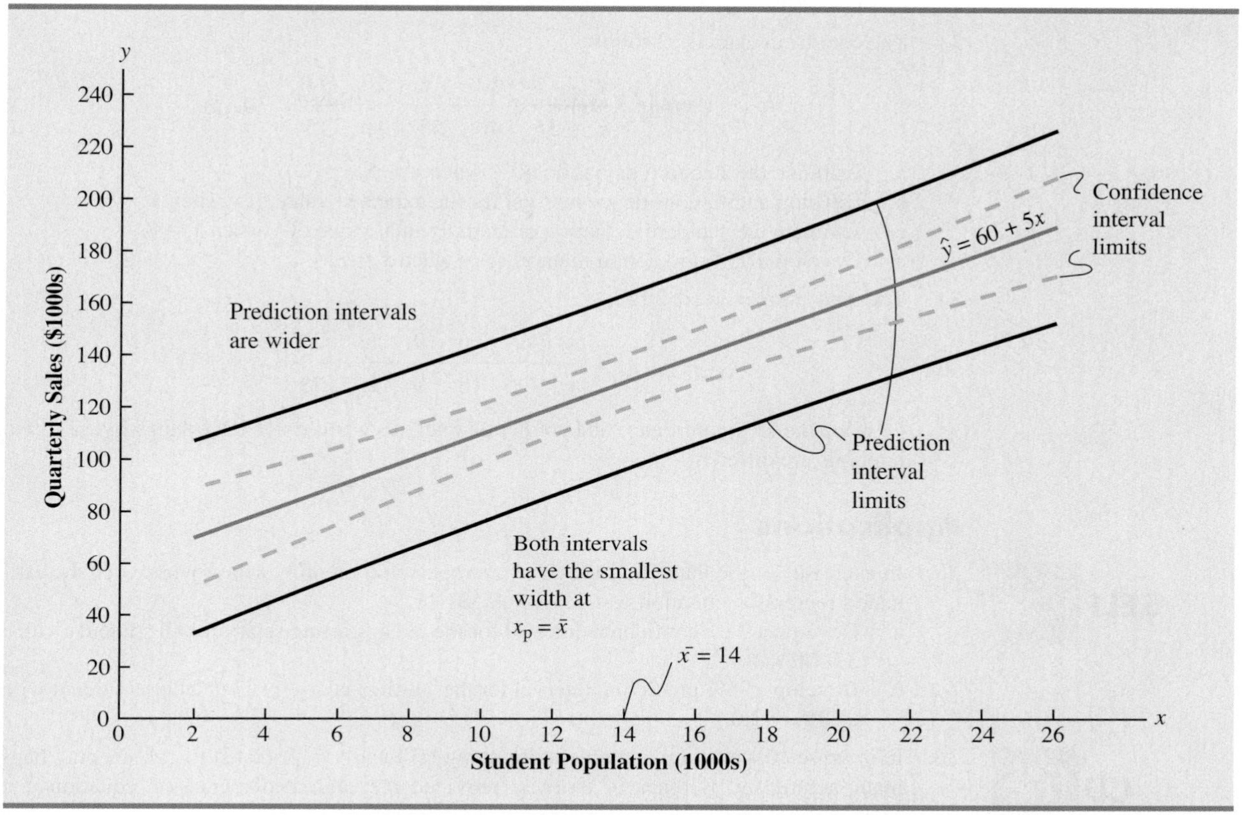

In dollars, this prediction interval is \$110,000 ± \$33,875 or \$76,125 to \$143,875. Note that the prediction interval for an individual restaurant located near a campus with 10,000 students is wider than the confidence interval for the mean sales of all restaurants located near campuses with 10,000 students. The difference reflects the fact that we are able to estimate the mean value of y more precisely than we can an individual value of y.

In general, the lines for the confidence interval limits and the prediction interval limits both have curvature.

Both confidence interval estimates and prediction interval estimates are most precise when the value of the independent variable is $x_p = \bar{x}$. The general shapes of confidence intervals and the wider prediction intervals are shown together in Figure 14.9.

Exercises

Methods

SELF test

32. The data from exercise 1 follow.

x_i	1	2	3	4	5
y_i	3	7	5	11	14

a. Use equation (14.23) to estimate the standard deviation of $\hat{y}_p$ when $x = 4$.
b. Use expression (14.24) to develop a 95% confidence interval for the expected value of y when $x = 4$.

c. Use equation (14.26) to estimate the standard deviation of an individual value of y when $x = 4$.

d. Use expression (14.27) to develop a 95% prediction interval for y when $x = 4$.

33. The data from exercise 2 follow.

x_i	3	12	6	20	14
y_i	55	40	55	10	15

a. Estimate the standard deviation of $\hat{y}_p$ when $x = 8$.
b. Develop a 95% confidence interval for the expected value of y when $x = 8$.
c. Estimate the standard deviation of an individual value of y when $x = 8$.
d. Develop a 95% prediction interval for y when $x = 8$.

34. The data from exercise 3 follow.

x_i	2	6	9	13	20
y_i	7	18	9	26	23

Develop the 95% confidence and prediction intervals when $x = 12$. Explain why these two intervals are different.

Applications

SELF test

35. In exercise 18, the data on grade point average x and monthly salary y provided the estimated regression equation $\hat{y} = 1790.5 + 581.1x$.

a. Develop a 95% confidence interval for the mean starting salary for all students with a 3.0 GPA.

b. Develop a 95% prediction interval for the starting salary for Joe Heller, a student with a GPA of 3.0.

CD file

SleepingBags

36. In exercise 10, data on x = temperature rating (F°) and y = price ($) for 11 sleeping bags manufactured by Bergans of Norway provided the estimated regression equation $\hat{y} = 359.2668 - 5.2772x$. For these data $s = 37.9372$.

a. Develop a point estimate of the price for a sleeping bag with a temperature rating of 30.
b. Develop a 95% confidence interval for the mean overall temperature rating for all sleeping bags with a temperature rating of 30.
c. Suppose that Bergans developed a new model with a temperature rating of 30. Develop a 95% prediction interval for the price of this new model.
d. Discuss the differences in your answers to parts (b) and (c).

37. In exercise 13, data were given on the adjusted gross income x and the amount of itemized deductions taken by taxpayers. Data were reported in thousands of dollars. With the estimated regression equation $\hat{y} = 4.68 + .16x$, the point estimate of a reasonable level of total itemized deductions for a taxpayer with an adjusted gross income of $52,500 is $13,080.

a. Develop a 95% confidence interval for the mean amount of total itemized deductions for all taxpayers with an adjusted gross income of $52,500.
b. Develop a 95% prediction interval estimate for the amount of total itemized deductions for a particular taxpayer with an adjusted gross income of $52,500.
c. If the particular taxpayer referred to in part (b) claimed total itemized deductions of $20,400, would the IRS agent's request for an audit appear to be justified?
d. Use your answer to part (b) to give the IRS agent a guideline as to the amount of total itemized deductions a taxpayer with an adjusted gross income of $52,500 should claim before an audit is recommended.

38. Refer to Exercise 21, where data on the production volume x and total cost y for a particular manufacturing operation were used to develop the estimated regression equation $\hat{y} = 1246.67 + 7.6x$.

a. The company's production schedule shows that 500 units must be produced next month. What is the point estimate of the total cost for next month?

b. Develop a 99% prediction interval for the total cost for next month.
c. If an accounting cost report at the end of next month shows that the actual production cost during the month was \$6000, should managers be concerned about incurring such a high total cost for the month? Discuss.

39. Almost all U.S. light-rail systems use electric cars that run on tracks built at street level. The Federal Transit Administration claims light-rail is one of the safest modes of travel, with an accident rate of .99 accidents per million passenger miles as compared to 2.29 for buses. The following data show the miles of track and the weekday ridership in thousands of passengers for six light-rail systems (*USA Today,* January 7, 2003).

City	Miles of Track	Ridership (1000s)
Cleveland	15	15
Denver	17	35
Portland	38	81
Sacramento	21	31
San Diego	47	75
San Jose	31	30
St. Louis	34	42

a. Use these data to develop an estimated regression equation that could be used to predict the ridership given the miles of track.
b. Did the estimated regression equation provide a good fit? Explain.
c. Develop a 95% confidence interval for the mean weekday ridership for all light-rail systems with 30 miles of track.
d. Suppose that Charlotte is considering construction of a light-rail system with 30 miles of track. Develop a 95% prediction interval for the weekday ridership for the Charlotte system. Do you think that the prediction interval you developed would be of value to Charlotte planners in anticipating the number of weekday riders for their new light-rail system? Explain.

14.7 Computer Solution

Performing the regression analysis computations without the help of a computer can be quite time consuming. In this section we discuss how the computational burden can be minimized by using a computer software package such as Minitab.

We entered Armand's student population and sales data into a Minitab worksheet. The independent variable was named Pop and the dependent variable was named Sales to assist with interpretation of the computer output. Using Minitab, we obtained the printout for Armand's Pizza Parlors shown in Figure 14.10.* The interpretation of this printout follows.

1. Minitab prints the estimated regression equation as Sales = 60.0 + 5.00 Pop.
2. A table is printed that shows the values of the coefficients b_0 and b_1, the standard deviation of each coefficient, the t value obtained by dividing each coefficient value by its standard deviation, and the p-value associated with the t test. Because the p-value is zero (to three decimal places), the sample results indicate that the null hypothesis (H_0: $\beta_1 = 0$) should be rejected. Alternatively, we could compare 8.62 (located in the t-ratio column) to the appropriate critical value. This procedure for the t test was described in Section 14.5.

*The Minitab steps necessary to generate the output are given in Appendix 14.3.

FIGURE 14.10 MINITAB OUTPUT FOR THE ARMAND'S PIZZA PARLORS PROBLEM

```
The regression equation is
Sales = 60.0 + 5.00 Pop                    <-- Estimated regression equation

Predictor      Coef    SE Coef      T       p
Constant     60.000      9.226   6.50   0.000
Pop          5.0000     0.5803   8.62   0.000

S = 13.83      R-sq = 90.3%      R-sq(adj) = 89.1%

Analysis of Variance

SOURCE           DF      SS       MS        F       p
Regression        1   14200    14200    74.25   0.000   <-- ANOVA table
Residual Error    8    1530      191
Total             9   15730

Predicted Values for New Observations

New
Obs      Fit    SE Fit        95% C.I.            95% P.I.      <-- Interval estimates
  1   110.00     4.95    (98.58, 121.42)   (76.12, 143.88)
```

3. Minitab prints the standard error of the estimate, $s = 13.83$, as well as information about the goodness of fit. Note that "R-sq = 90.3%" is the coefficient of determination expressed as a percentage. The value "R-Sq (adj) = 89.1%" is discussed in Chapter 15.
4. The ANOVA table is printed below the heading Analysis of Variance. Minitab uses the label Residual Error for the error source of variation. Note that DF is an abbreviation for degrees of freedom and that MSR is given as 14,200 and MSE as 191. The ratio of these two values provides the F value of 74.25 and the corresponding p-value of 0.000. Because the p-value is zero (to three decimal places), the relationship between Sales and Pop is judged statistically significant.
5. The 95% confidence interval estimate of the expected sales and the 95% prediction interval estimate of sales for an individual restaurant located near a campus with 10,000 students are printed below the ANOVA table. The confidence interval is (98.58, 121.42) and the prediction interval is (76.12, 143.88) as we showed in Section 14.6.

Exercises

Applications

SELF test

40. The commercial division of a real estate firm is conducting a regression analysis of the relationship between x, annual gross rents (in thousands of dollars), and y, selling price (in thousands of dollars) for apartment buildings. Data were collected on several properties recently sold and the following computer output was obtained.

```
The regression equation is
Y = 20.0 + 7.21 X

Predictor         Coef      SE Coef        T
Constant        20.000       3.2213     6.21
X                7.210       1.3626     5.29

Analysis of Variance

SOURCE                  DF          SS
Regression               1     41587.3
Residual Error           7
Total                    8     51984.1
```

a. How many apartment buildings were in the sample?
b. Write the estimated regression equation.
c. What is the value of s_{b_1}?
d. Use the F statistic to test the significance of the relationship at a .05 level of significance.
e. Estimate the selling price of an apartment building with gross annual rents of \$50,000.

41. Following is a portion of the computer output for a regression analysis relating y = maintenance expense (dollars per month) to x = usage (hours per week) of a particular brand of computer terminal.

```
The regression equation is
Y = 6.1092 + .8951 X

Predictor         Coef      SE Coef
Constant        6.1092       0.9361
X               0.8951       0.1490

Analysis of Variance

SOURCE                  DF         SS          MS
Regression               1    1575.76     1575.76
Residual Error           8     349.14       43.64
Total                    9    1924.90
```

a. Write the estimated regression equation.
b. Use a t test to determine whether monthly maintenance expense is related to usage at the .05 level of significance.
c. Use the estimated regression equation to predict monthly maintenance expense for any terminal that is used 25 hours per week.

42. A regression model relating x, number of salespersons at a branch office, to y, annual sales at the office (in thousands of dollars) provided the following computer output from a regression analysis of the data.

```
The regression equation is
Y = 80.0 + 50.00 X

Predictor        Coef    SE Coef      T
Constant         80.0     11.333   7.06
X                50.0      5.482   9.12

Analysis of Variance

SOURCE            DF         SS         MS
Regression         1     6828.6     6828.6
Residual Error    28     2298.8       82.1
Total             29     9127.4
```

a. Write the estimated regression equation.
b. How many branch offices were involved in the study?
c. Compute the F statistic and test the significance of the relationship at a .05 level of significance.
d. Predict the annual sales at the Memphis branch office. This branch employs 12 salespersons.

43. Health experts recommend that runners drink 4 ounces of water every 15 minutes they run. Although handheld bottles work well for many types of runs, all-day cross-country runs require hip-mounted or over-the-shoulder hydration systems. In addition to carrying more water, hip-mounted or over-the-shoulder hydration systems offer more storage space for food and extra clothing. As the capacity increases, however, the weight and cost of these larger-capacity systems also increase. The following data show the weight (ounces) and the price for 26 hip-mounted or over-the-shoulder hydration systems (*Trail Runner Gear Guide,* 2003).

CD file
Hydration1

Model	Weight (oz.)	Price ($)
Fastdraw	3	10
Fastdraw Plus	4	12
Fitness	5	12
Access	7	20
Access Plus	8	25
Solo	9	25
Serenade	9	35
Solitaire	11	35
Gemini	21	45
Shadow	15	40
SipStream	18	60
Express	9	30
Lightning	12	40
Elite	14	60
Extender	16	65
Stinger	16	65
GelFlask Belt	3	20
GelDraw	1	7
GelFlask Clip-on Holster	2	10
GelFlask Holster SS	1	10
Strider (W)	8	30

Model	Weight (oz.)	Price ($)
Walkabout (W)	14	40
Solitude I.C.E.	9	35
Getaway I.C.E.	19	55
Profile I.C.E.	14	50
Traverse I.C.E.	13	60

a. Use these data to develop an estimated regression equation that could be used to predict the price of a hydration system given its weight.
b. Test the significance of the relationship at the .05 level of significance.
c. Did the estimated regression equation provide a good fit? Explain.
d. Assume that the estimated regression equation developed in part (a) will also apply to hydration systems produced by other companies. Develop a 95% confidence interval estimate of the price for all hydration systems that weigh 10 ounces.
e. Assume that the estimated regression equation developed in part (a) will also apply to hydration systems produced by other companies. Develop a 95% prediction interval estimate of the price for the Back Draft system produced by Eastern Mountain Sports. The Back Draft system weighs 10 ounces.

44. Cushman & Wakefield, Inc., collects data showing the office building vacancy rates and rental rates for markets in the United States. The following data show the overall vacancy rates (%) and the average rental rates (per square foot) for the central business district for 18 selected markets.

CD file

OffRates

Market	Vacancy Rate (%)	Average Rate ($)
Atlanta	21.9	18.54
Boston	6.0	33.70
Hartford	22.8	19.67
Baltimore	18.1	21.01
Washington	12.7	35.09
Philadelphia	14.5	19.41
Miami	20.0	25.28
Tampa	19.2	17.02
Chicago	16.0	24.04
San Francisco	6.6	31.42
Phoenix	15.9	18.74
San Jose	9.2	26.76
West Palm Beach	19.7	27.72
Detroit	20.0	18.20
Brooklyn	8.3	25.00
Downtown, NY	17.1	29.78
Midtown, NY	10.8	37.03
Midtown South, NY	11.1	28.64

a. Develop a scatter diagram for these data; plot the vacancy rate on the horizontal axis.
b. Does there appear to be any relationship between vacancy rates and rental rates?
c. Develop the estimated regression equation that could be used to predict the average rental rate given the overall vacancy rate.
d. Test the significance of the relationship at the .05 level of significance.

e. Did the estimated regression equation provide a good fit? Explain.
f. Predict the expected rental rate for markets with a 25% vacancy rate in the central business district.
g. The overall vacancy rate in the central business district in Ft. Lauderdale is 11.3%. Predict the expected rental rate for Ft. Lauderdale.

14.8 Residual Analysis: Validating Model Assumptions

Residual analysis *is the primary tool for determining whether the assumed regression model is appropriate.*

As we noted previously, the *residual* for observation *i* is the difference between the observed value of the dependent variable (y_i) and the estimated value of the dependent variable ($\hat{y}_i$).

RESIDUAL FOR OBSERVATION *i*

$$y_i - \hat{y}_i \tag{14.28}$$

where

y_i is the observed value of the dependent variable
$\hat{y}_i$ is the estimated value of the dependent variable

In other words, the *i*th residual is the error resulting from using the estimated regression equation to predict the value of the dependent variable. The residuals for the Armand's Pizza Parlors example are computed in Table 14.7. The observed values of the dependent variable are in the second column and the estimated values of the dependent variable, obtained using the estimated regression equation $\hat{y} = 60 + 5x$, are in the third column. An analysis of the corresponding residuals in the fourth column will help determine whether the assumptions made about the regression model are appropriate.

Let us now review the regression assumptions for the Armand's Pizza Parlors example. A simple linear regression model was assumed.

$$y = \beta_0 + \beta_1 x + \epsilon \tag{14.29}$$

TABLE 14.7 RESIDUALS FOR ARMAND'S PIZZA PARLORS

Student Population x_i	Sales y_i	Estimated Sales $\hat{y}_i = 60 + 5x_i$	Residuals $y_i - \hat{y}_i$
2	58	70	−12
6	105	90	15
8	88	100	−12
8	118	100	18
12	117	120	−3
16	137	140	−3
20	157	160	−3
20	169	160	9
22	149	170	−21
26	202	190	12

This model indicates that we assumed quarterly sales (y) to be a linear function of the size of the student population (x) plus an error term ϵ. In Section 14.4 we made the following assumptions about the error term ϵ.

1. $E(\epsilon) = 0$.
2. The variance of ϵ, denoted by σ^2, is the same for all values of x.
3. The values of ϵ are independent.
4. The error term ϵ has a normal distribution.

These assumptions provide the theoretical basis for the t test and the F test used to determine whether the relationship between x and y is significant, and for the confidence and prediction interval estimates presented in Section 14.6. If the assumptions about the error term ϵ appear questionable, the hypothesis tests about the significance of the regression relationship and the interval estimation results may not be valid.

The residuals provide the best information about ϵ; hence an analysis of the residuals is an important step in determining whether the assumptions for ϵ are appropriate. Much of residual analysis is based on an examination of graphical plots. In this section, we discuss the following residual plots.

1. A plot of the residuals against values of the independent variable x
2. A plot of residuals against the predicted values of the dependent variable $\hat{y}$
3. A standardized residual plot
4. A normal probability plot

Residual Plot Against x

A **residual plot** against the independent variable x is a graph in which the values of the independent variable are represented by the horizontal axis and the corresponding residual values are represented by the vertical axis. A point is plotted for each residual. The first coordinate for each point is given by the value of x_i and the second coordinate is given by the corresponding value of the residual $y_i - \hat{y}_i$. For a residual plot against x with the Armand's Pizza Parlors data from Table 14.7, the coordinates of the first point are $(2, -12)$, corresponding to $x_1 = 2$ and $y_1 - \hat{y}_1 = -12$; the coordinates of the second point are $(6, 15)$, corresponding to $x_2 = 6$ and $y_2 - \hat{y}_2 = 15$; and so on. Figure 14.11 shows the resulting residual plot.

Before interpreting the results for this residual plot, let us consider some general patterns that might be observed in any residual plot. Three examples appear in Figure 14.12. If the assumption that the variance of ϵ is the same for all values of x and the assumed regression model is an adequate representation of the relationship between the variables, the residual plot should give an overall impression of a horizontal band of points such as the one in Panel A of Figure 14.12. However, if the variance of ϵ is not the same for all values of x—for example, if variability about the regression line is greater for larger values of x—a pattern such as the one in Panel B of Figure 14.12 could be observed. In this case, the assumption of a constant variance of ϵ is violated. Another possible residual plot is shown in Panel C. In this case, we would conclude that the assumed regression model is not an adequate representation of the relationship between the variables. A curvilinear regression model or multiple regression model should be considered.

Now let us return to the residual plot for Armand's Pizza Parlors shown in Figure 14.11. The residuals appear to approximate the horizontal pattern in Panel A of Figure 14.12. Hence, we conclude that the residual plot does not provide evidence that the assumptions made for Armand's regression model should be challenged. At this point, we are confident in the conclusion that Armand's simple linear regression model is valid.

FIGURE 14.11 PLOT OF THE RESIDUALS AGAINST THE INDEPENDENT VARIABLE x FOR ARMAND'S PIZZA PARLORS

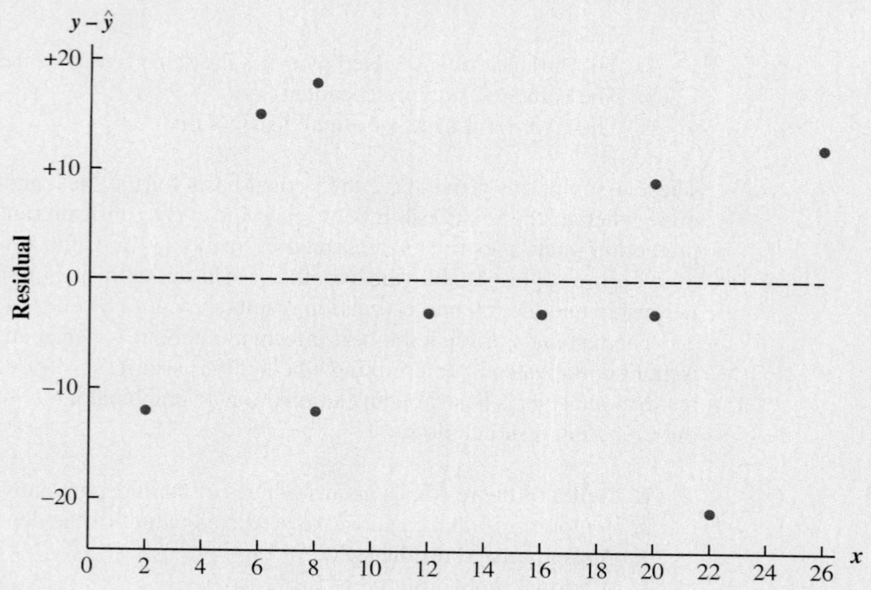

Experience and good judgment are always factors in the effective interpretation of residual plots. Seldom does a residual plot conform precisely to one of the patterns in Figure 14.12. Yet analysts who frequently conduct regression studies and frequently review residual plots become adept at understanding the differences between patterns that are reasonable and patterns that indicate the assumptions of the model should be questioned. A residual plot provides one technique to assess the validity of the assumptions for a regression model.

Residual Plot Against $\hat{y}$

Another residual plot represents the predicted value of the dependent variable $\hat{y}$ on the horizontal axis and the residual values on the vertical axis. A point is plotted for each residual. The first coordinate for each point is given by $\hat{y}_i$ and the second coordinate is given by the corresponding value of the ith residual $y_i - \hat{y}_i$. With the Armand's data from Table 14.7, the coordinates of the first point are (70, −12), corresponding to $\hat{y}_1 = 70$ and $y_1 - \hat{y}_1 = -12$; the coordinates of the second point are (90, 15); and so on. Figure 14.13 provides the residual plot. Note that the pattern of this residual plot is the same as the pattern of the residual plot against the independent variable x. It is not a pattern that would lead us to question the model assumptions. For simple linear regression, both the residual plot against x and the residual plot against $\hat{y}$ provide the same pattern. For multiple regression analysis, the residual plot against $\hat{y}$ is more widely used because of the presence of more than one independent variable.

Standardized Residuals

Many of the residual plots provided by computer software packages use a standardized version of the residuals. As demonstrated in preceding chapters, a random variable is standardized by subtracting its mean and dividing the result by its standard deviation. With the

FIGURE 14.12 RESIDUAL PLOTS FROM THREE REGRESSION STUDIES

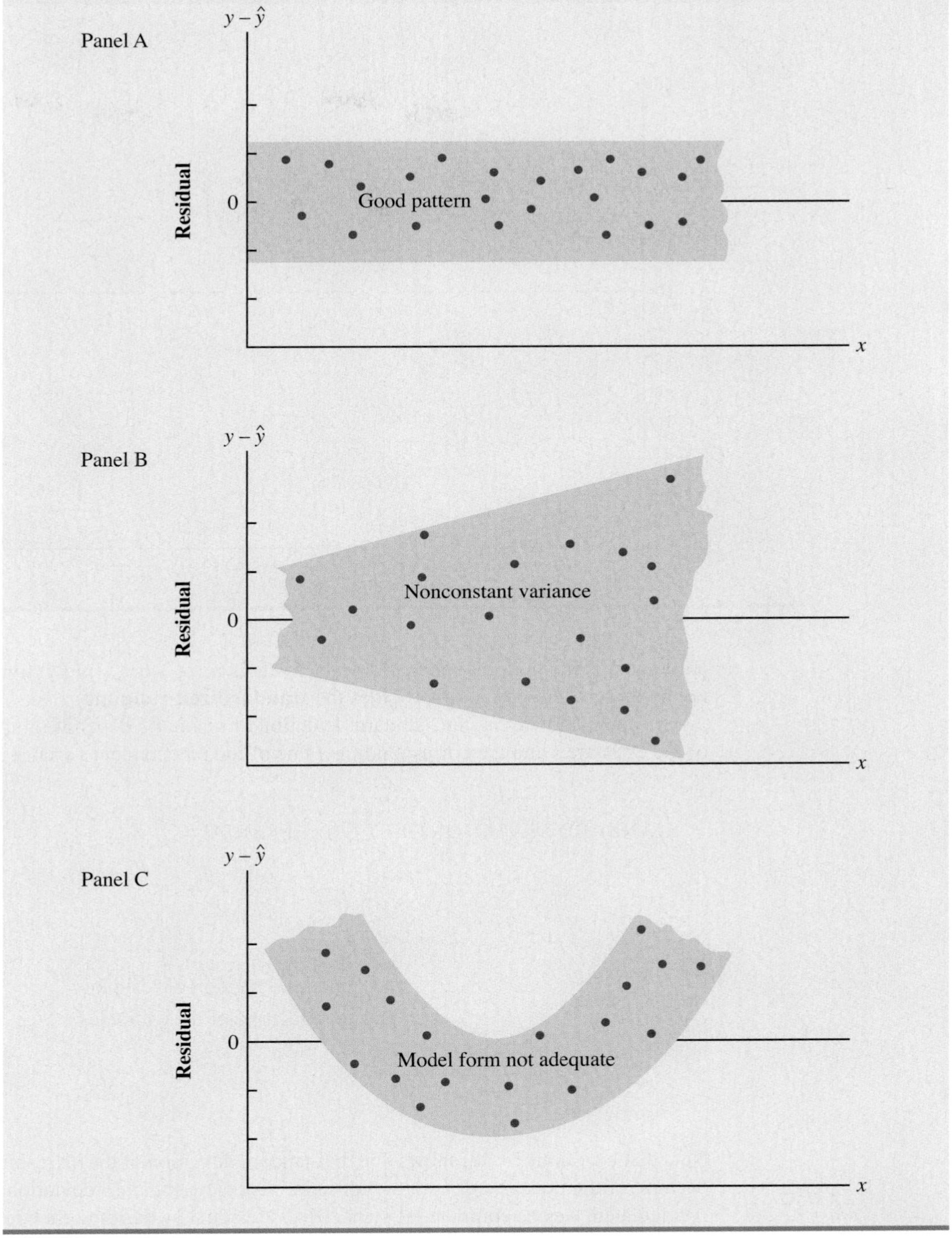

FIGURE 14.13 PLOT OF THE RESIDUALS AGAINST THE PREDICTED VALUES $\hat{y}$ FOR ARMAND'S PIZZA PARLORS

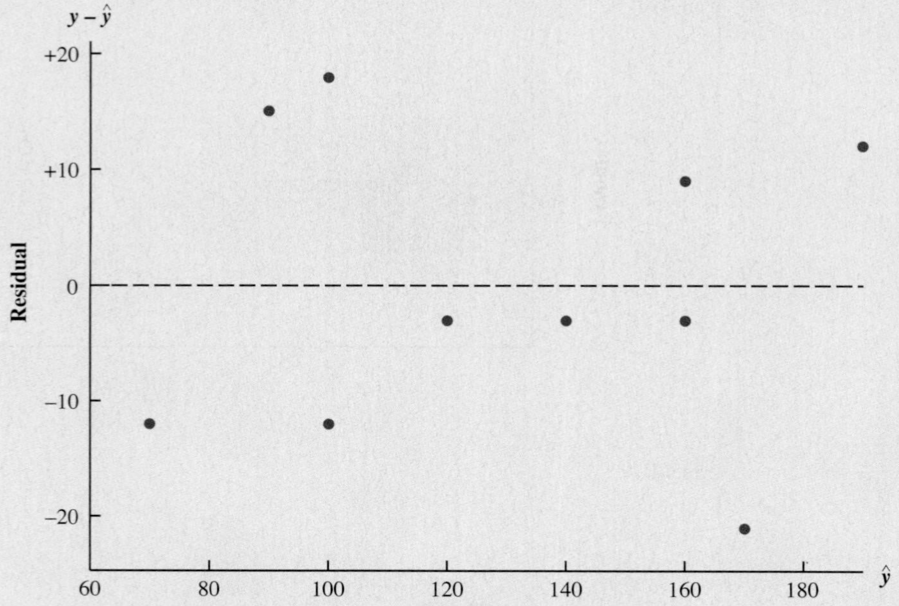

least squares method, the mean of the residuals is zero. Thus, simply dividing each residual by its standard deviation provides the **standardized residual.**

It can be shown that the standard deviation of residual i depends on the standard error of the estimate s and the corresponding value of the independent variable x_i.

STANDARD DEVIATION OF THE ith RESIDUAL*

$$s_{y_i - \hat{y}_i} = s\sqrt{1 - h_i} \tag{14.30}$$

where

$$s_{y_i - \hat{y}_i} = \text{the standard deviation of residual } i$$
$$s = \text{the standard error of the estimate}$$
$$h_i = \frac{1}{n} + \frac{(x_i - \bar{x})^2}{\Sigma(x_i - \bar{x})^2} \tag{14.31}$$

Note that equation (14.30) shows that the standard deviation of the ith residual depends on x_i because of the presence of h_i in the formula.† Once the standard deviation of each residual is calculated, we can compute the standardized residual by dividing each residual by its corresponding standard deviation.

*This equation actually provides an estimate of the standard deviation of the ith residual, because s is used instead of σ.

†h_i is referred to as the *leverage* of observation i. Leverage will be discussed further when we consider influential observations in Section 14.9.

TABLE 14.8 COMPUTATION OF STANDARDIZED RESIDUALS FOR ARMAND'S PIZZA PARLORS

Restaurant i	x_i	$x_i - \bar{x}$	$(x_i - \bar{x})^2$	$\frac{(x_i - \bar{x})^2}{\Sigma(x_i - \bar{x})^2}$	h_i	$s_{y_i - \hat{y}_i}$	$y_i - \hat{y}_i$	Standardized Residual
1	2	−12	144	.2535	.3535	11.1193	−12	−1.0792
2	6	−8	64	.1127	.2127	12.2709	15	1.2224
3	8	−6	36	.0634	.1634	12.6493	−12	−.9487
4	8	−6	36	.0634	.1634	12.6493	18	1.4230
5	12	−2	4	.0070	.1070	13.0682	−3	−.2296
6	16	2	4	.0070	.1070	13.0682	−3	−.2296
7	20	6	36	.0634	.1634	12.6493	−3	−.2372
8	20	6	36	.0634	.1634	12.6493	9	.7115
9	22	8	64	.1127	.2127	12.2709	−21	−1.7114
10	26	12	144	.2535	.3535	11.1193	12	1.0792
		Total	568					

Note: The values of the residuals were computed in Table 14.7.

STANDARDIZED RESIDUAL FOR OBSERVATION i

$$\frac{y_i - \hat{y}_i}{s_{y_i - \hat{y}_i}} \tag{14.32}$$

Table 14.8 shows the calculation of the standardized residuals for Armand's Pizza Parlors. Recall that previous calculations showed $s = 13.829$. Figure 14.14 is the plot of the standardized residuals against the independent variable x.

Small departures from normality do not have a great effect on the statistical tests used in regression analysis.

The standardized residual plot can provide insight about the assumption that the error term ϵ has a normal distribution. If this assumption is satisfied, the distribution of the standardized residuals should appear to come from a standard normal probability distribution.* Thus, when looking at a standardized residual plot, we should expect to see approximately 95% of the standardized residuals between −2 and +2. We see in Figure 14.14 that for the Armand's example all standardized residuals are between −2 and +2. Therefore, on the basis of the standardized residuals, this plot gives us no reason to question the assumption that ϵ has a normal distribution.

Because of the effort required to compute the estimated values of $\hat{y}$, the residuals, and the standardized residuals, most statistical packages provide these values as optional regression output. Hence, residual plots can be easily obtained. For large problems computer packages are the only practical means for developing the residual plots discussed in this section.

Normal Probability Plot

Another approach for determining the validity of the assumption that the error term has a normal distribution is the **normal probability plot**. To show how a normal probability plot is developed, we introduce the concept of *normal scores*.

Suppose 10 values are selected randomly from a normal probability distribution with a mean of zero and a standard deviation of one, and that the sampling process is repeated over and over with the values in each sample of 10 ordered from smallest to largest. For now, let

*Because s is used instead of σ in equation (14.30), the probability distribution of the standardized residuals is not technically normal. However, in most regression studies, the sample size is large enough that a normal approximation is very good.

FIGURE 14.14 PLOT OF THE STANDARDIZED RESIDUALS AGAINST THE INDEPENDENT VARIABLE x FOR ARMAND'S PIZZA PARLORS

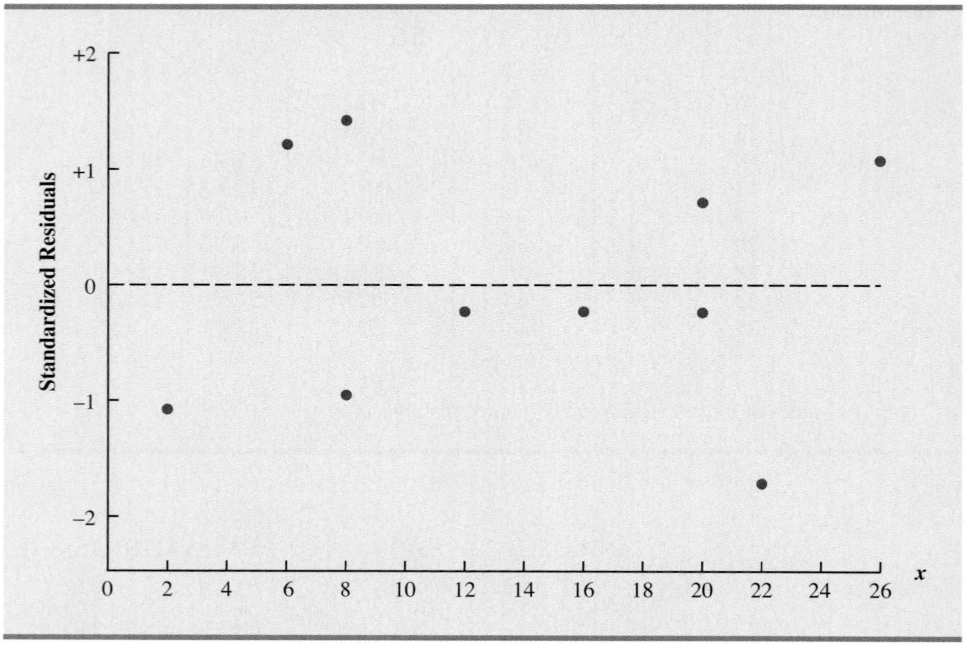

TABLE 14.9

NORMAL SCORES FOR $n = 10$

Order Statistic	Normal Score
1	−1.55
2	−1.00
3	−.65
4	−.37
5	−.12
6	.12
7	.37
8	.65
9	1.00
10	1.55

TABLE 14.10

NORMAL SCORES AND ORDERED STANDARDIZED RESIDUALS FOR ARMAND'S PIZZA PARLORS

Normal Scores	Ordered Standardized Residuals
−1.55	−1.7114
−1.00	−1.0792
−.65	−.9487
−.37	−.2372
−.12	−.2296
.12	−.2296
.37	.7115
.65	1.0792
1.00	1.2224
1.55	1.4230

us consider only the smallest value in each sample. The random variable representing the smallest value obtained in repeated sampling is called the first-order statistic.

Statisticians show that for samples of size 10 from a standard normal probability distribution, the expected value of the first-order statistic is −1.55. This expected value is called a normal score. For the case with a sample of size $n = 10$, there are 10 order statistics and 10 normal scores (see Table 14.9). In general, a data set consisting of n observations will have n order statistics and hence n normal scores.

Let us now show how the 10 normal scores can be used to determine whether the standardized residuals for Armand's Pizza Parlors appear to come from a standard normal probability distribution. We begin by ordering the 10 standardized residuals from Table 14.8. The 10 normal scores and the ordered standardized residuals are shown together in Table 14.10. If the normality assumption is satisfied, the smallest standardized residual should be close to the smallest normal score, the next smallest standardized residual should be close to the next smallest normal score, and so on. If we were to develop a plot with the normal scores on the horizontal axis and the corresponding standardized residuals on the vertical axis, the plotted points should cluster closely around a 45-degree line passing through the origin if the standardized residuals are approximately normally distributed. Such a plot is referred to as a *normal probability plot.*

Figure 14.15 is the normal probability plot for the Armand's Pizza Parlors example. Judgment is used to determine whether the pattern observed deviates from the line enough to conclude that the standardized residuals are not from a standard normal probability distribution. In Figure 14.15, we see that the points are grouped closely about the line. We therefore conclude that the assumption of the error term having a normal probability distribution is reasonable. In general, the more closely the points are clustered about the 45-degree line, the stronger the evidence supporting the normality assumption. Any substantial curvature in the normal probability plot is evidence that the residuals have not come from a normal distribution. Normal scores and the associated normal probability plot can be obtained easily from statistical packages such as Minitab.

FIGURE 14.15 NORMAL PROBABILITY PLOT FOR ARMAND'S PIZZA PARLORS

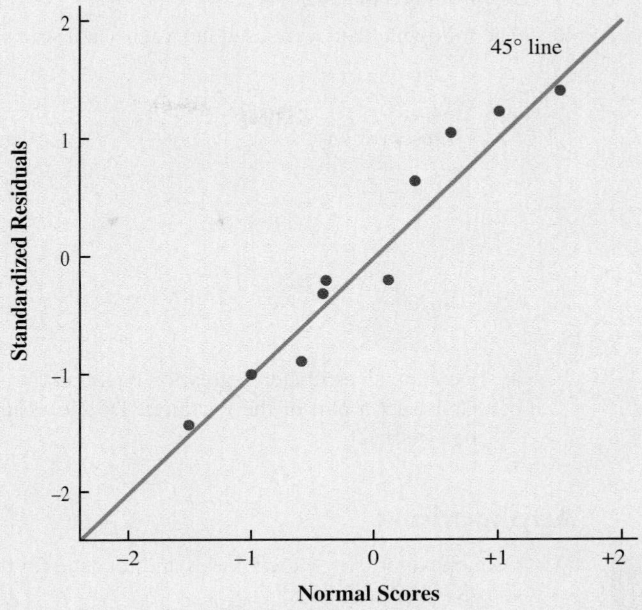

NOTES AND COMMENTS

1. We use residual and normal probability plots to validate the assumptions of a regression model. If our review indicates that one or more assumptions are questionable, a different regression model or a transformation of the data should be considered. The appropriate corrective action when the assumptions are violated must be based on good judgment; recommendations from an experienced statistician can be valuable.

2. Analysis of residuals is the primary method statisticians use to verify that the assumptions associated with a regression model are valid. Even if no violations are found, it does not necessarily follow that the model will yield good predictions. However, if additional statistical tests support the conclusion of significance and the coefficient of determination is large, we should be able to develop good estimates and predictions using the estimated regression equation.

Exercises

Methods

SELF test

45. Given are data for two variables, x and y.

x_i	6	11	15	18	20
y_i	6	8	12	20	30

a. Develop an estimated regression equation for these data.
b. Compute the residuals.
c. Develop a plot of the residuals against the independent variable x. Do the assumptions about the error terms seem to be satisfied?

d. Compute the standardized residuals.
e. Develop a plot of the standardized residuals against $\hat{y}$. What conclusions can you draw from this plot?

46. The following data were used in a regression study.

Observation	x_i	y_i	Observation	x_i	y_i
1	2	4	6	7	6
2	3	5	7	7	9
3	4	4	8	8	5
4	5	6	9	9	11
5	7	4			

a. Develop an estimated regression equation for these data.
b. Construct a plot of the residuals. Do the assumptions about the error term seem to be satisfied?

Applications

SELF test

47. Data on advertising expenditures and revenue (in thousands of dollars) for the Four Seasons Restaurant follow.

Advertising Expenditures	Revenue
1	19
2	32
4	44
6	40
10	52
14	53
20	54

a. Let x equal advertising expenditures and y equal revenue. Use the method of least squares to develop a straight line approximation of the relationship between the two variables.
b. Test whether revenue and advertising expenditures are related at a .05 level of significance.
c. Prepare a residual plot of $y - \hat{y}$ versus $\hat{y}$. Use the result from part (a) to obtain the values of $\hat{y}$.
d. What conclusions can you draw from residual analysis? Should this model be used, or should we look for a better one?

48. Refer to exercise 9, where an estimated regression equation relating years of experience and annual sales was developed.
   a. Compute the residuals and construct a residual plot for this problem.
   b. Do the assumptions about the error terms seem reasonable in light of the residual plot?

49. American Depository Receipts (ADRs) are certificates traded on the NYSE representing shares of a foreign company held on deposit in a bank in its home country. The following table shows the price/earnings (P/E) ratio and the percentage return on investment (ROE) for 10 Indian companies that are likely new ADRs (*Bloomberg Personal Finance*, April 2000).

CD file
ADRs

	ROE	P/E
Bharti Televentures	6.43	36.88
Gujarat Ambuja Cements	13.49	27.03
Hindalco Industries	14.04	10.83
ICICI	20.67	5.15
Mahanagar Telephone Nigam	22.74	13.35
NIIT	46.23	95.59
Pentamedia Graphics	28.90	54.85
Satyam Computer Services	54.01	189.21
Silverline Technologies	28.02	75.86
Videsh Sanchar Nigam	27.04	13.17

a. Use a computer package to develop an estimated regression equation relating y = P/E and x = ROE.
b. Construct a residual plot of the standardized residuals against the independent variable.
c. Do the assumptions about the error terms and model form seem reasonable in light of the residual plot?

14.9 Residual Analysis: Outliers and Influential Observations

In Section 14.8 we showed how residual analysis could be used to determine when violations of assumptions about the regression model occur. In this section, we discuss how residual analysis can be used to identify observations that can be classified as outliers or as being especially influential in determining the estimated regression equation. Some steps that should be taken when such observations occur are discussed.

Detecting Outliers

Figure 14.16 is a scatter diagram for a data set that contains an **outlier**, a data point (observation) that does not fit the trend shown by the remaining data. Outliers represent observations that are suspect and warrant careful examination. They may represent erroneous data;

FIGURE 14.16 DATA SET WITH AN OUTLIER

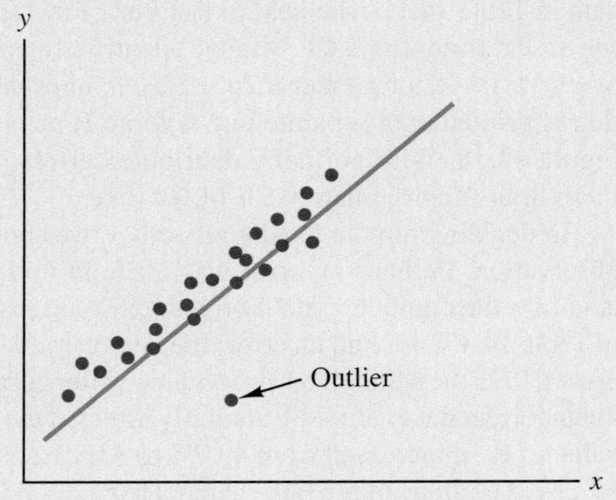

FIGURE 14.17 SCATTER DIAGRAM FOR OUTLIER DATA SET

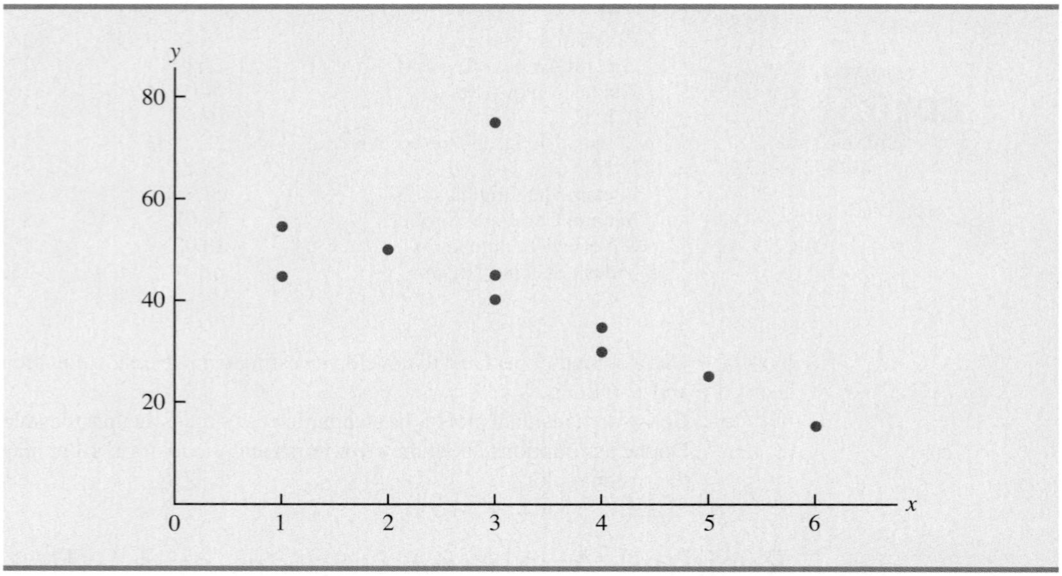

TABLE 14.11 DATA SET ILLUSTRATING THE EFFECT OF AN OUTLIER

x_i	y_i
1	45
1	55
2	50
3	75
3	40
3	45
4	30
4	35
5	25
6	15

if so, the data should be corrected. They may signal a violation of model assumptions; if so, another model should be considered. Finally, they may simply be unusual values that occurred by chance. In this case, they should be retained.

To illustrate the process of detecting outliers, consider the data set in Table 14.11; Figure 14.17 is a scatter diagram. Except for observation 4 ($x_4 = 3, y_4 = 75$), a pattern suggesting a negative linear relationship is apparent. Indeed, given the pattern of the rest of the data, we would expect y_4 to be much smaller and hence would identify the corresponding observation as an outlier. For the case of simple linear regression, one can often detect outliers by simply examining the scatter diagram.

The standardized residuals can also be used to identify outliers. If an observation deviates greatly from the pattern of the rest of the data (e.g., the outlier in Figure 14.16), the corresponding standardized residual will be large in absolute value. Many computer packages automatically identify observations with standardized residuals that are large in absolute value. In Figure 14.18 we show the Minitab output from a regression analysis of the data in Table 14.11. The next to last line of the output shows that the standardized residual for observation 4 is 2.67. Minitab identifies any observation with a standardized residual of less than -2 or greater than $+2$ as an unusual observation; in such cases, the observation is printed on a separate line with an R next to the standardized residual, as shown in Figure 14.18. With normally distributed errors, standardized residuals should be outside these limits approximately 5% of the time.

In deciding how to handle an outlier, we should first check to see whether it is a valid observation. Perhaps an error was made in initially recording the data or in entering the data into the computer file. For example, suppose that in checking the data for the outlier in Table 14.17, we find an error; the correct value for observation 4 is $x_4 = 3, y_4 = 30$. Figure 14.19 is the Minitab output obtained after correction of the value of y_4. We see that using the incorrect data value substantially affected the goodness of fit. With the correct data, the value of R-sq increased from 49.7% to 83.8% and the value of b_0 decreased from 64.958 to 59.237. The slope of the line changed from -7.331 to -6.949. The identification of the outlier enabled us to correct the data error and improve the regression results.

FIGURE 14.18 MINITAB OUTPUT FOR REGRESSION ANALYSIS OF THE OUTLIER DATA SET

```
The regression equation is
y = 65.0 - 7.33 x

Predictor     Coef  SE Coef      T      p
Constant    64.958    9.258   7.02  0.000
X           -7.331    2.608  -2.81  0.023

S = 12.67   R-sq = 49.7%   R-sq(adj) = 43.4%

Analysis of Variance

SOURCE           DF      SS      MS     F      p
Regression        1  1268.2  1268.2  7.90  0.023
Residual Error    8  1284.3   160.5
Total             9  2552.5

Unusual Observations
Obs     x      y    Fit  SE Fit  Residual  St Resid
  4  3.00  75.00  42.97    4.04     32.03     2.67R

R denotes an observation with a large standardized residual.
```

FIGURE 14.19 MINITAB OUTPUT FOR THE REVISED OUTLIER DATA SET

```
The regression equation is
Y = 59.2 - 6.95 X

Predictor     Coef  SE Coef      T      p
Constant    59.237    3.835  15.45  0.000
X           -6.949    1.080  -6.43  0.000

S = 5.248   R-sq = 83.8%   R-sq(adj) = 81.8%

Analysis of Variance

SOURCE           DF      SS      MS      F      p
Regression        1  1139.7  1139.7  41.38  0.000
Residual Error    8   220.3    27.5
Total             9  1360.0
```

Detecting Influential Observations

Sometimes one or more observations exert a strong influence on the results obtained. Figure 14.20 shows an example of an **influential observation** in simple linear regression. The estimated regression line has a negative slope. However, if the influential observation were dropped from the data set, the slope of the estimated regression line would change from negative to positive and the y-intercept would be smaller. Clearly, this one observation is

FIGURE 14.20 DATA SET WITH AN INFLUENTIAL OBSERVATION

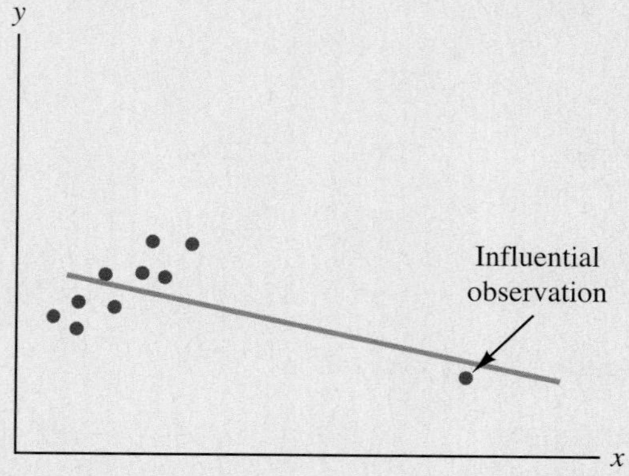

much more influential in determining the estimated regression line than any of the others; dropping one of the other observations from the data set would have little effect on the estimated regression equation.

Influential observations can be identified from a scatter diagram when only one independent variable is present. An influential observation may be an outlier (an observation with a y value that deviates substantially from the trend), it may correspond to an x value far away from its mean (e.g., see Figure 14.20), or it may be caused by a combination of the two (a somewhat off-trend y value and a somewhat extreme x value).

Because influential observations may have such a dramatic effect on the estimated regression equation, they must be examined carefully. We should first check to make sure that no error was made in collecting or recording the data. If an error occurred, it can be corrected and a new estimated regression equation can be developed. If the observation is valid, we might consider ourselves fortunate to have it. Such a point, if valid, can contribute to a better understanding of the appropriate model and can lead to a better estimated regression equation. The presence of the influential observation in Figure 14.20, if valid, would suggest trying to obtain data on intermediate values of x to understand better the relationship between x and y.

Observations with extreme values for the independent variables are called **high leverage points**. The influential observation in Figure 14.20 is a point with high leverage. The leverage of an observation is determined by how far the values of the independent variables are from their mean values. For the single-independent-variable case, the leverage of the ith observation, denoted h_i, can be computed by using equation (14.33).

LEVERAGE OF OBSERVATION i

$$h_i = \frac{1}{n} + \frac{(x_i - \bar{x})^2}{\Sigma(x_i - \bar{x})^2} \tag{14.33}$$

From the formula, it is clear that the farther x_i is from its mean $\bar{x}$, the higher the leverage of observation i.

Many statistical packages automatically identify observations with high leverage as part of the standard regression output. As an illustration of how the Minitab statistical package identifies points with high leverage, let us consider the data set in Table 14.12.

FIGURE 14.21 SCATTER DIAGRAM FOR THE DATA SET WITH A HIGH LEVERAGE OBSERVATION

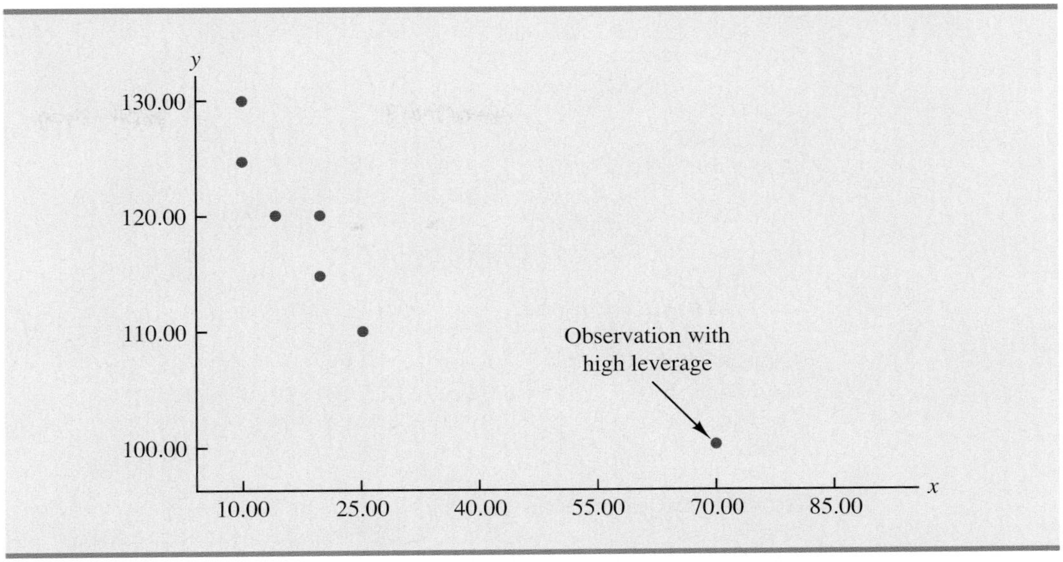

TABLE 14.12

DATA SET WITH A HIGH LEVERAGE OBSERVATION

x_i	y_i
10	125
10	130
15	120
20	115
20	120
25	110
70	100

Computer software packages are essential for performing the computations to identify influential observations. Minitab's selection rule is discussed here.

From Figure 14.21, a scatter diagram for the data set in Table 14.12, it is clear that observation 7 ($x = 70$, $y = 100$) is an observation with an extreme value of x. Hence, we would expect it to be identified as a point with high leverage. For this observation, the leverage is computed by using equation (14.33) as follows.

$$h_7 = \frac{1}{n} + \frac{(x_7 - \bar{x})^2}{\Sigma(x_i - \bar{x})^2} = \frac{1}{7} + \frac{(70 - 24.286)^2}{2621.43} = .94$$

For the case of simple linear regression, Minitab identifies observations as having high leverage if $h_i > 6/n$ or .99, whichever is smaller. For the data set in Table 14.12, $6/n = 6/7 = .86$. Because $h_7 = .94 > .86$, Minitab will identify observation 7 as an observation whose x value gives it large influence. Figure 14.22 shows the Minitab output for a regression analysis of this data set. Observation 7 ($x = 70$, $y = 100$) is identified as having large influence; it is printed on a separate line at the bottom, with an X in the right margin.

Influential observations that are caused by an interaction of large residuals and high leverage can be difficult to detect. Diagnostic procedures are available that take both into account in determining when an observation is influential. One such measure, called Cook's D statistic, will be discussed in Chapter 15.

NOTES AND COMMENTS

Once an observation is identified as potentially influential because of a large residual or high leverage, its impact on the estimated regression equation should be evaluated. More advanced texts discuss diagnostics for doing so. However, if one is not familiar with the more advanced material, a simple procedure is to run the regression analysis with and without the observation. This approach will reveal the influence of the observation on the results.

FIGURE 14.22 MINITAB OUTPUT FOR THE DATA SET WITH A HIGH LEVERAGE OBSERVATION

```
The regression equation is
y = 127 - 0.425 x

Predictor        Coef   SE Coef       T      p
Constant      127.466     2.961   43.04  0.000
X            -0.42507   0.09537   -4.46  0.007

S = 4.883   R-sq = 79.9%   R-sq(adj) = 75.9%

Analysis of Variance

SOURCE            DF       SS       MS      F      p
Regression         1   473.65   473.65  19.87  0.007
Residual Error     5   119.21    23.84
Total              6   592.86

Unusual Observations
Obs      x        y     Fit  SE Fit  Residual  St Resid
  7   70.0   100.00   97.71    4.73      2.29    1.91 X

X denotes an observation whose X value gives it large influence.
```

Exercises

Methods

SELF test

50. Consider the following data for two variables, x and y.

x_i	135	110	130	145	175	160	120
y_i	145	100	120	120	130	130	110

a. Compute the standardized residuals for these data. Do the data include any outliers? Explain.
b. Plot the standardized residuals against $\hat{y}$. Does this plot reveal any outliers?
c. Develop a scatter diagram for these data. Does the scatter diagram indicate any outliers in the data? In general, what implications does this finding have for simple linear regression?

51. Consider the following data for two variables, x and y.

x_i	4	5	7	8	10	12	12	22
y_i	12	14	16	15	18	20	24	19

a. Compute the standardized residuals for these data. Do the data include any outliers? Explain.
b. Compute the leverage values for these data. Do there appear to be any influential observations in these data? Explain.
c. Develop a scatter diagram for these data. Does the scatter diagram indicate any influential observations? Explain.

Applications

SELF test

52. The following data show the media expenditures ($ millions) and the shipments in bbls. (millions) for 10 major brands of beer.

CD file
Beer

Brand	Media Expenditures ($ millions)	Shipments
Budweiser	120.0	36.3
Bud Light	68.7	20.7
Miller Lite	100.1	15.9
Coors Light	76.6	13.2
Busch	8.7	8.1
Natural Light	0.1	7.1
Miller Genuine Draft	21.5	5.6
Miller High Life	1.4	4.4
Busch Light	5.3	4.3
Milwaukee's Best	1.7	4.3

a. Develop the estimated regression equation for these data.
b. Use residual analysis to determine whether any outliers and/or influential observations are present. Briefly summarize your findings and conclusions.

53. Health experts recommend that runners drink 4 ounces of water every 15 minutes they run. Runners who run three to eight hours need a larger-capacity hip-mounted or over-the-shoulder hydration system. The following data show the liquid volume (fl oz) and the price for 26 Ultimate Direction hip-mounted or over-the-shoulder hydration systems (*Trail Runner Gear Guide,* 2003).

CD file
Hydration2

Model	Volume (fl oz)	Price ($)
Fastdraw	20	10
Fastdraw Plus	20	12
Fitness	20	12
Access	20	20
Access Plus	24	25
Solo	20	25
Serenade	20	35
Solitaire	20	35
Gemini	40	45
Shadow	64	40
SipStream	96	60
Express	20	30
Lightning	28	40
Elite	40	60
Extender	40	65
Stinger	32	65
GelFlask Belt	4	20
GelDraw	4	7
GelFlask Clip-on Holster	4	10
GelFlask Holster SS	4	10
Strider (W)	20	30
Walkabout (W)	230	40
Solitude I.C.E.	20	35
Getaway I.C.E.	40	55
Profile I.C.E.	64	50
Traverse I.C.E.	64	60

a. Develop the estimated regression equation that can be used to predict the price of a hydration system given its liquid volume.
b. Use residual analysis to determine whether any outliers or influential observations are present. Briefly summarize your findings and conclusions.

54. The market capitalization and the salary of the chief executive officer (CEO) for 20 companies are shown in the following table (*The Wall Street Journal,* February 24, 2000, and April 6, 2000).

CD file CEO

	Market Cap. ($ millions)	CEO Salary ($1000s)
Anheuser-Busch	32,977.4	1,130
AT&T	162,365.1	1,400
Charles Schwab	31,363.8	800
Chevron	56,849.0	1,350
DuPont	68,848.0	1,000
General Electric	507,216.8	3,325
Gillette	44,180.1	978
IBM	194,455.9	2,000
Johnson & Johnson	143,131.0	1,365
Kimberly-Clark	35,377.5	950
Merrill Lynch	31,062.1	700
Motorola	92,923.7	1,275
Philip Morris	54,421.2	1,625
Procter & Gamble	144,152.9	1,318.3
Qualcomm	116,840.8	773
Schering-Plough	62,259.4	1,200
Sun Microsystems	120,966.5	116
Texaco	30,040.7	950
USWest	36,450.8	897
Walt Disney	61,288.1	750

a. Develop the estimated regression equation that can be used to predict the CEO salary given the market capitalization.
b. Use residual analysis to determine whether any outliers and/or influential observations are present. Briefly summarize your findings and conclusions.

Summary

In this chapter we showed how regression analysis can be used to determine how a dependent variable y is related to an independent variable x. In simple linear regression, the regression model is $y = \beta_0 + \beta_1 x + \epsilon$. The simple linear regression equation $E(y) = \beta_0 + \beta_1 x$ describes how the mean or expected value of y is related to x. We used sample data and the least squares method to develop the estimated regression equation $\hat{y} = b_0 + b_1 x$. In effect, b_0 and b_1 are the sample statistics used to estimate the unknown model parameters β_0 and β_1.

The coefficient of determination was presented as a measure of the goodness of fit for the estimated regression equation; it can be interpreted as the proportion of the variation in the dependent variable y that can be explained by the estimated regression equation. We reviewed correlation as a descriptive measure of the strength of a linear relationship between two variables.

The assumptions about the regression model and its associated error term ϵ were discussed, and t and F tests, based on those assumptions, were presented as a means for determining whether the relationship between two variables is statistically significant. We showed how to use the estimated regression equation to develop confidence interval estimates of the mean value of y and prediction interval estimates of individual values of y.

The chapter concluded with a section on the computer solution of regression problems and two sections on the use of residual analysis to validate the model assumptions and to identify outliers and influential observations.

Glossary

Dependent variable The variable that is being predicted or explained. It is denoted by y.

Independent variable The variable that is doing the predicting or explaining. It is denoted by x.

Simple linear regression Regression analysis involving one independent variable and one dependent variable in which the relationship between the variables is approximated by a straight line.

Regression model The equation that describes how y is related to x and an error term; in simple linear regression, the regression model is $y = \beta_0 + \beta_1 x + \epsilon$.

Regression equation The equation that describes how the mean or expected value of the dependent variable is related to the independent variable; in simple linear regression, $E(y) = \beta_0 + \beta_1 x$.

Estimated regression equation The estimate of the regression equation developed from sample data by using the least squares method. For simple linear regression, the estimated regression equation is $\hat{y} = b_0 + b_1 x$.

Least squares method A procedure used to develop the estimated regression equation. The objective is to minimize $\Sigma(y_i - \hat{y}_i)^2$.

Scatter diagram A graph of bivariate data in which the independent variable is on the horizontal axis and the dependent variable is on the vertical axis.

Coefficient of determination A measure of the goodness of fit of the estimated regression equation. It can be interpreted as the proportion of the variability in the dependent variable y that is explained by the estimated regression equation.

***i*th residual** The difference between the observed value of the dependent variable and the value predicted using the estimated regression equation; for the ith observation the ith residual is $y_i - \hat{y}_i$.

Correlation coefficient A measure of the strength of the linear relationship between two variables (previously discussed in Chapter 3).

Mean square error The unbiased estimate of the variance of the error term σ^2. It is denoted by MSE or s^2.

Standard error of the estimate The square root of the mean square error, denoted by s. It is the estimate of σ, the standard deviation of the error term ϵ.

ANOVA table The analysis of variance table used to summarize the computations associated with the F test for significance.

Confidence interval The interval estimate of the mean value of y for a given value of x.

Prediction interval The interval estimate of an individual value of y for a given value of x.

Residual analysis The analysis of the residuals used to determine whether the assumptions made about the regression model appear to be valid. Residual analysis is also used to identify outliers and influential observations.

Residual plot Graphical representation of the residuals that can be used to determine whether the assumptions made about the regression model appear to be valid.

Standardized residual The value obtained by dividing a residual by its standard deviation.

Normal probability plot A graph of the standardized residuals plotted against values of the normal scores. This plot helps determine whether the assumption that the error term has a normal probability distribution appears to be valid.

Outlier A data point or observation that does not fit the trend shown by the remaining data.

Influential observation An observation that has a strong influence or effect on the regression results.

High leverage points Observations with extreme values for the independent variables.

Key Formulas

Simple Linear Regression Model

$$y = \beta_0 + \beta_1 x + \epsilon \tag{14.1}$$

Simple Linear Regression Equation

$$E(y) = \beta_0 + \beta_1 x \tag{14.2}$$

Estimated Simple Linear Regression Equation

$$\hat{y} = b_0 + b_1 x \tag{14.3}$$

Least Squares Criterion

$$\min \Sigma(y_i - \hat{y}_i)^2 \tag{14.5}$$

Slope and *y*-Intercept for the Estimated Regression Equation

$$b_1 = \frac{\Sigma(x_i - \bar{x})(y_i - \bar{y})}{\Sigma(x_i - \bar{x})^2} \tag{14.6}$$

$$b_0 = \bar{y} - b_1\bar{x} \tag{14.7}$$

Sum of Squares Due to Error

$$\text{SSE} = \Sigma(y_i - \hat{y}_i)^2 \tag{14.8}$$

Total Sum of Squares

$$\text{SST} = \Sigma(y_i - \bar{y})^2 \tag{14.9}$$

Sum of Squares Due to Regression

$$\text{SSR} = \Sigma(\hat{y}_i - \bar{y})^2 \tag{14.10}$$

Relationship Among SST, SSR, and SSE

$$\text{SST} = \text{SSR} + \text{SSE} \tag{14.11}$$

Coefficient of Determination

$$r^2 = \frac{\text{SSR}}{\text{SST}} \tag{14.12}$$

Sample Correlation Coefficient

$$\begin{aligned} r_{xy} &= (\text{sign of } b_1)\sqrt{\text{Coefficient of determination}} \\ &= (\text{sign of } b_1)\sqrt{r^2} \end{aligned} \tag{14.13}$$

Mean Square Error (Estimate of σ^2)

$$s^2 = \text{MSE} = \frac{\text{SSE}}{n - 2} \tag{14.15}$$

Standard Error of the Estimate

$$s = \sqrt{\text{MSE}} = \sqrt{\frac{\text{SSE}}{n - 2}} \tag{14.16}$$

Standard Deviation of b_1

$$\sigma_{b_1} = \frac{\sigma}{\sqrt{\Sigma(x_i - \bar{x})^2}} \tag{14.17}$$

Estimated Standard Deviation of b_1

$$s_{b_1} = \frac{s}{\sqrt{\Sigma(x_i - \bar{x})^2}} \tag{14.18}$$

***t* Test Statistic**

$$t = \frac{b_1}{s_{b_1}} \tag{14.19}$$

Mean Square Regression

$$\text{MSR} = \frac{\text{SSR}}{\text{Number of independent variables}} \tag{14.20}$$

***F* Test Statistic**

$$F = \frac{\text{MSR}}{\text{MSE}} \tag{14.21}$$

Estimated Standard Deviation of $\hat{y}_p$

$$s_{\hat{y}_p} = s\sqrt{\frac{1}{n} + \frac{(x_p - \bar{x})^2}{\Sigma(x_i - \bar{x})^2}} \tag{14.23}$$

Confidence Interval for $E(y_p)$

$$\hat{y}_p \pm t_{\alpha/2} s_{\hat{y}_p} \tag{14.24}$$

Estimated Standard Deviation of an Individual Value

$$s_{\text{ind}} = s\sqrt{1 + \frac{1}{n} + \frac{(x_p - \bar{x})^2}{\Sigma(x_i - \bar{x})^2}} \tag{14.26}$$

Prediction Interval for y_p

$$\hat{y}_p \pm t_{\alpha/2} s_{\text{ind}} \tag{14.27}$$

Residual for Observation i

$$y_i - \hat{y}_i \tag{14.28}$$

Standard Deviation of the *i*th Residual

$$s_{y_i - \hat{y}_i} = s\sqrt{1 - h_i} \tag{14.30}$$

Standardized Residual for Observation *i*

$$\frac{y_i - \hat{y}_i}{s_{y_i - \hat{y}_i}} \tag{14.32}$$

Leverage of Observation *i*

$$h_i = \frac{1}{n} + \frac{(x_i - \bar{x})^2}{\Sigma(x_i - \bar{x})^2} \tag{14.33}$$

Supplementary Exercises

55. Does a high value of r^2 imply that two variables are causally related? Explain.
56. In your own words, explain the difference between an interval estimate of the mean value of y for a given x and an interval estimate for an individual value of y for a given x.
57. What is the purpose of testing whether $\beta_1 = 0$? If we reject $\beta_1 = 0$, does it imply a good fit?
58. The data in the following table show the number of shares selling (millions) and the expected price (average of projected low price and projected high price) for 10 selected initial public stock offerings.

CD file
IPO

Company	Shares Selling	Expected Price ($)
American Physician	5.0	15
Apex Silver Mines	9.0	14
Dan River	6.7	15
Franchise Mortgage	8.75	17
Gene Logic	3.0	11
International Home Foods	13.6	19
PRT Group	4.6	13
Rayovac	6.7	14
RealNetworks	3.0	10
Software AG Systems	7.7	13

a. Develop an estimated regression equation with the number of shares selling as the independent variable and the expected price as the dependent variable.
b. At the .05 level of significance, is there a significant relationship between the two variables?
c. Did the estimated regression equation provide a good fit? Explain.
d. Use the estimated regression equation to estimate the expected price for a firm considering an initial public offering of 6 million shares.

59. Corporate share repurchase programs are often touted as a benefit for shareholders. But Robert Gabele, director of insider research for First Call/Thomson Financial, noted that many of these programs are undertaken solely to acquire stock for a company's incentive options for top managers. Across all companies, existing stock options in 1998 represented 6.2 percent of all common shares outstanding. The following data show the number of shares covered by option grants and the number of shares outstanding for 13 companies (*Bloomberg Personal Finance,* January/February 2000).

CD file
Options

	Shares of Option Grants Outstanding (millions)	Common Shares Outstanding (millions)
Adobe Systems	20.3	61.8
Apple Computer	52.7	160.9
Applied Materials	109.1	375.4
Autodesk	15.7	58.9
Best Buy	44.2	203.8
Fruit of the Loom	14.2	66.9
ITT Industries	18.0	87.9
Merrill Lynch	89.9	365.5
Novell	120.2	335.0
Parametric Technology	78.3	269.3
Reebok International	12.8	56.1
Silicon Graphics	52.6	188.8
Toys "R" Us	54.8	247.6

a. Develop the estimated regression equation that could be used to estimate the number of shares of option grants outstanding given the number of common shares outstanding.

b. Use the estimated regression equation to estimate the number of shares of option grants outstanding for a company that has 150 million shares of common stock outstanding.

c. Do you believe the estimated regression equation would provide a good prediction of the number of shares of option grants outstanding? Use r^2 to support your answer.

60. The Dow Jones Industrial Average (DJIA) and the Standard & Poor's 500 (S&P) indexes are used as measures of overall movement in the stock market. The DJIA is based on the price movements of 30 large companies; the S&P 500 is an index composed of 500 stocks. Some say the S&P 500 is a better measure of stock market performance because it is broader based. The closing prices for the DJIA and the S&P 500 for 20 weeks, beginning with September 9, 2005, follow (*Barron's*, January 30, 2006).

CD file
DJIAS&P500

Date	DJIA	S&P 500
September 9	10679	1241
September 16	10642	1238
September 23	10420	1215
September 30	10569	1229
October 7	10292	1196
October 14	10287	1187
October 21	10215	1180
October 28	10403	1198
November 4	10531	1220
November 11	10686	1235
November 18	10766	1248
November 25	10932	1268
December 2	10878	1265
December 9	10779	1259
December 16	10876	1267
December 23	10883	1269
December 30	10718	1248
January 6	10959	1285
January 13	10960	1288
January 20	10667	1261

a. Develop a scatter diagram for these data with DJIA as the independent variable.
b. Develop the estimated regression equation.
c. Test for a significant relationship. Use $\alpha = .05$.
d. Did the estimated regression equation provide a good fit? Explain.
e. Suppose that the closing price for the DJIA is 11,000. Estimate the closing price for the S&P 500.
f. Should we be concerned that the DJIA value of 11,000 used to predict the S&P 500 in part (e) is beyond the range of the data used to develop the estimated regression equation?

61. Jensen Tire & Auto is in the process of deciding whether to purchase a maintenance contract for its new computer wheel alignment and balancing machine. Managers feel that maintenance expense should be related to usage, and they collected the following information on weekly usage (hours) and annual maintenance expense (in hundreds of dollars).

CD file
Jensen

Weekly Usage (hours)	Annual Maintenance Expense
13	17.0
10	22.0
20	30.0
28	37.0
32	47.0
17	30.5
24	32.5
31	39.0
40	51.5
38	40.0

a. Develop the estimated regression equation that relates annual maintenance expense to weekly usage.
b. Test the significance of the relationship in part (a) at a .05 level of significance.
c. Jensen expects to use the new machine 30 hours per week. Develop a 95% prediction interval for the company's annual maintenance expense.
d. If the maintenance contract costs $3000 per year, would you recommend purchasing it? Why or why not?

62. In a manufacturing process the assembly line speed (feet per minute) was thought to affect the number of defective parts found during the inspection process. To test this theory, managers devised a situation in which the same batch of parts was inspected visually at a variety of line speeds. They collected the following data.

Line Speed	Number of Defective Parts Found
20	21
20	19
40	15
30	16
60	14
40	17

a. Develop the estimated regression equation that relates line speed to the number of defective parts found.

b. At a .05 level of significance, determine whether line speed and number of defective parts found are related.
c. Did the estimated regression equation provide a good fit to the data?
d. Develop a 95% confidence interval to predict the mean number of defective parts for a line speed of 50 feet per minute.

63. A sociologist was hired by a large city hospital to investigate the relationship between the number of unauthorized days that employees are absent per year and the distance (miles) between home and work for the employees. A sample of 10 employees was chosen, and the following data were collected.

CD file
Absent

Distance to Work	Number of Days Absent
1	8
3	5
4	8
6	7
8	6
10	3
12	5
14	2
14	4
18	2

a. Develop a scatter diagram for these data. Does a linear relationship appear reasonable? Explain.
b. Develop the least squares estimated regression equation.
c. Is there a significant relationship between the two variables? Use $\alpha = .05$.
d. Did the estimated regression equation provide a good fit? Explain.
e. Use the estimated regression equation developed in part (b) to develop a 95% confidence interval for the expected number of days absent for employees living 5 miles from the company.

64. The regional transit authority for a major metropolitan area wants to determine whether there is any relationship between the age of a bus and the annual maintenance cost. A sample of 10 buses resulted in the following data.

CD file
AgeCost

Age of Bus (years)	Maintenance Cost ($)
1	350
2	370
2	480
2	520
2	590
3	550
4	750
4	800
5	790
5	950

a. Develop the least squares estimated regression equation.
b. Test to see whether the two variables are significantly related with $\alpha = .05$.
c. Did the least squares line provide a good fit to the observed data? Explain.
d. Develop a 95% prediction interval for the maintenance cost for a specific bus that is 4 years old.

65. A marketing professor at Givens College is interested in the relationship between hours spent studying and total points earned in a course. Data collected on 10 students who took the course last quarter follow.

CD file
HoursPts

Hours Spent Studying	Total Points Earned
45	40
30	35
90	75
60	65
105	90
65	50
90	90
80	80
55	45
75	65

a. Develop an estimated regression equation showing how total points earned is related to hours spent studying.
b. Test the significance of the model with $\alpha = .05$.
c. Predict the total points earned by Mark Sweeney. He spent 95 hours studying.
d. Develop a 95% prediction interval for the total points earned by Mark Sweeney.

66. *Bloomberg Personal Finance* (July/August 2001) reported the market beta for Texas Instruments was 1.46. Market betas for individual stocks are determined by simple linear regression. For each stock, the dependent variable is its quarterly percentage return (capital appreciation plus dividends) minus the percentage return that could be obtained from a risk-free investment (the Treasury Bill rate is used as the risk-free rate). The independent variable is the quarterly percentage return (capital appreciation plus dividends) for the stock market (S&P 500) minus the percentage return from a risk-free investment. An estimated regression equation is developed with quarterly data; the market beta for the stock is the slope of the estimated regression equation (b_1). The value of the market beta is often interpreted as a measure of the risk associated with the stock. Market betas greater than 1 indicate that the stock is more volatile than the market average; market betas less than 1 indicate that the stock is less volatile than the market average. Suppose that the following figures are the differences between the percentage return and the risk-free return for 10 quarters for the S&P 500 and Horizon Technology.

CD file
MktBeta

S&P 500	Horizon
1.2	−0.7
−2.5	−2.0
−3.0	−5.5
2.0	4.7
5.0	1.8
1.2	4.1
3.0	2.6
−1.0	2.0
.5	−1.3
2.5	5.5

a. Develop an estimated regression equation that can be used to determine the market beta for Horizon Technology. What is Horizon Technology's market beta?
b. Test for a significant relationship at the .05 level of significance.
c. Did the estimated regression equation provide a good fit? Explain.
d. Use the market betas of Texas Instruments and Horizon Technology to compare the risk associated with the two stocks.

67. The Transactional Records Access Clearinghouse at Syracuse University reported data showing the odds of an Internal Revenue Service audit. The following table shows the average adjusted gross income reported and the percent of the returns that were audited for 20 selected IRS districts.

CD file
IRSAudit

District	Adjusted Gross Income ($)	Percent Audited
Los Angeles	36,664	1.3
Sacramento	38,845	1.1
Atlanta	34,886	1.1
Boise	32,512	1.1
Dallas	34,531	1.0
Providence	35,995	1.0
San Jose	37,799	0.9
Cheyenne	33,876	0.9
Fargo	30,513	0.9
New Orleans	30,174	0.9
Oklahoma City	30,060	0.8
Houston	37,153	0.8
Portland	34,918	0.7
Phoenix	33,291	0.7
Augusta	31,504	0.7
Albuquerque	29,199	0.6
Greensboro	33,072	0.6
Columbia	30,859	0.5
Nashville	32,566	0.5
Buffalo	34,296	0.5

a. Develop the estimated regression equation that could be used to predict the percent audited given the average adjusted gross income reported.
b. At the .05 level of significance, determine whether the adjusted gross income and the percent audited are related.
c. Did the estimated regression equation provide a good fit? Explain.
d. Use the estimated regression equation developed in part (a) to calculate a 95% confidence interval for the expected percent audited for districts with an average adjusted gross income of $35,000.

68. The Australian Public Service Commission's State of the Service Report 2002–2003 reported job satisfaction ratings for employees. One of the survey questions asked employees to choose the five most important workplace factors (from a list of factors) that most affected how satisfied they were with their job. Respondents were then asked to indicate their level of satisfaction with their top five factors. The following data show the percentage of employees who nominated the factor in their top five, and a corresponding satisfaction rating measured using the percentage of employees who nominated the factor in the top five and who were "very satisfied" or "satisfied" with the factor in their current workplace (www.apsc.gov.au/stateoftheservice).

CD file
JobSat

Workplace Factor	Top Five (%)	Satisfaction Rating (%)
Appropriate workload	30	49
Chance to be creative/innovative	38	64
Chance to make a useful contribution to society	40	67
Duties/expectations made clear	40	69
Flexible working arrangements	55	86
Good working relationships	60	85
Interesting work provided	48	74
Opportunities for career development	33	43
Opportunities to develop my skills	46	66
Opportunities to utilize my skills	50	70
Regular feedback/recognition for effort	42	53
Salary	47	62
Seeing tangible results from my work	42	69

a. Develop a scatter diagram with Top Five (%) on the horizontal axis and Satisfaction Rating (%) on the vertical axis.
b. What does the scatter diagram developed in part (a) indicate about the relationship between the two variables?
c. Develop the estimated regression equation that could be used to predict the Satisfaction Rating (%) given the Top Five (%).
d. Test for a significant relationship at the .05 level of significance.
e. Did the estimated regression equation provide a good fit? Explain.
f. What is the value of the sample correlation coefficient?

Case Problem 1 Measuring Stock Market Risk

One measure of the risk or volatility of an individual stock is the standard deviation of the total return (capital appreciation plus dividends) over several periods of time. Although the standard deviation is easy to compute, it does not take into account the extent to which the price of a given stock varies as a function of a standard market index, such as the S&P 500. As a result, many financial analysts prefer to use another measure of risk referred to as *beta*.

CD file
Beta

Betas for individual stocks are determined by simple linear regression. The dependent variable is the total return for the stock and the independent variable is the total return for the stock market.* For this case problem we will use the S&P 500 index as the measure of the total return for the stock market, and an estimated regression equation will be developed using monthly data. The beta for the stock is the slope of the estimated regression equation (b_1). The data file Beta on the CD accompanying the text provides the total return (capital appreciation plus dividends) over 36 months for eight widely traded common stocks and the S&P 500.

The value of beta for the stock market will always be 1; thus, stocks that tend to rise and fall with the stock market will also have a beta close to 1. Betas greater than 1 indicate that the stock is more volatile than the market, and betas less than 1 indicate that the stock is less volatile than the market. For instance, if a stock has a beta of 1.4, it is 40% *more* volatile than the market, and if a stock has a beta of .4, it is 60% *less* volatile than the market.

*Various sources use different approaches for computing betas. For instance, some sources subtract the return that could be obtained from a risk-free investment (e.g., T-bills) from the dependent variable and the independent variable before computing the estimated regression equation. Some also use different indexes for the total return of the stock market; for instance, *Value Line* computes betas using the New York Stock Exchange composite index.

Managerial Report

You have been assigned to analyze the risk characteristics of these stocks. Prepare a report that includes but is not limited to the following items.

a. Compute descriptive statistics for each stock and the S&P 500. Comment on your results. Which stocks are the most volatile?

b. Compute the value of beta for each stock. Which of these stocks would you expect to perform best in an up market? Which would you expect to hold their value best in a down market?

c. Comment on how much of the return for the individual stocks is explained by the market.

Case Problem 2 U.S. Department of Transportation

As part of a study on transportation safety, the U.S. Department of Transportation collected data on the number of fatal accidents per 1000 licenses and the percentage of licensed drivers under the age of 21 in a sample of 42 cities. Data collected over a one-year period follow. These data are available on the CD accompanying the text in the file named Safety.

CD file

Safety

Percent Under 21	Fatal Accidents per 1000 Licenses	Percent Under 21	Fatal Accidents per 1000 Licenses
13	2.962	17	4.100
12	0.708	8	2.190
8	0.885	16	3.623
12	1.652	15	2.623
11	2.091	9	0.835
17	2.627	8	0.820
18	3.830	14	2.890
8	0.368	8	1.267
13	1.142	15	3.224
8	0.645	10	1.014
9	1.028	10	0.493
16	2.801	14	1.443
12	1.405	18	3.614
9	1.433	10	1.926
10	0.039	14	1.643
9	0.338	16	2.943
11	1.849	12	1.913
12	2.246	15	2.814
14	2.855	13	2.634
14	2.352	9	0.926
11	1.294	17	3.256

Managerial Report

1. Develop numerical and graphical summaries of the data.
2. Use regression analysis to investigate the relationship between the number of fatal accidents and the percentage of drivers under the age of 21. Discuss your findings.
3. What conclusion and recommendations can you derive from your analysis?

Case Problem 3 Alumni Giving

Alumni donations are an important source of revenue for colleges and universities. If administrators could determine the factors that influence increases in the percentage of alumni who make a donation, they might be able to implement policies that could lead to increased revenues. Research shows that students who are more satisfied with their contact with teachers are more likely to graduate. As a result, one might suspect that smaller class sizes and lower student-faculty ratios might lead to a higher percentage of satisfied graduates, which in turn might lead to increases in the percentage of alumni who make a donation. Table 14.13 shows data for 48 national universities (*America's Best Colleges,* Year 2000 Edition). The column labeled % of Classes Under 20 shows the percentage of classes offered with fewer than 20 students. The column labeled Student/Faculty Ratio is the number of students enrolled divided by the total number of faculty. Finally, the column labeled Alumni Giving Rate is the percentage of alumni that made a donation to the university.

Managerial Report

1. Develop numerical and graphical summaries of the data.
2. Use regression analysis to develop an estimated regression equation that could be used to predict the alumni giving rate given the percentage of classes with fewer than 20 students.
3. Use regression analysis to develop an estimated regression equation that could be used to predict the alumni giving rate given the student-faculty ratio.
4. Which of the two estimated regression equations provides the best fit? For this estimated regression equation, perform an analysis of the residuals and discuss your findings and conclusions.
5. What conclusions and recommendations can you derive from your analysis?

Case Problem 4 Major League Baseball Team Values

A group led by John Henry paid $700 million to purchase the Boston Red Sox in 2002, even though the Red Sox had not won the World Series since 1918 and posted an operating loss of $11.4 million for 2001. Moreover, *Forbes* magazine estimates that the current value of the team is actually $426 million. *Forbes* attributes the difference between the current value for a team and the price investors are willing to pay to the fact that the purchase of a team often includes the acquisition of a grossly undervalued cable network. For instance, in purchasing the Boston Red Sox, the new owners also got an 80% interest in the New England Sports Network. Table 14.14 shows data for the 30 major league teams (*Forbes,* April 15, 2002). The column labeled Value contains the values of the teams based on current stadium deals, without deduction for debt. The column labeled Income indicates the earnings before interest, taxes, and depreciation.

Managerial Report

1. Develop numerical and graphical summaries of the data.
2. Use regression analysis to investigate the relationship between value and income. Discuss your findings.
3. Use regression analysis to investigate the relationship between value and revenue. Discuss your findings.
4. What conclusions and recommendations can you derive from your analysis?

CD file
Alumni

TABLE 14.13 DATA FOR 48 NATIONAL UNIVERSITIES

	% of Classes Under 20	Student/Faculty Ratio	Alumni Giving Rate
Boston College	39	13	25
Brandeis University	68	8	33
Brown University	60	8	40
California Institute of Technology	65	3	46
Carnegie Mellon University	67	10	28
Case Western Reserve Univ.	52	8	31
College of William and Mary	45	12	27
Columbia University	69	7	31
Cornell University	72	13	35
Dartmouth College	61	10	53
Duke University	68	8	45
Emory University	65	7	37
Georgetown University	54	10	29
Harvard University	73	8	46
Johns Hopkins University	64	9	27
Lehigh University	55	11	40
Massachusetts Inst. of Technology	65	6	44
New York University	63	13	13
Northwestern University	66	8	30
Pennsylvania State Univ.	32	19	21
Princeton University	68	5	67
Rice University	62	8	40
Stanford University	69	7	34
Tufts University	67	9	29
Tulane University	56	12	17
U. of California–Berkeley	58	17	18
U. of California–Davis	32	19	7
U. of California–Irvine	42	20	9
U. of California–Los Angeles	41	18	13
U. of California–San Diego	48	19	8
U. of California–Santa Barbara	45	20	12
U. of Chicago	65	4	36
U. of Florida	31	23	19
U. of Illinois–Urbana Champaign	29	15	23
U. of Michigan–Ann Arbor	51	15	13
U. of North Carolina–Chapel Hill	40	16	26
U. of Notre Dame	53	13	49
U. of Pennsylvania	65	7	41
U. of Rochester	63	10	23
U. of Southern California	53	13	22
U. of Texas–Austin	39	21	13
U. of Virginia	44	13	28
U. of Washington	37	12	12
U. of Wisconsin–Madison	37	13	13
Vanderbilt University	68	9	31
Wake Forest University	59	11	38
Washington University–St. Louis	73	7	33
Yale University	77	7	50

TABLE 14.14 DATA FOR MAJOR LEAGUE BASEBALL TEAMS

CD file
MLB

Team	Value	Revenue	Income
New York Yankees	730	215	18.7
New York Mets	482	169	14.3
Los Angeles Dodgers	435	143	−29.6
Boston Red Sox	426	152	−11.4
Atlanta Braves	424	160	9.5
Seattle Mariners	373	166	14.1
Cleveland Indians	360	150	−3.6
Texas Rangers	356	134	−6.5
San Francisco Giants	355	142	16.8
Colorado Rockies	347	129	6.7
Houston Astros	337	125	4.1
Baltimore Orioles	319	133	3.2
Chicago Cubs	287	131	7.9
Arizona Diamondbacks	280	127	−3.9
St. Louis Cardinals	271	123	−5.1
Detroit Tigers	262	114	12.3
Pittsburgh Pirates	242	108	9.5
Milwaukee Brewers	238	108	18.8
Philadelphia Phillies	231	94	2.6
Chicago White Sox	223	101	−3.8
San Diego Padres	207	92	5.7
Cincinnati Reds	204	87	4.3
Anaheim Angels	195	103	5.7
Toronto Blue Jays	182	91	−20.6
Oakland Athletics	157	90	6.8
Kansas City Royals	152	85	2.2
Tampa Bay Devil Rays	142	92	−6.1
Florida Marlins	137	81	1.4
Minnesota Twins	127	75	3.6
Montreal Expos	108	63	−3.4

Appendix 14.1 Calculus-Based Derivation of Least Squares Formulas

As mentioned in the chapter, the least squares method is a procedure for determining the values of b_0 and b_1 that minimize the sum of squared residuals. The sum of squared residuals is given by

$$\Sigma(y_i - \hat{y}_i)^2$$

Substituting $\hat{y}_i = b_0 + b_1x_i$, we get

$$\Sigma(y_i - b_0 - b_1x_i)^2 \tag{14.34}$$

as the expression that must be minimized.

To minimize expression (14.34), we must take the partial derivatives with respect to b_0 and b_1, set them equal to zero, and solve. Doing so, we get

$$\frac{\partial \Sigma(y_i - b_0 - b_1x_i)^2}{\partial b_0} = -2\Sigma(y_i - b_0 - b_1x_i) = 0 \tag{14.35}$$

$$\frac{\partial \Sigma(y_i - b_0 - b_1x_i)^2}{\partial b_1} = -2\Sigma x_i(y_i - b_0 - b_1x_i) = 0 \tag{14.36}$$

Dividing equation (14.35) by two and summing each term individually yields

$$-\Sigma y_i + \Sigma b_0 + \Sigma b_1x_i = 0$$

Bringing Σy_i to the other side of the equal sign and noting that $\Sigma b_0 = nb_0$, we obtain

$$nb_0 + (\Sigma x_i)b_1 = \Sigma y_i \tag{14.37}$$

Similar algebraic simplification applied to equation (14.36) yields

$$(\Sigma x_i)b_0 + (\Sigma x_i^2)b_1 = \Sigma x_iy_i \tag{14.38}$$

Equations (14.37) and (14.38) are known as the *normal equations*. Solving equation (14.37) for b_0 yields

$$b_0 = \frac{\Sigma y_i}{n} - b_1\frac{\Sigma x_i}{n} \tag{14.39}$$

Using equation (14.39) to substitute for b_0 in equation (14.38) provides

$$\frac{\Sigma x_i \Sigma y_i}{n} - \frac{(\Sigma x_i)^2}{n}b_1 + (\Sigma x_i^2)b_1 = \Sigma x_iy_i \tag{14.40}$$

By rearranging the terms in equation (14.40), we obtain

$$b_1 = \frac{\Sigma x_iy_i - (\Sigma x_i \Sigma y_i)/n}{\Sigma x_i^2 - (\Sigma x_i)^2/n} = \frac{\Sigma(x_i - \bar{x})(y_i - \bar{y})}{\Sigma(x_i - \bar{x})^2} \tag{14.41}$$

Because $\bar{y} = \Sigma y_i/n$ and $\bar{x} = \Sigma x_i/n$, we can rewrite equation (14.39) as

$$b_0 = \bar{y} - b_1\bar{x} \tag{14.42}$$

Equations (14.41) and (14.42) are the formulas (14.6) and (14.7) we used in the chapter to compute the coefficients in the estimated regression equation.

Appendix 14.2 A Test for Significance Using Correlation

Using the sample correlation coefficient r_{xy}, we can determine whether the linear relationship between x and y is significant by testing the following hypotheses about the population correlation coefficient ρ_{xy}.

$$H_0\text{: } \rho_{xy} = 0$$
$$H_a\text{: } \rho_{xy} \neq 0$$

If H_0 is rejected, we can conclude that the population correlation coefficient is not equal to zero and that the linear relationship between the two variables is significant. This test for significance follows.

A TEST FOR SIGNIFICANCE USING CORRELATION

$$H_0\colon \rho_{xy} = 0$$
$$H_a\colon \rho_{xy} \neq 0$$

TEST STATISTIC

$$t = r_{xy}\sqrt{\frac{n-2}{1-r_{xy}^2}} \tag{14.43}$$

REJECTION RULE

p-value approach: Reject H_0 if p-value $\leq \alpha$
Critical value approach: Reject H_0 if $t \leq -t_{\alpha/2}$ or if $t \geq t_{\alpha/2}$

where $t_{\alpha/2}$ is based on a t distribution with $n - 2$ degrees of freedom.

In Section 14.4, we found that the sample with $n = 10$ provided the sample correlation coefficient for student population and quarterly sales of $r_{xy} = .9501$. The test statistic is

$$t = r_{xy}\sqrt{\frac{n-2}{1-r_{xy}^2}} = .9501\sqrt{\frac{10-2}{1-(.9501)^2}} = 8.61$$

The t distribution table shows that with $n - 2 = 10 - 2 = 8$ degrees of freedom, $t = 3.355$ provides an area of .005 in the upper tail. Thus, the area in the upper tail of the t distribution corresponding to the test statistic $t = 8.61$ must be less than .005. Because this test is a two-tailed test, we double this value to conclude that the p-value associated with $t = 8.62$ must be less than $2(.005) = .01$. Excel or Minitab show the p-value $= .000$. Because the p-value is less than $\alpha = .01$, we reject H_0 and conclude that ρ_{xy} is not equal to zero. This evidence is sufficient to conclude that a significant linear relationship exists between student population and quarterly sales.

Note that the test statistic t and the conclusion of a significant relationship are identical to the results obtained in Section 14.5 for the t test conducted using Armand's estimated regression equation $\hat{y} = 60 + 5x$. Performing regression analysis provides the conclusion of a significant relationship between x and y and in addition provides the equation showing how the variables are related. Most analysts therefore use modern computer packages to perform regression analysis and find that using correlation as a test of significance is unnecessary.

Appendix 14.3 Regression Analysis with Minitab

CD file
Armand's

In Section 14.7 we discussed the computer solution of regression problems by showing Minitab's output for the Armand's Pizza Parlors problem. In this appendix, we describe the steps required to generate the Minitab computer solution. First, the data must be entered in a Minitab worksheet. Student population data are entered in column C1 and quarterly sales data are entered in column C2. The variable names Pop and Sales are entered as the column headings on the worksheet. In subsequent steps, we refer to the data by using the variable names Pop and Sales or the column indicators C1 and C2. The following steps describe how to use Minitab to produce the regression results shown in Figure 14.10.

Step 1. Select the **Stat** menu
Step 2. Select the **Regression** menu
Step 3. Choose **Regression**
Step 4. When the Regression dialog box appears:
Enter Sales in the **Response** box
Enter Pop in the **Predictors** box
Click the **Options** button
When the Regression-Options dialog box appears:
Enter 10 in the **Prediction intervals for new observations** box
Click **OK**
When the Regression dialog box reappears:
Click **OK**

The Minitab regression dialog box provides additional capabilities that can be obtained by selecting the desired options. For instance, to obtain a residual plot that shows the predicted value of the dependent variable $\hat{y}$ on the horizontal axis and the standardized residual values on the vertical axis, step 4 would be as follows:

Step 4. When the Regression dialog box appears:
Enter Sales in the **Response** box
Enter Pop in the **Predictors** box
Click the **Graphs** button
When the Regression-Graphs dialog box appears:
Select **Standardized** under Residuals for Plots
Select **Residuals versus fits** under Residual Plots
Click **OK**
When the Regression dialog box reappears:
Click **OK**

Appendix 14.4 Regression Analysis with Excel

CD file
Armand's

In this appendix we will illustrate how Excel's Regression tool can be used to perform the regression analysis computations for the Armand's Pizza Parlors problem. Refer to Figure 14.23 as we describe the steps involved. The labels Restaurant, Population, and Sales are entered into cells A1:C1 of the worksheet. To identify each of the 10 observations, we entered the numbers 1 through 10 into cells A2:A11. The sample data are entered into cells B2:C11. The following steps describe how to use Excel to produce the regression results.

Step 1. Select the **Tools** menu
Step 2. Choose **Data Analysis**
Step 3. Choose **Regression** from the list of Analysis Tools
Step 4. Click **OK**
Step 5. When the Regression dialog box appears:
Enter C1:C11 in the **Input Y Range** box
Enter B1:B11 in the **Input X Range** box
Select **Labels**
Select **Confidence Level**
Enter 99 in the **Confidence Level** box
Select **Output Range**
Enter A13 in the **Output Range** box
(Any upper-left-hand corner cell indicating where the output is to begin may be entered here.)
Click **OK**

FIGURE 14.23 EXCEL SOLUTION TO THE ARMAND'S PIZZA PARLORS PROBLEM

	A	B	C	D	E	F	G	H	I	J
1	**Restaurant**	**Population**	**Sales**							
2	1	2	58							
3	2	6	105							
4	3	8	88							
5	4	8	118							
6	5	12	117							
7	6	16	137							
8	7	20	157							
9	8	20	169							
10	9	22	149							
11	10	26	202							
12										
13	SUMMARY OUTPUT									
14										
15	*Regression Statistics*									
16	Multiple R	0.9501								
17	R Square	0.9027								
18	Adjusted R Square	0.8906								
19	Standard Error	13.8293								
20	Observations	10								
21										
22	ANOVA									
23		*df*	*SS*	*MS*	*F*	*Significance F*				
24	Regression	1	14200	14200	74.2484	2.55E-05				
25	Residual	8	1530	191.25						
26	Total	9	15730							
27										
28		*Coefficients*	*Standard Error*	*t Stat*	*P-value*	*Lower 95%*	*Upper 95%*	*Lower 99.0%*	*Upper 99.0%*	
29	Intercept	60	9.2260	6.5033	0.0002	38.7247	81.2753	29.0431	90.9569	
30	Population	5	0.5803	8.6167	2.55E-05	3.6619	6.3381	3.0530	6.9470	
31										
32										
33										
34										

The first section of the output, titled *Regression Statistics,* contains summary statistics such as the coefficient of determination (R Square). The second section of the output, titled ANOVA, contains the analysis of variance table. The last section of the output, which is not titled, contains the estimated regression coefficients and related information. We will begin our discussion of the interpretation of the regression output with the information contained in cells A28:I30.

Interpretation of Estimated Regression Equation Output

The y intercept of the estimated regression line, $b_0 = 60$, is shown in cell B29, and the slope of the estimated regression line, $b_1 = 5$, is shown in cell B30. The label Intercept in cell A29 and the label Population in cell A30 are used to identify these two values.

In Section 14.5 we showed that the estimated standard deviation of b_1 is $s_{b_1} = .5803$. Note that the value in cell C30 is .5803. The label Standard Error in cell C28 is Excel's way of indicating that the value in cell C30 is the standard error, or standard deviation, of b_1. Recall that the t test for a significant relationship required the computation of the t statistic, $t = b_1/s_{b_1}$. For the Armand's data, the value of t that we computed was $t = 5/.5803 = 8.62$. The label in cell D28, *t Stat,* reminds us that cell D30 contains the value of the t test statistic.

The value in cell E30 is the p-value associated with the t test for significance. Excel has displayed the p-value in cell E30 using scientific notation. To obtain the decimal value, we move the decimal point 5 places to the left, obtaining a value of .0000255. Because the p-value $= .0000255 < \alpha = .01$, we can reject H_0 and conclude that we have a significant relationship between student population and quarterly sales.

The information in cells F28:I30 can be used to develop confidence interval estimates of the y intercept and slope of the estimated regression equation. Excel always provides the lower and upper limits for a 95% confidence interval. Recall that in step 4 we selected Confidence Level and entered 99 in the Confidence Level box. As a result, Excel's Regression tool also provides the lower and upper limits for a 99% confidence interval. The value in cell H30 is the lower limit for the 99% confidence interval estimate of β_1 and the value in cell I30 is the upper limit. Thus, after rounding, the 99% confidence interval estimate of β_1 is 3.05 to 6.95. The values in cells F30 and G30 provide the lower and upper limits for the 95% confidence interval. Thus, the 95% confidence interval is 3.66 to 6.34.

Interpretation of ANOVA Output

The information in cells A22:F26 is a summary of the analysis of variance computations. The three sources of variation are labeled Regression, Residual, and Total. The label *df* in cell B23 stands for degrees of freedom, the label *SS* in cell C23 stands for sum of squares, and the label *MS* in cell D23 stands for mean square.

In Section 14.5 we stated that the mean square error, obtained by dividing the error or residual sum of squares by its degrees of freedom, provides an estimate of σ^2. The value in cell D25, 191.25, is the mean square error for the Armand's regression output. In Section 14.5 we showed that an F test could also be used to test for significance in regression. The value in cell F24, .0000255, is the p-value associated with the F test for significance. Because the p-value $= .0000255 < \alpha = .01$, we can reject H_0 and conclude that we have a significant relationship between student population and quarterly sales. The label Excel uses to identify the p-value for the F test for significance, shown in cell F23, is *Significance F.*

The label Significance F may be more meaningful if you think of the value in cell F24 as the observed level of significance for the F test.

Interpretation of Regression Statistics Output

The coefficient of determination, .9027, appears in cell B17; the corresponding label, R Square, is shown in cell A17. The square root of the coefficient of determination provides the sample correlation coefficient of .9501 shown in cell B16. Note that Excel uses the label Multiple R (cell A16) to identify this value. In cell A19, the label Standard Error is used to identify the value of the standard error of the estimate shown in cell B19. Thus, the standard error of the estimate is 13.8293. We caution the reader to keep in mind that in the Excel output, the label Standard Error appears in two different places. In the Regression Statistics section of the output, the label Standard Error refers to the estimate of σ. In the Estimated Regression Equation section of the output, the label *Standard Error* refers to s_{b_1} the standard deviation of the sampling distribution of b_1.

CHAPTER 15

Multiple Regression

CONTENTS

STATISTICS *in* PRACTICE

INTERNATIONAL PAPER*
PURCHASE, NEW YORK

International Paper is the world's largest paper and forest products company. The company employs more than 117,000 people in its operations in nearly 50 countries, and exports its products to more than 130 nations. International Paper produces building materials such as lumber and plywood; consumer packaging materials such as disposable cups and containers; industrial packaging materials such as corrugated boxes and shipping containers; and a variety of papers for use in photocopiers, printers, books, and advertising materials.

To make paper products, pulp mills process wood chips and chemicals to produce wood pulp. The wood pulp is then used at a paper mill to produce paper products. In the production of white paper products, the pulp must be bleached to remove any discoloration. A key bleaching agent used in the process is chlorine dioxide, which, because of its combustible nature, is usually produced at a pulp mill facility and then piped in solution form into the bleaching tower of the pulp mill. To improve one of the processes used to produce chlorine dioxide, researchers studied the process's control and efficiency. One aspect of the study looked at the chemical-feed rate for chlorine dioxide production.

To produce the chlorine dioxide, four chemicals flow at metered rates into the chlorine dioxide generator. The chlorine dioxide produced in the generator flows to an absorber where chilled water absorbs the chlorine dioxide gas to form a chlorine dioxide solution. The solution is then piped into the paper mill. A key part of controlling the process involves the chemical-feed rates. Historically, experienced operators set the chemical-feed rates, but this approach led to overcontrol by the operators. Consequently, chemical engineers at the mill requested that a set of control equations, one for each chemical feed, be developed to aid the operators in setting the rates.

Multiple regression analysis assisted in the development of a better bleaching process for making white paper products. © Lester Lefkowitz/Corbis.

Using multiple regression analysis, statistical analysts developed an estimated multiple regression equation for each of the four chemicals used in the process. Each equation related the production of chlorine dioxide to the amount of chemical used and the concentration level of the chlorine dioxide solution. The resulting set of four equations was programmed into a microcomputer at each mill. In the new system, operators enter the concentration of the chlorine dioxide solution and the desired production rate; the computer software then calculates the chemical feed needed to achieve the desired production rate. After the operators began using the control equations, the chlorine dioxide generator efficiency increased, and the number of times the concentrations fell within acceptable ranges increased significantly.

This example shows how multiple regression analysis can be used to develop a better bleaching process for producing white paper products. In this chapter we will discuss how computer software packages are used for such purposes. Most of the concepts introduced in Chapter 14 for simple linear regression can be directly extended to the multiple regression case.

*The authors are indebted to Marian Williams and Bill Griggs for providing this Statistics in Practice. This application was originally developed at Champion International Corporation, which became part of International Paper in 2000.

In Chapter 14 we presented simple linear regression and demonstrated its use in developing an estimated regression equation that describes the relationship between two variables. Recall that the variable being predicted or explained is called the dependent variable and the variable being used to predict or explain the dependent variable is called the independent variable. In this chapter we continue our study of regression analysis by considering situations involving two or more independent variables. This subject area, called **multiple regression analysis**, enables us to consider more factors and thus obtain better estimates than are possible with simple linear regression.

15.1 Multiple Regression Model

Multiple regression analysis is the study of how a dependent variable y is related to two or more independent variables. In the general case, we will use p to denote the number of independent variables.

Regression Model and Regression Equation

The concepts of a regression model and a regression equation introduced in the preceding chapter are applicable in the multiple regression case. The equation that describes how the dependent variable y is related to the independent variables $x_1, x_2, \ldots, x_p$ and an error term is called the **multiple regression model**. We begin with the assumption that the multiple regression model takes the following form.

MULTIPLE REGRESSION MODEL

$$y = \beta_0 + \beta_1 x_1 + \beta_2 x_2 + \cdots + \beta_p x_p + \epsilon \quad \textbf{(15.1)}$$

In the multiple regression model, $\beta_0, \beta_1, \beta_2, \ldots, \beta_p$ are the parameters and the error term ϵ (the Greek letter epsilon) is a random variable. A close examination of this model reveals that y is a linear function of $x_1, x_2, \ldots, x_p$ (the $\beta_0 + \beta_1 x_1 + \beta_2 x_2 + \cdots + \beta_p x_p$ part) plus the error term ϵ. The error term accounts for the variability in y that cannot be explained by the linear effect of the p independent variables.

In Section 15.4 we will discuss the assumptions for the multiple regression model and ϵ. One of the assumptions is that the mean or expected value of ϵ is zero. A consequence of this assumption is that the mean or expected value of y, denoted $E(y)$, is equal to $\beta_0 + \beta_1 x_1 + \beta_2 x_2 + \cdots + \beta_p x_p$. The equation that describes how the mean value of y is related to $x_1, x_2, \ldots, x_p$ is called the **multiple regression equation**.

MULTIPLE REGRESSION EQUATION

$$E(y) = \beta_0 + \beta_1 x_1 + \beta_2 x_2 + \cdots + \beta_p x_p \quad \textbf{(15.2)}$$

Estimated Multiple Regression Equation

If the values of $\beta_0, \beta_1, \beta_2, \ldots, \beta_p$ were known, equation (15.2) could be used to compute the mean value of y at given values of $x_1, x_2, \ldots, x_p$. Unfortunately, these parameter values will not, in general, be known and must be estimated from sample data. A simple random sample is used to compute sample statistics $b_0, b_1, b_2, \ldots, b_p$ that are used as the point estimators of the parameters $\beta_0, \beta_1, \beta_2, \ldots, \beta_p$. These sample statistics provide the following **estimated multiple regression equation**.

ESTIMATED MULTIPLE REGRESSION EQUATION

$$\hat{y} = b_0 + b_1x_1 + b_2x_2 + \cdots + b_px_p \tag{15.3}$$

where

$b_0, b_1, b_2, \ldots, b_p$ are the estimates of $\beta_0, \beta_1, \beta_2, \ldots, \beta_p$
$\hat{y}$ = estimated value of the dependent variable

The estimation process for multiple regression is shown in Figure 15.1.

15.2 Least Squares Method

In Chapter 14, we used the **least squares method** to develop the estimated regression equation that best approximated the straight-line relationship between the dependent and independent variables. This same approach is used to develop the estimated multiple regression equation. The least squares criterion is restated as follows.

LEAST SQUARES CRITERION

$$\min \Sigma(y_i - \hat{y}_i)^2 \tag{15.4}$$

In simple linear regression, b_0 and b_1 were the sample statistics used to estimate the parameters β_0 and β_1. Multiple regression parallels this statistical inference process, with b_0, b_1, b_2, . . . b_p denoting the sample statistics used to estimate the parameters $\beta_0, \beta_1, \beta_2, \ldots, \beta_p$.

FIGURE 15.1 THE ESTIMATION PROCESS FOR MULTIPLE REGRESSION

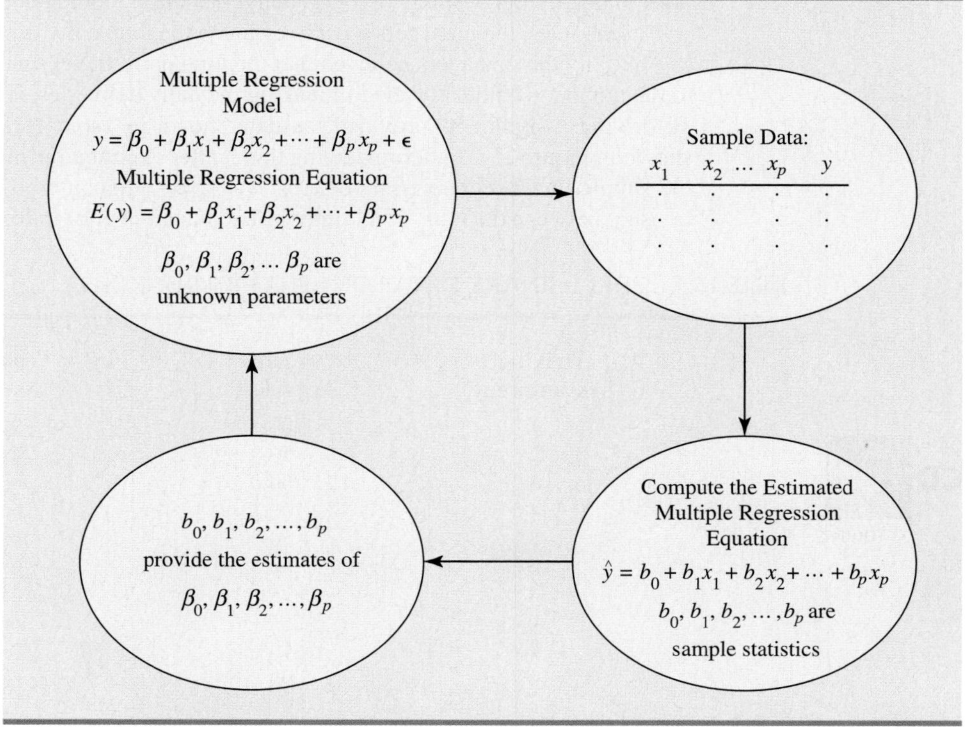

where

y_i = observed value of the dependent variable for the ith observation
$\hat{y}_i$ = estimated value of the dependent variable for the ith observation

The estimated values of the dependent variable are computed by using the estimated multiple regression equation,

$$\hat{y} = b_0 + b_1x_1 + b_2x_2 + \cdots + b_px_p$$

As expression (15.4) shows, the least squares method uses sample data to provide the values of $b_0, b_1, b_2, \ldots, b_p$ that make the sum of squared residuals [the deviations between the observed values of the dependent variable (y_i) and the estimated values of the dependent variable ($\hat{y}_i$)] a minimum.

In Chapter 14 we presented formulas for computing the least squares estimators b_0 and b_1 for the estimated simple linear regression equation $\hat{y} = b_0 + b_1x$. With relatively small data sets, we were able to use those formulas to compute b_0 and b_1 by manual calculations. In multiple regression, however, the presentation of the formulas for the regression coefficients $b_0, b_1, b_2, \ldots, b_p$ involves the use of matrix algebra and is beyond the scope of this text. Therefore, in presenting multiple regression, we focus on how computer software packages can be used to obtain the estimated regression equation and other information. The emphasis will be on how to interpret the computer output rather than on how to make the multiple regression computations.

An Example: Butler Trucking Company

As an illustration of multiple regression analysis, we will consider a problem faced by the Butler Trucking Company, an independent trucking company in southern California. A major portion of Butler's business involves deliveries throughout its local area. To develop better work schedules, the managers want to estimate the total daily travel time for their drivers.

Initially the managers believed that the total daily travel time would be closely related to the number of miles traveled in making the daily deliveries. A simple random sample of 10 driving assignments provided the data shown in Table 15.1 and the scatter diagram shown in Figure 15.2. After reviewing this scatter diagram, the managers hypothesized that the simple linear regression model $y = \beta_0 + \beta_1x_1 + \epsilon$ could be used to describe the relationship between the total travel time (y) and the number of miles traveled (x_1). To estimate

TABLE 15.1 PRELIMINARY DATA FOR BUTLER TRUCKING

CD file
Butler

Driving Assignment	x_1 = Miles Traveled	y = Travel Time (hours)
1	100	9.3
2	50	4.8
3	100	8.9
4	100	6.5
5	50	4.2
6	80	6.2
7	75	7.4
8	65	6.0
9	90	7.6
10	90	6.1

FIGURE 15.2 SCATTER DIAGRAM OF PRELIMINARY DATA FOR BUTLER TRUCKING

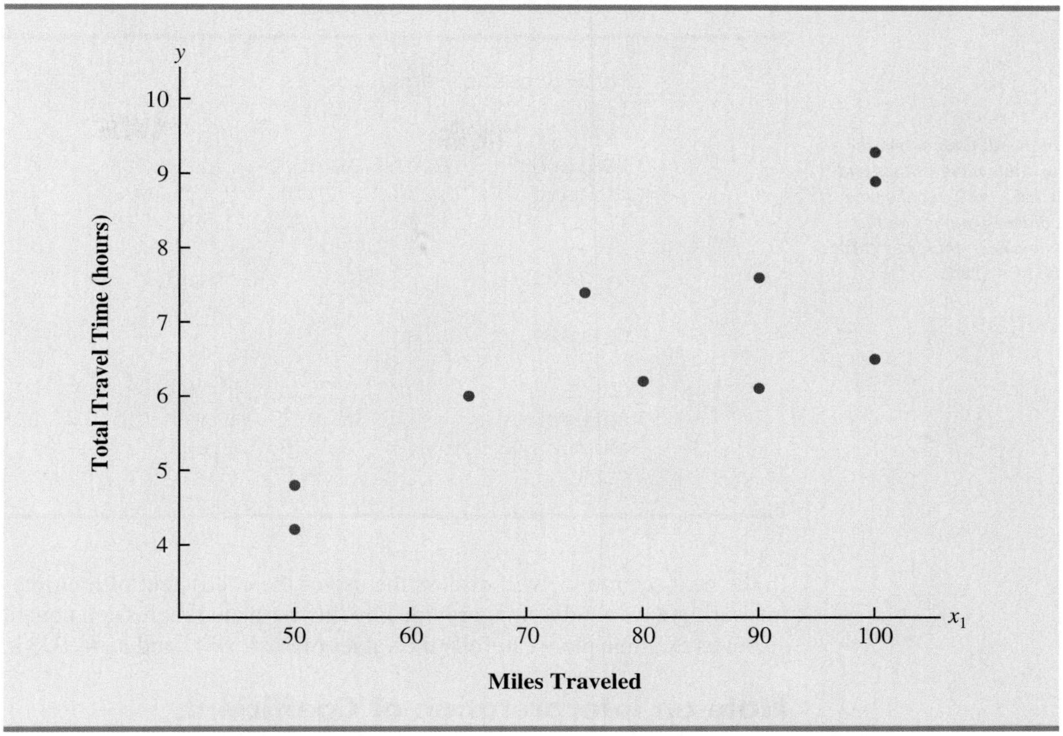

the parameters β_0 and β_1, the least squares method was used to develop the estimated regression equation.

$$\hat{y} = b_0 + b_1x_1 \tag{15.5}$$

In Figure 15.3, we show the Minitab computer output from applying simple linear regression to the data in Table 15.1. The estimated regression equation is

$$\hat{y} = 1.27 + .0678x_1$$

At the .05 level of significance, the F value of 15.81 and its corresponding p-value of .004 indicate that the relationship is significant; that is, we can reject H_0: $\beta_1 = 0$ because the p-value is less than $\alpha = .05$. Note that the same conclusion is obtained from the t value of 3.98 and its associated p-value of .004. Thus, we can conclude that the relationship between the total travel time and the number of miles traveled is significant; longer travel times are associated with more miles traveled. With a coefficient of determination (expressed as a percentage) of R-sq $= 66.4\%$, we see that 66.4% of the variability in travel time can be explained by the linear effect of the number of miles traveled. This finding is fairly good, but the managers might want to consider adding a second independent variable to explain some of the remaining variability in the dependent variable.

In attempting to identify another independent variable, the managers felt that the number of deliveries could also contribute to the total travel time. The Butler Trucking data, with the number of deliveries added, are shown in Table 15.2. The Minitab computer solution with both miles traveled (x_1) and number of deliveries (x_2) as independent variables is shown in Figure 15.4. The estimated regression equation is

$$\hat{y} = -.869 + .0611x_1 + .923x_2 \tag{15.6}$$

FIGURE 15.3 MINITAB OUTPUT FOR BUTLER TRUCKING WITH ONE INDEPENDENT VARIABLE

```
The regression equation is
Time = 1.27 + 0.0678 Miles

Predictor      Coef   SE Coef     T      p
Constant      1.274     1.401  0.91  0.390
Miles       0.06783   0.01706  3.98  0.004

S = 1.002   R-sq = 66.4%   R-sq(adj) = 62.2%

Analysis of Variance

SOURCE          DF      SS      MS      F      p
Regression       1  15.871  15.871  15.81  0.004
Residual Error   8   8.029   1.004
Total            9  23.900
```

In the Minitab output the variable names Miles *and* Time *were entered as the column headings on the worksheet; thus,* x_1 = Miles *and* y = Time.

In the next section we will discuss the use of the coefficient of multiple determination in measuring how good a fit is provided by this estimated regression equation. Before doing so, let us examine more carefully the values of $b_1 = .0611$ and $b_2 = .923$ in equation (15.6).

Note on Interpretation of Coefficients

One observation can be made at this point about the relationship between the estimated regression equation with only the miles traveled as an independent variable and the equation that includes the number of deliveries as a second independent variable. The value of b_1 is not the same in both cases. In simple linear regression, we interpret b_1 as an estimate of the change in y for a one-unit change in the independent variable. In multiple regression analysis, this interpretation must be modified somewhat. That is, in multiple regression analysis, we interpret each regression coefficient as follows: b_i represents an estimate of the change in y corresponding to a one-unit change in x_i when all other independent variables are held constant. In the Butler Trucking example involving two independent variables, $b_1 = .0611$. Thus,

TABLE 15.2 DATA FOR BUTLER TRUCKING WITH MILES TRAVELED (x_1) AND NUMBER OF DELIVERIES (x_2) AS THE INDEPENDENT VARIABLES

CD file Butler

Driving Assignment	x_1 = Miles Traveled	x_2 = Number of Deliveries	y = Travel Time (hours)
1	100	4	9.3
2	50	3	4.8
3	100	4	8.9
4	100	2	6.5
5	50	2	4.2
6	80	2	6.2
7	75	3	7.4
8	65	4	6.0
9	90	3	7.6
10	90	2	6.1

FIGURE 15.4 MINITAB OUTPUT FOR BUTLER TRUCKING WITH TWO INDEPENDENT VARIABLES

```
The regression equation is
Time = - 0.869 + 0.0611 Miles + 0.923 Deliveries

Predictor        Coef    SE Coef       T      p
Constant      -0.8687     0.9515   -0.91  0.392
Miles        0.061135   0.009888    6.18  0.000
Deliveries     0.9234     0.2211    4.18  0.004

S = 0.5731   R-sq = 90.4%   R-sq(adj) = 87.6%

Analysis of Variance

SOURCE           DF       SS       MS       F      p
Regression        2   21.601   10.800   32.88  0.000
Residual Error    7    2.299    0.328
Total             9   23.900
```

In the Minitab output the variable names Miles, Deliveries, *and* Time *were entered as the column headings on the worksheet; thus,* x_1 = Miles, x_2 = Deliveries, *and* y = Time.

.0611 hours is an estimate of the expected increase in travel time corresponding to an increase of one mile in the distance traveled when the number of deliveries is held constant. Similarly, because $b_2 = .923$, an estimate of the expected increase in travel time corresponding to an increase of one delivery when the number of miles traveled is held constant is .923 hours.

Exercises

Note to student: The exercises involving data in this and subsequent sections were designed to be solved using a computer software package.

Methods

1. The estimated regression equation for a model involving two independent variables and 10 observations follows.

$$\hat{y} = 29.1270 + .5906x_1 + .4980x_2$$

   a. Interpret b_1 and b_2 in this estimated regression equation.
   b. Estimate y when $x_1 = 180$ and $x_2 = 310$.

SELF test

2. Consider the following data for a dependent variable y and two independent variables, x_1 and x_2.

CD file
Exer2

x_1	x_2	y
30	12	94
47	10	108
25	17	112
51	16	178
40	5	94
51	19	175
74	7	170

(continued)

x_1	x_2	y
36	12	117
59	13	142
76	16	211

a. Develop an estimated regression equation relating y to x_1. Estimate y if $x_1 = 45$.
b. Develop an estimated regression equation relating y to x_2. Estimate y if $x_2 = 15$.
c. Develop an estimated regression equation relating y to x_1 and x_2. Estimate y if $x_1 = 45$ and $x_2 = 15$.

3. In a regression analysis involving 30 observations, the following estimated regression equation was obtained.

$$\hat{y} = 17.6 + 3.8x_1 - 2.3x_2 + 7.6x_3 + 2.7x_4$$

a. Interpret b_1, b_2, b_3, and b_4 in this estimated regression equation.
b. Estimate y when $x_1 = 10$, $x_2 = 5$, $x_3 = 1$, and $x_4 = 2$.

Applications

4. A shoe store developed the following estimated regression equation relating sales to inventory investment and advertising expenditures.

$$\hat{y} = 25 + 10x_1 + 8x_2$$

where

x_1 = inventory investment ($1000s)
x_2 = advertising expenditures ($1000s)
y = sales ($1000s)

a. Estimate sales resulting from a $15,000 investment in inventory and an advertising budget of $10,000.
b. Interpret b_1 and b_2 in this estimated regression equation.

SELF test

5. The owner of Showtime Movie Theaters, Inc., would like to estimate weekly gross revenue as a function of advertising expenditures. Historical data for a sample of eight weeks follow.

CD file
Showtime

Weekly Gross Revenue ($1000s)	Television Advertising ($1000s)	Newspaper Advertising ($1000s)
96	5.0	1.5
90	2.0	2.0
95	4.0	1.5
92	2.5	2.5
95	3.0	3.3
94	3.5	2.3
94	2.5	4.2
94	3.0	2.5

a. Develop an estimated regression equation with the amount of television advertising as the independent variable.
b. Develop an estimated regression equation with both television advertising and newspaper advertising as the independent variables.
c. Is the estimated regression equation coefficient for television advertising expenditures the same in part (a) and in part (b)? Interpret the coefficient in each case.

d. What is the estimate of the weekly gross revenue for a week when \$3500 is spent on television advertising and \$1800 is spent on newspaper advertising?

6. In baseball, a team's success is often thought to be a function of the team's hitting and pitching performance. One measure of hitting performance is the number of home runs the team hits, and one measure of pitching performance is the earned run average for the team's pitching staff. It is generally believed that teams that hit more home runs and have a lower earned run average will win a higher percentage of the games played. The following data show the proportion of games won, the number of team home runs (HR), and the earned run average (ERA) for the 16 teams in the National League for the 2003 Major League Baseball season (www.usatoday.com, January 7, 2004).

CD file MLB

Team	Proportion Won	HR	ERA	Team	Proportion Won	HR	ERA
Arizona	0.519	152	3.857	Milwaukee	0.420	196	5.058
Atlanta	0.623	235	4.106	Montreal	0.512	144	4.027
Chicago	0.543	172	3.842	New York	0.410	124	4.517
Cincinnati	0.426	182	5.127	Philadelphia	0.531	166	4.072
Colorado	0.457	198	5.269	Pittsburgh	0.463	163	4.664
Florida	0.562	157	4.059	San Diego	0.395	128	4.904
Houston	0.537	191	3.880	San Francisco	0.621	180	3.734
Los Angeles	0.525	124	3.162	St. Louis	0.525	196	4.642

a. Determine the estimated regression equation that could be used to predict the proportion of games won given the number of team home runs.
b. Determine the estimated regression equation that could be used to predict the proportion of games won given the earned run average for the team's pitching staff.
c. Determine the estimated regression equation that could be used to predict the proportion of games won given the number of team home runs and the earned run average for the team's pitching staff.
d. For the 2003 season San Diego won only 39.5% of the games they played, the lowest in the National League. To improve next year's record, the team is trying to acquire new players who will increase the number of team home runs to 180 and decrease the earned run average for the team's pitching staff to 4.0. Use the estimated regression equation developed in part (c) to estimate the percentage of games San Diego will win if they have 180 team home runs and have an earned run average of 4.0.

7. Designers of backpacks use exotic material such as supernylon Delrin, high-density polyethylene, aircraft aluminum, and thermomolded foam to make packs that fit comfortably and distribute weight to eliminate pressure points. The following data show the capacity (cubic inches), comfort rating, and price for 10 backpacks tested by *Outside Magazine.* Comfort was measured using a rating from 1 to 5, with a rating of 1 denoting average comfort and a rating of 5 denoting excellent comfort (*Outside Buyer's Guide,* 2001).

CD file Backpack

Manufacturer and Model	Capacity	Comfort	Price
Camp Trails Paragon II	4330	2	\$190
EMS 5500	5500	3	219
Lowe Alpomayo 90+20	5500	4	249
Marmot Muir	4700	3	249
Kelly Bigfoot 5200	5200	4	250
Gregory Whitney	5500	4	340
Osprey 75	4700	4	389
Arc'Teryx Bora 95	5500	5	395
Dana Design Terraplane LTW	5800	5	439
The Works @ Mystery Ranch Jazz	5000	5	525

a. Determine the estimated regression equation that can be used to predict the price of a backpack given the capacity and the comfort rating.
b. Interpret b_1 and b_2.
c. Predict the price for a backpack with a capacity of 4500 cubic inches and a comfort rating of 4.

8. The following table gives the annual return, the safety rating (0 = riskiest, 10 = safest), and the annual expense ratio for 20 foreign funds (*Mutual Funds,* March 2000).

CD file ForFunds

	Safety Rating	Annual Expense Ratio (%)	Annual Return (%)
Accessor Int'l Equity "Adv"	7.1	1.59	49
Aetna "I" International	7.2	1.35	52
Amer Century Int'l Discovery "Inv"	6.8	1.68	89
Columbia International Stock	7.1	1.56	58
Concert Inv "A" Int'l Equity	6.2	2.16	131
Dreyfus Founders Int'l Equity "F"	7.4	1.80	59
Driehaus International Growth	6.5	1.88	99
Excelsior "Inst" Int'l Equity	7.0	0.90	53
Julius Baer International Equity	6.9	1.79	77
Marshall International Stock "Y"	7.2	1.49	54
MassMutual Int'l Equity "S"	7.1	1.05	57
Morgan Grenfell Int'l Sm Cap "Inst"	7.7	1.25	61
New England "A" Int'l Equity	7.0	1.83	88
Pilgrim Int'l Small Cap "A"	7.0	1.94	122
Republic International Equity	7.2	1.09	71
Sit International Growth	6.9	1.50	51
Smith Barney "A" Int'l Equity	7.0	1.28	60
State St Research "S" Int'l Equity	7.1	1.65	50
Strong International Stock	6.5	1.61	93
Vontobel International Equity	7.0	1.50	47

a. Develop an estimated regression equation relating the annual return to the safety rating and the annual expense ratio.
b. Estimate the annual return for a firm that has a safety rating of 7.5 and annual expense ratio of 2.

9. Waterskiing and wakeboarding are two popular water-sports. Finding a model that best suits your intended needs, whether it is waterskiing, wakeboading, or general boating, can be a difficult task. *WaterSki* magazine did extensive testing for 88 boats and provided a wide variety of information to help consumers select the best boat. A portion of the data they reported for 20 boats with a length of between 20 and 22 feet follows (*WaterSki*, January/February 2006). Beam is the maximum width of the boat in inches, HP is the horsepower of the boat's engine, and TopSpeed is the top speed in miles per hour (mph).

CD file Boats

Make and Model	Beam	HP	TopSpeed
Calabria Cal Air Pro V-2	100	330	45.3
Correct Craft Air Nautique 210	91	330	47.3
Correct Craft Air Nautique SV-211	93	375	46.9
Correct Craft Ski Nautique 206 Limited	91	330	46.7
Gekko GTR 22	96	375	50.1
Gekko GTS 20	83	375	52.2
Malibu Response LXi	93.5	340	47.2
Malibu Sunsettter LXi	98	400	46
Malibu Sunsetter 21 XTi	98	340	44

Make and Model	Beam	HP	TopSpeed
Malibu Sunscape 21 LSV	98	400	47.5
Malibu Wakesetter 21 XTi	98	340	44.9
Malibu Wakesetter VLX	98	400	47.3
Malibu vRide	93.5	340	44.5
Malibu Ride XTi	93.5	320	44.5
Mastercraft ProStar 209	96	350	42.5
Mastercraft X-1	90	310	45.8
Mastercraft X-2	94	310	42.8
Mastercraft X-9	96	350	43.2
MB Sports 190 Plus	92	330	45.3
Svfara SVONE	91	330	47.7

a. Using these data, develop an estimated regression equation relating the top speed with the boat's beam and horsepower rating.

b. The Svfara SV609 has a beam of 85 inches and an engine with a 330 horsepower rating. Use the estimated regression equation developed in part (a) to estimate the top speed for the Svfara SV609.

10. The National Basketball Association (NBA) records a variety of statistics for each team. Four of these statistics are the proportion of games won (PCT), the proportion of field goals made by the team (FG%), the proportion of three-point shots made by the team's opponent (Opp 3 Pt%), and the number of turnovers committed by the team's opponent (Opp TO). The following data show the values of these statistics for the 29 teams in the NBA for a portion of the 2004 season (www.nba.com, January 3, 2004).

CD file

NBA

Team	PCT	FG%	Opp 3 Pt%	Opp TO	Team	PCT	FG%	Opp 3 Pt%	Opp TO
Atlanta	0.265	0.435	0.346	13.206	Minnesota	0.677	0.473	0.348	13.839
Boston	0.471	0.449	0.369	16.176	New Jersey	0.563	0.435	0.338	17.063
Chicago	0.313	0.417	0.372	15.031	New Orleans	0.636	0.421	0.330	16.909
Cleveland	0.303	0.438	0.345	12.515	New York	0.412	0.442	0.330	13.588
Dallas	0.581	0.439	0.332	15.000	Orlando	0.242	0.417	0.360	14.242
Denver	0.606	0.431	0.366	17.818	Philadelphia	0.438	0.428	0.364	16.938
Detroit	0.606	0.423	0.262	15.788	Phoenix	0.364	0.438	0.326	16.515
Golden State	0.452	0.445	0.384	14.290	Portland	0.484	0.447	0.367	12.548
Houston	0.548	0.426	0.324	13.161	Sacramento	0.724	0.466	0.327	15.207
Indiana	0.706	0.428	0.317	15.647	San Antonio	0.688	0.429	0.293	15.344
L.A. Clippers	0.464	0.424	0.326	14.357	Seattle	0.533	0.436	0.350	16.767
L.A. Lakers	0.724	0.465	0.323	16.000	Toronto	0.516	0.424	0.314	14.129
Memphis	0.485	0.432	0.358	17.848	Utah	0.531	0.456	0.368	15.469
Miami	0.424	0.410	0.369	14.970	Washington	0.300	0.411	0.341	16.133
Milwaukee	0.500	0.438	0.349	14.750					

a. Determine the estimated regression equation that can be used to predict the proportion of games won given the proportion of field goals made by the team.

b. Provide an interpretation for the slope of the estimated regression equation developed in part (a).

c. Determine the estimated regression equation that can be used to predict the proportion of games won given the proportion of field goals made by the team, the proportion of three-point shots made by the team's opponent, and the number of turnovers committed by the team's opponent.

d. Discuss the practical implications of the estimated regression equation developed in part (c).

e. Estimate the proportion of games won for a team with the following values for the three independent variables: FG% = .45, Opp 3 Pt% = .34, and Opp TO = 17.

15.3 Multiple Coefficient of Determination

In simple linear regression we showed that the total sum of squares can be partitioned into two components: the sum of squares due to regression and the sum of squares due to error. The same procedure applies to the sum of squares in multiple regression.

RELATIONSHIP AMONG SST, SSR, AND SSE

$$\text{SST} = \text{SSR} + \text{SSE} \tag{15.7}$$

where

$$\text{SST} = \text{total sum of squares} = \Sigma(y_i - \bar{y})^2$$
$$\text{SSR} = \text{sum of squares due to regression} = \Sigma(\hat{y}_i - \bar{y})^2$$
$$\text{SSE} = \text{sum of squares due to error} = \Sigma(y_i - \hat{y}_i)^2$$

Because of the computational difficulty in computing the three sums of squares, we rely on computer packages to determine those values. The analysis of variance part of the Minitab output in Figure 15.4 shows the three values for the Butler Trucking problem with two independent variables: SST = 23.900, SSR = 21.601, and SSE = 2.299. With only one independent variable (number of miles traveled), the Minitab output in Figure 15.3 shows that SST = 23.900, SSR = 15.871, and SSE = 8.029. The value of SST is the same in both cases because it does not depend on $\hat{y}$, but SSR increases and SSE decreases when a second independent variable (number of deliveries) is added. The implication is that the estimated multiple regression equation provides a better fit for the observed data.

In Chapter 14, we used the coefficient of determination, $r^2 = \text{SSR/SST}$, to measure the goodness of fit for the estimated regression equation. The same concept applies to multiple regression. The term **multiple coefficient of determination** indicates that we are measuring the goodness of fit for the estimated multiple regression equation. The multiple coefficient of determination, denoted R^2, is computed as follows.

MULTIPLE COEFFICIENT OF DETERMINATION

$$R^2 = \frac{\text{SSR}}{\text{SST}} \tag{15.8}$$

The multiple coefficient of determination can be interpreted as the proportion of the variability in the dependent variable that can be explained by the estimated multiple regression equation. Hence, when multiplied by 100, it can be interpreted as the percentage of the variability in y that can be explained by the estimated regression equation.

In the two-independent-variable Butler Trucking example, with SSR = 21.601 and SST = 23.900, we have

$$R^2 = \frac{21.601}{23.900} = .904$$

Therefore, 90.4% of the variability in travel time y is explained by the estimated multiple regression equation with miles traveled and number of deliveries as the independent variables. In Figure 15.4, we see that the multiple coefficient of determination is also provided by the Minitab output; it is denoted by R-sq = 90.4%.

Adding independent variables causes the prediction errors to become smaller, thus reducing the sum of squares due to error, SSE. Because SSR = SST − SSE, when SSE becomes smaller, SSR becomes larger, causing R^2 = SSR/SST to increase.

Figure 15.3 shows that the R-sq value for the estimated regression equation with only one independent variable, number of miles traveled (x_1), is 66.4%. Thus, the percentage of the variability in travel times that is explained by the estimated regression equation increases from 66.4% to 90.4% when number of deliveries is added as a second independent variable. In general, R^2 always increases as independent variables are added to the model.

Many analysts prefer adjusting R^2 for the number of independent variables to avoid overestimating the impact of adding an independent variable on the amount of variability explained by the estimated regression equation. With n denoting the number of observations and p denoting the number of independent variables, the **adjusted multiple coefficient of determination** is computed as follows.

If a variable is added to the model, R^2 becomes larger even if the variable added is not statistically significant. The adjusted multiple coefficient of determination compensates for the number of independent variables in the model.

ADJUSTED MULTIPLE COEFFICIENT OF DETERMINATION

$$R_{\text{a}}^2 = 1 - (1 - R^2)\frac{n - 1}{n - p - 1} \tag{15.9}$$

For the Butler Trucking example with $n = 10$ and $p = 2$, we have

$$R_{\text{a}}^2 = 1 - (1 - .904)\frac{10 - 1}{10 - 2 - 1} = .88$$

Thus, after adjusting for the two independent variables, we have an adjusted multiple coefficient of determination of .88. This value is provided by the Minitab output in Figure 15.4 as R-sq(adj) = 87.6%; the value we calculated differs because we used a rounded value of R^2 in the calculation.

NOTES AND COMMENTS

If the value of R^2 is small and the model contains a large number of independent variables, the adjusted coefficient of determination can take a negative value; in such cases, Minitab sets the adjusted coefficient of determination to zero.

Exercises

Methods

11. In exercise 1, the following estimated regression equation based on 10 observations was presented.

$$\hat{y} = 29.1270 + .5906x_1 + .4980x_2$$

The values of SST and SSR are 6724.125 and 6216.375, respectively.

a. Find SSE.
b. Compute R^2.
c. Compute R_{a}^2.
d. Comment on the goodness of fit.

SELF test

12. In exercise 2, 10 observations were provided for a dependent variable y and two independent variables x_1 and x_2; for these data SST = 15,182.9, and SSR = 14,052.2.

a. Compute R^2.
b. Compute R_{a}^2.
c. Does the estimated regression equation explain a large amount of the variability in the data? Explain.

13. In exercise 3, the following estimated regression equation based on 30 observations was presented.

$$\hat{y} = 17.6 + 3.8x_1 - 2.3x_2 + 7.6x_3 + 2.7x_4$$

The values of SST and SSR are 1805 and 1760, respectively.

a. Compute R^2.
b. Compute R_a^2.
c. Comment on the goodness of fit.

Applications

14. In exercise 4, the following estimated regression equation relating sales to inventory investment and advertising expenditures was given.

$$\hat{y} = 25 + 10x_1 + 8x_2$$

The data used to develop the model came from a survey of 10 stores; for those data, SST = 16,000 and SSR = 12,000.

a. For the estimated regression equation given, compute R^2.
b. Compute R_a^2.
c. Does the model appear to explain a large amount of variability in the data? Explain.

SELF test

15. In exercise 5, the owner of Showtime Movie Theaters, Inc., used multiple regression analysis to predict gross revenue (y) as a function of television advertising (x_1) and newspaper advertising (x_2). The estimated regression equation was

$$\hat{y} = 83.2 + 2.29x_1 + 1.30x_2$$

CD file Showtime

The computer solution provided SST = 25.5 and SSR = 23.435.

a. Compute and interpret R^2 and R_a^2.
b. When television advertising was the only independent variable, $R^2 = .653$ and $R_a^2 = .595$. Do you prefer the multiple regression results? Explain.

CD file MLB

16. In exercise 6, data were given on the proportion of games won, the number of team home runs, and the earned run average for the team's pitching staff for the 16 teams in the National League for the 2003 Major League Baseball season (http://www.usatoday.com, January 7, 2004).

a. Did the estimated regression equation that uses only the number of home runs as the independent variable to predict the proportion of games won provide a good fit? Explain.
b. Discuss the benefits of using both the number of home runs and the earned run average to predict the proportion of games won.

CD file Boats

17. In exercise 9, an estimated regression equation was developed relating the top speed for a boat to the boat's beam and horsepower rating.

a. Compute and interpret and R^2 and R_a^2.
b. Does the estimated regression equation provide a good fit to the data? Explain.

CD file NBA

18. Refer to exercise 10, where data were reported on a variety of statistics for the 29 teams in the National Basketball Association for a portion of the 2004 season (www.nba.com, January 3, 2004).

a. In part (c) of exercise 10, an estimated regression equation was developed relating the proportion of games won given the percentage of field goals made by the team, the proportion of three-point shots made by the team's opponent, and the number of turnovers committed by the team's opponent. What are the values of R^2 and R_a^2?
b. Does the estimated regression equation provide a good fit to the data? Explain.

15.4 Model Assumptions

In Section 15.1 we introduced the following multiple regression model.

MULTIPLE REGRESSION MODEL

$$y = \beta_0 + \beta_1 x_1 + \beta_2 x_2 + \cdots + \beta_p x_p + \epsilon \quad \textbf{(15.10)}$$

The assumptions about the error term ϵ in the multiple regression model parallel those for the simple linear regression model.

ASSUMPTIONS ABOUT THE ERROR TERM ϵ IN THE MULTIPLE REGRESSION MODEL $y = \beta_0 + \beta_1 x_1 + \cdots + \beta_p x_p + \epsilon$

1. The error term ϵ is a random variable with mean or expected value of zero; that is, $E(\epsilon) = 0$.
   Implication: For given values of $x_1, x_2, \ldots, x_p$, the expected, or average, value of y is given by

   $$E(y) = \beta_0 + \beta_1 x_1 + \beta_2 x_2 + \cdots + \beta_p x_p. \quad \textbf{(15.11)}$$

   Equation (15.11) is the multiple regression equation we introduced in Section 15.1. In this equation, $E(y)$ represents the average of all possible values of y that might occur for the given values of $x_1, x_2, \ldots, x_p$.
2. The variance of ϵ is denoted by σ^2 and is the same for all values of the independent variables $x_1, x_2, \ldots, x_p$.
   Implication: The variance of y about the regression line equals σ^2 and is the same for all values of $x_1, x_2, \ldots, x_p$.
3. The values of ϵ are independent.
   Implication: The value of ϵ for a particular set of values for the independent variables is not related to the value of ϵ for any other set of values.
4. The error term ϵ is a normally distributed random variable reflecting the deviation between the y value and the expected value of y given by $\beta_0 + \beta_1 x_1 + \beta_2 x_2 + \cdots + \beta_p x_p$.
   Implication: Because $\beta_0, \beta_1, \ldots, \beta_p$ are constants for the given values of $x_1, x_2, \ldots, x_p$, the dependent variable y is also a normally distributed random variable.

To obtain more insight about the form of the relationship given by equation (15.11), consider the following two-independent-variable multiple regression equation.

$$E(y) = \beta_0 + \beta_1 x_1 + \beta_2 x_2$$

The graph of this equation is a plane in three-dimensional space. Figure 15.5 provides an example of such a graph. Note that the value of ϵ shown is the difference between the actual y value and the expected value of y, $E(y)$, when $x_1 = x_1^*$ and $x_2 = x_2^*$.

FIGURE 15.5 GRAPH OF THE REGRESSION EQUATION FOR MULTIPLE REGRESSION ANALYSIS WITH TWO INDEPENDENT VARIABLES

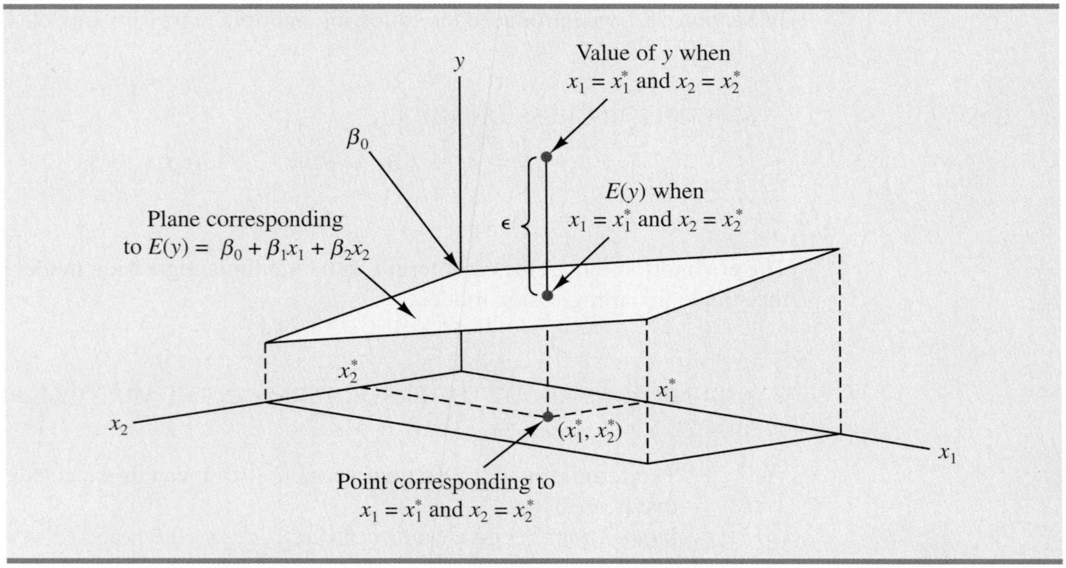

In regression analysis, the term *response variable* is often used in place of the term *dependent variable.* Furthermore, since the multiple regression equation generates a plane or surface, its graph is called a *response surface.*

15.5 Testing for Significance

In this section we show how to conduct significance tests for a multiple regression relationship. The significance tests we used in simple linear regression were a t test and an F test. In simple linear regression, both tests provide the same conclusion; that is, if the null hypothesis is rejected, we conclude that $\beta_1 \neq 0$. In multiple regression, the t test and the F test have different purposes.

1. The F test is used to determine whether a significant relationship exists between the dependent variable and the set of all the independent variables; we will refer to the F test as the test for *overall significance.*
2. If the F test shows an overall significance, the t test is used to determine whether each of the individual independent variables is significant. A separate t test is conducted for each of the independent variables in the model; we refer to each of these t tests as a test for *individual significance.*

In the material that follows, we will explain the F test and the t test and apply each to the Butler Trucking Company example.

F Test

The multiple regression model as defined in Section 15.4 is

$$y = \beta_0 + \beta_1 x_1 + \beta_2 x_2 + \cdots + \beta_p x_p + \epsilon$$

The hypotheses for the F test involve the parameters of the multiple regression model.

$$H_0\colon \beta_1 = \beta_2 = \cdots = \beta_p = 0$$
$$H_a\colon \text{One or more of the parameters is not equal to zero}$$

If H_0 is rejected, the test gives us sufficient statistical evidence to conclude that one or more of the parameters is not equal to zero and that the overall relationship between y and the set of independent variables $x_1, x_2, \ldots, x_p$ is significant. However, if H_0 cannot be rejected, we do not have sufficient evidence to conclude that a significant relationship is present.

Before describing the steps of the F test, we need to review the concept of *mean square.* A mean square is a sum of squares divided by its corresponding degrees of freedom. In the multiple regression case, the total sum of squares has $n - 1$ degrees of freedom, the sum of squares due to regression (SSR) has p degrees of freedom, and the sum of squares due to error has $n - p - 1$ degrees of freedom. Hence, the mean square due to regression (MSR) is SSR/p and the mean square due to error (MSE) is SSE/$(n - p - 1)$.

$$\text{MSR} = \frac{\text{SSR}}{p} \tag{15.12}$$

and

$$\text{MSE} = \frac{\text{SSE}}{n - p - 1} \tag{15.13}$$

As discussed in Chapter 14, MSE provides an unbiased estimate of σ^2, the variance of the error term ϵ. If H_0: $\beta_1 = \beta_2 = \cdots = \beta_p = 0$ is true, MSR also provides an unbiased estimate of σ^2, and the value of MSR/MSE should be close to 1. However, if H_0 is false, MSR overestimates σ^2 and the value of MSR/MSE becomes larger. To determine how large the value of MSR/MSE must be to reject H_0, we make use of the fact that if H_0 is true and the assumptions about the multiple regression model are valid, the sampling distribution of MSR/MSE is an F distribution with p degrees of freedom in the numerator and $n - p - 1$ in the denominator. A summary of the F test for significance in multiple regression follows.

***F* TEST FOR OVERALL SIGNIFICANCE**

H_0: $\beta_1 = \beta_2 = \cdots = \beta_p = 0$

H_a: One or more of the parameters is not equal to zero

TEST STATISTIC

$$F = \frac{\text{MSR}}{\text{MSE}} \tag{15.14}$$

REJECTION RULE

p-value approach:	Reject H_0 if p-value $\leq \alpha$
Critical value approach:	Reject H_0 if $F \geq F_\alpha$

where F_α is based on an F distribution with p degrees of freedom in the numerator and $n - p - 1$ degrees of freedom in the denominator.

Let us apply the F test to the Butler Trucking Company multiple regression problem. With two independent variables, the hypotheses are written as follows.

H_0: $\beta_1 = \beta_2 = 0$

H_a: β_1 and/or β_2 is not equal to zero

FIGURE 15.6 MINITAB OUTPUT FOR BUTLER TRUCKING WITH TWO INDEPENDENT VARIABLES, MILES TRAVELED (x_1) AND NUMBER OF DELIVERIES (x_2)

```
The regression equation is
Time = - 0.869 + 0.0611 Miles + 0.923 Deliveries

Predictor        Coef    SE Coef       T      p
Constant      -0.8687     0.9515   -0.91  0.392
Miles        0.061135   0.009888    6.18  0.000
Deliveries     0.9234     0.2211    4.18  0.004

S = 0.5731   R-sq = 90.4%   R-sq(adj) = 87.6%

Analysis of Variance

SOURCE           DF       SS       MS       F      p
Regression        2   21.601   10.800   32.88  0.000
Residual Error    7    2.299    0.328
Total             9   23.900
```

Figure 15.6 is the Minitab output for the multiple regression model with miles traveled (x_1) and number of deliveries (x_2) as the two independent variables. In the analysis of variance part of the output, we see that MSR = 10.8 and MSE = .328. Using equation (15.14), we obtain the test statistic.

$$F = \frac{10.8}{.328} = 32.9$$

Note that the F value on the Minitab output is $F = 32.88$; the value we calculated differs because we used rounded values for MSR and MSE in the calculation. Using $\alpha = .01$, the p-value $= 0.000$ in the last column of the analysis of variance table (Figure 15.6) indicates that we can reject H_0: $\beta_1 = \beta_2 = 0$ because the p-value is less than $\alpha = .01$. Alternatively, Table 4 of Appendix B shows that with two degrees of freedom in the numerator and seven degrees of freedom in the denominator, $F_{.01} = 9.55$. With $32.9 > 9.55$, we reject H_0: $\beta_1 = \beta_2 = 0$ and conclude that a significant relationship is present between travel time y and the two independent variables, miles traveled and number of deliveries.

As noted previously, the mean square error provides an unbiased estimate of σ^2, the variance of the error term ϵ. Referring to Figure 15.6, we see that the estimate of σ^2 is MSE = .328. The square root of MSE is the estimate of the standard deviation of the error term. As defined in Section 14.5, this standard deviation is called the standard error of the estimate and is denoted s. Hence, we have $s = \sqrt{\text{MSE}} = \sqrt{.328} = .573$. Note that the value of the standard error of the estimate appears in the Minitab output in Figure 15.6.

Table 15.3 is the general analysis of variance (ANOVA) table that provides the F test results for a multiple regression model. The value of the F test statistic appears in the last column and can be compared to F_α with p degrees of freedom in the numerator and $n - p - 1$ degrees of freedom in the denominator to make the hypothesis test conclusion. By reviewing the Minitab output for Butler Trucking Company in Figure 15.6, we see that Minitab's analysis of variance table contains this information. Moreover, Minitab also provides the p-value corresponding to the F test statistic.

TABLE 15.3 ANOVA TABLE FOR A MULTIPLE REGRESSION MODEL WITH p INDEPENDENT VARIABLES

Source	Sum of Squares	Degrees of Freedom	Mean Square	F
Regression	SSR	p	$\text{MSR} = \dfrac{\text{SSR}}{p}$	$F = \dfrac{\text{MSR}}{\text{MSE}}$
Error	SSE	$n - p - 1$	$\text{MSE} = \dfrac{\text{SSE}}{n - p - 1}$	
Total	SST	$n - 1$		

t Test

If the F test shows that the multiple regression relationship is significant, a t test can be conducted to determine the significance of each of the individual parameters. The t test for individual significance follows.

t TEST FOR INDIVIDUAL SIGNIFICANCE

For any parameter β_i

$$H_0: \beta_i = 0$$
$$H_a: \beta_i \neq 0$$

TEST STATISTIC

$$t = \frac{b_i}{s_{b_i}} \qquad \textbf{(15.15)}$$

REJECTION RULE

p-value approach: Reject H_0 if p-value $\leq \alpha$
Critical value approach: Reject H_0 if $t \leq -t_{\alpha/2}$ or if $t \geq t_{\alpha/2}$

where $t_{\alpha/2}$ is based on a t distribution with $n - p - 1$ degrees of freedom.

In the test statistic, s_{b_i} is the estimate of the standard deviation of b_i. The value of s_{b_i} will be provided by the computer software package.

Let us conduct the t test for the Butler Trucking regression problem. Refer to the section of Figure 15.6 that shows the Minitab output for the t-ratio calculations. Values of b_1, b_2, s_{b_1}, and s_{b_2} are as follows.

$$b_1 = .061135 \quad s_{b_1} = .009888$$
$$b_2 = .9234 \quad s_{b_2} = .2211$$

Using equation (15.15), we obtain the test statistic for the hypotheses involving parameters β_1 and β_2.

$$t = .061135/.009888 = 6.18$$
$$t = .9234/.2211 = 4.18$$

Note that both of these t-ratio values and the corresponding p-values are provided by the Minitab output in Figure 15.6. Using $\alpha = .01$, the p-values of .000 and .004 on the Minitab output indicate that we can reject H_0: $\beta_1 = 0$ and H_0: $\beta_2 = 0$. Hence, both parameters are statistically significant. Alternatively, Table 2 of Appendix B shows that with $n - p - 1 = 10 - 2 - 1 = 7$ degrees of freedom, $t_{.005} = 3.499$. With $6.18 > 3.499$, we reject H_0: $\beta_1 = 0$. Similarly, with $4.18 > 3.499$, we reject H_0: $\beta_2 = 0$.

Multicollinearity

We use the term *independent variable* in regression analysis to refer to any variable being used to predict or explain the value of the dependent variable. The term does not mean, however, that the independent variables themselves are independent in any statistical sense. On the contrary, most independent variables in a multiple regression problem are correlated to some degree with one another. For example, in the Butler Trucking example involving the two independent variables x_1 (miles traveled) and x_2 (number of deliveries), we could treat the miles traveled as the dependent variable and the number of deliveries as the independent variable to determine whether those two variables are themselves related. We could then compute the sample correlation coefficient $r_{x_1x_2}$ to determine the extent to which the variables are related. Doing so yields $r_{x_1x_2} = .16$. Thus, we find some degree of linear association between the two independent variables. In multiple regression analysis, **multicollinearity** refers to the correlation among the independent variables.

To provide a better perspective of the potential problems of multicollinearity, let us consider a modification of the Butler Trucking example. Instead of x_2 being the number of deliveries, let x_2 denote the number of gallons of gasoline consumed. Clearly, x_1 (the miles traveled) and x_2 are related; that is, we know that the number of gallons of gasoline used depends on the number of miles traveled. Hence, we would conclude logically that x_1 and x_2 are highly correlated independent variables.

Assume that we obtain the equation $\hat{y} = b_0 + b_1x_1 + b_2x_2$ and find that the F test shows the relationship to be significant. Then suppose we conduct a t test on β_1 to determine whether $\beta_1 \neq 0$, and we cannot reject H_0: $\beta_1 = 0$. Does this result mean that travel time is not related to miles traveled? Not necessarily. What it probably means is that with x_2 already in the model, x_1 does not make a significant contribution to determining the value of y. This interpretation makes sense in our example; if we know the amount of gasoline consumed, we do not gain much additional information useful in predicting y by knowing the miles traveled. Similarly, a t test might lead us to conclude $\beta_2 = 0$ on the grounds that, with x_1 in the model, knowledge of the amount of gasoline consumed does not add much.

A sample correlation coefficient greater than +.7 or less than −.7 for two independent variables is a rule of thumb warning of potential problems with multicollinearity.

To summarize, in t tests for the significance of individual parameters, the difficulty caused by multicollinearity is that it is possible to conclude that none of the individual parameters are significantly different from zero when an F test on the overall multiple regression equation indicates a significant relationship. This problem is avoided when there is little correlation among the independent variables.

Statisticians have developed several tests for determining whether multicollinearity is high enough to cause problems. According to the rule of thumb test, multicollinearity is a potential problem if the absolute value of the sample correlation coefficient exceeds .7 for any two of the independent variables. The other types of tests are more advanced and beyond the scope of this text.

When the independent variables are highly correlated, it is not possible to determine the separate effect of any particular independent variable on the dependent variable.

If possible, every attempt should be made to avoid including independent variables that are highly correlated. In practice, however, strict adherence to this policy is rarely possible. When decision makers have reason to believe substantial multicollinearity is present, they must realize that separating the effects of the individual independent variables on the dependent variable is difficult.

NOTES AND COMMENTS

Ordinarily, multicollinearity does not affect the way in which we perform our regression analysis or interpret the output from a study. However, when multicollinearity is severe—that is, when two or more of the independent variables are highly correlated with one another—we can have difficulty interpreting the results of t tests on the individual parameters. In addition to the type of problem illustrated in this section, severe cases of multicollinearity have been shown to result in least squares estimates that have the wrong sign. That is, in simulated studies where researchers created the underlying regression model and then applied the least squares technique to develop estimates of β_0, β_1, β_2, and so on, it has been shown that under conditions of high multicollinearity the least squares estimates can have a sign opposite that of the parameter being estimated. For example, b_2 might actually be $+10$ and β_2, its estimate, might turn out to be -2. Thus, little faith can be placed in the individual coefficients if multicollinearity is present to a high degree.

Exercises

Methods

SELF test

19. In exercise 1, the following estimated regression equation based on 10 observations was presented.

$$\hat{y} = 29.1270 + .5906x_1 + .4980x_2$$

Here SST = 6724.125, SSR = 6216.375, $s_{b_1} = .0813$, and $s_{b_2} = .0567$.

a. Compute MSR and MSE.
b. Compute F and perform the appropriate F test. Use $\alpha = .05$.
c. Perform a t test for the significance of β_1. Use $\alpha = .05$.
d. Perform a t test for the significance of β_2. Use $\alpha = .05$.

20. Refer to the data presented in exercise 2. The estimated regression equation for these data is

$$\hat{y} = -18.4 + 2.01x_1 + 4.74x_2$$

Here SST = 15,182.9, SSR = 14,052.2, $s_{b_1} = .2471$, and $s_{b_2} = .9484$.

a. Test for a significant relationship among x_1, x_2, and y. Use $\alpha = .05$.
b. Is β_1 significant? Use $\alpha = .05$.
c. Is β_2 significant? Use $\alpha = .05$.

21. The following estimated regression equation was developed for a model involving two independent variables.

$$\hat{y} = 40.7 + 8.63x_1 + 2.71x_2$$

After x_2 was dropped from the model, the least squares method was used to obtain an estimated regression equation involving only x_1 as an independent variable.

$$\hat{y} = 42.0 + 9.01x_1$$

a. Give an interpretation of the coefficient of x_1 in both models.
b. Could multicollinearity explain why the coefficient of x_1 differs in the two models? If so, how?

Applications

22. In exercise 4, the following estimated regression equation relating sales to inventory investment and advertising expenditures was given.

$$\hat{y} = 25 + 10x_1 + 8x_2$$

The data used to develop the model came from a survey of 10 stores; for these data SST = 16,000 and SSR = 12,000.

a. Compute SSE, MSE, and MSR.
b. Use an F test and a .05 level of significance to determine whether there is a relationship among the variables.

SELF test

23. Refer to exercise 5.

a. Use $\alpha = .01$ to test the hypotheses

$$H_0: \beta_1 = \beta_2 = 0$$
$$H_a: \beta_1 \text{ and/or } \beta_2 \text{ is not equal to zero}$$

for the model $y = \beta_0 + \beta_1 x_1 + \beta_2 x_2 + \epsilon$, where

$$x_1 = \text{television advertising (\$1000s)}$$
$$x_2 = \text{newspaper advertising (1000s)}$$

b. Use $\alpha = .05$ to test the significance of β_1. Should x_1 be dropped from the model?
c. Use $\alpha = .05$ to test the significance of β_2. Should x_2 be dropped from the model?

CD file
MLB

24. Refer to the data in exercise 6. Use the number of team home runs and the earned run average for the team's pitching staff to predict the proportion of games won.

a. Use the F test to determine the overall significance of the relationship. What is your conclusion at the .05 level of significance?
b. Use the t test to determine the significance of each independent variable. What is your conclusion at the .05 level of significance?

25. *Barron's* conducts an annual review of online brokers, including both brokers that can be accessed via a Web browser, as well as direct-access brokers that connect customers directly with the broker's network server. Each broker's offerings and performance are evaluated in six areas, using a point value of 0–5 in each category. The results are weighted to obtain an overall score, and a final star rating, ranging from zero to five stars, is assigned to each broker. Trade execution, ease of use, and range of offerings are three of the areas evaluated. A point value of 5 in the trade execution area means the order entry and execution process flowed easily from one step to the next. A value of 5 in the ease of use area means that the site was easy to use and can be tailored to show what the user wants to see. A value of 5 in the range offerings area means that all of the investment transactions can be executed online. The following data show the point values for trade execution, ease of use, range of offerings, and the star rating for a sample of 10 of the online brokers that *Barron's* evaluated (*Barron's,* March 10, 2003).

CD file
Brokers

Broker	Trade Execution	Use	Range	Rating
Wall St. Access	3.7	4.5	4.8	4.0
E*TRADE (Power)	3.4	3.0	4.2	3.5
E*TRADE (Standard)	2.5	4.0	4.0	3.5
Preferred Trade	4.8	3.7	3.4	3.5
my Track	4.0	3.5	3.2	3.5
TD Waterhouse	3.0	3.0	4.6	3.5
Brown & Co.	2.7	2.5	3.3	3.0
Brokerage America	1.7	3.5	3.1	3.0
Merrill Lynch Direct	2.2	2.7	3.0	2.5
Strong Funds	1.4	3.6	2.5	2.0

a. Determine the estimated regression equation that can be used to predict the star rating given the point values for execution, ease of use, and range of offerings.
b. Use the F test to determine the overall significance of the relationship. What is the conclusion at the .05 level of significance?
c. Use the t test to determine the significance of each independent variable. What is your conclusion at the .05 level of significance?
d. Remove any independent variable that is not significant from the estimated regression equation. What is your recommended estimated regression equation? Compare the R^2 with the value of R^2 from part (a). Discuss the differences.

CD file
NBA

26. In exercise 10 an estimated regression equation was developed relating the proportion of games won given the proportion of field goals made by the team, the proportion of three-point shots made by the team's opponent, and the number of turnovers committed by the team's opponent.
a. Use the F test to determine the overall significance of the relationship. What is your conclusion at the .05 level of significance?
b. Use the t test to determine the significance of each independent variable. What is your conclusion at the .05 level of significance?

15.6 Using the Estimated Regression Equation for Estimation and Prediction

The procedures for estimating the mean value of y and predicting an individual value of y in multiple regression are similar to those in regression analysis involving one independent variable. First, recall that in Chapter 14 we showed that the point estimate of the expected value of y for a given value of x was the same as the point estimate of an individual value of y. In both cases, we used $\hat{y} = b_0 + b_1x$ as the point estimate.

In multiple regression we use the same procedure. That is, we substitute the given values of $x_1, x_2, \ldots, x_p$ into the estimated regression equation and use the corresponding value of $\hat{y}$ as the point estimate. Suppose that for the Butler Trucking example we want to use the estimated regression equation involving x_1 (miles traveled) and x_2 (number of deliveries) to develop two interval estimates:

1. A *confidence interval* of the mean travel time for all trucks that travel 100 miles and make two deliveries
2. A *prediction interval* of the travel time for *one specific* truck that travels 100 miles and makes two deliveries

Using the estimated regression equation $\hat{y} = -.869 + .0611x_1 + .923x_2$ with $x_1 = 100$ and $x_2 = 2$, we obtain the following value of $\hat{y}$.

$$\hat{y} = -.869 + .0611(100) + .923(2) = 7.09$$

Hence, the point estimate of travel time in both cases is approximately seven hours.

To develop interval estimates for the mean value of y and for an individual value of y, we use a procedure similar to that for regression analysis involving one independent variable. The formulas required are beyond the scope of the text, but computer packages for multiple regression analysis will often provide confidence intervals once the values of $x_1, x_2, \ldots, x_p$ are specified by the user. In Table 15.4 we show the 95% confidence and prediction intervals for the Butler Trucking example for selected values of x_1 and x_2; these values were obtained using Minitab. Note that the interval estimate for an individual value of y is wider than the interval estimate for the expected value of y. This difference simply reflects the fact that for given values of x_1 and x_2 we can estimate the mean travel time for all trucks with more precision than we can predict the travel time for one specific truck.

TABLE 15.4 THE 95% CONFIDENCE AND PREDICTION INTERVALS FOR BUTLER TRUCKING

Value of x_1	Value of x_2	Confidence Interval Lower Limit	Confidence Interval Upper Limit	Prediction Interval Lower Limit	Prediction Interval Upper Limit
50	2	3.146	4.924	2.414	5.656
50	3	4.127	5.789	3.368	6.548
50	4	4.815	6.948	4.157	7.607
100	2	6.258	7.926	5.500	8.683
100	3	7.385	8.645	6.520	9.510
100	4	8.135	9.742	7.362	10.515

Exercises

Methods

27. In exercise 1, the following estimated regression equation based on 10 observations was presented.

$$\hat{y} = 29.1270 + .5906x_1 + .4980x_2$$

a. Develop a point estimate of the mean value of y when $x_1 = 180$ and $x_2 = 310$.
b. Develop a point estimate for an individual value of y when $x_1 = 180$ and $x_2 = 310$.

SELF test

28. Refer to the data in exercise 2. The estimated regression equation for those data is

$$\hat{y} = -18.4 + 2.01x_1 + 4.74x_2$$

a. Develop a 95% confidence interval for the mean value of y when $x_1 = 45$ and $x_2 = 15$.
b. Develop a 95% prediction interval for y when $x_1 = 45$ and $x_2 = 15$.

Applications

SELF test

29. In exercise 5, the owner of Showtime Movie Theaters, Inc., used multiple regression analysis to predict gross revenue (y) as a function of television advertising (x_1) and newspaper advertising (x_2). The estimated regression equation was

$$\hat{y} = 83.2 + 2.29x_1 + 1.30x_2$$

a. What is the gross revenue expected for a week when \$3500 is spent on television advertising ($x_1 = 3.5$) and \$1800 is spent on newspaper advertising ($x_2 = 1.8$)?
b. Provide a 95% confidence interval for the mean revenue of all weeks with the expenditures listed in part (a).
c. Provide a 95% prediction interval for next week's revenue, assuming that the advertising expenditures will be allocated as in part (a).

CD file Boats

30. In exercise 9 an estimated regression equation was developed relating the top speed for a boat to the boat's beam and horsepower rating.
    a. Develop a 95% confidence interval for the mean top speed of a boat with a beam of 85 inches and an engine with a 330 horsepower rating.

b. The Svfara SV609 has a beam of 85 inches and an engine with a 330 horsepower rating. Develop a 95% confidence interval for the mean top speed for the Svfara SV609.

31. The Buyer's Guide section of the Web site for *Car and Driver* magazine provides reviews and road tests for cars, trucks, SUVs, and vans. The average ratings of overall quality, vehicle styling, braking, handling, fuel economy, interior comfort, acceleration, dependability, fit and finish, transmission, and ride are summarized for each vehicle using a scale ranging from 1 (worst) to 10 (best). A portion of the data for 14 Sports/GT cars is shown here (www.caranddriver.com, January 7, 2004).

CD file
SportsCar

Sports/GT	Overall	Handling	Dependability	Fit and Finish
Acura 3.2CL	7.80	7.83	8.17	7.67
Acura RSX	9.02	9.46	9.35	8.97
Audi TT	9.00	9.58	8.74	9.38
BMW 3-Series/M3	8.39	9.52	8.39	8.55
Chevrolet Corvette	8.82	9.64	8.54	7.87
Ford Mustang	8.34	8.85	8.70	7.34
Honda Civic Si	8.92	9.31	9.50	7.93
Infiniti G35	8.70	9.34	8.96	8.07
Mazda RX-8	8.58	9.79	8.96	8.12
Mini Cooper	8.76	10.00	8.69	8.33
Mitsubishi Eclipse	8.17	8.95	8.25	7.36
Nissan 350Z	8.07	9.35	7.56	8.21
Porsche 911	9.55	9.91	8.86	9.55
Toyota Celica	8.77	9.29	9.04	7.97

a. Develop an estimated regression equation using handling, dependability, and fit and finish to predict overall quality.
b. Another Sports/GT car rated by *Car and Driver* is the Honda Accord. The ratings for handling, dependability, and fit and finish for the Honda Accord were 8.28, 9.06, and 8.07, respectively. Estimate the overall rating for this car.
c. Provide a 95% confidence interval for overall quality for all sports and GT cars with the characteristics listed in part (a).
d. Provide a 95% prediction interval for overall quality for the Honda Accord described in part (b).
e. The overall rating reported by *Car and Driver* for the Honda Accord was 8.65. How does this rating compare to the estimates you developed in parts (b) and (d)?

15.7 Qualitative Independent Variables

The independent variables may be qualitative or quantitative.

Thus far, the examples we have considered involved quantitative independent variables such as student population, distance traveled, and number of deliveries. In many situations, however, we must work with **qualitative independent variables** such as gender (male, female), method of payment (cash, credit card, check), and so on. The purpose of this section is to show how qualitative variables are handled in regression analysis. To illustrate the use and interpretation of a qualitative independent variable, we will consider a problem facing the managers of Johnson Filtration, Inc.

An Example: Johnson Filtration, Inc.

Johnson Filtration, Inc., provides maintenance service for water-filtration systems throughout southern Florida. Customers contact Johnson with requests for maintenance service on

TABLE 15.5 DATA FOR THE JOHNSON FILTRATION EXAMPLE

Service Call	Months Since Last Service	Type of Repair	Repair Time in Hours
1	2	electrical	2.9
2	6	mechanical	3.0
3	8	electrical	4.8
4	3	mechanical	1.8
5	2	electrical	2.9
6	7	electrical	4.9
7	9	mechanical	4.2
8	8	mechanical	4.8
9	4	electrical	4.4
10	6	electrical	4.5

their water-filtration systems. To estimate the service time and the service cost, Johnson's managers want to predict the repair time necessary for each maintenance request. Hence, repair time in hours is the dependent variable. Repair time is believed to be related to two factors, the number of months since the last maintenance service and the type of repair problem (mechanical or electrical). Data for a sample of 10 service calls are reported in Table 15.5.

Let y denote the repair time in hours and x_1 denote the number of months since the last maintenance service. The regression model that uses only x_1 to predict y is

$$y = \beta_0 + \beta_1 x_1 + \epsilon$$

Using Minitab to develop the estimated regression equation, we obtained the output shown in Figure 15.7. The estimated regression equation is

$$\hat{y} = 2.15 + .304x_1 \tag{15.16}$$

At the .05 level of significance, the p-value of .016 for the t (or F) test indicates that the number of months since the last service is significantly related to repair time. R-sq = 53.4% indicates that x_1 alone explains 53.4% of the variability in repair time.

In the Minitab output the variable names Months *and* Time *were entered as the column headings on the worksheet; thus,* $x_1 =$ Months *and* $y =$ Time.

FIGURE 15.7 MINITAB OUTPUT FOR JOHNSON FILTRATION WITH MONTHS SINCE LAST SERVICE (x_1) AS THE INDEPENDENT VARIABLE

```
The regression equation is
Time = 2.15 + 0.304 Months

Predictor     Coef  SE Coef     T      p
Constant    2.1473   0.6050  3.55  0.008
Months      0.3041   0.1004  3.03  0.016

S = 0.7810    R-sq = 53.4%    R-sq(adj) = 47.6%

Analysis of Variance

SOURCE           DF       SS      MS     F      p
Regression        1   5.5960  5.5960  9.17  0.016
Residual Error    8   4.8800  0.6100
Total             9  10.4760
```

TABLE 15.6 DATA FOR THE JOHNSON FILTRATION EXAMPLE WITH TYPE OF REPAIR INDICATED BY A DUMMY VARIABLE ($x_2 = 0$ FOR MECHANICAL; $x_2 = 1$ FOR ELECTRICAL)

Customer	Months Since Last Service (x_1)	Type of Repair (x_2)	Repair Time in Hours (y)
1	2	1	2.9
2	6	0	3.0
3	8	1	4.8
4	3	0	1.8
5	2	1	2.9
6	7	1	4.9
7	9	0	4.2
8	8	0	4.8
9	4	1	4.4
10	6	1	4.5

CD file

Johnson

To incorporate the type of repair into the regression model, we define the following variable.

$$x_2 = \begin{cases} 0 \text{ if the type of repair is mechanical} \\ 1 \text{ if the type of repair is electrical} \end{cases}$$

In regression analysis x_2 is called a **dummy** or ***indicator* variable**. Using this dummy variable, we can write the multiple regression model as

$$y = \beta_0 + \beta_1 x_1 + \beta_2 x_2 + \epsilon$$

Table 15.6 is the revised data set that includes the values of the dummy variable. Using Minitab and the data in Table 15.6, we can develop estimates of the model parameters. The Minitab output in Figure 15.8 shows that the estimated multiple regression equation is

$$\hat{y} = .93 + .388x_1 + 1.26x_2 \quad \textbf{(15.17)}$$

At the .05 level of significance, the p-value of .001 associated with the F test ($F = 21.36$) indicates that the regression relationship is significant. The t test part of the printout in Figure 15.8 shows that both months since last service (p-value $= .000$) and type of repair (p-value $= .005$) are statistically significant. In addition, R-sq $= 85.9\%$ and R-sq(adj) $=$ 81.9% indicate that the estimated regression equation does a good job of explaining the variability in repair times. Thus, equation (15.17) should prove helpful in estimating the repair time necessary for the various service calls.

Interpreting the Parameters

The multiple regression equation for the Johnson Filtration example is

$$E(y) = \beta_0 + \beta_1 x_1 + \beta_2 x_2 \quad \textbf{(15.18)}$$

To understand how to interpret the parameters β_0, β_1, and β_2 when a qualitative variable is present, consider the case when $x_2 = 0$ (mechanical repair). Using $E(y \mid \text{mechanical})$ to denote the mean or expected value of repair time *given* a mechanical repair, we have

$$E(y \mid \text{mechanical}) = \beta_0 + \beta_1 x_1 + \beta_2(0) = \beta_0 + \beta_1 x_1 \quad \textbf{(15.19)}$$

FIGURE 15.8 MINITAB OUTPUT FOR JOHNSON FILTRATION WITH MONTHS SINCE LAST SERVICE (x_1) AND TYPE OF REPAIR (x_2) AS THE INDEPENDENT VARIABLES

In the Minitab output the variable names Months, Type, *and* Time *were entered as the column headings on the worksheet; thus,* x_1 = Months, x_2 = Type, *and* y = Time.

```
The regression equation is
Time = 0.930 + 0.388 Months + 1.26 Type

Predictor       Coef   SE Coef      T      p
Constant      0.9305    0.4670   1.99  0.087
Months       0.38762   0.06257   6.20  0.000
Type          1.2627    0.3141   4.02  0.005

S = 0.4590   R-sq = 85.9%   R-sq(adj) = 81.9%

Analysis of Variance

SOURCE           DF        SS      MS      F      p
Regression        2    9.0009  4.5005  21.36  0.001
Residual Error    7    1.4751  0.2107
Total             9   10.4760
```

Similarly, for an electrical repair ($x_2 = 1$), we have

$$E(y \mid \text{electrical}) = \beta_0 + \beta_1 x_1 + \beta_2(1) = \beta_0 + \beta_1 x_1 + \beta_2 \qquad \textbf{(15.20)}$$
$$= (\beta_0 + \beta_2) + \beta_1 x_1$$

Comparing equations (15.19) and (15.20), we see that the mean repair time is a linear function of x_1 for both mechanical and electrical repairs. The slope of both equations is β_1, but the y-intercept differs. The y-intercept is β_0 in equation (15.19) for mechanical repairs and $(\beta_0 + \beta_2)$ in equation (15.20) for electrical repairs. The interpretation of β_2 is that it indicates the difference between the mean repair time for an electrical repair and the mean repair time for a mechanical repair.

If β_2 is positive, the mean repair time for an electrical repair will be greater than that for a mechanical repair; if β_2 is negative, the mean repair time for an electrical repair will be less than that for a mechanical repair. Finally, if $\beta_2 = 0$, there is no difference in the mean repair time between electrical and mechanical repairs and the type of repair is not related to the repair time.

Using the estimated multiple regression equation $\hat{y} = .93 + .388x_1 + 1.26x_2$, we see that .93 is the estimate of β_0 and 1.26 is the estimate of β_2. Thus, when $x_2 = 0$ (mechanical repair)

$$\hat{y} = .93 + .388x_1 \qquad \textbf{(15.21)}$$

and when $x_2 = 1$ (electrical repair)

$$\hat{y} = .93 + .388x_1 + 1.26(1) \qquad \textbf{(15.22)}$$
$$= 2.19 + .388x_1$$

In effect, the use of a dummy variable for type of repair provides two equations that can be used to predict the repair time, one corresponding to mechanical repairs and one

FIGURE 15.9 SCATTER DIAGRAM FOR THE JOHNSON FILTRATION REPAIR DATA FROM TABLE 15.6

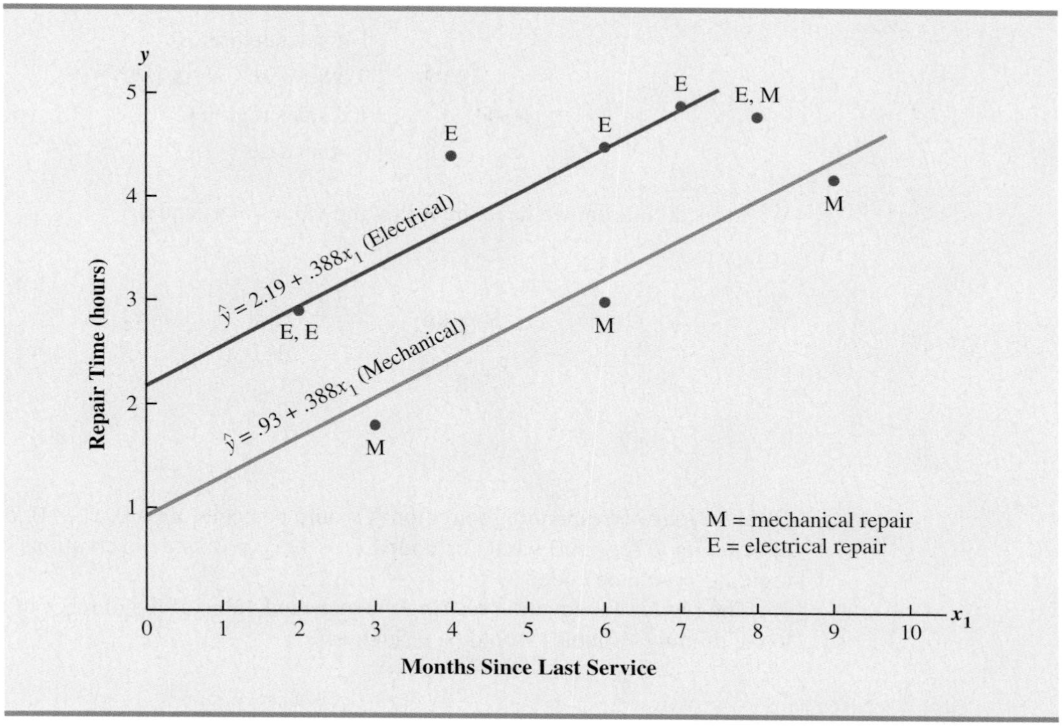

corresponding to electrical repairs. In addition, with $b_2 = 1.26$, we learn that, on average, electrical repairs require 1.26 hours longer than mechanical repairs.

Figure 15.9 is the plot of the Johnson data from Table 15.6. Repair time in hours (y) is represented by the vertical axis and months since last service (x_1) is represented by the horizontal axis. A data point for a mechanical repair is indicated by an M and a data point for an electrical repair is indicated by an E. Equations (15.21) and (15.22) are plotted on the graph to show graphically the two equations that can be used to predict the repair time, one corresponding to mechanical repairs and one corresponding to electrical repairs.

More Complex Qualitative Variables

A qualitative variable with k levels must be modeled using k − 1 dummy variables. Care must be taken in defining and interpreting the dummy variables.

Because the qualitative variable for the Johnson Filtration example had two levels (mechanical and electrical), defining a dummy variable with zero indicating a mechanical repair and one indicating an electrical repair was easy. However, when a qualitative variable has more than two levels, care must be taken in both defining and interpreting the dummy variables. As we will show, if a qualitative variable has k levels, $k - 1$ dummy variables are required, with each dummy variable being coded as 0 or 1.

For example, suppose a manufacturer of copy machines organized the sales territories for a particular state into three regions: A, B, and C. The managers want to use regression analysis to help predict the number of copiers sold per week. With the number of units sold as the dependent variable, they are considering several independent variables (the number of sales personnel, advertising expenditures, and so on). Suppose the managers believe sales region is also an important factor in predicting the number of copiers sold. Because sales region is a qualitative variable with three levels, A, B and C, we will need $3 - 1 = 2$ dummy variables to represent the sales region. Each variable can be coded 0 or 1 as follows.

$$x_1 = \begin{cases} 1 \text{ if sales region B} \\ 0 \text{ otherwise} \end{cases}$$

$$x_2 = \begin{cases} 1 \text{ if sales region C} \\ 0 \text{ otherwise} \end{cases}$$

With this definition, we have the following values of x_1 and x_2.

Region	x_1	x_2
A	0	0
B	1	0
C	0	1

Observations corresponding to region A would be coded $x_1 = 0, x_2 = 0$; observations corresponding to region B would be coded $x_1 = 1, x_2 = 0$; and observations corresponding to region C would be coded $x_1 = 0, x_2 = 1$.

The regression equation relating the expected value of the number of units sold, $E(y)$, to the dummy variables would be written as

$$E(y) = \beta_0 + \beta_1 x_1 + \beta_2 x_2$$

To help us interpret the parameters β_0, β_1, and β_2, consider the following three variations of the regression equation.

$$\begin{aligned} E(y \mid \text{region A}) &= \beta_0 + \beta_1(0) + \beta_2(0) = \beta_0 \\ E(y \mid \text{region B}) &= \beta_0 + \beta_1(1) + \beta_2(0) = \beta_0 + \beta_1 \\ E(y \mid \text{region C}) &= \beta_0 + \beta_1(0) + \beta_2(1) = \beta_0 + \beta_2 \end{aligned}$$

Thus, β_0 is the mean or expected value of sales for region A; β_1 is the difference between the mean number of units sold in region B and the mean number of units sold in region A; and β_2 is the difference between the mean number of units sold in region C and the mean number of units sold in region A.

Two dummy variables were required because sales region is a qualitative variable with three levels. But the assignment of $x_1 = 0, x_2 = 0$ to indicate region A, $x_1 = 1, x_2 = 0$ to indicate region B, and $x_1 = 0, x_2 = 1$ to indicate region C was arbitrary. For example, we could have chosen $x_1 = 1$, $x_2 = 0$ to indicate region A, $x_1 = 0$, $x_2 = 0$ to indicate region B, and $x_1 = 0, x_2 = 1$ to indicate region C. In that case, β_1 would have been interpreted as the mean difference between regions A and B and β_2 as the mean difference between regions C and B.

The important point to remember is that when a qualitative variable has k levels, $k - 1$ dummy variables are required in the multiple regression analysis. Thus, if the sales region example had a fourth region, labeled D, three dummy variables would be necessary. For example, the three dummy variables can be coded as follows.

$$x_1 = \begin{cases} 1 \text{ if sales region B} \\ 0 \text{ otherwise} \end{cases} \quad x_2 = \begin{cases} 1 \text{ if sales region C} \\ 0 \text{ otherwise} \end{cases} \quad x_3 = \begin{cases} 1 \text{ if sales region D} \\ 0 \text{ otherwise} \end{cases}$$

Exercises

Methods

SELF test

32. Consider a regression study involving a dependent variable y, a quantitative independent variable x_1, and a qualitative variable with two levels (level 1 and level 2).
    a. Write a multiple regression equation relating x_1 and the qualitative variable to y.
    b. What is the expected value of y corresponding to level 1 of the qualitative variable?
    c. What is the expected value of y corresponding to level 2 of the qualitative variable?
    d. Interpret the parameters in your regression equation.

33. Consider a regression study involving a dependent variable y, a quantitative independent variable x_1, and a qualitative independent variable with three possible levels (level 1, level 2, and level 3).
    a. How many dummy variables are required to represent the qualitative variable?
    b. Write a multiple regression equation relating x_1 and the qualitative variable to y.
    c. Interpret the parameters in your regression equation.

Applications

SELF test

34. Management proposed the following regression model to predict sales at a fast-food outlet.

$$y = \beta_0 + \beta_1 x_1 + \beta_2 x_2 + \beta_3 x_3 + \epsilon$$

where

$$x_1 = \text{number of competitors within one mile}$$
$$x_2 = \text{population within one mile (1000s)}$$
$$x_3 = \begin{cases} 1 \text{ if drive-up window present} \\ 0 \text{ otherwise} \end{cases}$$
$$y = \text{sales (\$1000s)}$$

The following estimated regression equation was developed after 20 outlets were surveyed.

$$\hat{y} = 10.1 - 4.2x_1 + 6.8x_2 + 15.3x_3$$

    a. What is the expected amount of sales attributable to the drive-up window?
    b. Predict sales for a store with two competitors, a population of 8000 within one mile, and no drive-up window.
    c. Predict sales for a store with one competitor, a population of 3000 within one mile, and a drive-up window.

35. Refer to the Johnson Filtration problem introduced in this section. Suppose that in addition to information on the number of months since the machine was serviced and whether a mechanical or an electrical repair was necessary, the managers obtained a list showing which repairperson performed the service. The revised data follow.

CD file
Repair

Repair Time in Hours	Months Since Last Service	Type of Repair	Repairperson
2.9	2	Electrical	Dave Newton
3.0	6	Mechanical	Dave Newton
4.8	8	Electrical	Bob Jones

(continued)

Repair Time in Hours	Months Since Last Service	Type of Repair	Repairperson
1.8	3	Mechanical	Dave Newton
2.9	2	Electrical	Dave Newton
4.9	7	Electrical	Bob Jones
4.2	9	Mechanical	Bob Jones
4.8	8	Mechanical	Bob Jones
4.4	4	Electrical	Bob Jones
4.5	6	Electrical	Dave Newton

a. Ignore for now the months since the last maintenance service (x_1) and the repairperson who performed the service. Develop the estimated simple linear regression equation to predict the repair time (y) given the type of repair (x_2). Recall that $x_2 = 0$ if the type of repair is mechanical and 1 if the type of repair is electrical.

b. Does the equation that you developed in part (a) provide a good fit for the observed data? Explain.

c. Ignore for now the months since the last maintenance service and the type of repair associated with the machine. Develop the estimated simple linear regression equation to predict the repair time given the repairperson who performed the service. Let $x_3 = 0$ if Bob Jones performed the service and $x_3 = 1$ if Dave Newton performed the service.

d. Does the equation that you developed in part (c) provide a good fit for the observed data? Explain.

36. This problem is an extension of the situation described in exercise 35.

a. Develop the estimated regression equation to predict the repair time given the number of months since the last maintenance service, the type of repair, and the repairperson who performed the service.

b. At the .05 level of significance, test whether the estimated regression equation developed in part (a) represents a significant relationship between the independent variables and the dependent variable.

c. Is the addition of the independent variable x_3, the repairperson who performed the service, statistically significant? Use $\alpha = .05$. What explanation can you give for the results observed?

37. The National Football League rates prospects by position on a scale that ranges from 5 to 9. The ratings are interpreted as follows: 8–9 should start the first year; 7.0–7.9 should start; 6.0–6.9 will make the team as backup; and 5.0–5.9 can make the club and contribute. The following table shows the position, weight, time in seconds to run 40 yards, and ratings for 25 NFL prospects (*USA Today,* April 14, 2000).

CD file

Football

	Position	Weight (pounds)	Time (seconds)	Rating
Cosey Coleman	Guard	322	5.38	7.4
Travis Claridge	Guard	303	5.18	7.0
Kaulana Noa	Guard	317	5.34	6.8
Leander Jordan	Guard	330	5.46	6.7
Chad Clifton	Guard	334	5.18	6.3
Manula Savea	Guard	308	5.32	6.1
Ryan Johanningmeir	Guard	310	5.28	6.0
Mark Tauscher	Guard	318	5.37	6.0
Blaine Saipaia	Guard	321	5.25	6.0
Richard Mercier	Guard	295	5.34	5.8
Damion McIntosh	Guard	328	5.31	5.3

	Position	Weight (pounds)	Time (seconds)	Rating
Jeno James	Guard	320	5.64	5.0
Al Jackson	Guard	304	5.20	5.0
Chris Samuels	Offensive tackle	325	4.95	8.5
Stockar McDougle	Offensive tackle	361	5.50	8.0
Chris McIngosh	Offensive tackle	315	5.39	7.8
Adrian Klemm	Offensive tackle	307	4.98	7.6
Todd Wade	Offensive tackle	326	5.20	7.3
Marvel Smith	Offensive tackle	320	5.36	7.1
Michael Thompson	Offensive tackle	287	5.05	6.8
Bobby Williams	Offensive tackle	332	5.26	6.8
Darnell Alford	Offensive tackle	334	5.55	6.4
Terrance Beadles	Offensive tackle	312	5.15	6.3
Tutan Reyes	Offensive tackle	299	5.35	6.1
Greg Robinson-Ran	Offensive tackle	333	5.59	6.0

a. Develop a dummy variable that will account for the player's position.
b. Develop an estimated regression equation to show how rating is related to position, weight, and time to run 40 yards.
c. At the .05 level of significance, test whether the estimated regression equation developed in part (b) indicates a significant relationship between the independent variables and the dependent variable.
d. Does the estimated regression equation provide a good fit for the observed data? Explain.
e. Is position a significant factor in the player's rating? Use $\alpha = .05$. Explain.
f. Suppose a new offensive tackle prospect who weighs 300 pounds ran the 40 yards in 5.1 seconds. Use the estimated regression equation developed in part (b) to estimate the rating for this player.

38. A 10-year study conducted by the American Heart Association provided data on how age, blood pressure, and smoking relate to the risk of strokes. Assume that the following data are from a portion of this study. Risk is interpreted as the probability (times 100) that the patient will have a stroke over the next 10-year period. For the smoking variable, define a dummy variable with 1 indicating a smoker and 0 indicating a nonsmoker.

CD file
Stroke

Risk	Age	Pressure	Smoker
12	57	152	No
24	67	163	No
13	58	155	No
56	86	177	Yes
28	59	196	No
51	76	189	Yes
18	56	155	Yes
31	78	120	No
37	80	135	Yes
15	78	98	No
22	71	152	No
36	70	173	Yes
15	67	135	Yes
48	77	209	Yes
15	60	199	No
36	82	119	Yes
8	66	166	No
34	80	125	Yes
3	62	117	No
37	59	207	Yes

a. Develop an estimated regression equation that relates risk of a stroke to the person's age, blood pressure, and whether the person is a smoker.
b. Is smoking a significant factor in the risk of a stroke? Explain. Use $\alpha = .05$.
c. What is the probability of a stroke over the next 10 years for Art Speen, a 68-year-old smoker who has blood pressure of 175? What action might the physician recommend for this patient?

15.8 Residual Analysis

In Chapter 14 we pointed out that standardized residuals are frequently used in residual plots and in the identification of outliers. The general formula for the standardized residual for observation i follows.

STANDARDIZED RESIDUAL FOR OBSERVATION i

$$\frac{y_i - \hat{y}_i}{s_{y_i - \hat{y}_i}} \tag{15.23}$$

where

$$s_{y_i - \hat{y}_i} = \text{the standard deviation of residual } i$$

The general formula for the standard deviation of residual i is defined as follows.

STANDARD DEVIATION OF RESIDUAL i

$$s_{y_i - \hat{y}_i} = s\sqrt{1 - h_i} \tag{15.24}$$

where

$$s = \text{standard error of the estimate}$$
$$h_i = \text{leverage of observation } i$$

As we stated in Chapter 14, the **leverage** of an observation is determined by how far the values of the independent variables are from their means. The computation of h_i, $s_{y_i - \hat{y}_i}$, and hence the standardized residual for observation i in multiple regression analysis is too complex to be done by hand. However, the standardized residuals can be easily obtained as part of the output from statistical software packages. Table 15.7 lists the predicted values, the residuals, and the standardized residuals for the Butler Trucking example presented previously in this chapter; we obtained these values by using the Minitab statistical software package. The predicted values in the table are based on the estimated regression equation $\hat{y} = -.869 + .0611x_1 + .923x_2$.

The standardized residuals and the predicted values of y from Table 15.7 are used in Figure 15.10, the standardized residual plot for the Butler Trucking multiple regression example. This standardized residual plot does not indicate any unusual abnormalities. Also, all of the standardized residuals are between -2 and $+2$; hence, we have no reason to question the assumption that the error term ϵ is normally distributed. We conclude that the model assumptions are reasonable.

TABLE 15.7 RESIDUALS AND STANDARDIZED RESIDUALS FOR THE BUTLER TRUCKING REGRESSION ANALYSIS

Miles Traveled (x_1)	Deliveries (x_2)	Travel Time (y)	Predicted Value ($\hat{y}$)	Residual ($y - \hat{y}$)	Standardized Residual
100	4	9.3	8.93846	0.361541	0.78344
50	3	4.8	4.95830	−0.158304	−0.34962
100	4	8.9	8.93846	−0.038460	−0.08334
100	2	6.5	7.09161	−0.591609	−1.30929
50	2	4.2	4.03488	0.165121	0.38167
80	2	6.2	5.86892	0.331083	0.65431
75	3	7.4	6.48667	0.913331	1.68917
65	4	6.0	6.79875	−0.798749	−1.77372
90	3	7.6	7.40369	0.196311	0.36703
90	2	6.1	6.48026	−0.380263	−0.77639

A normal probability plot also can be used to determine whether the distribution of ϵ appears to be normal. The procedure and interpretation for a normal probability plot were discussed in Section 14.8. The same procedure is appropriate for multiple regression. Again, we would use a statistical software package to perform the computations and provide the normal probability plot.

Detecting Outliers

An **outlier** is an observation that is unusual in comparison with the other data; in other words, an outlier does not fit the pattern of the other data. In Chapter 14 we showed an example of an outlier and discussed how standardized residuals can be used to detect outliers.

FIGURE 15.10 STANDARDIZED RESIDUAL PLOT FOR BUTLER TRUCKING

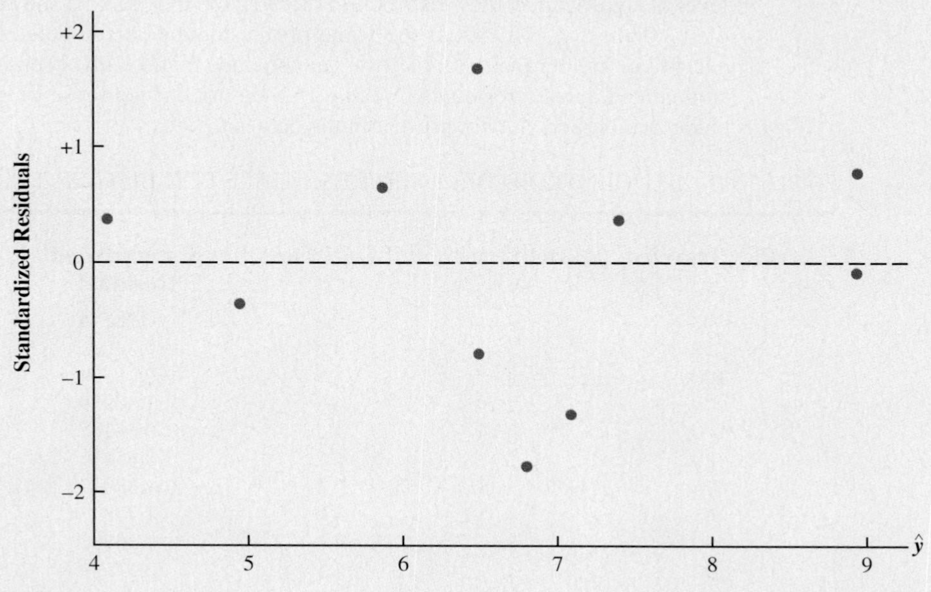

Minitab classifies an observation as an outlier if the value of its standardized residual is less than −2 or greater than +2. Applying this rule to the standardized residuals for the Butler Trucking example (see Table 15.7), we do not detect any outliers in the data set.

In general, the presence of one or more outliers in a data set tends to increase s, the standard error of the estimate, and hence increase $s_{y-\hat{y}_i}$, the standard deviation of residual i. Because $s_{y_i-\hat{y}_i}$ appears in the denominator of the formula for the standardized residual (15.23), the size of the standardized residual will decrease as s increases. As a result, even though a residual may be unusually large, the large denominator in expression (15.23) may cause the standardized residual rule to fail to identify the observation as being an outlier. We can circumvent this difficulty by using a form of the standardized residuals called **studentized deleted residuals**.

Studentized Deleted Residuals and Outliers

Suppose the ith observation is deleted from the data set and a new estimated regression equation is developed with the remaining $n - 1$ observations. Let $s_{(i)}$ denote the standard error of the estimate based on the data set with the ith observation deleted. If we compute the standard deviation of residual i using $s_{(i)}$ instead of s, and then compute the standardized residual for observation i using the revised $s_{y_i-\hat{y}_i}$ value, the resulting standardized residual is called a studentized deleted residual. If the ith observation is an outlier, $s_{(i)}$ will be less than s. The absolute value of the ith studentized deleted residual therefore will be larger than the absolute value of the standardized residual. In this sense, studentized deleted residuals may detect outliers that standardized residuals do not detect.

Many statistical software packages provide an option for obtaining studentized deleted residuals. Using Minitab, we obtained the studentized deleted residuals for the Butler Trucking example; the results are reported in Table 15.8. The t distribution can be used to determine whether the studentized deleted residuals indicate the presence of outliers. Recall that p denotes the number of independent variables and n denotes the number of observations. Hence, if we delete the ith observation, the number of observations in the reduced data set is $n - 1$; in this case the error sum of squares has $(n - 1) - p - 1$ degrees of freedom. For the Butler Trucking example with $n = 10$ and $p = 2$, the degrees of freedom for the error sum of squares with the ith observation deleted is $9 - 2 - 1 = 6$. At a .05 level of significance, the t distribution (Table 2 of Appendix B) shows that with six degrees of freedom, $t_{.025} = 2.447$. If the value of the ith studentized deleted residual is less than −2.447 or greater than +2.447, we can conclude that the ith observation is an outlier. The studentized deleted residuals in Table 15.8 do not exceed those limits; therefore, we conclude that outliers are not present in the data set.

TABLE 15.8 STUDENTIZED DELETED RESIDUALS FOR BUTLER TRUCKING

Miles Traveled (x_1)	Deliveries (x_2)	Travel Time (y)	Standardized Residual	Studentized Deleted Residual
100	4	9.3	0.78344	0.75939
50	3	4.8	−0.34962	−0.32654
100	4	8.9	−0.08334	−0.07720
100	2	6.5	−1.30929	−1.39494
50	2	4.2	0.38167	0.35709
80	2	6.2	0.65431	0.62519
75	3	7.4	1.68917	2.03187
65	4	6.0	−1.77372	−2.21314
90	3	7.6	0.36703	0.34312
90	2	6.1	−0.77639	−0.75190

TABLE 15.9 LEVERAGE AND COOK'S DISTANCE MEASURES FOR BUTLER TRUCKING

Miles Traveled (x_1)	Deliveries (x_2)	Travel Time (y)	Leverage (h_i)	Cook's D (D_i)
100	4	9.3	.351704	.110994
50	3	4.8	.375863	.024536
100	4	8.9	.351704	.001256
100	2	6.5	.378451	.347923
50	2	4.2	.430220	.036663
80	2	6.2	.220557	.040381
75	3	7.4	.110009	.117562
65	4	6.0	.382657	.650029
90	3	7.6	.129098	.006656
90	2	6.1	.269737	.074217

Influential Observations

In Section 14.9 we discussed how the leverage of an observation can be used to identify observations for which the value of the independent variable may have a strong influence on the regression results. As we indicated in the discussion of standardized residuals, the leverage of an observation, denoted h_i, measures how far the values of the independent variables are from their mean values. The leverage values are easily obtained as part of the output from statistical software packages. Minitab computes the leverage values and uses the rule of thumb $h_i > 3(p + 1)/n$ to identify **influential observations.** For the Butler Trucking example with $p = 2$ independent variables and $n = 10$ observations, the critical value for leverage is $3(2 + 1)/10 = .9$. The leverage values for the Butler Trucking example obtained by using Minitab are reported in Table 15.9. Because h_i does not exceed .9, we do not detect influential observations in the data set.

Using Cook's Distance Measure to Identify Influential Observations

TABLE 15.10 DATA SET ILLUSTRATING POTENTIAL PROBLEM USING THE LEVERAGE CRITERION

x_i	y_i	Leverage h_i
1	18	.204170
1	21	.204170
2	22	.164205
3	21	.138141
4	23	.125977
4	24	.125977
5	26	.127715
15	39	.909644

A problem that can arise in using leverage to identify influential observations is that an observation can be identified as having high leverage and not necessarily be influential in terms of the resulting estimated regression equation. For example, Table 15.10 is a data set consisting of eight observations and their corresponding leverage values (obtained by using Minitab). Because the leverage for the eighth observation is $.91 > .75$ (the critical leverage value), this observation is identified as influential. Before reaching any final conclusions, however, let us consider the situation from a different perspective.

Figure 15.11 shows the scatter diagram corresponding to the data set in Table 15.10. We used Minitab to develop the following estimated regression equation for these data.

$$\hat{y} = 18.2 + 1.39x$$

The straight line in Figure 15.11 is the graph of this equation. Now, let us delete the observation $x = 15$, $y = 39$ from the data set and fit a new estimated regression equation to the remaining seven observations; the new estimated regression equation is

$$\hat{y} = 18.1 + 1.42x$$

We note that the y-intercept and slope of the new estimated regression equation are not significantly different from the values obtained by using all the data. Although the leverage

FIGURE 15.11 SCATTER DIAGRAM FOR THE DATA SET IN TABLE 15.10

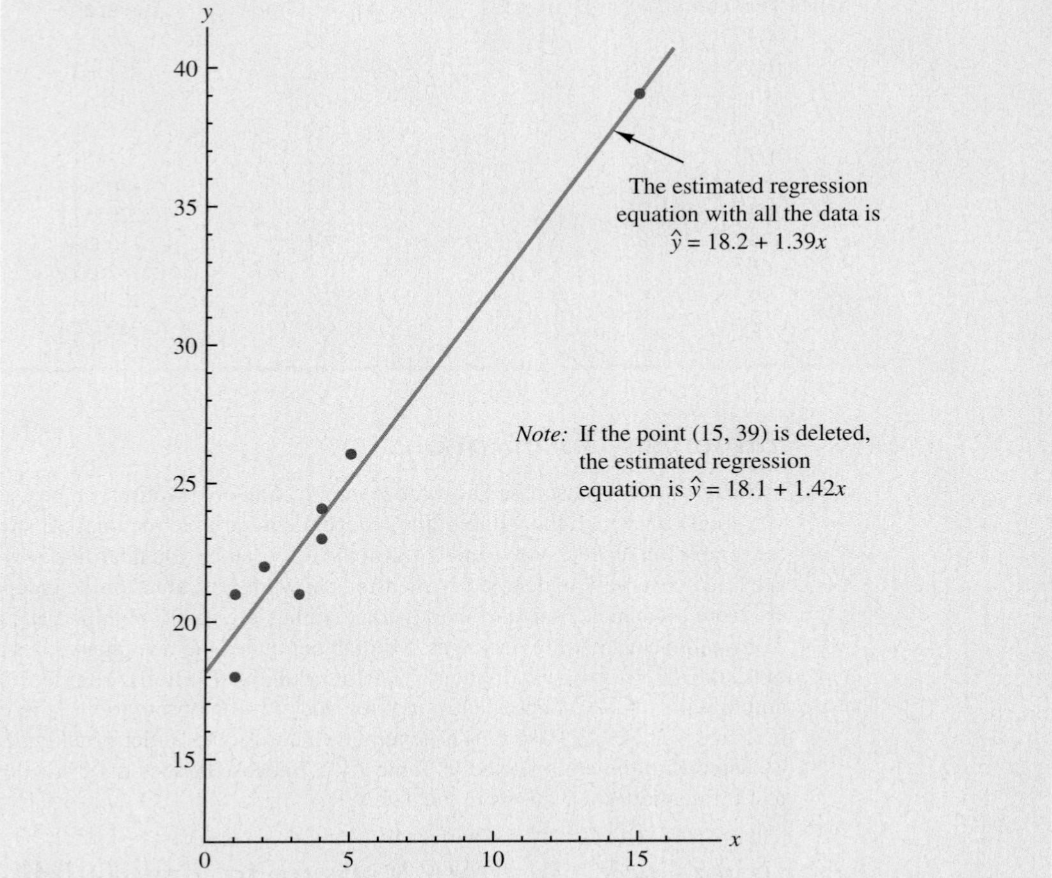

criterion identified the eighth observation as influential, this observation clearly had little influence on the results obtained. Thus, in some situations using only leverage to identify influential observations can lead to wrong conclusions.

Cook's distance measure uses both the leverage of observation i, h_i, and the residual for observation i, $(y_i - \hat{y}_i)$, to determine whether the observation is influential.

COOK'S DISTANCE MEASURE

$$D_i = \frac{(y_i - \hat{y}_i)^2}{(p - 1)s^2}\left[\frac{h_i}{(1 - h_i)^2}\right] \tag{15.25}$$

where

D_i = Cook's distance measure for observation i
$y_i - \hat{y}_i$ = the residual for observation i
h_i = the leverage for observation i
p = the number of independent variables
s = the standard error of the estimate

The value of Cook's distance measure will be large and indicate an influential observation if the residual or the leverage is large. As a rule of thumb, values of $D_i > 1$ indicate that the ith observation is influential and should be studied further. The last column of Table 15.9 provides Cook's distance measure for the Butler Trucking problem as given by Minitab. Observation 8 with $D_i = .650029$ has the most influence. However, applying the rule $D_i > 1$, we should not be concerned about the presence of influential observations in the Butler Trucking data set.

NOTES AND COMMENTS

1. The procedures for identifying outliers and influential observations provide warnings about the potential effects some observations may have on the regression results. Each outlier and influential observation warrants careful examination. If data errors are found, the errors can be corrected and the regression analysis repeated. In general, outliers and influential observations should not be removed from the data set unless clear evidence shows that they are not based on elements of the population being studied and should not have been included in the original data set.

2. To determine whether the value of Cook's distance measure D_i is large enough to conclude that the ith observation is influential, we can also compare the value of D_i to the 50th percentile of an F distribution (denoted $F_{.50}$) with $p + 1$ numerator degrees of freedom and $n - p - 1$ denominator degrees of freedom. F tables corresponding to a .50 level of significance must be available to carry out the test. The rule of thumb we provided ($D_i > 1$) is based on the fact that the table value is close to one for a wide variety of cases.

Exercises

Methods

SELF test

39. Data for two variables, x and y, follow.

x_i	1	2	3	4	5
y_i	3	7	5	11	14

a. Develop the estimated regression equation for these data.
b. Plot the standardized residuals versus $\hat{y}$. Do there appear to be any outliers in these data? Explain.
c. Compute the studentized deleted residuals for these data. At the .05 level of significance, can any of these observations be classified as an outlier? Explain.

40. Data for two variables, x and y, follow.

x_i	22	24	26	28	40
y_i	12	21	31	35	70

a. Develop the estimated regression equation for these data.
b. Compute the studentized deleted residuals for these data. At the .05 level of significance, can any of these observations be classified as an outlier? Explain.
c. Compute the leverage values for these data. Do there appear to be any influential observations in these data? Explain.
d. Compute Cook's distance measure for these data. Are any observations influential? Explain.

Applications

SELF test

41. Exercise 5 gave the following data on weekly gross revenue, television advertising, and newspaper advertising for Showtime Movie Theaters.

CD file
Showtime

Weekly Gross Revenue ($1000s)	Television Advertising ($1000s)	Newspaper Advertising ($1000s)
96	5.0	1.5
90	2.0	2.0
95	4.0	1.5
92	2.5	2.5
95	3.0	3.3
94	3.5	2.3
94	2.5	4.2
94	3.0	2.5

a. Find an estimated regression equation relating weekly gross revenue to television and newspaper advertising.
b. Plot the standardized residuals against $\hat{y}$. Does the residual plot support the assumptions about ϵ? Explain.
c. Check for any outliers in these data. What are your conclusions?
d. Are there any influential observations? Explain.

42. The following data show the curb weight, horsepower, and ¼-mile speed for 16 popular sports and GT cars. Suppose that the price of each sports and GT car is also available. The complete data set is as follows:

CD file
Auto2

Sports & GT Car	Price ($1000s)	Curb Weight (lb.)	Horsepower	Speed at ¼ mile (mph)
Accura Integra Type R	25.035	2577	195	90.7
Accura NSX-T	93.758	3066	290	108.0
BMW Z3 2.8	40.900	2844	189	93.2
Chevrolet Camaro Z28	24.865	3439	305	103.2
Chevrolet Corvette Convertible	50.144	3246	345	102.1
Dodge Viper RT/10	69.742	3319	450	116.2
Ford Mustang GT	23.200	3227	225	91.7
Honda Prelude Type SH	26.382	3042	195	89.7
Mercedes-Benz CLK320	44.988	3240	215	93.0
Mercedes-Benz SLK230	42.762	3025	185	92.3
Mitsubishi 3000GT VR-4	47.518	3737	320	99.0
Nissan 240SX SE	25.066	2862	155	84.6
Pontiac Firebird Trans Am	27.770	3455	305	103.2
Porsche Boxster	45.560	2822	201	93.2
Toyota Supra Turbo	40.989	3505	320	105.0
Volvo C70	41.120	3285	236	97.0

a. Find the estimated regression equation, which uses price and horsepower to predict ¼-mile speed.
b. Plot the standardized residuals against $\hat{y}$. Does the residual plot support the assumption about ϵ? Explain.
c. Check for any outliers. What are your conclusions?
d. Are there any influential observations? Explain.

CD file

LPGA

43. The Ladies Professional Golfers Association (LPGA) maintains statistics on performance and earnings for members of the LPGA Tour. Year-end performance statistics for the 30 players who had the highest total earnings in LPGA Tour events for 2005 appear on the data disk in the file named LPGA (www.lpga.com, 2006). Earnings ($1000) is the total earnings in thousands of dollars; Scoring Avg. is the average score for all events; Greens in Reg. is the percentage of time a player is able to hit the green in regulation; and Putting Avg. is the average number of putts taken on greens hit in regulation. A green is considered hit in regulation if any part of the ball is touching the putting surface and the difference between the value of par for the hole and the number of strokes taken to hit the green is at least 2.
    a. Develop an estimated regression equation that can be used to predict the average score for all events given the percentage of time a player is able to hit the green in regulation and the average number of putts taken on greens hit in regulation.
    b. Plot the standardized residuals against $\hat{y}$. Does the residual plot support the assumption about ϵ? Explain.
    c. Check for any outliers. What are your conclusions?
    d. Are there any influential observations? Explain.

15.9 Logistic Regression

In many regression applications the dependent variable may only assume two discrete values. For instance, a bank might like to develop an estimated regression equation for predicting whether a person will be approved for a credit card. The dependent variable can be coded as $y = 1$ if the bank approves the request for a credit card and $y = 0$ if the bank rejects the request for a credit card. Using logistic regression we can estimate the probability that the bank will approve the request for a credit card given a particular set of values for the chosen independent variables.

Let us consider an application of logistic regression involving a direct mail promotion being used by Simmons Stores. Simmons owns and operates a national chain of women's apparel stores. Five thousand copies of an expensive four-color sales catalog have been printed, and each catalog includes a coupon that provides a $50 discount on purchases of $200 or more. The catalogs are expensive and Simmons would like to send them to only those customers who have the highest probability of using the coupon.

Management thinks that annual spending at Simmons Stores and whether a customer has a Simmons credit card are two variables that might be helpful in predicting whether a customer who receives the catalog will use the coupon. Simmons conducted a pilot study using a random sample of 50 Simmons credit card customers and 50 other customers who do not have a Simmons credit card. Simmons sent the catalog to each of the 100 customers selected. At the end of a test period, Simmons noted whether the customer used the coupon. The sample data for the first 10 catalog recipients are shown in Table 15.11. The amount each customer spent last year at Simmons is shown in thousands of dollars and the credit card information has been coded as 1 if the customer has a Simmons credit card and 0 if not. In the Coupon column, a 1 is recorded if the sampled customer used the coupon and 0 if not.

We might think of building a multiple regression model using the data in Table 15.11 to help Simmons predict whether a catalog recipient will use the coupon. We would use Annual Spending and Simmons Card as independent variables and Coupon as the dependent variable. Because the dependent variable may only assume the values of 0 or 1, however, the ordinary multiple regression model is not applicable. This example shows the type of situation for which logistic regression was developed. Let us see how logistic regression can be used to help Simmons predict which type of customer is most likely to take advantage of their promotion.

TABLE 15.11 SAMPLE DATA FOR SIMMONS STORES

Customer	Annual Spending ($1000)	Simmons Card	Coupon
1	2.291	1	0
2	3.215	1	0
3	2.135	1	0
4	3.924	0	0
5	2.528	1	0
6	2.473	0	1
7	2.384	0	0
8	7.076	0	0
9	1.182	1	1
10	3.345	0	0

CD file
Simmons

Logistic Regression Equation

In many ways logistic regression is like ordinary regression. It requires a dependent variable, y, and one or more independent variables. In multiple regression analysis, the mean or expected value of y is referred to as the multiple regression equation.

$$E(y) = \beta_0 + \beta_1 x_1 + \beta_2 x_2 + \cdots + \beta_p x_p \tag{15.26}$$

In logistic regression, statistical theory as well as practice has shown that the relationship between $E(y)$ and $x_1, x_2, \ldots, x_p$ is better described by the following nonlinear equation.

LOGISTIC REGRESSION EQUATION

$$E(y) = \frac{e^{\beta_0 + \beta_1 x_1 + \beta_2 x_2 + \cdots + \beta_p x_p}}{1 + e^{\beta_0 + \beta_1 x_1 + \beta_2 x_2 + \cdots + \beta_p x_p}} \tag{15.27}$$

If the two values of the dependent variable y are coded as 0 or 1, the value of $E(y)$ in equation (15.27) provides the *probability* that $y = 1$ given a particular set of values for the independent variables $x_1, x_2, \ldots, x_p$. Because of the interpretation of $E(y)$ as a probability, the **logistic regression equation** is often written as follows.

INTERPRETATION OF $E(y)$ AS A PROBABILITY IN LOGISTIC REGRESSION

$$E(y) = P(y = 1 | x_1, x_2, \ldots, x_p) \tag{15.28}$$

To provide a better understanding of the characteristics of the logistic regression equation, suppose the model involves only one independent variable x and the values of the model parameters are $\beta_0 = -7$ and $\beta_1 = 3$. The logistic regression equation corresponding to these parameter values is

$$E(y) = P(y = 1 | x) = \frac{e^{\beta_0 + \beta_1 x}}{1 + e^{\beta_0 + \beta_1 x}} = \frac{e^{-7+3x}}{1 + e^{-7+3x}} \tag{15.29}$$

FIGURE 15.12 LOGISTIC REGRESSION EQUATION FOR $\beta_0 = -7$ AND $\beta_1 = 3$

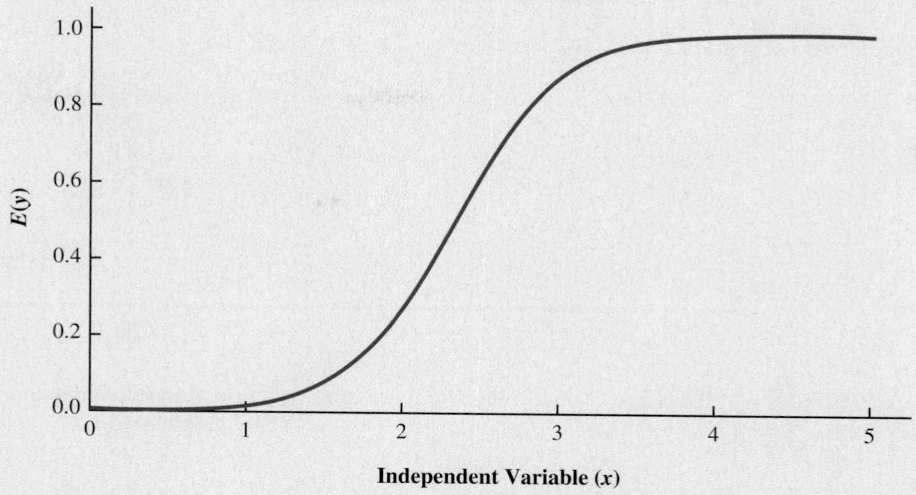

Figure 15.12 shows a graph of equation (15.29). Note that the graph is S-shaped. The value of $E(y)$ ranges from 0 to 1, with the value of $E(y)$ gradually approaching 1 as the value of x becomes larger and the value of $E(y)$ approaching 0 as the value of x becomes smaller. Note also that the values of $E(y)$, representing probability, increase fairly rapidly as x increases from 2 to 3. The fact that the values of $E(y)$ range from 0 to 1 and that the curve is S-shaped makes equation (15.29) ideally suited to model the probability the dependent variable is equal to 1.

Estimating the Logistic Regression Equation

In simple linear and multiple regression the least squares method is used to compute b_0, $b_1, \ldots, b_p$ as estimates of the model parameters ($\beta_0, \beta_1, \ldots, \beta_p$). The nonlinear form of the logistic regression equation makes the method of computing estimates more complex and beyond the scope of this text. We will use computer software to provide the estimates. The **estimated logistic regression equation** is

ESTIMATED LOGISTIC REGRESSION EQUATION

$$\hat{y} = \text{estimate of } P(y = 1|x_1, x_2, \ldots, x_p) = \frac{e^{b_0 + b_1x_1 + b_2x_2 + \cdots + b_px_p}}{1 + e^{b_0 + b_1x_1 + b_2x_2 + \cdots + b_px_p}} \qquad \textbf{(15.30)}$$

Here, $\hat{y}$ provides an estimate of the probability that $y = 1$, given a particular set of values for the independent variables.

Let us now return to the Simmons Stores example. The variables in the study are defined as follows:

$$y = \begin{cases} 0 \text{ if the customer did not use the coupon} \\ 1 \text{ if the customer used the coupon} \end{cases}$$

$$x_1 = \text{annual spending at Simmons Stores (\$1000s)}$$

$$x_2 = \begin{cases} 0 \text{ if the customer does not have a Simmons credit card} \\ 1 \text{ if the customer has a Simmons credit card} \end{cases}$$

FIGURE 15.13 PARTIAL LOGISTIC REGRESSION OUTPUT FOR THE SIMMONS STORES EXAMPLE

In the Minitab output, x_1 = Spending and x_2 = Card.

```
Logistic Regression Table
                                                       Odds     95% CI
Predictor      Coef   SE Coef       Z      p    Ratio   Lower  Upper
Constant    -2.1464    0.5772   -3.72  0.000
Spending     0.3416    0.1287    2.66  0.008     1.41    1.09   1.81
Card         1.0987    0.4447    2.47  0.013     3.00    1.25   7.17

Log-Likelihood = -60.487
Test that all slopes are zero: G = 13.628, DF = 2, P-Value = 0.001
```

Thus, we choose a logistic regression equation with two independent variables.

$$E(y) = \frac{e^{\beta_0+\beta_1x_1+\beta_2x_2}}{1 + e^{\beta_0+\beta_1x_1+\beta_2x_2}} \tag{15.31}$$

In Appendix 15.3 we show how Minitab is used to generate the output in Figure 15.13.

Using the sample data (see Table 15.11), Minitab's binary logistic regression procedure was used to compute estimates of the model parameters β_0, β_1, and β_2. A portion of the output obtained is shown in Figure 15.13. We see that $b_0 = -2.1464$, $b_1 = 0.3416$, and $b_2 = 1.0987$. Thus, the estimated logistic regression equation is

$$\hat{y} = \frac{e^{b_0+b_1x_1+b_2x_2}}{1 + e^{b_0+b_1x_1+b_2x_2}} = \frac{e^{-2.1464+0.3416x_1+1.0987x_2}}{1 + e^{-2.1464+0.3416x_1+1.0987x_2}} \tag{15.32}$$

We can now use equation (15.32) to estimate the probability of using the coupon for a particular type of customer. For example, to estimate the probability of using the coupon for customers who spend \$2000 annually and do not have a Simmons credit card, we substitute $x_1 = 2$ and $x_2 = 0$ into equation (15.32).

$$\hat{y} = \frac{e^{-2.1464+0.3416(2)+1.0987(0)}}{1 + e^{-2.1464+0.3416(2)+1.0987(0)}} = \frac{e^{-1.4632}}{1 + e^{-1.4632}} = \frac{.2315}{1.2315} = 0.1880$$

Thus, an estimate of the probability of using the coupon for this particular group of customers is approximately 0.19. Similarly, to estimate the probability of using the coupon for customers who spent \$2000 last year and have a Simmons credit card, we substitute $x_1 = 2$ and $x_2 = 1$ into equation (15.32).

$$\hat{y} = \frac{e^{-2.1464+0.3416(2)+1.0987(1)}}{1 + e^{-2.1464+0.3416(2)+1.0987(1)}} = \frac{e^{-0.3645}}{1 + e^{-0.3645}} = \frac{.6945}{1.6945} = 0.4099$$

Thus, for this group of customers, the probability of using the coupon is approximately 0.41. It appears that the probability of using the coupon is much higher for customers with a Simmons credit card. Before reaching any conclusions, however, we need to assess the statistical significance of our model.

Testing for Significance

Testing for significance in logistic regression is similar to testing for significance in multiple regression. First we conduct a test for overall significance. For the Simmons Stores example, the hypotheses for the test of overall significance follow:

$$H_0\colon \beta_1 = \beta_2 = 0$$
$$H_a\colon \text{One or both of the parameters is not equal to zero}$$

The test for overall significance is based upon the value of a G test statistic. If the null hypothesis is true, the sampling distribution of G follows a chi-square distribution with degrees of freedom equal to the number of independent variables in the model. Although the computation of G is beyond the scope of the book, the value of G and its corresponding p-value are provided as part of Minitab's binary logistic regression output. Referring to the last line in Figure 15.13, we see that the value of G is 13.628, its degrees of freedom are 2, and its p-value is 0.001. Thus, at any level of significance $\alpha \geq .001$, we would reject the null hypothesis and conclude that the overall model is significant.

If the G test shows an overall significance, a z test can be used to determine whether each of the individual independent variables is making a significant contribution to the overall model. For the independent variables x_i, the hypotheses are

$$H_0\colon \beta_i = 0$$
$$H_a\colon \beta_i \neq 0$$

If the null hypothesis is true, the value of the estimated coefficient divided by its standard error follows a standard normal probability distribution. The column labeled Z in the Minitab output contains the values of $z_i = b_i/s_{b_i}$ for each of the estimated coefficients and the column labeled p contains the corresponding p-values. Suppose we use $\alpha = .05$ to test for the significance of the independent variables in the Simmons model. For the independent variable x_1 the z value is 2.66 and the corresponding p-value is .008. Thus, at the .05 level of significance we can reject $H_0\colon \beta_1 = 0$. In a similar fashion we can also reject $H_0\colon \beta_2 = 0$ because the p-value corresponding to $z = 2.47$ is .013. Hence, at the .05 level of significance, both independent variables are statistically significant.

Managerial Use

We described how to develop the estimated logistic regression equation and how to test it for significance. Let us now use it to make a decision recommendation concerning the Simmons Stores catalog promotion. For Simmons Stores, we already computed $P(y = 1|x_1 = 2, x_2 = 1) = .4099$ and $P(y = 1|x_1 = 2, x_2 = 0) = .1880$. These probabilities indicate that for customers with annual spending of \$2000 the presence of a Simmons credit card increases the probability of using the coupon. In Table 15.12 we show estimated probabilities for values of annual spending ranging from \$1000 to \$7000 for both customers who have a Simmons credit card and customers who do not have a Simmons credit card. How can Simmons use this information to better target customers for the new promotion? Suppose Simmons wants to send the promotional catalog only to customers who have a 0.40 or higher probability of using the coupon. Using the estimated probabilities in Table 15.12, Simmons promotion strategy would be:

Customers who have a Simmons credit card: Send the catalog to every customer who spent \$2000 or more last year.

TABLE 15.12 ESTIMATED PROBABILITIES FOR SIMMONS STORES

		Annual Spending						
		\$1000	**\$2000**	**\$3000**	**\$4000**	**\$5000**	**\$6000**	**\$7000**
Credit Card	**Yes**	0.3305	0.4099	0.4943	0.5790	0.6593	0.7314	0.7931
	No	0.1413	0.1880	0.2457	0.3143	0.3921	0.4758	0.5609

Customers who do not have a Simmons credit card: Send the catalog to every customer who spent \$6000 or more last year.

Looking at the estimated probabilities further, we see that the probability of using the coupon for customers who do not have a Simmons credit card but spend \$5000 annually is 0.3921. Thus, Simmons may want to consider revising this strategy by including those customers who do not have a credit card, as long as they spent \$5000 or more last year.

Interpreting the Logistic Regression Equation

Interpreting a regression equation involves relating the independent variables to the business question that the equation was developed to answer. With logistic regression, it is difficult to interpret the relation between the independent variables and the probability that $y = 1$ directly because the logistic regression equation is nonlinear. However, statisticians have shown that the relationship can be interpreted indirectly using a concept called the odds ratio.

The **odds in favor of an event occurring** is defined as the probability the event will occur divided by the probability the event will not occur. In logistic regression the event of interest is always $y = 1$. Given a particular set of values for the independent variables, the odds in favor of $y = 1$ can be calculated as follows:

$$\text{odds} = \frac{P(y = 1 \mid x_1, x_2, \ldots, x_p)}{P(y = 0 \mid x_1, x_2, \ldots, x_p)} = \frac{P(y = 1 \mid x_1, x_2, \ldots, x_p)}{1 - P(y = 1 \mid x_1, x_2, \ldots, x_p)} \tag{15.33}$$

The **odds ratio** measures the impact on the odds of a one-unit increase in only one of the independent variables. The odds ratio is the odds that $y = 1$ given that one of the independent variables has been increased by one unit (odds_1) divided by the odds that $y = 1$ given no change in the values for the independent variables (odds_0).

ODDS RATIO

$$\text{Odds Ratio} = \frac{\text{odds}_1}{\text{odds}_0} \tag{15.34}$$

For example, suppose we want to compare the odds of using the coupon for customers who spend \$2000 annually and have a Simmons credit card ($x_1 = 2$ and $x_2 = 1$) to the odds of using the coupon for customers who spend \$2000 annually and do not have a Simmons credit card ($x_1 = 2$ and $x_2 = 0$). We are interested in interpreting the effect of a one-unit increase in the independent variable x_2. In this case

$$\text{odds}_1 = \frac{P(y = 1 \mid x_1 = 2, x_2 = 1)}{1 - P(y = 1 \mid x_1 = 2, x_2 = 1)}$$

and

$$\text{odds}_0 = \frac{P(y = 1|x_1 = 2, x_2 = 0)}{1 - P(y = 1|x_1 = 2, x_2 = 0)}$$

Previously we showed that an estimate of the probability that $y = 1$ given $x_1 = 2$ and $x_2 = 1$ is .4099, and an estimate of the probability that $y = 1$ given $x_1 = 2$ and $x_2 = 0$ is .1880. Thus,

$$\text{estimate of odds}_1 = \frac{.4099}{1 - .4099} = .6946$$

and

$$\text{estimate of odds}_0 = \frac{.1880}{1 - .1880} = .2315$$

The estimated odds ratio is

$$\text{Estimated odds ratio} = \frac{.6946}{.2315} = 3.00$$

Thus, we can conclude that the estimated odds in favor of using the coupon for customers who spent \$2000 last year and have a Simmons credit card are 3 times greater than the estimated odds in favor of using the coupon for customers who spent \$2000 last year and do not have a Simmons credit card.

The odds ratio for each independent variable is computed while holding all the other independent variables constant. But it does not matter what constant values are used for the other independent variables. For instance, if we computed the odds ratio for the Simmons credit card variable (x_2) using \$3000, instead of \$2000, as the value for the annual spending variable (x_1), we would still obtain the same value for the estimated odds ratio (3.00). Thus, we can conclude that the estimated odds of using the coupon for customers who have a Simmons credit card are 3 times greater than the estimated odds of using the coupon for customers who do not have a Simmons credit card.

The odds ratio is standard output for logistic regression software packages. Refer to the Minitab output in Figure 15.13. The column with the heading Odds Ratio contains the estimated odds ratios for each of the independent variables. The estimated odds ratio for x_1 is 1.41 and the estimated odds ratio for x_2 is 3.00. We already showed how to interpret the estimated odds ratio for the binary independent variable x_2. Let us now consider the interpretation of the estimated odds ratio for the continuous independent variable x_1.

The value of 1.41 in the Odds Ratio column of the Minitab output tells us that the estimated odds in favor of using the coupon for customers who spent \$3000 last year is 1.41 times greater than the estimated odds in favor of using the coupon for customers who spent \$2000 last year. Moreover, this interpretation is true for any one-unit change in x_1. For instance, the estimated odds in favor of using the coupon for someone who spent \$5000 last year is 1.41 times greater than the odds in favor of using the coupon for a customer who spent \$4000 last year. But suppose we are interested in the change in the odds for an increase of more than one unit for an independent variable. Note that x_1 can range from 1 to 7. The odds ratio given by the Minitab output does not answer this question. To answer this question we must explore the relationship between the odds ratio and the regression coefficients.

A unique relationship exists between the odds ratio for a variable and its corresponding regression coefficient. For each independent variable in a logistic regression equation it can be shown that

$$\text{Odds ratio} = e^{\beta_i}$$

To illustrate this relationship, consider the independent variable x_1 in the Simmons example. The estimated odds ratio for x_1 is

$$\text{Estimated odds ratio} = e^{b_1} = e^{.3416} = 1.41$$

Similarly, the estimated odds ratio for x_2 is

$$\text{Estimated odds ratio} = e^{b_2} = e^{1.0987} = 3.00$$

This relationship between the odds ratio and the coefficients of the independent variables makes it easy to compute estimates of the odds ratios once we develop estimates of the model parameters. Moreover, it also provides us with the ability to investigate changes in the odds ratio of more than or less than one unit for a continuous independent variable.

The odds ratio for an independent variable represents the change in the odds for a one-unit change in the independent variable holding all the other independent variables constant. Suppose that we want to consider the effect of a change of more than one unit, say c units. For instance, suppose in the Simmons example that we want to compare the odds of using the coupon for customers who spend \$5000 annually ($x_1 = 5$) to the odds of using the coupon for customers who spend \$2000 annually ($x_1 = 2$). In this case $c = 5 - 2 = 3$ and the corresponding estimated odds ratio is

$$e^{cb_1} = e^{3(.3416)} = e^{1.0248} = 2.79$$

This result indicates that the estimated odds of using the coupon for customers who spend \$5000 annually is 2.79 times greater than the estimated odds of using the coupon for customers who spend \$2000 annually. In other words, the estimated odds ratio for an increase of \$3000 in annual spending is 2.79.

In general, the odds ratio enables us to compare the odds for two different events. If the value of the odds ratio is 1, the odds for both events are the same. Thus, if the independent variable we are considering (such as Simmons credit card status) has a positive impact on the probability of the event occurring, the corresponding odds ratio will be greater than 1. Most logistic regression software packages provide a confidence interval for the odds ratio. The Minitab output in Figure 15.13 provides a 95% confidence interval for each of the odds ratios. For example, the point estimate of the odds ratio for x_1 is 1.41 and the 95% confidence interval is 1.09 to 1.81. Because the confidence interval does not contain the value of 1, we can conclude that x_1, has a significant effect on the estimated odds ratio. Similarly, the 95% confidence interval for the odds ratio for x_2 is 1.25 to 7.17. Because this interval does not contain the value of 1, we can also conclude that x_2 has a significant effect on the odds ratio.

Logit Transformation

An interesting relationship can be observed between the odds in favor of $y = 1$ and the exponent for e in the logistic regression equation. It can be shown that

$$\ln(\text{odds}) = \beta_0 + \beta_1 x_1 + \beta_2 x_2 + \cdots + \beta_p x_p$$

This equation shows that the natural logarithm of the odds in favor of $y = 1$ is a linear function of the independent variables. This linear function is called the **logit**. We will use the notation $g(x_1, x_2, \ldots, x_p)$ to denote the logit.

LOGIT

$$g(x_1, x_2, \ldots, x_p) = \beta_0 + \beta_1 x_1 + \beta_2 x_2 + \cdots + \beta_p x_p \qquad \textbf{(15.35)}$$

Substituting $g(x_1, x_2, \ldots, x_p)$ for $\beta_1 + \beta_1 x_1 + \beta_2 x_2 + \cdots + \beta_p x_p$ in equation (15.27), we can write the logistic regression equation as

$$E(y) = \frac{e^{g(x_1, x_2, \ldots, x_p)}}{1 + e^{g(x_1, x_2, \ldots, x_p)}} \tag{15.36}$$

Once we estimate the parameters in the logistic regression equation, we can compute an estimate of the logit. Using $\hat{g}(x_1, x_2, \ldots, x_p)$ to denote the **estimated logit**, we obtain

ESTIMATED LOGIT

$$\hat{g}(x_1, x_2, \ldots, x_p) = b_0 + b_1 x_1 + b_2 x_2 + \cdots + b_p x_p \tag{15.37}$$

Thus, in terms of the estimated logit, the estimated regression equation is

$$\hat{y} = \frac{e^{b_0 + b_1 x_1 + b_2 x_2 + \cdots + b_p x_p}}{1 + e^{b_0 + b_1 x_1 + b_2 x_2 + \cdots + b_p x_p}} = \frac{e^{\hat{g}(x_1, x_2, \ldots, x_p)}}{1 + e^{\hat{g}(x_1, x_2, \ldots, x_p)}} \tag{15.38}$$

For the Simmons Stores example, the estimated logit is

$$\hat{g}(x_1, x_2) = -2.1464 + 0.3416x_1 + 1.0987x_2$$

and the estimated regression equation is

$$\hat{y} = \frac{e^{\hat{g}(x_1, x_2)}}{1 + e^{\hat{g}(x_1, x_2)}} = \frac{e^{-2.1464 + 0.3416x_1 + 1.0987x_2}}{1 + e^{-2.1464 + 0.3416x_1 + 1.0987x_2}}$$

Thus, because of the unique relationship between the estimated logit and the estimated logistic regression equation, we can compute the estimated probabilities for Simmons Stores by dividing $e^{\hat{g}(x_1, x_2)}$ by $1 + e^{\hat{g}(x_1, x_2)}$.

NOTES AND COMMENTS

1. Because of the unique relationship between the estimated coefficients in the model and the corresponding odds ratios, the overall test for significance based upon the G statistic is also a test of overall significance for the odds ratios. In addition, the z test for the individual significance of a model parameter also provides a statistical test of significance for the corresponding odds ratio.
2. In simple and multiple regression, the coefficient of determination is used to measure the goodness of fit. In logistic regression, no single measure provides a similar interpretation. A discussion of goodness of fit is beyond the scope of our introductory treatment of logistic regression.

Exercises

Applications

CD file
Simmons

44. Refer to the Simmons Stores example introduced in this section. The dependent variable is coded as $y = 1$ if the customer used the coupon and 0 if not. Suppose that the only information available to help predict whether the customer will use the coupon is the customer's credit card status, coded as $x = 1$ if the customer has a Simmons credit card and $x = 0$ if not.
    a. Write the logistic regression equation relating x to y.
    b. What is the interpretation of $E(y)$ when $x = 0$?

c. For the Simmons data in Table 15.11, use Minitab to compute the estimated logit.
d. Use the estimated logit computed in part (c) to compute an estimate of the probability of using the coupon for customers who do not have a Simmons credit card and an estimate of the probability of using the coupon for customers who have a Simmons credit card.
e. What is the estimate of the odds ratio? What is its interpretation?

45. In Table 15.12 we provided estimates of the probability using the coupon in the Simmons Stores catalog promotion. A different value is obtained for each combination of values for the independent variables.
a. Compute the odds in favor of using the coupon for a customer with annual spending of \$4000 who does not have a Simmons credit card ($x_1 = 4, x_2 = 0$).
b. Use the information in Table 15.12 and part (a) to compute the odds ratio for the Simmons credit card variable $x_2 = 0$, holding annual spending constant at $x_1 = 4$.
c. In the text, the odds ratio for the credit card variable was computed using the information in the \$2000 column of Table 15.12. Did you get the same value for the odds ratio in part (b)?

46. Community Bank would like to increase the number of customers who use payroll direct deposit. Management is considering a new sales campaign that will require each branch manager to call each customer who does not currently use payroll direct deposit. As an incentive to sign up for payroll direct deposit, each customer contacted will be offered free checking for two years. Because of the time and cost associated with the new campaign, management would like to focus their efforts on customers who have the highest probability of signing up for payroll direct deposit. Management believes that the average monthly balance in a customer's checking account may be a useful predictor of whether the customer will sign up for direct payroll deposit. To investigate the relationship between these two variables, Community Bank tried the new campaign using a sample of 50 checking account customers who do not currently use payroll direct deposit. The sample data show the average monthly checking account balance (in hundreds of dollars) and whether the customer contacted signed up for payroll direct deposit (coded 1 if the customer signed up for payroll direct deposit and 0 if not). The data are contained in the data set named Bank; a portion of the data follows.

CD file

Bank

Customer	x = Monthly Balance	y = Direct Deposit
1	1.22	0
2	1.56	0
3	2.10	0
4	2.25	0
5	2.89	0
6	3.55	0
7	3.56	0
8	3.65	1
⋮	⋮	⋮
48	18.45	1
49	24.98	0
50	26.05	1

a. Write the logistic regression equation relating x to y.
b. For the Community Bank data, use Minitab to compute the estimated logistic regression equation.
c. Conduct a test of significance using the G test statistic. Use $\alpha = .05$.

d. Estimate the probability that customers with an average monthly balance of $1000 will sign up for direct payroll deposit.
e. Suppose Community Bank only wants to contact customers who have a .50 or higher probability of signing up for direct payroll deposit. What is the average monthly balance required to achieve this level of probability?
f. What is the estimate of the odds ratio? What is its interpretation?

47. Over the past few years the percentage of students who leave Lakeland College at the end of the first year has increased. Last year Lakeland started a voluntary one-week orientation program to help first-year students adjust to campus life. If Lakeland is able to show that the orientation program has a positive effect on retention, they will consider making the program a requirement for all first-year students. Lakeland's administration also suspects that students with lower GPAs have a higher probability of leaving Lakeland at the end of the first year. In order to investigate the relation of these variables to retention, Lakeland selected a random sample of 100 students from last year's entering class. The data are contained in the data set named Lakeland; a portion of the data follows.

CD file
Lakeland

Student	GPA	Program	Return
1	3.78	1	1
2	2.38	0	1
3	1.30	0	0
4	2.19	1	0
5	3.22	1	1
6	2.68	1	1
⋮	⋮	⋮	⋮
98	2.57	1	1
99	1.70	1	1
100	3.85	1	1

The dependent variable was coded as $y = 1$ if the student returned to Lakeland for the sophomore year and $y = 0$ if not. The two independent variables are:

$$x_1 = \text{GPA at the end of the first semester}$$

$$x_2 = \begin{cases} 0 \text{ if the student did not attend the orientation program} \\ 1 \text{ if the student attended the orientation program} \end{cases}$$

a. Write the logistic regression equation relating x_1 and x_2 to y.
b. What is the interpretation of $E(y)$ when $x_2 = 0$?
c. Use both independent variables and Minitab to compute the estimated logit.
d. Conduct a test for overall significance using $\alpha = .05$.
e. Use $\alpha = .05$ to determine whether each of the independent variables is significant.
f. Use the estimated logit computed in part (c) to compute an estimate of the probability that students with a 2.5 grade point average who did not attend the orientation program will return to Lakeland for their sophomore year. What is the estimated probability for students with a 2.5 grade point average who attended the orientation program?
g. What is the estimate of the odds ratio for the orientation program? Interpret it.
h. Would you recommend making the orientation program a required activity? Why or why not?

48. *Consumer Reports* conducted a taste test on 19 brands of boxed chocolates. The following data show the price per serving, based on the FDA serving size of 1.4 ounces, and the quality rating for the 19 chocolates tested (*Consumer Reports,* February 2002).

CD file
Chocolate

Manufacturer	Price	Rating
Bernard Callebaut	3.17	Very Good
Candinas	3.58	Excellent
Fannie May	1.49	Good
Godiva	2.91	Very Good
Hershey's	0.76	Good
L.A. Burdick	3.70	Very Good
La Maison du Chocolate	5.08	Excellent
Leonidas	2.11	Very Good
Lindt	2.20	Good
Martine's	4.76	Excellent
Michael Recchiuti	7.05	Very Good
Neuchatel	3.36	Good
Neuchatel Sugar Free	3.22	Good
Richard Donnelly	6.55	Very Good
Russell Stover	0.70	Good
See's	1.06	Very Good
Teuscher Lake of Zurich	4.66	Very Good
Whitman's	0.70	Fair
Whitman's Sugar Free	1.21	Fair

Suppose that you would like to determine whether products that cost more rate higher in quality. For the purpose of this exercise, use the following binary dependent variable:

$y = 1$ if the quality rating is very good or excellent and 0 if good or fair

a. Write the logistic regression equation relating x = price per serving to y.
b. Use Minitab to compute the estimated logit.
c. Use the estimated logit computed in part (b) to compute an estimate of the probability a chocolate that has a price per serving of $4.00 will have a quality rating of very good or excellent.
d. What is the estimate of the odds ratio? What is its interpretation?

Summary

In this chapter, we introduced multiple regression analysis as an extension of simple linear regression analysis presented in Chapter 14. Multiple regression analysis enables us to understand how a dependent variable is related to two or more independent variables. The regression equation $E(y) = \beta_0 + \beta_1 x_1 + \beta_2 x_2 + \cdots + \beta_p x_p$ shows that the expected value or mean value of the dependent variable y is related to the values of the independent variables $x_1, x_2, \ldots, x_p$. Sample data and the least squares method are used to develop the estimated regression equation $\hat{y} = b_0 + b_1 x_1 + b_2 x_2 + \ldots + b_p x_p$. In effect $b_0, b_1, b_2, \ldots, b_p$ are sample statistics used to estimate the unknown model parameters $\beta_0, \beta_1, \beta_2, \ldots, \beta_p$. Computer printouts were used throughout the chapter to emphasize the fact that statistical software packages are the only realistic means of performing the numerous computations required in multiple regression analysis.

The multiple coefficient of determination was presented as a measure of the goodness of fit of the estimated regression equation. It determines the proportion of the variation of y that can be explained by the estimated regression equation. The adjusted multiple coefficient of determination is a similar measure of goodness of fit that adjusts for the number of independent variables and thus avoids overestimating the impact of adding more independent variables.

An F test and a t test were presented as ways to determine statistically whether the relationship among the variables is significant. The F test is used to determine whether there is a significant overall relationship between the dependent variable and the set of all independent variables. The t test is used to determine whether there is a significant relationship between the dependent variable and an individual independent variable given the other independent variables in the regression model. Correlation among the independent variables, known as multicollinearity, was discussed.

The section on qualitative independent variables showed how dummy variables can be used to incorporate qualitative data into multiple regression analysis. The section on residual analysis showed how residual analysis can be used to validate the model assumptions, detect outliers, and identify influential observations. Standardized residuals, leverage, studentized deleted residuals, and Cook's distance measure were discussed. The chapter concluded with a section on how logistic regression can be used to model situations in which the dependent variable may only assume two values.

Glossary

Multiple regression analysis Regression analysis involving two or more independent variables.

Multiple regression model The mathematical equation that describes how the dependent variable y is related to the independent variables $x_1, x_2, \ldots, x_p$ and an error term ϵ.

Multiple regression equation The mathematical equation relating the expected value or mean value of the dependent variable to the values of the independent variables; that is, $E(y) = \beta_0 + \beta_1 x_1 + \beta_2 x_2 + \cdots + \beta_p x_p$.

Estimated multiple regression equation The estimate of the multiple regression equation based on sample data and the least squares method; it is $\hat{y} = b_0 + b_1 x_1 + b_2 x_2 + \cdots + b_p x_p$.

Least squares method The method used to develop the estimated regression equation. It minimizes the sum of squared residuals (the deviations between the observed values of the dependent variable, y_i, and the estimated values of the dependent variable, $\hat{y}_i$).

Multiple coefficient of determination A measure of the goodness of fit of the estimated multiple regression equation. It can be interpreted as the proportion of the variability in the dependent variable that is explained by the estimated regression equation.

Adjusted multiple coefficient of determination A measure of the goodness of fit of the estimated multiple regression equation that adjusts for the number of independent variables in the model and thus avoids overestimating the impact of adding more independent variables.

Multicollinearity The term used to describe the correlation among the independent variables.

Qualitative independent variable An independent variable with qualitative data.

Dummy variable A variable used to model the effect of qualitative independent variables. A dummy variable may take only the value zero or one.

Leverage A measure of how far the values of the independent variables are from their mean values.

Outlier An observation that does not fit the pattern of the other data.

Studentized deleted residuals Standardized residuals that are based on a revised standard error of the estimate obtained by deleting observation i from the data set and then performing the regression analysis and computations.

Influential observation An observation that has a strong influence on the regression results.

Cook's distance measure A measure of the influence of an observation based on both the leverage of observation i and the residual for observation i.

Logistic regression equation The mathematical equation relating $E(y)$, the probability that $y = 1$, to the values of the independent variables; that is, $E(y) = P(y = 1|x_1, x_2, \ldots, x_p) = \dfrac{e^{\beta_0+\beta_1 x_1+\beta_2 x_2+\cdots+\beta_p x_p}}{1 + e^{\beta_0+\beta_1 x_1+\beta_2 x_2+\cdots+\beta_p x_p}}$.

Estimated logistic regression equation The estimate of the logistic regression equation based on sample data; that is, $\hat{y}$ = estimate of $P(y = 1|x_1, x_2, \ldots, x_p) = \dfrac{e^{b_0+b_1x_1+b_2x_2+\cdots+b_px_p}}{1 + e^{b_0+b_1x_1+b_2x_2+\cdots+b_px_p}}$.

Odds in favor of an event occurring The probability the event will occur divided by the probability the event will not occur.

Odds ratio The odds that $y = 1$ given that one of the independent variables increased by one unit (odds_1) divided by the odds that $y = 1$ given no change in the values for the independent variables (odds_0); that is, Odds ratio $= \text{odds}_1/\text{odds}_0$.

Logit The natural logarithm of the odds in favor of $y = 1$; that is, $g(x_1, x_2, \ldots, x_p) = \beta_0 + \beta_1x_1 + \beta_2x_2 + \cdots + \beta_px_p$.

Estimated logit An estimate of the logit based on sample data; that is, $\hat{g}(x_1, x_2, \ldots, x_p) = b_0 + b_1x_1 + b_2x_2 + \cdots + b_px_p$.

Key Formulas

Multiple Regression Model

$$y = \beta_0 + \beta_1x_1 + \beta_2x_2 + \cdots + \beta_px_p + \epsilon \qquad (15.1)$$

Multiple Regression Equation

$$E(y) = \beta_0 + \beta_1x_1 + \beta_2x_2 + \cdots + \beta_px_p \qquad (15.2)$$

Estimated Multiple Regression Equation

$$\hat{y} = b_0 + b_1x_1 + b_2x_2 + \cdots + b_px_p \qquad (15.3)$$

Least Squares Criterion

$$\min \Sigma(y_i - \hat{y}_i)^2 \qquad (15.4)$$

Relationship Among SST, SSR, and SSE

$$\text{SST} = \text{SSR} + \text{SSE} \qquad (15.7)$$

Multiple Coefficient of Determination

$$R^2 = \frac{\text{SSR}}{\text{SST}} \qquad (15.8)$$

Adjusted Multiple Coefficient of Determination

$$R_a^2 = 1 - (1 - R^2)\frac{n-1}{n-p-1} \qquad (15.9)$$

Mean Square Regression

$$\text{MSR} = \frac{\text{SSR}}{p} \qquad (15.12)$$

Mean Square Error

$$\text{MSE} = \frac{\text{SSE}}{n - p - 1} \tag{15.13}$$

F Test Statistic

$$F = \frac{\text{MSR}}{\text{MSE}} \tag{15.14}$$

t Test Statistic

$$t = \frac{b_i}{s_{b_i}} \tag{15.15}$$

Standardized Residual for Observation *i*

$$\frac{y_i - \hat{y}_i}{s_{y_i - \hat{y}_i}} \tag{15.23}$$

Standard Deviation of Residual *i*

$$s_{y_i - \hat{y}_i} = s\sqrt{1 - h_i} \tag{15.24}$$

Cook's Distance Measure

$$D_i = \frac{(y_i - \hat{y}_i)^2}{(p - 1)s^2}\left[\frac{h_i}{(1 - h_i)^2}\right] \tag{15.25}$$

Logistic Regression Equation

$$E(y) = \frac{e^{\beta_0 + \beta_1 x_1 + \beta_2 x_2 + \cdots + \beta_p x_p}}{1 + e^{\beta_0 + \beta_1 x_1 + \beta_2 x_2 + \cdots + \beta_p x_p}} \tag{15.27}$$

Estimated Logistic Regression Equation

$$\hat{y} = \text{estimate of } P(y = 1 | x_1, x_2, \ldots, x_p) = \frac{e^{b_0 + b_1 x_1 + b_2 x_2 + \cdots + b_p x_p}}{1 + e^{b_0 + b_1 x_1 + b_2 x_2 + \cdots + b_p x_p}} \tag{15.30}$$

Odds Ratio

$$\text{Odds ratio} = \frac{\text{odds}_1}{\text{odds}_0} \tag{15.34}$$

Logit

$$g(x_1, x_2, \ldots, x_p) = \beta_0 + \beta_1 x_1 + \beta_2 x_2 + \cdots + \beta_p x_p \tag{15.35}$$

Estimated Logit

$$\hat{g}(x_1, x_2, \ldots, x_p) = b_0 + b_1 x_1 + b_2 x_2 + \cdots + b_p x_p \tag{15.37}$$

Supplementary Exercises

49. The admissions officer for Clearwater College developed the following estimated regression equation relating the final college GPA to the student's SAT mathematics score and high-school GPA.

$$\hat{y} = -1.41 + .0235x_1 + .00486x_2$$

where

$$x_1 = \text{high-school grade point average}$$
$$x_2 = \text{SAT mathematics score}$$
$$y = \text{final college grade point average}$$

a. Interpret the coefficients in this estimated regression equation.
b. Estimate the final college GPA for a student who has a high-school average of 84 and a score of 540 on the SAT mathematics test.

50. The personnel director for Electronics Associates developed the following estimated regression equation relating an employee's score on a job satisfaction test to his or her length of service and wage rate.

$$\hat{y} = 14.4 - 8.69x_1 + 13.5x_2$$

where

$$x_1 = \text{length of service (years)}$$
$$x_2 = \text{wage rate (dollars)}$$
$$y = \text{job satisfaction test score (higher scores indicate greater job satisfaction)}$$

a. Interpret the coefficients in this estimated regression equation.
b. Develop an estimate of the job satisfaction test score for an employee who has four years of service and makes \$6.50 per hour.

51. A partial computer output from a regression analysis follows.

```
The regression equation is
Y = 8.103 + 7.602 X1 + 3.111 X2

Predictor          Coef       SE Coef        T
Constant         _______       2.667       _____
X1               _______       2.105       _____
X2               _______       0.613       _____

S = 3.335      R-sq = 92.3%      R-sq(adj) = _____%

Analysis of Variance

SOURCE            DF         SS         MS        F
Regression      ______      1612      ______    ______
Residual Error    12       ______     ______
Total           ______     ______
```

a. Compute the appropriate t-ratios.
b. Test for the significance of β_1 and β_2 at $\alpha = .05$.
c. Compute the entries in the DF, SS, and MS columns.
d. Compute R_a^2.

52. Recall that in exercise 49, the admissions officer for Clearwater College developed the following estimated regression equation relating final college GPA to the student's SAT mathematics score and high-school GPA.

$$\hat{y} = -1.41 + .0235x_1 + .00486x_2$$

where

$$x_1 = \text{high-school grade point average}$$
$$x_2 = \text{SAT mathematics score}$$
$$y = \text{final college grade point average}$$

A portion of the Minitab computer output follows.

```
The regression equation is
Y = -1.41 + .0235 X1 + .00486 X2

Predictor          Coef       SE Coef          T
Constant        -1.4053        0.4848      _____
X1             0.023467      0.008666      _____
X2               ______      0.001077      _____

S = 0.1298     R-sq = _____     R-sq(adj) = _____

Analysis of Variance

SOURCE            DF          SS          MS        F
Regression      _____     1.76209      _____    _____
Residual Error  _____     _______      _____
Total               9     1.88000
```

a. Complete the missing entries in this output.
b. Compute F and test at a .05 level of significance to see whether a significant relationship is present.
c. Did the estimated regression equation provide a good fit to the data? Explain.
d. Use the t test and $\alpha = .05$ to test H_0: $\beta_1 = 0$ and H_0: $\beta_2 = 0$.

53. Recall that in exercise 50 the personnel director for Electronics Associates developed the following estimated regression equation relating an employee's score on a job satisfaction test to length of service and wage rate.

$$\hat{y} = 14.4 - 8.69x_1 + 13.5x_2$$

where

$$x_1 = \text{length of service (years)}$$
$$x_2 = \text{wage rate (dollars)}$$
$$y = \text{job satisfaction test score (higher scores indicate greater job satisfaction)}$$

A portion of the Minitab computer output follows.

```
The regression equation is
Y = 14.4 - 8.69 X1 + 13.52 X2

Predictor         Coef        SE Coef        T
Constant        14.448          8.191     1.76
X1              ______          1.555    _____
X2              13.517          2.085    _____

S = 3.773     R-sq = ______%  R-sq(adj) = ______%

Analysis of Variance

SOURCE            DF          SS        MS        F
Regression         2      ______     _____   ______
Residual Error ______      71.17     _____
Total              7       720.0
```

a. Complete the missing entries in this output.
b. Compute F and test using $\alpha = .05$ to see whether a significant relationship is present.
c. Did the estimated regression equation provide a good fit to the data? Explain.
d. Use the t test and $\alpha = .05$ to test H_0: $\beta_1 = 0$ and H_0: $\beta_2 = 0$.

54. *SmartMoney* magazine evaluated 65 metropolitan areas to determine where home values are headed. An ideal city would get a score of 100 if all factors measured were as favorable as possible. Areas with a score of 60 or greater are considered to be primed for price appreciation, and areas with a score of below 50 may see housing values erode. Two of the factors evaluated were the recession resistance of the area and its affordability. Both of these factors were rated using a scale ranging from 0 (low score) to 10 (high score). The data obtained for a sample of 20 cities evaluated by *SmartMoney* follow (*SmartMoney,* February 2002).

CD file
HomeValue

Metro Area	Recession Resistance	Affordability	Score
Tucson	10	7	70.7
Fort Worth	10	7	68.5
San Antonio	6	8	65.5
Richmond	8	6	63.6
Indianapolis	4	8	62.5
Philadelphia	0	10	61.9
Atlanta	2	6	60.7
Phoenix	4	5	60.3
Cincinnati	2	7	57.0
Miami	6	5	56.5
Hartford	0	7	56.2
Birmingham	0	8	55.7
San Diego	8	2	54.6
Raleigh	2	7	50.9
Oklahoma City	1	6	49.6
Orange County	4	2	49.1
Denver	4	4	48.6
Los Angeles	0	7	45.7
Detroit	0	5	44.3
New Orleans	0	5	41.2

a. Develop an estimated regression equation that can be used to predict the score given the recession resistance rating. At the .05 level of significance, test for a significant relationship.
b. Did the estimated regression equation developed in part (a) provide a good fit to the data? Explain.
c. Develop an estimated regression equation that can be used to predict the score given the recession resistance rating and the affordability rating. At the .05 level of significance, test for overall significance.

55. *Consumer Reports* provided extensive testing and ratings for 24 treadmills. An overall score, based primarily on ease of use, ergonomics, exercise range, and quality, was developed for each treadmill tested. In general, a higher overall score indicates better performance. The following data show the price, the quality rating, and overall score for the 24 treadmills (*Consumer Reports*, February 2006).

CD file
Treadmills

Brand & Model	Price	Quality	Score
Landice L7	2900	Excellent	86
NordicTrack S3000	3500	Very good	85
SportsArt 3110	2900	Excellent	82
Precor	3500	Excellent	81
True Z4 HRC	2300	Excellent	81
Vision Fitness T9500	2000	Excellent	81
Precor M 9.31	3000	Excellent	79
Vision Fitness T9200	1300	Very good	78
Star Trac TR901	3200	Very good	72
Trimline T350HR	1600	Very good	72
Schwinn 820p	1300	Very good	69
Bowflex 7-Series	1500	Excellent	83
NordicTrack S1900	2600	Very good	83
Horizon Fitness PST8	1600	Very good	82
Horizon Fitness 5.2T	1800	Very good	80
Evo by Smooth Fitness FX30	1700	Very good	75
ProForm 1000S	1600	Very good	75
Horizon Fitness CST4.5	1000	Very good	74
Keys Fitness 320t	1200	Very good	73
Smooth Fitness 7.1HR Pro	1600	Very good	73
NordicTrack C2300	1000	Good	70
Spirit Inspire	1400	Very good	70
ProForm 750	1000	Good	67
Image 19.0 R	600	Good	66

a. Use these data to develop an estimated regression equation that could be used to estimate the overall score given the price.
b. Use $\alpha = .05$ to test for overall significance.
c. To incorporate the effect of quality, a qualitative variable with three levels, we used two dummy variables, Quality-E and Quality-VG. Each variable is coded 0 or 1 as follows.

$$\text{Quality-E} = \begin{cases} 1 \text{ if quality rating is excellent} \\ 0 \text{ otherwise} \end{cases}$$

$$\text{Quality-VG} = \begin{cases} 1 \text{ if quality rating is very good} \\ 0 \text{ otherwise} \end{cases}$$

Develop an estimated regression equation that could be used to estimate the overall score given the price and the quality rating.

d. For the estimated regression equation developed in part (c), test for overall significance using $\alpha = .10$.
e. For the estimated regression equation developed in part (c), use the t test to determine the significance of each independent variable. Use $\alpha = .10$.
f. Develop a standardized residual plot. Does the pattern of the residual plot appear to be reasonable?
g. Do the data contain any outliers or influential observations?
h. Estimate the overall score for a treadmill with a price of \$2000 and a good quality rating. How much would the estimate change if the quality rating were very good? Explain.

56. The U.S. Department of Energy's *Fuel Economy Guide* provides fuel efficiency data for cars and trucks. A portion of the data for 35 standard pickup trucks produced by Chevrolet and General Motors follows (www.fueleconomy.gov, March 21, 2003). The column labeled Drive identifies whether the vehicle has two-wheel drive (2WD) or four-wheel drive (4WD). The column labeled Displacement shows the engine's displacement in liters, the column labeled Cylinders specifies the number of cylinders the engine has, and the column labeled Transmission shows whether the truck has an automatic transmission or a manual transmission. The column labeled City MPG shows the fuel efficiency rating for the truck for city driving in terms of miles per gallon (mpg).

CD file
FuelEcon

Truck	Name	Drive	Displacement	Cylinders	Transmission	City MPG
1	C1500 Silverado	2WD	4.3	6	Auto	15
2	C1500 Silverado	2WD	4.3	6	Manual	15
3	C1500 Silverado	2WD	4.8	8	Auto	15
4	C1500 Silverado	2WD	4.8	8	Manual	16
5	C1500 Silverado	2WD	5.3	8	Auto	11
⋮	⋮	⋮	⋮	⋮	⋮	⋮
32	K1500 Sierra	4WD	5.3	8	Auto	15
33	K1500 Sierra	4WD	5.3	8	Auto	15
34	Sonoma	4WD	4.3	6	Auto	17
35	Sonoma	4WD	4.3	6	Manual	15

a. Develop an estimated regression equation that can be used to predict the fuel efficiency for city driving given the engine's displacement. Test for significance using $\alpha = .05$.
b. Consider the addition of the dummy variable Drive4, where the value of Drive4 is 0 if the truck has two-wheel drive and 1 if the truck has four-wheel drive. Develop the estimated regression equation that can be used to predict the fuel efficiency for city driving given the engine's displacement and the dummy variable Drive4.
c. Use $\alpha = .05$ to determine whether the dummy variable added in part (b) is significant.
d. Consider the addition of the dummy variable EightCyl, where the value of EightCyl is 0 if the truck's engine has six cylinders and 1 if the truck's engine has eight cylinders. Develop the estimated regression equation that can be used to predict the fuel efficiency for city driving given the engine's displacement and the dummy variables Drive4 and EightCyl.
e. For the estimated regression equation developed in part (d), test for overall significance and individual significance using $\alpha = .05$.

57. Today's marketplace offers a wide choice to buyers of sport utility vehicles (SUVs) and pickup trucks. An important factor to many buyers is the resale value of the vehicle. The following table shows the resale value (%) after two years and the suggested retail price for 10 SUVs, 10 small pickup trucks, and 10 large pickup trucks (*Kiplinger's New Cars & Trucks 2000 Buyer's Guide*).

CD file
Trucks

	Type of Vehicle	Suggested Retail Price ($)	Resale Value (%)
Chevrolet Blazer LS	sport utility	19,495	55
Ford Explorer Sport	sport utility	20,495	57
GMC Yukon XL 1500	sport utility	26,789	67
Honda CR-V	sport utility	18,965	65
Isuzu VehiCross	sport utility	30,186	62
Jeep Cherokee Limited	sport utility	25,745	57
Mercury Mountaineer	sport utility	29,895	59
Nissan Pathfinder XE	sport utility	26,919	54
Toyota 4Runner	sport utility	22,418	55
Toyota RAV4	sport utility	17,148	55
Chevrolet S-10 Extended Cab	small pickup	18,847	46
Dodge Dakota Club Cab Sport	small pickup	16,870	53
Ford Ranger XLT Regular Cab	small pickup	18,510	48
Ford Ranger XLT Supercab	small pickup	20,225	55
GMC Sonoma Regular Cab	small pickup	16,938	44
Isuzu Hombre Spacecab	small pickup	18,820	41
Mazda B4000 SE Cab Plus	small pickup	23,050	51
Nissan Frontier XE Regular Cab	small pickup	12,110	51
Toyota Tacoma Xtracab	small pickup	18,228	49
Toyota Tacoma Xtracab V6	small pickup	19,318	50
Chevrolet K2500	full-size pickup	24,417	60
Chevrolet Silverado 2500 Ext	full-size pickup	24,140	64
Dodge Ram 1500	full-size pickup	17,460	54
Dodge Ram Quad Cab 2500	full-size pickup	32,770	63
Dodge Ram Regular Cab 2500	full-size pickup	23,140	59
Ford F150 XL	full-size pickup	22,875	58
Ford F-350 Super Duty Crew Cab XL	full-size pickup	34,295	64
GMC New Sierra 1500 Ext Cab	full-size pickup	27,089	68
Toyota Tundra Access Cab Limited	full-size pickup	25,605	53
Toyota Tundra Regular Cab	full-size pickup	15,835	58

a. Develop an estimated regression equation that can be used to predict the resale value given the suggested retail price. At the .05 level of significance, test for a significant relationship.
b. Did the estimated regression equation developed in part (a) provide a good fit to the data? Explain.
c. Develop an estimated regression equation that can be used to predict the resale value given the suggested retail price and the type of vehicle.
d. Use the F test to determine the significance of the regression results. At a .05 level of significance, what is your conclusion?

Case Problem 1 Consumer Research, Inc.

Consumer Research, Inc., is an independent agency that conducts research on consumer attitudes and behaviors for a variety of firms. In one study, a client asked for an investigation of consumer characteristics that can be used to predict the amount charged by credit card users. Data were collected on annual income, household size, and annual credit card charges for a sample of 50 consumers. The following data are on the CD accompanying the text in the data set named Consumer.

CD file
Consumer

Income ($1000s)	Household Size	Amount Charged ($)	Income ($1000s)	Household Size	Amount Charged ($)
54	3	4016	54	6	5573
30	2	3159	30	1	2583
32	4	5100	48	2	3866
50	5	4742	34	5	3586
31	2	1864	67	4	5037
55	2	4070	50	2	3605
37	1	2731	67	5	5345
40	2	3348	55	6	5370
66	4	4764	52	2	3890
51	3	4110	62	3	4705
25	3	4208	64	2	4157
48	4	4219	22	3	3579
27	1	2477	29	4	3890
33	2	2514	39	2	2972
65	3	4214	35	1	3121
63	4	4965	39	4	4183
42	6	4412	54	3	3730
21	2	2448	23	6	4127
44	1	2995	27	2	2921
37	5	4171	26	7	4603
62	6	5678	61	2	4273
21	3	3623	30	2	3067
55	7	5301	22	4	3074
42	2	3020	46	5	4820
41	7	4828	66	4	5149

Managerial Report

1. Use methods of descriptive statistics to summarize the data. Comment on the findings.
2. Develop estimated regression equations, first using annual income as the independent variable and then using household size as the independent variable. Which variable is the better predictor of annual credit card charges? Discuss your findings.
3. Develop an estimated regression equation with annual income and household size as the independent variables. Discuss your findings.
4. What is the predicted annual credit card charge for a three-person household with an annual income of $40,000?
5. Discuss the need for other independent variables that could be added to the model. What additional variables might be helpful?

Case Problem 2 Predicting Student Proficiency Test Scores

In order to predict how a school district would have scored when accounting for poverty and other income measures, *The Cincinnati Enquirer* gathered data from the Ohio Department of Education's Education Management Services and the Ohio Department of Taxation (*The Cincinnati Enquirer,* November 30, 1997). First, the newspaper obtained passage-rate data on the math, reading, science, writing, and citizenship proficiency exams given to fourth-, sixth-, ninth-, and twelfth-graders in early 1996. By combining these data, they computed an overall percentage of students that passed the tests for each district.

The percentage of a school district's students on Aid for Dependent Children (ADC), the percentage who qualify for free or reduced-price lunches, and the district's median family income were also recorded. A portion of the data collected for the 608 school districts follows. The complete data set is available on the CD accompanying the text in the data set named Enquirer.

CD file

Enquirer

Rank	School District	County	% Passed	% on ADC	% Free Lunch	Median Income ($)
1	Ottawa Hills Local	Lucas	93.85	0.11	0.00	48231
2	Wyoming City	Hamilton	93.08	2.95	4.59	42672
3	Oakwood City	Montgomery	92.92	0.20	0.38	42403
4	Madeira City	Hamilton	92.37	1.50	4.83	32889
5	Indian Hill Ex Vill	Hamilton	91.77	1.23	2.70	44135
6	Solon City	Cuyahoga	90.77	0.68	2.24	34993
7	Chagrin Falls Ex Vill	Cuyahoga	89.89	0.47	0.44	38921
8	Mariemont City	Hamilton	89.80	3.00	2.97	31823
9	Upper Arlington City	Franklin	89.77	0.24	0.92	38358
10	Granville Ex Vill	Licking	89.22	1.14	0.00	36235
⋮	⋮	⋮	⋮	⋮	⋮	⋮

The data have been ranked based on the values in the column labeled % Passed; these data are the overall percentage of students passing the tests. Data in the column labeled % on ADC are the percentage of each school district's students on ADC, and the data in the column labeled % Free Lunch are the percentage of students who qualify for free or reduced-price lunches. The column labeled Median Income shows each district's median family income. Also shown for each school district is the county in which the school district is located. Note that in some cases the value in the % Free Lunch column is 0, indicating that the district did not participate in the free lunch program.

Managerial Report

Use the methods presented in this and previous chapters to analyze this data set. Present a summary of your analysis, including key statistical results, conclusions, and recommendations, in a managerial report. Include any technical material you feel is appropriate in an appendix.

Case Problem 3 Alumni Giving

Alumni donations are an important source of revenue for colleges and universities. If administrators could determine the factors that could lead to increases in the percentage of alumni who make a donation, they might be able to implement policies that could lead to increased revenues. Research shows that students who are more satisfied with their contact with teachers are more likely to graduate. As a result, one might suspect that smaller class sizes and lower student-faculty ratios might lead to a higher percentage of satisfied graduates, which in turn might lead to increases in the percentage of alumni who make a donation. Table 15.13 shows data for 48 national universities (*America's Best Colleges,* Year 2000 Edition). The column labeled Graduation Rate is the percentage of students who initially enrolled at the university and graduated. The column labeled % of Classes Under 20 shows the percentage of classes

TABLE 15.13 DATA FOR 48 NATIONAL UNIVERSITIES

CD file
Alumni

	State	Graduation Rate	% of Classes Under 20	Student-Faculty Ratio	Alumni Giving Rate
Boston College	MA	85	39	13	25
Brandeis University	MA	79	68	8	33
Brown University	RI	93	60	8	40
California Institute of Technology	CA	85	65	3	46
Carnegie Mellon University	PA	75	67	10	28
Case Western Reserve Univ.	OH	72	52	8	31
College of William and Mary	VA	89	45	12	27
Columbia University	NY	90	69	7	31
Cornell University	NY	91	72	13	35
Dartmouth College	NH	94	61	10	53
Duke University	NC	92	68	8	45
Emory University	GA	84	65	7	37
Georgetown University	DC	91	54	10	29
Harvard University	MA	97	73	8	46
Johns Hopkins University	MD	89	64	9	27
Lehigh University	PA	81	55	11	40
Massachusetts Inst. of Technology	MA	92	65	6	44
New York University	NY	72	63	13	13
Northwestern University	IL	90	66	8	30
Pennsylvania State Univ.	PA	80	32	19	21
Princeton University	NJ	95	68	5	67
Rice University	TX	92	62	8	40
Stanford University	CA	92	69	7	34
Tufts University	MA	87	67	9	29
Tulane University	LA	72	56	12	17
U. of California–Berkeley	CA	83	58	17	18
U. of California–Davis	CA	74	32	19	7
U. of California–Irvine	CA	74	42	20	9
U. of California–Los Angeles	CA	78	41	18	13
U. of California–San Diego	CA	80	48	19	8
U. of California–Santa Barbara	CA	70	45	20	12
U. of Chicago	IL	84	65	4	36
U. of Florida	FL	67	31	23	19
U. of Illinois–Urbana Champaign	IL	77	29	15	23
U. of Michigan–Ann Arbor	MI	83	51	15	13
U. of North Carolina–Chapel Hill	NC	82	40	16	26
U. of Notre Dame	IN	94	53	13	49
U. of Pennsylvania	PA	90	65	7	41
U. of Rochester	NY	76	63	10	23
U. of Southern California	CA	70	53	13	22
U. of Texas–Austin	TX	66	39	21	13
U. of Virginia	VA	92	44	13	28
U. of Washington	WA	70	37	12	12
U. of Wisconsin–Madison	WI	73	37	13	13
Vanderbilt University	TN	82	68	9	31
Wake Forest University	NC	82	59	11	38
Washington University–St. Louis	MO	86	73	7	33
Yale University	CT	94	77	7	50

offered with fewer than 20 students. The column labeled Student-Faculty Ratio is the number of students enrolled divided by the total number of faculty. Finally, the column labeled Alumni Giving Rate is the percentage of alumni who made a donation to the university.

Managerial Report

1. Use methods of descriptive statistics to summarize the data.
2. Develop an estimated regression equation that can be used to predict the alumni giving rate given the number of students who graduate. Discuss your findings.
3. Develop an estimated regression equation that could be used to predict the alumni giving rate using the data provided.
4. What conclusions and recommendations can you derive from your analysis?

Case Problem 4 Predicting Winning Percentage for the NFL

CD file

NFLStats

The National Football League (NFL) records a variety of performance data for individuals and teams (www.nfl.com). Some of the year-end performance data for the 2005 season appear on the data disk in the file named NFLStats. Each row of the data set corresponds to an NFL team, and the teams are ranked by winning percentage. Descriptions for the data follow:

WinPct	Percentage of games won
DefYds/G	Average number of yards per game given up on defense
RushYds/G	Average number of rushing yards per game
PassYds/G	Average number of passing yards per game
FGPct	Percentage of field goals
TakeInt	Takeaway interceptions; the total number of interceptions made by the team's defense
TakeFum	Takeaway fumbles; the total number of fumbles recovered by the team's defense
GiveInt	Giveaway interceptions; the total number of interceptions made by the team's offense
GiveFum	Giveaway fumbles; the total number of fumbles made by the team's offense

Managerial Report

1. Use methods of descriptive statistics to summarize the data. Comment on the findings.
2. Develop an estimated regression equation that can be used to predict WinPct using DefYds/G, RushYds/G, PassYds/G, and FGPct. Discuss your findings.
3. Starting with the estimated regression equation developed in part (2), delete any independent variables that are not significant and develop a new estimated regression equation that can be used to predict WinPct. Use $\alpha = .05$.
4. Some football analysts believe that turnovers are one of the most important factors in determining a team's success. With Takeaways = TakeInt + TakeFum and Giveaways = GiveInt + GiveFum, let NetDiff = Takeaways − Giveaways. Develop an estimated regression equation that can be used to predict WinPct using NetDiff. Compare your results with the estimated regression equation developed in part (3).
5. Develop an estimated regression equation that can be used to predict WinPct using all the data provided.

Appendix 15.1 Multiple Regression with Minitab

CD file
Butler

In Section 15.2 we discussed the computer solution of multiple regression problems by showing Minitab's output for the Butler Trucking Company problem. In this appendix we describe the steps required to generate the Minitab computer solution. First, the data must be entered in a Minitab worksheet. The miles traveled are entered in column C1, the number of deliveries are entered in column C2, and the travel times (hours) are entered in column C3. The variable names Miles, Deliveries, and Time were entered as the column headings on the worksheet. In subsequent steps, we refer to the data by using the variable names Miles, Deliveries, and Time or the column indicators C1, C2, and C3. The following steps describe how to use Minitab to produce the regression results shown in Figure 15.4.

Step 1. Select the **Stat** menu
Step 2. Select the **Regression** menu
Step 3. Choose **Regression**
Step 4. When the **Regression** dialog box appears
Enter Time in the **Response** box
Enter Miles and Deliveries in the **Predictors** box
Click **OK**

Appendix 15.2 Multiple Regression with Excel

CD file
Butler

In Section 15.2 we discussed the computer solution of multiple regression problems by showing Minitab's output for the Butler Trucking Company problem. In this appendix we describe how to use Excel's Regression tool to develop the estimated multiple regression equation for the Butler Trucking problem. Refer to Figure 15.14 as we describe the tasks involved. First, the labels Assignment, Miles, Deliveries, and Time are entered into cells A1:D1 of the worksheet, and the sample data into cells B2:D11. The numbers 1–10 in cells A2:A11 identify each observation.

The following steps describe how to use the Regression tool for the multiple regression analysis.

Step 1. Select the **Tools** menu
Step 2. Choose **Data Analysis**
Step 3. Choose **Regression** from the list of Analysis Tools
Step 4. When the Regression dialog box appears
Enter D1:D11 in the **Input Y Range** box
Enter B1:C11 in the **Input X Range** box
Select **Labels**
Select **Confidence Level**
Enter 99 in the **Confidence Level** box
Select **Output Range**
Enter A13 in the **Output Range** box (to identify the upper left corner of the section of the worksheet where the output will appear)
Click **OK**

In the Excel output shown in Figure 15.14 the label for the independent variable x_1 is Miles (see cell A30), and the label for the independent variable x_2 is Deliveries (see cell A31). The estimated regression equation is

$$\hat{y} = -.8687 + .0611x_1 + .9234x_2$$

FIGURE 15.14 EXCEL OUTPUT FOR BUTLER TRUCKING WITH TWO INDEPENDENT VARIABLES

	A	B	C	D	E	F	G	H	I	J
1	**Assignment**	**Miles**	**Deliveries**	**Time**						
2	1	100	4	9.3						
3	2	50	3	4.8						
4	3	100	4	8.9						
5	4	100	2	6.5						
6	5	50	2	4.2						
7	6	80	2	6.2						
8	7	75	3	7.4						
9	8	65	4	6						
10	9	90	3	7.6						
11	10	90	2	6.1						
12										
13	SUMMARY OUTPUT									
14										
15	*Regression Statistics*									
16	Multiple R	0.9507								
17	R Square	0.9038								
18	Adjusted R Square	0.8763								
19	Standard Error	0.5731								
20	Observations	10								
21										
22	ANOVA									
23		*df*	*SS*	*MS*	*F*	*Significance F*				
24	Regression	2	21.6006	10.8003	32.8784	0.0003				
25	Residual	7	2.2994	0.3285						
26	Total	9	23.9							
27										
28		*Coefficients*	*Standard Error*	*t Stat*	*P-value*	*Lower 95%*	*Upper 95%*	*Lower 99.0%*	*Upper 99.0%*	
29	Intercept	-0.8687	0.9515	-0.9129	0.3916	-3.1188	1.3813	-4.1986	2.4612	
30	Miles	0.0611	0.0099	6.1824	0.0005	0.0378	0.0845	0.0265	0.0957	
31	Deliveries	0.9234	0.2211	4.1763	0.0042	0.4006	1.4463	0.1496	1.6972	
32										

Note that using Excel's Regression tool for multiple regression is almost the same as using it for simple linear regression. The major difference is that in the multiple regression case a larger range of cells is required in order to identify the independent variables.

Appendix 15.3 Logistic Regression with Minitab

CD file
Simmons

Minitab calls logistic regression with a dependent variable that can only assume the values 0 and 1 Binary Logistic Regression. In this appendix we describe the steps required to use Minitab's Binary Logistic Regression procedure to generate the computer output for the Simmons Stores problem shown in Figure 15.13. First, the data must be entered in a Minitab worksheet. The amounts customers spent last year at Simmons (in thousands of dollars) are entered into column C2, the credit card data (1 if a Simmons card; 0 otherwise) are entered into column C3, and the coupon use data (1 if the customer used the coupon; 0 otherwise) are entered in column C4. The variable names Spending, Card, and Coupon are entered as the column headings on the worksheet. In subsequent steps, we refer to the data by using the variable names Spending, Card, and Coupon or the column indicators C2, C3, and C4. The following steps will generate the logistic regression output.

Step 1. Select the **Stat** menu
Step 2. Select the **Regression** menu
Step 3. Choose **Binary Logistic Regression**
Step 4. When the **Binary Logistic Regression** dialog box appears
Enter Coupon in the **Response** box
Enter Spending and Card in the **Model** box
Click **OK**

The information in Figure 15.13 will now appear as a portion of the output.

CHAPTER 16

Regression Analysis: Model Building

CONTENTS

STATISTICS *in* PRACTICE

MONSANTO COMPANY*

ST. LOUIS, MISSOURI

Monsanto Company traces its roots to one entrepreneur's investment of $500 and a dusty warehouse on the Mississippi riverfront, where in 1901 John F. Queeney began manufacturing saccharin. Today, Monsanto is one of the nation's largest chemical companies, producing more than a thousand products ranging from industrial chemicals to synthetic playing surfaces used in modern sports stadiums. Monsanto is a worldwide corporation with manufacturing facilities, laboratories, technical centers, and marketing operations in 65 countries.

Monsanto's Nutrition Chemical Division manufactures and markets a methionine supplement used in poultry, swine, and cattle feed products. Because poultry growers work with high volumes and low profit margins, cost-effective poultry feed products with the best possible nutrition value are needed. Optimal feed composition will result in rapid growth and high final body weight for a given level of feed intake. The chemical industry works closely with poultry growers to optimize poultry feed products. Ultimately, success depends on keeping the cost of poultry low in comparison with the cost of beef and other meat products.

Monsanto used regression analysis to model the relationship between body weight y and the amount of methionine x added to the poultry feed. Initially, the following simple linear estimated regression equation was developed.

$$\hat{y} = .21 + .42x$$

This estimated regression equation proved statistically significant; however, the analysis of the residuals indicated that a curvilinear relationship would be a better model of the relationship between body weight and methionine.

Monsanto researchers used regression analysis to develop an optimal feed composition for poultry growers. © PhotoDisc/Getty Images.

Further research conducted by Monsanto showed that although small amounts of methionine tended to increase body weight, at some point body weight leveled off and additional amounts of the methionine were of little or no benefit. In fact, when the amount of methionine increased beyond nutritional requirements, body weight tended to decline. The following estimated multiple regression equation was used to model the curvilinear relationship between body weight and methionine.

$$\hat{y} = -1.89 + 1.32x - .506x^2$$

Use of the regression results enabled Monsanto to determine the optimal level of methionine to be used in poultry feed products.

In this chapter we will extend the discussion of regression analysis by showing how curvilinear models such as the one used by Monsanto can be developed. In addition, we will describe a variety of tools that help determine which independent variables lead to the best estimated regression equation.

*The authors are indebted to James R. Ryland and Robert M. Schisla, Senior Research Specialists, Monsanto Nutrition Chemical Division, for providing this Statistics in Practice.

Model building is the process of developing an estimated regression equation that describes the relationship between a dependent variable and one or more independent variables. The major issues in model building are finding the proper functional form of the relationship and selecting the independent variables to be included in the model. In Section 16.1 we establish the framework for model building by introducing the concept of a general linear model. Section 16.2, which provides the foundation for the more sophisticated computer-based procedures, introduces a general approach for determining when to add or delete independent variables. In Section 16.3 we consider a larger regression problem involving eight independent variables and 25 observations; this problem is used to illustrate the variable selection procedures presented in Section 16.4, including stepwise regression, the forward selection procedure, the backward elimination procedure, and best-subsets regression. In Section 16.5 we show how multiple regression analysis can provide another approach to solving experimental design problems, and in Section 16.6 we show how the Durbin-Watson test can be used to detect serial or autocorrelation.

16.1 General Linear Model

Suppose we collected data for one dependent variable y and k independent variables $x_1, x_2, \ldots, x_k$. Our objective is to use these data to develop an estimated regression equation that provides the best relationship between the dependent and independent variables. As a general framework for developing more complex relationships among the independent variables, we introduce the concept of a **general linear model** involving p independent variables.

If you can write a regression model in the form of equation (16.1), the standard multiple regression procedures described in Chapter 15 are applicable.

GENERAL LINEAR MODEL

$$y = \beta_0 + \beta_1 z_1 + \beta_2 z_2 + \cdots + \beta_p z_p + \epsilon \tag{16.1}$$

In equation (16.1), each of the independent variables z_j (where $j = 1, 2, \ldots, p$) is a function of $x_1, x_2, \ldots, x_k$ (the variables for which data are collected). In some cases, each z_j may be a function of only one x variable. The simplest case is when we collect data for just one variable x_1 and want to estimate y by using a straight-line relationship. In this case $z_1 = x_1$ and equation (16.1) becomes

$$y = \beta_0 + \beta_1 x_1 + \epsilon \tag{16.2}$$

Equation (16.2) is the simple linear regression model introduced in Chapter 14 with the exception that the independent variable is labeled x_1 instead of x. In the statistical modeling literature, this model is called a *simple first-order model with one predictor variable.*

TABLE 16.1

DATA FOR THE REYNOLDS EXAMPLE

Months Employed	Scales Sold
41	375
106	296
76	317
10	376
22	162
12	150
85	367
111	308
40	189
51	235
9	83
12	112
6	67
56	325
19	189

CD file

Reynolds

Modeling Curvilinear Relationships

More complex types of relationships can be modeled with equation (16.1). To illustrate, let us consider the problem facing Reynolds, Inc., a manufacturer of industrial scales and laboratory equipment. Managers at Reynolds want to investigate the relationship between length of employment of their salespeople and the number of electronic laboratory scales sold. Table 16.1 gives the number of scales sold by 15 randomly selected salespeople for the most recent sales period and the number of months each salesperson has been employed by the firm. Figure 16.1 is the scatter diagram for these data. The scatter diagram indicates a possible curvilinear relationship between the length of time employed and the number of units sold. Before considering how to develop a curvilinear relationship for Reynolds, let us consider the Minitab output in Figure 16.2 corresponding to a simple first-order model; the estimated regression is

$$\text{Sales} = 111 + 2.38 \text{ Months}$$

where

$$\text{Sales} = \text{number of electronic laboratory scales sold}$$
$$\text{Months} = \text{the number of months the salesperson has been employed}$$

FIGURE 16.1 SCATTER DIAGRAM FOR THE REYNOLDS EXAMPLE

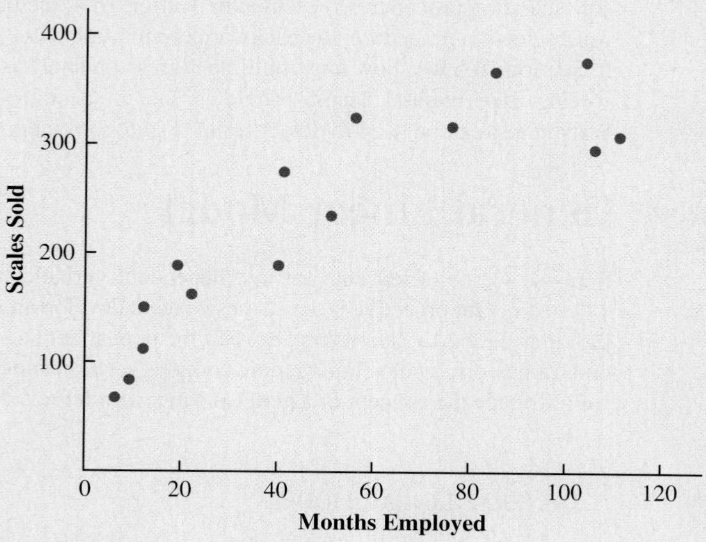

Figure 16.3 is the corresponding standardized residual plot. Although the computer output shows that the relationship is significant (p-value = .000) and that a linear relationship explains a high percentage of the variability in sales (R-sq = 78.1%), the standardized residual plot suggests that a curvilinear relationship is needed.

To account for the curvilinear relationship, we set $z_1 = x_1$ and $z_2 = x_1^2$ in equation (16.1) to obtain the model

$$y = \beta_0 + \beta_1 x_1 + \beta_2 x_1^2 + \epsilon \tag{16.3}$$

This model is called a *second-order model with one predictor variable.* To develop an estimated regression equation corresponding to this second-order model, the statistical

FIGURE 16.2 MINITAB OUTPUT FOR THE REYNOLDS EXAMPLE: FIRST-ORDER MODEL

```
The regression equation is
Sales = 111 + 2.38 Months

Predictor      Coef   SE Coef      T      p
Constant     111.23     21.63   5.14  0.000
Months       2.3768    0.3489   6.81  0.000

S = 49.52    R-sq = 78.1%    R-sq(adj) = 76.4%

Analysis of Variance

SOURCE          DF      SS      MS      F      p
Regression       1  113783  113783  46.41  0.000
Residual Error  13   31874    2452
Total           14  145657
```

FIGURE 16.3 STANDARDIZED RESIDUAL PLOT FOR THE REYNOLDS EXAMPLE: FIRST-ORDER MODEL

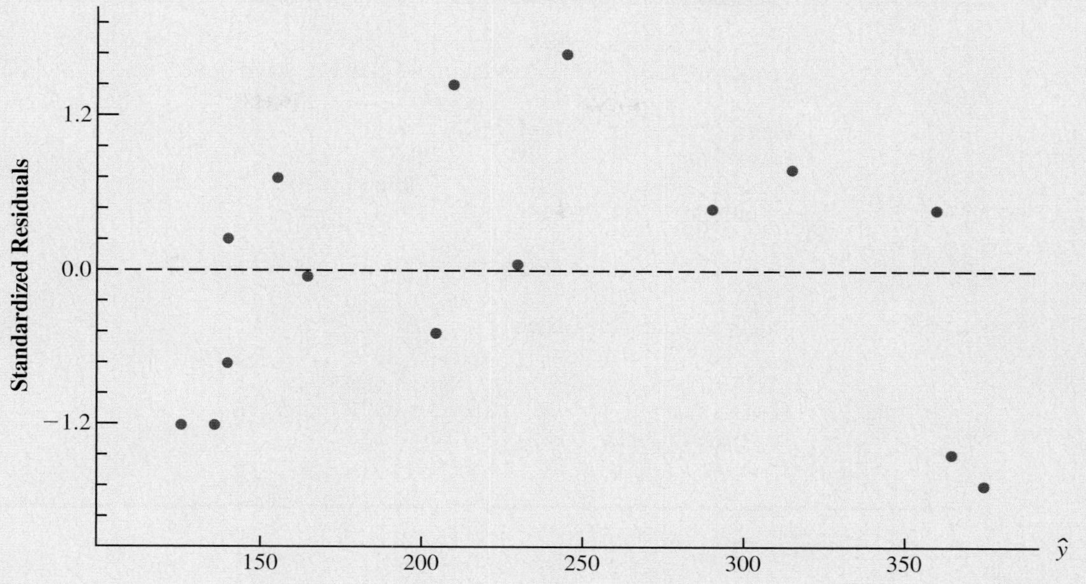

software package we are using needs the original data in Table 16.1, as well as that data corresponding to adding a second independent variable that is the square of the number of months the employee has been with the firm. In Figure 16.4 we show the Minitab output corresponding to the second-order model; the estimated regression equation is

The data for the MonthsSq *independent variable is obtained by squaring the values of* Months.

$$\text{Sales} = 45.3 + 6.34 \text{ Months} - .0345 \text{ MonthsSq}$$

where

MonthsSq = the square of the number of months the salesperson has been employed

Figure 16.5 is the corresponding standardized residual plot. It shows that the previous curvilinear pattern has been removed. At the .05 level of significance, the computer output shows that the overall model is significant (p-value for the F test is 0.000); note also that the p-value corresponding to the t-ratio for MonthsSq (p-value = .002) is less than .05, and hence we can conclude that adding MonthsSq to the model involving Months is significant. With an R-sq(adj) value of 88.6%, we should be pleased with the fit provided by this estimated regression equation. More important, however, is seeing how easy it is to handle curvilinear relationships in regression analysis.

Clearly, many types of relationships can be modeled by using equation (16.1). The regression techniques with which we have been working are definitely not limited to linear, or straight-line, relationships. In multiple regression analysis the word *linear* in the term "general linear model" refers only to the fact that $\beta_0, \beta_1, \ldots, \beta_p$ all have exponents of 1; it does not imply that the relationship between y and the x_i's is linear. Indeed, in this section we have seen one example of how equation (16.1) can be used to model a curvilinear relationship.

FIGURE 16.4 MINITAB OUTPUT FOR THE REYNOLDS EXAMPLE: SECOND-ORDER MODEL

```
The regression equation is
Sales = 45.3 + 6.34 Months - 0.0345 MonthsSq

Predictor         Coef   SE Coef      T      p
Constant         45.35     22.77   1.99  0.070
Months           6.345     1.058   6.00  0.000
MonthsSq     -0.034486  0.008948  -3.85  0.002

S = 34.45   R-sq = 90.2%   R-sq(adj) = 88.6%

Analysis of Variance

SOURCE          DF      SS     MS      F      p
Regression       2  131413  65707  55.36  0.000
Residual Error  12   14244   1187
Total           14  145657
```

FIGURE 16.5 STANDARDIZED RESIDUAL PLOT FOR THE REYNOLDS EXAMPLE: SECOND-ORDER MODEL

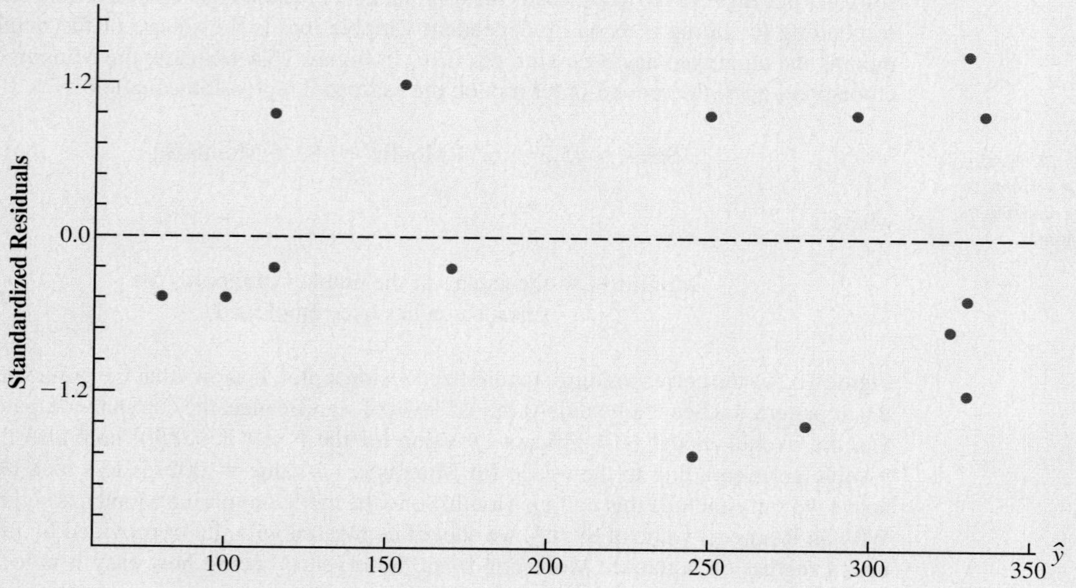

Interaction

If the original data set consists of observations for y and two independent variables x_1 and x_2, we can develop a second-order model with two predictor variables by setting $z_1 = x_1$, $z_2 = x_2$, $z_3 = x_1^2$, $z_4 = x_2^2$, and $z_5 = x_1x_2$ in the general linear model of equation (16.1). The model obtained is

$$y = \beta_0 + \beta_1x_1 + \beta_2x_2 + \beta_3x_1^2 + \beta_4x_2^2 + \beta_5x_1x_2 + \epsilon \tag{16.4}$$

In this second-order model, the variable $z_5 = x_1x_2$ is added to account for the potential effects of the two variables acting together. This type of effect is called **interaction**.

To provide an illustration of interaction and what it means, let us review the regression study conducted by Tyler Personal Care for one of its new shampoo products. Two factors believed to have the most influence on sales are unit selling price and advertising expenditure. To investigate the effects of these two variables on sales, prices of \$2.00, \$2.50, and \$3.00 were paired with advertising expenditures of \$50,000 and \$100,000 in 24 test markets. The unit sales (in thousands) that were observed are reported in Table 16.2.

Table 16.3 is a summary of these data. Note that the sample mean sales corresponding to a price of \$2.00 and an advertising expenditure of \$50,000 is 461,000, and the sample mean sales corresponding to a price of \$2.00 and an advertising expenditure of \$100,000 is 808,000. Hence, with price held constant at \$2.00, the difference in mean sales between advertising expenditures of \$50,000 and \$100,000 is 808,000 − 461,000 = 347,000 units. When the price of the product is \$2.50, the difference in mean sales is 646,000 − 364,000 = 282,000 units. Finally, when the price is \$3.00, the difference in mean sales is 375,000 − 332,000 = 43,000 units. Clearly, the difference in mean sales between advertising expenditures of \$50,000 and \$100,000 depends on the price of the product. In other words, at higher selling prices, the effect of increased advertising expenditure diminishes. These observations provide evidence of interaction between the price and advertising expenditure variables.

To provide another perspective of interaction, Figure 16.6 shows the sample mean sales for the six price-advertising expenditure combinations. This graph also shows that the effect of advertising expenditure on mean sales depends on the price of the product; we again see

TABLE 16.2 DATA FOR THE TYLER PERSONAL CARE EXAMPLE

Price	Advertising Expenditure (\$1000s)	Sales (1000s)	Price	Advertising Expenditure (\$1000s)	Sales (1000s)
\$2.00	50	478	\$2.00	100	810
\$2.50	50	373	\$2.50	100	653
\$3.00	50	335	\$3.00	100	345
\$2.00	50	473	\$2.00	100	832
\$2.50	50	358	\$2.50	100	641
\$3.00	50	329	\$3.00	100	372
\$2.00	50	456	\$2.00	100	800
\$2.50	50	360	\$2.50	100	620
\$3.00	50	322	\$3.00	100	390
\$2.00	50	437	\$2.00	100	790
\$2.50	50	365	\$2.50	100	670
\$3.00	50	342	\$3.00	100	393

CD file
Tyler

TABLE 16.3 MEAN UNIT SALES (1000s) FOR THE TYLER PERSONAL CARE EXAMPLE

		Price		
		$2.00	**$2.50**	**$3.00**
Advertising Expenditure	**$50,000**	461	364	332
	$100,000	808	646	375

Mean sales of 808,000 units when price = $2.00 and advertising expenditure = $100,000

FIGURE 16.6 MEAN UNIT SALES (1000s) AS A FUNCTION OF SELLING PRICE AND ADVERTISING EXPENDITURE

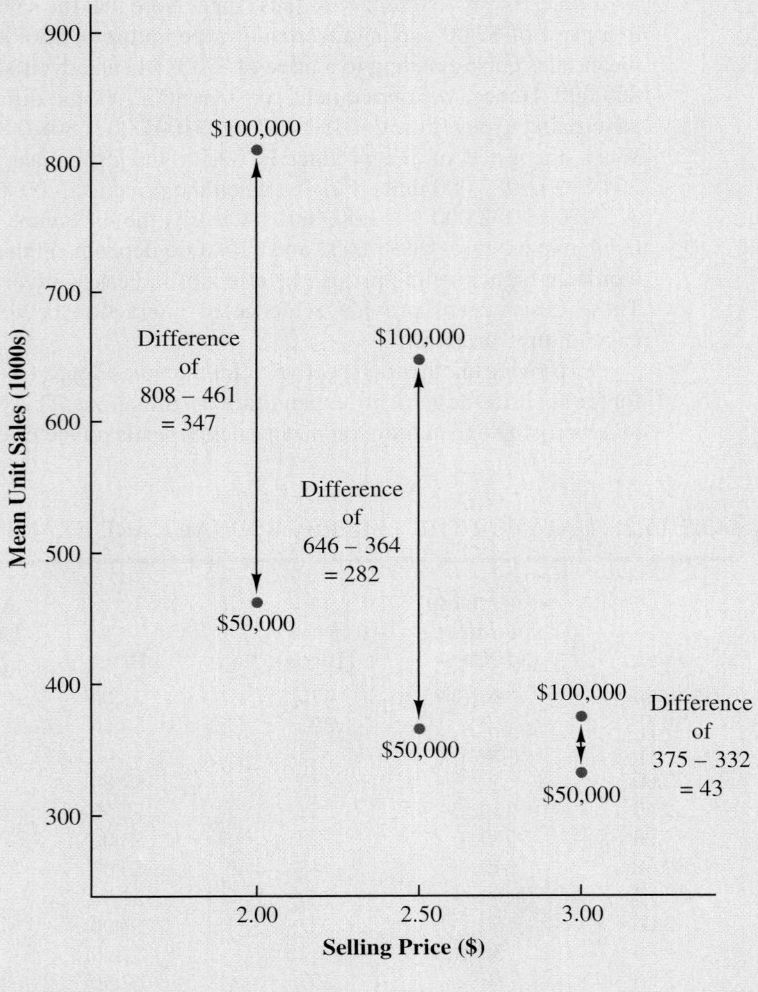

the effect of interaction. When interaction between two variables is present, we cannot study the effect of one variable on the response y independently of the other variable. In other words, meaningful conclusions can be developed only if we consider the joint effect that both variables have on the response.

To account for the effect of interaction, we will use the following regression model.

$$y = \beta_0 + \beta_1 x_1 + \beta_2 x_2 + \beta_3 x_1 x_2 + \epsilon \quad (16.5)$$

where

$$\begin{aligned} y &= \text{unit sales (1000s)} \\ x_1 &= \text{price (\$)} \\ x_2 &= \text{advertising expenditure (\$1000s)} \end{aligned}$$

Note that equation (16.5) reflects Tyler's belief that the number of units sold depends linearly on selling price and advertising expenditure (accounted for by the $\beta_1 x_1$ and $\beta_2 x_2$ terms), and that there is interaction between the two variables (accounted for by the $\beta_3 x_1 x_2$ term).

To develop an estimated regression equation, a general linear model involving three independent variables (z_1, z_2, and z_3) was used.

$$y = \beta_0 + \beta_1 z_1 + \beta_2 z_2 + \beta_3 z_3 + \epsilon \quad (16.6)$$

where

$$\begin{aligned} z_1 &= x_1 \\ z_2 &= x_2 \\ z_3 &= x_1 x_2 \end{aligned}$$

Figure 16.7 is the Minitab output corresponding to the interaction model for the Tyler Personal Care example. The resulting estimated regression equation is

$$\text{Sales} = -276 + 175 \text{ Price} + 19.7 \text{ AdvExp} - 6.08 \text{ PriceAdv}$$

where

The data for the PriceAdv *independent variable is obtained by multiplying each value of* Price *times the corresponding value of* AdvExp.

$$\begin{aligned} \text{Sales} &= \text{unit sales (1000s)} \\ \text{Price} &= \text{price of the product (\$)} \\ \text{AdvExp} &= \text{advertising expenditure (\$1000s)} \\ \text{PriceAdv} &= \text{interaction term (Price times AdvExp)} \end{aligned}$$

Because the model is significant (p-value for the F test is 0.000) and the p-value corresponding to the t test for PriceAdv is 0.000, we conclude that interaction is significant given the linear effect of the price of the product and the advertising expenditure. Thus, the regression results show that the effect of advertising expenditure on sales depends on the price.

Transformations Involving the Dependent Variable

In showing how the general linear model can be used to model a variety of possible relationships between the independent variables and the dependent variable, we have focused attention on transformations involving one or more of the independent variables. Often it

FIGURE 16.7 MINITAB OUTPUT FOR THE TYLER PERSONAL CARE EXAMPLE

```
The regression equation is
Sales = - 276 + 175 Price + 19.7 AdvExpen - 6.08 PriceAdv

Predictor      Coef   SE Coef       T      p
Constant     -275.8     112.8   -2.44  0.024
Price        175.00     44.55    3.93  0.001
Adver        19.680     1.427   13.79  0.000
PriceAdv    -6.0800    0.5635  -10.79  0.000

S = 28.17   R-sq = 97.8%   R-sq(adj) = 97.5%

Analysis of Variance

SOURCE          DF      SS      MS       F      p
Regression       3  709316  236439  297.87  0.000
Residual Error  20   15875     794
Total           23  725191
```

TABLE 16.4 MILES-PER-GALLON RATINGS AND WEIGHTS FOR 12 AUTOMOBILES

Weight	Miles per Gallon
2289	28.7
2113	29.2
2180	34.2
2448	27.9
2026	33.3
2702	26.4
2657	23.9
2106	30.5
3226	18.1
3213	19.5
3607	14.3
2888	20.9

CD file MPG

is worthwhile to consider transformations involving the dependent variable y. As an illustration of when we might want to transform the dependent variable, consider the data in Table 16.4, which shows the miles-per-gallon ratings and weights for 12 automobiles. The scatter diagram in Figure 16.8 indicates a negative linear relationship between these two variables. Therefore, we use a simple first-order model to relate the two variables. The Minitab output is shown in Figure 16.9; the resulting estimated regression equation is

$$\text{MPG} = 56.1 - 0.0116 \text{ Weight}$$

where

$$\text{MPG} = \text{miles-per-gallon rating}$$
$$\text{Weight} = \text{weight of the car in pounds}$$

The model is significant (p-value for the F test is 0.000) and the fit is very good (R-sq = 93.5%). However, we note in Figure 16.9 that observation 3 is identified as having a large standardized residual.

Figure 16.10 is the standardized residual plot corresponding to the first-order model. The pattern we observe does not look like the horizontal band we should expect to find if the assumptions about the error term are valid. Instead, the variability in the residuals appears to increase as the value of $\hat{y}$ increases. In other words, we see the wedge-shaped pattern referred to in Chapters 14 and 15 as being indicative of a nonconstant variance. We are not justified in reaching any conclusions about the statistical significance of the resulting estimated regression equation when the underlying assumptions for the tests of significance do not appear to be satisfied.

Often the problem of nonconstant variance can be corrected by transforming the dependent variable to a different scale. For instance, if we work with the logarithm of the dependent variable instead of the original dependent variable, the effect will be to compress the values of the dependent variable and thus diminish the effects of nonconstant variance. Most statistical packages provide the ability to apply logarithmic transformations using either the base 10 (common logarithm) or the base $e = 2.71828\ldots$ (natural logarithm). We

FIGURE 16.8 SCATTER DIAGRAM FOR THE MILES-PER-GALLON EXAMPLE

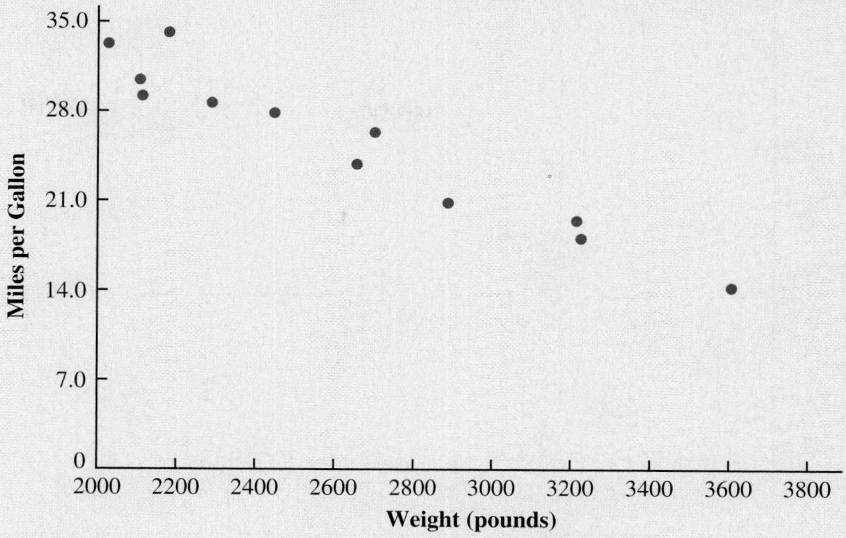

FIGURE 16.9 MINITAB OUTPUT FOR THE MILES-PER-GALLON EXAMPLE

```
The regression equation is
MPG = 56.1 - 0.0116 Weight

Predictor         Coef     SE Coef        T      p
Constant        56.096       2.582    21.72  0.000
Weight      -0.0116436   0.0009677   -12.03  0.000

S = 1.671   R-sq = 93.5%   R-sq(adj) = 92.9%

Analysis of Variance

SOURCE          DF      SS      MS       F      p
Regression       1  403.98  403.98  144.76  0.000
Residual Error  10   27.91    2.79
Total           11  431.88

Unusual Observations
Obs  Weight     MPG     Fit  SE Fit  Residual  St Resid
  3    2180  34.200  30.713   0.644     3.487     2.26R

R denotes an observation with a large standardized residual.
```

FIGURE 16.10 STANDARDIZED RESIDUAL PLOT FOR THE MILES-PER-GALLON EXAMPLE

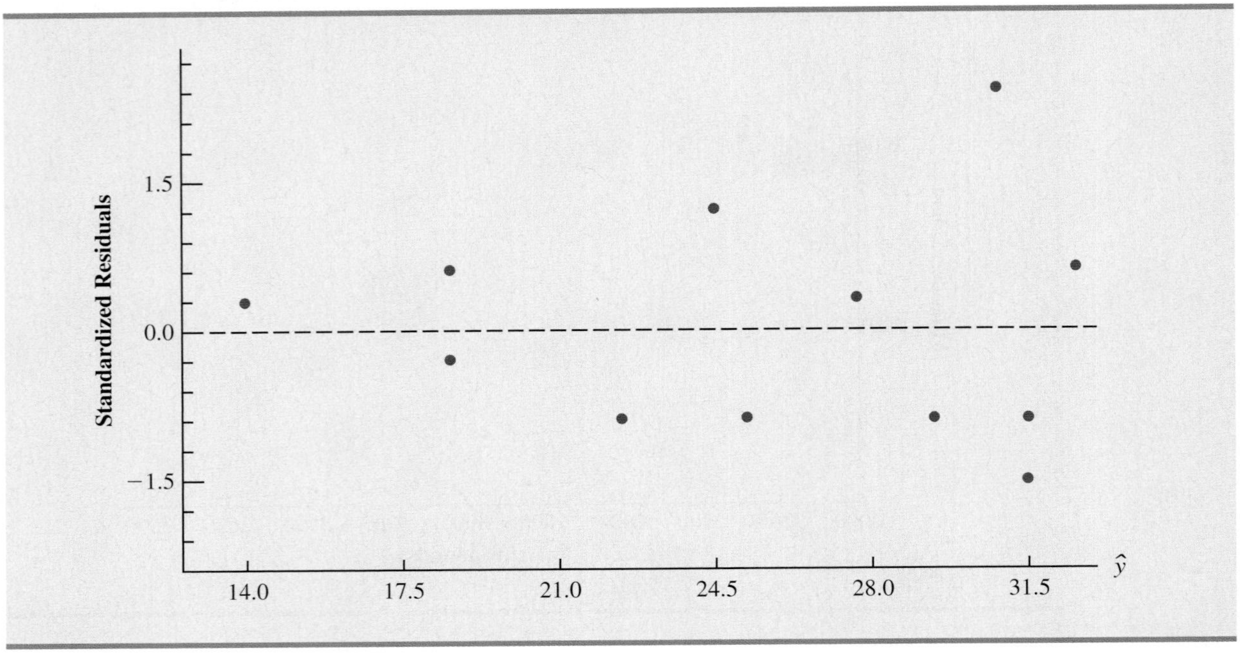

applied a natural logarithmic transformation to the miles-per-gallon data and developed the estimated regression equation relating weight to the natural logarithm of miles-per-gallon. The regression results obtained by using the natural logarithm of miles-per-gallon as the dependent variable, labeled LogeMPG in the output, are shown in Figure 16.11; Figure 16.12 is the corresponding standardized residual plot.

Looking at the residual plot in Figure 16.12, we see that the wedge-shaped pattern has now disappeared. Moreover, none of the observations are identified as having a large

FIGURE 16.11 MINITAB OUTPUT FOR THE MILES-PER-GALLON EXAMPLE: LOGARITHMIC TRANSFORMATION

```
The regression equation is
LogeMPG = 4.52 -0.000501 Weight

Predictor          Coef      SE Coef        T      p
Constant        4.52423      0.09932    45.55  0.000
Weight      -0.00050110   0.00003722   -13.46  0.000

S = 0.06425   R-sq = 94.8%   R-sq(adj) = 94.2%

Analysis of Variance

SOURCE           DF        SS        MS       F      p
Regression        1   0.74822   0.74822  181.22  0.000
Residual Error   10   0.04129   0.00413
Total            11   0.78950
```

FIGURE 16.12 STANDARDIZED RESIDUAL PLOT FOR THE MILES-PER-GALLON EXAMPLE: LOGARITHMIC TRANSFORMATION

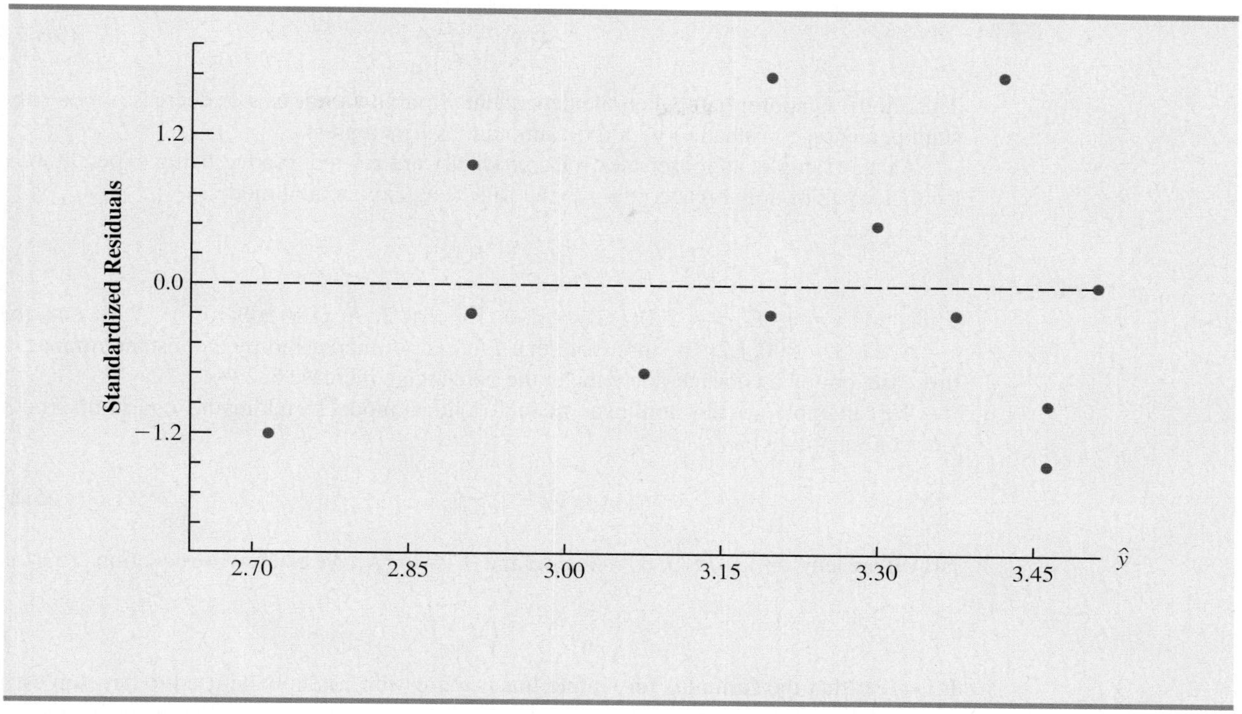

standardized residual. The model with the logarithm of miles per gallon as the dependent variable is statistically significant and provides an excellent fit to the observed data. Hence, we would recommend using the estimated regression equation

$$\text{LogeMPG} = 4.52 - 0.000501 \text{ Weight}$$

To estimate the miles-per-gallon rating for an automobile that weighs 2500 pounds, we first develop an estimate of the logarithm of the miles-per-gallon rating.

$$\text{LogeMPG} = 4.52 - 0.000501(2500) = 3.2675$$

The miles-per-gallon estimate is obtained by finding the number whose natural logarithm is 3.2675. Using a calculator with an exponential function, or raising e to the power 3.2675, we obtain 26.2 miles per gallon.

Another approach to problems of nonconstant variance is to use $1/y$ as the dependent variable instead of y. This type of transformation is called a *reciprocal transformation.* For instance, if the dependent variable is measured in miles per gallon, the reciprocal transformation would result in a new dependent variable whose units would be 1/(miles per gallon) or gallons per mile. In general, there is no way to determine whether a logarithmic transformation or a reciprocal transformation will perform best without actually trying each of them.

Nonlinear Models That Are Intrinsically Linear

Models in which the parameters ($\beta_0, \beta_1, \ldots, \beta_p$) have exponents other than 1 are called nonlinear models. However, for the case of the exponential model, we can perform a transformation of variables that will enable us to perform regression analysis with equation (16.1), the general linear model. The exponential model involves the following regression equation.

$$E(y) = \beta_0\beta_1^x \tag{16.7}$$

This model is appropriate when the dependent variable y increases or decreases by a constant percentage, instead of by a fixed amount, as x increases.

As an example, suppose sales for a product y are related to advertising expenditure x (in thousands of dollars) according to the following exponential model.

$$E(y) = 500(1.2)^x$$

Thus, for $x = 1$, $E(y) = 500(1.2)^1 = 600$; for $x = 2$, $E(y) = 500(1.2)^2 = 720$; and for $x = 3$, $E(y) = 500(1.2)^3 = 864$. Note that $E(y)$ is not increasing by a constant amount in this case, but by a constant percentage; the percentage increase is 20%.

We can transform this nonlinear model to a linear model by taking the logarithm of both sides of equation (16.7).

$$\log E(y) = \log \beta_0 + x \log \beta_1 \tag{16.8}$$

Now if we let $y' = \log E(y)$, $\beta_0' = \log \beta_0$, and $\beta_1' = \log \beta_1$, we can rewrite equation (16.8) as

$$y' = \beta_0' + \beta_1' x$$

It is clear that the formulas for simple linear regression can now be used to develop estimates of β_0' and β_1'. Denoting the estimates as b_0' and b_1' leads to the following estimated regression equation.

$$\hat{y}' = b_0' + b_1' x \tag{16.9}$$

To obtain predictions of the original dependent variable y given a value of x, we would first substitute the value of x into equation (16.9) and compute $\hat{y}'$. The antilog of $\hat{y}'$ would be the prediction of y, or the expected value of y.

Many nonlinear models cannot be transformed into an equivalent linear model. However, such models have had limited use in business and economic applications. Furthermore, the mathematical background needed for study of such models is beyond the scope of this text.

Exercises

Methods

SELF test

1. Consider the following data for two variables, x and y.

x	22	24	26	30	35	40
y	12	21	33	35	40	36

   a. Develop an estimated regression equation for the data of the form $\hat{y} = b_0 + b_1x$.
   b. Use the results from part (a) to test for a significant relationship between x and y. Use $\alpha = .05$.
   c. Develop a scatter diagram for the data. Does the scatter diagram suggest an estimated regression equation of the form $\hat{y} = b_0 + b_1x + b_2x^2$? Explain.

d. Develop an estimated regression equation for the data of the form $\hat{y} = b_0 + b_1x + b_2x^2$.
e. Refer to part (d). Is the relationship between x, x^2, and y significant? Use $\alpha = .05$.
f. Predict the value of y when $x = 25$.

2. Consider the following data for two variables, x and y.

x	9	32	18	15	26
y	10	20	21	16	22

a. Develop an estimated regression equation for the data of the form $\hat{y} = b_0 + b_1x$. Comment on the adequacy of this equation for predicting y.
b. Develop an estimated regression equation for the data of the form $\hat{y} = b_0 + b_1x + b_2x^2$. Comment on the adequacy of this equation for predicting y.
c. Predict the value of y when $x = 20$.

3. Consider the following data for two variables, x and y.

x	2	3	4	5	7	7	7	8	9
y	4	5	4	6	4	6	9	5	11

a. Does there appear to be a linear relationship between x and y? Explain.
b. Develop the estimated regression equation relating x and y.
c. Plot the standardized residuals versus $\hat{y}$ for the estimated regression equation developed in part (b). Do the model assumptions appear to be satisfied? Explain.
d. Perform a logarithmic transformation on the dependent variable y. Develop an estimated regression equation using the transformed dependent variable. Do the model assumptions appear to be satisfied by using the transformed dependent variable? Does a reciprocal transformation work better in this case? Explain.

Applications

4. A highway department is studying the relationship between traffic flow and speed. The following model has been hypothesized.

$$y = \beta_0 + \beta_1x + \epsilon$$

where

y = traffic flow in vehicles per hour
x = vehicle speed in miles per hour

The following data were collected during rush hour for six highways leading out of the city.

Traffic Flow (y)	Vehicle Speed (x)
1256	35
1329	40
1226	30
1335	45
1349	50
1124	25

a. Develop an estimated regression equation for the data.
b. Use $\alpha = .01$ to test for a significant relationship.

SELF test

5. In working further with the problem of exercise 4, statisticians suggested the use of the following curvilinear estimated regression equation.

$$\hat{y} = b_0 + b_1x + b_2x^2$$

a. Use the data of exercise 4 to estimate the parameters of this estimated regression equation.
b. Use $\alpha = .01$ to test for a significant relationship.
c. Estimate the traffic flow in vehicles per hour at a speed of 38 miles per hour.

6. A study of emergency service facilities investigated the relationship between the number of facilities and the average distance traveled to provide the emergency service. The following table gives the data collected.

Number of Facilities	Average Distance (miles)
9	1.66
11	1.12
16	.83
21	.62
27	.51
30	.47

a. Develop a scatter diagram for these data, treating average distance traveled as the dependent variable.
b. Does a simple linear model appear to be appropriate? Explain.
c. Develop an estimated regression equation for the data that you believe will best explain the relationship between these two variables.

7. An important factor in purchasing a suitable computer monitor is the field of view. If a monitor has a wide field of view, slight head turns can still provide an acceptable image and someone standing next to the monitor can still clearly see the image on the screen. In a review of 19-inch LCD monitors, *PC World* found that although all the monitors they tested claimed a 170-degree arc—both horizontally and vertically—the actual angles for the monitors ranged from 108 to 167 degrees. The following data show the horizontal viewing angle for eight 19-inch monitors and *PC World*'s overall rating based upon image quality, price, features, and support policies (*PC World,* February 2003).

CD file

Monitors

Monitor	Angle	Rating
Samsung SyncMaster 191T	167	86
ViewSonic VX900	159	82
Sceptre Technologies X9S-Naga	126	81
Planar PL191M	108	81
Dell UltraSharp 1900FP	153	81
AOC LM914	123	81
KDS USA Radius Rad-9	118	80
NEC MultiSync LCD 1920NX	123	80
Iiyama Pro Lite 4821DT-BK	119	80

a. Develop a scatter diagram for these data with horizontal viewing angles as the independent variable.
b. Does a simple linear regression model appear to be appropriate?
c. Develop an estimated regression equation for the data you believe will best explain the relationship between these two variables.

8. Corvette, Ferrari, and Jaguar produced a variety of classic cars that continue to increase in value. The following data, based upon the Martin Rating System for Collectible Cars, show the rarity rating (1–20) and the high price ($1000) for 15 classic cars (www.businessweek.com, February 2006).

CD file ClassicCars

Year	Make	Model	Rating	Price ($1000)
1984	Chevrolet	Corvette	18	1600
1956	Chevrolet	Corvette 265/225-hp	19	4000
1963	Chevrolet	Corvette coupe (340-bhp 4-speed)	18	1000
1978	Chevrolet	Corvette coupe Silver Anniversary	19	1300
1960–1963	Ferrari	250 GTE 2+2	16	350
1962–1964	Ferrari	250 GTL Lusso	19	2650
1962	Ferrari	250 GTO	18	375
1967–1968	Ferrari	275 GTB/4 NART Spyder	17	450
1968–1973	Ferrari	365 GTB/4 Daytona	17	140
1962–1967	Jaguar	E-type OTS	15	77.5
1969–1971	Jaguar	E-type Series II OTS	14	62
1971–1974	Jaguar	E-type Series III OTS	16	125
1951–1954	Jaguar	XK 120 roadster (steel)	17	400
1950–1953	Jaguar	XK C-type	16	250
1956–1957	Jaguar	XKSS	13	70

a. Develop a scatter diagram of the data using the rarity rating as the independent variable and price as the independent variable. Does a simple linear regression model appear to be appropriate?
b. Develop an estimated multiple regression equation with x = rarity rating and x^2 as the two independent variables.
c. Consider the nonlinear relationship shown by equation (16.7). Use logarithms to develop an estimated regression equation for this model.
d. Do you prefer the estimated regression equation developed in part (b) or part (c)? Explain.

9. Almost all U.S. light-rail systems use electric cars that run on tracks built at street level. According to the Federal Transit Administration, light-rail is one of the safest modes of travel, with an accident rate of .99 accidents per million passenger miles as compared to 2.29 for buses. The following data show the miles of track and the weekday ridership in thousands of passengers for selected light-rail systems (*USA Today,* January 7, 2003).

CD file LightRail

City	Miles	Riders
Los Angeles	22	70
San Diego	47	75
Portland	38	81
Sacramento	21	31
San Jose	31	30
San Francisco	73	164
Philadelphia	69	84
Boston	51	231
Denver	17	35
Salt Lake City	18	28

(*continued*)

City	Miles	Riders
Dallas	44	39
New Orleans	16	14
St. Louis	34	42
Pittsburgh	18	25
Buffalo	6	23
Cleveland	15	15
Newark	9	8

a. Develop a scatter diagram for these data, treating the number of miles of track as the independent variable. Does a simple linear regression model appear to be appropriate?
b. Use a simple linear regression model to develop an estimated regression equation to predict the weekday ridership given the miles of track. Construct a standardized residual plot. Based upon the standardized residual plot, does a simple linear regression model appear to be appropriate?
c. Perform a logarithmic transformation on the dependent variable. Develop an estimated regression equation using the transformed dependent variable. Do the model assumptions appear to be satisfied by using the transformed dependent variable?
d. Perform a reciprocal transformation on the dependent variable. Develop an estimated regression equation using the transformed dependent variable.
e. What estimated regression equation would you recommend? Explain.

16.2 Determining When to Add or Delete Variables

In this section we will show how an F test can be used to determine whether it is advantageous to add one or more independent variables to a multiple regression model. This test is based on a determination of the amount of reduction in the error sum of squares resulting from adding one or more independent variables to the model. We will first illustrate how the test can be used in the context of the Butler Trucking example.

In Chapter 15, the Butler Trucking example was introduced to illustrate the use of multiple regression analysis. Recall that the managers wanted to develop an estimated regression equation to predict total daily travel time for trucks using two independent variables: miles traveled and number of deliveries. With miles traveled x_1 as the only independent variable, the least squares procedure provided the following estimated regression equation.

$$\hat{y} = 1.27 + .0678x_1$$

In Chapter 15 we showed that the error sum of squares for this model was SSE = 8.029. When x_2, the number of deliveries, was added as a second independent variable, we obtained the following estimated regression equation.

$$\hat{y} = -.869 + .0611x_1 + .923x_2$$

The error sum of squares for this model was SSE = 2.299. Clearly, adding x_2 resulted in a reduction of SSE. The question we want to answer is: Does adding the variable x_2 lead to a *significant* reduction in SSE?

We use the notation SSE(x_1) to denote the error sum of squares when x_1 is the only independent variable in the model, SSE(x_1, x_2) to denote the error sum of squares when x_1 and

x_2 are both in the model, and so on. Hence, the reduction in SSE resulting from adding x_2 to the model involving just x_1 is

$$\text{SSE}(x_1) - \text{SSE}(x_1, x_2) = 8.029 - 2.299 = 5.730$$

An F test is conducted to determine whether this reduction is significant.

The numerator of the F statistic is the reduction in SSE divided by the number of independent variables added to the original model. Here only one variable, x_2, has been added; thus, the numerator of the F statistic is

$$\frac{\text{SSE}(x_1) - \text{SSE}(x_1, x_2)}{1} = 5.730$$

The result is a measure of the reduction in SSE per independent variable added to the model. The denominator of the F statistic is the mean square error for the model that includes all of the independent variables. For Butler Trucking this corresponds to the model containing both x_1 and x_2; thus, $p = 2$ and

$$\text{MSE} = \frac{\text{SSE}(x_1, x_2)}{n - p - 1} = \frac{2.299}{7} = .3284$$

The following F statistic provides the basis for testing whether the addition of x_2 is statistically significant.

$$F = \frac{\dfrac{\text{SSE}(x_1) - \text{SSE}(x_1, x_2)}{1}}{\dfrac{\text{SSE}(x_1, x_2)}{n - p - 1}} \tag{16.10}$$

The numerator degrees of freedom for this F test is equal to the number of variables added to the model, and the denominator degrees of freedom is equal to $n - p - 1$.

For the Butler Trucking problem, we obtain

$$F = \frac{\dfrac{5.730}{1}}{\dfrac{2.299}{7}} = \frac{5.730}{.3284} = 17.45$$

Refer to Table 4 of Appendix B. We find that for a level of significance of $\alpha = .05$, $F_{.05} = 5.59$. Because $F = 17.45 > F_{.05} = 5.59$, we can reject the null hypothesis that x_2 is not statistically significant; in other words, adding x_2 to the model involving only x_1 results in a significant reduction in the error sum of squares.

When we want to test for the significance of adding only one more independent variable to a model, the result found with the F test just described could also be obtained by using the t test for the significance of an individual parameter (described in Section 15.4). Indeed, the F statistic we just computed is the square of the t statistic used to test the significance of an individual parameter.

Because the t test is equivalent to the F test when only one independent variable is being added to the model, we can now further clarify the proper use of the t test for testing the significance of an individual parameter. If an individual parameter is not significant, the corresponding variable can be dropped from the model. However, if the t test shows that two or more parameters are not significant, no more than one independent variable can ever be dropped from a model on the basis of a t test; if one variable is dropped, a second variable that was not significant initially might become significant.

We now turn to a consideration of whether the addition of more than one independent variable—as a set—results in a significant reduction in the error sum of squares.

General Case

Consider the following multiple regression model involving q independent variables, where $q < p$.

$$y = \beta_0 + \beta_1 x_1 + \beta_2 x_2 + \cdots + \beta_q x_q + \epsilon \tag{16.11}$$

If we add variables $x_{q+1}, x_{q+2}, \ldots, x_p$ to this model, we obtain a model involving p independent variables.

$$\begin{aligned} y = \beta_0 &+ \beta_1 x_1 + \beta_2 x_2 + \cdots + \beta_q x_q \\ &+ \beta_{q+1} x_{q+1} + \beta_{q+2} x_{q+2} + \cdots + \beta_p x_p + \epsilon \end{aligned} \tag{16.12}$$

To test whether the addition of $x_{q+1}, x_{q+2}, \ldots, x_p$ is statistically significant, the null and alternative hypotheses can be stated as follows.

H_0: $\beta_{q+1} = \beta_{q+2} = \cdots = \beta_p = 0$
H_a: One or more of the parameters is not equal to zero

The following F statistic provides the basis for testing whether the additional independent variables are statistically significant.

$$F = \frac{\dfrac{\text{SSE}(x_1, x_2, \ldots, x_q) - \text{SSE}(x_1, x_2, \ldots, x_q, x_{q+1}, \ldots, x_p)}{p - q}}{\dfrac{\text{SSE}(x_1, x_2, \ldots, x_q, x_{q+1}, \ldots, x_p)}{n - p - 1}} \tag{16.13}$$

This computed F value is then compared with F_α, the table value with $p - q$ numerator degrees of freedom and $n - p - 1$ denominator degrees of freedom. If $F > F_\alpha$, we reject H_0 and conclude that the set of additional independent variables is statistically significant. Note that for the special case where $q = 1$ and $p = 2$, equation (16.13) reduces to equation (16.10).

Many computer packages, such as Minitab, provide extra sums of squares corresponding to the order in which each independent variable enters the model; in such cases, the computation of the F test for determining whether to add or delete a set of variables is simplified.

Many students find equation (16.13) somewhat complex. To provide a simpler description of this F ratio, we can refer to the model with the smaller number of independent variables as the reduced model and the model with the larger number of independent variables as the full model. If we let SSE(reduced) denote the error sum of squares for the reduced model and SSE(full) denote the error sum of squares for the full model, we can write the numerator of (16.13) as

$$\frac{\text{SSE(reduced)} - \text{SSE(full)}}{\text{number of extra terms}} \tag{16.14}$$

Note that "number of extra terms" denotes the difference between the number of independent variables in the full model and the number of independent variables in the reduced model. The denominator of equation (16.13) is the error sum of squares for the full model divided by the corresponding degrees of freedom; in other words, the denominator is the mean square error for the full model. Denoting the mean square error for the full model as MSE(full) enables us to write it as

$$F = \frac{\dfrac{\text{SSE(reduced)} - \text{SSE(full)}}{\text{number of extra terms}}}{\text{MSE(full)}} \tag{16.15}$$

To illustrate the use of this F statistic, suppose we have a regression problem involving 30 observations. One model with the independent variables x_1, x_2, and x_3 has an error sum of squares of 150 and a second model with the independent variables x_1, x_2, x_3, x_4, and x_5 has an error sum of squares of 100. Did the addition of the two independent variables x_4 and x_5 result in a significant reduction in the error sum of squares?

First, note that the degrees of freedom for SST is $30 - 1 = 29$ and that the degrees of freedom for the regression sum of squares for the full model is five (the number of independent variables in the full model). Thus, the degrees of freedom for the error sum of squares for the full model is $29 - 5 = 24$, and hence MSE(full) $= 100/24 = 4.17$. Therefore the F statistic is

$$F = \frac{\dfrac{150 - 100}{2}}{4.17} = 6.00$$

This computed F value is compared with the table F value with two numerator and 24 denominator degrees of freedom. At the .05 level of significance, Table 4 of Appendix B shows $F_{.05} = 3.40$. Because $F = 6.00$ is greater than 3.40, we conclude that the addition of variables x_4 and x_5 is statistically significant.

Use of p-Values

The p-value criterion can also be used to determine whether it is advantageous to add one or more independent variables to a multiple regression model. In the preceding example, we showed how to perform an F test to determine if the addition of two independent variables, x_4 and x_5, to a model with three independent variables, x_1, x_2, and x_3, was statistically significant. For this example, the computed F statistic was 6.00 and we concluded (by comparing $F = 6.00$ to the critical value $F_{.05} = 3.40$) that the addition of variables x_4 and x_5 was significant. The p-value associated with $F = 6.00$ (2 numerator and 24 denominator degrees of freedom) is .008. With a p-value $= .008 < \alpha = .05$, we also conclude that the addition of the two independent variables is statistically significant. It is difficult to determine the p-value directly from tables of the F distribution, but computer software packages, such as Minitab or Excel, make computing the p-value easy.

NOTES AND COMMENTS

Computation of the F statistic can also be based on the difference in the regression sums of squares. To show this form of the F statistic, we first note that

$$\text{SSE(reduced)} = \text{SST} - \text{SSR(reduced)}$$
$$\text{SSE(full)} = \text{SST} - \text{SSR(full)}$$

Hence

$$\begin{aligned}\text{SSE(reduced)} - \text{SSE(full)} &= [\text{SST} - \text{SSR(reduced)}] - [\text{SST} - \text{SSR(full)}]\\ &= \text{SSR(full)} - \text{SSR(reduced)}\end{aligned}$$

Thus,

$$F = \frac{\dfrac{\text{SSR(full)} - \text{SSR(reduced)}}{\text{number of extra terms}}}{\text{MSE(full)}}$$

Exercises

Methods

10. In a regression analysis involving 27 observations, the following estimated regression equation was developed.

$$\hat{y} = 25.2 + 5.5x_1$$

For this estimated regression equation SST = 1550 and SSE = 520.

a. At $\alpha = .05$, test whether x_1 is significant.

Suppose that variables x_2 and x_3 are added to the model and the following regression equation is obtained.

$$\hat{y} = 16.3 + 2.3x_1 + 12.1x_2 - 5.8x_3$$

For this estimated regression equation SST = 1550 and SSE = 100.

b. Use an F test and a .05 level of significance to determine whether x_2 and x_3 contribute significantly to the model.

SELF test

11. In a regression analysis involving 30 observations, the following estimated regression equation was obtained.

$$\hat{y} = 17.6 + 3.8x_1 - 2.3x_2 + 7.6x_3 + 2.7x_4$$

For this estimated regression equation SST = 1805 and SSR = 1760.

a. At $\alpha = .05$, test the significance of the relationship among the variables.

Suppose variables x_1 and x_4 are dropped from the model and the following estimated regression equation is obtained.

$$\hat{y} = 11.1 - 3.6x_2 + 8.1x_3$$

For this model SST = 1805 and SSR = 1705.

b. Compute SSE(x_1, x_2, x_3, x_4).
c. Compute SSE(x_2, x_3).
d. Use an F test and a .05 level of significance to determine whether x_1 and x_4 contribute significantly to the model.

Applications

CD file

LPGATour

12. The Ladies Professional Golfers Association (LPGA) maintains statistics on performance and earnings for members of the LPGA Tour. Year-end performance statistics for the 30 players who had the highest total earnings in LPGA Tour events for 2005 appear on the data disk in the file named LPGATour (www.lpga.com, 2006). Earnings ($1000) is the total earnings in thousands of dollars; Scoring Avg. is the average score for all events; Greens in Reg. is the percentage of time a player is able to hit the green in regulation; Putting Avg. is the average number of putts taken on greens hit in regulation; and Sand Saves is the percentage of time a player is able to get "up and down" once in a greenside sand bunker. A green is considered hit in regulation if any part of the ball is touching the putting surface

and the difference between the value of par for the hole and the number of strokes taken to hit the green is at least 2.

a. Develop an estimated regression equation that can be used to predict the average score for all events given the average number of putts taken on greens hit in regulation.
b. Develop an estimated regression equation that can be used to predict the average score for all events given the percentage of time a player is able to hit the green in regulation, the average number of putts taken on greens hit in regulation, and the percentage of time a player is able to get "up and down" once in a greenside sand bunker.
c. At the .05 level of significance, test whether the two independent variables added in part (b), the percentage of time a player is able to hit the green in regulation and the percentage of time a player is able to get "up and down" once in a greenside sand bunker, contribute significantly to the estimated regression equation developed in part (a). Explain.

CD file
LPGATour

13. Refer to exercise 12.
a. Develop an estimated regression equation that can be used to predict the total earnings for all events given the average number of putts taken on greens hit in regulation.
b. Develop an estimated regression equation that can be used to predict the total earnings for all events given the percentage of time a player is able to hit the green in regulation, the average number of putts taken on greens hit in regulation, and the percentage of time a player is able to get "up and down" once in a greenside sand bunker.
c. At the .05 level of significance, test whether the two independent variables added in part (b), the percentage of time a player is able to hit the green in regulation and the percentage of time a player is able to get "up and down" once in a greenside sand bunker, contribute significantly to the estimated regression equation developed in part (a). Explain.
d. In general, lower scores should lead to higher earnings. To investigate this option to predicting total earnings, develop an estimated regression equation that can be used to predict total earnings for all events given the average score for all events. Would you prefer to use this equation to predict total earnings or the estimated regression equation developed in part (b)? Explain.

14. A 10-year study conducted by the American Heart Association provided data on how age, blood pressure, and smoking relate to the risk of strokes. Data from a portion of this study follow. Risk is interpreted as the probability (times 100) that a person will have a stroke over the next 10-year period. For the smoker variable, 1 indicates a smoker and 0 indicates a nonsmoker.

CD file
Stroke

Risk	Age	Blood Pressure	Smoker
12	57	152	0
24	67	163	0
13	58	155	0
56	86	177	1
28	59	196	0
51	76	189	1
18	56	155	1
31	78	120	0
37	80	135	1
15	78	98	0
22	71	152	0
36	70	173	1

(continued)

Risk	Age	Blood Pressure	Smoker
15	67	135	1
48	77	209	1
15	60	199	0
36	82	119	1
8	66	166	0
34	80	125	1
3	62	117	0
37	59	207	1

a. Develop an estimated regression equation that can be used to predict the risk of stroke given the age and blood-pressure level.
b. Consider adding two independent variables to the model developed in part (a), one for the interaction between age and blood-pressure level and the other for whether the person is a smoker. Develop an estimated regression equation using these four independent variables.
c. At a .05 level of significance, test to see whether the addition of the interaction term and the smoker variable contribute significantly to the estimated regression equation developed in part (a).

15. The National Football League rates prospects by position on a scale that ranges from 5 to 9. The ratings are interpreted as follows: 8–9 should start the first year; 7.0–7.9 should start; 6.0–6.9 will make the team as backup; and 5.0–5.9 can make the club and contribute. The following table shows the position, weight, time in seconds to run 40 yards, and ratings for 40 NFL prospects (*USA Today,* April 14, 2000).

CD file
NFL

Observation	Name	Position	Weight	Time	Rating
1	Peter Warrick	Wide receiver	194	4.53	9.0
2	Plaxico Burress	Wide receiver	231	4.52	8.8
3	Sylvester Morris	Wide receiver	216	4.59	8.3
4	Travis Taylor	Wide receiver	199	4.36	8.1
5	Laveranues Coles	Wide receiver	192	4.29	8.0
6	Dez White	Wide receiver	218	4.49	7.9
7	Jerry Porter	Wide receiver	221	4.55	7.4
8	Ron Dugans	Wide receiver	206	4.47	7.1
9	Todd Pinkston	Wide receiver	169	4.37	7.0
10	Dennis Northcutt	Wide receiver	175	4.43	7.0
11	Anthony Lucas	Wide receiver	194	4.51	6.9
12	Darrell Jackson	Wide receiver	197	4.56	6.6
13	Danny Farmer	Wide receiver	217	4.60	6.5
14	Sherrod Gideon	Wide receiver	173	4.57	6.4
15	Trevor Gaylor	Wide receiver	199	4.57	6.2
16	Cosey Coleman	Guard	322	5.38	7.4
17	Travis Claridge	Guard	303	5.18	7.0
18	Kaulana Noa	Guard	317	5.34	6.8
19	Leander Jordan	Guard	330	5.46	6.7
20	Chad Clifton	Guard	334	5.18	6.3
21	Manula Savea	Guard	308	5.32	6.1
22	Ryan Johanningmeir	Guard	310	5.28	6.0
23	Mark Tauscher	Guard	318	5.37	6.0
24	Blaine Saipaia	Guard	321	5.25	6.0
25	Richard Mercier	Guard	295	5.34	5.8
26	Damion McIntosh	Guard	328	5.31	5.3
27	Jeno James	Guard	320	5.64	5.0

Observation	Name	Position	Weight	Time	Rating
28	Al Jackson	Guard	304	5.20	5.0
29	Chris Samuels	Offensive tackle	325	4.95	8.5
30	Stockar McDougle	Offensive tackle	361	5.50	8.0
31	Chris McIngosh	Offensive tackle	315	5.39	7.8
32	Adrian Klemm	Offensive tackle	307	4.98	7.6
33	Todd Wade	Offensive tackle	326	5.20	7.3
34	Marvel Smith	Offensive tackle	320	5.36	7.1
35	Michael Thompson	Offensive tackle	287	5.05	6.8
36	Bobby Williams	Offensive tackle	332	5.26	6.8
37	Darnell Alford	Offensive tackle	334	5.55	6.4
38	Terrance Beadles	Offensive tackle	312	5.15	6.3
39	Tutan Reyes	Offensive tackle	299	5.35	6.1
40	Greg Robinson-Ran	Offensive tackle	333	5.59	6.0

a. Develop dummy variables that will account for the player's position.
b. Develop an estimated regression equation to show how rating is related to position, weight, and time to run 40 yards.
c. At the .05 level of significance, test whether the estimated regression equation developed in part (b) represents a significant relationship between the independent variables and the dependent variable.
d. Is position a significant factor in the player's rating? Use $\alpha = .05$. Explain.

16.3 Analysis of a Larger Problem

In introducing multiple regression analysis, we used the Butler Trucking example extensively. The small size of this problem was an advantage in exploring introductory concepts, but would make it difficult to illustrate some of the variable selection issues involved in model building. To provide an illustration of the variable selection procedures discussed in the next section, we introduce a data set consisting of 25 observations on eight independent variables. Permission to use these data was provided by Dr. David W. Cravens of the Department of Marketing at Texas Christian University. Consequently, we refer to the data set as the Cravens data.*

The Cravens data are for a company that sells products in several sales territories, each of which is assigned to a single sales representative. A regression analysis was conducted to determine whether a variety of predictor (independent) variables could explain sales in each territory. A random sample of 25 sales territories resulted in the data in Table 16.5; the variable definitions are given in Table 16.6.

As a preliminary step, let us consider the sample correlation coefficients between each pair of variables. Figure 16.13 is the correlation matrix obtained using Minitab. Note that the sample correlation coefficient between Sales and Time is .623, between Sales and Poten is .598, and so on.

Looking at the sample correlation coefficients between the independent variables, we see that the correlation between Time and Accounts is .758; hence, if Accounts were used as an independent variable, Time would not add much more explanatory power to the model. Recall the rule-of-thumb test from the discussion of multicollinearity in Section 15.4: multicollinearity can cause problems if the absolute value of the sample correlation coefficient

*For details see David W. Cravens, Robert B. Woodruff, and Joe C. Stamper, "An Analytical Approach for Evaluating Sales Territory Performance," *Journal of Marketing*, 36 (January 1972): 31–37. Copyright © 1972 American Marketing Association.

TABLE 16.5 CRAVENS DATA

CD file
Cravens

Sales	Time	Poten	AdvExp	Share	Change	Accounts	Work	Rating
3,669.88	43.10	74,065.1	4,582.9	2.51	0.34	74.86	15.05	4.9
3,473.95	108.13	58,117.3	5,539.8	5.51	0.15	107.32	19.97	5.1
2,295.10	13.82	21,118.5	2,950.4	10.91	−0.72	96.75	17.34	2.9
4,675.56	186.18	68,521.3	2,243.1	8.27	0.17	195.12	13.40	3.4
6,125.96	161.79	57,805.1	7,747.1	9.15	0.50	180.44	17.64	4.6
2,134.94	8.94	37,806.9	402.4	5.51	0.15	104.88	16.22	4.5
5,031.66	365.04	50,935.3	3,140.6	8.54	0.55	256.10	18.80	4.6
3,367.45	220.32	35,602.1	2,086.2	7.07	−0.49	126.83	19.86	2.3
6,519.45	127.64	46,176.8	8,846.2	12.54	1.24	203.25	17.42	4.9
4,876.37	105.69	42,053.2	5,673.1	8.85	0.31	119.51	21.41	2.8
2,468.27	57.72	36,829.7	2,761.8	5.38	0.37	116.26	16.32	3.1
2,533.31	23.58	33,612.7	1,991.8	5.43	−0.65	142.28	14.51	4.2
2,408.11	13.82	21,412.8	1,971.5	8.48	0.64	89.43	19.35	4.3
2,337.38	13.82	20,416.9	1,737.4	7.80	1.01	84.55	20.02	4.2
4,586.95	86.99	36,272.0	10,694.2	10.34	0.11	119.51	15.26	5.5
2,729.24	165.85	23,093.3	8,618.6	5.15	0.04	80.49	15.87	3.6
3,289.40	116.26	26,878.6	7,747.9	6.64	0.68	136.58	7.81	3.4
2,800.78	42.28	39,572.0	4,565.8	5.45	0.66	78.86	16.00	4.2
3,264.20	52.84	51,866.1	6,022.7	6.31	−0.10	136.58	17.44	3.6
3,453.62	165.04	58,749.8	3,721.1	6.35	−0.03	138.21	17.98	3.1
1,741.45	10.57	23,990.8	861.0	7.37	−1.63	75.61	20.99	1.6
2,035.75	13.82	25,694.9	3,571.5	8.39	−0.43	102.44	21.66	3.4
1,578.00	8.13	23,736.3	2,845.5	5.15	0.04	76.42	21.46	2.7
4,167.44	58.44	34,314.3	5,060.1	12.88	0.22	136.58	24.78	2.8
2,799.97	21.14	22,809.5	3,552.0	9.14	−0.74	88.62	24.96	3.9

exceeds .7 for any two of the independent variables. If possible, then, we should avoid including both Time and Accounts in the same regression model. The sample correlation coefficient of .549 between Change and Rating is also high and may warrant further consideration.

Looking at the sample correlation coefficients between Sales and each of the independent variables can give us a quick indication of which independent variables are, by themselves, good predictors. We see that the single best predictor of Sales is Accounts, because

TABLE 16.6 VARIABLE DEFINITIONS FOR THE CRAVENS DATA

Variable	Definition
Sales	Total sales credited to the sales representative
Time	Length of time employed in months
Poten	Market potential; total industry sales in units for the sales territory*
AdvExp	Advertising expenditure in the sales territory
Share	Market share; weighted average for the past four years
Change	Change in the market share over the previous four years
Accounts	Number of accounts assigned to the sales representative*
Work	Workload; a weighted index based on annual purchases and concentrations of accounts
Rating	Sales representative overall rating on eight performance dimensions; an aggregate rating on a 1–7 scale

*These data were coded to preserve confidentiality.

FIGURE 16.13 SAMPLE CORRELATION COEFFICIENTS FOR THE CRAVENS DATA

	Sales	Time	Poten	AdvExp	Share	Change	Accounts	Work
Time	0.623							
Poten	0.598	0.454						
AdvExp	0.596	0.249	0.174					
Share	0.484	0.106	-0.211	0.264				
Change	0.489	0.251	0.268	0.377	0.085			
Accounts	0.754	0.758	0.479	0.200	0.403	0.327		
Work	-0.117	-0.179	-0.259	-0.272	0.349	-0.288	-0.199	
Rating	0.402	0.101	0.359	0.411	-0.024	0.549	0.229	-0.277

it has the highest sample correlation coefficient (.754). Recall that for the case of one independent variable, the square of the sample correlation coefficient is the coefficient of determination. Thus, Accounts can explain $(.754)^2(100)$, or 56.85%, of the variability in Sales. The next most important independent variables are Time, Poten, and AdvExp, each with a sample correlation coefficient of approximately .6.

Although there are potential multicollinearity problems, let us consider developing an estimated regression equation using all eight independent variables. The Minitab computer package provided the results in Figure 16.14. The eight-variable multiple regression model has an adjusted coefficient of determination of 88.3%. Note, however, that the p-values for the t tests of individual parameters show that only Poten, AdvExp, and Share are significant at the $\alpha = .05$ level, given the effect of all the other variables. Hence, we might be

FIGURE 16.14 MINITAB OUTPUT FOR THE MODEL INVOLVING ALL EIGHT INDEPENDENT VARIABLES

```
The regression equation is
Sales = - 1508 + 2.01 Time + 0.0372 Poten + 0.151 AdvExp + 199 Share
        + 291 Change + 5.55 Accounts + 19.8 Work + 8 Rating

Predictor        Coef    SE Coef      T      p
Constant       1507.8      778.6  -1.94  0.071
Time            2.010      1.931   1.04  0.313
Poten        0.037205   0.008202   4.54  0.000
AdvExp        0.15099    0.04711   3.21  0.006
Share          199.02      67.03   2.97  0.009
Change          290.9      186.8   1.56  0.139
Accounts        5.551      4.776   1.16  0.262
Work            19.79      33.68   0.59  0.565
Rating            8.2      128.5   0.06  0.950

S = 449.0   R-sq = 92.2%    R-sq(adj) = 88.3%

Analysis of Variance

SOURCE          DF        SS       MS      F      p
Regression       8  38153568  4769196  23.65  0.000
Residual Error  16   3225984   201624
Total           24  41379552
```

FIGURE 16.15 MINITAB OUTPUT FOR THE MODEL INVOLVING Poten, AdvExp, AND Share

```
The regression equation is
Sales = - 1604 + 0.0543 Poten + 0.167 AdvExp + 283 Share

Predictor       Coef    SE Coef       T      p
Constant     -1603.6      505.6   -3.17  0.005
Poten       0.054286   0.007474    7.26  0.000
AdvExp       0.16748    0.04427    3.78  0.001
Share         282.75      48.76    5.80  0.000

S = 545.5   R-sq = 84.9%   R-sq(adj) = 82.7%

Analysis of Variance

SOURCE          DF        SS        MS       F      p
Regression       3  35130240  11710080   39.35  0.000
Residual Error  21   6249310    297586
Total           24  41379552
```

inclined to investigate the results that would be obtained if we used just those three variables. Figure 16.15 shows the Minitab results obtained for the estimated regression equation with those three variables. We see that the estimated regression equation has an adjusted coefficient of determination of 82.7%, which, although not quite as good as that for the eight-independent-variable estimated regression equation, is high.

How can we find an estimated regression equation that will do the best job given the data available? One approach is to compute all possible regressions. That is, we could develop eight one-variable estimated regression equations (each of which corresponds to one of the independent variables), 28 two-variable estimated regression equations (the number of combinations of eight variables taken two at a time), and so on. In all, for the Cravens data, 255 different estimated regression equations involving one or more independent variables would have to be fitted to the data.

With the excellent computer packages available today, it is possible to compute all possible regressions. But doing so involves a great amount of computation and requires the model builder to review a large volume of computer output, much of which is associated with obviously poor models. Statisticians prefer a more systematic approach to selecting the subset of independent variables that provide the best estimated regression equation. In the next section, we introduce some of the more popular approaches.

16.4 Variable Selection Procedures

Variable selection procedures are particularly useful in the early stages of building a model, but they cannot substitute for experience and judgment on the part of the analyst.

In this section we discuss four **variable selection procedures**: stepwise regression, forward selection, backward elimination, and best-subsets regression. Given a data set with several possible independent variables, we can use these procedures to identify which independent variables provide the best model. The first three procedures are iterative; at each step of the procedure a single independent variable is added or deleted and the new model is evaluated. The process continues until a stopping criterion indicates that the procedure cannot find a better model. The last procedure (best subsets) is not a one-variable-at-a-time procedure; it evaluates regression models involving different subsets of the independent variables.

In the stepwise regression, forward selection, and backward elimination procedures, the criterion for selecting an independent variable to add or delete from the model at each step is based on the F statistic introduced in Section 16.2. Suppose, for instance, that we are considering adding x_2 to a model involving x_1 or deleting x_2 from a model involving x_1 and x_2. To test whether the addition or deletion of x_2 is statistically significant, the null and alternative hypotheses can be stated as follows:

$$H_0: \beta_2 = 0$$
$$H_a: \beta_2 \neq 0$$

In Section 16.2 (see equation (16.10)) we showed that

$$F = \frac{\dfrac{\text{SSE}(x_1) - \text{SSE}(x_1, x_2)}{1}}{\dfrac{\text{SSE}(x_1, x_2)}{n - p - 1}}$$

can be used as a criterion for determining whether the presence of x_2 in the model causes a significant reduction in the error sum of squares. The p-value corresponding to this F statistic is the criterion used to determine whether an independent variable should be added or deleted from the regression model. The usual rejection rule applies: Reject H_0 if p-value $\leq \alpha$.

Stepwise Regression

The stepwise regression procedure begins each step by determining whether any of the variables *already in the model* should be removed. It does so by first computing an F statistic and a corresponding p-value for each independent variable in the model. The level of significance α for determining whether an independent variable should be removed from the model is referred to in Minitab as *Alpha to remove*. If the p-value for any independent variable is greater than *Alpha to remove,* the independent variable with the largest p-value is removed from the model and the stepwise regression procedure begins a new step.

If no independent variable can be removed from the model, the procedure attempts to enter another independent variable into the model. It does so by first computing an F statistic and corresponding p-value for each independent variable that is not in the model. The level of significance α for determining whether an independent variable should be entered into the model is referred to in Minitab as *Alpha to enter.* The independent variable with the smallest p-value is entered into the model provided its p-value is less than *Alpha to enter.* The procedure continues in this manner until no independent variables can be deleted from or added to the model.

Figure 16.16 shows the results obtained by using the Minitab stepwise regression procedure for the Cravens data using values of .05 for *Alpha to remove* and .05 for *Alpha to enter.* The stepwise procedure terminated after four steps. The estimated regression equation identified by the Minitab stepwise regression procedure is

$$\hat{y} = -1441.93 + 9.2 \text{ Accounts} + .175 \text{ AdvExp} + .0382 \text{ Poten} + 190 \text{ Share}$$

Because the one-at-a-time procedures do not consider every possible subset for a given number of independent variables, they will not necessarily select the model with the highest R-sq value.

Note also in Figure 16.16 that $s = \sqrt{\text{MSE}}$ has been reduced from 881 with the best one-variable model (using Accounts) to 454 after four steps. The value of R-sq has been increased from 56.85% to 90.04%, and the recommended estimated regression equation has an R-Sq(adj) value of 88.05%.

In summary, at each step of the stepwise regression procedure the first consideration is to see whether any independent variable can be removed from the current model. If none

FIGURE 16.16 MINITAB STEPWISE REGRESSION OUTPUT FOR THE CRAVENS DATA

```
Alpha-to-Enter: 0.05      Alpha-to-Remove: 0.05

Response is Sales on 8 predictors, with N = 25

    Step          1        2         3          4
Constant     709.32    50.29   -327.24   -1441.93

Accounts       21.7     19.0      15.6        9.2
T-Value        5.50     6.41      5.19       3.22
P-Value       0.000    0.000     0.000      0.004

AdvExp                 0.227     0.216      0.175
T-Value                 4.50      4.77       4.74
P-Value                0.000     0.000      0.000

Poten                           0.0219     0.0382
T-Value                           2.53       4.79
P-Value                          0.019      0.000

Share                                         190
T-Value                                      3.82
P-Value                                     0.001

S               881      650       583        454
R-Sq          56.85    77.51     82.77      90.04
R-Sq(adj)     54.97    75.47     80.31      88.05
C-p            67.6     27.2      18.4        5.4
```

of the independent variables can be removed from the model, the procedure checks to see whether any of the independent variables that are not currently in the model can be entered. Because of the nature of the stepwise regression procedure, an independent variable can enter the model at one step, be removed at a subsequent step, and then enter the model at a later step. The procedure stops when no independent variables can be removed from or entered into the model.

Forward Selection

The forward selection procedure starts with no independent variables. It adds variables one at a time using the same procedure as stepwise regression for determining whether an independent variable should be entered into the model. However, the forward selection procedure does not permit a variable to be removed from the model once it has been entered. The procedure stops if the p-value for each of the independent variables not in the model is greater than *Alpha to enter.*

The estimated regression equation obtained using Minitab's forward selection procedure is

$$\hat{y} = -1441.93 + 9.2 \text{ Accounts} + .175 \text{ AdvExp} + .0382 \text{ Poten} + 190 \text{ Share}$$

Thus, for the Cravens data, the forward selection procedure (using .05 for *Alpha to enter*) leads to the same estimated regression equation as the stepwise procedure.

Backward Elimination

The backward elimination procedure begins with a model that includes all the independent variables. It then deletes one independent variable at a time using the same procedure as stepwise regression. However, the backward elimination procedure does not permit an independent variable to be reentered once it has been removed. The procedure stops when none of the independent variables in the model have a p-value greater than *Alpha to remove.*

The estimated regression equation obtained using Minitab's backward elimination procedure for the Cravens data (using .05 for *Alpha to remove*) is

$$\hat{y} = -1312 + 3.8 \text{ Time} + .0444 \text{ Poten} + .152 \text{ AdvExp} + 259 \text{ Share}$$

Comparing the estimated regression equation identified using the backward elimination procedure to the estimated regression equation identified using the forward selection procedure, we see that three independent variables—AdvExp, Poten, and Share—are common to both. However, the backward elimination procedure has included Time instead of Accounts.

Forward selection and backward elimination may lead to different models.

Forward selection and backward elimination are the two extremes of model building; the forward selection procedure starts with no independent variables in the model and adds independent variables one at a time, whereas the backward elimination procedure starts with all independent variables in the model and deletes variables one at a time. The two procedures may lead to the same estimated regression equation. It is possible, however, for them to lead to two different estimated regression equations, as we saw with the Cravens data. Deciding which estimated regression equation to use remains a topic for discussion. Ultimately, the analyst's judgment must be applied. The best-subsets model building procedure we discuss next provides additional model-building information to be considered before a final decision is made.

Best-Subsets Regression

Stepwise regression, forward selection, and backward elimination are approaches to choosing the regression model by adding or deleting independent variables one at a time. None of them guarantees that the best model for a given number of variables will be found. Hence, these one-variable-at-a-time methods are properly viewed as heuristics for selecting a good regression model.

Some software packages use a procedure called best-subsets regression that enables the user to find, given a specified number of independent variables, the best regression model. Minitab has such a procedure. Figure 16.17 is a portion of the computer output obtained by using the best-subsets procedure for the Cravens data set.

This output identifies the two best one-variable estimated regression equations, the two best two-variable equations, the two best three-variable equations, and so on. The criterion used in determining which estimated regression equations are best for any number of predictors is the value of the coefficient of determination (R-sq). For instance, Accounts, with an R-sq = 56.8%, provides the best estimated regression equation using only one independent variable; AdvExp and Accounts, with an R-sq = 77.5%, provides the best estimated regression equation using two independent variables; and Poten, AdvExp, and Share, with an R-sq = 84.9%, provides the best estimated regression equation with three independent variables. For the Cravens data, the adjusted coefficient of determination (Adj. R-sq = 89.4%) is largest for the model with six independent variables: Time, Poten, AdvExp, Share, Change, and Accounts. However, the best model with four independent variables (Poten, AdvExp, Share, Accounts) has an adjusted coefficient of determination almost as high (88.1%). All other things being equal, a simpler model with fewer variables is usually preferred.

FIGURE 16.17 PORTION OF MINITAB BEST-SUBSETS REGRESSION OUTPUT

Vars	R-sq	Adj. R-sq	s	Time	Poten	AdvExp	Share	Change	Accounts	Work	RatIng
1	56.8	55.0	881.09						X		
1	38.8	36.1	1049.3	X							
2	77.5	75.5	650.39			X			X		
2	74.6	72.3	691.11		X			X			
3	84.9	82.7	545.52		X	X	X				
3	82.8	80.3	582.64		X	X			X		
4	90.0	88.1	453.84		X	X	X		X		
4	89.6	87.5	463.93	X	X	X	X				
5	91.5	89.3	430.21	X	X	X	X	X			
5	91.2	88.9	436.75		X	X	X	X	X		
6	92.0	89.4	427.99	X	X	X	X	X	X		
6	91.6	88.9	438.20		X	X	X	X	X	X	
7	92.2	89.0	435.66	X	X	X	X	X	X	X	
7	92.0	88.8	440.29	X	X	X	X	X	X		X
8	92.2	88.3	449.02	X	X	X	X	X	X	X	X

Making the Final Choice

The analysis performed on the Cravens data to this point is good preparation for choosing a final model, but more analysis should be conducted before the final choice. As we noted in Chapters 14 and 15, a careful analysis of the residuals should be done. We want the residual plot for the chosen model to resemble approximately a horizontal band. Let us assume the residuals are not a problem and that we want to use the results of the best-subsets procedure to help choose the model.

The best-subsets procedure shows us that the best four-variable model contains the independent variables Poten, AdvExp, Share, and Accounts. This result also happens to be the four-variable model identified with the stepwise regression procedure. Table 16.7 is helpful in making the final choice. It shows several possible models consisting of some or all of these four independent variables.

TABLE 16.7 SELECTED MODELS INVOLVING Accounts, AdvExp, Poten, AND Share

Model	Independent Variables	Adj. R-sq
1	Accounts	55.0
2	AdvExp, Accounts	75.5
3	Poten, Share	72.3
4	Poten, AdvExp, Accounts	80.3
5	Poten, AdvExp, Share	82.7
6	Poten, AdvExp, Share, Accounts	88.1

From Table 16.7, we see that the model with just AdvExp and Accounts is good. The adjusted coefficient of determination is 75.5%, and the model with all four variables provides only a 12.6-percentage-point improvement. The simpler two-variable model might be preferred, for instance, if it is difficult to measure market potential (Poten). However, if the data are readily available and highly accurate predictions of sales are needed, the model builder would clearly prefer the model with all four variables.

NOTES AND COMMENTS

1. The stepwise procedure requires that *Alpha to remove* be greater than or equal to *Alpha to enter*. This requirement prevents the same variable from being removed and then reentered at the same step.
2. Functions of the independent variables can be used to create new independent variables for use with any of the procedures in this section. For instance, if we wanted x_1x_2 in the model to account for interaction, we would use the data for x_1 and x_2 to create the data for $z = x_1x_2$.
3. None of the procedures that add or delete variables one at a time can be guaranteed to identify the best regression model. But they are excellent approaches to finding good models—especially when little multicollinearity is present.

Exercises

Applications

CD file Layoffs

16. A study provided data on variables that may be related to the number of weeks a manufacturing worker has been jobless. The dependent variable in the study (Weeks) was defined as the number of weeks a worker has been jobless due to a layoff. The following independent variables were used in the study.

Age	The age of the worker
Educ	The number of years of education
Married	A dummy variable; 1 if married, 0 otherwise
Head	A dummy variable; 1 if the head of household, 0 otherwise
Tenure	The number of years on the previous job
Manager	A dummy variable; 1 if management occupation, 0 otherwise
Sales	A dummy variable; 1 if sales occupation, 0 otherwise

The data are available on the CD accompanying the text in the file named Layoffs.

a. Develop the best one-variable estimated regression equation.
b. Use the stepwise procedure to develop the best estimated regression equation. Use values of .05 for *Alpha to enter* and *Alpha to remove*.
c. Use the forward selection procedure to develop the best estimated regression equation. Use a value of .05 for *Alpha to enter*.
d. Use the backward elimination procedure to develop the best estimated regression equation. Use a value of .05 for *Alpha to remove*.
e. Use the best-subsets regression procedure to develop the best estimated regression equation.

CD file LPGATour2

17. The Ladies Professional Golfers Association (LPGA) maintains statistics on performance and earnings for members of the LPGA Tour. Year-end performance statistics for the 30 players who had the highest total earnings in LPGA Tour events for 2005 appear on the data disk in the file named LPGATour2 (www.lpga.com, 2006). Earnings ($1000)

is the total earnings in thousands of dollars; Scoring Avg. is the average score for all events; Drive Average is the average length of a players drive in yards; Greens in Reg. is the percentage of time a player is able to hit the green in regulation; Putting Avg. is the average number of putts taken on greens hit in regulation; and Sand Saves is the percentage of time a player is able to get "up and down" once in a greenside sand bunker. A green is considered hit in regulation if any part of the ball is touching the putting surface and the difference between the value of par for the hole and the number of strokes taken to hit the green is at least 2. Let DriveGreens denote a new independent variable that represents the interaction between the average length of a player's drive and the percentage of time a player is able to hit the green in regulation. Use the methods in this section to develop the best estimated multiple regression equation for estimating a player's average score for all events.

18. Jeff Sagarin has been providing sports ratings for *USA Today* since 1985. In baseball his predicted RPG (runs/game) statistic takes into account the entire player's offensive statistics, and is claimed to be the best measure of a player's true offensive value. The following data show the RPG and a variety of offensive statistics for the 2005 Major League Baseball (MLB) season for 20 members of the New York Yankees (www.usatoday.com, March 3, 2006). The labels on columns are defined as follows: RPG, predicted runs per game statistic; H, hits; 2B, doubles; 3B, triples; HR, home runs; RBI, runs batted in; BB, bases on balls (walks); SO, strikeouts; SB, stolen bases; CS, caught stealing; OBP, on-base percentage; SLG, slugging percentage; and AVG, batting average.

CD file
Yankees

Player	RPG	H	2B	3B	HR	RBI	BB	SO	SB	CS	OBP	SLG	AVG
D Jeter	6.51	202	25	5	19	70	77	117	14	5	0.389	0.45	0.309
H Matsui	6.32	192	45	3	23	116	63	78	2	2	0.367	0.496	0.305
A Rodriguez	9.06	194	29	1	48	130	91	139	21	6	0.421	0.61	0.321
G Sheffield	6.93	170	27	0	34	123	78	76	10	2	0.379	0.512	0.291
R Cano	5.01	155	34	4	14	62	16	68	1	3	0.32	0.458	0.297
B Williams	4.14	121	19	1	12	64	53	75	1	2	0.321	0.367	0.249
J Posada	5.36	124	23	0	19	71	66	94	1	0	0.352	0.43	0.262
J Giambi	9.11	113	14	0	32	87	108	109	0	0	0.44	0.535	0.271
T Womack	2.91	82	8	1	0	15	12	49	27	5	0.276	0.28	0.249
T Martinez	5.08	73	9	0	17	49	38	54	2	0	0.328	0.439	0.241
M Bellhorn	4.07	63	20	0	8	30	52	112	3	0	0.324	0.357	0.21
R Sierra	3.27	39	12	0	4	29	9	41	0	0	0.265	0.371	0.229
J Flaherty	1.83	21	5	0	2	11	6	26	0	0	0.206	0.252	0.165
B Crosby	3.48	27	0	1	1	6	4	14	4	1	0.304	0.327	0.276
M Lawton	5.15	6	0	0	2	4	7	8	1	0	0.263	0.25	0.125
R Sanchez	3.36	12	1	0	0	2	2	3	0	1	0.326	0.302	0.279
A Phillips	2.13	6	4	0	1	4	1	13	0	0	0.171	0.325	0.15
M Cabrera	1.19	4	0	0	0	0	0	2	0	0	0.211	0.211	0.211
R Johnson	3.44	4	2	0	0	0	1	4	0	0	0.3	0.333	0.222
F Escalona	5.31	4	1	0	0	2	1	4	0	0	0.375	0.357	0.286

Let the dependent variable be the RPG statistic.

a. Develop the best one-variable estimated regression equation.
b. Use the methods in this section to develop the best estimated multiple regression equation for estimating a player's RPG.

CD file
Stroke

19. Refer to exercise 14. Using age, blood pressure, whether a person is a smoker, and any interaction involving those variables, develop an estimated regression equation that can be used to predict risk. Briefly describe the process you used to develop an estimated regression equation for these data.

16.5 Multiple Regression Approach to Experimental Design

In Section 15.7 we discussed the use of dummy variables in multiple regression analysis. In this section we show how the use of dummy variables in a multiple regression equation can provide another approach to solving experimental design problems. We will demonstrate the multiple regression approach to experimental design by applying it to the Chemitech, Inc., completely randomized design introduced in Chapter 13.

Recall that Chemitech developed a new filtration system for municipal water supplies. The components for the new filtration system will be purchased from several suppliers, and Chemitech will assemble the components at its plant in Columbia, South Carolina. Three different assembly methods, referred to as methods A, B, and C, have been proposed. Managers at Chemitech want to determine which assembly method can produce the greatest number of filtration systems per week.

A random sample of 15 employees was selected, and each of the three assembly methods was randomly assigned to 5 employees. The number of units assembled by each employee is shown in Table 16.8. The sample mean number of units produced with each of the three assembly methods is as follows:

Assembly Method	Mean Number Produced
A	62
B	66
C	52

Although method B appears to result in higher production rates than either of the other methods, the issue is whether the three sample means observed are different enough for us to conclude that the means of the populations corresponding to the three methods of assembly are different.

We begin the regression approach to this problem by defining dummy variables that will be used to indicate which assembly method was used. Because the Chemitech problem has three assembly methods or treatments, we need two dummy variables. In general, if the factor being investigated involves k distinct levels or treatments, we need to define $k - 1$ dummy variables. For the Chemitech experiment we define dummy variables A and B as shown in Table 16.9.

TABLE 16.8 NUMBER OF UNITS PRODUCED BY 15 WORKERS

	Method	
A	**B**	**C**
58	58	48
64	69	57
55	71	59
66	64	47
67	68	49

TABLE 16.9 DUMMY VARIABLES FOR THE CHEMITECH EXPERIMENT

A	B	
1	0	Observation is associated with assembly method A
0	1	Observation is associated with assembly method B
0	0	Observation is associated with assembly method C

We can use the dummy variables to relate the number of units produced per week, y, to the method of assembly the employee uses.

$$\begin{aligned} E(y) &= \text{Expected value of the number of units produced per week} \\ &= \beta_0 + \beta_1\text{A} + \beta_2\text{B} \end{aligned}$$

Thus, if we are interested in the expected value of the number of units assembled per week for an employee who uses method C, our procedure for assigning numerical values to the dummy variables would result in setting A = B = 0. The multiple regression equation then reduces to

$$E(y) = \beta_0 + \beta_1(0) + \beta_2(0) = \beta_0$$

We can interpret β_0 as the expected value of the number of units assembled per week for an employee who uses method C. In other words, β_0 is the mean number of units assembled per week using method C.

Next let us consider the forms of the multiple regression equation for each of the other methods. For method A the values of the dummy variables are A = 1 and B = 0, and

$$E(y) = \beta_0 + \beta_1(1) + \beta_2(0) = \beta_0 + \beta_1$$

For method B we set A = 0 and B = 1, and

$$E(y) = \beta_0 + \beta_1(0) + \beta_2(1) = \beta_0 + \beta_2$$

We see that $\beta_0 + \beta_1$ represents the mean number of units assembled per week using method A, and $\beta_0 + \beta_2$ represents the mean number of units assembled per week using method B.

We now want to estimate the coefficient of, β_0, β_1, and β_2 and hence develop an estimate of the mean number of units assembled per week for each method. Table 16.10 shows the sample data, consisting of 15 observations of A, B, and y. Figure 16.18 shows the corresponding Minitab multiple regression output. We see that the estimates of β_0, β_1, and β_2 are $b_0 = 52$, $b_1 = 10$, and $b_2 = 14$. Thus, the best estimate of the mean number of units assembled per week for each assembly method is as follows:

Assembly Method	**Estimate of $E(y)$**
A	$b_0 + b_1 = 52 + 10 = 62$
B	$b_0 = 52 + 14 = 66$
C	$b_0 = 52$

Note that the estimate of the mean number of units produced with each of the three assembly methods obtained from the regression analysis is the same as the sample mean shown previously.

TABLE 16.10 INPUT DATA FOR THE CHEMITECH COMPLETELY RANDOMIZED DESIGN

A	B	y
1	0	58
1	0	64
1	0	55
1	0	66
1	0	67
0	1	58
0	1	69
0	1	71
0	1	64
0	1	68
0	0	48
0	0	57
0	0	59
0	0	47
0	0	49

Now let us see how we can use the output from the multiple regression analysis to perform the ANOVA test on the difference among the means for the three plants. First, we observe that if the means do not differ

$$E(y) \text{ for method A} - E(y) \text{ for method C} = 0$$
$$E(y) \text{ for method B} - E(y) \text{ for method C} = 0$$

Because β_0 equals $E(y)$ for method C and $\beta_0 + \beta_1$ equals $E(y)$ for method A, the first difference is equal to $(\beta_0 + \beta_1) - \beta_0 = \beta_1$. Moreover, because $\beta_0 + \beta_2$ equals $E(y)$ for

FIGURE 16.18 MULTIPLE REGRESSION OUTPUT FOR THE CHEMITECH COMPLETELY RANDOMIZED DESIGN

```
The regression equation is
y = 52.0 + 10.0 A + 14.0 B

Predictor      Coef   SE Coef      T      P
Constant     52.000     2.380  21.84  0.000
A            10.000     3.367   2.97  0.012
B            14.000     3.367   4.16  0.001

S = 5.32291    R-Sq = 60.5%    R-Sq(adj) = 53.9%

Analysis of Variance

SOURCE          DF      SS      MS     F      P
Regression       2  520.00  260.00  9.18  0.004
Residual Error  12  340.00   28.33
Total           14  860.00
```

method B, the second difference is equal to $(\beta_0 + \beta_2) - \beta_0 = \beta_2$. We would conclude that the three methods do not differ if $\beta_1 = 0$ and $\beta_2 = 0$. Hence, the null hypothesis for a test for difference of means can be stated as

$$H_0 : \beta_1 = \beta_2 = 0$$

Suppose the level of significance is $\alpha = .05$. Recall that to test this type of null hypothesis about the significance of the regression relationship we use the F test for overall significance. The Minitab output in Figure 16.18 shows that the p-value corresponding to $F = 9.18$ is .004. Because the p-value $= .004 < \alpha = .05$, we reject $H_0 : \beta_1 = \beta_2 = 0$ and conclude that the means for the three assembly methods are not the same. Because the F test shows that the multiple regression relationship is significant, a t test can be conducted to determine the significance of the individual parameters, β_1 and β_2. Using $\alpha = .05$, the p-values of .012 and .001 on the Minitab output indicate that we can reject $H_0 : \beta_1 = 0$ and $H_0 : \beta_2 = 0$. Hence, both parameters are statistically significant. Thus, we can also conclude that the means for methods A and C are different and that the means for methods B and C are different.

Exercises

Methods

SELF test

20. Consider a completely randomized design involving four treatments: A, B, C, and D. Write a multiple regression equation that can be used to analyze these data. Define all variables.

21. Write a multiple regression equation that can be used to analyze the data for a randomized block design involving three treatments and two blocks. Define all variables.

22. Write a multiple regression equation that can be used to analyze the data for a two-factorial design with two levels for factor A and three levels for factor B. Define all variables.

Applications

SELF test

23. The Jacobs Chemical Company wants to estimate the mean time (minutes) required to mix a batch of material on machines produced by three different manufacturers. To limit the cost of testing, four batches of material were mixed on machines produced by each of the three manufacturers. The times needed to mix the material follow.

Manufacturer 1	Manufacturer 2	Manufacturer 3
20	28	20
26	26	19
24	31	23
22	27	22

a. Write a multiple regression equation that can be used to analyze the data.
b. What are the best estimates of the coefficients in your regression equation?
c. In terms of the regression equation coefficients, what hypotheses must we test to see whether the mean time to mix a batch of material is the same for all three manufacturers?
d. For an $\alpha = .05$ level of significance, what conclusion should be drawn?

24. Four different paints are advertised as having the same drying time. To check the manufacturers' claims, five samples were tested for each of the paints. The time in minutes until

the paint was dry enough for a second coat to be applied was recorded for each sample. The data obtained follow.

Paint 1	Paint 2	Paint 3	Paint 4
128	144	133	150
137	133	143	142
135	142	137	135
124	146	136	140
141	130	131	153

a. Use $\alpha = .05$ to test for any significant differences in mean drying time among the paints.
b. What is your estimate of mean drying time for paint 2? How is it obtained from the computer output?

25. An automobile dealer conducted a test to determine whether the time needed to complete a minor engine tune-up depends on whether a computerized engine analyzer or an electronic analyzer is used. Because tune-up time varies among compact, intermediate, and full-sized cars, the three types of cars were used as blocks in the experiment. The data (time in minutes) obtained follow.

		Car		
		Compact	**Intermediate**	**Full Size**
Analyzer	**Computerized**	50	55	63
	Electronic	42	44	46

Use $\alpha = .05$ to test for any significant differences.

26. A mail-order catalog firm designed a factorial experiment to test the effect of the size of a magazine advertisement and the advertisement design on the number (in thousands) of catalog requests received. Three advertising designs and two sizes of advertisements were considered. The following data were obtained. Test for any significant effects due to type of design, size of advertisement, or interaction. Use $\alpha = .05$.

		Size of Advertisement	
		Small	**Large**
Design	**A**	8	12
		12	8
	B	22	26
		14	30
	C	10	18
		18	14

16.6 Autocorrelation and the Durbin-Watson Test

Often, the data used for regression studies in business and economics are collected over time. It is not uncommon for the value of y at time t, denoted by y_t, to be related to the value of y at previous time periods. In such cases, we say **autocorrelation** (also called **serial correlation**) is present in the data. If the value of y in time period t is related to its value in

FIGURE 16.19 TWO DATA SETS WITH FIRST-ORDER AUTOCORRELATION

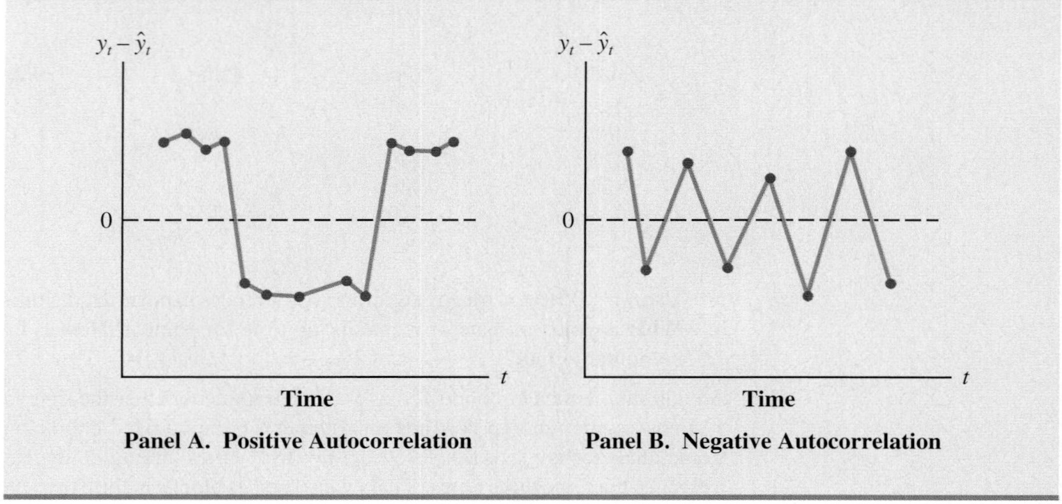

time period $t - 1$, first-order autocorrelation is present. If the value of y in time period t is related to the value of y in time period $t - 2$, second-order autocorrelation is present, and so on.

When autocorrelation is present, one of the assumptions of the regression model is violated: the error terms are not independent. In the case of first-order autocorrelation, the error at time t, denoted ϵ_t, will be related to the error at time period $t - 1$, denoted ϵ_{t-1}. Two cases of first-order autocorrelation are illustrated in Figure 16.19. Panel A is the case of positive autocorrelation; panel B is the case of negative autocorrelation. With positive autocorrelation we expect a positive residual in one period to be followed by a positive residual in the next period, a negative residual in one period to be followed by a negative residual in the next period, and so on. With negative autocorrelation, we expect a positive residual in one period to be followed by a negative residual in the next period, then a positive residual, and so on.

When autocorrelation is present, serious errors can be made in performing tests of statistical significance based upon the assumed regression model. It is therefore important to be able to detect autocorrelation and take corrective action. We will show how the Durbin-Watson statistic can be used to detect first-order autocorrelation.

Suppose the values of ϵ are not independent but are related in the following manner:

$$\epsilon_t = \rho\epsilon_{t-1} + z_t \tag{16.16}$$

where ρ is a parameter with an absolute value less than one and z_t is a normally and independently distributed random variable with a mean of zero and a variance of σ^2. From equation (16.16) we see that if $\rho = 0$, the error terms are not related, and each has a mean of zero and a variance of σ^2. In this case, there is no autocorrelation and the regression assumptions are satisfied. If $\rho > 0$, we have positive autocorrelation; if $\rho < 0$, we have negative autocorrelation. In either of these cases, the regression assumptions about the error term are violated.

The **Durbin-Watson test** for autocorrelation uses the residuals to determine whether $\rho = 0$. To simplify the notation for the Durbin-Watson statistic, we denote the ith residual by $e_i = y_i - \hat{y}_i$. The Durbin-Watson test statistic is computed as follows.

DURBIN-WATSON TEST STATISTIC

$$d = \frac{\sum_{t=2}^{n}(e_t - e_{t-1})^2}{\sum_{t=1}^{n} e_t^2} \tag{16.17}$$

If successive values of the residuals are close together (positive autocorrelation), the value of the Durbin-Watson test statistic will be small. If successive values of the residuals are far apart (negative autocorrelation), the value of the Durbin-Watson statistic will be large.

The Durbin-Watson test statistic ranges in value from zero to four, with a value of two indicating no autocorrelation is present. Durbin and Watson developed tables that can be used to determine when their test statistic indicates the presence of autocorrelation. Table 16.11 shows lower and upper bounds (d_L and d_U) for hypothesis tests using $\alpha = .05$; n denotes the number of observations. The null hypothesis to be tested is always that there is no autocorrelation.

$$H_0: \rho = 0$$

The alternative hypothesis to test for positive autocorrelation is

$$H_a: \rho > 0$$

The alternative hypothesis to test for negative autocorrelation is

$$H_a: \rho < 0$$

TABLE 16.11 CRITICAL VALUES FOR THE DURBIN-WATSON TEST FOR AUTOCORRELATION

Note: Entries in the table are the critical values for a one-tailed Durbin-Watson test for autocorrelation. For a two-tailed test, the level of significance is doubled.

Significance Points of d_L and d_U: $\alpha = .05$
Number of Independent Variables

	1		2		3		4		5	
n*	d_L	d_U	d_L	d_U	d_L	d_U	d_L	d_U	d_L	d_U
15	1.08	1.36	.95	1.54	.82	1.75	.69	1.97	.56	2.21
20	1.20	1.41	1.10	1.54	1.00	1.68	.90	1.83	.79	1.99
25	1.29	1.45	1.21	1.55	1.12	1.66	1.04	1.77	.95	1.89
30	1.35	1.49	1.28	1.57	1.21	1.65	1.14	1.74	1.07	1.83
40	1.44	1.54	1.39	1.60	1.34	1.66	1.29	1.72	1.23	1.79
50	1.50	1.59	1.46	1.63	1.42	1.67	1.38	1.72	1.34	1.77
70	1.58	1.64	1.55	1.67	1.52	1.70	1.49	1.74	1.46	1.77
100	1.65	1.69	1.63	1.72	1.61	1.74	1.59	1.76	1.57	1.78

* Interpolate linearly for intermediate n values.

FIGURE 16.20 HYPOTHESIS TEST FOR AUTOCORRELATION USING THE DURBIN-WATSON TEST

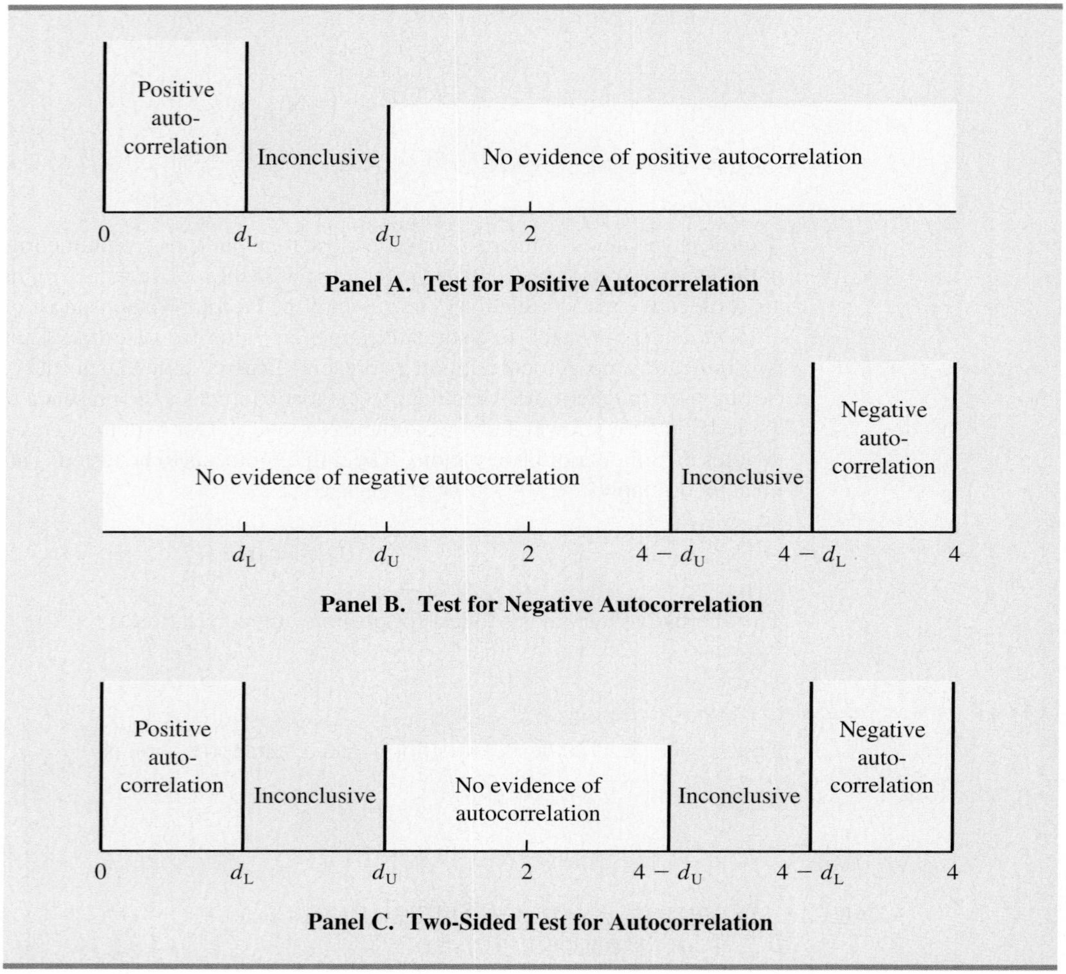

A two-sided test is also possible. In this case the alternative hypothesis is

$$H_a\colon \rho \neq 0$$

Figure 16.20 shows how the values of d_L and d_U in Table 16.11 are used to test for autocorrelation. Panel A illustrates the test for positive autocorrelation. If $d < d_L$, we conclude that positive autocorrelation is present. If $d_L \leq d \leq d_U$, we say the test is inconclusive. If $d > d_U$, we conclude that there is no evidence of positive autocorrelation.

Panel B illustrates the test for negative autocorrelation. If $d > 4 - d_L$, we conclude that negative autocorrelation is present. If $4 - d_U \leq d \leq 4 - d_L$, we say the test is inconclusive. If $d < 4 - d_U$, we conclude that there is no evidence of negative autocorrelation.

Panel C illustrates the two-sided test. If $d < d_L$ or $d > 4 - d_L$, we reject H_0 and conclude that autocorrelation is present. If $d_L \leq d \leq d_U$ or $4 - d_U \leq d \leq 4 - d_L$, we say the test is inconclusive. If $d_U < d < 4 - d_U$, we conclude that there is no evidence of autocorrelation.

If significant autocorrelation is identified, we should investigate whether we omitted one or more key independent variables that have time-ordered effects on the dependent variable. If no such variables can be identified, including an independent variable that measures the time of the observation (for instance, the value of this variable could be one for the first observation, two for the second observation, and so on) will sometimes eliminate or reduce the autocorrelation. When these attempts to reduce or remove autocorrelation do not work, transformations on the dependent or independent variables can prove helpful; a discussion of such transformations can be found in more advanced texts on regression analysis.

Note that the Durbin-Watson tables list the smallest sample size as 15. The reason is that the test is generally inconclusive for smaller sample sizes; in fact, many statisticians believe the sample size should be at least 50 for the test to produce worthwhile results.

Exercises

Applications

27. The following data show the daily closing prices (in dollars per share) for IBM for November 3, 2005, through December 1, 2005 (*Compustat,* February 26, 2006).

CD file

IBM

Date	Price ($)
Nov. 3	82.87
Nov. 4	83.00
Nov. 7	83.61
Nov. 8	83.15
Nov. 9	82.84
Nov. 10	83.99
Nov. 11	84.55
Nov. 14	84.36
Nov. 15	85.53
Nov. 16	86.54
Nov. 17	86.89
Nov. 18	87.77
Nov. 21	87.29
Nov. 22	87.99
Nov. 23	88.80
Nov. 25	88.80
Nov. 28	89.11
Nov. 29	89.10
Nov. 30	88.90
Dec. 1	89.21

a. Define the independent variable Period, where Period = 1 corresponds to the data for November 3, Period = 2 corresponds to the data for November 4, and so on. Develop the estimated regression equation that can be used to predict the closing price given the value of Period.

b. At the .05 level of significance, test for any positive autocorrelation in the data.

28. Refer to the Cravens data set in Table 16.5. In Section 16.3 we showed that the estimated regression equation involving Accounts, AdvExp, Poten, and Share had an adjusted coefficient of determination of 88.1%. Use the .05 level of significance and apply the Durbin-Watson test to determine whether positive autocorrelation is present.

Summary

In this chapter we discussed several concepts used by model builders to help identify the best estimated regression equation. First, we introduced the concept of a general linear model to show how the methods discussed in Chapters 14 and 15 could be extended to handle curvilinear relationships and interaction effects. Then we discussed how transformations involving the dependent variable could be used to account for problems such as nonconstant variance in the error term.

In many applications of regression analysis, a large number of independent variables are considered. We presented a general approach based on an F statistic for adding or deleting variables from a regression model. We then introduced a larger problem involving 25 observations and eight independent variables. We saw that one issue encountered in solving larger problems is finding the best subset of the independent variables. To help in that task, we discussed several variable selection procedures: stepwise regression, forward selection, backward elimination, and best-subsets regression.

In Section 16.5, we extended the discussion of how multiple regression models could be developed to provide another approach for solving analysis of variance and experimental design problems. The chapter concluded with an application of residual analysis to show the Durbin-Watson test for autocorrelation.

Glossary

General linear model A model of the form $y = \beta_0 + \beta_1 z_1 + \beta_2 z_2 + \cdots + \beta_p z_p + \epsilon$, where each of the independent variables z_j $(j = 1, 2, \ldots, p)$ is a function of $x_1, x_2, \ldots, x_k$, the variables for which data have been collected.

Interaction The effect of two independent variables acting together.

Variable selection procedures Methods for selecting a subset of the independent variables for a regression model.

Autocorrelation Correlation in the errors that arises when the error terms at successive points in time are related.

Serial correlation Same as autocorrelation.

Durbin-Watson test A test to determine whether first-order autocorrelation is present.

Key Formulas

General Linear Model

$$y = \beta_0 + \beta_1 z_1 + \beta_2 z_2 + \cdots + \beta_p z_p + \epsilon \tag{16.1}$$

F Test Statistic for Adding or Deleting $p - q$ Variables

$$F = \frac{\dfrac{\text{SSE}(x_1, x_2, \ldots, x_q) - \text{SSE}(x_1, x_2, \ldots, x_q, x_{q+1}, \ldots, x_p)}{p - q}}{\dfrac{\text{SSE}(x_1, x_2, \ldots, x_q, x_{q+1}, \ldots, x_p)}{n - p - 1}} \tag{16.13}$$

First-Order Autocorrelation

$$\epsilon_t = \rho\epsilon_{t-1} + z_t \tag{16.16}$$

Durbin-Watson Test Statistic

$$d = \frac{\sum_{t=2}^{n}(e_t - e_{t-1})^2}{\sum_{t=1}^{n} e_t^2} \qquad (16.17)$$

Supplementary Exercises

29. Lower prices for color laser printers make them a great alternative to inkjet printers. *PC World* reviewed and rated 10 color laser printers. The following data show the price, printing speed for color graphics in pages per minute (ppm), and the overall *PC World* rating for each printer tested (*PC World,* December 2005).

CD file ColorPrinter

Make and Model	Speed (ppm)	Rating
Dell 3000cn	3.4	83
Oki Data C5200n	5.2	81
Konica Minolta MagiColor 2430DL	2.7	79
Brother HL-2700CN	3.1	78
Lexmark C522n	3.8	77
HP Color LaserJet 3600n	5.6	74
Xerox Phaser 6120n	1.6	73
Konica Minolta MagiColor 2450	1.6	71
HP Color LaserJet 2600n	2.6	70
HP Color LaserJet 2550L	1.1	61

a. Develop a scatter diagram of the data using the printing speed as the independent variable. Does a simple linear regression model appear to be appropriate?
b. Develop an estimated multiple regression equation with x = speed and x^2 as the two independent variables.
c. Consider the nonlinear model shown by equation (16.7). Use logarithms to transform this nonlinear model into an equivalent linear model, and develop the corresponding estimated regression equation. Does the estimated regression equation provide a better fit than the estimated regression equation developed in part (b)?

30. Many international funds offer more reasonable equity valuations than those found in the United States. Because international markets often move in different directions than the U.S. market, investments in foreign markets can also reduce an investor's overall risk. The following table shows the fund type (load or no-load), expense ratio (%), safety rating (0 = riskiest, 10 = safest), and the one-year performance through December 10, 1999, for 20 international funds (*Mutual Funds,* February 2000).

CD file MutFunds

	Fund Type	Expense Ratio (%)	Safety Rating	Performance (%)
ABN AMRO Int'l Equity "Com"	No-load	1.38	6.9	36
Accessor Int'l Equity "Adv"	No-load	1.59	7.1	42
Artisan International	No-load	1.45	6.8	72
Columbia Int'l Stock	No-load	1.56	7.1	54
Concert Inv. "A" Int'l Equity	Load	2.16	6.3	116
Diversified Invstr Int'l Eqty	No-load	1.40	7.3	54

(*continued*)

	Fund Type	Expense Ratio (%)	Safety Rating	Performance (%)
Driehaus Int'l Growth	No-load	1.88	6.5	92
Founders Passport	No-load	1.52	7.0	86
Guardian Baillie Fifford Int'l "A"	Load	1.62	7.1	37
Jamestown Int'l Equity	No-load	1.56	7.1	35
Julius Baer Int'l Equity	No-load	1.79	6.9	71
Aetna "I" Int'l	No-load	1.35	7.3	46
Pilgrim Int'l Value "A"	Load	1.80	7.1	42
Fidelity Diversified Int'l	No-load	1.48	7.5	42
Putnam "A" Int'l Growth	Load	1.59	6.9	55
Sit Int'l Growth	No-load	1.50	6.9	49
Touchstone Int'l Equity "A"	Load	1.60	7.5	35
United Int'l Growth "A"	Load	1.28	7.1	47
Vontobel Int'l Equity	No-load	1.50	7.0	43
Waddell & Reed Int'l Growth "B"	Load	2.46	7.0	75

a. Use the methods in this chapter to develop an estimated regression equation that can be used to estimate the performance of a fund on the basis of the data provided.

b. Did the estimated regression equation developed in part (a) provide a good fit? Explain.

c. Acorn International is a no-load fund that has an annual expense ratio of 1.12% and a safety rating of 7.6. Use the estimated regression equation developed in part (a) to estimate the one-year performance for Acorn International.

31. A study investigated the relationship between audit delay (Delay), the length of time from a company's fiscal year-end to the date of the auditor's report, and variables that describe the client and the auditor. Some of the independent variables that were included in this study follow.

Industry	A dummy variable coded 1 if the firm was an industrial company or 0 if the firm was a bank, savings and loan, or insurance company.
Public	A dummy variable coded 1 if the company was traded on an organized exchange or over the counter; otherwise coded 0.
Quality	A measure of overall quality of internal controls, as judged by the auditor, on a five-point scale ranging from "virtually none" (1) to "excellent" (5).
Finished	A measure ranging from 1 to 4, as judged by the auditor, where 1 indicates "all work performed subsequent to year-end" and 4 indicates "most work performed prior to year-end."

A sample of 40 companies provided the following data.

CD file
Audit

Delay	Industry	Public	Quality	Finished
62	0	0	3	1
45	0	1	3	3
54	0	0	2	2
71	0	1	1	2
91	0	0	1	1
62	0	0	4	4
61	0	0	3	2
69	0	1	5	2
80	0	0	1	1
52	0	0	5	3

Delay	Industry	Public	Quality	Finished
47	0	0	3	2
65	0	1	2	3
60	0	0	1	3
81	1	0	1	2
73	1	0	2	2
89	1	0	2	1
71	1	0	5	4
76	1	0	2	2
68	1	0	1	2
68	1	0	5	2
86	1	0	2	2
76	1	1	3	1
67	1	0	2	3
57	1	0	4	2
55	1	1	3	2
54	1	0	5	2
69	1	0	3	3
82	1	0	5	1
94	1	0	1	1
74	1	1	5	2
75	1	1	4	3
69	1	0	2	2
71	1	0	4	4
79	1	0	5	2
80	1	0	1	4
91	1	0	4	1
92	1	0	1	4
46	1	1	4	3
72	1	0	5	2
85	1	0	5	1

a. Develop the estimated regression equation using all of the independent variables.
b. Did the estimated regression equation developed in part (a) provide a good fit? Explain.
c. Develop a scatter diagram showing Delay as a function of Finished. What does this scatter diagram indicate about the relationship between Delay and Finished?
d. On the basis of your observations about the relationship between Delay and Finished, develop an alternative estimated regression equation to the one developed in (a) to explain as much of the variability in Delay as possible.

32. Refer to the data in exercise 31. Consider a model in which only Industry is used to predict Delay. At a .01 level of significance, test for any positive autocorrelation in the data.

33. Refer to the data in exercise 31.
a. Develop an estimated regression equation that can be used to predict Delay by using Industry and Quality.
b. Plot the residuals obtained from the estimated regression equation developed in part (a) as a function of the order in which the data are presented. Does any autocorrelation appear to be present in the data? Explain.
c. At the .05 level of significance, test for any positive autocorrelation in the data.

34. A study was conducted to investigate browsing activity by shoppers. Shoppers were classified as nonbrowsers, light browsers, and heavy browsers. For each shopper in the study, a measure was obtained to determine how comfortable the shopper was in the store. Higher scores indicated greater comfort. Assume that the following data are from this study. Use a .05 level of significance to test for differences in comfort levels among the three types of browsers.

CD file
Browsing

Nonbrowser	Light Browser	Heavy Browser
4	5	5
5	6	7
6	5	5
3	4	7
3	7	4
4	4	6
5	6	5
4	5	7

35. *Money* magazine reported price and related data for 418 of the most popular vehicles of the 2003 model year. One of the variables reported was the vehicle's resale value, expressed as a percentage of the manufacturer's suggested resale price. The data were classified according to size and type of vehicle. The following table shows the resale value for 10 randomly selected small cars, 10 randomly selected mid-size cars, 10 randomly selected luxury cars, and 10 randomly selected sports cars (*Money,* March 2003).

CD file
Resale

Small	Mid-size	Luxury	Sports
26	26	36	41
31	29	38	39
41	41	38	30
32	27	39	34
27	26	35	40
34	33	26	43
31	27	40	42
38	29	47	39
27	35	41	44
42	39	32	50

Use $\alpha = .05$ and test for any significant difference in the mean resale value among the four types of vehicles.

Case Problem 1 Analysis of PGA Tour Statistics

CD file
PGATour

The Professional Golfers Association (PGA) maintains data on performance and earnings for members of the PGA Tour. Year-end performance data for the 125 players who had the highest total earnings in PGA Tour events for 2005 appear on the data disk in the file named PGATour (www.pgatour.com, 2006). Each row of the data set corresponds to a PGA Tour player, and the data have been sorted based on total earnings. Descriptions for the data follow.

Earnings	Total earnings in PGA Tour events
Scoring Avg.	Average score for all events
Yards/Drive	Average number of yards per drive (The length of a drive is measured to the point where the drive comes to rest, regardless of whether it is in the fairway.)
Driving Acc.	The percentage of time a player is able to hit the fairway with a tee shot
Greens in Reg.	The percentage of time a player is able to hit the green in regulation (A green is considered hit in regulation if any part of the ball is touching the putting surface and the difference between the value of par for the hole and the number of strokes taken to hit the green is at least 2.)

Putting Avg.	Average number of putts taken on greens hit in regulation
Save Pct.	Percentage of time a player is able to get "up and down" once in a greenside sand bunker

Managerial Report

Suppose you are hired by the commissioner of the PGA Tour to analyze the data for a presentation to be made at the annual PGA Tour meeting. The commissioner asks whether it would be possible to use these data to determine the performance measures that are the best predictors of a player's average score. Use the methods presented in this and previous chapters to analyze the data. Prepare a report for the PGA Tour commissioner that summarizes your analysis, including key statistical results, conclusions, and recommendations. Include any appropriate technical material in an appendix.

Case Problem 2 Fuel Economy for Cars

CD file
Cars

Posted on every new car sold in the United States is a fuel economy rating that shows the miles per gallon the car is expected to achieve in actual city and highway use. Data showing these ratings for all cars and trucks are available in the U.S. Department of Energy's *Fuel Economy Guide*. A portion of the data for 230 cars is available on the CD accompanying the text in the file named Cars (www.fueleconomy.gov, March 21, 2003). Descriptions for the data, which appear on the disk, follow.

Class	The class of the car (Compact, Midsize, Large)
Manufacturer	The manufacturer of the car
carline name	The name of the car
displ	The displacement of the engine in liters
cyl	The number of cylinders in the engine (4, 6, 8)
trans	The type of transmission (Automatic, Manual)
cty	The fuel economy rating for city driving in miles per gallon
hwy	The fuel economy rating for highway driving in miles per gallon

Managerial Report

Use the methods presented in this and previous chapters to analyze this data set. The objective of your study is to develop an estimated regression equation that can be used to estimate the fuel economy rating for city driving and an estimated regression equation that can be used to estimate the fuel economy rating for highway driving. Present a summary of your analysis, including key statistical results, conclusions, and recommendations, in a managerial report. Include any appropriate technical material (computer output, residual plots, etc.) in an appendix.

Case Problem 3 Predicting Graduation Rates for Colleges and Universities

The percentage of students who enroll at a college or university and actually graduate is an important statistic for university administrators. Some of the factors related to the graduation rate include the percentage of classes with fewer than 20 students, the percentage of classes with more than 50 students, the student-faculty ratio, the percentage of students who apply to the university and are admitted, the percentage of first-year students in the top 10% of their high school class, and the academic reputation of the university. To study the effect of these factors on the graduation rate, data for 48 national universities was collected (*America's Best Colleges,* Year 2000 Edition). These data are available on the CD accompanying the text in the file named GradRate. Descriptions for data, which appear on the disk, follow.

CD file GradRate

Region	The region of the country in which the university is located (North, South, Midwest, West)
Graduation Rate	The percentage of students who enroll at the university and graduate
% of Classes Under 20	The percentage of classes with fewer than 20 students
% of Classes of 50 or More	The percentage of classes with more than 50 students
Student-Faculty Ratio	The ratio of the number of students enrolled divided by the total number of faculty
Acceptance Rate	The percentage of students who apply and are accepted
1st-Year Students in Top 10% of HS Class	The percentage of students admitted who were in the top 10% of their high school class
Academic Reputation Score	A measure of the school's reputation determined by surveying administrators at other universities: measured on a scale from 1 (marginal) to 5 (distinguished)

Managerial Report

Use the methods presented in this and previous chapters to analyze this data set. Present a summary of your analysis, including key statistical results, conclusions, and recommendations, in a managerial report. Include any appropriate technical material (computer output, residual plots, etc.) in an appendix.

Appendix 16.1 Variable Selection Procedures with Minitab

In Section 16.4 we discussed the use of variable selection procedures in solving multiple regression problems. In Figure 16.16 we showed the Minitab stepwise regression output for the Cravens data, and in Figure 16.17 we showed the Minitab best-subsets output. In this appendix we describe the steps required to generate the output in both of these figures, as well as the steps required to use the forward selection and backward elimination procedures. First, the data in Table 16.5 must be entered in a Minitab worksheet. The values of Sales, Time, Poten, AdvExp, Share, Change, Accounts, Work, and Rating are entered into columns C1–C9 of a Minitab worksheet.

Using Minitab's Stepwise Procedure

The following steps can be used to produce the Minitab stepwise regression output for the Cravens data.

Step 1. Select the **Stat** menu
Step 2. Select the **Regression** menu
Step 3. Choose **Stepwise**

Step 4. When the **Stepwise Regression** dialog box appears:
Enter Sales in the **Response** box
Enter Time, Poten, AdvExp, Share, Change, Accounts, Work, and Rating in the **Predictors** box
Select the **Methods** button
Step 5. When the **Stepwise-Methods** dialog box appears:
Select **Stepwise (forward and backward)**
Enter .05 in the **Alpha to enter** box
Enter .05 in the **Alpha to remove** box
Click **OK**
Step 6. When the **Stepwise Regression** dialog box reappears:
Click **OK**

Using Minitab's Forward Selection Procedure

To use Minitab's forward selection procedure, we simply modify step 5 in Minitab's stepwise regression procedure as shown here:

Step 5. When the **Stepwise-Methods** dialog box appears:
Select **Forward selection**
Enter .05 in the **Alpha to enter** box
Click **OK**

Using Minitab's Backward Elimination Procedure

To use Minitab's backward elimination procedure, we simply modify step 5 in Minitab's stepwise regression procedure as shown here:

Step 5. When the **Stepwise-Methods** dialog box appears:
Select **Backward elimination**
Enter .05 in the **Alpha to remove** box
Click **OK**

Using Minitab's Best-Subsets Procedure

The following steps can be used to produce the Minitab best-subsets regression output for the Craven data.

Step 1. Select the **Stat** menu
Step 2. Select the **Regression** menu
Step 3. Choose **Best Subsets**
Step 4. When the **Best Subsets Regression** dialog box appears:
Enter Sales in the **Response** box
Enter Time, Poten, AdvExp, Share, Change, Accounts, Work, and Rating in the **Predictors** box
Click **OK**

CHAPTER 18

Forecasting

CONTENTS

STATISTICS in PRACTICE

NEVADA OCCUPATIONAL HEALTH CLINIC*
SPARKS, NEVADA

Nevada Occupational Health Clinic is a privately owned medical clinic in Sparks, Nevada. The clinic specializes in industrial medicine, operating at the same site for more than 20 years. The clinic had been in a rapid growth phase, with monthly billings increasing from $57,000 to more than $300,000 in 26 months, when the main clinic building burned to the ground.

The clinic's insurance policy covered physical property and equipment as well as loss of income due to the interruption of regular business operations. Settling the property insurance claim was a relatively straightforward matter of determining the value of the physical property and equipment lost during the fire. However, determining the value of the income lost during the seven months that it took to rebuild the clinic was a complicated matter involving negotiations between the business owners and the insurance company. No preestablished rules could help calculate "what would have happened" to the clinic's billings if the fire had not occurred.

A fire closed the Nevada Occupational Health Clinic for seven months. © PhotoDisc/Getty Images.

To estimate the lost income, the clinic used a forecasting method to project the growth in business that would have been realized during the seven-month lost-business period. The actual history of billings prior to the fire provided the basis for a forecasting model with linear trend and seasonal components as discussed in this chapter. This forecasting model enabled the clinic to establish an accurate estimate of the loss, which eventually was accepted by the insurance company.

*The authors are indebted to Bard Betz, Director of Operations, and Curtis Brauer, Executive Administrative Assistant, Nevada Occupational Health Clinic, for providing this Statistics in Practice.

An essential aspect of managing any organization is planning for the future. Indeed, the long-run success of an organization is closely related to how well management is able to anticipate the future and develop appropriate strategies. Good judgment, intuition, and an awareness of the state of the economy may give a manager a rough idea or "feeling" of what is likely to happen in the future. However, converting that feeling into a number that can be used as next quarter's sales volume or next year's raw material cost is difficult. The purpose of this chapter is to introduce several forecasting methods.

Most companies can forecast total demand for all products with errors of less than 5%. However, forecasting demand for individual products can result in significantly higher errors.

Suppose we are asked to provide quarterly forecasts of the sales volume for a particular product during the coming one-year period. Production schedules, raw material purchasing, inventory policies, and sales quotas will all be affected by the quarterly forecasts we provide. Consequently, poor forecasts may result in poor planning and hence increased costs for the firm. How should we go about providing the quarterly sales volume forecasts?

A forecast is simply a prediction of what will happen in the future. Managers must learn to accept the fact that regardless of the technique used, they will not be able to develop perfect forecasts.

We will certainly want to review the actual sales data for the product in past periods. Using these historical data, we can identify the general level of sales and any trend such as an increase or decrease in sales volume over time. A further review of the data might reveal a seasonal pattern such as peak sales occurring in the third quarter of each year and sales volume bottoming out during the first quarter. By reviewing historical data, we can often develop a better understanding of the pattern of past sales, leading to better predictions of future sales for the product.

Historical sales form a time series. A **time series** is a set of observations on a variable measured at successive points in time or over successive periods of time. In this chapter, we will introduce several procedures for analyzing time series. The objective of such analyses is to provide good **forecasts** or predictions of future values of the time series.

Forecasting methods can be classified as quantitative or qualitative. Quantitative forecasting methods can be used when (1) past information about the variable being forecast is available, (2) the information can be quantified, and (3) a reasonable assumption is that the pattern of the past will continue into the future. In such cases, a forecast can be developed using a time series method or a causal method.

If the historical data are restricted to past values of the variable, the forecasting procedure is called a *time series method.* The objective of time series methods is to discover a pattern in the historical data and then extrapolate the pattern into the future; the forecast is based solely on past values of the variable and/or on past forecast errors. In this chapter we discuss three time series methods: smoothing (moving averages, weighted moving averages, and exponential smoothing), trend projection, and trend projection adjusted for seasonal influence.

Causal forecasting methods are based on the assumption that the variable we are forecasting has a cause-effect relationship with one or more other variables. In this chapter we discuss the use of regression analysis as a causal forecasting method. For instance, the sales volume for many products is influenced by advertising expenditures, so regression analysis may be used to develop an equation showing how these two variables are related. Then, once the advertising budget is set for the next period, we could substitute this value into the equation to develop a prediction or forecast of the sales volume for that period. Note that if a time series method was used to develop the forecast, advertising expenditures would not be considered; that is, a time series method would base the forecast solely on past sales.

Qualitative methods generally involve the use of expert judgment to develop forecasts. For instance, a panel of experts might develop a consensus forecast of the prime rate for a year from now. An advantage of qualitative procedures is that they can be applied when the information on the variable being forecast cannot be quantified and when historical data are either not applicable or unavailable. Figure 18.1 provides an overview of the types of forecasting methods.

18.1 Components of a Time Series

The pattern or behavior of the data in a time series involves several components. The usual assumption is that four separate components—trend, cyclical, seasonal, and irregular—combine to provide specific values for the time series. Let us look more closely at each of these components.

Trend Component

In time series analysis, the measurements may be taken every hour, day, week, month, or year, or at any other regular interval.* Although time series data generally exhibit random fluctuations, the time series may still show gradual shifts or movements to relatively higher or lower values over a longer period of time. The gradual shifting of the time series is referred to as the **trend** in the time series; this shifting or trend is usually the result of long-term factors such as changes in the population, demographic characteristics of the population, technology, and/or consumer preferences.

For example, a manufacturer of photographic equipment may see substantial month-to-month variability in the number of cameras sold. However, in reviewing the sales over the past 10 to 15 years, the manufacturer may find a gradual increase in the annual sales volume.

*We limit our discussion to time series in which the values of the series are recorded at equal intervals. Cases in which the observations are not made at unequal intervals are beyond the scope of this text.

FIGURE 18.1 OVERVIEW OF FORECASTING METHODS

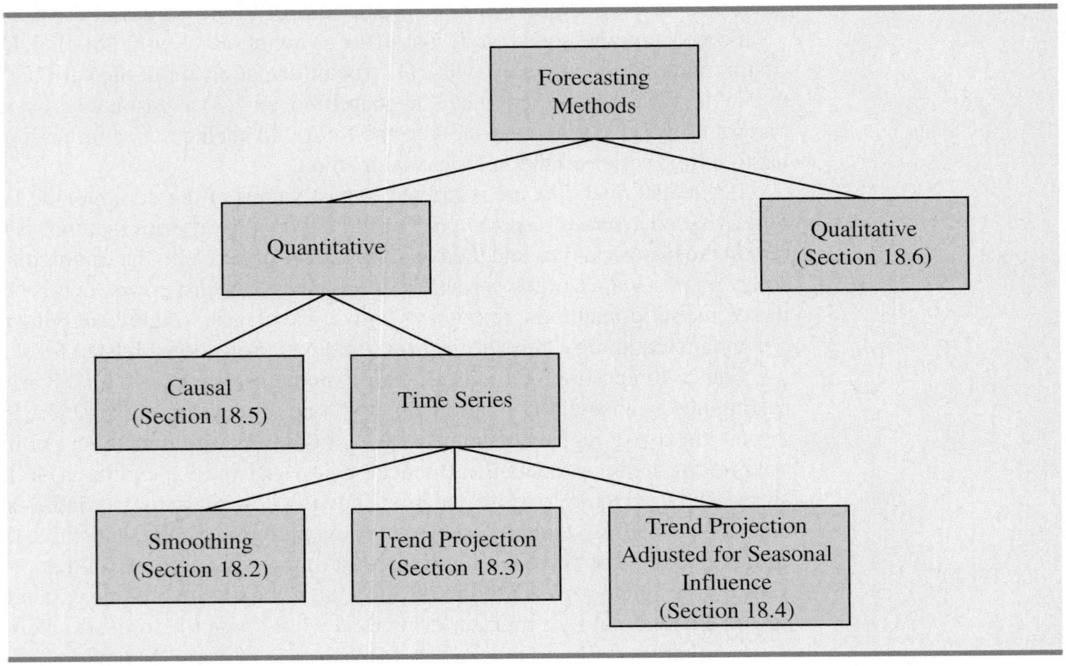

Suppose the sales volume was approximately 17,000 cameras in 1996, 23,000 cameras in 2001, and 25,000 cameras in 2006. This gradual growth in sales over time shows an upward trend for the time series. Figure 18.2 shows a straight line that may be a good approximation of the trend in camera sales. Although the trend for camera sales appears to be linear and increasing over time, sometimes the trend in a time series can be described better by some other patterns.

FIGURE 18.2 LINEAR TREND OF CAMERA SALES

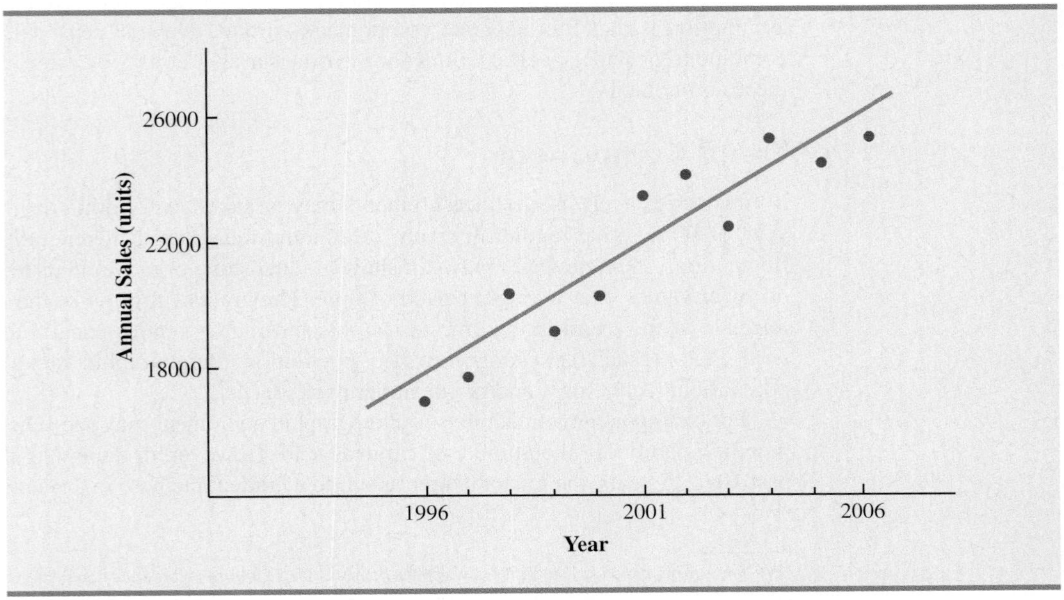

FIGURE 18.3 EXAMPLES OF SOME POSSIBLE TIME SERIES TREND PATTERNS

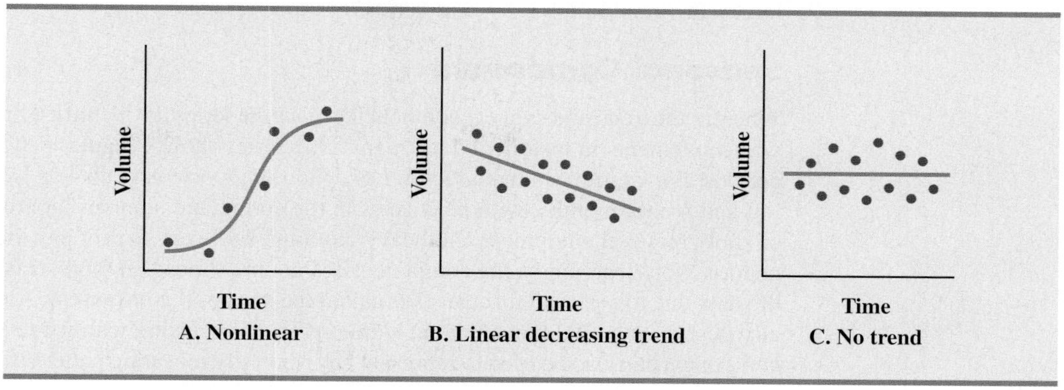

Figure 18.3 shows some other possible time series trend patterns. Panel A shows a nonlinear trend; in this case, the time series indicates little growth initially, then a period of rapid growth, and finally a leveling off. This trend might be a good approximation of sales for a product from introduction through a growth period and into a period of market saturation. The linear decreasing trend in panel B is useful for a time series displaying a steady decrease over time. The horizontal line in panel C represents a time series with no consistent increase or decrease over time and thus no trend.

Cyclical Component

Although a time series may exhibit a trend over long periods of time, all future values of the time series will not fall exactly on the trend line. In fact, time series often show alternating sequences of points below and above the trend line. Any recurring sequence of points above and below the trend line lasting more than one year can be attributed to the **cyclical component** of the time series. Figure 18.4 shows the graph of a time series with an obvious cyclical component. The observations are taken at intervals one year apart.

Many time series exhibit cyclical behavior with regular runs of observations below and above the trend line. Generally, this component of the time series is due to multiyear cyclical movements in the economy. For example, periods of moderate inflation followed by

FIGURE 18.4 TREND AND CYCLICAL COMPONENTS OF A TIME SERIES WITH DATA POINTS ONE YEAR APART

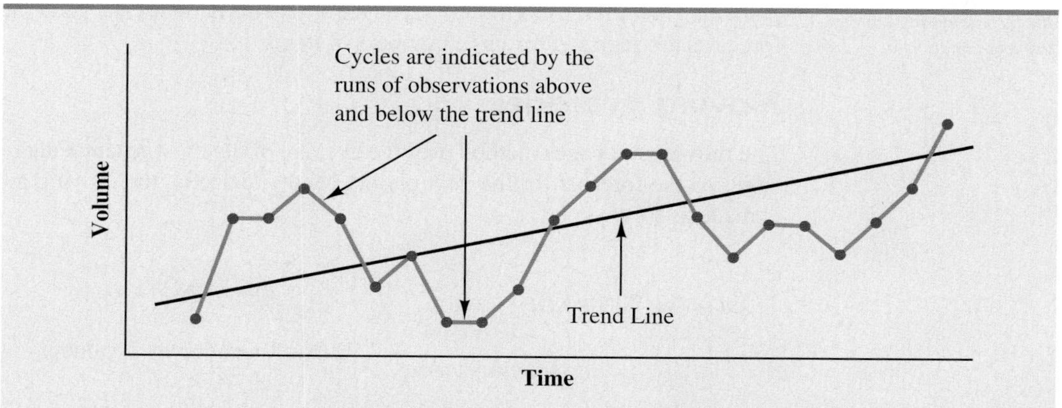

periods of rapid inflation can lead to time series that alternate below and above a generally increasing trend line (e.g., a time series for housing costs).

Seasonal Component

Whereas the trend and cyclical components of a time series are identified by analyzing multi-year movements in historical data, many time series show a regular pattern over one-year periods. For example, a manufacturer of swimming pools expects low sales activity in the fall and winter months, with peak sales in the spring and summer months. Manufacturers of snow removal equipment and heavy clothing, however, expect just the opposite yearly pattern. Not surprisingly, the component of the time series that represents the variability in the data due to seasonal influences is called the **seasonal component**. Although we generally think of seasonal movement in a time series as occurring within one year, the seasonal component can also be used to represent any regularly repeating pattern that is less than one year in duration. For example, daily traffic volume data show within-the-day "seasonal" behavior, with peak levels occurring during rush hours, moderate flow during the rest of the day and early evening, and light flow from midnight to early morning.

Irregular Component

The **irregular component** of the time series is the residual, or "catch-all," factor that accounts for the deviations of the actual time series values from those expected given the effects of the trend, cyclical, and seasonal components. The irregular component is caused by the short-term, unanticipated, and nonrecurring factors that affect the time series. Because this component accounts for the random variability in the time series, it is unpredictable. We cannot attempt to predict its impact on the time series.

18.2 Smoothing Methods

Many manufacturing environments require forecasts for thousands of items weekly or monthly. Thus, in choosing a forecasting technique, simplicity and ease of use are important criteria. The data requirements for the techniques presented in this section are minimal, and the techniques are easy to use and understand.

In this section we discuss three forecasting methods: moving averages, weighted moving averages, and exponential smoothing. The objective of each of these methods is to "smooth out" the random fluctuations caused by the irregular component of the time series; therefore they are referred to as smoothing methods. Smoothing methods are appropriate for a stable time series—that is, one that exhibits no significant trend, cyclical, or seasonal effects—because they adapt well to changes in the level of the time series. However, without modification, they do not work as well when significant trend, cyclical, or seasonal variations are present.

Smoothing methods are easy to use and generally provide a high level of accuracy for short-range forecasts, such as a forecast for the next time period. One of the methods, exponential smoothing, has minimal data requirements and thus is a good method to use when forecasts are required for large numbers of items.

Moving Averages

The **moving averages** method uses the average of the most recent n data values in the time series as the forecast for the next period. Mathematically, the moving average calculation is made as follows.

MOVING AVERAGE

$$\text{Moving average} = \frac{\Sigma(\text{most recent } n \text{ data values})}{n} \tag{18.1}$$

TABLE 18.1

GASOLINE SALES TIME SERIES

Week	Sales (1000s of gallons)
1	17
2	21
3	19
4	23
5	18
6	16
7	20
8	18
9	22
10	20
11	15
12	22

The term *moving* is used because every time a new observation becomes available for the time series, it replaces the oldest observation in equation (18.1) and a new average is computed. As a result, the average will change, or move, as new observations become available.

To illustrate the moving averages method, consider the 12 weeks of data in Table 18.1 and Figure 18.5. These data show the number of gallons of gasoline sold by a gasoline distributor in Bennington, Vermont, over the past 12 weeks. Figure 18.5 indicates that, although random variability is present, the time series appears to be stable over time. Hence, the smoothing methods of this section are applicable.

To use moving averages to forecast gasoline sales, we must first select the number of data values to be included in the moving average. As an example, let us compute forecasts using a three-week moving average. The moving average calculation for the first three weeks of the gasoline sales time series is

$$\text{Moving average (weeks 1–3)} = \frac{17 + 21 + 19}{3} = 19$$

CD file

Gasoline

We then use this moving average as the forecast for week 4. Because the actual value observed in week 4 is 23, the forecast error in week 4 is $23 - 19 = 4$. In general, the error associated with any forecast is the difference between the observed value of the time series and the forecast.

The calculation for the second three-week moving average is

$$\text{Moving average (weeks 2–4)} = \frac{21 + 19 + 23}{3} = 21$$

FIGURE 18.5 GASOLINE SALES TIME SERIES

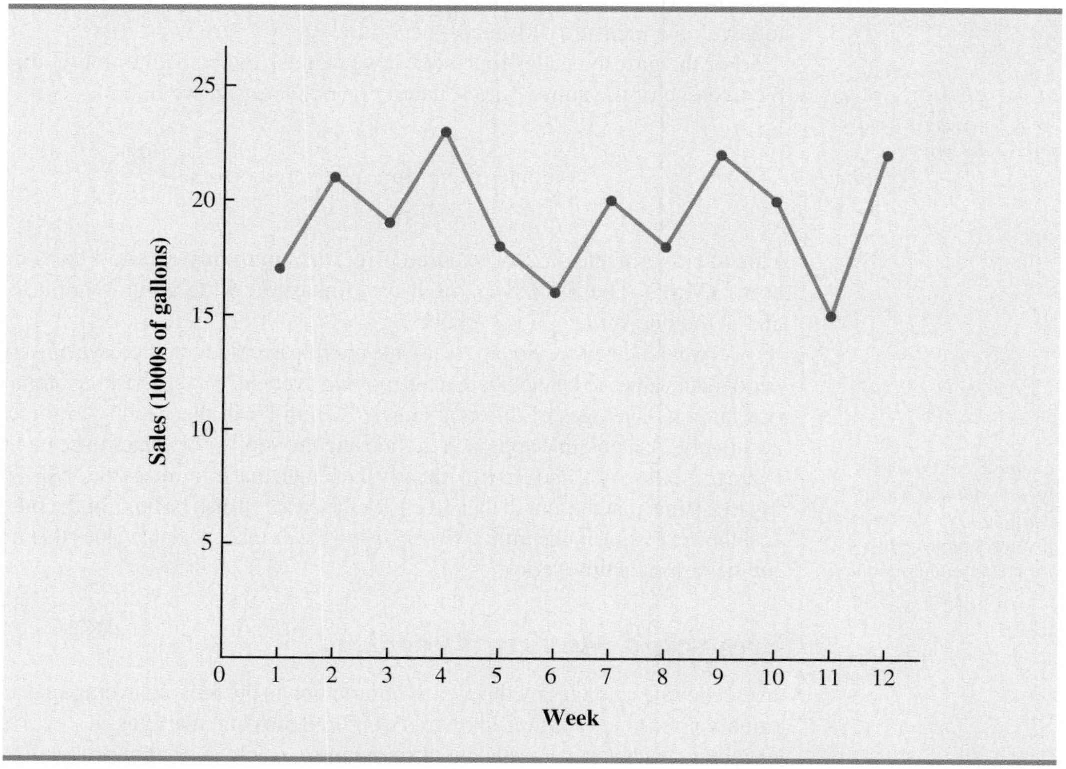

TABLE 18.2 SUMMARY OF THREE-WEEK MOVING AVERAGE CALCULATIONS

Week	Time Series Value	Moving Average Forecast	Forecast Error	Squared Forecast Error
1	17			
2	21			
3	19			
4	23	19	4	16
5	18	21	−3	9
6	16	20	−4	16
7	20	19	1	1
8	18	18	0	0
9	22	18	4	16
10	20	20	0	0
11	15	20	−5	25
12	22	19	3	9
		Totals	0	92

Hence, the forecast for week 5 is 21. The error associated with this forecast is $18 - 21 = -3$. Thus, the forecast error may be positive or negative depending on whether the forecast is too low or too high. A complete summary of the three-week moving average calculations for the gasoline sales time series is provided in Table 18.2 and Figure 18.6.

Forecast accuracy is not the only consideration. Sometimes the most accurate method requires data on related time series that are difficult or costly to obtain. Trade-offs are often made between cost and forecast accuracy.

Forecast Accuracy An important consideration in selecting a forecasting method is the accuracy of the forecast. Clearly, we want forecast errors to be small. The last two columns of Table 18.2, which contain the forecast errors and the squared forecast errors, can be used to develop a measure of forecast accuracy.

For the gasoline sales time series, we can use the last column of Table 18.2 to compute the average of the sum of the squared errors. Doing so we obtain

$$\text{Average of the sum of squared errors} = \frac{92}{9} = 10.22$$

This average of the sum of squared errors is commonly referred to as the **mean squared error (MSE)**. The MSE is an often-used measure of the accuracy of a forecasting method and is the one we use in this chapter.

Exercise 2 at the end of the section will ask you to consider four-week and five-week moving averages for the gasoline sales data.

As we indicated previously, to use the moving averages method, we must first select the number of data values to be included in the moving average. Not surprisingly, for a particular time series, moving averages of different lengths will differ in their ability to forecast the time series accurately. One possible approach to choosing the number of values to be included in the moving average is to use trial and error to identify the length that minimizes the MSE. Then, if we are willing to assume that the length that is best for the past will also be best for the future, we would forecast the next value in the time series by using the number of data values that minimized the MSE for the historical time series.

Weighted Moving Averages

In the moving averages method, each observation in the moving average calculation receives the same weight. One variation, known as **weighted moving averages**, involves selecting a different weight for each data value and then computing a weighted average of the most recent n values as

FIGURE 18.6 GASOLINE SALES TIME SERIES AND THREE-WEEK MOVING AVERAGE FORECASTS

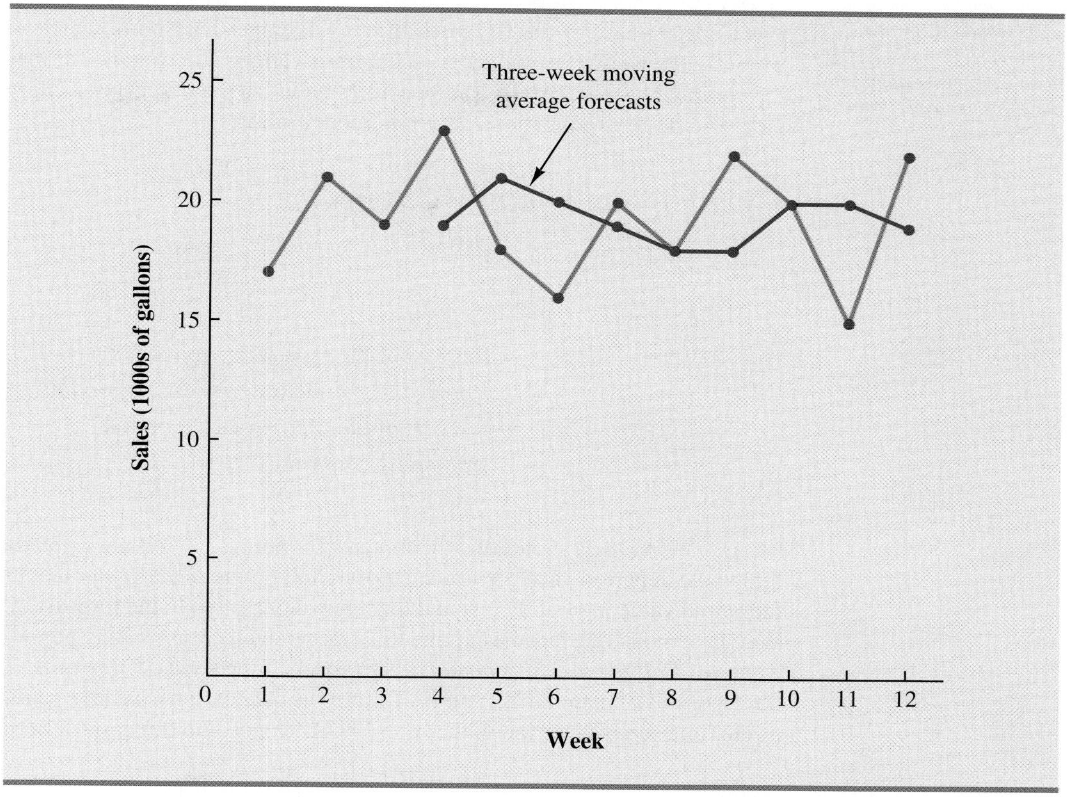

the forecast. In most cases, the most recent observation receives the most weight, and the weight decreases for older data values. For example, we can use the gasoline sales time series to illustrate the computation of a weighted three-week moving average, with the most recent observation receiving a weight three times as great as that given the oldest observation, and the next oldest observation receiving a weight twice as great as the oldest. For week 4 the computation is:

$$\text{Forecast for week 4} = \tfrac{1}{6}(17) + \tfrac{2}{6}(21) + \tfrac{3}{6}(19) = 19.33$$

Note that for the weighted moving average the sum of the weights is equal to 1. Actually the sum of the weights for the simple moving average also equalled 1: Each weight was 1/3. However, recall that the simple or unweighted moving average provided a forecast of 19.

Forecast Accuracy To use the weighted moving averages method we must first select the number of data values to be included in the weighted moving average and then choose weights for each of the data values. In general, if we believe that the recent past is a better predictor of the future than the distant past, larger weights should be given to the more recent observations. However, when the time series is highly variable, selecting approximately equal weights for the data values may be best. Note that the only requirement in selecting the weights is that their sum must equal 1. To determine whether one particular combination of number of data values and weights provides a more accurate forecast than another combination, we will continue to use the MSE criterion as the measure of forecast accuracy. That is, if we assume that the combination that is best for the past will also be best for the future, we would use the combination of number of data values and weights that minimized MSE for the historical time series to forecast the next value in the time series.

Exponential Smoothing

Exponential smoothing is simple and has few data requirements, which makes it an inexpensive approach for firms that make many forecasts each period.

Exponential smoothing uses a weighted average of past time series values as the forecast; it is a special case of the weighted moving averages method in which we select only one weight—the weight for the most recent observation. The weights for the other data values are computed automatically and become smaller as the observations move farther into the past. The basic exponential smoothing model follows.

EXPONENTIAL SMOOTHING MODEL

$$F_{t+1} = \alpha Y_t + (1 - \alpha)F_t \tag{18.2}$$

where

$$
\begin{aligned}
F_{t+1} &= \text{forecast of the time series for period } t + 1 \\
Y_t &= \text{actual value of the time series in period } t \\
F_t &= \text{forecast of the time series for period } t \\
\alpha &= \text{smoothing constant } (0 \leq \alpha \leq 1)
\end{aligned}
$$

Equation (18.2) shows that the forecast for period $t + 1$ is a weighted average of the actual value in period t and the forecast for period t; note in particular that the weight given to the actual value in period t is α and that the weight given to the forecast in period t is $1 - \alpha$. We can demonstrate that the exponential smoothing forecast for any period is also a weighted average of *all the previous actual values* for the time series with a time series consisting of three periods of data: Y_1, Y_2, and Y_3. To start the calculations, we let F_1 equal the actual value of the time series in period 1; that is, $F_1 = Y_1$. Hence, the forecast for period 2 is

$$
\begin{aligned}
F_2 &= \alpha Y_1 + (1 - \alpha)F_1 \\
&= \alpha Y_1 + (1 - \alpha)Y_1 \\
&= Y_1
\end{aligned}
$$

Thus, the exponential smoothing forecast for period 2 is equal to the actual value of the time series in period 1.

The forecast for period 3 is

$$F_3 = \alpha Y_2 + (1 - \alpha)F_2 = \alpha Y_2 + (1 - \alpha)Y_1$$

Finally, substituting this expression for F_3 in the expression for F_4, we obtain

$$
\begin{aligned}
F_4 &= \alpha Y_3 + (1 - \alpha)F_3 \\
&= \alpha Y_3 + (1 - \alpha)[\alpha Y_2 + (1 - \alpha)Y_1] \\
&= \alpha Y_3 + \alpha(1 - \alpha)Y_2 + (1 - \alpha)^2 Y_1
\end{aligned}
$$

The term exponential smoothing *comes from the exponential nature of the weighting scheme for the historical values.*

Hence, F_4 is a weighted average of the first three time series values. The sum of the coefficients, or weights, for Y_1, Y_2, and Y_3 equals one. A similar argument can be made to show that, in general, any forecast F_{t+1} is a weighted average of all the previous time series values.

Despite the fact that exponential smoothing provides a forecast that is a weighted average of all past observations, all past data do not need to be saved to compute the forecast for the next period. In fact, once the **smoothing constant** α is selected, only two pieces of information are needed to compute the forecast. Equation (18.2) shows that with a given α we can compute the forecast for period $t + 1$ simply by knowing the actual and forecast time series values for period t—that is, Y_t and F_t.

To illustrate the exponential smoothing approach to forecasting, consider the gasoline sales time series in Table 18.1 and Figure 18.5. As indicated, the exponential smoothing forecast for period 2 is equal to the actual value of the time series in period 1. Thus, with $Y_1 = 17$, we will set $F_2 = 17$ to start the exponential smoothing computations. Referring to the time series data in Table 18.1, we find an actual time series value in period 2 of $Y_2 = 21$. Thus, period 2 has a forecast error of $21 - 17 = 4$.

Continuing with the exponential smoothing computations using a smoothing constant of $\alpha = .2$, we obtain the following forecast for period 3.

$$F_3 = .2Y_2 + .8F_2 = .2(21) + .8(17) = 17.8$$

Once the actual time series value in period 3, $Y_3 = 19$, is known, we can generate a forecast for period 4 as follows.

$$F_4 = .2Y_3 + .8F_3 = .2(19) + .8(17.8) = 18.04$$

By continuing the exponential smoothing calculations, we can determine the weekly forecast values and the corresponding weekly forecast errors, as shown in Table 18.3. Note that we have not shown an exponential smoothing forecast or the forecast error for period 1 because no forecast was made. For week 12, we have $Y_{12} = 22$ and $F_{12} = 18.48$. Can we use this information to generate a forecast for week 13 before the actual value of week 13 becomes known? Using the exponential smoothing model, we have

$$F_{13} = .2Y_{12} + .8F_{12} = .2(22) + .8(18.48) = 19.18$$

Thus, the exponential smoothing forecast of the amount sold in week 13 is 19.18, or 19,180 gallons of gasoline. With this forecast, the firm can make plans and decisions accordingly. The accuracy of the forecast will not be known until the end of week 13.

Figure 18.7 is the plot of the actual and forecast time series values. Note in particular how the forecasts "smooth out" the irregular fluctuations in the time series.

Forecast Accuracy In the preceding exponential smoothing calculations, we used a smoothing constant of $\alpha = .2$. Although any value of α between 0 and 1 is acceptable, some

TABLE 18.3 SUMMARY OF THE EXPONENTIAL SMOOTHING FORECASTS AND FORECAST ERRORS FOR GASOLINE SALES WITH SMOOTHING CONSTANT $\alpha = .2$

Week (t)	Time Series Value (Y_t)	Exponential Smoothing Forecast (F_t)	Forecast Error ($Y_t - F_t$)
1	17		
2	21	17.00	4.00
3	19	17.80	1.20
4	23	18.04	4.96
5	18	19.03	−1.03
6	16	18.83	−2.83
7	20	18.26	1.74
8	18	18.61	−.61
9	22	18.49	3.51
10	20	19.19	.81
11	15	19.35	−4.35
12	22	18.48	3.52

FIGURE 18.7 ACTUAL AND FORECAST GASOLINE SALES TIME SERIES WITH SMOOTHING CONSTANT $\alpha = .2$

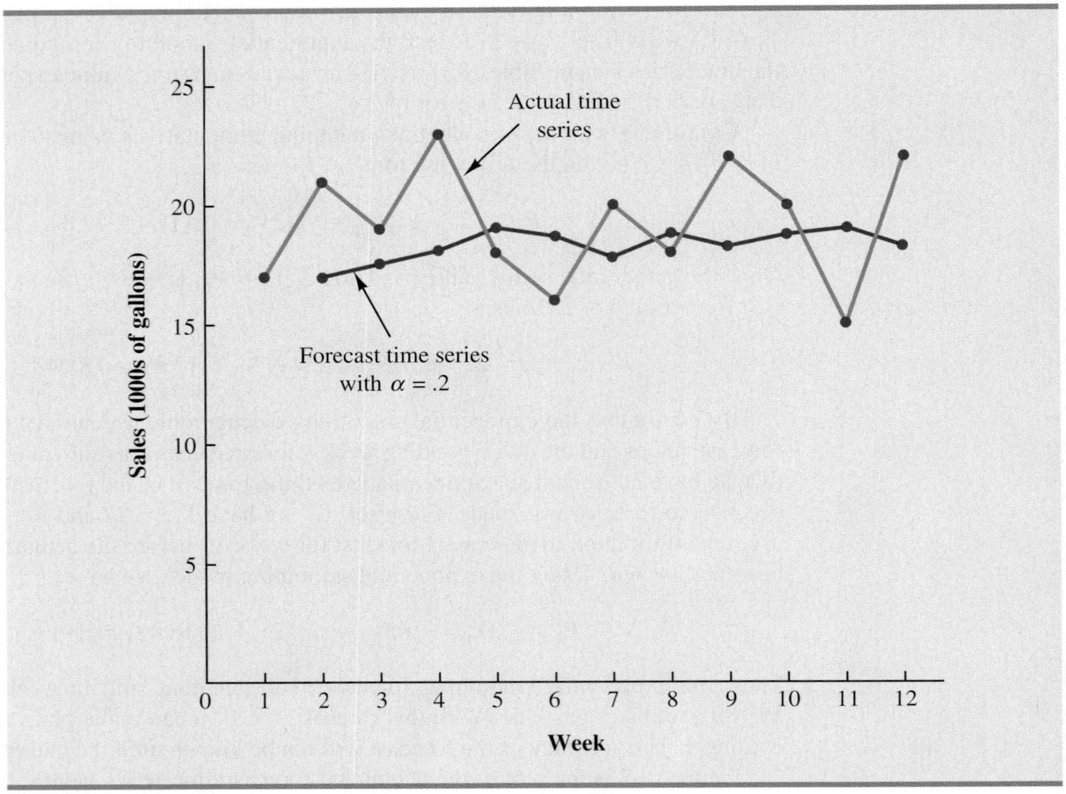

values will yield better forecasts than others. Insight into choosing a good value for α can be obtained by rewriting the basic exponential smoothing model as follows.

$$F_{t+1} = \alpha Y_t + (1 - \alpha)F_t$$
$$F_{t+1} = \alpha Y_t + F_t - \alpha F_t$$
$$F_{t+1} = \underset{\text{Forecast in period } t}{F_t} + \alpha\underbrace{(Y_t - F_t)}_{\text{Forecast error in period } t} \quad \textbf{(18.3)}$$

Thus, the new forecast F_{t+1} is equal to the previous forecast F_t plus an adjustment, which is α times the most recent forecast error, $Y_t - F_t$. That is, the forecast in period $t + 1$ is obtained by adjusting the forecast in period t by a fraction of the forecast error. If the time series contains substantial random variability, a small value of the smoothing constant is preferred. The reason for this choice is that, because much of the forecast error is due to random variability, we do not want to overreact and adjust the forecasts too quickly. For a time series with relatively little random variability, larger values of the smoothing constant provide the advantage of quickly adjusting the forecasts when forecasting errors occur and thus allowing the forecasts to react faster to changing conditions.

The criterion we will use to determine a desirable value for the smoothing constant α is the same as the criterion we proposed for determining the number of periods of data to include in the moving averages calculation. That is, we choose the value of α that minimizes the mean squared error (MSE). A summary of the MSE calculations for the exponential

TABLE 18.4 MSE COMPUTATIONS FOR FORECASTING GASOLINE SALES WITH $\alpha = .2$

Week (t)	Time Series Value (Y_t)	Forecast (F_t)	Forecast Error ($Y_t - F_t$)	Squared Forecast Error $(Y_t - F_t)^2$
1	17			
2	21	17.00	4.00	16.00
3	19	17.80	1.20	1.44
4	23	18.04	4.96	24.60
5	18	19.03	−1.03	1.06
6	16	18.83	−2.83	8.01
7	20	18.26	1.74	3.03
8	18	18.61	−.61	.37
9	22	18.49	3.51	12.32
10	20	19.19	.81	.66
11	15	19.35	−4.35	18.92
12	22	18.48	3.52	12.39
			Total	98.80

$$\text{MSE} = \frac{98.80}{11} = 8.98$$

smoothing forecast of gasoline sales with $\alpha = .2$ is shown in Table 18.4. Note that there is one less squared error term than the number of time periods, because we had no past values with which to make a forecast for period 1. Would a different value of α provide better results in terms of a lower MSE value? Perhaps the most straightforward way to answer this question is simply to try another value for α. We will then compare its mean squared error with the MSE value of 8.98 obtained by using a smoothing constant of $\alpha = .2$.

The exponential smoothing results with $\alpha = .3$ are shown in Table 18.5. With MSE = 9.35, we see that for the current data set, a smoothing constant of $\alpha = .3$ results in less forecast

TABLE 18.5 MSE COMPUTATIONS FOR FORECASTING GASOLINE SALES WITH $\alpha = .3$

Week (t)	Time Series Value (Y_t)	Forecast (F_t)	Forecast Error ($Y_t - F_t$)	Squared Forecast Error $(Y_t - F_t)^2$
1	17			
2	21	17.00	4.00	16.00
3	19	18.20	.80	.64
4	23	18.44	4.56	20.79
5	18	19.81	−1.81	3.28
6	16	19.27	−3.27	10.69
7	20	18.29	1.71	2.92
8	18	18.80	−.80	.64
9	22	18.56	3.44	11.83
10	20	19.59	.41	.17
11	15	19.71	−4.71	22.18
12	22	18.30	3.70	13.69
			Total	102.83

$$\text{MSE} = \frac{102.83}{11} = 9.35$$

accuracy than a smoothing constant of $\alpha = .2$. Thus, we would be inclined to prefer the original smoothing constant of $\alpha = .2$. Using a trial-and-error calculation with other values of α, we can find a "good" value for the smoothing constant. This value can be used in the exponential smoothing model to provide forecasts for the future. At a later date, after new time series observations are obtained, we analyze the newly collected time series data to determine whether the smoothing constant should be revised to provide better forecasting results.

NOTES AND COMMENTS

1. Another measure of forecast accuracy is the *mean absolute deviation* (MAD). This measure is simply the average of the absolute values of all the forecast errors. Using the errors given in Table 18.2, we obtain

$$\text{MAD} = \frac{4 + 3 + 4 + 1 + 0 + 4 + 0 + 5 + 3}{9} = 2.67$$

One major difference between MSE and MAD is that the MSE measure is influenced much more by large forecast errors than by small errors (because for the MSE measure the errors are squared). The selection of the best measure of forecasting accuracy is not a simple matter. Indeed, forecasting experts often disagree as to which measure should be used. We use the MSE measure in this chapter.

2. Spreadsheet packages are an effective aid in choosing a good value of α for exponential smoothing and selecting weights for the weighted moving averages method. With the time series data and the forecasting formulas in the spreadsheets, you can experiment with different values of α (or moving average weights) and choose the value(s) of α providing the smallest MSE or MAD.

Exercises

Methods

SELF test

1. Consider the following time series data.

Week	1	2	3	4	5	6
Value	8	13	15	17	16	9

   a. Develop a three-week moving average for this time series. What is the forecast for week 7?
   b. Compute the MSE for the three-week moving average.
   c. Use $\alpha = .2$ to compute the exponential smoothing values for the time series. What is the forecast for week 7?
   d. Compare the three-week moving average forecast with the exponential smoothing forecast using $\alpha = .2$. Which appears to provide the better forecast?
   e. Use a smoothing constant of .4 to compute the exponential smoothing values. Does a smoothing constant of .2 or .4 appear to provide the better forecast? Explain.

CD file Gasoline

2. Refer to the gasoline sales time series data in Table 18.1.
   a. Compute four-week and five-week moving averages for the time series.
   b. Compute the MSE for the four-week and five-week moving average forecasts.
   c. What appears to be the best number of weeks of past data to use in the moving average computation? Remember that the MSE for the three-week moving average is 10.22.

CD file Gasoline

3. Refer again to the gasoline sales time series data in Table 18.1.
   a. Using a weight of 1/2 for the most recent observation, 1/3 for the second most recent, and 1/6 for third most recent, compute a three-week weighted moving average for the time series.

b. Compute the MSE for the weighted moving average in part (a). Do you prefer this weighted moving average to the unweighted moving average? Remember that the MSE for the unweighted moving average is 10.22.

c. Suppose you are allowed to choose any weights as long as they sum to one. Could you always find a set of weights that would make the MSE smaller for a weighted moving average than for an unweighted moving average? Why or why not?

CD file

Gasoline

4. With the gasoline time series data from Table 18.1, show the exponential smoothing forecasts using $\alpha = .1$. Applying the MSE criterion, would you prefer a smoothing constant of $\alpha = .1$ or $\alpha = .2$ for the gasoline sales time series?

5. With a smoothing constant of $\alpha = .2$, equation (18.2) shows that the forecast for week 13 of the gasoline sales data from Table 18.1 is given by $F_{13} = .2Y_{12} + .8F_{12}$. However, the forecast for week 12 is given by $F_{12} = .2Y_{11} + .8F_{11}$. Thus, we could combine these two results to show that the forecast for week 13 can be written

$$F_{13} = .2Y_{12} + .8(.2Y_{11} + .8F_{11}) = .2Y_{12} + .16Y_{11} + .64F_{11}$$

a. Making use of the fact that $F_{11} = .2Y_{10} = .8F_{10}$ (and similarly for F_{10} and F_9), continue to expand the expression for F_{13} until it is written in terms of the past data values Y_{12}, Y_{11}, Y_{10}, Y_9, Y_8, and the forecast for period 8.

b. Refer to the coefficients or weights for the past values Y_{12}, Y_{11}, Y_{10}, Y_9, Y_8; what observation can you make about how exponential smoothing weights past data values in arriving at new forecasts? Compare this weighting pattern with the weighting pattern of the moving averages method.

Applications

6. For the Hawkins Company, the monthly percentages of all shipments received on time over the past 12 months are 80, 82, 84, 83, 83, 84, 85, 84, 82, 83, 84, and 83.

a. Compare a three-month moving average forecast with an exponential smoothing forecast for $\alpha = .2$. Which provides the better forecasts?

b. What is the forecast for next month?

7. Corporate triple A bond interest rates for 12 consecutive months follow.

9.5 9.3 9.4 9.6 9.8 9.7 9.8 10.5 9.9 9.7 9.6 9.6

a. Develop three-month and four-month moving averages for this time series. Does the three-month or four-month moving average provide the better forecasts? Explain.

b. What is the moving average forecast for the next month?

SELF test

8. The values of Alabama building contracts (in millions of dollars) for a 12-month period follow.

240 350 230 260 280 320 220 310 240 310 240 230

a. Compare a three-month moving averages forecast with an exponential smoothing forecast. Use $\alpha = .2$. Which provides the better forecasts?

b. What is the forecast for the next month?

9. The following time series shows the sales of a particular product over the past 12 months.

Month	Sales	Month	Sales
1	105	7	145
2	135	8	140
3	120	9	100
4	105	10	80
5	90	11	100
6	120	12	110

a. Use $\alpha = .3$ to compute the exponential smoothing values for the time series.
b. Use a smoothing constant of .5 to compute the exponential smoothing values. Does a smoothing constant of .3 or .5 appear to provide the better forecasts?

10. Ten weeks of data on the Commodity Futures Index are 7.35, 7.40, 7.55, 7.56, 7.60, 7.52, 7.52, 7.70, 7.62, and 7.55.
    a. Compute the exponential smoothing values for $\alpha = .2$.
    b. Compute the exponential smoothing values for $\alpha = .3$.
    c. Which exponential smoothing model provides the better forecasts? Forecast week 11.

11. The following data represent 15 quarters of manufacturing capacity utilization (in percentages).

CD file
MfgCap

Quarter/Year	Utilization (%)	Quarter/Year	Utilization (%)
1/2003	82.5	1/2005	78.8
2/2003	81.3	2/2005	78.7
3/2003	81.3	3/2005	78.4
4/2003	79.0	4/2005	80.0
1/2004	76.6	1/2006	80.7
2/2004	78.0	2/2006	80.7
3/2004	78.4	3/2006	80.8
4/2004	78.0		

a. Compute three- and four-quarter moving averages for this time series. Which moving average provides the better forecast for the fourth quarter of 2006?
b. Use smoothing constants of $\alpha = .4$ and $\alpha = .5$ to develop forecasts for the fourth quarter of 2006. Which smoothing constant provides the better forecast?
c. On the basis of the analyses in parts (a) and (b), which method—moving averages or exponential smoothing—provides the better forecast? Explain.

18.3 Trend Projection

In this section we show how to forecast a time series that has a long-term linear trend. The type of time series for which the trend projection method is applicable shows a consistent increase or decrease over time; because it is not stable, the smoothing methods described in the preceding section are not applicable.

TABLE 18.6
BICYCLE SALES TIME SERIES

Year (t)	Sales (1000s) (Y_t)
1	21.6
2	22.9
3	25.5
4	21.9
5	23.9
6	27.5
7	31.5
8	29.7
9	28.6
10	31.4

Consider the time series for bicycle sales of a particular manufacturer over the past 10 years, as shown in Table 18.6 and Figure 18.8. Note that 21,600 bicycles were sold in year 1, 22,900 were sold in year 2, and so on. In year 10, the most recent year, 31,400 bicycles were sold. Although Figure 18.8 shows some up and down movement over the past 10 years, the time series seems to have an overall increasing or upward trend.

We do not want the trend component of a time series to follow each and every up and down movement. Rather, the trend component should reflect the gradual shifting—in this case, growth—of the time series values. After we view the time series data in Table 18.6 and the graph in Figure 18.8, we might agree that a linear trend as shown in Figure 18.9 provides a reasonable description of the long-run movement in the series.

CD file
Bicycle

We use the bicycle sales data to illustrate the calculations involved in applying regression analysis to identify a linear trend. Recall that in the discussion of simple linear regression in Chapter 14, we described how the least squares method is used to find the best straight-line relationship between two variables. We will use that same methodology to develop the trend line for the bicycle sales time series. Specifically, we will be using regression analysis to estimate the relationship between time and sales volume.

FIGURE 18.8 BICYCLE SALES TIME SERIES

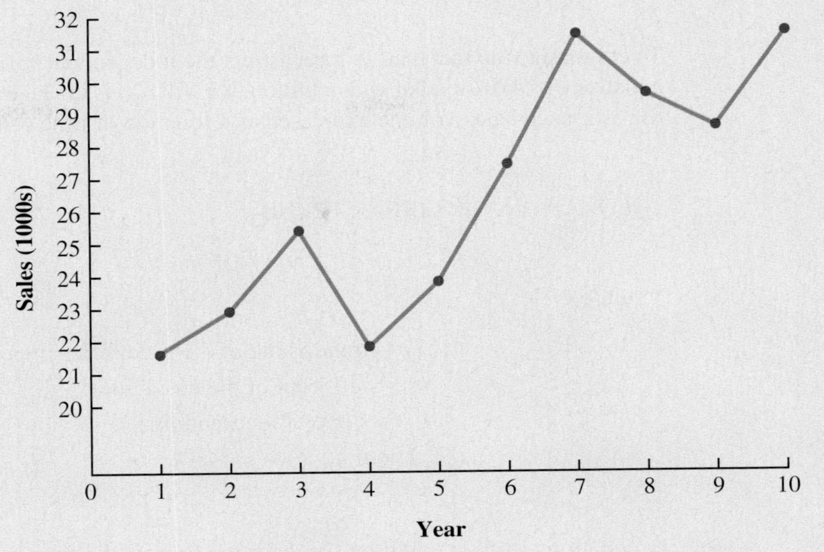

FIGURE 18.9 TREND REPRESENTED BY A LINEAR FUNCTION FOR BICYCLE SALES

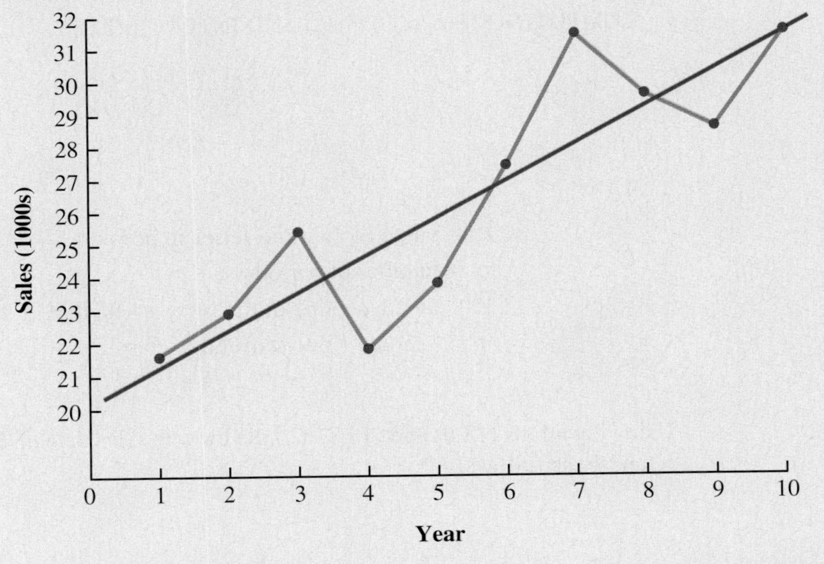

In Chapter 14 the estimated regression equation describing a straight-line relationship between an independent variable x and a dependent variable y was written

$$\hat{y} = b_0 + b_1 x \qquad \textbf{(18.4)}$$

To emphasize the fact that, in forecasting, the independent variable is time, we will use t in equation (18.4) instead of x; in addition, we will use T_t in place of $\hat{y}$. Thus, for a linear trend, the estimated sales volume expressed as a function of time can be written as follows.

EQUATION FOR LINEAR TREND

$$T_t = b_0 + b_1 t \qquad \textbf{(18.5)}$$

where

T_t = trend value of the time series in period t
b_0 = intercept of the trend line
b_1 = slope of the trend line
t = time

In equation (18.5), we will let $t = 1$ for the time of the first observation on the time series data, $t = 2$ for the time of the second observation, and so on. Note that for the time series on bicycle sales, $t = 1$ corresponds to the oldest time series value and $t = 10$ corresponds to the most recent year's data. Formulas for computing the estimated regression coefficients (b_1 and b_0) in equation (18.5) follow.

COMPUTING THE SLOPE (b_1) AND INTERCEPT (b_0)

$$b_1 = \frac{\Sigma t Y_t - (\Sigma t \Sigma Y_t)/n}{\Sigma t^2 - (\Sigma t)^2/n} \qquad \textbf{(18.6)}$$

$$b_0 = \bar{Y} - b_1 \bar{t} \qquad \textbf{(18.7)}$$

where

Y_t = value of the time series in period t
n = number of periods
$\bar{Y}$ = average value of the time series; that is, $\bar{Y} = \Sigma Y_t/n$
$\bar{t}$ = average value of t; that is, $\bar{t} = \Sigma t/n$

Using equations (18.6) and (18.7) and the bicycle sales data of Table 18.6, we can compute b_0 and b_1 as follows:

t	Y_t	tY_t	t^2
1	21.6	21.6	1
2	22.9	45.8	4
3	25.5	76.5	9
4	21.9	87.6	16
5	23.9	119.5	25
6	27.5	165.0	36

	t	Y_t	tY_t	t^2
	7	31.5	220.5	49
	8	29.7	237.6	64
	9	28.6	257.4	81
	10	31.4	314.0	100
Totals	55	264.5	1545.5	385

$$\bar{t} = \frac{55}{10} = 5.5$$

$$\bar{Y} = \frac{264.5}{10} = 26.45$$

$$b_1 = \frac{1545.5 - (55)(264.5)/10}{385 - (55)^2/10} = 1.10$$

$$b_0 = 26.45 - 1.10(5.5) = 20.4$$

Therefore,

$$T_t = 20.4 + 1.1t \tag{18.8}$$

is the expression for the linear trend component for the bicycle sales time series.

Before the trend equation is used to develop a forecast, a statistical test of significance (see Chapter 14) should be conducted. In practice, such a test would be a routine part of fitting the trend line.

The slope of 1.1 indicates that over the past 10 years the firm experienced average growth in sales of about 1100 units per year. If we assume that the past 10-year trend in sales is a good indicator of the future, equation (18.8) can be used to project the trend component of the time series. For example, substituting $t = 11$ into equation (18.8) yields next year's trend projection, T_{11}.

$$T_{11} = 20.4 + 1.1(11) = 32.5$$

Thus, using the trend component only, we would forecast sales of 32,500 bicycles next year.

The use of a linear function to model the trend is common. However, as we discussed previously, sometimes time series have a curvilinear, or nonlinear, trend similar to those in Figure 18.10. In Chapter 16 we discussed how regression analysis can be used to model curvilinear relationships of the type shown in panel A of Figure 18.10. More advanced texts discuss in detail how to develop regression models for more complex relationships, such as the one shown in panel B of Figure 18.10.

FIGURE 18.10 SOME POSSIBLE FORMS OF NONLINEAR TREND PATTERNS

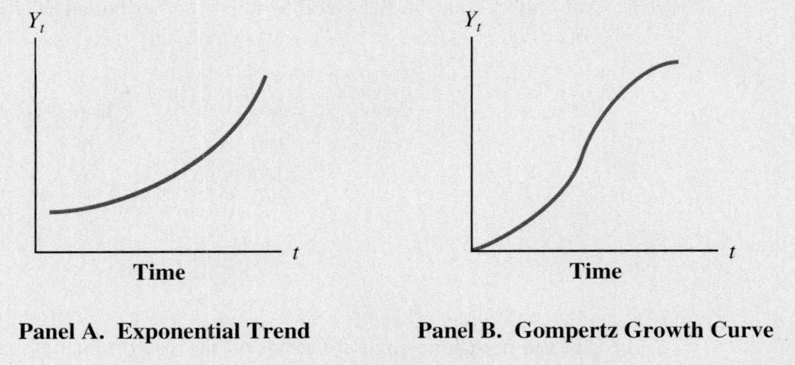

Exercises

Methods

SELF test

12. Consider the following time series.

t	1	2	3	4	5
Y_t	6	11	9	14	15

Develop an equation for the linear trend component of this time series. What is the forecast for $t = 6$?

13. Consider the following time series.

t	1	2	3	4	5	6
Y_t	205	202	195	190	191	188

Develop an equation for the linear trend component for this time series. What is the forecast for $t = 7$?

Applications

SELF test

14. The enrollment data (in thousands) for a state college over the past six years are shown.

Year	1	2	3	4	5	6
Enrollment	20.5	20.2	19.5	19.0	19.1	18.8

Develop the equation for the linear trend component of this time series. Comment on what is happening to enrollment at this institution.

15. The following table gives average attendance figures for home football games at a major university for the past seven years. Develop the equation for the linear trend component of this time series.

Year	Attendance
1	28,000
2	30,000
3	31,500
4	30,400
5	30,500
6	32,200
7	30,800

16. Automobile sales at B.J. Scott Motors, Inc., provided the following 10-year time series.

Year	Sales	Year	Sales
1	400	6	260
2	390	7	300
3	320	8	320
4	340	9	340
5	270	10	370

Plot the time series and comment on the appropriateness of a linear trend. What type of functional form do you believe would be most appropriate for the trend pattern of this time series?

17. The president of a small manufacturing firm is concerned about the continual increase in manufacturing costs over the past several years. The following figures provide a time series of the cost per unit for the firm's leading product over the past eight years.

Year	Cost/Unit ($)	Year	Cost/Unit ($)
1	20.00	5	26.60
2	24.50	6	30.00
3	28.20	7	31.00
4	27.50	8	36.00

a. Show a graph of this time series. Does a linear trend appear to be present?
b. Develop the equation for the linear trend component of the time series. What is the average cost increase that the firm has been realizing per year?

18. The following data show the percentage of rural, urban, and suburban Americans who have a high-speed Internet connection at home (Pew Internet Rural Broadband Internet Use Memo, February 2006).

CD file
Broadband

Year	Rural	Urban	Suburban
2001	3	9	9
2002	6	18	17
2003	9	21	23
2004	16	29	29
2005	24	38	40

a. For each group, develop a linear trend equation.
b. Use the trend equations developed in part (a) to compare the growth rates for the three groups.
c. For each group, use the trend equation to develop a forecast for 2006.

19. The following data show the average monthly cellular telephone bill (*The New York Times Almanac*, 2006).

Year	Amount ($)
1998	39.43
1999	41.24
2000	45.27
2001	47.37
2002	48.40
2003	49.91

a. Graph this time series. Does a trend appear to be present?
b. Develop a linear trend equation for this time series.
c. Use the trend equation to estimate the average monthly bill for 2004.

20. Gross revenue data (in millions of dollars) for Regional Airlines for a 10-year period follow.

Year	Revenue	Year	Revenue
1	2428	6	4264
2	2951	7	4738
3	3533	8	4460
4	3618	9	5318
5	3616	10	6915

a. Develop a linear trend equation for this time series. Comment on what the equation tells about the gross revenue for Regional Airlines for the 10-year period.
b. Provide the forecasts for gross revenue for years 11 and 12.

21. FRED® (Federal Reserve Economic Data), a database of more than 3000 U.S. economic time series, contains historical data on foreign exchange rates. The following data show the foreign exchange rate for the United States and Canada (http://research.stlouisfed.org/fred2/). The units for Rate are the number of Canadian dollars to one U.S. dollar.

Date	Rate
April 2005	1.2359
May 2005	1.2555
June 2005	1.2402
July 2005	1.2229
August 2005	1.2043
September 2005	1.1777
October 2005	1.1774
November 2005	1.1815
December 2005	1.1615
January 2006	1.1572

a. Graph this time series. Does a linear trend appear to be present?
b. Develop the equation for the linear trend component for the time series.
c. Use the trend equation to forecast the exchange rate for February 2006.
d. Would you feel comfortable using the trend equation to forecast the exchange rate for July 2006?

18.4 Trend and Seasonal Components

We showed how to forecast a time series that has a trend component. In this section we extend the discussion by showing how to forecast a time series that has both trend and seasonal components.

Many situations in business and economics involve period-to-period comparisons. We might be interested to learn that unemployment is up 2% compared to last month, steel production is up 5% over last month, or that the production of electric power is down 3% from the previous month. Care must be exercised in using such information, however, because whenever a seasonal influence is present, such comparisons may be misleading. For instance, the fact that electric power consumption is down 3% from August to September might be only the seasonal effect associated with a decrease in the use of air conditioning and not because of a long-term decline in the use of electric power. Indeed, after adjusting for the seasonal effect, we might even find that the use of electric power increased.

Removing the seasonal effect from a time series is known as deseasonalizing the time series. After we do so, period-to-period comparisons are more meaningful and can help identify whether a trend exists. The approach we take in this section is appropriate in situations when only seasonal effects are present or in situations when both seasonal and trend components are present. The first step is to compute seasonal indexes and use them to deseasonalize the data. Then, if a trend is apparent in the deseasonalized data, we use regression analysis on the deseasonalized data to estimate the trend component.

Multiplicative Model

In addition to a trend component (T) and a seasonal component (S), we will assume that the time series involves an irregular component (I). The irregular component accounts for any random effects in the time series that cannot be explained by the trend and seasonal components. Using T_t, S_t, and I_t to identify the trend, seasonal, and irregular components at time t, we will assume that the time series value, denoted Y_t, can be described by the following **multiplicative time series model**.

$$Y_t = T_t \times S_t \times I_t \tag{18.9}$$

TABLE 18.7

QUARTERLY DATA FOR TELEVISION SET SALES

Year	Quarter	Sales (1000s)
1	1	4.8
	2	4.1
	3	6.0
	4	6.5
2	1	5.8
	2	5.2
	3	6.8
	4	7.4
3	1	6.0
	2	5.6
	3	7.5
	4	7.8
4	1	6.3
	2	5.9
	3	8.0
	4	8.4

CD file

TVSales

In this model, T_t is the trend measured in units of the item being forecast. However, the S_t and I_t components are measured in relative terms, with values above 1.00 indicating effects above the trend and values below 1.00 indicating effects below the trend.

We will illustrate the use of the multiplicative model with trend, seasonal, and irregular components by working with the quarterly data in Table 18.7 and Figure 18.11. These data show television set sales (in thousands of units) for a particular manufacturer over the past four years. We begin by showing how to identify the seasonal component of the time series.

Calculating the Seasonal Indexes

Figure 18.11 indicates that sales are lowest in the second quarter of each year and increase in quarters 3 and 4. Thus, we conclude that a seasonal pattern exists for television set sales. The computational procedure used to identify each quarter's seasonal influence begins by computing a moving average to separate the combined seasonal and irregular components, S_t and I_t, from the trend component T_t.

To do so, we use one year of data in each calculation. Because we are working with a quarterly series, we will use four data values in each moving average. The moving average calculation for the first four quarters of the television set sales data is

$$\text{First moving average} = \frac{4.8 + 4.1 + 6.0 + 6.5}{4} = \frac{21.4}{4} = 5.35$$

Note that the moving average calculation for the first four quarters yields the average quarterly sales over year 1 of the time series. Continuing the moving average calculations, we

FIGURE 18.11 QUARTERLY TELEVISION SET SALES TIME SERIES

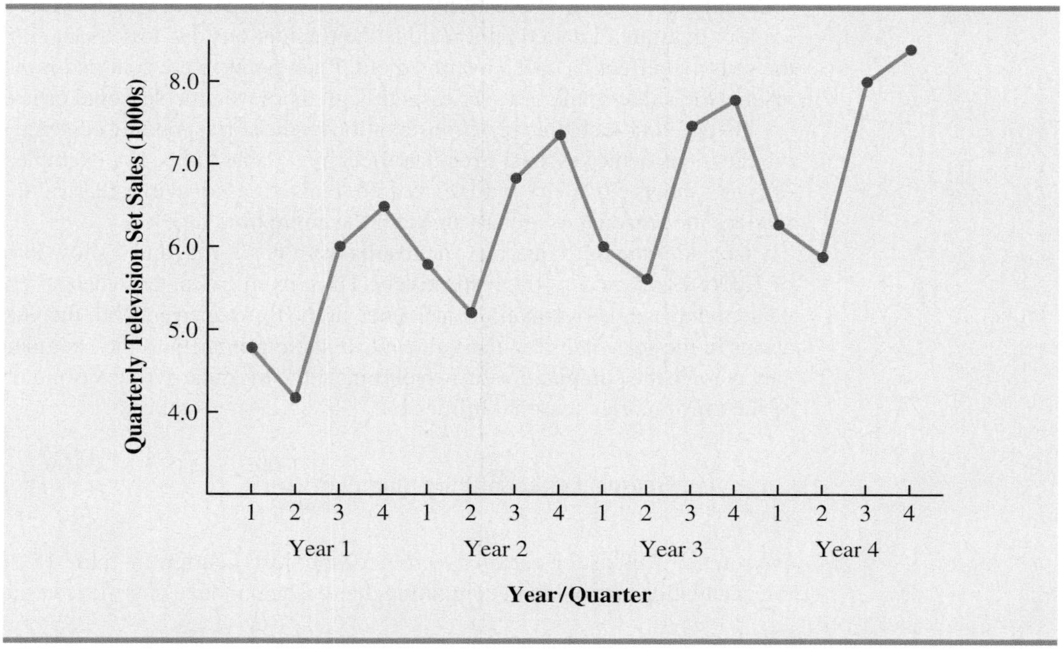

next add the 5.8 value for the first quarter of year 2 and drop the 4.8 for the first quarter of year 1. Thus, the second moving average is

$$\text{Second moving average} = \frac{4.1 + 6.0 + 6.5 + 5.8}{4} = \frac{22.4}{4} = 5.60$$

Similarly, the third moving average calculation is $(6.0 + 6.5 + 5.8 + 5.2)/4 = 5.875$.

Before we proceed with the moving average calculations for the entire time series, we return to the first moving average calculation, which resulted in a value of 5.35. The 5.35 value represents an average quarterly sales volume (across all seasons) for year 1. As we look back at the calculation of the 5.35 value, associating 5.35 with the "middle" quarter of the moving average group makes sense. Note, however, that we encounter some difficulty in identifying the middle quarter; with four quarters in the moving average there is no middle quarter. The 5.35 value corresponds to the last half of quarter 2 and the first half of quarter 3. Similarly, if we go to the next moving average value of 5.60, the middle corresponds to the last half of quarter 3 and the first half of quarter 4.

Recall that the reason for computing moving averages is to isolate the combined seasonal and irregular components. However, the moving average values we computed do not correspond directly to the original quarters of the time series. We can resolve this difficulty by using the midpoints between successive moving average values. For example, if 5.35 corresponds to the first half of quarter 3 and 5.60 corresponds to the last half of quarter 3, we can use $(5.35 + 5.60)/2 = 5.475$ as the moving average value for quarter 3. Similarly, we associate a moving average value of $(5.60 + 5.875)/2 = 5.738$ with quarter 4. The result is a *centered moving average.* Table 18.8 shows a complete summary of the moving average calculations for the television set sales data.

If the number of data points in a moving average calculation is an odd number, the middle point will correspond to one of the periods in the time series. In such cases, we would not have to center the moving average values to correspond to a particular time period as we have done in the calculations in Table 18.8.

What do the centered moving averages in Table 18.8 tell us about this time series? Figure 18.12 is a plot of the actual time series values and the centered moving average values. Note particularly how the centered moving average values tend to "smooth out" both the seasonal and irregular fluctuations in the time series. The moving average values computed for four quarters of data do not include the fluctuations due to seasonal influences because the seasonal effect has been averaged out. Each point in the centered moving average represents the value of the time series as though there were no seasonal or irregular influence.

By dividing each time series observation by the corresponding centered moving average, we can identify the seasonal irregular effect in the time series. For example, the third quarter of year 1 shows $6.0/5.475 = 1.096$ as the combined seasonal irregular value. Table 18.9 summarizes the seasonal irregular values for the entire time series.

Consider the third quarter. The results from years 1, 2, and 3 show third-quarter values of 1.096, 1.075, and 1.109, respectively. Thus, in all cases, the seasonal irregular value appears to have an above-average influence in the third quarter. With the year-to-year fluctuations in the seasonal irregular value attributable primarily to the irregular component, we can average the computed values to eliminate the irregular influence and obtain an estimate of the third-quarter seasonal influence.

$$\text{Seasonal effect of third quarter} = \frac{1.096 + 1.075 + 1.109}{3} = 1.09$$

We refer to 1.09 as the *seasonal index* for the third quarter. In Table 18.10 we summarize the calculations involved in computing the seasonal indexes for the television set sales time

TABLE 18.8 CENTERED MOVING AVERAGE CALCULATIONS FOR THE TELEVISION SET SALES TIME SERIES

Year	Quarter	Sales (1000s)	Four-Quarter Moving Average	Centered Moving Average
1	1	4.8		
	2	4.1		
			5.350	
	3	6.0		5.475
			5.600	
	4	6.5		5.738
			5.875	
2	1	5.8		5.975
			6.075	
	2	5.2		6.188
			6.300	
	3	6.8		6.325
			6.350	
	4	7.4		6.400
			6.450	
3	1	6.0		6.538
			6.625	
	2	5.6		6.675
			6.725	
	3	7.5		6.763
			6.800	
	4	7.8		6.838
			6.875	
4	1	6.3		6.938
			7.000	
	2	5.9		7.075
			7.150	
	3	8.0		
	4	8.4		

series. Thus, the seasonal indexes for the four quarters are: quarter 1, .93; quarter 2, .84; quarter 3, 1.09; and quarter 4, 1.14.

Interpretation of the values in Table 18.10 provides some observations about the seasonal component in television set sales. The best sales quarter is the fourth quarter, with sales averaging 14% above the average quarterly value. The worst, or slowest, sales quarter is the second quarter; its seasonal index of .84 shows that the sales average is 16% below the average quarterly sales. The seasonal component corresponds clearly to the intuitive expectation that television viewing interest and thus television purchase patterns tend to peak in the fourth quarter because of the coming winter season and reduction in outdoor activities. The low second-quarter sales reflect the reduced interest in television viewing due to the spring and presummer activities of potential customers.

One final adjustment is sometimes necessary in obtaining the seasonal indexes. The multiplicative model requires that the average seasonal index equal 1.00, so the sum of the four seasonal indexes in Table 18.10 must equal 4.00. In other words the seasonal effects must even out over the year. The average of the seasonal indexes in our example is equal to

FIGURE 18.12 QUARTERLY TELEVISION SET SALES TIME SERIES AND CENTERED MOVING AVERAGE

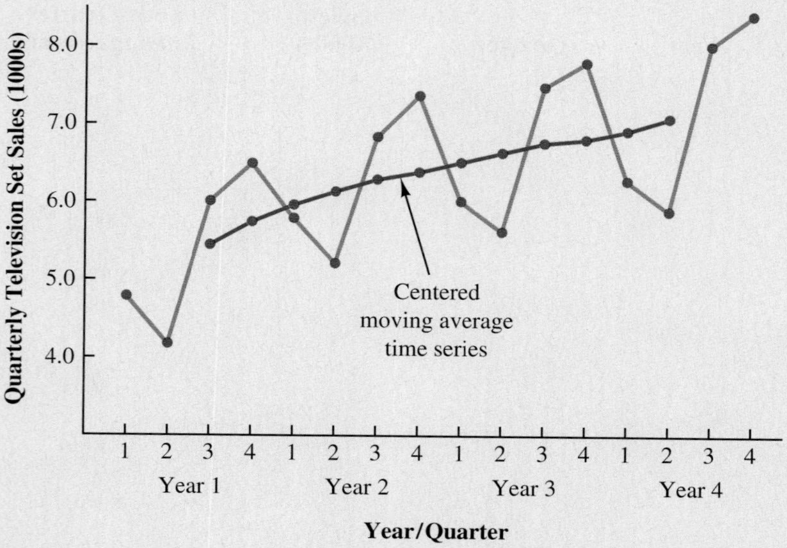

TABLE 18.9 SEASONAL IRREGULAR VALUES FOR THE TELEVISION SET SALES TIME SERIES

Year	Quarter	Sales (1000s)	Centered Moving Average	Seasonal Irregular Value
1	1	4.8		
	2	4.1		
	3	6.0	5.475	1.096
	4	6.5	5.738	1.133
2	1	5.8	5.975	.971
	2	5.2	6.188	.840
	3	6.8	6.325	1.075
	4	7.4	6.400	1.156
3	1	6.0	6.538	.918
	2	5.6	6.675	.839
	3	7.5	6.763	1.109
	4	7.8	6.838	1.141
4	1	6.3	6.938	.908
	2	5.9	7.075	.834
	3	8.0		
	4	8.4		

TABLE 18.10 SEASONAL INDEX CALCULATIONS FOR THE TELEVISION SET SALES TIME SERIES

Quarter	Seasonal Irregular Component Values (S_tI_t)	Seasonal Index (S_t)
1	.971, .918, .908	.93
2	.840, .839, .834	.84
3	1.096, 1.075, 1.109	1.09
4	1.133, 1.156, 1.141	1.14

1.00, and hence this type of adjustment is not necessary. In other cases, a slight adjustment may be necessary. To make the adjustment, multiply each seasonal index by the number of seasons divided by the sum of the unadjusted seasonal indexes. For instance, for quarterly data multiply each seasonal index by 4/(sum of the unadjusted seasonal indexes). Some of the exercises will require this adjustment to obtain the appropriate seasonal indexes.

Deseasonalizing the Time Series

With deseasonalized data, comparing sales in successive periods makes sense. With data that have not been deseasonalized, relevant comparisons can often be made between sales in the current period and sales in the same period one year ago.

The purpose of finding seasonal indexes is to remove the seasonal effects from a time series. This process is referred to as *deseasonalizing* the time series. Economic time series adjusted for seasonal variations (**deseasonalized time series**) are often reported in publications such as the *Survey of Current Business, The Wall Street Journal,* and *BusinessWeek.* Using the notation of the multiplicative model, we have

$$Y_t = T_t \times S_t \times I_t$$

By dividing each time series observation by the corresponding seasonal index, we remove the effect of season from the time series. The deseasonalized time series for television set sales is summarized in Table 18.11. A graph of the deseasonalized television set sales time series is shown in Figure 18.13.

Using the Deseasonalized Time Series to Identify Trend

Although the graph in Figure 18.13 shows some random up and down movement over the past 16 quarters, the time series seems to have an upward linear trend. To identify this trend, we will use the same procedure as in the preceding section; in this case, the data are quarterly deseasonalized sales values. Thus, for a linear trend, the estimated sales volume expressed as a function of time is

$$T_t = b_0 + b_1 t$$

where

T_t = trend value for television set sales in period t
b_0 = intercept of the trend line
b_1 = slope of the trend line

As before, $t = 1$ corresponds to the time of the first observation for the time series, $t = 2$ corresponds to the time of the second observation, and so on. Thus, for the deseasonalized

TABLE 18.11 DESEASONALIZED VALUES FOR THE TELEVISION SET SALES TIME SERIES

Year	Quarter	Sales (1000s) (Y_t)	Seasonal Index (S_t)	Deseasonalized Sales ($Y_t/S_t = T_tI_t$)
1	1	4.8	.93	5.16
	2	4.1	.84	4.88
	3	6.0	1.09	5.50
	4	6.5	1.14	5.70
2	1	5.8	.93	6.24
	2	5.2	.84	6.19
	3	6.8	1.09	6.24
	4	7.4	1.14	6.49
3	1	6.0	.93	6.45
	2	5.6	.84	6.67
	3	7.5	1.09	6.88
	4	7.8	1.14	6.84
4	1	6.3	.93	6.77
	2	5.9	.84	7.02
	3	8.0	1.09	7.34
	4	8.4	1.14	7.37

television set sales time series, $t = 1$ corresponds to the first deseasonalized quarterly sales value and $t = 16$ corresponds to the most recent deseasonalized quarterly sales value. The formulas for computing the value of b_0 and the value of b_1 follow.

$$b_1 = \frac{\Sigma tY_t - (\Sigma t \Sigma Y_t)/n}{\Sigma t^2 - (\Sigma t)^2/n}$$

$$b_0 = \bar{Y} - b_1\bar{t}$$

FIGURE 18.13 DESEASONALIZED TELEVISION SET SALES TIME SERIES

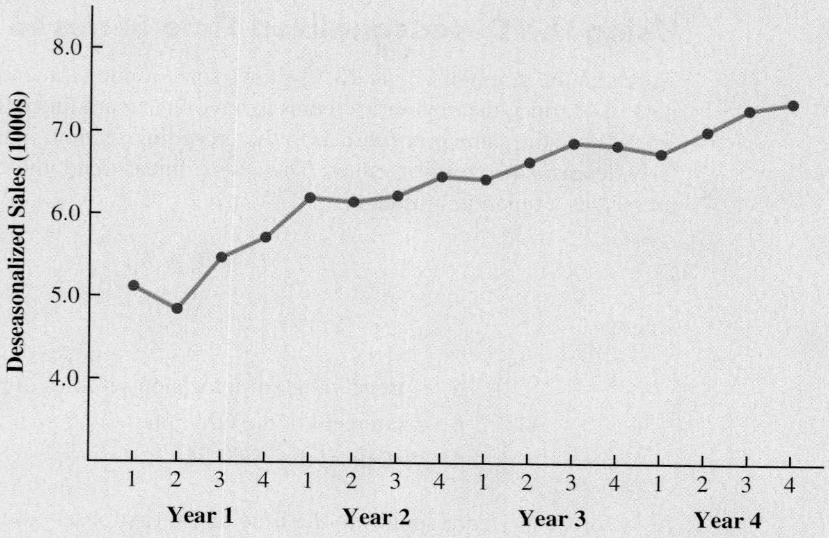

Note, however, that Y_t now refers to the deseasonalized time series value at time t and not to the actual value of the time series. Using the given relationships for b_0 and b_1 and the deseasonalized sales data of Table 18.11, we have the following calculations.

	t	Y_t (Deseasonalized)	tY_t	t^2
	1	5.16	5.16	1
	2	4.88	9.76	4
	3	5.50	16.50	9
	4	5.70	22.80	16
	5	6.24	31.20	25
	6	6.19	37.14	36
	7	6.24	43.68	49
	8	6.49	51.92	64
	9	6.45	58.05	81
	10	6.67	66.70	100
	11	6.88	75.68	121
	12	6.84	82.08	144
	13	6.77	88.01	169
	14	7.02	98.28	196
	15	7.34	110.10	225
	16	7.37	117.92	256
Totals	136	101.74	914.98	1496

where

$$\bar{t} = \frac{136}{16} = 8.5$$

$$\bar{Y} = \frac{101.74}{16} = 6.359$$

$$b_1 = \frac{914.98 - (136)(101.74)/16}{1496 - (136)^2/16} = 0.148$$

$$b_0 = 6.359 - 0.148(8.5) = 5.101$$

Therefore,

$$T_t = 5.101 + 0.148t$$

is the expression for the linear trend component of the deseasonalized time series.

The slope of 0.148 indicates that over the past 16 quarters, the firm averaged deseasonalized growth in sales of about 148 sets per quarter. If we assume that the past 16-quarter trend in sales data is a reasonably good indicator of the future, this equation can be used to project the trend component of the deseasonalized time series for future quarters. For example, substituting $t = 17$ into the equation yields next quarter's deseasonalized trend projection, T_{17}.

$$T_{17} = 5.101 + 0.148(17) = 7.617$$

TABLE 18.12 QUARTERLY FORECASTS FOR THE TELEVISION SET SALES TIME SERIES

Year	Quarter	Deseasonalized Trend Forecast	Seasonal Index (see Table 18.11)	Quarterly Forecast
5	1	7617	.93	(7617)(.93) = 7084
	2	7765	.84	(7765)(.84) = 6523
	3	7913	1.09	(7913)(1.09) = 8625
	4	8061	1.14	(8061)(1.14) = 9190

Thus, the trend component yields a deseasonalized sales forecast of 7617 television sets for the next quarter. Similarly, the trend component produces deseasonalized sales forecasts of 7765, 7913, and 8061 television sets in quarters 18, 19, and 20, respectively.

Seasonal Adjustments

The final step in developing the forecast when both trend and seasonal components are present is to use the seasonal index to adjust the deseasonalized trend projection. Returning to the television set sales example, we have a deseasonalized trend projection for the next four quarters. Now we must adjust the forecast for the seasonal effect. The seasonal index for the first quarter of year 5 ($t = 17$) is 0.93, so we obtain the quarterly forecast by multiplying the deseasonalized forecast based on trend ($T_{17} = 7617$) by the seasonal index (0.93). Thus, the forecast for the next quarter is 7617(0.93) = 7084. Table 18.12 gives the quarterly forecast for quarters 17 through 20. The high-volume fourth quarter has a 9190-unit forecast, and the low-volume second quarter has a 6523-unit forecast.

Models Based on Monthly Data

In the preceding television set sales example, we used quarterly data to illustrate the computation of seasonal indexes. However, many businesses use monthly rather than quarterly forecasts. In such cases, the procedures introduced in this section can be applied with minor modifications. First, a 12-month moving average replaces the four-quarter moving average; second, 12 monthly seasonal indexes, rather than four quarterly seasonal indexes, must be computed. Other than these changes, the computational and forecasting procedures are identical.

Cyclical Component

Mathematically, the multiplicative model of equation (18.9) can be expanded to include a cyclical component.

$$Y_t = T_t \times C_t \times S_t \times I_t \tag{18.10}$$

The cyclical component, like the seasonal component, is expressed as a percentage of trend. As mentioned in Section 18.1, this component is attributable to multiyear cycles in the time series. It is analogous to the seasonal component, but over a longer period of time. However, because of the length of time involved, obtaining enough relevant data to estimate the cyclical component is often difficult. Another difficulty is that cycles usually vary in length. We leave further discussion of the cyclical component to texts on forecasting methods.

Exercises

Methods

SELF test

22. Consider the following time series data.

Quarter	Year 1	Year 2	Year 3
1	4	6	7
2	2	3	6
3	3	5	6
4	5	7	8

a. Show the four-quarter and centered moving average values for this time series.
b. Compute seasonal indexes for the four quarters.

Applications

23. The quarterly sales data (number of copies sold) for a college textbook over the past three years follow.

Quarter	Year 1	Year 2	Year 3
1	1690	1800	1850
2	940	900	1100
3	2625	2900	2930
4	2500	2360	2615

a. Show the four-quarter and centered moving average values for this time series.
b. Compute seasonal indexes for the four quarters.
c. When does the textbook publisher have the largest seasonal index? Does this result appear reasonable? Explain.

24. Identify the monthly seasonal indexes for the three years of expenses for a six-unit apartment house in southern Florida as given here. Use a 12-month moving average calculation.

CD file

AptExp

	Expenses		
	Year 1	Year 2	Year 3
January	170	180	195
February	180	205	210
March	205	215	230
April	230	245	280
May	240	265	290
June	315	330	390
July	360	400	420
August	290	335	330
September	240	260	290
October	240	270	295
November	230	255	280
December	195	220	250

25. Air pollution control specialists in southern California monitor the amount of ozone, carbon dioxide, and nitrogen dioxide in the air on an hourly basis. The hourly time series data exhibit seasonality, with the levels of pollutants showing patterns over the hours in the day. On July 15, 16, and 17, the following levels of nitrogen dioxide were observed in the downtown area for the 12 hours from 6:00 A.M. to 6:00 P.M.

CD file
Pollution

July 15:	25	28	35	50	60	60	40	35	30	25	25	20
July 16:	28	30	35	48	60	65	50	40	35	25	20	20
July 17:	35	42	45	70	72	75	60	45	40	25	25	25

a. Identify the hourly seasonal indexes for the 12 readings each day.
b. With the seasonal indexes from part (a), the data were deseasonalized; the trend equation developed for the deseasonalized data was $T_t = 32.983 + .3922t$. Using the trend component only, develop forecasts for the 12 hours for July 18.
c. Use the seasonal indexes from part (a) to adjust the trend forecasts developed in part (b).

26. Electric power consumption is measured in kilowatt-hours (kWh). The local utility company offers an interrupt program whereby commercial customers that participate receive favorable rates but must agree to cut back consumption if the utility requests them to do so. Timko Products cut back consumption at 12:00 noon Thursday. To assess the savings, the utility must estimate Timko's usage without the interrupt. The period of interrupted service was from noon to 8:00 P.M. Data on electric power consumption for the previous 72 hours are available.

CD file
Power

Time Period	Monday	Tuesday	Wednesday	Thursday
12–4 A.M.	—	19,281	31,209	27,330
4–8 A.M.	—	33,195	37,014	32,715
8–12 noon	—	99,516	119,968	152,465
12–4 P.M.	124,299	123,666	156,033	
4–8 P.M.	113,545	111,717	128,889	
8–12 midnight	41,300	48,112	73,923	

a. Is there a seasonal effect over the 24-hour period? Compute seasonal indexes for the six 4-hour periods.
b. Use trend adjusted for seasonal indexes to estimate Timko's normal usage over the period of interrupted service.

18.5 Regression Analysis

In the discussion of regression analysis in Chapters 14, 15, and 16, we showed how one or more independent variables could be used to predict the value of a single dependent variable. Looking at regression analysis as a forecasting tool, we can view the time series value that we want to forecast as the dependent variable. Hence, if we can identify a good set of related independent, or predictor, variables we may be able to develop an estimated regression equation for predicting or forecasting the time series.

The approach we used in Section 18.3 to fit a linear trend line to the bicycle sales time series is a special case of regression analysis. In that example, two variables—bicycle sales and time—were shown to be linearly related.* The inherent complexity of most real-world problems necessitates the consideration of more than one variable to predict the variable of

*In a purely technical sense, the number of bicycles sold is not viewed as being related to time; instead, time is used as a surrogate for variables to which the number of bicycles sold is actually related but which are either unknown or too difficult or too costly to measure.

interest. The statistical technique known as multiple regression analysis can be used in such situations.

Recall that to develop an estimated multiple regression equation, we need a sample of observations for the dependent variable and all independent variables. In time series analysis the n periods of time series data provide a sample of n observations on each variable that can be used in the analysis. For a function involving k independent variables, we use the following notation.

$$Y_t = \text{value of the time series in period } t$$
$$x_{1t} = \text{value of independent variable 1 in period } t$$
$$x_{2t} = \text{value of independent variable 2 in period } t$$
$$\vdots$$
$$x_{kt} = \text{value of independent variable } k \text{ in period } t$$

The n periods of data necessary to develop the estimated regression equation would appear as shown in the following table.

Period	Time Series (Y_t)	Value of Independent Variables						
		x_{1t}	x_{2t}	x_{3t}	.	.	.	x_{kt}
1	Y_1	x_{11}	x_{21}	x_{31}	.	.	.	x_{k1}
2	Y_2	x_{12}	x_{22}	x_{32}	.	.	.	x_{k2}
.	.	.	.	.	.	.	.	.
.	.	.	.	.	.	.	.	.
.	.	.	.	.	.	.	.	.
n	Y_n	x_{1n}	x_{2n}	x_{3n}	.	.	.	x_{kn}

As you might imagine, several choices are possible for the independent variables in a forecasting model. One possible choice for an independent variable is simply time. It was the choice made in Section 18.3 when we estimated the trend of the time series using a linear function of the independent variable time. Letting $x_{1t} = t$, we obtain an estimated regression equation of the form

$$\hat{Y}_t = b_0 + b_1 t$$

where $\hat{Y}_t$ is the estimate of the time series value Y_t and where b_0 and b_1 are the estimated regression coefficients. In a more complex model, additional terms could be added corresponding to time raised to other powers. For example, if $x_{2t} = t^2$ and $x_{3t} = t^3$, the estimated regression equation would become

$$\begin{aligned}\hat{Y}_t &= b_0 + b_1 x_{1t} + b_2 x_{2t} + b_3 x_{3t} \\ &= b_0 + b_1 t + b_2 t^2 + b_3 t^3\end{aligned}$$

Note that this model provides a forecast of a time series with curvilinear characteristics over time.

Other regression-based forecasting models have a mixture of economic and demographic independent variables. For example, in forecasting sales of refrigerators, we might select the following independent variables.

x_{1t} = price in period t
x_{2t} = total industry sales in period $t - 1$
x_{3t} = number of building permits for new houses in period $t - 1$
x_{4t} = population forecast for period t
x_{5t} = advertising budget for period t

According to the usual multiple regression procedure, an estimated regression equation with five independent variables would be used to develop forecasts.

Spyros Makridakis, a noted forecasting expert, conducted research showing that simple techniques usually outperform more complex procedures for short-term forecasting. Using a more sophisticated and expensive procedure will not guarantee better forecasts.

Whether a regression approach provides a good forecast depends largely on how well we are able to identify and obtain data for independent variables that are closely related to the time series. Generally, during the development of an estimated regression equation, we will want to consider many possible sets of independent variables. Thus, part of the regression analysis procedure should be the selection of the set of independent variables that provides the best forecasting model.

In the chapter introduction we stated that **causal forecasting models** use other time series related to the one being forecast in an effort to explain the cause of a time series' behavior. Regression analysis is the tool most often used in developing such causal models. The related time series become the independent variables, and the time series being forecast is the dependent variable.

In another type of regression-based forecasting model, the independent variables are all previous values of the same time series. For example, if the time series values are denoted $Y_1, Y_2, \ldots, Y_n$, then with a dependent variable Y_t, we might try to find an estimated regression equation relating Y_t to the most recent times series values Y_{t-1}, Y_{t-2}, and so on. With the three most recent periods as independent variables, the estimated regression equation would be

$$\hat{Y}_t = b_0 + b_1 Y_{t-1} + b_2 Y_{t-2} + b_3 Y_{t-3}$$

Regression models in which the independent variables are previous values of the time series are referred to as **autoregressive models**.

Finally, another regression-based forecasting approach incorporates a mixture of the independent variables previously discussed. For example, we might select a combination of time variables, some economic/demographic variables, and some previous values of the time series variable itself.

18.6 Qualitative Approaches

If historical data are not available, managers must use a qualitative technique to develop forecasts. But the cost of using qualitative techniques can be high because of the time commitment required from the people involved.

In the preceding sections we discussed several types of quantitative forecasting methods. Most of those techniques require historical data on the variable of interest, so they cannot be applied when historical data are not available. Furthermore, even when such data are available, a significant change in environmental conditions affecting the time series may make the use of past data questionable in predicting future values of the time series. For example, a government-imposed gasoline rationing program would raise questions about the validity of a gasoline sales forecast based on historical data. Qualitative forecasting techniques afford an alternative in these and other cases.

Delphi Method

One of the most commonly used qualitative forecasting techniques is the **Delphi method**, originally developed by a research group at the Rand Corporation. It is an attempt to develop forecasts through "group consensus." In its usual application, the members of a panel of experts—all of whom are physically separated from and unknown to each other—are asked to respond to a series of questionnaires. The responses from the first questionnaire are tabulated and used to prepare a second questionnaire that contains information and opinions of the entire group. Each respondent is then asked to reconsider and possibly revise his or her previous response in light of the group information provided. This process continues until the coordinator feels that some degree of consensus has been reached. The goal of the Delphi method is not to produce a single answer as output, but instead to produce a relatively narrow spread of opinions within which the majority of experts concur.

Expert Judgment

Empirical evidence and theoretical arguments suggest that between 5 and 20 experts should be used in judgmental forecasting. However, in situations involving exponential growth, judgmental forecasts may be inappropriate.

Qualitative forecasts often are based on the judgment of a single expert or represent the consensus of a group of experts. For example, each year a group of experts at Merrill Lynch gather to forecast the level of the Dow Jones Industrial Average and the prime rate for the next year. In doing so, the experts individually consider information that they believe will influence the stock market and interest rates; then they combine their conclusions into a forecast. No formal model is used, and no two experts are likely to consider the same information in the same way.

Expert judgment is a forecasting method that is commonly recommended when conditions in the past are not likely to hold in the future. Even though no formal quantitative model is used, expert judgment has provided good forecasts in many situations.

Scenario Writing

The qualitative procedure known as **scenario writing** consists of developing a conceptual scenario of the future based on a well-defined set of assumptions. Different sets of assumptions lead to different scenarios. The job of the decision maker is to decide how likely each scenario is and then to make decisions accordingly.

Intuitive Approaches

Subjective or *intuitive qualitative* approaches are based on the ability of the human mind to process a variety of information that, in most cases, is difficult to quantify. These techniques are often used in group work, wherein a committee or panel seeks to develop new ideas or solve complex problems through a series of "brainstorming sessions." In such sessions, individuals are freed from the usual group restrictions of peer pressure and criticism because they can present any idea or opinion without regard to its relevancy and, even more important, without fear of criticism.

Summary

This chapter provided an introduction to the basic methods of time series analysis and forecasting. First, we showed that to explain the behavior of a time series, it is often helpful to think of the time series as consisting of four separate components: trend, cyclical, seasonal, and irregular. By isolating these components and measuring their apparent effect, one can forecast future values of the time series.

We discussed how smoothing methods can be used to forecast a time series that exhibits no significant trend, seasonal, or cyclical effect. The moving averages approach consists of computing an average of past data values and then using that average as the forecast for the next period. In the exponential smoothing method, a weighted average of past time series values is used to compute a forecast.

For time series that have only a long-term trend, we showed how regression analysis could be used to make trend projections. For time series in which both trend and seasonal influences are significant, we showed how to isolate the effects of the two factors and prepare better forecasts. Finally, regression analysis was described as a procedure for developing causal forecasting models. A causal forecasting model is one that relates the time series value (dependent variable) to other independent variables that are believed to explain (cause) the time series behavior.

Qualitative forecasting methods were discussed as approaches that could be used when little or no historical data are available. These methods are also considered most appropriate when the past pattern of the time series is not expected to continue into the future.

Glossary

Time series A set of observations on a variable measured at successive points in time or over successive periods of time.

Forecast A prediction of future values of a time series.

Trend The long-run shift or movement in the time series observable over several periods of time.

Cyclical component The component of the time series that results in periodic above-trend and below-trend behavior of the time series lasting more than one year.

Seasonal component The component of the time series that shows a periodic pattern over one year or less.

Irregular component The component of the time series that reflects the random variation of the time series values beyond what can be explained by the trend, cyclical, and seasonal components.

Moving averages A method of forecasting or smoothing a time series that uses the average of the most recent n data values in the time series as the forecast for the next period.

Mean squared error (MSE) A measure of the accuracy of a forecasting method. This measure is the average of the sum of the squared differences between the forecast values and the actual time series values.

Weighted moving averages A method of forecasting or smoothing a time series by computing a weighted average of past data values. The sum of the weights must equal one.

Exponential smoothing A forecasting technique that uses a weighted average of past time series values as the forecast.

Smoothing constant A parameter of the exponential smoothing model that provides the weight given to the most recent time series value in the calculation of the forecast value.

Multiplicative time series model A model whereby the separate components of the time series are multiplied together to identify the actual time series value. When the four components of trend, cyclical, seasonal, and irregular are assumed present, we obtain $Y_t = T_t \times C_t \times S_t \times I_t$. When the cyclical component is not modeled, we obtain $Y_t = T_t \times S_t \times I_t$.

Deseasonalized time series A time series from which the effect of season has been removed by dividing each original time series observation by the corresponding seasonal index.

Causal forecasting methods Forecasting methods that relate a time series to other variables that are believed to explain or cause its behavior.

Autoregressive model A time series model whereby a regression relationship based on past time series values is used to predict the future time series values.

Delphi method A qualitative forecasting method that obtains forecasts through group consensus.

Scenario writing A qualitative forecasting method that consists of developing a conceptual scenario of the future based on a well-defined set of assumptions.

Key Formulas

Moving Average

$$\text{Moving average} = \frac{\Sigma(\text{most recent } n \text{ data values})}{n} \quad \textbf{(18.1)}$$

Exponential Smoothing Model

$$F_{t+1} = \alpha Y_t + (1 - \alpha)F_t \quad \textbf{(18.2)}$$

Equation for Linear Trend

$$T_t = b_0 + b_1 t \quad \textbf{(18.5)}$$

Multiplicative Time Series Model with Trend, Seasonal, and Irregular Components

$$Y_t = T_t \times S_t \times I_t \quad \textbf{(18.9)}$$

Multiplicative Time Series Model with Trend, Cyclical, Seasonal, and Irregular Components

$$Y_t = T_t \times C_t \times S_t \times I_t \quad \textbf{(18.10)}$$

Supplementary Exercises

27. Moving averages often are used to identify movements in stock prices. Daily closing prices (in dollars per share) for IBM for August 24, 2005, through September 16, 2005, follow (*Compustat,* February 26, 2006).

CD file
IBM

Day	Price($)	Day	Price($)
August 24	81.32	September 7	80.98
August 25	81.10	September 8	80.80
August 26	80.38	September 9	81.44
August 29	81.34	September 12	81.48
August 30	80.54	September 13	80.75
August 31	80.62	September 14	80.48
September 1	79.54	September 15	80.01
September 2	79.46	September 16	80.33
September 6	81.02		

a. Use a three-day moving average to smooth the time series. Forecast the closing price for September 19, 2005 (next trading day).
b. Use exponential smoothing with a smoothing constant of $\alpha = .6$ to smooth the time series. Forecast the closing price for September 19, 2005 (next trading day).
c. Which of the two methods do you prefer? Why?

28. In 2005, Xerox Corporation's revenue from color products and services was \$4.6 billion, or 30% of Xerox's total revenue. The following data show the quarterly percentage change in revenue for 12 quarters (*Democrat and Chronicle,* March 5, 2006).

Year	Quarter	%Growth
2003	1	15
	2	19
	3	15
	4	20
2004	1	26
	2	17
	3	18
	4	21
2005	1	15
	2	17
	3	22
	4	17

a. Use exponential smoothing to forecast this time series. Consider smoothing constants of $\alpha = .1$, $\alpha = .2$, and $\alpha = .3$. What value of the smoothing constant provides the best forecast?

b. What is the forecast of the percentage change for the first quarter of 2006?

29. The following table reports the percentage of stocks in a typical portfolio in nine quarters from 2005 to 2007.

Quarter	Stock %
1st—2005	29.8
2nd—2005	31.0
3rd—2005	29.9
4th—2005	30.1
1st—2006	32.2
2nd—2006	31.5
3rd—2006	32.0
4th—2006	31.9
1st—2007	30.0

a. Use exponential smoothing to forecast this time series. Consider smoothing constants of $\alpha = .2$, .3, and .4. What value of the smoothing constant provides the best forecast?

b. What is the forecast of the percentage of stocks in a typical portfolio for the second quarter of 2007?

30. A chain of grocery stores noted the weekly demand (in cases) reported in the following table for a particular brand of automatic dishwasher detergent. Use exponential smoothing with $\alpha = .2$ to develop a forecast for week 11.

Week	Demand	Week	Demand
1	22	6	24
2	18	7	20
3	23	8	19
4	21	9	18
5	17	10	21

31. United Dairies, Inc., supplies milk to several independent grocers throughout Dade County, Florida. Managers at United Dairies want to develop a forecast of the number of half-gallons of milk sold per week. Sales data for the past 12 weeks follow.

Week	Sales	Week	Sales
1	2750	7	3300
2	3100	8	3100
3	3250	9	2950
4	2800	10	3000
5	2900	11	3200
6	3050	12	3150

Use exponential smoothing with $\alpha = .4$ to develop a forecast of demand for week 13.

32. The Garden Avenue Seven sells CDs of its musical performances. The following table reports sales (in units) for the past 18 months. The group's manager wants an accurate method for forecasting future sales.

CD file

CDSales

Month	Sales	Month	Sales	Month	Sales
1	293	7	381	13	549
2	283	8	431	14	544
3	322	9	424	15	601
4	355	10	433	16	587
5	346	11	470	17	644
6	379	12	481	18	660

a. Use exponential smoothing with $\alpha = .3$, .4, and .5. Which value of α provides the best forecasts?
b. Use trend projection to provide a forecast. What is the value of MSE?
c. Which method of forecasting would you recommend to the manager? Why?

33. The Mayfair Department Store in Davenport, Iowa, is trying to determine the amount of sales lost while it was shut down during July and August because of damage caused by the Mississippi River flood. Sales data for January through June follow.

Month	Sales ($1000s)	Month	Sales ($1000s)
January	185.72	April	210.36
February	167.84	May	255.57
March	205.11	June	261.19

a. Use exponential smoothing, with $\alpha = .4$, to develop a forecast for July and August. (*Hint:* Use the forecast for July as the actual sales in July in developing the August forecast.) Comment on the use of exponential smoothing for forecasts more than one period into the future.
b. Use trend projection to forecast sales for July and August.
c. Mayfair's insurance company proposed a settlement based on lost sales of $240,000 in July and August. Is this amount fair? If not, what amount would you recommend as a counteroffer?

34. Canton Supplies, Inc., is a service firm that employs approximately 100 individuals. Managers of Canton Supplies are concerned about meeting monthly cash obligations and want to

develop a forecast of monthly cash requirements. Because of a recent change in operating policy, only the past seven months of data are considered to be relevant. With the following historical data, use trend projection to develop a forecast of cash requirements for each of the next two months.

Month	1	2	3	4	5	6	7
Cash Required ($1000s)	205	212	218	224	230	240	246

35. The following five years of data show the average minimum balance to avoid fees for checking accounts that pay interest (*USA Today,* December 6, 2005).

CD file
AcctBal

Date	Balance ($)
Spring 2000	1522.41
Fall 2000	1659.63
Spring 2001	1678.34
Fall 2001	1707.55
Spring 2002	1767.36
Fall 2002	1866.17
Spring 2003	2015.04
Fall 2003	2257.82
Spring 2004	2425.83
Fall 2004	2086.93
Spring 2005	2295.85
Fall 2005	2294.61

a. Graph this time series. Does a linear trend appear to be present?
b. Develop the equation for the linear trend component for the time series.
c. Use the trend equation to forecast the minimum average balance to avoid account fees for Spring 2006.

36. The Costello Music Company has been in business for five years. During that time, sales of pianos increased from 12 units in the first year to 76 units in the most recent year. Fred Costello, the firm's owner, wants to develop a forecast of piano sales for the coming year. The historical data follow.

Year	1	2	3	4	5
Sales	12	28	34	50	76

a. Show a graph of this time series. Does a linear trend appear to be present?
b. Develop the equation for the linear trend component for the time series. What is the average increase in sales that the firm has been realizing per year?

37. Hudson Marine has been an authorized dealer for C&D marine radios for the past seven years. The following table reports the number of radios sold each year.

Year	1	2	3	4	5	6	7
Number Sold	35	50	75	90	105	110	130

a. Show a graph of this time series. Does a linear trend appear to be present?
b. Develop the equation for the linear trend component of the time series.
c. Use the linear trend developed in part (b) to develop a forecast for annual sales in year 8.

38. The League of American Theatres and Producers, Inc., collects a variety of statistics for Broadway plays, such as the gross revenue, the length of play run, and the number of new

productions. The following data show the season attendance (in millions) for Broadway shows from 1990 to 2001 (*The World Almanac,* 2002).

Season	Attendance (millions)	Season	Attendance (millions)
1990–1991	7.3	1996–1997	10.6
1991–1992	7.4	1997–1998	11.5
1992–1993	7.9	1998–1999	11.7
1993–1994	8.1	1999–2000	11.4
1994–1995	9.0	2000–2001	11.9
1995–1996	9.5		

a. Plot the time series and comment on the appropriateness of a linear trend.
b. Develop the equation for the linear trend component for this time series.
c. What is the average increase in attendance per season?
d. Use the trend equation to forecast attendance for the 2001–2002 season.

39. Over the past 25 years the United States Golf Association (USGA) tested thousands of golf balls for conformance with the overall distance standard. The following table gives the number of golf balls tested by the USGA by year from 1992 to 2002 (*Golf Journal,* October 2002).

Year	Number	Year	Number
1992	465	1997	919
1993	602	1998	916
1994	646	1999	861
1995	755	2000	834
1996	807	2001	821

Plot the time series and comment on the appropriateness of a linear trend. What type of functional form do you believe would be most appropriate for the trend pattern of this time series?

40. Refer to the Hudson Marine problem in exercise 37. Suppose the quarterly sales values for the seven years of historical data are as follow.

Year	Quarter 1	Quarter 2	Quarter 3	Quarter 4	Total Yearly Sales
1	6	15	10	4	35
2	10	18	15	7	50
3	14	26	23	12	75
4	19	28	25	18	90
5	22	34	28	21	105
6	24	36	30	20	110
7	28	40	35	27	130

a. Show the four-quarter moving average values for this time series. Plot both the original time series and the moving average series on the same graph.
b. Compute the seasonal indexes for the four quarters.
c. When does Hudson Marine experience the largest seasonal effect? Does this result seem reasonable? Explain.

41. Consider the Costello Music Company problem in exercise 36. The quarterly sales data follow.

Year	Quarter 1	Quarter 2	Quarter 3	Quarter 4	Total Yearly Sales
1	4	2	1	5	12
2	6	4	4	14	28
3	10	3	5	16	34
4	12	9	7	22	50
5	18	10	13	35	76

a. Compute the seasonal indexes for the four quarters.
b. When does Costello Music experience the largest seasonal effect? Does this result appear reasonable? Explain.

42. Refer to the Hudson Marine data in exercise 40.
a. Deseasonalize the data and use the deseasonalized time series to identify the trend.
b. Use the results of part (a) to develop a quarterly forecast for next year based on trend.
c. Use the seasonal indexes developed in exercise 40 to adjust the forecasts developed in part (b) to account for the effect of season.

43. Consider the Costello Music Company time series in exercise 41.
a. Deseasonalize the data and use the deseasonalized time series to identify the trend.
b. Use the results of part (a) to develop a quarterly forecast for next year based on trend.
c. Use the seasonal indexes developed in exercise 41 to adjust the forecasts developed in part (b) to account for the effect of season.

Case Problem 1 Forecasting Food and Beverage Sales

The Vintage Restaurant, on Captiva Island near Fort Myers, Florida, is owned and operated by Karen Payne. The restaurant just completed its third year of operation. During that time, Karen sought to establish a reputation for the restaurant as a high-quality dining establishment that specializes in fresh seafood. Through the efforts of Karen and her staff, her restaurant has become one of the best and fastest-growing restaurants on the island.

Karen believes that to plan for the growth of the restaurant in the future, she needs to develop a system that will enable her to forecast food and beverage sales by month for up to one year in advance. Karen compiled the following data (in thousands of dollars) on total food and beverage sales for the three years of operation.

CD file
Vintage

Month	First Year	Second Year	Third Year
January	242	263	282
February	235	238	255
March	232	247	265
April	178	193	205
May	184	193	210
June	140	149	160
July	145	157	166
August	152	161	174
September	110	122	126
October	130	130	148
November	152	167	173
December	206	230	235

Managerial Report

Perform an analysis of the sales data for the Vintage Restaurant. Prepare a report for Karen that summarizes your findings, forecasts, and recommendations. Include the following:

1. A graph of the time series.
2. An analysis of the seasonality of the data. Indicate the seasonal indexes for each month, and comment on the high and low seasonal sales months. Do the seasonal indexes make intuitive sense? Discuss.
3. A forecast of sales for January through December of the fourth year.
4. Recommendations as to when the system that you develop should be updated to account for new sales data.
5. Any detailed calculations of your analysis in the appendix of your report.

Assume that January sales for the fourth year turn out to be $295,000. What was your forecast error? If this error is large, Karen may be puzzled about the difference between your forecast and the actual sales value. What can you do to resolve her uncertainty in the forecasting procedure?

Case Problem 2 Forecasting Lost Sales

The Carlson Department Store suffered heavy damage when a hurricane struck on August 31, 2006. The store was closed for four months (September 2006 through December 2006), and Carlson is now involved in a dispute with its insurance company about the amount of lost sales during the time the store was closed. Two key issues must be resolved: (1) the amount of sales Carlson would have made if the hurricane had not struck and (2) whether Carlson is entitled to any compensation for excess sales due to increased business activity after the storm. More than $8 billion in federal disaster relief and insurance money came into the county, resulting in increased sales at department stores and numerous other businesses.

Table 18.13 gives Carlson's sales data for the 48 months preceding the storm. Table 18.14 reports total sales for the 48 months preceding the storm for all department stores in the county, as well as the total sales in the county for the four months the Carlson Department Store was closed. Carlson's managers asked you to analyze these data and develop estimates of the lost sales at the Carlson Department Store for the months of September

TABLE 18.13 SALES FOR CARLSON DEPARTMENT STORE, SEPTEMBER 2002 THROUGH AUGUST 2006 ($ MILLIONS)

Month	2002	2003	2004	2005	2006
January		1.45	2.31	2.31	2.56
February		1.80	1.89	1.99	2.28
March		2.03	2.02	2.42	2.69
April		1.99	2.23	2.45	2.48
May		2.32	2.39	2.57	2.73
June		2.20	2.14	2.42	2.37
July		2.13	2.27	2.40	2.31
August		2.43	2.21	2.50	2.23
September	1.71	1.90	1.89	2.09	
October	1.90	2.13	2.29	2.54	
November	2.74	2.56	2.83	2.97	
December	4.20	4.16	4.04	4.35	

TABLE 18.14 DEPARTMENT STORE SALES FOR THE COUNTY, SEPTEMBER 2002 THROUGH DECEMBER 2006 ($ MILLIONS)

Month	2002	2003	2004	2005	2006
January		46.8	46.8	43.8	48.0
February		48.0	48.6	45.6	51.6
March		60.0	59.4	57.6	57.6
April		57.6	58.2	53.4	58.2
May		61.8	60.6	56.4	60.0
June		58.2	55.2	52.8	57.0
July		56.4	51.0	54.0	57.6
August		63.0	58.8	60.6	61.8
September	55.8	57.6	49.8	47.4	69.0
October	56.4	53.4	54.6	54.6	75.0
November	71.4	71.4	65.4	67.8	85.2
December	117.6	114.0	102.0	100.2	121.8

through December 2006. They also asked you to determine whether a case can be made for excess storm-related sales during the same period. If such a case can be made, Carlson is entitled to compensation for excess sales it would have earned in addition to ordinary sales.

Managerial Report

Prepare a report for the managers of the Carlson Department Store that summarizes your findings, forecasts, and recommendations. Include the following:

1. An estimate of sales had there been no hurricane.
2. An estimate of countywide department store sales had there been no hurricane.
3. An estimate of lost sales for the Carlson Department Store for September through December 2006.

In addition, use the countywide actual department stores sales for September through December 2006 and the estimate in part (2) to make a case for or against excess storm-related sales.

Appendix 18.1 Forecasting with Minitab

In this appendix we show how Minitab can be used to develop forecasts using three forecasting methods: moving averages, exponential smoothing, and trend projection.

Moving Averages

CD file
Gasoline

To show how Minitab can be used to develop forecasts using the moving averages method, we will develop a forecast for the gasoline sales time series in Table 18.1 and Figure 18.5. The sales data for the 12 weeks are entered into column 2 of the worksheet. The following steps can be used to produce a three-week moving average forecast for week 13.

Step 1. Select the **Stat** menu
Step 2. Choose **Time Series**
Step 3. Choose **Moving Average**

Step 4. When the Moving Average dialog box appears:
Enter C2 in the **Variable** box
Enter 3 in the **MA length** box
Select **Generate forecasts**
Enter 1 in the **Number of forecasts** box
Enter 12 in the **Starting from origin** box
Click **OK**

The three-week moving average forecast for week 13 is shown in the session window. The mean square error of 10.22 is labeled as MSD in the Minitab output. Many other output options are available, including a summary table similar to Table 18.2 and graphical output similar to Figure 18.6.

Exponential Smoothing

CD file
Gasoline

To show how Minitab can be used to develop an exponential smoothing forecast, we will again develop a forecast of sales in week 13 for the gasoline sales time series in Table 18.1 and Figure 18.5. The sales data for the 12 weeks are entered into column 2 of the worksheet. The following steps can be used to produce a forecast for week 13 using a smoothing constant of $\alpha = .2$.

Step 1. Select the **Stat** menu
Step 2. Choose **Time Series**
Step 3. Choose **Single Exp Smoothing**
Step 4. When the Single Exponential Smoothing dialog box appears:
Enter C2 in the **Variable** box
Select the **Use** option for the Weight to Use in Smoothing
Enter 0.2 in the Use box
Select **Generate forecasts**
Enter 1 in the **Number of forecasts** box
Enter 12 in the **Starting from origin** box
Select **Options**
Step 5. When the Single Exponential Smoothing—Options dialog box appears:
Enter 1 in the **Use average of first** box
Click **OK**
Step 6. When the Single Exponential Smoothing dialog box appears:
Click **OK**

The exponential smoothing forecast for week 13 is shown in the session window. The mean square error is labeled as MSD in the Minitab output.* Many other output options are available, including a summary table similar to Table 18.3 and graphical output similar to Figure 18.7.

Trend Projection

CD file
Bicycle

To show how Minitab can be used for trend projection, we develop a forecast for the bicycle sales time series in Table 18.6 and Figure 18.8. The year numbers are entered into column C1 and the sales data are entered into column C2 of the worksheet. The following steps can be used to produce a forecast for week 13 using trend projection.

*The value of MSD computed by Minitab is not the same as the value of MSE that appears in Table 18.4. Minitab uses a forecast of 17 for week 1 and computes MSD using all 12 time periods of data. In Section 18.2 we compute MSE using only the data for weeks 2 through 12, because we had no past values with which to make a forecast for period 1.

Step 1. Select the **Stat** menu
Step 2. Choose **Time Series**
Step 3. Choose **Trend Analysis**
Step 4. When the Trend Analysis dialog box appears:
Enter C2 in the **Variable** box
Choose **Linear** for the Model Type
Select **Generate forecasts**
Enter 1 in the **Number of forecasts** box
Enter 10 in the **Starting from origin** box
Click **OK**

The equation for linear trend and the forecast for the next period are shown in the session window.

Appendix 18.2 Forecasting with Excel

In this appendix we show how Excel can be used to develop forecasts using three forecasting methods: moving averages, exponential smoothing, and trend projection.

Moving Averages

CD file
Gasoline

To show how Excel can be used to develop forecasts using the moving averages method, we will develop a forecast for the gasoline sales time series in Table 18.1 and Figure 18.5. The sales data for the 12 weeks are entered into worksheet rows 2 through 13 of column B. The following steps can be used to produce a three-week moving average.

Step 1. Select the **Tools** menu
Step 2. Choose **Data Analysis**
Step 3. Choose **Moving Average** from the list of Analysis Tools
Click **OK**
Step 4. When the Moving Average dialog box appears:
Enter B2:B13 in the **Input Range** box
Enter 3 in the **Interval** box
Enter C2 in the **Output Range** box
Click **OK**

The three-week moving average forecasts will appear in column B of the worksheet. Forecasts for periods of other length can be computed easily by entering a different value in the **Interval** box.

Exponential Smoothing

CD file
Gasoline

To show how Excel can be used for exponential smoothing, we again develop a forecast for the gasoline sales time series in Table 18.1 and Figure 18.5. The sales data for the 12 weeks are entered into worksheet rows 2 through 13 of column B. The following steps can be used to produce a forecast using a smoothing constant of $\alpha = .2$.

Step 1. Select the **Tools** menu
Step 2. Choose **Data Analysis**
Step 3. Choose **Exponential Smoothing** from the list of Analysis Tools
Click **OK**
Step 4. When the Exponential Smoothing dialog box appears:
Enter B2:B13 in the **Input Range** box
Enter .8 in the **Damping factor** box
Enter C2 in the **Output Range** box
Click **OK**

The exponential smoothing forecasts will appear in column C of the worksheet. Note that the value we entered in the Damping factor box is $1 - \alpha$; forecasts for other smoothing constants can be computed easily by entering a different value for $1 - \alpha$ in the Damping factor box.

Trend Projection

CD file
Bicycle

To show how Excel can be used for trend projection, we develop a forecast for the bicycle sales time series in Table 18.6 and Figure 18.8. The data, with appropriate labels in row 1, are entered into worksheet rows 1 through 11 of columns A and B. The following steps can be used to produce a forecast for year 11 by trend projection.

Step 1. Select an empty cell in the worksheet
Step 2. Select the **Insert** menu
Step 3. Choose **Function**
Step 4. When the Insert Function dialog box appears:
Choose **Statistical** in the Or select a category box
Choose **Forecast** in the Select a function box
Click **OK**
Step 5. When the Forecast Arguments dialog box appears:
Enter 11 in the **x** box
Enter B2:B11 in the **Known y's** box
Enter A2:A11 in the **Known x's** box
Click **OK**

The forecast for year 11, in this case 32.5, will appear in the cell selected in step 1.

Statistical Methods for Quality Control

CONTENTS

STATISTICS *in* PRACTICE

DOW CHEMICAL COMPANY*
FREEPORT, TEXAS

In 1940 the Dow Chemical Company purchased 800 acres of Texas land on the Gulf Coast to build a magnesium production facility. That original site has expanded to cover more than 5000 acres and holds one of the largest petrochemical complexes in the world. Among the products from Dow Texas Operations are magnesium, styrene, plastics, adhesives, solvent, glycol, and chlorine. Some products are made solely for use in other processes, but many end up as essential ingredients in products such as pharmaceuticals, toothpastes, dog food, water hoses, ice chests, milk cartons, garbage bags, shampoos, and furniture.

Dow's Texas Operations produce more than 30% of the world's magnesium, an extremely lightweight metal used in products ranging from tennis racquets to suitcases to "mag" wheels. The Magnesium Department was the first group in Texas Operations to train its technical people and managers in the use of statistical quality control. Some of the earliest successful applications of statistical quality control were in chemical processing.

In one application involving the operation of a drier, samples of the output were taken at periodic intervals; the average value for each sample was computed and recorded on a chart called an $\bar{x}$ chart. Such a chart enabled Dow analysts to monitor trends in the output that might indicate the process was not operating correctly. In one instance, analysts began to observe values for the sample mean that were not indicative of a process operating within its design limits. On further examination of the control chart and the operation itself, the analysts found that the variation could be traced to problems involving one operator. The $\bar{x}$ chart recorded after retraining the operator showed a significant improvement in the process quality.

Statistical quality control has enabled Dow Chemical Company to improve its processing methods and output. © PR Newswire Dow Chemical USA.

Dow achieves quality improvements everywhere it applies statistical quality control. Documented savings of several hundred thousand dollars per year are realized, and new applications are continually being discovered.

In this chapter we will show how an $\bar{x}$ chart such as the one used by Dow can be developed. Such charts are a part of statistical quality control known as statistical process control. We will also discuss methods of quality control for situations in which a decision to accept or reject a group of items is based on a sample.

*The authors are indebted to Clifford B. Wilson, Magnesium Technical Manager, The Dow Chemical Company, for providing this Statistics in Practice.

The American Society for Quality (ASQ) defines quality as "the totality of features and characteristics of a product or service that bears on its ability to satisfy given needs." In other words, quality measures how well a product or service meets customer needs. Organizations recognize that to be competitive in today's global economy, they must strive for a high level of quality. As a result, they place increased emphasis on methods for monitoring and maintaining quality.

Today, the customer-driven focus that is fundamental to high-performing organizations has changed the scope that quality issues encompass, from simply eliminating defects on a production line to developing broad-based corporate quality strategies. Broadening the scope of quality naturally leads to the concept of **total quality (TQ)**.

> Total Quality (TQ) is a people-focused management system that aims at continual increase in customer satisfaction at continually lower real cost. TQ is a total system approach (not a

separate area or work program) and an integral part of high-level strategy; it works horizontally across function and departments, involves all employees, top to bottom, and extends backward and forward to include the supply chain and the customer chain. TQ stresses learning and adaptation to continual change as keys to organization success.*

Regardless of how it is implemented in different organizations, total quality is based on three fundamental principles: a focus on customers and stakeholders; participation and teamwork throughout the organization; and a focus on continuous improvement and learning. In the first section of the chapter we provide a brief introduction to three quality management frameworks: the Malcolm Baldrige Quality Award, ISO 9000 standards, and the Six Sigma philosophy. In the last two sections we introduce two statistical tools that can be used to monitor quality: statistical process control and acceptance sampling.

20.1 Philosophies and Frameworks

After World War II, Dr. W. Edwards Deming became a consultant to Japanese industry; he is credited with being the person who convinced top managers in Japan to use the methods of statistical quality control.

Two individuals who have had great influence on quality are Dr. W. Edwards Deming and Joseph Juran. These men helped educate the Japanese in quality management shortly after World War II. Although quality is everybody's job, Deming stressed that the focus on quality must be led by managers. He developed a list of 14 points that he believed represent the key responsibilities of managers. For instance, Deming stated that managers must cease dependence on mass inspection; must end the practice of awarding business solely on the basis of price; must seek continual improvement in all production processes and service; must foster a team-oriented environment; and must eliminate goals, slogans, and work standards that prescribe numerical quotas. Perhaps most important, managers must create a work environment in which a commitment to quality and productivity is maintained at all times.

Juran proposed a simple definition of quality: *fitness for use.* Juran's approach to quality focused on three quality processes: quality planning, quality control, and quality improvement. In contrast to Deming's philosophy, which required a major cultural change in the organization, Juran's programs were designed to improve quality by working within the current organizational system. Nonetheless, the two philosophies are similar in that they both focus on the need for top management to be involved and stress the need for continuous improvement, the importance of training, and the use of quality control techniques.

Many other individuals played significant roles in the quality movement, including Philip B. Crosby, A. V. Feigenbaum, Karou Ishikawa, and Genichi Taguchi. More specialized texts dealing exclusively with quality provide details of the contributions of each of these individuals. The contributions of all individuals involved in the quality movement helped define a set of best practices and led to numerous awards and certification programs. The two most significant programs are the U.S. Malcolm Baldrige National Quality Award and the international ISO 9000 certification process. In recent years, use of Six Sigma—a methodology for improving organizational performance based on rigorous data collection and statistical analysis—has also increased.

Malcolm Baldrige National Quality Award

The Malcolm Baldrige National Quality Award is given by the president of the United States to organizations that apply and are judged to be outstanding in seven areas: leadership; strategic planning; customer and market focus; measurement, analysis, and knowledge management; human resource focus; process management; and business results. Congress established the award program in 1987 to recognize U.S. organizations for their

*J. R. Evans and W. M. Lindsay, *The Management and Control of Quality*, 6th ed. (Cincinnati, OH: South-Western, 2005), pp. 18–19.

The U.S. Commerce Department's National Institute of Standards and Technology (NIST) manages the Baldrige National Quality Program. More information can be obtained at www.quality.nist.gov.

achievements in quality and performance and to raise awareness about the importance of quality as a competitive edge. The award is named for Malcolm Baldrige who served as Secretary of Commerce from 1981 until his death in 1987.

Since the presentation of the first awards in 1988, the Baldrige National Quality Program has grown in stature and impact. Approximately 2 million copies of the criteria have been distributed since 1988, and wide-scale reproduction by organizations and electronic access add to that number significantly. For the eighth year in a row, a hypothetical stock index, made up of publicly traded U.S. companies that have received the Baldrige Award, outperformed the Standard & Poor's 500. In 2003, the "Baldrige Index" outperformed the S&P 500 by 4.4 to 1. At the 2003 Baldrige Award Ceremony, Bob Barnett, executive vice president of Motorola, Inc., said, "We applied for the Award, not with the idea of winning, but with the goal of receiving the evaluation of the Baldrige Examiners. That evaluation was comprehensive, professional, and insightful . . . making it perhaps the most cost-effective, value-added business consultation available anywhere in the world today."

ISO 9000

ISO 9000 is a series of five international standards published in 1987 by the International Organization for Standardization (ISO), Geneva, Switzerland. Companies can use the standards to help determine what is needed to maintain an efficient quality conformance system. For example, the standards describe the need for an effective quality system, for ensuring that measuring and testing equipment is calibrated regularly, and for maintaining an adequate record-keeping system. ISO 9000 registration determines whether a company complies with its own quality system. Overall, ISO 9000 registration covers less than 10% of the Baldrige Award criteria.

Six Sigma

In the late 1980s Motorola recognized the need to improve the quality of its products and services; their goal was to achieve a level of quality so good that for every million opportunities no more than 3.4 defects will occur. This level of quality is referred to as the six sigma level of quality, and the methodology created to reach this quality goal is referred to as **Six Sigma**.

An organization may undertake two kinds of Six Sigma projects:

- DMAIC (Define, Measure, Analyze, Improve, and Control) to help redesign existing processes
- DFSS (Design for Six Sigma) to design new products, processes, or services

In helping to redesign existing processes and design new processes, Six Sigma places a heavy emphasis on statistical analysis and careful measurement. Today, Six Sigma is a major tool in helping organizations achieve Baldrige levels of business performance and process quality. Many Baldrige examiners view Six Sigma as the ideal approach for implementing Baldrige improvement programs.

Six Sigma Limits and Defects per Million Opportunities In Six Sigma terminology, a *defect* is any mistake or error that is passed on to the customer. The Six Sigma process defines quality performance as defects per million opportunities (dpmo). As we indicated previously, Six Sigma represents a quality level of at most 3.4 dpmo. To illustrate how this quality level is measured, let us consider the situation at KJW Packaging.

KJW operates a production line where boxes of cereal are filled. The filling process has a mean of $\mu = 16.05$ ounces and a standard deviation of $\sigma = .10$ ounces. In addition, assume the filling weights are normally distributed. The distribution of filling weights is shown in Figure 20.1. Suppose management considers 15.45 to 16.65 ounces to be acceptable quality

FIGURE 20.1 NORMAL DISTRIBUTION OF CEREAL BOX FILLING WEIGHTS WITH A PROCESS MEAN $\mu = 16.05$

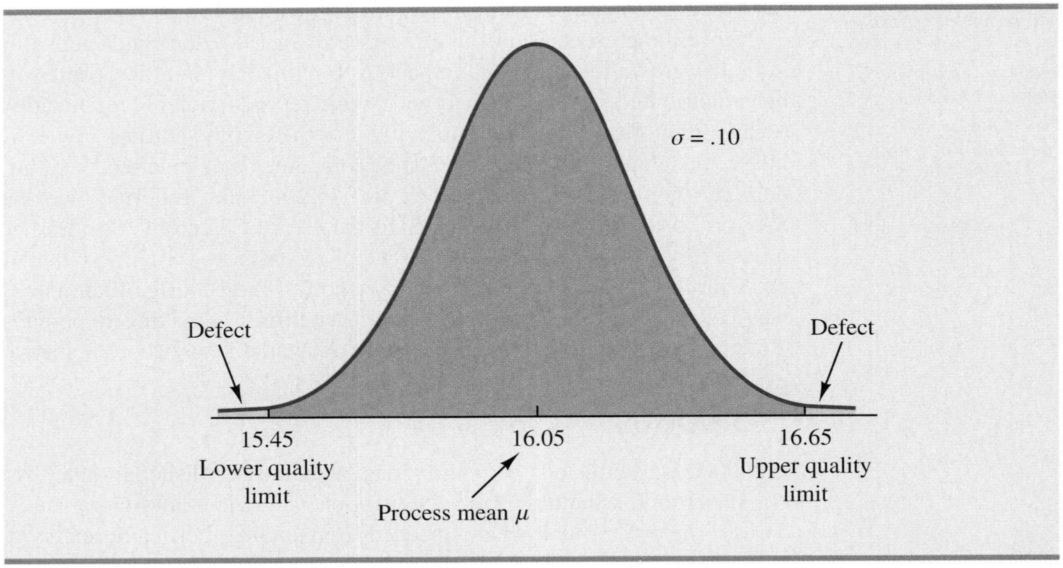

limits for the filling process. Thus, any box of cereal that contains less than 15.45 or more than 16.65 ounces is considered to be a defect. Using Excel or Minitab, it can be shown that 99.9999998% of the boxes filled will have between $16.05 - 6(.10) = 15.45$ ounces and $16.05 + 6(.10) = 16.65$ ounces. In other words, only .0000002% of the boxes filled will contain less than 15.45 ounces or more than 16.65 ounces. Thus, the likelihood of obtaining a defective box of cereal from the filling process appears to be extremely unlikely, because on average only two boxes in 10 million will be defective.

Motorola's early work on Six Sigma convinced them that a process mean can shift on average by as much as 1.5 standard deviations. For instance, suppose that the process mean for KJW increases by 1.5 standard deviations or $1.5(.10) = .15$ ounces. With such a shift, the normal distribution of filling weights would now be centered at $\mu = 16.05 + .15 = 16.20$ ounces. With a process mean of $\mu = 16.05$ ounces, the probability of obtaining a box of cereal with more than 16.65 ounces is extremely small. But how does this probability change if the mean of the process shifts up to $\mu = 16.20$ ounces? Figure 20.2 shows that for this case, the upper quality limit of 16.65 is 4.5 standard deviations to the right of the new mean $\mu = 16.20$ ounces. Using this mean and Excel or Minitab, we find that the probability of obtaining a box with more than 16.65 ounces is .0000034. Thus, if the process mean shifts up by 1.5 standard deviations, approximately $1{,}000{,}000(.0000034) = 3.4$ boxes of cereal will exceed the upper limit of 16.65 ounces. In Six Sigma terminology, the quality level of the process is said to be 3.4 defects per million opportunities. If management of KJW considers 15.45 to 16.65 ounces to be acceptable quality limits for the filling process, the KJW filling process would be considered a Six Sigma process. Thus, if the process mean stays within 1.5 standard deviations of its target value $\mu = 16.05$ ounces, a maximum of only 3.4 defects per million boxes filled can be expected.

Organizations that want to achieve and maintain a Six Sigma level of quality must emphasize methods for monitoring and maintaining quality. *Quality assurance* refers to the entire system of policies, procedures, and guidelines established by an organization to achieve and maintain quality. Quality assurance consists of two principal functions: quality engineering and quality control. The object of *quality engineering* is to include quality in the

FIGURE 20.2 NORMAL DISTRIBUTION OF CEREAL BOX FILLING WEIGHTS WITH A PROCESS MEAN $\mu = 16.20$

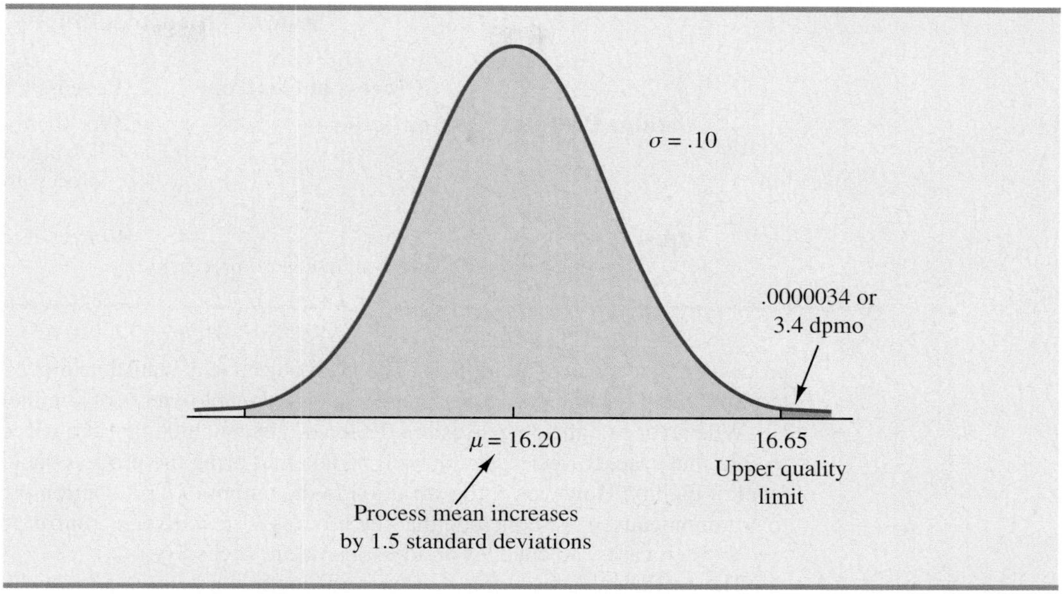

design of products and processes and to identify quality problems prior to production. **Quality control** consists of a series of inspections and measurements used to determine whether quality standards are being met. If quality standards are not being met, corrective or preventive action can be taken to achieve and maintain conformance. In the next two sections we present two statistical methods used in quality control. The first method, *statistical process control,* uses graphical displays known as control charts to monitor a process; the goal is to determine whether the process can be continued or whether corrective action should be taken to achieve a desired quality level. The second method, *acceptance sampling,* is used in situations where a decision to accept or reject a group of items must be based on the quality found in a sample.

20.2 Statistical Process Control

In this section we consider quality control procedures for a production process whereby goods are manufactured continuously. On the basis of sampling and inspection of production output, a decision will be made to either continue the production process or adjust it to bring the items or goods being produced up to acceptable quality standards.

Continuous improvement is one of the most important concepts of the total quality management movement. The most important use of a control chart is in improving the process.

Despite high standards of quality in manufacturing and production operations, machine tools will invariably wear out, vibrations will throw machine settings out of adjustment, purchased materials will be defective, and human operators will make mistakes. Any or all of these factors can result in poor quality output. Fortunately, procedures are available for monitoring production output so that poor quality can be detected early and the production process can be adjusted or corrected.

If the variation in the quality of the production output is due to **assignable causes** such as tools wearing out, incorrect machine settings, poor quality raw materials, or operator error, the process should be adjusted or corrected as soon as possible. Alternatively, if the variation is due to what are called **common causes**—that is, randomly occurring variations in materials, temperature, humidity, and so on, which the manufacturer cannot possibly control—the

TABLE 20.1 THE OUTCOMES OF STATISTICAL PROCESS CONTROL

		State of Production Process	
		H_0 True Process in Control	H_0 False Process Out of Control
Decision	Continue Process	Correct decision	Type II error (allowing an out-of-control process to continue)
	Adjust Process	Type I error (adjusting an in-control process)	Correct decision

process does not need to be adjusted. The main objective of statistical process control is to determine whether variations in output are due to assignable causes or common causes.

Whenever assignable causes are detected, we conclude that the process is *out of control.* In that case, corrective action will be taken to bring the process back to an acceptable level of quality. However, if the variation in the output of a production process is due only to common causes, we conclude that the process is *in statistical control,* or simply *in control;* in such cases, no changes or adjustments are necessary.

Process control procedures are closely related to hypothesis testing procedures discussed earlier in this text. Control charts provide an ongoing test of the hypothesis that the process is in control.

The statistical procedures for process control are based on the hypothesis testing methodology presented in Chapter 9. The null hypothesis H_0 is formulated in terms of the production process being in control. The alternative hypothesis H_a is formulated in terms of the production process being out of control. Table 20.1 shows that correct decisions to continue an in-control process and adjust an out-of-control process are possible. However, as with other hypothesis testing procedures, both a Type I error (adjusting an in-control process) and a Type II error (allowing an out-of-control process to continue) are also possible.

Control Charts

A **control chart** provides a basis for deciding whether the variation in the output is due to common causes (in control) or assignable causes (out of control). Whenever an out-of-control situation is detected, adjustments or other corrective action will be taken to bring the process back into control.

Control charts based on data that can be measured on a continuous scale are called variables control charts. The $\bar{x}$ chart is a variables control chart.

Control charts can be classified by the type of data they contain. An **$\bar{x}$ chart** is used if the quality of the output of the process is measured in terms of a variable such as length, weight, temperature, and so on. In that case, the decision to continue or to adjust the production process will be based on the mean value found in a sample of the output. To introduce some of the concepts common to all control charts, let us consider some specific features of an $\bar{x}$ chart.

Figure 20.3 shows the general structure of an $\bar{x}$ chart. The center line of the chart corresponds to the mean of the process when the process is *in control.* The vertical line identifies the scale of measurement for the variable of interest. Each time a sample is taken from the production process, a value of the sample mean $\bar{x}$ is computed and a data point showing the value of $\bar{x}$ is plotted on the control chart.

The two lines labeled UCL and LCL are important in determining whether the process is in control or out of control. The lines are called the *upper control limit* and the *lower control limit,* respectively. They are chosen so that when the process is in control, there will be a high probability that the value of $\bar{x}$ will be between the two control limits. Values outside the control limits provide strong statistical evidence that the process is out of control and corrective action should be taken.

Over time, more and more data points will be added to the control chart. The order of the data points will be from left to right as the process is sampled. In essence, every time a

FIGURE 20.3 $\bar{x}$ CHART STRUCTURE

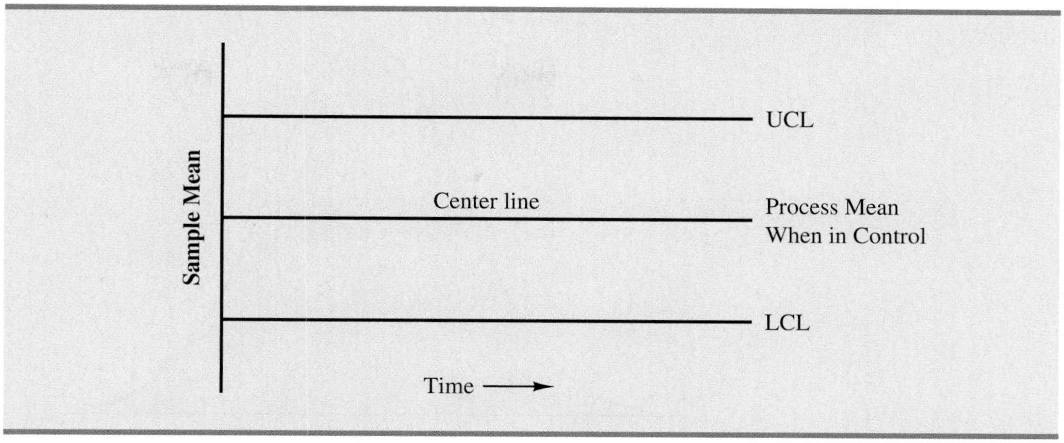

point is plotted on the control chart, we are carrying out a hypothesis test to determine whether the process is in control.

In addition to the $\bar{x}$ chart, other control charts can be used to monitor the range of the measurements in the sample (***R* chart**), the proportion defective in the sample (***p* chart**), and the number of defective items in the sample (***np* chart**). In each case, the control chart has a LCL, a center line, and an UCL similar to the $\bar{x}$ chart in Figure 20.3. The major difference among the charts is what the vertical axis measures; for instance, in a p chart the measurement scale denotes the proportion of defective items in the sample instead of the sample mean. In the following discussion, we will illustrate the construction and use of the $\bar{x}$ chart, R chart, p chart, and np chart.

$\bar{x}$ Chart: Process Mean and Standard Deviation Known

To illustrate the construction of an $\bar{x}$ chart, let us reconsider the situation at KJW Packaging. Recall that KJW operates a production line where cartons of cereal are filled. When the process is operating correctly—and hence the system is in control—the mean filling weight is $\mu = 16.05$ ounces, and the process standard deviation is $\sigma = .10$ ounces. In addition, the filling weights are assumed to be normally distributed. This distribution is shown in Figure 20.4.

The sampling distribution of $\bar{x}$, as presented in Chapter 7, can be used to determine the variation that can be expected in $\bar{x}$ values for a process that is in control. Let us first briefly review the properties of the sampling distribution of $\bar{x}$. First, recall that the expected value or mean of $\bar{x}$ is equal to μ, the mean filling weight when the production line is in control. For samples of size n, the equation for the standard deviation of $\bar{x}$, called the standard error of the mean, is

$$\sigma_{\bar{x}} = \frac{\sigma}{\sqrt{n}} \tag{20.1}$$

In addition, because the filling weights are normally distributed, the sampling distribution of $\bar{x}$ is normally distributed for any sample size. Thus, the sampling distribution of $\bar{x}$ is a normal distribution with mean μ and standard deviation $\sigma_{\bar{x}}$. This distribution is shown in Figure 20.5.

The sampling distribution of $\bar{x}$ is used to determine what values of $\bar{x}$ are reasonable if the process is in control. The general practice in quality control is to define as reasonable any value of $\bar{x}$ that is within 3 standard deviations, or standard errors, above or below the mean value. Recall from the study of the normal probability distribution that approximately 99.7% of the values of a normally distributed random variable are within ± 3 standard

FIGURE 20.4 NORMAL DISTRIBUTION OF CEREAL CARTON FILLING WEIGHTS

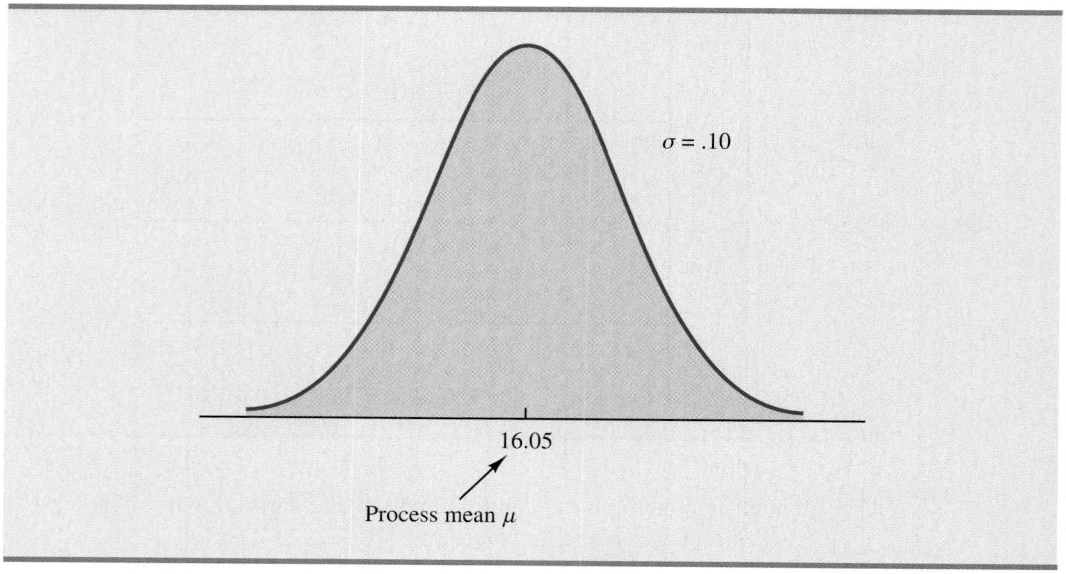

FIGURE 20.5 SAMPLING DISTRIBUTION OF $\bar{x}$ FOR A SAMPLE OF n FILLING WEIGHTS

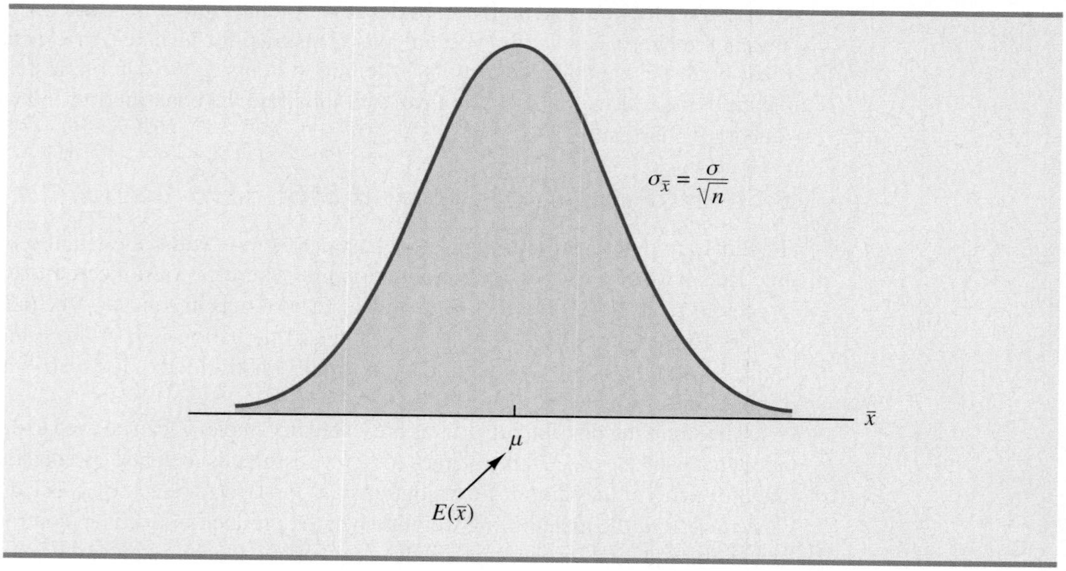

deviations of its mean value. Thus, if a value of $\bar{x}$ is within the interval $\mu - 3\sigma_{\bar{x}}$ to $\mu + 3\sigma_{\bar{x}}$, we will assume that the process is in control. In summary, then, the control limits for an $\bar{x}$ chart are as follows.

CONTROL LIMITS FOR AN $\bar{x}$ CHART: PROCESS MEAN AND STANDARD DEVIATION KNOWN

$$\text{UCL} = \mu + 3\sigma_{\bar{x}} \quad \textbf{(20.2)}$$

$$\text{LCL} = \mu - 3\sigma_{\bar{x}} \quad \textbf{(20.3)}$$

FIGURE 20.6 THE $\bar{x}$ CHART FOR THE CEREAL CARTON FILLING PROCESS

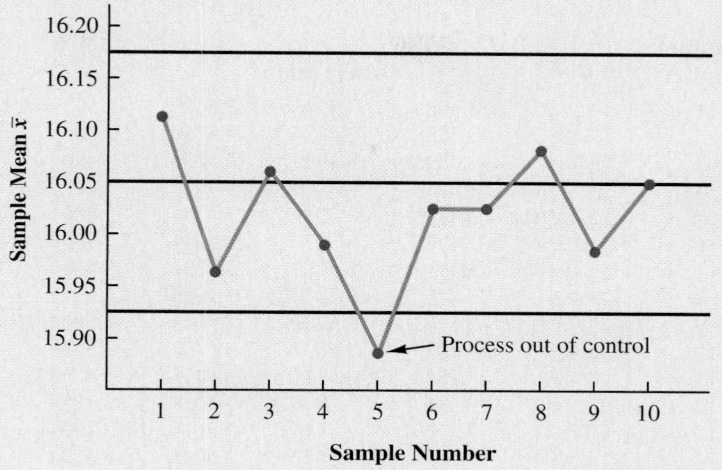

Reconsider the KJW Packaging example with the process distribution of filling weights shown in Figure 20.4 and the sampling distribution of $\bar{x}$ shown in Figure 20.5. Assume that a quality control inspector periodically samples six cartons and uses the sample mean filling weight to determine whether the process is in control or out of control. Using equation (20.1), we find that the standard error of the mean is $\sigma_{\bar{x}} = \sigma/\sqrt{n} = .10/\sqrt{6} = .04$. Thus, with the process mean at 16.05, the control limits are UCL $= 16.05 + 3(.04) = 16.17$ and LCL $= 16.05 - 3(.04) = 15.93$. Figure 20.6 is the control chart with the results of 10 samples taken over a 10-hour period. For ease of reading, the sample numbers 1 through 10 are listed below the chart.

Note that the mean for the fifth sample in Figure 20.6 shows that the process is out of control. The fifth sample mean is below the LCL, indicating that assignable causes of output variation are present and that underfilling is occurring. As a result, corrective action was taken at this point to bring the process back into control. The fact that the remaining points on the $\bar{x}$ chart are within the upper and lower control limits indicates that the corrective action was successful.

$\bar{x}$ Chart: Process Mean and Standard Deviation Unknown

In the KJW Packaging example, we showed how an $\bar{x}$ chart can be developed when the mean and standard deviation of the process are known. In most situations, the process mean and standard deviation must be estimated by using samples that are selected from the process when it is in control. For instance, KJW might select a random sample of five boxes each morning and five boxes each afternoon for 10 days of in-control operation. For each subgroup, or sample, the mean and standard deviation of the sample are computed. The overall averages of both the sample means and the sample standard deviations are used to construct control charts for both the process mean and the process standard deviation.

It is important to maintain control over both the mean and the variability of a process.

In practice, it is more common to monitor the variability of the process by using the range instead of the standard deviation because the range is easier to compute. The range can be used to provide good estimates of the process standard deviation; thus it can be used to construct upper and lower control limits for the $\bar{x}$ chart with little computational effort. To illustrate, let us consider the problem facing Jensen Computer Supplies, Inc.

Jensen Computer Supplies (JCS) manufactures 3.5-inch-diameter computer disks; they just finished adjusting their production process so that it is operating in control. Suppose

TABLE 20.2 DATA FOR THE JENSEN COMPUTER SUPPLIES PROBLEM

CD file
Jensen

Sample Number	Observations					Sample Mean $\bar{x}_j$	Sample Range R_j
1	3.5056	3.5086	3.5144	3.5009	3.5030	3.5065	.0135
2	3.4882	3.5085	3.4884	3.5250	3.5031	3.5026	.0368
3	3.4897	3.4898	3.4995	3.5130	3.4969	3.4978	.0233
4	3.5153	3.5120	3.4989	3.4900	3.4837	3.5000	.0316
5	3.5059	3.5113	3.5011	3.4773	3.4801	3.4951	.0340
6	3.4977	3.4961	3.5050	3.5014	3.5060	3.5012	.0099
7	3.4910	3.4913	3.4976	3.4831	3.5044	3.4935	.0213
8	3.4991	3.4853	3.4830	3.5083	3.5094	3.4970	.0264
9	3.5099	3.5162	3.5228	3.4958	3.5004	3.5090	.0270
10	3.4880	3.5015	3.5094	3.5102	3.5146	3.5047	.0266
11	3.4881	3.4887	3.5141	3.5175	3.4863	3.4989	.0312
12	3.5043	3.4867	3.4946	3.5018	3.4784	3.4932	.0259
13	3.5043	3.4769	3.4944	3.5014	3.4904	3.4935	.0274
14	3.5004	3.5030	3.5082	3.5045	3.5234	3.5079	.0230
15	3.4846	3.4938	3.5065	3.5089	3.5011	3.4990	.0243
16	3.5145	3.4832	3.5188	3.4935	3.4989	3.5018	.0356
17	3.5004	3.5042	3.4954	3.5020	3.4889	3.4982	.0153
18	3.4959	3.4823	3.4964	3.5082	3.4871	3.4940	.0259
19	3.4878	3.4864	3.4960	3.5070	3.4984	3.4951	.0206
20	3.4969	3.5144	3.5053	3.4985	3.4885	3.5007	.0259

random samples of five disks were selected during the first hour of operation, five disks were selected during the second hour of operation, and so on, until 20 samples were obtained. Table 20.2 provides the diameter of each disk sampled as well as the mean $\bar{x}_j$ and range R_j for each of the samples.

The estimate of the process mean μ is given by the overall sample mean.

OVERALL SAMPLE MEAN

$$\bar{\bar{x}} = \frac{\bar{x}_1 + \bar{x}_2 + \cdots + \bar{x}_k}{k} \tag{20.4}$$

where

$\bar{x}_j$ = mean of the jth sample $j = 1, 2, \ldots, k$
k = number of samples

For the JCS data in Table 20.2, the overall sample mean is $\bar{\bar{x}} = 3.4995$. This value will be the center line for the $\bar{x}$ chart. The range of each sample, denoted R_j, is simply the difference between the largest and smallest values in each sample. The average range for k samples is computed as follows.

AVERAGE RANGE

$$\bar{R} = \frac{R_1 + R_2 + \cdots + R_k}{k} \tag{20.5}$$

where

$$R_j = \text{range of the } j\text{th sample}, j = 1, 2, \ldots, k$$
$$k = \text{number of samples}$$

For the JCS data in Table 20.2, the average range is $\bar{R} = .0253$.

In the preceding section we showed that the upper and lower control limits for the $\bar{x}$ chart are

$$\bar{x} \pm 3\frac{\sigma}{\sqrt{n}} \tag{20.6}$$

The overall sample mean $\bar{\bar{x}}$ is used to estimate μ and the sample ranges are used to develop an estimate of σ.

Hence, to construct the control limits for the $\bar{x}$ chart, we need to estimate μ and σ, the mean and standard deviation of the process. An estimate of μ is given by $\bar{\bar{x}}$. An estimate of σ can be developed by using the range data.

It can be shown that an estimator of the process standard deviation σ is the average range divided by d_2, a constant that depends on the sample size n. That is,

$$\text{Estimator of } \sigma = \frac{\bar{R}}{d_2} \tag{20.7}$$

The *American Society for Testing and Materials Manual on Presentation of Data and Control Chart Analysis* provides values for d_2 as shown in Table 20.3. For instance, when $n = 5$, $d_2 = 2.326$, and the estimate of σ is the average range divided by 2.326. If we substitute $\bar{R}/d_2$ for σ in expression (20.6), we can write the control limits for the $\bar{x}$ chart as

$$\bar{\bar{x}} \pm 3\frac{\bar{R}/d_2}{\sqrt{n}} = \bar{\bar{x}} \pm \frac{3}{d_2\sqrt{n}}\bar{R} = \bar{\bar{x}} \pm A_2\bar{R} \tag{20.8}$$

Note that $A_2 = 3/(d_2\sqrt{n})$ is a constant that depends only on the sample size. Values for A_2 are provided in Table 20.3. For $n = 5$, $A_2 = .577$; thus, the control limits for the $\bar{x}$ chart are

$$3.4995 \pm (.577)(.0253) = 3.4995 \pm .0146$$

Hence, UCL = 3.514 and LCL = 3.485.

Figure 20.7 shows the $\bar{x}$ chart for the Jensen Computer Supplies problem. We used the data in Table 20.2 and Minitab's control chart routine to construct the chart. The center line is shown at the overall sample mean $\bar{\bar{x}} = 3.4995$. The upper control limit (UCL) is 3.514 and the lower control (LCL) is 3.485. The $\bar{x}$ chart shows the 20 sample means plotted over time. Because all 20 sample means are within the control limits,we confirm that the process was in control during the sampling period.

R Chart

Let us now consider a range chart (*R* chart) that can be used to control the variability of a process. To develop the *R* chart, we need to think of the range of a sample as a random variable with its own mean and standard deviation. The average range $\bar{R}$ provides an estimate

TABLE 20.3 FACTORS FOR $\bar{x}$ AND R CONTROL CHARTS

Observations in Sample, n	d_2	A_2	d_3	D_3	D_4
2	1.128	1.880	0.853	0	3.267
3	1.693	1.023	0.888	0	2.574
4	2.059	0.729	0.880	0	2.282
5	2.326	0.577	0.864	0	2.114
6	2.534	0.483	0.848	0	2.004
7	2.704	0.419	0.833	0.076	1.924
8	2.847	0.373	0.820	0.136	1.864
9	2.970	0.337	0.808	0.184	1.816
10	3.078	0.308	0.797	0.223	1.777
11	3.173	0.285	0.787	0.256	1.744
12	3.258	0.266	0.778	0.283	1.717
13	3.336	0.249	0.770	0.307	1.693
14	3.407	0.235	0.763	0.328	1.672
15	3.472	0.223	0.756	0.347	1.653
16	3.532	0.212	0.750	0.363	1.637
17	3.588	0.203	0.744	0.378	1.622
18	3.640	0.194	0.739	0.391	1.608
19	3.689	0.187	0.734	0.403	1.597
20	3.735	0.180	0.729	0.415	1.585
21	3.778	0.173	0.724	0.425	1.575
22	3.819	0.167	0.720	0.434	1.566
23	3.858	0.162	0.716	0.443	1.557
24	3.895	0.157	0.712	0.451	1.548
25	3.931	0.153	0.708	0.459	1.541

Source: Adapted from Table 27 of ASTM STP 15D, *ASTM Manual on Presentation of Data and Control Chart Analysis.* Copyright 1976 American Society for Testing and Materials, Philadelphia, PA. Reprinted with permission.

FIGURE 20.7 $\bar{x}$ CHART FOR THE JENSEN COMPUTER SUPPLIES PROBLEM

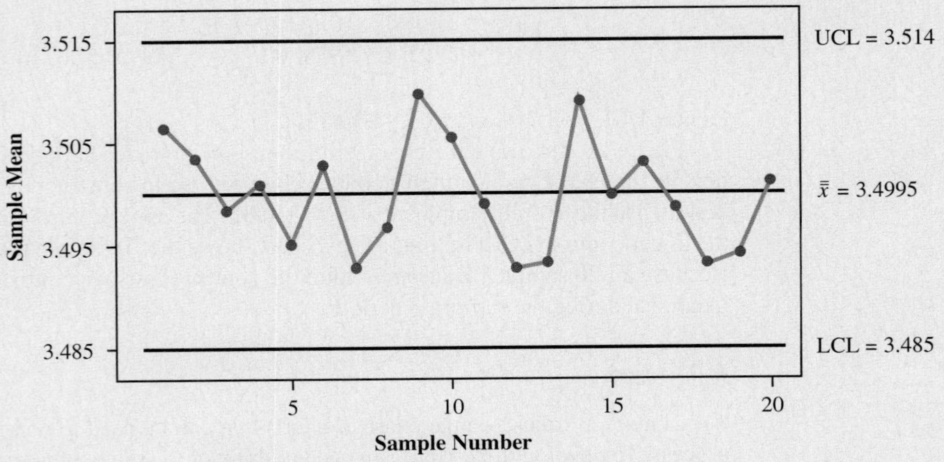

of the mean of this random variable. Moreover, it can be shown that an estimate of the standard deviation of the range is

$$\hat{\sigma}_R = d_3 \frac{\bar{R}}{d_2} \tag{20.9}$$

where d_2 and d_3 are constants that depend on the sample size; values of d_2 and d_3 are also provided in Table 20.3. Thus, the UCL for the R chart is given by

$$\bar{R} + 3\hat{\sigma}_R = \bar{R}\left(1 + 3\frac{d_3}{d_2}\right) \tag{20.10}$$

and the LCL is

$$\bar{R} - 3\hat{\sigma}_R = \bar{R}\left(1 - 3\frac{d_3}{d_2}\right) \tag{20.11}$$

If we let

$$D_4 = 1 + 3\frac{d_3}{d_2} \tag{20.12}$$

$$D_3 = 1 - 3\frac{d_3}{d_2} \tag{20.13}$$

we can write the control limits for the R chart as

$$\text{UCL} = \bar{R}D_4 \tag{20.14}$$

$$\text{LCL} = \bar{R}D_3 \tag{20.15}$$

Values for D_3 and D_4 are also provided in Table 20.3. Note that for $n = 5$, $D_3 = 0$, and $D_4 = 2.114$. Thus, with $\bar{R} = .0253$, the control limits are

$$\text{UCL} = .0253(2.114) = .053$$
$$\text{LCL} = .0253(0) = 0$$

If the R chart indicates that the process is out of control, the $\bar{x}$ chart should not be interpreted until the R chart indicates the process variability is in control.

Figure 20.8 shows the R chart for the Jensen Computer Supplies problem. We used the data in Table 20.2 and Minitab's control chart routine to construct the chart. The center line is shown at the overall mean of the 20 sample ranges, $\bar{R} = .0253$. The UCL is .053 and the LCL is .000. The R chart shows the 20 sample ranges plotted over time. Because all 20 sample ranges are within the control limits, we confirm that the process was in control during the sampling period.

p Chart

Control charts that are based on data indicating the presence of a defect or a number of defects are called attributes control charts. A p chart is an attributes control chart.

Let us consider the case in which the output quality is measured by either nondefective or defective items. The decision to continue or to adjust the production process will be based on $\bar{p}$, the proportion of defective items found in a sample. The control chart used for proportion-defective data is called a p chart.

To illustrate the construction of a p chart, consider the use of automated mail-sorting machines in a post office. These automated machines scan the zip codes on letters and divert each letter to its proper carrier route. Even when a machine is operating properly, some

FIGURE 20.8 *R* CHART FOR THE JENSEN COMPUTER SUPPLIES PROBLEM

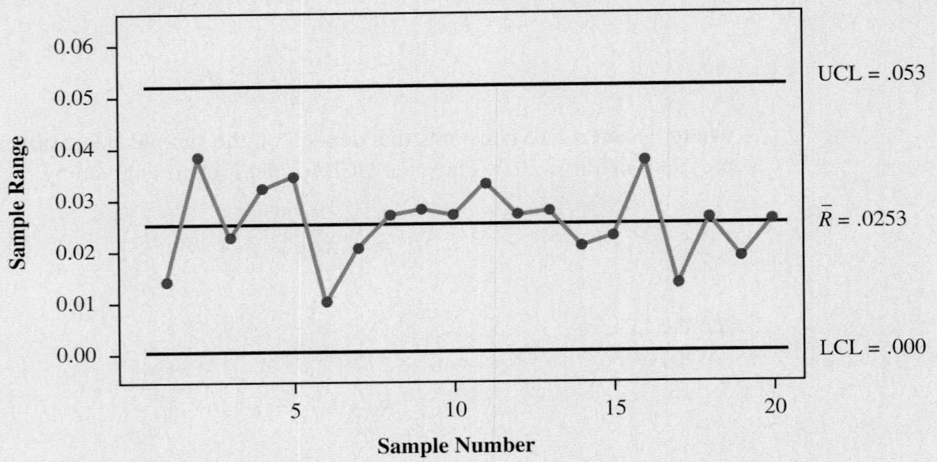

letters are diverted to incorrect routes. Assume that when a machine is operating correctly, or in a state of control, 3% of the letters are incorrectly diverted. Thus p, the proportion of letters incorrectly diverted when the process is in control, is .03.

The sampling distribution of $\bar{p}$, as presented in Chapter 7, can be used to determine the variation that can be expected in $\bar{p}$ values for a process that is in control. Recall that the expected value or mean of $\bar{p}$ is p, the proportion defective when the process is in control. With samples of size n, the formula for the standard deviation of $\bar{p}$, called the standard error of the proportion, is

$$\sigma_{\bar{p}} = \sqrt{\frac{p(1-p)}{n}} \quad \textbf{(20.16)}$$

We also learned in Chapter 7 that the sampling distribution of $\bar{p}$ can be approximated by a normal distribution whenever the sample size is large. With $\bar{p}$, the sample size can be considered large whenever the following two conditions are satisfied.

$$np \geq 5$$
$$n(1-p) \geq 5$$

In summary, whenever the sample size is large, the sampling distribution of $\bar{p}$ can be approximated by a normal distribution with mean p and standard deviation $\sigma_{\bar{p}}$. This distribution is shown in Figure 20.9.

To establish control limits for a p chart, we follow the same procedure we used to establish control limits for an $\bar{x}$ chart. That is, the limits for the control chart are set at 3 standard deviations, or standard errors, above and below the proportion defective when the process is in control. Thus, we have the following control limits.

CONTROL LIMITS FOR A p CHART

$$\text{UCL} = p + 3\sigma_{\bar{p}} \quad \textbf{(20.17)}$$
$$\text{LCL} = p - 3\sigma_{\bar{p}} \quad \textbf{(20.18)}$$

FIGURE 20.9 SAMPLING DISTRIBUTION OF $\bar{p}$

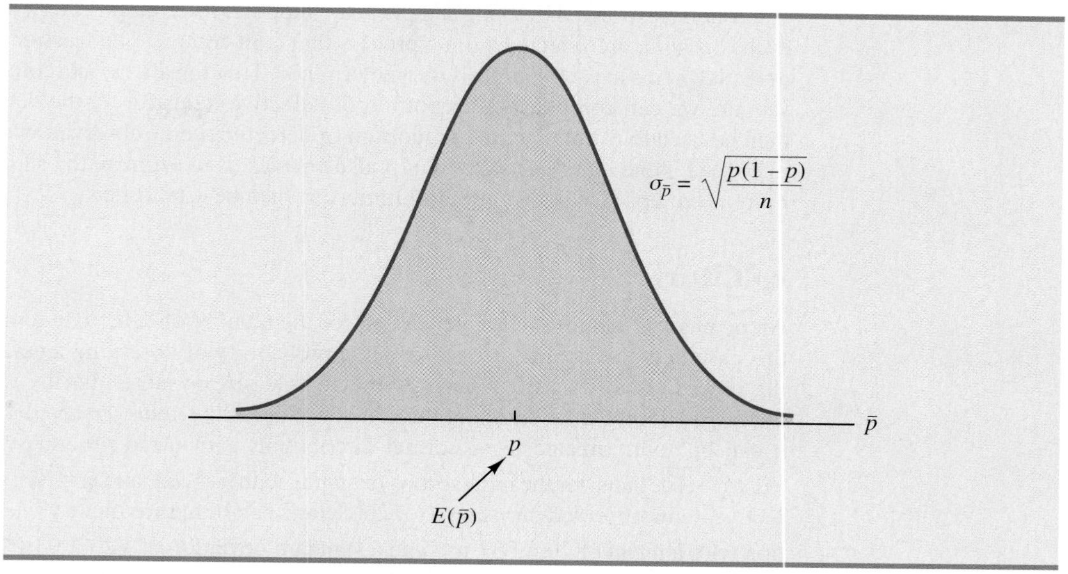

With $p = .03$ and samples of size $n = 200$, equation (20.16) shows that the standard error is

$$\sigma_{\bar{p}} = \sqrt{\frac{.03(1 - .03)}{200}} = .0121$$

Hence, the control limits are UCL $= .03 + 3(.0121) = .0663$, and LCL $= .03 - 3(.0121) = -.0063$. Whenever equation (20.18) provides a negative value for LCL, LCL is set equal to zero in the control chart.

Figure 20.10 is the control chart for the mail-sorting process. The points plotted show the sample proportion defective found in samples of letters taken from the process. All points are within the control limits, providing no evidence to conclude that the sorting process is out of control.

FIGURE 20.10 p CHART FOR THE PROPORTION DEFECTIVE IN A MAIL-SORTING PROCESS

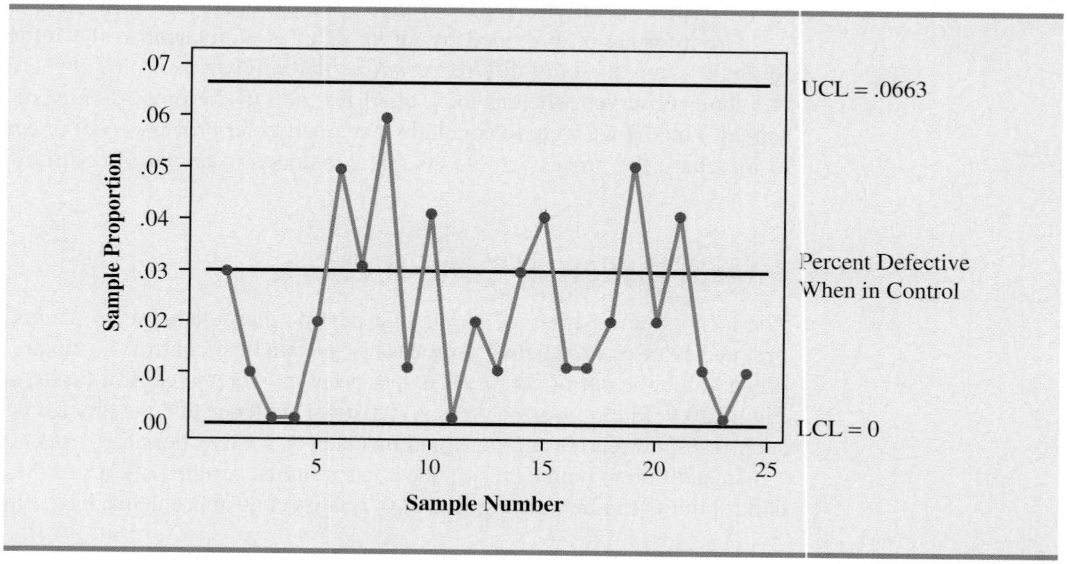

If the proportion of defective items for a process that is in control is not known, that value is first estimated by using sample data. Suppose, for example, that k different samples, each of size n, are selected from a process that is in control. The fraction or proportion of defective items in each sample is then determined. Treating all the data collected as one large sample, we can compute the proportion of defective items for all the data; that value can then be used to estimate p, the proportion of defective items observed when the process is in control. Note that this estimate of p also enables us to estimate the standard error of the proportion; upper and lower control limits can then be established.

np Chart

An np chart is a control chart developed for the number of defective items in a sample. In this case, n is the sample size and p is the probability of observing a defective item when the process is in control. Whenever the sample size is large, that is, when $np \geq 5$ and $n(1 - p) \geq 5$, the distribution of the number of defective items observed in a sample of size n can be approximated by a normal distribution with mean np and standard deviation $\sqrt{np(1 - p)}$. Thus, for the mail-sorting example, with $n = 200$ and $p = .03$, the number of defective items observed in a sample of 200 letters can be approximated by a normal distribution with a mean of $200(.03) = 6$ and a standard deviation of $\sqrt{200(.03)(.97)} = 2.4125$.

The control limits for an np chart are set at 3 standard deviations above and below the expected number of defective items observed when the process is in control. Thus, we have the following control limits.

CONTROL LIMITS FOR AN *np* CHART

$$UCL = np + 3\sqrt{np(1 - p)} \tag{20.19}$$

$$LCL = np - 3\sqrt{np(1 - p)} \tag{20.20}$$

For the mail-sorting process example, with $p = .03$ and $n = 200$, the control limits are $UCL = 6 + 3(2.4125) = 13.2375$, and $LCL = 6 - 3(2.4125) = -1.2375$. When LCL is negative, LCL is set equal to zero in the control chart. Hence, if the number of letters diverted to incorrect routes is greater than 13, the process is concluded to be out of control.

The information provided by an np chart is equivalent to the information provided by the p chart; the only difference is that the np chart is a plot of the number of defective items observed whereas the p chart is a plot of the proportion of defective items observed. Thus, if we were to conclude that a particular process is out of control on the basis of a p chart, the process would also be concluded to be out of control on the basis of an np chart.

Interpretation of Control Charts

The location and pattern of points in a control chart enable us to determine, with a small probability of error, whether a process is in statistical control. A primary indication that a process may be out of control is a data point outside the control limits, such as point 5 in Figure 20.6. Finding such a point is statistical evidence that the process is out of control; in such cases, corrective action should be taken as soon as possible.

In addition to points outside the control limits, certain patterns of the points within the control limits can be warning signals of quality control problems. For example, assume that all the data points are within the control limits but that a large number of points are on one side of the center line. This pattern may indicate that an equipment problem, a change in materials, or some other assignable cause of a shift in quality has occurred. Careful investigation of the production process should be undertaken to determine whether quality has changed.

Even if all points are within the upper and lower control limits, a process may not be in control. Trends in the sample data points or unusually long runs above or below the center line may also indicate out-of-control conditions.

Another pattern to watch for in control charts is a gradual shift, or trend, over time. For example, as tools wear out, the dimensions of machined parts will gradually deviate from their designed levels. Gradual changes in temperature or humidity, general equipment deterioration, dirt buildup, or operator fatigue may also result in a trend pattern in control charts. Six or seven points in a row that indicate either an increasing or decreasing trend should be cause for concern, even if the data points are all within the control limits. When such a pattern occurs, the process should be reviewed for possible changes or shifts in quality. Corrective action to bring the process back into control may be necessary.

NOTES AND COMMENTS

1. Because the control limits for the $\bar{x}$ chart depend on the value of the average range, these limits will not have much meaning unless the process variability is in control. In practice, the R chart is usually constructed before the $\bar{x}$ chart; if the R chart indicates that the process variability is in control, then the $\bar{x}$ chart is constructed. Minitab's Xbar-R option provides the $\bar{x}$ chart and the R chart simultaneously. The steps of this procedure are described in Appendix 20.1.
2. An np chart is used to monitor a process in terms of the number of defects. The Motorola Six Sigma Quality Level sets a goal of producing no more than 3.4 defects per million operations; this goal implies $p = .0000034$.

Exercises

Methods

1. A process that is in control has a mean of $\mu = 12.5$ and a standard deviation of $\sigma = .8$.
   a. Construct the $\bar{x}$ control chart for this process if samples of size 4 are to be used.
   b. Repeat part (a) for samples of size 8 and 16.
   c. What happens to the limits of the control chart as the sample size is increased? Discuss why this is reasonable.
2. Twenty-five samples, each of size 5, were selected from a process that was in control. The sum of all the data collected was 677.5 pounds.
   a. What is an estimate of the process mean (in terms of pounds per unit) when the process is in control?
   b. Develop the $\bar{x}$ control chart for this process if samples of size 5 will be used. Assume that the process standard deviation is .5 when the process is in control, and that the mean of the process is the estimate developed in part (a).
3. Twenty-five samples of 100 items each were inspected when a process was considered to be operating satisfactorily. In the 25 samples, a total of 135 items were found to be defective.
   a. What is an estimate of the proportion defective when the process is in control?
   b. What is the standard error of the proportion if samples of size 100 will be used for statistical process control?
   c. Compute the upper and lower control limits for the control chart.

SELF test

4. A process sampled 20 times with a sample of size 8 resulted in $\bar{\bar{x}} = 28.5$ and $\bar{R} = 1.6$. Compute the upper and lower control limits for the $\bar{x}$ and R charts for this process.

Applications

5. Temperature is used to measure the output of a production process. When the process is in control, the mean of the process is $\mu = 128.5$ and the standard deviation is $\sigma = .4$.
   a. Construct the $\bar{x}$ chart for this process if samples of size 6 are to be used.
   b. Is the process in control for a sample providing the following data?

128.8	128.2	129.1	128.7	128.4	129.2

   c. Is the process in control for a sample providing the following data?

129.3	128.7	128.6	129.2	129.5	129.0

6. A quality control process monitors the weight per carton of laundry detergent. Control limits are set at UCL = 20.12 ounces and LCL = 19.90 ounces. Samples of size 5 are used for the sampling and inspection process. What are the process mean and process standard deviation for the manufacturing operation?

7. The Goodman Tire and Rubber Company periodically tests its tires for tread wear under simulated road conditions. To study and control the manufacturing process, 20 samples, each containing three radial tires, were chosen from different shifts over several days of operation, with the following results. Assuming that these data were collected when the manufacturing process was believed to be operating in control, develop the R and $\bar{x}$ charts.

CD file

Tires

Sample	Tread Wear*		
1	31	42	28
2	26	18	35
3	25	30	34
4	17	25	21
5	38	29	35
6	41	42	36
7	21	17	29
8	32	26	28
9	41	34	33
10	29	17	30
11	26	31	40
12	23	19	25
13	17	24	32
14	43	35	17
15	18	25	29
16	30	42	31
17	28	36	32
18	40	29	31
19	18	29	28
20	22	34	26

*Hundredths of an inch

8. Over several weeks of normal, or in-control, operation, 20 samples of 150 packages each of synthetic-gut tennis strings were tested for breaking strength. A total of 141 packages of the 3000 tested failed to conform to the manufacturer's specifications.
   a. What is an estimate of the process proportion defective when the system is in control?
   b. Compute the upper and lower control limits for a p chart.
   c. With the results of part (b), what conclusion should be made about the process if tests on a new sample of 150 packages find 12 defective? Do there appear to be assignable causes in this situation?
   d. Compute the upper and lower control limits for an np chart.

e. Answer part (c) using the results of part (d).
f. Which control chart would be preferred in this situation? Explain.

9. An automotive industry supplier produces pistons for several models of automobiles. Twenty samples, each consisting of 200 pistons, were selected when the process was known to be operating correctly. The numbers of defective pistons found in the samples follow.

8	10	6	4	5	7	8	12	8	15
14	10	10	7	5	8	6	10	4	8

a. What is an estimate of the proportion defective for the piston manufacturing process when it is in control?
b. Construct the p chart for the manufacturing process, assuming each sample has 200 pistons.
c. With the results of part (b), what conclusion should be made if a sample of 200 has 20 defective pistons?
d. Compute the upper and lower control limits for an np chart.
e. Answer part (c) using the results of part (d).

20.3 Acceptance Sampling

In acceptance sampling, the items of interest can be incoming shipments of raw materials or purchased parts as well as finished goods from final assembly. Suppose we want to decide whether to accept or reject a group of items on the basis of specified quality characteristics. In quality control terminology, the group of items is a **lot**, and **acceptance sampling** is a statistical method that enables us to base the accept-reject decision on the inspection of a sample of items from the lot.

The general steps of acceptance sampling are shown in Figure 20.11. After a lot is received, a sample of items is selected for inspection. The results of the inspection are compared to specified quality characteristics. If the quality characteristics are satisfied, the lot is accepted and sent to production or shipped to customers. If the lot is rejected, managers must decide on its disposition. In some cases, the decision may be to keep the lot and remove the unacceptable or nonconforming items. In other cases, the lot may be returned to the supplier at the supplier's expense; the extra work and cost placed on the supplier can motivate the supplier to provide high-quality lots. Finally, if the rejected lot consists of finished goods, the goods must be scrapped or reworked to meet acceptable quality standards.

Acceptance sampling has the following advantages over 100% inspection:
1. Usually less expensive
2. Less product damage due to less handling and testing
3. Fewer inspectors required
4. The only approach possible if destructive testing must be used

The statistical procedure of acceptance sampling is based on the hypothesis testing methodology presented in Chapter 9. The null and alternative hypotheses are stated as follows.

$$H_0\text{: Good-quality lot}$$
$$H_a\text{: Poor-quality lot}$$

Table 20.4 shows the results of the hypothesis testing procedure. Note that correct decisions correspond to accepting a good-quality lot and rejecting a poor-quality lot. However, as with other hypothesis testing procedures, we need to be aware of the possibilities of making a Type I error (rejecting a good-quality lot) or a Type II error (accepting a poor-quality lot).

The probability of a Type I error creates a risk for the producer of the lot and is known as the **producer's risk**. For example, a producer's risk of .05 indicates a 5% chance that a good-quality lot will be erroneously rejected. The probability of a Type II error, on the other hand, creates a risk for the consumer of the lot and is known as the **consumer's risk**. For example, a consumer's risk of .10 means a 10% chance that a poor-quality lot will be erroneously accepted and thus used in production or shipped to the customer. Specific values for the producer's risk and the consumer's risk can be controlled by the person designing the acceptance sampling procedure. To illustrate how to assign risk values, let us consider the problem faced by KALI, Inc.

FIGURE 20.11 ACCEPTANCE SAMPLING PROCEDURE

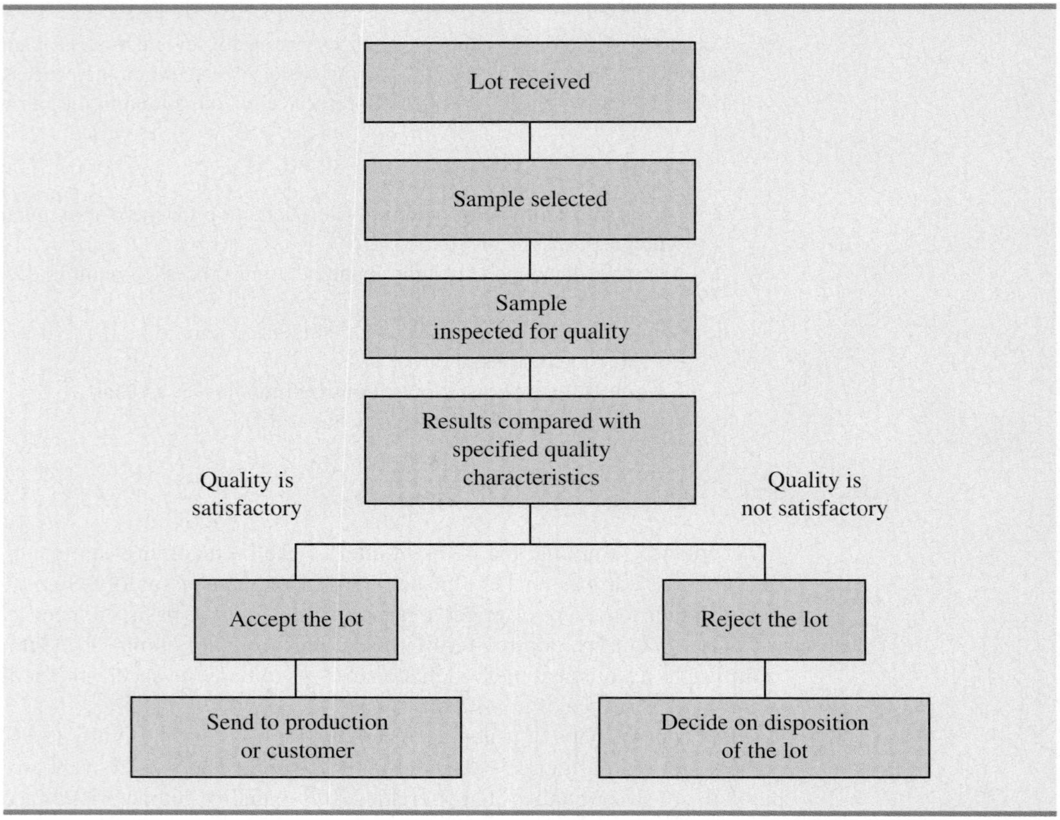

KALI, Inc.: An Example of Acceptance Sampling

KALI, Inc., manufactures home appliances that are marketed under a variety of trade names. However, KALI does not manufacture every component used in its products. Several components are purchased directly from suppliers. For example, one of the components that KALI purchases for use in home air conditioners is an overload protector, a device that turns off the compressor if it overheats. The compressor can be seriously damaged if the overload protector does not function properly, and therefore KALI is concerned about the quality of the overload protectors. One way to ensure quality would be to test every component

TABLE 20.4 THE OUTCOMES OF ACCEPTANCE SAMPLING

		State of the Lot	
		H_0 True Good-Quality Lot	**H_0 False Poor-Quality Lot**
Decision	**Accept the Lot**	Correct decision	Type II error (accepting a poor-quality lot)
	Reject the Lot	Type I error (rejecting a good-quality lot)	Correct decision

received through an approach known as 100% inspection. However, to determine proper functioning of an overload protector, the device must be subjected to time-consuming and expensive tests, and KALI cannot justify testing every overload protector it receives.

Instead, KALI uses an acceptance sampling plan to monitor the quality of the overload protectors. The acceptance sampling plan requires that KALI's quality control inspectors select and test a sample of overload protectors from each shipment. If very few defective units are found in the sample, the lot is probably of good quality and should be accepted. However, if a large number of defective units are found in the sample, the lot is probably of poor quality and should be rejected.

An acceptance sampling plan consists of a sample size n and an acceptance criterion c. The **acceptance criterion** is the maximum number of defective items that can be found in the sample and still indicate an acceptable lot. For example, for the KALI problem let us assume that a sample of 15 items will be selected from each incoming shipment or lot. Furthermore, assume that the manager of quality control states that the lot can be accepted only if no defective items are found. In this case, the acceptance sampling plan established by the quality control manager is $n = 15$ and $c = 0$.

This acceptance sampling plan is easy for the quality control inspector to implement. The inspector simply selects a sample of 15 items, performs the tests, and reaches a conclusion based on the following decision rule.

- *Accept the lot* if zero defective items are found.
- *Reject the lot* if one or more defective items are found.

Before implementing this acceptance sampling plan, the quality control manager wants to evaluate the risks or errors possible under the plan. The plan will be implemented only if both the producer's risk (Type I error) and the consumer's risk (Type II error) are controlled at reasonable levels.

Computing the Probability of Accepting a Lot

The key to analyzing both the producer's risk and the consumer's risk is a "what-if" type of analysis. That is, we will assume that a lot has some known percentage of defective items and compute the probability of accepting the lot for a given sampling plan. By varying the assumed percentage of defective items, we can examine the effect of the sampling plan on both types of risks.

Let us begin by assuming that a large shipment of overload protectors has been received and that 5% of the overload protectors in the shipment are defective. For a shipment or lot with 5% of the items defective, what is the probability that the $n = 15$, $c = 0$ sampling plan will lead us to accept the lot? Because each overload protector tested will be either defective or nondefective and because the lot size is large, the number of defective items in a sample of 15 has a *binomial distribution.* The binomial probability function, which was presented in Chapter 5, follows.

BINOMIAL PROBABILITY FUNCTION FOR ACCEPTANCE SAMPLING

$$f(x) = \frac{n!}{x!(n-x)!} p^x (1-p)^{(n-x)} \tag{20.21}$$

where

n = the sample size
p = the proportion of defective items in the lot
x = the number of defective items in the sample
$f(x)$ = the probability of x defective items in the sample

For the KALI acceptance sampling plan, $n = 15$; thus, for a lot with 5% defective ($p = .05$), we have

$$f(x) = \frac{15!}{x!(15-x)!}(.05)^x(1-.05)^{(15-x)} \tag{20.22}$$

Using equation (20.22), $f(0)$ will provide the probability that zero overload protectors will be defective and the lot will be accepted. In using equation (20.22), recall that $0! = 1$. Thus, the probability computation for $f(0)$ is

$$f(0) = \frac{15!}{0!(15-0)!}(.05)^0(1-.05)^{(15-0)}$$
$$= \frac{15!}{0!(15)!}(.05)^0(.95)^{15} = (.95)^{15} = .4633$$

We now know that the $n = 15$, $c = 0$ sampling plan has a .4633 probability of accepting a lot with 5% defective items. Hence, there must be a corresponding $1 - .4633 = .5367$ probability of rejecting a lot with 5% defective items.

Binomial probabilities can also be computed using Excel or Minitab.

Tables of binomial probabilities (see Table 5, Appendix B) can help reduce the computational effort in determining the probabilities of accepting lots. Selected binomial probabilities for $n = 15$ and $n = 20$ are listed in Table 20.5. Using this table, we can determine that if the lot contains 10% defective items, there is a .2059 probability that the $n = 15$, $c = 0$ sampling plan will indicate an acceptable lot. The probability that the $n = 15$, $c = 0$

TABLE 20.5 SELECTED BINOMIAL PROBABILITIES FOR SAMPLES OF SIZE 15 AND 20

		p								
n	*x*	.01	.02	.03	.04	.05	.10	.15	.20	.25
15	0	.8601	.7386	.6333	.5421	.4633	.2059	.0874	.0352	.0134
	1	.1303	.2261	.2938	.3388	.3658	.3432	.2312	.1319	.0668
	2	.0092	.0323	.0636	.0988	.1348	.2669	.2856	.2309	.1559
	3	.0004	.0029	.0085	.0178	.0307	.1285	.2184	.2501	.2252
	4	.0000	.0002	.0008	.0022	.0049	.0428	.1156	.1876	.2252
	5	.0000	.0000	.0001	.0002	.0006	.0105	.0449	.1032	.1651
	6	.0000	.0000	.0000	.0000	.0000	.0019	.0132	.0430	.0917
	7	.0000	.0000	.0000	.0000	.0000	.0003	.0030	.0138	.0393
	8	.0000	.0000	.0000	.0000	.0000	.0000	.0005	.0035	.0131
	9	.0000	.0000	.0000	.0000	.0000	.0000	.0001	.0007	.0034
	10	.0000	.0000	.0000	.0000	.0000	.0000	.0000	.0001	.0007
20	0	.8179	.6676	.5438	.4420	.3585	.1216	.0388	.0115	.0032
	1	.1652	.2725	.3364	.3683	.3774	.2702	.1368	.0576	.0211
	2	.0159	.0528	.0988	.1458	.1887	.2852	.2293	.1369	.0669
	3	.0010	.0065	.0183	.0364	.0596	.1901	.2428	.2054	.1339
	4	.0000	.0006	.0024	.0065	.0133	.0898	.1821	.2182	.1897
	5	.0000	.0000	.0002	.0009	.0022	.0319	.1028	.1746	.2023
	6	.0000	.0000	.0000	.0001	.0003	.0089	.0454	.1091	.1686
	7	.0000	.0000	.0000	.0000	.0000	.0020	.0160	.0545	.1124
	8	.0000	.0000	.0000	.0000	.0000	.0004	.0046	.0222	.0609
	9	.0000	.0000	.0000	.0000	.0000	.0001	.0011	.0074	.0271
	10	.0000	.0000	.0000	.0000	.0000	.0000	.0002	.0020	.0099
	11	.0000	.0000	.0000	.0000	.0000	.0000	.0000	.0005	.0030
	12	.0000	.0000	.0000	.0000	.0000	.0000	.0000	.0001	.0008

TABLE 20.6 PROBABILITY OF ACCEPTING THE LOT FOR THE KALI PROBLEM WITH $n = 15$ AND $c = 0$

Percent Defective in the Lot	Probability of Accepting the Lot
1	.8601
2	.7386
3	.6333
4	.5421
5	.4633
10	.2059
15	.0874
20	.0352
25	.0134

sampling plan will lead to the acceptance of lots with 1%, 2%, 3%, . . . defective items is summarized in Table 20.6.

Using the probabilities in Table 20.6, a graph of the probability of accepting the lot versus the percent defective in the lot can be drawn as shown in Figure 20.12. This graph, or curve, is called the **operating characteristic (OC) curve** for the $n = 15$, $c = 0$ acceptance sampling plan.

Perhaps we should consider other sampling plans, ones with different sample sizes n or different acceptance criteria c. First consider the case in which the sample size remains $n = 15$ but the acceptance criterion increases from $c = 0$ to $c = 1$. That is, we will now accept the lot if zero or one defective component is found in the sample. For a lot with 5% defective items ($p = .05$), Table 20.5 shows that with $n = 15$ and $p = .05$, $f(0) = .4633$

FIGURE 20.12 OPERATING CHARACTERISTIC CURVE FOR THE $n = 15$, $c = 0$ ACCEPTANCE SAMPLING PLAN

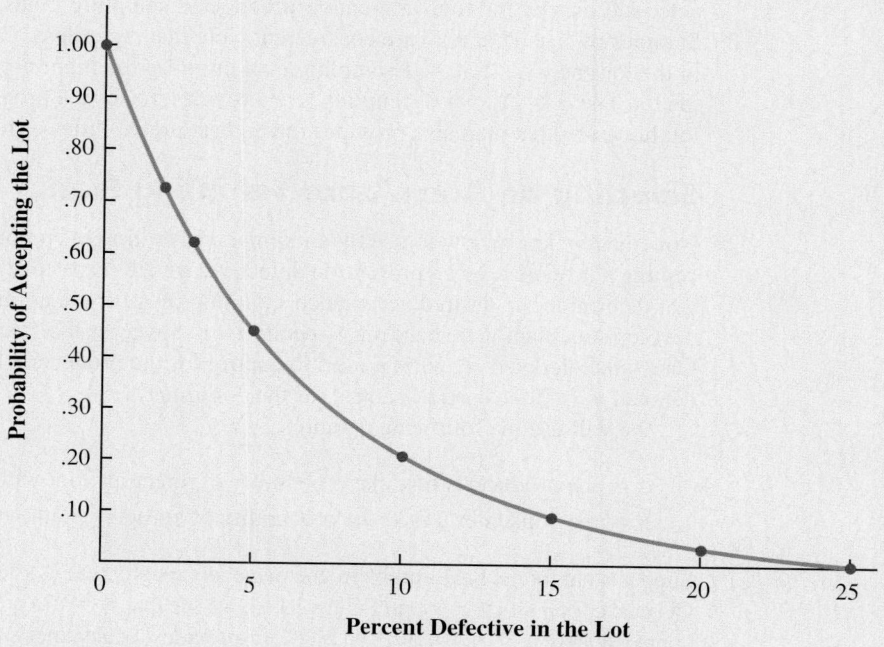

FIGURE 20.13 OPERATING CHARACTERISTIC CURVES FOR FOUR ACCEPTANCE SAMPLING PLANS

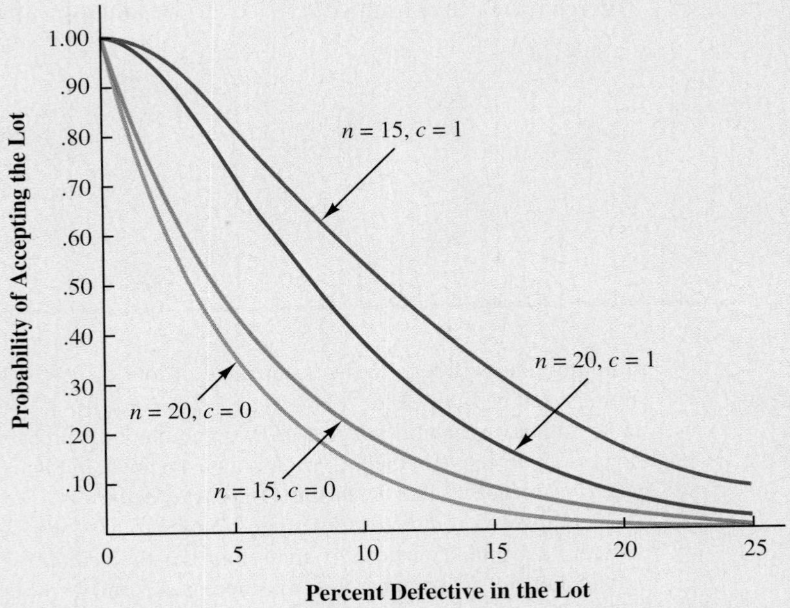

and $f(1) = .3658$. Thus, there is a $.4633 + .3658 = .8291$ probability that the $n = 15, c = 1$ plan will lead to the acceptance of a lot with 5% defective items.

Continuing these calculations we obtain Figure 20.13, which shows the operating characteristic curves for four alternative acceptance sampling plans for the KALI problem. Samples of size 15 and 20 are considered. Note that regardless of the proportion defective in the lot, the $n = 15$, $c = 1$ sampling plan provides the highest probabilities of accepting the lot. The $n = 20$, $c = 0$ sampling plan provides the lowest probabilities of accepting the lot; however, that plan also provides the highest probabilities of rejecting the lot.

Selecting an Acceptance Sampling Plan

Now that we know how to use the binomial distribution to compute the probability of accepting a lot with a given proportion defective, we are ready to select the values of n and c that determine the desired acceptance sampling plan for the application being studied. To develop this plan, managers must specify two values for the fraction defective in the lot. One value, denoted p_0, will be used to control for the producer's risk, and the other value, denoted p_1, will be used to control for the consumer's risk.

We will use the following notation.

α = the producer's risk; the probability of rejecting a lot with p_0 defective items

β = the consumer's risk; the probability of accepting a lot with p_1 defective items

Suppose that for the KALI problem, the managers specify that $p_0 = .03$ and $p_1 = .15$. From the OC curve for $n = 15$, $c = 0$ in Figure 20.14, we see that $p_0 = .03$ provides a producer's risk of approximately $1 - .63 = .37$, and $p_1 = .15$ provides a consumer's risk of approximately .09. Thus, if the managers are willing to tolerate both a .37 probability of rejecting a lot with 3%

FIGURE 20.14 OPERATING CHARACTERISTIC CURVE FOR $n = 15$, $c = 0$ WITH $p_0 = .03$ AND $p_1 = .15$

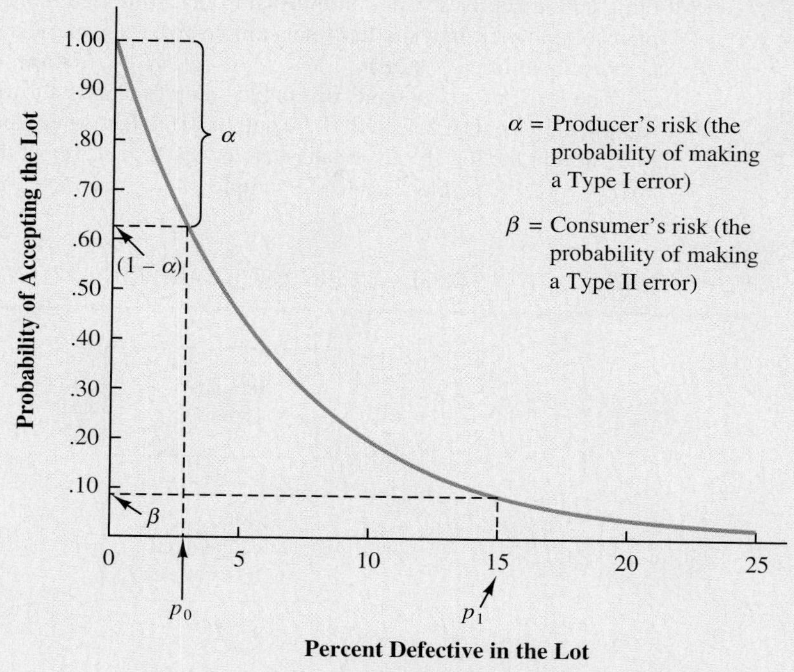

defective items (producer's risk) and a .09 probability of accepting a lot with 15% defective items (consumer's risk), the $n = 15$, $c = 0$ acceptance sampling plan would be acceptable.

Suppose, however, that the managers request a producer's risk of $\alpha = .10$ and a consumer's risk of $\beta = .20$. We see that now the $n = 15$, $c = 0$ sampling plan has a better-than-desired consumer's risk but an unacceptably large producer's risk. The fact that $\alpha = .37$ indicates that 37% of the lots will be erroneously rejected when only 3% of the items in them are defective. The producer's risk is too high, and a different acceptance sampling plan should be considered.

Exercise 13 at the end of this section will ask you to compute the producer's risk and the consumer's risk for the $n = 20$, $c = 1$ sampling plan.

Using $p_0 = .03$, $\alpha = .10$, $p_1 = .15$, and $\beta = .20$, Figure 20.13 shows that the acceptance sampling plan with $n = 20$ and $c = 1$ comes closest to meeting both the producer's and the consumer's risk requirements.

As shown in this section, several computations and several operating characteristic curves may need to be considered to determine the sampling plan with the desired producer's and consumer's risk. Fortunately, tables of sampling plans are published. For example, the American Military Standard Table, MIL-STD-105D, provides information helpful in designing acceptance sampling plans. More advanced texts on quality control, such as those listed in the bibliography, describe the use of such tables. The advanced texts also discuss the role of sampling costs in determining the optimal sampling plan.

Multiple Sampling Plans

The acceptance sampling procedure we presented for the KALI problem is a *single-sample* plan. It is called a single-sample plan because only one sample or sampling stage is used. After the number of defective components in the sample is determined, a decision must be made to accept or reject the lot. An alternative to the single-sample plan is a **multiple sampling plan**, in which two or more stages of sampling are used. At each stage a decision is made among three possibilities: stop sampling and accept the lot, stop sampling and reject the lot, or continue sampling. Although more complex, multiple sampling plans often result in a smaller total sample size than single-sample plans with the same α and β probabilities.

The logic of a two-stage, or double-sample, plan is shown in Figure 20.15. Initially a sample of n_1 items is selected. If the number of defective components x_1 is less than or equal to c_1, accept the lot. If x_1 is greater than or equal to c_2, reject the lot. If x_1 is between c_1 and c_2 ($c_1 < x_1 < c_2$), select a second sample of n_2 items. Determine the combined, or total,

FIGURE 20.15 A TWO-STAGE ACCEPTANCE SAMPLING PLAN

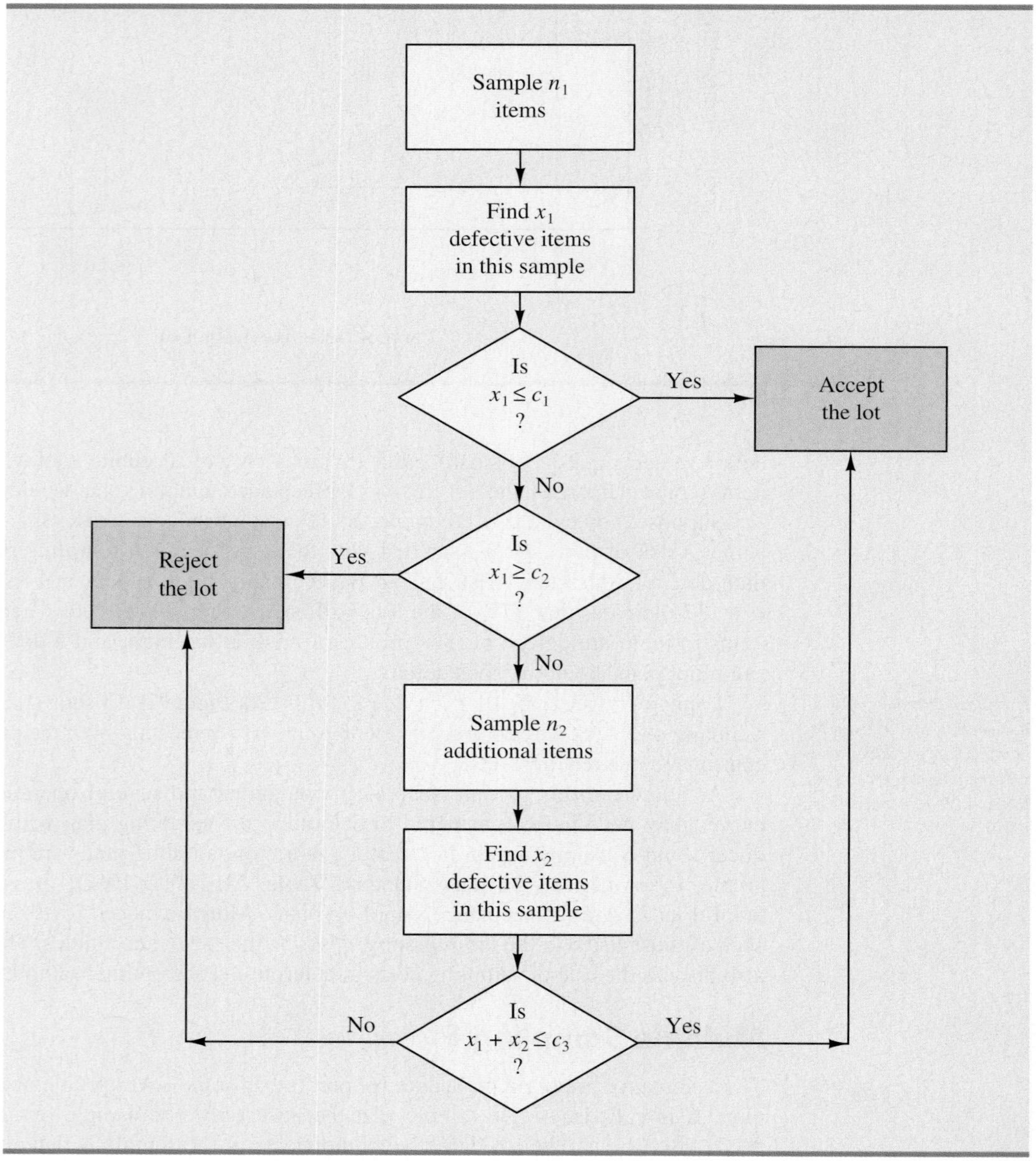

number of defective components from the first sample (x_1) and the second sample (x_2). If $x_1 + x_2 \leq c_3$, accept the lot; otherwise reject the lot. The development of the double-sample plan is more difficult because the sample sizes n_1 and n_2 and the acceptance numbers c_1, c_2, and c_3 must meet both the producer's and consumer's risks desired.

NOTES AND COMMENTS

1. The use of the binomial distribution for acceptance sampling is based on the assumption of large lots. If the lot size is small, the hypergeometric distribution is appropriate. Experts in the field of quality control indicate that the Poisson distribution provides a good approximation for acceptance sampling when the sample size is at least 16, the lot size is at least 10 times the sample size, and p is less than .1. For larger sample sizes, the normal approximation to the binomial distribution can be used.
2. In the MIL-ST-105D sampling tables, p_0 is called the acceptable quality level (AQL). In some sampling tables, p_1 is called the lot tolerance percent defective (LTPD) or the rejectable quality level (RQL). Many of the published sampling plans also use quality indexes such as the indifference quality level (IQL) and the average outgoing quality limit (AOQL). The more advanced texts listed in the bibliography provide a complete discussion of these other indexes.
3. In this section we provided an introduction to *attributes sampling plans.* In these plans each item sampled is classified as nondefective or defective. In *variables sampling plans,* a sample is taken and a measurement of the quality characteristic is taken. For example, for gold jewelry a measurement of quality may be the amount of gold it contains. A simple statistic such as the average amount of gold in the sample jewelry is computed and compared with an allowable value to determine whether to accept or reject the lot.

Exercises

Methods

SELF test

10. For an acceptance sampling plan with $n = 25$ and $c = 0$, find the probability of accepting a lot that has a defect rate of 2%. What is the probability of accepting the lot if the defect rate is 6%?
11. Consider an acceptance sampling plan with $n = 20$ and $c = 0$. Compute the producer's risk for each of the following cases.
    a. The lot has a defect rate of 2%.
    b. The lot has a defect rate of 6%.
12. Repeat exercise 11 for the acceptance sampling plan with $n = 20$ and $c = 1$. What happens to the producer's risk as the acceptance number c is increased? Explain.

Applications

13. Refer to the KALI problem presented in this section. The quality control manager requested a producer's risk of .10 when p_0 was .03 and a consumer's risk of .20 when p_1 was .15. Consider the acceptance sampling plan based on a sample size of 20 and an acceptance number of 1. Answer the following questions.
    a. What is the producer's risk for the $n = 20$, $c = 1$ sampling plan?
    b. What is the consumer's risk for the $n = 20$, $c = 1$ sampling plan?
    c. Does the $n = 20$, $c = 1$ sampling plan satisfy the risks requested by the quality control manager? Discuss.
14. To inspect incoming shipments of raw materials, a manufacturer is considering samples of sizes 10, 15, and 20. Use the binomial probabilities from Table 5 of Appendix B to select a sampling plan that provides a producer's risk of $\alpha = .03$ when p_0 is .05 and a consumer's risk of $\beta = .12$ when p_1 is .30.

15. A domestic manufacturer of watches purchases quartz crystals from a Swiss firm. The crystals are shipped in lots of 1000. The acceptance sampling procedure uses 20 randomly selected crystals.
    a. Construct operating characteristic curves for acceptance numbers of 0, 1, and 2.
    b. If p_0 is .01 and $p_1 = .08$, what are the producer's and consumer's risks for each sampling plan in part (a)?

Summary

In this chapter we discussed how statistical methods can be used to assist in the control of quality. We first presented the $\bar{x}$, R, p, and np control charts as graphical aids in monitoring process quality. Control limits are established for each chart; samples are selected periodically, and the data points plotted on the control chart. Data points outside the control limits indicate that the process is out of control and that corrective action should be taken. Patterns of data points within the control limits can also indicate potential quality control problems and suggest that corrective action may be warranted.

We also considered the technique known as acceptance sampling. With this procedure, a sample is selected and inspected. The number of defective items in the sample provides the basis for accepting or rejecting the lot. The sample size and the acceptance criterion can be adjusted to control both the producer's risk (Type I error) and the consumer's risk (Type II error).

Glossary

Total quality (TQ) A total system approach to improving customer satisfaction and lowering real cost through a strategy of continuous improvement and learning.

Six Sigma A methodology that uses measurement and statistical analysis to achieve a level of quality so good that for every million opportunities no more than 3.4 defects will occur.

Quality control A series of inspections and measurements that determine whether quality standards are being met.

Assignable causes Variations in process outputs that are due to factors such as machine tools wearing out, incorrect machine settings, poor-quality raw materials, operator error, and so on. Corrective action should be taken when assignable causes of output variation are detected.

Common causes Normal or natural variations in process outputs that are due purely to chance. No corrective action is necessary when output variations are due to common causes.

Control chart A graphical tool used to help determine whether a process is in control or out of control.

$\bar{x}$ chart A control chart used when the quality of the output of a process is measured in terms of the mean value of a variable such as a length, weight, temperature, and so on.

***R* chart** A control chart used when the quality of the output of a process is measured in terms of the range of a variable.

***p* chart** A control chart used when the quality of the output of a process is measured in terms of the proportion defective.

***np* chart** A control chart used to monitor the quality of the output of a process in terms of the number of defective items.

Lot A group of items such as incoming shipments of raw materials or purchased parts as well as finished goods from final assembly.

Acceptance sampling A statistical method in which the number of defective items found in a sample is used to determine whether a lot should be accepted or rejected.

Producer's risk The risk of rejecting a good-quality lot; a Type I error.

Consumer's risk The risk of accepting a poor-quality lot; a Type II error.

Acceptance criterion The maximum number of defective items that can be found in the sample and still indicate an acceptable lot.

Operating characteristic (OC) curve A graph showing the probability of accepting the lot as a function of the percentage defective in the lot. This curve can be used to help determine whether a particular acceptance sampling plan meets both the producer's and the consumer's risk requirements.

Multiple sampling plan A form of acceptance sampling in which more than one sample or stage is used. On the basis of the number of defective items found in a sample, a decision will be made to accept the lot, reject the lot, or continue sampling.

Key Formulas

Standard Error of the Mean

$$\sigma_{\bar{x}} = \frac{\sigma}{\sqrt{n}} \tag{20.1}$$

Control Limits for an $\bar{x}$ Chart: Process Mean and Standard Deviation Known

$$\text{UCL} = \mu + 3\sigma_{\bar{x}} \tag{20.2}$$
$$\text{LCL} = \mu - 3\sigma_{\bar{x}} \tag{20.3}$$

Overall Sample Mean

$$\bar{\bar{x}} = \frac{\bar{x}_1 + \bar{x}_2 + \cdots + \bar{x}_k}{k} \tag{20.4}$$

Average Range

$$\bar{R} = \frac{R_1 + R_2 + \cdots + R_k}{k} \tag{20.5}$$

Control Limits for an $\bar{x}$ Chart: Process Mean and Standard Deviation Unknown

$$\bar{\bar{x}} \pm A_2\bar{R} \tag{20.8}$$

Control Limits for an *R* Chart

$$\text{UCL} = \bar{R}D_4 \tag{20.14}$$
$$\text{LCL} = \bar{R}D_3 \tag{20.15}$$

Standard Error of the Proportion

$$\sigma_{\bar{p}} = \sqrt{\frac{p(1-p)}{n}} \tag{20.16}$$

Control Limits for a *p* Chart

$$\text{UCL} = p + 3\sigma_{\bar{p}} \tag{20.17}$$
$$\text{LCL} = p - 3\sigma_{\bar{p}} \tag{20.18}$$

Control Limits for an *np* Chart

$$\text{UCL} = np + 3\sqrt{np(1-p)} \tag{20.19}$$
$$\text{LCL} = np - 3\sqrt{np(1-p)} \tag{20.20}$$

Binomial Probability Function for Acceptance Sampling

$$f(x) = \frac{n!}{x!(n-x)!} p^x (1-p)^{(n-x)} \qquad (20.21)$$

Supplementary Exercises

16. Samples of size 5 provided the following 20 sample means for a production process that is believed to be in control.

95.72	95.24	95.18
95.44	95.46	95.32
95.40	95.44	95.08
95.50	95.80	95.22
95.56	95.22	95.04
95.72	94.82	95.46
95.60	95.78	

a. Based on these data, what is an estimate of the mean when the process is in control?
b. Assume that the process standard deviation is $\sigma = .50$. Develop the $\bar{x}$ control chart for this production process. Assume that the mean of the process is the estimate developed in part (a).
c. Do any of the 20 sample means indicate that the process was out of control?

17. Product filling weights are normally distributed with a mean of 350 grams and a standard deviation of 15 grams.
a. Develop the control limits for the $\bar{x}$ chart for samples of size 10, 20, and 30.
b. What happens to the control limits as the sample size is increased?
c. What happens when a Type I error is made?
d. What happens when a Type II error is made?
e. What is the probability of a Type I error for samples of size 10, 20, and 30?
f. What is the advantage of increasing the sample size for control chart purposes? What error probability is reduced as the sample size is increased?

18. Twenty-five samples of size 5 resulted in $\bar{\bar{x}} = 5.42$ and $\bar{R} = 2.0$. Compute control limits for the $\bar{x}$ and R charts, and estimate the standard deviation of the process.

19. The following are quality control data for a manufacturing process at Kensport Chemical Company. The data show the temperature in degrees centigrade at five points in time during a manufacturing cycle. The company is interested in using control charts to monitor the temperature of its manufacturing process. Construct the $\bar{x}$ chart and R chart. What conclusions can be made about the quality of the process?

Sample	$\bar{x}$	R	Sample	$\bar{x}$	R
1	95.72	1.0	11	95.80	.6
2	95.24	.9	12	95.22	.2
3	95.18	.8	13	95.56	1.3
4	95.44	.4	14	95.22	.5
5	95.46	.5	15	95.04	.8
6	95.32	1.1	16	95.72	1.1
7	95.40	.9	17	94.82	.6
8	95.44	.3	18	95.46	.5
9	95.08	.2	19	95.60	.4
10	95.50	.6	20	95.74	.6

20. The following were collected for the Master Blend Coffee production process. The data show the filling weights based on samples of 3-pound cans of coffee. Use these data to construct the $\bar{x}$ and R charts. What conclusions can be made about the quality of the production process?

CD file

Coffee

	Observations				
Sample	1	2	3	4	5
1	3.05	3.08	3.07	3.11	3.11
2	3.13	3.07	3.05	3.10	3.10
3	3.06	3.04	3.12	3.11	3.10
4	3.09	3.08	3.09	3.09	3.07
5	3.10	3.06	3.06	3.07	3.08
6	3.08	3.10	3.13	3.03	3.06
7	3.06	3.06	3.08	3.10	3.08
8	3.11	3.08	3.07	3.07	3.07
9	3.09	3.09	3.08	3.07	3.09
10	3.06	3.11	3.07	3.09	3.07

21. Consider the following situations. Comment on whether the situation might cause concern about the quality of the process.
   a. A p chart has LCL = 0 and UCL = .068. When the process is in control, the proportion defective is .033. Plot the following seven sample results: .035, .062, .055, .049, .058, .066, and .055. Discuss.
   b. An $\bar{x}$ chart has LCL = 22.2 and UCL = 24.5. The mean is $\mu = 23.35$ when the process is in control. Plot the following seven sample results: 22.4, 22.6, 22.65, 23.2, 23.4, 23.85, and 24.1. Discuss.

22. Managers of 1200 different retail outlets make twice-a-month restocking orders from a central warehouse. Past experience shows that 4% of the orders result in one or more errors such as wrong item shipped, wrong quantity shipped, and item requested but not shipped. Random samples of 200 orders are selected monthly and checked for accuracy.
   a. Construct a control chart for this situation.
   b. Six months of data show the following numbers of orders with one or more errors: 10, 15, 6, 13, 8, and 17. Plot the data on the control chart. What does your plot indicate about the order process?

23. An $n = 10$, $c = 2$ acceptance sampling plan is being considered; assume that $p_0 = .05$ and $p_1 = .20$.
   a. Compute both producer's and consumer's risk for this acceptance sampling plan.
   b. Would the producer, the consumer, or both be unhappy with the proposed sampling plan?
   c. What change in the sampling plan, if any, would you recommend?

24. An acceptance sampling plan with $n = 15$ and $c = 1$ has been designed with a producer's risk of .075.
   a. Was the value of p_0 .01, .02, .03, .04, or .05? What does this value mean?
   b. What is the consumer's risk associated with this plan if p_1 is .25?

25. A manufacturer produces lots of a canned food product. Let p denote the proportion of the lots that do not meet the product quality specifications. An $n = 25$, $c = 0$ acceptance sampling plan will be used.
   a. Compute points on the operating characteristic curve when $p = .01, .03, .10$, and .20.
   b. Plot the operating characteristic curve.
   c. What is the probability that the acceptance sampling plan will reject a lot containing .01 defective?

Appendix 20.1 Control Charts with Minitab

CD file

Jensen

In this appendix we describe the steps required to generate Minitab control charts using the Jensen sample data shown in Table 20.2. The sample number appears in column C1. The first observation is in column C2, the second observation is in column C3, and so on. The following steps describe how to use Minitab to produce both the $\bar{x}$ chart and R chart simultaneously.

Step 1. Select the **Stat** menu
Step 2. Choose **Control Charts**
Step 3. Choose **Variables Charts for Subgroups**
Step 4. Choose **Xbar-R**
Step 5. When the Xbar-R Chart dialog box appears:
Select **Observations for a subgroup are in one row of columns**
In the box below, enter C2-C6
Select **Xbar-R Options**
Step 6. When the Xbar-R-Options dialog box appears:
Select the **Tests** tab
Choose **One point > 3.0 standard deviations from center line***
Click **OK**
Step 7. When the Xbar-R Chart dialog box appears:
Click **OK**

The $\bar{x}$ chart and the R chart will be shown together on the Minitab output. The choices available under step 3 of the preceding Minitab procedure provide access to a variety of control chart options. For example, the $\bar{x}$ and the R chart can be selected separately. Additional options include the p chart, the np chart, and others.

*Minitab provides several additional tests for detecting special causes of variation and out-of-control conditions. The user may select several of these tests simultaneously.

APPENDIXES

Appendix A: References and Bibliography

General

Bowerman, B. L., and R. T. O'Connell. *Applied Statistics: Improving Business Processes*. Irwin, 1996.

Freedman, D., R. Pisani, and R. Purves. *Statistics*, 3rd ed. W. W. Norton, 1997.

Hogg, R. V., and A. T. Craig. *Introduction to Mathematical Statistics,* 5th ed. Prentice Hall, 1994.

Hogg, R. V., and E. A. Tanis. *Probability and Statistical Inference,* 6th ed. Prentice Hall, 2001.

Joiner, B. L., and B. F. Ryan. *Minitab Handbook.* Brooks/Cole, 2000.

Miller, I., and M. Miller. *John E. Freund's Mathematical Statistics.* Prentice Hall, 1998.

Moore, D. S., and G. P. McCabe. *Introduction to the Practice of Statistics,* 4th ed. Freeman, 2003.

Roberts, H. *Data Analysis for Managers with Minitab.* Scientific Press, 1991.

Tanur, J. M. *Statistics: A Guide to the Unknown,* 4th ed. Brooks/Cole, 2002.

Tukey, J. W. *Exploratory Data Analysis.* Addison-Wesley, 1977.

Experimental Design

Cochran, W. G., and G. M. Cox. *Experimental Designs,* 2d ed. Wiley, 1992.

Hicks, C. R., and K. V. Turner. *Fundamental Concepts in the Design of Experiments,* 5th ed. Oxford University Press, 1999.

Montgomery, D. C. *Design and Analysis of Experiments,* 5th ed. Wiley, 2000.

Winer, B. J., K. M. Michels, and D. R. Brown. *Statistical Principles in Experimental Design,* 3rd ed. McGraw-Hill, 1991.

Wu, C. F. Jeff, and M. Hamada. *Experiments: Planning, Analysis, and Parameter Optimization.* Wiley, 2000.

Forecasting

Bowerman, B. L., and R. T. O'Connell. *Forecasting and Time Series: An Applied Approach,* 3rd ed. Brooks/Cole, 2000.

Box, G. E. P., G. C. Reinsel, and G. Jenkins. *Time Series Analysis: Forecasting and Control,* 3rd ed. Prentice Hall, 1994.

Makridakis, S., S. C. Wheelwright, and R. J. Hyndman. *Forecasting: Methods and Applications,* 3rd ed. Wiley, 1997.

Index Numbers

U.S. Department of Commerce. *Survey of Current Business.*

U.S. Department of Labor, Bureau of Labor Statistics. *CPI Detailed Report.*

U.S. Department of Labor. *Producer Price Indexes.*

Nonparametric Methods

Conover, W. J. *Practical Nonparametric Statistics,* 3rd ed. Wiley, 1998.

Gibbons, J. D., and S. Chakraborti. *Nonparametric Statistical Inference,* 3rd ed. Marcel Dekker, 1992.

Siegel, S., and N. J. Castellan. *Nonparametric Statistics for the Behavioral Sciences,* 2d ed. McGraw-Hill, 1990.

Sprent, P. *Applied Non-Parametric Statistical Methods.* CRC, 1993.

Probability

Hogg, R. V., and E. A. Tanis. *Probability and Statistical Inference,* 6th ed. Prentice Hall, 2001.

Ross, S. M. *Introduction to Probability Models,* 7th ed. Academic Press, 2000.

Wackerly, D. D., W. Mendenhall, and R. L. Scheaffer. *Mathematical Statistics with Applications,* 6th ed. Duxbury Press, 2002.

Quality Control

Deming, W. E. *Quality, Productivity, and Competitive Position.* MIT, 1982.

Evans, J. R., and W. M. Lindsay. *The Management and Control of Quality,* 5th ed. South-Western, 2001.

Gryna, F. M., and I. M. Juran. *Quality Planning and Analysis: From Product Development Through Use,* 3rd ed. McGraw-Hill, 1993.

Ishikawa, K. *Introduction to Quality Control.* Kluwer Academic, 1991.

Montgomery, D. C. *Introduction to Statistical Quality Control,* 4th ed. Wiley, 2000.

Regression Analysis

Belsley, D. A. *Conditioning Diagnostics: Collinearity and Weak Data in Regression.* Wiley, 1991.

Chatterjee, S., and B. Price. *Regression Analysis by Example,* 3rd ed. Wiley, 1999.

Draper, N. R., and H. Smith. *Applied Regression Analysis,* 3rd ed. Wiley, 1998.

Graybill, F. A., and H. Iyer. *Regression Analysis: Concepts and Applications.* Duxbury Press, 1994.

Hosmer, D. W., and S. Lemeshow. *Applied Logistic Regression,* 2d ed. Wiley, 2000.

Kleinbaum, D. G., L. L. Kupper, and K. E. Muller. *Applied Regression Analysis and Other Multivariate Methods,* 3rd ed. Duxbury Press, 1997.

Kutner, M. H., C. J. Nachtschiem, W. Wasserman, and J. Neter. *Applied Linear Statistical Models,* 4th ed. Irwin, 1996.

Mendenhall, M., and T. Sincich. *A Second Course in Statistics: Regression Analysis,* 5th ed. Prentice Hall, 1996.

Myers, R. H. *Classical and Modern Regression with Applications,* 2d ed. PWS, 1990.

Decision Analysis

Chernoff, H., and L. E. Moses. *Elementary Decision Theory.* Dover, 1987.

Clemen, R. T., and T. Reilly. *Making Hard Decisions with Decision Tools.* Duxbury Press, 2001.

Goodwin, P., and G. Wright. *Decision Analysis for Management Judgment,* 2d ed. Wiley, 1999.

Pratt, J. W., H. Raiffa, and R. Schlaifer. *Introduction to Statistical Decision Theory.* MIT Press, 1995.

Raiffa, H. *Decision Analysis.* McGraw-Hill, 1997.

Sampling

Cochran, W. G. *Sampling Techniques,* 3rd ed. Wiley, 1977.

Deming, W. E. *Some Theory of Sampling.* Dover, 1984.

Hansen, M. H., W. N. Hurwitz, W. G. Madow, and M. N. Hanson. *Sample Survey Methods and Theory.* Wiley, 1993.

Kish, L. *Survey Sampling.* Wiley, 1995.

Levy, P. S., and S. Lemeshow. *Sampling of Populations: Methods and Applications,* 3rd ed. Wiley, 1999.

Scheaffer, R. L., W. Mendenhall, and L. Ott. *Elementary Survey Sampling,* 5th ed. Duxbury Press, 1996.

Appendix B: Tables

TABLE 1 CUMULATIVE PROBABILITIES FOR THE STANDARD NORMAL DISTRIBUTION

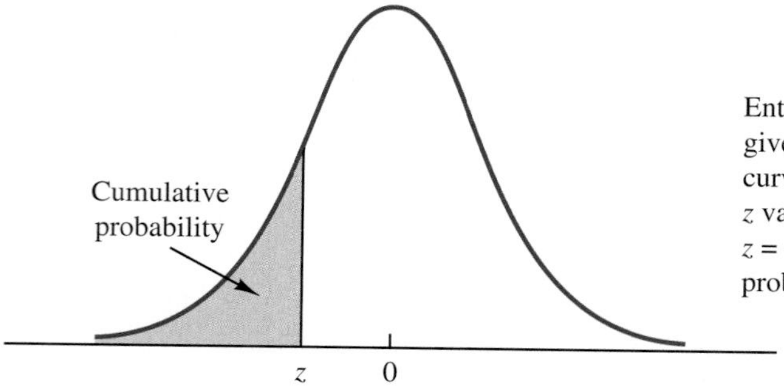

Entries in the table give the area under the curve to the left of the z value. For example, for $z = -.85$, the cumulative probability is .1977.

z	.00	.01	.02	.03	.04	.05	.06	.07	.08	.09
−3.0	.0013	.0013	.0013	.0012	.0012	.0011	.0011	.0011	.0010	.0010
−2.9	.0019	.0018	.0018	.0017	.0016	.0016	.0015	.0015	.0014	.0014
−2.8	.0026	.0025	.0024	.0023	.0023	.0022	.0021	.0021	.0020	.0019
−2.7	.0035	.0034	.0033	.0032	.0031	.0030	.0029	.0028	.0027	.0026
−2.6	.0047	.0045	.0044	.0043	.0041	.0040	.0039	.0038	.0037	.0036
−2.5	.0062	.0060	.0059	.0057	.0055	.0054	.0052	.0051	.0049	.0048
−2.4	.0082	.0080	.0078	.0075	.0073	.0071	.0069	.0068	.0066	.0064
−2.3	.0107	.0104	.0102	.0099	.0096	.0094	.0091	.0089	.0087	.0084
−2.2	.0139	.0136	.0132	.0129	.0125	.0122	.0119	.0116	.0113	.0110
−2.1	.0179	.0174	.0170	.0166	.0162	.0158	.0154	.0150	.0146	.0143
−2.0	.0228	.0222	.0217	.0212	.0207	.0202	.0197	.0192	.0188	.0183
−1.9	.0287	.0281	.0274	.0268	.0262	.0256	.0250	.0244	.0239	.0233
−1.8	.0359	.0351	.0344	.0336	.0329	.0322	.0314	.0307	.0301	.0294
−1.7	.0446	.0436	.0427	.0418	.0409	.0401	.0392	.0384	.0375	.0367
−1.6	.0548	.0537	.0526	.0516	.0505	.0495	.0485	.0475	.0465	.0455
−1.5	.0668	.0655	.0643	.0630	.0618	.0606	.0594	.0582	.0571	.0559
−1.4	.0808	.0793	.0778	.0764	.0749	.0735	.0721	.0708	.0694	.0681
−1.3	.0968	.0951	.0934	.0918	.0901	.0885	.0869	.0853	.0838	.0823
−1.2	.1151	.1131	.1112	.1093	.1075	.1056	.1038	.1020	.1003	.0985
−1.1	.1357	.1335	.1314	.1292	.1271	.1251	.1230	.1210	.1190	.1170
−1.0	.1587	.1562	.1539	.1515	.1492	.1469	.1446	.1423	.1401	.1379
−.9	.1841	.1814	.1788	.1762	.1736	.1711	.1685	.1660	.1635	.1611
−.8	.2119	.2090	.2061	.2033	.2005	.1977	.1949	.1922	.1894	.1867
−.7	.2420	.2389	.2358	.2327	.2296	.2266	.2236	.2206	.2177	.2148
−.6	.2743	.2709	.2676	.2643	.2611	.2578	.2546	.2514	.2483	.2451
−.5	.3085	.3050	.3015	.2981	.2946	.2912	.2877	.2843	.2810	.2776
−.4	.3446	.3409	.3372	.3336	.3300	.3264	.3228	.3192	.3156	.3121
−.3	.3821	.3783	.3745	.3707	.3669	.3632	.3594	.3557	.3520	.3483
−.2	.4207	.4168	.4129	.4090	.4052	.4013	.3974	.3936	.3897	.3859
−.1	.4602	.4562	.4522	.4483	.4443	.4404	.4364	.4325	.4286	.4247
−.0	.5000	.4960	.4920	.4880	.4840	.4801	.4761	.4721	.4681	.4641

TABLE 1 CUMULATIVE PROBABILITIES FOR THE STANDARD NORMAL DISTRIBUTION (*Continued*)

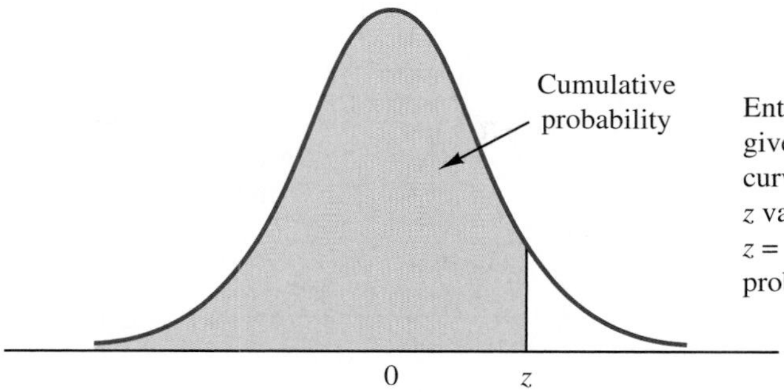

Entries in the table give the area under the curve to the left of the z value. For example, for $z = 1.25$, the cumulative probability is .8944.

z	.00	.01	.02	.03	.04	.05	.06	.07	.08	.09
.0	.5000	.5040	.5080	.5120	.5160	.5199	.5239	.5279	.5319	.5359
.1	.5398	.5438	.5478	.5517	.5557	.5596	.5636	.5675	.5714	.5753
.2	.5793	.5832	.5871	.5910	.5948	.5987	.6026	.6064	.6103	.6141
.3	.6179	.6217	.6255	.6293	.6331	.6368	.6406	.6443	.6480	.6517
.4	.6554	.6591	.6628	.6664	.6700	.6736	.6772	.6808	.6844	.6879
.5	.6915	.6950	.6985	.7019	.7054	.7088	.7123	.7157	.7190	.7224
.6	.7257	.7291	.7324	.7357	.7389	.7422	.7454	.7486	.7517	.7549
.7	.7580	.7611	.7642	.7673	.7704	.7734	.7764	.7794	.7823	.7852
.8	.7881	.7910	.7939	.7967	.7995	.8023	.8051	.8078	.8106	.8133
.9	.8159	.8186	.8212	.8238	.8264	.8289	.8315	.8340	.8365	.8389
1.0	.8413	.8438	.8461	.8485	.8508	.8531	.8554	.8577	.8599	.8621
1.1	.8643	.8665	.8686	.8708	.8729	.8749	.8770	.8790	.8810	.8830
1.2	.8849	.8869	.8888	.8907	.8925	.8944	.8962	.8980	.8997	.9015
1.3	.9032	.9049	.9066	.9082	.9099	.9115	.9131	.9147	.9162	.9177
1.4	.9192	.9207	.9222	.9236	.9251	.9265	.9279	.9292	.9306	.9319
1.5	.9332	.9345	.9357	.9370	.9382	.9394	.9406	.9418	.9429	.9441
1.6	.9452	.9463	.9474	.9484	.9495	.9505	.9515	.9525	.9535	.9545
1.7	.9554	.9564	.9573	.9582	.9591	.9599	.9608	.9616	.9625	.9633
1.8	.9641	.9649	.9656	.9664	.9671	.9678	.9686	.9693	.9699	.9706
1.9	.9713	.9719	.9726	.9732	.9738	.9744	.9750	.9756	.9761	.9767
2.0	.9772	.9778	.9783	.9788	.9793	.9798	.9803	.9808	.9812	.9817
2.1	.9821	.9826	.9830	.9834	.9838	.9842	.9846	.9850	.9854	.9857
2.2	.9861	.9864	.9868	.9871	.9875	.9878	.9881	.9884	.9887	.9890
2.3	.9893	.9896	.9898	.9901	.9904	.9906	.9909	.9911	.9913	.9913
2.4	.9918	.9920	.9922	.9925	.9927	.9929	.9931	.9932	.9934	.9936
2.5	.9938	.9940	.9941	.9943	.9945	.9946	.9948	.9949	.9951	.9952
2.6	.9953	.9955	.9956	.9957	.9959	.9960	.9961	.9962	.9963	.9964
2.7	.9965	.9966	.9967	.9968	.9969	.9970	.9971	.9972	.9973	.9974
2.8	.9974	.9975	.9976	.9977	.9977	.9978	.9979	.9979	.9980	.9981
2.9	.9981	.9982	.9982	.9983	.9984	.9984	.9985	.9985	.9986	.9986
3.0	.9986	.9987	.9987	.9988	.9988	.9989	.9989	.9989	.9990	.9990

TABLE 2 t DISTRIBUTION

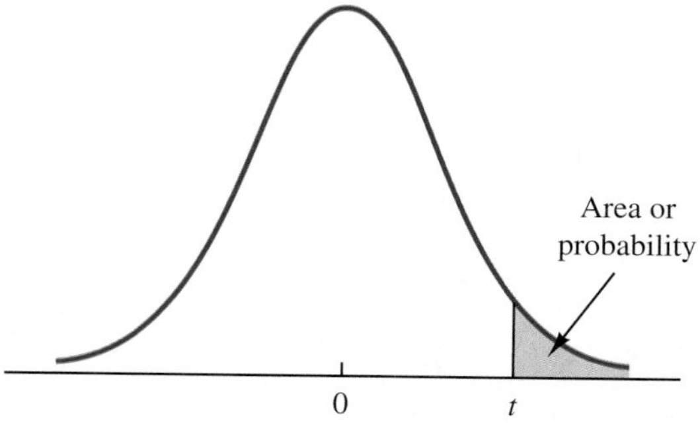

Entries in the table give t values for an area or probability in the upper tail of the t distribution. For example, with 10 degrees of freedom and a .05 area in the upper tail, $t_{.05} = 1.812$.

Degrees of Freedom	Area in Upper Tail					
	.20	.10	.05	.025	.01	.005
1	1.376	3.078	6.314	12.706	31.821	63.656
2	1.061	1.886	2.920	4.303	6.965	9.925
3	.978	1.638	2.353	3.182	4.541	5.841
4	.941	1.533	2.132	2.776	3.747	4.604
5	.920	1.476	2.015	2.571	3.365	4.032
6	.906	1.440	1.943	2.447	3.143	3.707
7	.896	1.415	1.895	2.365	2.998	3.499
8	.889	1.397	1.860	2.306	2.896	3.355
9	.883	1.383	1.833	2.262	2.821	3.250
10	.879	1.372	1.812	2.228	2.764	3.169
11	.876	1.363	1.796	2.201	2.718	3.106
12	.873	1.356	1.782	2.179	2.681	3.055
13	.870	1.350	1.771	2.160	2.650	3.012
14	.868	1.345	1.761	2.145	2.624	2.977
15	.866	1.341	1.753	2.131	2.602	2.947
16	.865	1.337	1.746	2.120	2.583	2.921
17	.863	1.333	1.740	2.110	2.567	2.898
18	.862	1.330	1.734	2.101	2.552	2.878
19	.861	1.328	1.729	2.093	2.539	2.861
20	.860	1.325	1.725	2.086	2.528	2.845
21	.859	1.323	1.721	2.080	2.518	2.831
22	.858	1.321	1.717	2.074	2.508	2.819
23	.858	1.319	1.714	2.069	2.500	2.807
24	.857	1.318	1.711	2.064	2.492	2.797
25	.856	1.316	1.708	2.060	2.485	2.787
26	.856	1.315	1.706	2.056	2.479	2.779
27	.855	1.314	1.703	2.052	2.473	2.771
28	.855	1.313	1.701	2.048	2.467	2.763
29	.854	1.311	1.699	2.045	2.462	2.756
30	.854	1.310	1.697	2.042	2.457	2.750
31	.853	1.309	1.696	2.040	2.453	2.744
32	.853	1.309	1.694	2.037	2.449	2.738
33	.853	1.308	1.692	2.035	2.445	2.733
34	.852	1.307	1.691	2.032	2.441	2.728

TABLE 2 *t* DISTRIBUTION (*Continued*)

Degrees of Freedom	Area in Upper Tail .20	.10	.05	.025	.01	.005
35	.852	1.306	1.690	2.030	2.438	2.724
36	.852	1.306	1.688	2.028	2.434	2.719
37	.851	1.305	1.687	2.026	2.431	2.715
38	.851	1.304	1.686	2.024	2.429	2.712
39	.851	1.304	1.685	2.023	2.426	2.708
40	.851	1.303	1.684	2.021	2.423	2.704
41	.850	1.303	1.683	2.020	2.421	2.701
42	.850	1.302	1.682	2.018	2.418	2.698
43	.850	1.302	1.681	2.017	2.416	2.695
44	.850	1.301	1.680	2.015	2.414	2.692
45	.850	1.301	1.679	2.014	2.412	2.690
46	.850	1.300	1.679	2.013	2.410	2.687
47	.849	1.300	1.678	2.012	2.408	2.685
48	.849	1.299	1.677	2.011	2.407	2.682
49	.849	1.299	1.677	2.010	2.405	2.680
50	.849	1.299	1.676	2.009	2.403	2.678
51	.849	1.298	1.675	2.008	2.402	2.676
52	.849	1.298	1.675	2.007	2.400	2.674
53	.848	1.298	1.674	2.006	2.399	2.672
54	.848	1.297	1.674	2.005	2.397	2.670
55	.848	1.297	1.673	2.004	2.396	2.668
56	.848	1.297	1.673	2.003	2.395	2.667
57	.848	1.297	1.672	2.002	2.394	2.665
58	.848	1.296	1.672	2.002	2.392	2.663
59	.848	1.296	1.671	2.001	2.391	2.662
60	.848	1.296	1.671	2.000	2.390	2.660
61	.848	1.296	1.670	2.000	2.389	2.659
62	.847	1.295	1.670	1.999	2.388	2.657
63	.847	1.295	1.669	1.998	2.387	2.656
64	.847	1.295	1.669	1.998	2.386	2.655
65	.847	1.295	1.669	1.997	2.385	2.654
66	.847	1.295	1.668	1.997	2.384	2.652
67	.847	1.294	1.668	1.996	2.383	2.651
68	.847	1.294	1.668	1.995	2.382	2.650
69	.847	1.294	1.667	1.995	2.382	2.649
70	.847	1.294	1.667	1.994	2.381	2.648
71	.847	1.294	1.667	1.994	2.380	2.647
72	.847	1.293	1.666	1.993	2.379	2.646
73	.847	1.293	1.666	1.993	2.379	2.645
74	.847	1.293	1.666	1.993	2.378	2.644
75	.846	1.293	1.665	1.992	2.377	2.643
76	.846	1.293	1.665	1.992	2.376	2.642
77	.846	1.293	1.665	1.991	2.376	2.641
78	.846	1.292	1.665	1.991	2.375	2.640
79	.846	1.292	1.664	1.990	2.374	2.639

TABLE 2 *t* DISTRIBUTION (*Continued*)

Degrees of Freedom	Area in Upper Tail .20	.10	.05	.025	.01	.005
80	.846	1.292	1.664	1.990	2.374	2.639
81	.846	1.292	1.664	1.990	2.373	2.638
82	.846	1.292	1.664	1.989	2.373	2.637
83	.846	1.292	1.663	1.989	2.372	2.636
84	.846	1.292	1.663	1.989	2.372	2.636
85	.846	1.292	1.663	1.988	2.371	2.635
86	.846	1.291	1.663	1.988	2.370	2.634
87	.846	1.291	1.663	1.988	2.370	2.634
88	.846	1.291	1.662	1.987	2.369	2.633
89	.846	1.291	1.662	1.987	2.369	2.632
90	.846	1.291	1.662	1.987	2.368	2.632
91	.846	1.291	1.662	1.986	2.368	2.631
92	.846	1.291	1.662	1.986	2.368	2.630
93	.846	1.291	1.661	1.986	2.367	2.630
94	.845	1.291	1.661	1.986	2.367	2.629
95	.845	1.291	1.661	1.985	2.366	2.629
96	.845	1.290	1.661	1.985	2.366	2.628
97	.845	1.290	1.661	1.985	2.365	2.627
98	.845	1.290	1.661	1.984	2.365	2.627
99	.845	1.290	1.660	1.984	2.364	2.626
100	.845	1.290	1.660	1.984	2.364	2.626
∞	.842	1.282	1.645	1.960	2.326	2.576

TABLE 3 CHI-SQUARE DISTRIBUTION

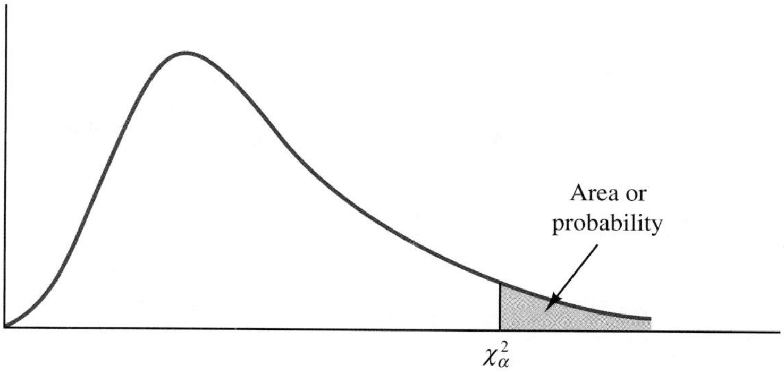

Entries in the table give χ^2_α values, where α is the area or probability in the upper tail of the chi-square distribution. For example, with 10 degrees of freedom and a .01 area in the upper tail, $\chi^2_{.01} = 23.209$.

Degrees of Freedom	Area in Upper Tail									
	.995	.99	.975	.95	.90	.10	.05	.025	.01	.005
1	.000	.000	.001	.004	.016	2.706	3.841	5.024	6.635	7.879
2	.010	.020	.051	.103	.211	4.605	5.991	7.378	9.210	10.597
3	.072	.115	.216	.352	.584	6.251	7.815	9.348	11.345	12.838
4	.207	.297	.484	.711	1.064	7.779	9.488	11.143	13.277	14.860
5	.412	.554	.831	1.145	1.610	9.236	11.070	12.832	15.086	16.750
6	.676	.872	1.237	1.635	2.204	10.645	12.592	14.449	16.812	18.548
7	.989	1.239	1.690	2.167	2.833	12.017	14.067	16.013	18.475	20.278
8	1.344	1.647	2.180	2.733	3.490	13.362	15.507	17.535	20.090	21.955
9	1.735	2.088	2.700	3.325	4.168	14.684	16.919	19.023	21.666	23.589
10	2.156	2.558	3.247	3.940	4.865	15.987	18.307	20.483	23.209	25.188
11	2.603	3.053	3.816	4.575	5.578	17.275	19.675	21.920	24.725	26.757
12	3.074	3.571	4.404	5.226	6.304	18.549	21.026	23.337	26.217	28.300
13	3.565	4.107	5.009	5.892	7.041	19.812	22.362	24.736	27.688	29.819
14	4.075	4.660	5.629	6.571	7.790	21.064	23.685	26.119	29.141	31.319
15	4.601	5.229	6.262	7.261	8.547	22.307	24.996	27.488	30.578	32.801
16	5.142	5.812	6.908	7.962	9.312	23.542	26.296	28.845	32.000	34.267
17	5.697	6.408	7.564	8.672	10.085	24.769	27.587	30.191	33.409	35.718
18	6.265	7.015	8.231	9.390	10.865	25.989	28.869	31.526	34.805	37.156
19	6.844	7.633	8.907	10.117	11.651	27.204	30.144	32.852	36.191	38.582
20	7.434	8.260	9.591	10.851	12.443	28.412	31.410	34.170	37.566	39.997
21	8.034	8.897	10.283	11.591	13.240	29.615	32.671	35.479	38.932	41.401
22	8.643	9.542	10.982	12.338	14.041	30.813	33.924	36.781	40.289	42.796
23	9.260	10.196	11.689	13.091	14.848	32.007	35.172	38.076	41.638	44.181
24	9.886	10.856	12.401	13.848	15.659	33.196	36.415	39.364	42.980	45.558
25	10.520	11.524	13.120	14.611	16.473	34.382	37.652	40.646	44.314	46.928
26	11.160	12.198	13.844	15.379	17.292	35.563	38.885	41.923	45.642	48.290
27	11.808	12.878	14.573	16.151	18.114	36.741	40.113	43.195	46.963	49.645
28	12.461	13.565	15.308	16.928	18.939	37.916	41.337	44.461	48.278	50.994
29	13.121	14.256	16.047	17.708	19.768	39.087	42.557	45.722	49.588	52.335

TABLE 3 CHI-SQUARE DISTRIBUTION (*Continued*)

Degrees of Freedom	Area in Upper Tail									
	.995	**.99**	**.975**	**.95**	**.90**	**.10**	**.05**	**.025**	**.01**	**.005**
30	13.787	14.953	16.791	18.493	20.599	40.256	43.773	46.979	50.892	53.672
35	17.192	18.509	20.569	22.465	24.797	46.059	49.802	53.203	57.342	60.275
40	20.707	22.164	24.433	26.509	29.051	51.805	55.758	59.342	63.691	66.766
45	24.311	25.901	28.366	30.612	33.350	57.505	61.656	65.410	69.957	73.166
50	27.991	29.707	32.357	34.764	37.689	63.167	67.505	71.420	76.154	79.490
55	31.735	33.571	36.398	38.958	42.060	68.796	73.311	77.380	82.292	85.749
60	35.534	37.485	40.482	43.188	46.459	74.397	79.082	83.298	88.379	91.952
65	39.383	41.444	44.603	47.450	50.883	79.973	84.821	89.177	94.422	98.105
70	43.275	45.442	48.758	51.739	55.329	85.527	90.531	95.023	100.425	104.215
75	47.206	49.475	52.942	56.054	59.795	91.061	96.217	100.839	106.393	110.285
80	51.172	53.540	57.153	60.391	64.278	96.578	101.879	106.629	112.329	116.321
85	55.170	57.634	61.389	64.749	68.777	102.079	107.522	112.393	118.236	122.324
90	59.196	61.754	65.647	69.126	73.291	107.565	113.145	118.136	124.116	128.299
95	63.250	65.898	69.925	73.520	77.818	113.038	118.752	123.858	129.973	134.247
100	67.328	70.065	74.222	77.929	82.358	118.498	124.342	129.561	135.807	140.170

TABLE 4 *F* DISTRIBUTION

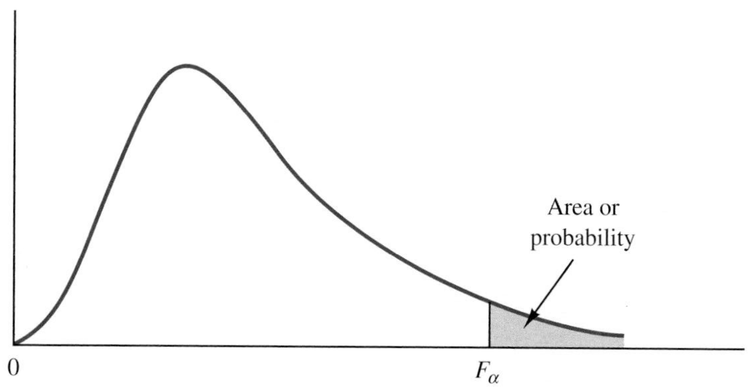

Entries in the table give F_α values, where α is the area or probability in the upper tail of the F distribution. For example, with 4 numerator degrees of freedom, 8 denominator degrees of freedom, and a .05 area in the upper tail, $F_{.05} = 3.84$.

Denominator Degrees of Freedom	Area in Upper Tail	Numerator Degrees of Freedom 1	2	3	4	5	6	7	8	9	10	15	20	25	30	40	60	100	1000
1	.10	39.86	49.50	53.59	55.83	57.24	58.20	58.91	59.44	59.86	60.19	61.22	61.74	62.05	62.26	62.53	62.79	63.01	63.30
	.05	161.45	199.50	215.71	224.58	230.16	233.99	236.77	238.88	240.54	241.88	245.95	248.02	249.26	250.10	251.14	252.20	253.04	254.19
	.025	647.79	799.48	864.15	899.60	921.83	937.11	948.20	956.64	963.28	968.63	984.87	993.08	998.09	1001.40	1005.60	1009.79	1013.16	1017.76
	.01	4052.18	4999.34	5403.53	5624.26	5763.96	5858.95	5928.33	5980.95	6022.40	6055.93	6156.97	6208.66	6239.86	6260.35	6286.43	6312.97	6333.92	6362.80
2	.10	8.53	9.00	9.16	9.24	9.29	9.33	9.35	9.37	9.38	9.39	9.42	9.44	9.45	9.46	9.47	9.47	9.48	9.49
	.05	18.51	19.00	19.16	19.25	19.30	19.33	19.35	19.37	19.38	19.40	19.43	19.45	19.46	19.46	19.47	19.48	19.49	19.49
	.025	38.51	39.00	39.17	39.25	39.30	39.33	39.36	39.37	39.39	39.40	39.43	39.45	39.46	39.46	39.47	39.48	39.49	39.50
	.01	98.50	99.00	99.16	99.25	99.30	99.33	99.36	99.38	99.39	99.40	99.43	99.45	99.46	99.47	99.48	99.48	99.49	99.50
3	.10	5.54	5.46	5.39	5.34	5.31	5.28	5.27	5.25	5.24	5.23	5.20	5.18	5.17	5.17	5.16	5.15	5.14	5.13
	.05	10.13	9.55	9.28	9.12	9.01	8.94	8.89	8.85	8.81	8.79	8.70	8.66	8.63	8.62	8.59	8.57	8.55	8.53
	.025	17.44	16.04	15.44	15.10	14.88	14.73	14.62	14.54	14.47	14.42	14.25	14.17	14.12	14.08	14.04	13.99	13.96	13.91
	.01	34.12	30.82	29.46	28.71	28.24	27.91	27.67	27.49	27.34	27.23	26.87	26.69	26.58	26.50	26.41	26.32	26.24	26.14
4	.10	4.54	4.32	4.19	4.11	4.05	4.01	3.98	3.95	3.94	3.92	3.87	3.84	3.83	3.82	3.80	3.79	3.78	3.76
	.05	7.71	6.94	6.59	6.39	6.26	6.16	6.09	6.04	6.00	5.96	5.86	5.80	5.77	5.75	5.72	5.69	5.66	5.63
	.025	12.22	10.65	9.98	9.60	9.36	9.20	9.07	8.98	8.90	8.84	8.66	8.56	8.50	8.46	8.41	8.36	8.32	8.26
	.01	21.20	18.00	16.69	15.98	15.52	15.21	14.98	14.80	14.66	14.55	14.20	14.02	13.91	13.84	13.75	13.65	13.58	13.47
5	.10	4.06	3.78	3.62	3.52	3.45	3.40	3.37	3.34	3.32	3.30	3.324	3.21	3.19	3.17	3.16	3.14	3.13	3.11
	.05	6.61.	5.79	5.41	5.19	5.05	4.95	4.88	4.82	4.77	4.74	4.62	4.56	4.52	4.50	4.46	4.43	4.41	4.37
	.025	10.01	8.43	7.76	7.39	7.15	6.98	6.85	6.76	6.68	6.62	6.43	6.33	6.27	6.23	6.18	6.12	6.08	6.02
	.01	16.26	13.27	12.06	11.39	10.97	10.67	10.46	10.29	10.16	10.05	9.72	9.55	9.45	9.38	9.29	9.20	9.13	9.03

TABLE 4 *F* DISTRIBUTION (*Continued*)

Denominator Degrees of Freedom	Area in Upper Tail	Numerator Degrees of Freedom 1	2	3	4	5	6	7	8	9	10	15	20	25	30	40	60	100	1000
6	.10	3.78	3.46	3.29	3.18	3.11	3.05	3.01	2.98	2.96	2.94	2.87	2.84	2.81	2.80	2.78	2.76	2.75	2.72
	.05	5.99	5.14	4.76	4.53	4.39	4.28	4.21	4.15	4.10	4.06	3.94	3.87	3.83	3.81	3.77	3.74	3.71	3.67
	.025	8.81	7.26	6.60	6.23	5.99	5.82	5.70	5.60	5.52	5.46	5.27	5.17	5.11	5.07	5.01	4.96	4.92	4.86
	.01	13.75	10.92	9.78	9.15	8.75	8.47	8.26	8.10	7.98	7.87	7.56	7.40	7.30	7.23	7.14	7.06	6.99	6.89
7	.10	3.59	3.26	3.07	2.96	2.88	2.83	2.78	2.75	2.72	2.70	2.63	2.59	2.57	2.56	2.54	2.51	2.50	2.47
	.05	5.59	4.74	4.35	4.12	3.97	3.87	3.79	3.73	3.68	3.64	3.51	3.44	3.40	3.38	3.34	3.30	3.27	3.23
	.025	8.07	6.54	5.89	5.52	5.29	5.12	4.99	4.90	4.82	4.76	4.57	4.47	4.40	4.36	4.31	4.25	4.21	4.15
	.01	12.25	9.55	8.45	7.85	7.46	7.19	6.99	6.84	6.72	6.62	6.31	6.16	6.06	5.99	5.91	5.82	5.75	5.66
8	.10	3.46	3.11	2.92	2.81	2.73	2.67	2.62	2.59	2.56	2.54	2.46	2.42	2.40	2.38	2.36	2.34	2.32	2.30
	.05	5.32	4.46	4.07	3.84	3.69	3.58	3.50	3.44	3.39	3.35	3.22	3.15	3.11	3.08	3.04	3.01	2.97	2.93
	.025	7.57	6.06	5.42	5.05	4.82	4.65	4.53	4.43	4.36	4.30	4.10	4.00	3.94	3.89	3.84	3.78	3.74	3.68
	.01	11.26	8.65	7.59	7.01	6.63	6.37	6.18	6.03	5.91	5.81	5.52	5.36	5.26	5.20	5.12	5.03	4.96	4.87
9	.10	3.36	3.01	2.81	2.69	2.61	2.55	2.51	2.47	2.44	2.42	2.34	2.30	2.27	2.25	2.23	2.21	2.19	2.16
	.05	5.12	4.26	3.86	3.63	3.48	3.37	3.29	3.23	3.18	3.14	3.01	2.94	2.89	2.86	2.83	2.79	2.76	2.71
	.025	7.21	5.71	5.08	4.72	4.48	4.32	4.20	4.10	4.03	3.96	3.77	3.67	3.60	3.56	3.51	3.45	3.40	3.34
	.01	10.56	8.02	6.99	6.42	6.06	5.80	5.61	5.47	5.35	5.26	4.96	4.81	4.71	4.65	4.57	4.48	4.41	4.32
10	.10	3.29	2.92	2.73	2.61	2.52	2.46	2.41	2.38	2.35	2.32	2.24	2.20	2.17	2.16	2.13	2.11	2.09	2.06
	.05	4.96	4.10	3.71	3.48	3.33	3.22	3.14	3.07	3.02	2.98	2.85	2.77	2.73	2.70	2.66	2.62	2.59	2.54
	.025	6.94	5.46	4.83	4.47	4.24	4.07	3.95	3.85	3.78	3.72	3.52	3.42	3.35	3.31	3.26	3.20	3.15	3.09
	.01	10.04	7.56	6.55	5.99	5.64	5.39	5.20	5.06	4.94	4.85	4.56	4.41	4.31	4.25	4.17	4.08	4.01	3.92
11	.10	3.23	2.86	2.66	2.54	2.45	2.39	2.34	2.30	2.27	2.25	2.17	2.12	2.10	2.08	2.05	2.03	2.01	1.98
	.05	4.84	3.98	3.59	3.36	3.20	3.09	3.01	2.95	2.90	2.85	2.72	2.65	2.60	2.57	2.53	2.49	2.46	2.41
	.025	6.72	5.26	4.63	4.28	4.04	3.88	3.76	3.66	3.59	3.53	3.33	3.23	3.16	3.12	3.06	3.00	2.96	2.89
	.01	9.65	7.21	6.22	5.67	5.32	5.07	4.89	4.74	4.63	4.54	4.25	4.10	4.01	3.94	3.86	3.78	3.71	3.61
12	.10	3.18	2.81	2.61	2.48	2.39	2.33	2.28	2.24	2.21	2.19	2.10	2.06	2.03	2.01	1.99	1.96	1.94	1.91
	.05	4.75	3.89	3.49	3.26	3.11	3.00	2.91	2.85	2.80	2.75	2.62	2.54	2.50	2.47	2.43	2.38	2.35	2.30
	.025	6.55	5.10	4.47	4.12	3.89	3.73	3.61	3.51	3.44	3.37	3.18	3.07	3.01	2.96	2.91	2.85	2.80	2.73
	.01	9.33	6.93	5.95	5.41	5.06	4.82	4.64	4.50	4.39	4.30	4.01	3.86	3.76	3.70	3.62	3.54	3.47	3.37
13	.10	3.14	2.76	2.56	2.43	2.35	2.28	2.23	2.20	2.16	2.14	2.05	2.01	1.98	1.96	1.93	1.90	1.88	1.85
	.05	4.67	3.81	3.41	3.18	3.03	2.92	2.83	2.77	2.71	2.67	2.53	2.46	2.41	2.38	2.34	2.30	2.26	2.21
	.025	6.41	4.97	4.35	4.00	3.77	3.60	3.48	3.39	3.31	3.25	3.05	2.95	2.88	2.84	2.78	2.72	2.67	2.60
	.01	9.07	6.70	5.74	5.21	4.86	4.62	4.44	4.30	4.19	4.10	3.82	3.66	3.57	3.51	3.43	3.34	3.27	3.18
14	.10	3.10	2.73	2.52	2.39	2.31	2.24	2.19	2.15	2.12	2.10	2.01	1.96	1.93	1.99	1.89	1.86	1.83	1.80
	.05	4.60	3.74	3.34	3.11	2.96	2.85	2.76	2.70	2.65	2.60	2.46	2.39	2.34	2.31	2.27	2.22	2.19	2.14
	.025	6.30	4.86	4.24	3.89	3.66	3.50	3.38	3.29	3.21	3.15	2.95	2.84	2.78	2.73	2.67	2.61	2.56	2.50
	.01	8.86	6.51	5.56	5.04	4.69	4.46	4.28	4.14	4.03	3.94	3.66	3.51	3.41	3.35	3.27	3.18	3.11	3.02
15	.10	3.07	2.70	2.49	2.36	2.27	2.21	2.16	2.12	2.09	2.06	1.97	1.92	1.89	1.87	1.85	1.82	1.79	1.76
	.05	4.54	3.68	3.29	3.06	2.90	2.79	2.71	2.64	2.59	2.54	2.40	2.33	2.28	2.25	2.20	2.16	2.12	2.07
	.025	6.20	4.77	4.15	3.80	3.58	3.41	3.29	3.20	3.12	3.06	2.86	2.76	2.69	2.64	2.59	2.52	2.47	2.40
	.01	8.68	6.36	5.42	4.89	4.56	4.32	4.14	4.00	3.89	3.80	3.52	3.37	3.28	3.21	3.13	3.05	2.98	2.88

Denominator Degrees of Freedom	Area in Upper Tail	Numerator Degrees of Freedom																	
		1	2	3	4	5	6	7	8	9	10	15	20	25	30	40	60	100	1000
16	.10	3.05	2.67	2.46	2.33	2.24	2.18	2.13	2.09	2.06	2.03	1.94	1.89	1.86	1.84	1.81	1.78	1.76	1.72
	.05	4.49	3.63	3.24	3.01	2.85	2.74	2.66	2.59	2.54	2.49	2.35	2.28	2.23	2.19	2.15	2.11	2.07	2.02
	.025	6.12	4.69	4.08	3.73	3.50	3.34	3.22	3.12	3.05	2.99	2.79	2.68	2.61	2.57	2.51	2.45	2.40	2.32
	.01	8.53	6.23	5.29	4.77	4.44	4.20	4.03	3.89	3.78	3.69	3.41	3.26	3.16	3.10	3.02	2.93	2.86	2.76
17	.10	3.03	2.64	2.44	2.31	2.22	2.15	2.10	2.06	2.03	2.00	1.91	1.86	1.83	1.81	1.78	1.75	1.73	1.69
	.05	4.45	3.59	3.20	2.96	2.81	2.70	2.61	2.55	2.49	2.45	2.31	2.23	2.18	2.15	2.10	2.06	2.02	1.97
	.025	6.04	4.62	4.01	3.66	3.44	3.28	3.16	3.06	2.98	2.92	2.72	2.62	2.55	2.50	2.44	2.38	2.33	2.26
	.01	8.40	6.11	5.19	4.67	4.34	4.10	3.93	3.79	3.68	3.59	3.31	3.16	3.07	3.00	2.92	2.83	2.76	2.66
18	.10	3.01	2.62	2.42	2.29	2.20	2.13	2.08	2.04	2.00	1.98	1.89	1.84	1.80	1.78	1.75	1.72	1.70	1.66
	.05	4.41	3.55	3.16	2.93	2.77	2.66	2.58	2.51	2.46	2.41	2.27	2.19	2.14	2.11	2.06	2.02	1.98	1.92
	.025	5.98	4.56	3.95	3.61	3.38	3.22	3.10	3.01	2.93	2.87	2.67	2.56	2.49	2.44	2.38	2.32	2.27	2.20
	.01	8.29	6.01	5.09	4.58	4.25	4.01	3.84	3.71	3.60	3.51	3.23	3.08	2.98	2.92	2.84	2.75	2.68	2.58
19	.10	2.99	2.61	2.40	2.27	2.18	2.11	2.06	2.02	1.98	1.96	1.86	1.81	1.78	1.76	1.73	1.70	1.67	1.64
	.05	4.38	3.52	3.13	2.90	2.74	2.63	2.54	2.48	2.42	2.38	2.23	2.16	2.11	2.07	2.03	1.98	1.94	1.88
	.025	5.92	4.51	3.90	3.56	3.33	3.17	3.05	2.96	2.88	2.82	2.62	2.51	2.44	2.39	2.33	2.27	2.22	2.14
	.01	8.18	5.93	5.01	4.50	4.17	3.94	3.77	3.63	3.52	3.43	3.15	3.00	2.91	2.84	2.76	2.67	2.60	2.50
20	.10	2.97	2.59	2.38	2.25	2.16	2.09	2.04	2.00	1.96	1.94	1.84	1.79	1.76	1.74	1.71	1.68	1.65	1.61
	.05	4.35	3.49	3.10	2.87	2.71	2.60	2.51	2.45	2.39	2.35	2.20	2.12	2.07	2.04	1.99	1.95	1.91	1.85
	.025	5.87	4.46	3.86	3.51	3.29	3.13	3.01	2.91	2.84	2.77	2.57	2.46	2.40	2.35	2.29	2.22	2.17	2.09
	.01	8.10	5.85	4.94	4.43	4.10	3.87	3.70	3.56	3.46	3.37	3.09	2.94	2.84	2.78	2.69	2.61	2.54	2.43
21	.10	2.96	2.57	2.36	2.23	2.14	2.08	2.02	1.98	1.95	1.92	1.83	1.78	1.74	1.72	1.69	1.66	1.63	1.59
	.05	4.32	3.47	3.07	2.84	2.68	2.57	2.49	2.42	2.37	2.32	2.18	2.10	2.05	2.01	1.96	1.92	1.88	1.82
	.025	5.83	4.42	3.82	3.48	3.25	3.09	2.97	2.87	2.80	2.73	2.53	2.42	2.36	2.31	2.25	2.18	2.13	2.05
	.01	8.02	5.78	4.87	4.37	4.04	3.81	3.64	3.51	3.40	3.31	3.03	2.88	2.79	2.72	2.64	2.55	2.48	2.37
22	.10	2.95	2.56	2.35	2.22	2.13	2.06	2.01	1.97	1.93	1.90	1.81	1.76	1.73	1.70	1.67	1.64	1.61	1.57
	.05	4.30	3.44	3.05	2.82	2.66	2.55	2.46	2.40	2.34	2.30	2.15	2.07	2.02	1.98	1.94	1.89	1.85	1.79
	.025	5.79	4.38	3.78	3.44	3.22	3.05	2.93	2.84	2.76	2.70	2.50	2.39	2.32	2.27	2.21	2.14	2.09	2.01
	.01	7.95	5.72	4.82	4.31	3.99	3.76	3.59	3.45	3.35	3.26	2.98	2.83	2.73	2.67	2.58	2.50	2.42	2.32
23	.10	2.94	2.55	2.34	2.21	2.11	2.05	1.99	1.95	1.92	1.89	1.80	1.74	1.71	1.69	1.66	1.62	1.59	1.55
	.05	4.28	3.42	3.03	2.80	2.64	2.53	2.44	2.37	2.32	2.27	2.13	2.05	2.00	1.96	1.91	1.86	1.82	1.76
	.025	5.75	4.35	3.75	3.41	3.18	3.02	2.90	2.81	2.73	2.67	2.47	2.36	2.29	2.24	2.18	2.11	2.06	1.98
	.01	7.88	5.66	4.76	4.26	3.94	3.71	3.54	3.41	3.30	3.21	2.93	2.78	2.69	2.62	2.54	2.45	2.37	2.27
24	.10	2.93	2.54	2.33	2.19	2.10	2.04	1.98	1.94	1.91	1.88	1.78	1.73	1.70	1.67	1.64	1.61	1.58	1.54
	.05	4.26	3.40	3.01	2.78	2.62	2.51	2.42	2.36	2.30	2.25	2.11	2.03	1.97	1.94	1.89	1.84	1.80	1.74
	.025	5.72	4.32	3.72	3.38	3.15	2.99	2.87	2.78	2.70	2.64	2.44	2.33	2.26	2.21	2.15	2.08	2.02	1.94
	.01	7.82	5.61	4.72	4.22	3.90	3.67	3.50	3.36	3.26	3.17	2.89	2.74	2.64	2.58	2.49	2.40	2.33	2.22

TABLE 4 *F* DISTRIBUTION (*Continued*)

Denominator Degrees of Freedom	Area in Upper Tail	Numerator Degrees of Freedom																	
		1	2	3	4	5	6	7	8	9	10	15	20	25	30	40	60	100	1000
25	.10	2.92	2.53	2.32	2.18	2.09	2.02	1.97	1.93	1.89	1.87	1.77	1.72	1.68	1.66	1.63	1.59	1.56	1.52
	.05	4.24	3.39	2.99	2.76	2.60	2.49	2.40	2.34	2.28	2.24	2.09	2.01	1.96	1.92	1.87	1.82	1.78	1.72
	.025	5.69	4.29	3.69	3.35	3.13	2.97	2.85	2.75	2.68	2.61	2.41	2.30	2.23	2.18	2.12	2.05	2.00	1.91
	.01	7.77	5.57	4.68	4.18	3.85	3.63	3.46	3.32	3.22	3.13	2.85	2.70	2.60	2.54	2.45	2.36	2.29	2.18
26	.10	2.91	2.52	2.31	2.17	2.08	2.01	1.96	1.92	1.88	1.86	1.76	1.71	1.67	1.65	1.61	1.58	1.55	1.51
	.05	4.23	3.37	2.98	2.74	2.59	2.47	2.39	2.32	2.27	2.22	2.07	1.99	1.94	1.90	1.85	1.80	1.76	1.70
	.025	5.66	4.27	3.67	3.33	3.10	2.94	2.82	2.73	2.65	2.59	2.39	2.28	2.21	2.16	2.09	2.03	1.97	1.89
	.01	7.72	5.53	4.64	4.14	3.82	3.59	3.42	3.29	3.18	3.09	2.81	2.66	2.57	2.50	2.42	2.33	2.25	2.14
27	.10	2.90	2.51	2.30	2.17	2.07	2.00	1.95	1.91	1.87	1.85	1.75	1.70	1.66	1.64	1.60	1.57	1.54	1.50
	.05	4.21	3.35	2.96	2.73	2.57	2.46	2.37	2.31	2.25	2.20	2.06	1.97	1.92	1.88	1.84	1.79	1.74	1.68
	.025	5.63	4.24	3.65	3.31	3.08	2.92	2.80	2.71	2.63	2.57	2.36	2.25	2.18	2.13	2.07	2.00	1.94	1.86
	.01	7.68	5.49	4.60	4.11	3.78	3.56	3.39	3.26	3.15	3.06	2.78	2.63	2.54	2.47	2.38	2.29	2.22	2.11
28	.10	2.89	2.50	2.29	2.16	2.06	2.00	1.94	1.90	1.87	1.84	1.74	1.69	1.65	1.63	1.59	1.56	1.53	1.48
	.05	4.20	3.34	2.95	2.71	2.56	2.45	2.36	2.29	2.24	2.19	2.04	1.96	1.91	1.87	1.82	1.77	1.73	1.66
	.025	5.61	4.22	3.63	3.29	3.06	2.90	2.78	2.69	2.61	2.55	2.34	2.23	2.16	2.11	2.05	1.98	1.92	1.84
	.01	7.64	5.45	4.57	4.07	3.75	3.53	3.36	3.23	3.12	3.03	2.75	2.60	2.51	2.44	2.35	2.26	2.19	2.08
29	.10	2.89	2.50	2.28	2.15	2.06	1.99	1.93	1.89	1.86	1.83	1.73	1.68	1.64	1.62	1.58	1.55	1.52	1.47
	.05	4.18	3.33	2.93	2.70	2.55	2.43	2.35	2.28	2.22	2.18	2.03	1.94	1.89	1.85	1.81	1.75	1.71	1.65
	.025	5.59	4.20	3.61	3.27	3.04	2.88	2.76	2.67	2.59	2.53	2.32	2.21	2.14	2.09	2.03	1.96	1.90	1.82
	.01	7.60	5.42	4.54	4.04	3.73	3.50	3.33	3.20	3.09	3.00	2.73	2.57	2.48	2.41	2.33	2.23	2.16	2.05
30	.10	2.88	2.49	2.28	2.14	2.05	1.98	1.93	1.88	1.85	1.82	1.72	1.67	1.63	1.61	1.57	1.54	1.51	1.46
	.05	4.17	3.32	2.92	2.69	2.53	2.42	2.33	2.27	2.21	2.16	2.01	1.93	1.88	1.84	1.79	1.74	1.70	1.63
	.025	5.57	4.18	3.59	3.25	3.03	2.87	2.75	2.65	2.57	2.51	2.31	2.20	2.12	2.07	2.01	1.94	1.88	1.80
	.01	7.56	5.39	4.51	4.02	3.70	3.47	3.30	3.17	3.07	2.98	2.70	2.55	2.45	2.39	2.30	2.21	2.13	2.02
40	.10	2.84	2.44	2.23	2.09	2.00	1.93	1.87	1.83	1.79	1.76	1.66	1.61	1.57	1.54	1.51	1.47	1.43	1.38
	.05	4.08	3.23	2.84	2.61	2.45	2.34	2.25	2.18	2.12	2.08	1.92	1.84	1.78	1.74	1.69	1.64	1.59	1.52
	.025	5.42	4.05	3.46	3.13	2.90	2.74	2.62	2.53	2.45	2.39	2.18	2.07	1.99	1.94	1.88	1.80	1.74	1.65
	.01	7.31	5.18	4.31	3.83	3.51	3.29	3.12	2.99	2.89	2.80	2.52	2.37	2.27	2.20	2.11	2.02	1.94	1.82
60	.10	2.79	2.39	2.18	2.04	1.95	1.87	1.82	1.77	1.74	1.71	1.60	1.54	1.50	1.48	1.44	1.40	1.36	1.30
	.05	4.00	3.15	2.76	2.53	2.37	2.25	2.17	2.10	2.04	1.99	1.84	1.75	1.69	1.65	1.59	1.53	1.48	1.40
	.025	5.29	3.93	3.34	3.01	2.79	2.63	2.51	2.41	2.33	2.27	2.06	1.94	1.87	1.82	1.74	1.67	1.60	1.49
	.01	7.08	4.98	4.13	3.65	3.34	3.12	2.95	2.82	2.72	2.63	2.35	2.20	2.10	2.03	1.94	1.84	1.75	1.62
100	.10	2.76	2.36	2.14	2.00	1.91	1.83	1.78	1.73	1.69	1.66	1.56	1.49	1.45	1.42	1.38	1.34	1.29	1.22
	.05	3.94	3.09	2.70	2.46	2.31	2.19	2.10	2.03	1.97	1.93	1.77	1.68	1.62	1.57	1.52	1.45	1.39	1.30
	.025	5.18	3.83	3.25	2.92	2.70	2.54	2.42	2.32	2.24	2.18	1.97	1.85	1.77	1.71	1.64	1.56	1.48	1.36
	.01	6.90	4.82	3.98	3.51	3.21	2.99	2.82	2.69	2.59	2.50	2.22	2.07	1.97	1.89	1.80	1.69	1.60	1.45
1000	.10	2.71	2.31	2.09	1.95	1.85	1.78	1.72	1.68	1.64	1.61	1.49	1.43	1.38	1.35	1.30	1.25	1.20	1.08
	.05	3.85	3.00	2.61	2.38	2.22	2.11	2.02	1.95	1.89	1.84	1.68	1.58	1.52	1.47	1.41	1.33	1.26	1.11
	.025	5.04	3.70	3.13	2.80	2.58	2.42	2.30	2.20	2.13	2.06	1.85	1.72	1.64	1.58	1.50	1.41	1.32	1.13
	.01	6.66	4.63	3.80	3.34	3.04	2.82	2.66	2.53	2.43	2.34	2.06	1.90	1.79	1.72	1.61	1.50	1.38	1.16

TABLE 5 BINOMIAL PROBABILITIES

Entries in the table give the probability of x successes in n trials of a binomial experiment, where p is the probability of a success on one trial. For example, with six trials and $p = .05$, the probability of two successes is .0305.

		p								
n	*x*	.01	.02	.03	.04	.05	.06	.07	.08	.09
2	0	.9801	.9604	.9409	.9216	.9025	.8836	.8649	.8464	.8281
	1	.0198	.0392	.0582	.0768	.0950	.1128	.1302	.1472	.1638
	2	.0001	.0004	.0009	.0016	.0025	.0036	.0049	.0064	.0081
3	0	.9703	.9412	.9127	.8847	.8574	.8306	.8044	.7787	.7536
	1	.0294	.0576	.0847	.1106	.1354	.1590	.1816	.2031	.2236
	2	.0003	.0012	.0026	.0046	.0071	.0102	.0137	.0177	.0221
	3	.0000	.0000	.0000	.0001	.0001	.0002	.0003	.0005	.0007
4	0	.9606	.9224	.8853	.8493	.8145	.7807	.7481	.7164	.6857
	1	.0388	.0753	.1095	.1416	.1715	.1993	.2252	.2492	.2713
	2	.0006	.0023	.0051	.0088	.0135	.0191	.0254	.0325	.0402
	3	.0000	.0000	.0001	.0002	.0005	.0008	.0013	.0019	.0027
	4	.0000	.0000	.0000	.0000	.0000	.0000	.0000	.0000	.0001
5	0	.9510	.9039	.8587	.8154	.7738	.7339	.6957	.6591	.6240
	1	.0480	.0922	.1328	.1699	.2036	.2342	.2618	.2866	.3086
	2	.0010	.0038	.0082	.0142	.0214	.0299	.0394	.0498	.0610
	3	.0000	.0001	.0003	.0006	.0011	.0019	.0030	.0043	.0060
	4	.0000	.0000	.0000	.0000	.0000	.0001	.0001	.0002	.0003
	5	.0000	.0000	.0000	.0000	.0000	.0000	.0000	.0000	.0000
6	0	.9415	.8858	.8330	.7828	.7351	.6899	.6470	.6064	.5679
	1	.0571	.1085	.1546	.1957	.2321	.2642	.2922	.3164	.3370
	2	.0014	.0055	.0120	.0204	.0305	.0422	.0550	.0688	.0833
	3	.0000	.0002	.0005	.0011	.0021	.0036	.0055	.0080	.0110
	4	.0000	.0000	.0000	.0000	.0001	.0002	.0003	.0005	.0008
	5	.0000	.0000	.0000	.0000	.0000	.0000	.0000	.0000	.0000
	6	.0000	.0000	.0000	.0000	.0000	.0000	.0000	.0000	.0000
7	0	.9321	.8681	.8080	.7514	.6983	.6485	.6017	.5578	.5168
	1	.0659	.1240	.1749	.2192	.2573	.2897	.3170	.3396	.3578
	2	.0020	.0076	.0162	.0274	.0406	.0555	.0716	.0886	.1061
	3	.0000	.0003	.0008	.0019	.0036	.0059	.0090	.0128	.0175
	4	.0000	.0000	.0000	.0001	.0002	.0004	.0007	.0011	.0017
	5	.0000	.0000	.0000	.0000	.0000	.0000	.0000	.0001	.0001
	6	.0000	.0000	.0000	.0000	.0000	.0000	.0000	.0000	.0000
	7	.0000	.0000	.0000	.0000	.0000	.0000	.0000	.0000	.0000
8	0	.9227	.8508	.7837	.7214	.6634	.6096	.5596	.5132	.4703
	1	.0746	.1389	.1939	.2405	.2793	.3113	.3370	.3570	.3721
	2	.0026	.0099	.0210	.0351	.0515	.0695	.0888	.1087	.1288
	3	.0001	.0004	.0013	.0029	.0054	.0089	.0134	.0189	.0255
	4	.0000	.0000	.0001	.0002	.0004	.0007	.0013	.0021	.0031
	5	.0000	.0000	.0000	.0000	.0000	.0000	.0001	.0001	.0002
	6	.0000	.0000	.0000	.0000	.0000	.0000	.0000	.0000	.0000
	7	.0000	.0000	.0000	.0000	.0000	.0000	.0000	.0000	.0000
	8	.0000	.0000	.0000	.0000	.0000	.0000	.0000	.0000	.0000

TABLE 5 BINOMIAL PROBABILITIES (*Continued*)

		p								
n	*x*	**.01**	**.02**	**.03**	**.04**	**.05**	**.06**	**.07**	**.08**	**.09**
9	0	.9135	.8337	.7602	.6925	.6302	.5730	.5204	.4722	.4279
	1	.0830	.1531	.2116	.2597	.2985	.3292	.3525	.3695	.3809
	2	.0034	.0125	.0262	.0433	.0629	.0840	.1061	.1285	.1507
	3	.0001	.0006	.0019	.0042	.0077	.0125	.0186	.0261	.0348
	4	.0000	.0000	.0001	.0003	.0006	.0012	.0021	.0034	.0052
	5	.0000	.0000	.0000	.0000	.0000	.0001	.0002	.0003	.0005
	6	.0000	.0000	.0000	.0000	.0000	.0000	.0000	.0000	.0000
	7	.0000	.0000	.0000	.0000	.0000	.0000	.0000	.0000	.0000
	8	.0000	.0000	.0000	.0000	.0000	.0000	.0000	.0000	.0000
	9	.0000	.0000	.0000	.0000	.0000	.0000	.0000	.0000	.0000
10	0	.9044	.8171	.7374	.6648	.5987	.5386	.4840	.4344	.3894
	1	.0914	.1667	.2281	.2770	.3151	.3438	.3643	.3777	.3851
	2	.0042	.0153	.0317	.0519	.0746	.0988	.1234	.1478	.1714
	3	.0001	.0008	.0026	.0058	.0105	.0168	.0248	.0343	.0452
	4	.0000	.0000	.0001	.0004	.0010	.0019	.0033	.0052	.0078
	5	.0000	.0000	.0000	.0000	.0001	.0001	.0003	.0005	.0009
	6	.0000	.0000	.0000	.0000	.0000	.0000	.0000	.0000	.0001
	7	.0000	.0000	.0000	.0000	.0000	.0000	.0000	.0000	.0000
	8	.0000	.0000	.0000	.0000	.0000	.0000	.0000	.0000	.0000
	9	.0000	.0000	.0000	.0000	.0000	.0000	.0000	.0000	.0000
	10	.0000	.0000	.0000	.0000	.0000	.0000	.0000	.0000	.0000
12	0	.8864	.7847	.6938	.6127	.5404	.4759	.4186	.3677	.3225
	1	.1074	.1922	.2575	.3064	.3413	.3645	.3781	.3837	.3827
	2	.0060	.0216	.0438	.0702	.0988	.1280	.1565	.1835	.2082
	3	.0002	.0015	.0045	.0098	.0173	.0272	.0393	.0532	.0686
	4	.0000	.0001	.0003	.0009	.0021	.0039	.0067	.0104	.0153
	5	.0000	.0000	.0000	.0001	.0002	.0004	.0008	.0014	.0024
	6	.0000	.0000	.0000	.0000	.0000	.0000	.0001	.0001	.0003
	7	.0000	.0000	.0000	.0000	.0000	.0000	.0000	.0000	.0000
	8	.0000	.0000	.0000	.0000	.0000	.0000	.0000	.0000	.0000
	9	.0000	.0000	.0000	.0000	.0000	.0000	.0000	.0000	.0000
	10	.0000	.0000	.0000	.0000	.0000	.0000	.0000	.0000	.0000
	11	.0000	.0000	.0000	.0000	.0000	.0000	.0000	.0000	.0000
	12	.0000	.0000	.0000	.0000	.0000	.0000	.0000	.0000	.0000
15	0	.8601	.7386	.6333	.5421	.4633	.3953	.3367	.2863	.2430
	1	.1303	.2261	.2938	.3388	.3658	.3785	.3801	.3734	.3605
	2	.0092	.0323	.0636	.0988	.1348	.1691	.2003	.2273	.2496
	3	.0004	.0029	.0085	.0178	.0307	.0468	.0653	.0857	.1070
	4	.0000	.0002	.0008	.0022	.0049	.0090	.0148	.0223	.0317
	5	.0000	.0000	.0001	.0002	.0006	.0013	.0024	.0043	.0069
	6	.0000	.0000	.0000	.0000	.0000	.0001	.0003	.0006	.0011
	7	.0000	.0000	.0000	.0000	.0000	.0000	.0000	.0001	.0001
	8	.0000	.0000	.0000	.0000	.0000	.0000	.0000	.0000	.0000
	9	.0000	.0000	.0000	.0000	.0000	.0000	.0000	.0000	.0000
	10	.0000	.0000	.0000	.0000	.0000	.0000	.0000	.0000	.0000
	11	.0000	.0000	.0000	.0000	.0000	.0000	.0000	.0000	.0000
	12	.0000	.0000	.0000	.0000	.0000	.0000	.0000	.0000	.0000
	13	.0000	.0000	.0000	.0000	.0000	.0000	.0000	.0000	.0000
	14	.0000	.0000	.0000	.0000	.0000	.0000	.0000	.0000	.0000
	15	.0000	.0000	.0000	.0000	.0000	.0000	.0000	.0000	.0000

TABLE 5 BINOMIAL PROBABILITIES (*Continued*)

		p								
n	*x*	.01	.02	.03	.04	.05	.06	.07	.08	.09
18	0	.8345	.6951	.5780	.4796	.3972	.3283	.2708	.2229	.1831
	1	.1517	.2554	.3217	.3597	.3763	.3772	.3669	.3489	.3260
	2	.0130	.0443	.0846	.1274	.1683	.2047	.2348	.2579	.2741
	3	.0007	.0048	.0140	.0283	.0473	.0697	.0942	.1196	.1446
	4	.0000	.0004	.0016	.0044	.0093	.0167	.0266	.0390	.0536
	5	.0000	.0000	.0001	.0005	.0014	.0030	.0056	.0095	.0148
	6	.0000	.0000	.0000	.0000	.0002	.0004	.0009	.0018	.0032
	7	.0000	.0000	.0000	.0000	.0000	.0000	.0001	.0003	.0005
	8	.0000	.0000	.0000	.0000	.0000	.0000	.0000	.0000	.0001
	9	.0000	.0000	.0000	.0000	.0000	.0000	.0000	.0000	.0000
	10	.0000	.0000	.0000	.0000	.0000	.0000	.0000	.0000	.0000
	11	.0000	.0000	.0000	.0000	.0000	.0000	.0000	.0000	.0000
	12	.0000	.0000	.0000	.0000	.0000	.0000	.0000	.0000	.0000
	13	.0000	.0000	.0000	.0000	.0000	.0000	.0000	.0000	.0000
	14	.0000	.0000	.0000	.0000	.0000	.0000	.0000	.0000	.0000
	15	.0000	.0000	.0000	.0000	.0000	.0000	.0000	.0000	.0000
	16	.0000	.0000	.0000	.0000	.0000	.0000	.0000	.0000	.0000
	17	.0000	.0000	.0000	.0000	.0000	.0000	.0000	.0000	.0000
	18	.0000	.0000	.0000	.0000	.0000	.0000	.0000	.0000	.0000
20	0	.8179	.6676	.5438	.4420	.3585	.2901	.2342	.1887	.1516
	1	.1652	.2725	.3364	.3683	.3774	.3703	.3526	.3282	.3000
	2	.0159	.0528	.0988	.1458	.1887	.2246	.2521	.2711	.2818
	3	.0010	.0065	.0183	.0364	.0596	.0860	.1139	.1414	.1672
	4	.0000	.0006	.0024	.0065	.0133	.0233	.0364	.0523	.0703
	5	.0000	.0000	.0002	.0009	.0022	.0048	.0088	.0145	.0222
	6	.0000	.0000	.0000	.0001	.0003	.0008	.0017	.0032	.0055
	7	.0000	.0000	.0000	.0000	.0000	.0001	.0002	.0005	.0011
	8	.0000	.0000	.0000	.0000	.0000	.0000	.0000	.0001	.0002
	9	.0000	.0000	.0000	.0000	.0000	.0000	.0000	.0000	.0000
	10	.0000	.0000	.0000	.0000	.0000	.0000	.0000	.0000	.0000
	11	.0000	.0000	.0000	.0000	.0000	.0000	.0000	.0000	.0000
	12	.0000	.0000	.0000	.0000	.0000	.0000	.0000	.0000	.0000
	13	.0000	.0000	.0000	.0000	.0000	.0000	.0000	.0000	.0000
	14	.0000	.0000	.0000	.0000	.0000	.0000	.0000	.0000	.0000
	15	.0000	.0000	.0000	.0000	.0000	.0000	.0000	.0000	.0000
	16	.0000	.0000	.0000	.0000	.0000	.0000	.0000	.0000	.0000
	17	.0000	.0000	.0000	.0000	.0000	.0000	.0000	.0000	.0000
	18	.0000	.0000	.0000	.0000	.0000	.0000	.0000	.0000	.0000
	19	.0000	.0000	.0000	.0000	.0000	.0000	.0000	.0000	.0000
	20	.0000	.0000	.0000	.0000	.0000	.0000	.0000	.0000	.0000

TABLE 5 BINOMIAL PROBABILITIES (*Continued*)

		p								
n	*x*	.10	.15	.20	.25	.30	.35	.40	.45	.50
2	0	.8100	.7225	.6400	.5625	.4900	.4225	.3600	.3025	.2500
	1	.1800	.2550	.3200	.3750	.4200	.4550	.4800	.4950	.5000
	2	.0100	.0225	.0400	.0625	.0900	.1225	.1600	.2025	.2500
3	0	.7290	.6141	.5120	.4219	.3430	.2746	.2160	.1664	.1250
	1	.2430	.3251	.3840	.4219	.4410	.4436	.4320	.4084	.3750
	2	.0270	.0574	.0960	.1406	.1890	.2389	.2880	.3341	.3750
	3	.0010	.0034	.0080	.0156	.0270	.0429	.0640	.0911	.1250
4	0	.6561	.5220	.4096	.3164	.2401	.1785	.1296	.0915	.0625
	1	.2916	.3685	.4096	.4219	.4116	.3845	.3456	.2995	.2500
	2	.0486	.0975	.1536	.2109	.2646	.3105	.3456	.3675	.3750
	3	.0036	.0115	.0256	.0469	.0756	.1115	.1536	.2005	.2500
	4	.0001	.0005	.0016	.0039	.0081	.0150	.0256	.0410	.0625
5	0	.5905	.4437	.3277	.2373	.1681	.1160	.0778	.0503	.0312
	1	.3280	.3915	.4096	.3955	.3602	.3124	.2592	.2059	.1562
	2	.0729	.1382	.2048	.2637	.3087	.3364	.3456	.3369	.3125
	3	.0081	.0244	.0512	.0879	.1323	.1811	.2304	.2757	.3125
	4	.0004	.0022	.0064	.0146	.0284	.0488	.0768	.1128	.1562
	5	.0000	.0001	.0003	.0010	.0024	.0053	.0102	.0185	.0312
6	0	.5314	.3771	.2621	.1780	.1176	.0754	.0467	.0277	.0156
	1	.3543	.3993	.3932	.3560	.3025	.2437	.1866	.1359	.0938
	2	.0984	.1762	.2458	.2966	.3241	.3280	.3110	.2780	.2344
	3	.0146	.0415	.0819	.1318	.1852	.2355	.2765	.3032	.3125
	4	.0012	.0055	.0154	.0330	.0595	.0951	.1382	.1861	.2344
	5	.0001	.0004	.0015	.0044	.0102	.0205	.0369	.0609	.0938
	6	.0000	.0000	.0001	.0002	.0007	.0018	.0041	.0083	.0156
7	0	.4783	.3206	.2097	.1335	.0824	.0490	.0280	.0152	.0078
	1	.3720	.3960	.3670	.3115	.2471	.1848	.1306	.0872	.0547
	2	.1240	.2097	.2753	.3115	.3177	.2985	.2613	.2140	.1641
	3	.0230	.0617	.1147	.1730	.2269	.2679	.2903	.2918	.2734
	4	.0026	.0109	.0287	.0577	.0972	.1442	.1935	.2388	.2734
	5	.0002	.0012	.0043	.0115	.0250	.0466	.0774	.1172	.1641
	6	.0000	.0001	.0004	.0013	.0036	.0084	.0172	.0320	.0547
	7	.0000	.0000	.0000	.0001	.0002	.0006	.0016	.0037	.0078
8	0	.4305	.2725	.1678	.1001	.0576	.0319	.0168	.0084	.0039
	1	.3826	.3847	.3355	.2670	.1977	.1373	.0896	.0548	.0312
	2	.1488	.2376	.2936	.3115	.2965	.2587	.2090	.1569	.1094
	3	.0331	.0839	.1468	.2076	.2541	.2786	.2787	.2568	.2188
	4	.0046	.0185	.0459	.0865	.1361	.1875	.2322	.2627	.2734
	5	.0004	.0026	.0092	.0231	.0467	.0808	.1239	.1719	.2188
	6	.0000	.0002	.0011	.0038	.0100	.0217	.0413	.0703	.1094
	7	.0000	.0000	.0001	.0004	.0012	.0033	.0079	.0164	.0313
	8	.0000	.0000	.0000	.0000	.0001	.0002	.0007	.0017	.0039

TABLE 5 BINOMIAL PROBABILITIES (*Continued*)

		p								
n	*x*	.10	.15	.20	.25	.30	.35	.40	.45	.50
9	0	.3874	.2316	.1342	.0751	.0404	.0207	.0101	.0046	.0020
	1	.3874	.3679	.3020	.2253	.1556	.1004	.0605	.0339	.0176
	2	.1722	.2597	.3020	.3003	.2668	.2162	.1612	.1110	.0703
	3	.0446	.1069	.1762	.2336	.2668	.2716	.2508	.2119	.1641
	4	.0074	.0283	.0661	.1168	.1715	.2194	.2508	.2600	.2461
	5	.0008	.0050	.0165	.0389	.0735	.1181	.1672	.2128	.2461
	6	.0001	.0006	.0028	.0087	.0210	.0424	.0743	.1160	.1641
	7	.0000	.0000	.0003	.0012	.0039	.0098	.0212	.0407	.0703
	8	.0000	.0000	.0000	.0001	.0004	.0013	.0035	.0083	.0176
	9	.0000	.0000	.0000	.0000	.0000	.0001	.0003	.0008	.0020
10	0	.3487	.1969	.1074	.0563	.0282	.0135	.0060	.0025	.0010
	1	.3874	.3474	.2684	.1877	.1211	.0725	.0403	.0207	.0098
	2	.1937	.2759	.3020	.2816	.2335	.1757	.1209	.0763	.0439
	3	.0574	.1298	.2013	.2503	.2668	.2522	.2150	.1665	.1172
	4	.0112	.0401	.0881	.1460	.2001	.2377	.2508	.2384	.2051
	5	.0015	.0085	.0264	.0584	.1029	.1536	.2007	.2340	.2461
	6	.0001	.0012	.0055	.0162	.0368	.0689	.1115	.1596	.2051
	7	.0000	.0001	.0008	.0031	.0090	.0212	.0425	.0746	.1172
	8	.0000	.0000	.0001	.0004	.0014	.0043	.0106	.0229	.0439
	9	.0000	.0000	.0000	.0000	.0001	.0005	.0016	.0042	.0098
	10	.0000	.0000	.0000	.0000	.0000	.0000	.0001	.0003	.0010
12	0	.2824	.1422	.0687	.0317	.0138	.0057	.0022	.0008	.0002
	1	.3766	.3012	.2062	.1267	.0712	.0368	.0174	.0075	.0029
	2	.2301	.2924	.2835	.2323	.1678	.1088	.0639	.0339	.0161
	3	.0853	.1720	.2362	.2581	.2397	.1954	.1419	.0923	.0537
	4	.0213	.0683	.1329	.1936	.2311	.2367	.2128	.1700	.1208
	5	.0038	.0193	.0532	.1032	.1585	.2039	.2270	.2225	.1934
	6	.0005	.0040	.0155	.0401	.0792	.1281	.1766	.2124	.2256
	7	.0000	.0006	.0033	.0115	.0291	.0591	.1009	.1489	.1934
	8	.0000	.0001	.0005	.0024	.0078	.0199	.0420	.0762	.1208
	9	.0000	.0000	.0001	.0004	.0015	.0048	.0125	.0277	.0537
	10	.0000	.0000	.0000	.0000	.0002	.0008	.0025	.0068	.0161
	11	.0000	.0000	.0000	.0000	.0000	.0001	.0003	.0010	.0029
	12	.0000	.0000	.0000	.0000	.0000	.0000	.0000	.0001	.0002
15	0	.2059	.0874	.0352	.0134	.0047	.0016	.0005	.0001	.0000
	1	.3432	.2312	.1319	.0668	.0305	.0126	.0047	.0016	.0005
	2	.2669	.2856	.2309	.1559	.0916	.0476	.0219	.0090	.0032
	3	.1285	.2184	.2501	.2252	.1700	.1110	.0634	.0318	.0139
	4	.0428	.1156	.1876	.2252	.2186	.1792	.1268	.0780	.0417
	5	.0105	.0449	.1032	.1651	.2061	.2123	.1859	.1404	.0916
	6	.0019	.0132	.0430	.0917	.1472	.1906	.2066	.1914	.1527
	7	.0003	.0030	.0138	.0393	.0811	.1319	.1771	.2013	.1964
	8	.0000	.0005	.0035	.0131	.0348	.0710	.1181	.1647	.1964
	9	.0000	.0001	.0007	.0034	.0016	.0298	.0612	.1048	.1527
	10	.0000	.0000	.0001	.0007	.0030	.0096	.0245	.0515	.0916
	11	.0000	.0000	.0000	.0001	.0006	.0024	.0074	.0191	.0417
	12	.0000	.0000	.0000	.0000	.0001	.0004	.0016	.0052	.0139
	13	.0000	.0000	.0000	.0000	.0000	.0001	.0003	.0010	.0032
	14	.0000	.0000	.0000	.0000	.0000	.0000	.0000	.0001	.0005
	15	.0000	.0000	.0000	.0000	.0000	.0000	.0000	.0000	.0000

TABLE 5 BINOMIAL PROBABILITIES (*Continued*)

		p								
n	x	.10	.15	.20	.25	.30	.35	.40	.45	.50
18	0	.1501	.0536	.0180	.0056	.0016	.0004	.0001	.0000	.0000
	1	.3002	.1704	.0811	.0338	.0126	.0042	.0012	.0003	.0001
	2	.2835	.2556	.1723	.0958	.0458	.0190	.0069	.0022	.0006
	3	.1680	.2406	.2297	.1704	.1046	.0547	.0246	.0095	.0031
	4	.0700	.1592	.2153	.2130	.1681	.1104	.0614	.0291	.0117
	5	.0218	.0787	.1507	.1988	.2017	.1664	.1146	.0666	.0327
	6	.0052	.0301	.0816	.1436	.1873	.1941	.1655	.1181	.0708
	7	.0010	.0091	.0350	.0820	.1376	.1792	.1892	.1657	.1214
	8	.0002	.0022	.0120	.0376	.0811	.1327	.1734	.1864	.1669
	9	.0000	.0004	.0033	.0139	.0386	.0794	.1284	.1694	.1855
	10	.0000	.0001	.0008	.0042	.0149	.0385	.0771	.1248	.1669
	11	.0000	.0000	.0001	.0010	.0046	.0151	.0374	.0742	.1214
	12	.0000	.0000	.0000	.0002	.0012	.0047	.0145	.0354	.0708
	13	.0000	.0000	.0000	.0000	.0002	.0012	.0045	.0134	.0327
	14	.0000	.0000	.0000	.0000	.0000	.0002	.0011	.0039	.0117
	15	.0000	.0000	.0000	.0000	.0000	.0000	.0002	.0009	.0031
	16	.0000	.0000	.0000	.0000	.0000	.0000	.0000	.0001	.0006
	17	.0000	.0000	.0000	.0000	.0000	.0000	.0000	.0000	.0001
	18	.0000	.0000	.0000	.0000	.0000	.0000	.0000	.0000	.0000
20	0	.1216	.0388	.0115	.0032	.0008	.0002	.0000	.0000	.0000
	1	.2702	.1368	.0576	.0211	.0068	.0020	.0005	.0001	.0000
	2	.2852	.2293	.1369	.0669	.0278	.0100	.0031	.0008	.0002
	3	.1901	.2428	.2054	.1339	.0716	.0323	.0123	.0040	.0011
	4	.0898	.1821	.2182	.1897	.1304	.0738	.0350	.0139	.0046
	5	.0319	.1028	.1746	.2023	.1789	.1272	.0746	.0365	.0148
	6	.0089	.0454	.1091	.1686	.1916	.1712	.1244	.0746	.0370
	7	.0020	.0160	.0545	.1124	.1643	.1844	.1659	.1221	.0739
	8	.0004	.0046	.0222	.0609	.1144	.1614	.1797	.1623	.1201
	9	.0001	.0011	.0074	.0271	.0654	.1158	.1597	.1771	.1602
	10	.0000	.0002	.0020	.0099	.0308	.0686	.1171	.1593	.1762
	11	.0000	.0000	.0005	.0030	.0120	.0336	.0710	.1185	.1602
	12	.0000	.0000	.0001	.0008	.0039	.0136	.0355	.0727	.1201
	13	.0000	.0000	.0000	.0002	.0010	.0045	.0146	.0366	.0739
	14	.0000	.0000	.0000	.0000	.0002	.0012	.0049	.0150	.0370
	15	.0000	.0000	.0000	.0000	.0000	.0003	.0013	.0049	.0148
	16	.0000	.0000	.0000	.0000	.0000	.0000	.0003	.0013	.0046
	17	.0000	.0000	.0000	.0000	.0000	.0000	.0000	.0002	.0011
	18	.0000	.0000	.0000	.0000	.0000	.0000	.0000	.0000	.0002
	19	.0000	.0000	.0000	.0000	.0000	.0000	.0000	.0000	.0000
	20	.0000	.0000	.0000	.0000	.0000	.0000	.0000	.0000	.0000

TABLE 5 BINOMIAL PROBABILITIES (*Continued*)

		p								
n	*x*	**0.55**	**0.60**	**0.65**	**0.70**	**0.75**	**0.80**	**0.85**	**0.90**	**0.95**
2	0	0.2025	0.1600	0.1225	0.0900	0.0625	0.0400	0.0225	0.0100	0.0025
	1	0.4950	0.4800	0.4550	0.4200	0.3750	0.3200	0.2550	0.1800	0.0950
	2	0.3025	0.3600	0.4225	0.4900	0.5625	0.6400	0.7225	0.8100	0.9025
3	0	0.0911	0.0640	0.0429	0.0270	0.0156	0.0080	0.0034	0.0010	0.0001
	1	0.3341	0.2880	0.2389	0.1890	0.1406	0.0960	0.0574	0.0270	0.0071
	2	0.4084	0.4320	0.4436	0.4410	0.4219	0.3840	0.3251	0.2430	0.1354
	3	0.1664	0.2160	0.2746	0.3430	0.4219	0.5120	0.6141	0.7290	0.8574
4	0	0.0410	0.0256	0.0150	0.0081	0.0039	0.0016	0.0005	0.0001	0.0000
	1	0.2005	0.1536	0.1115	0.0756	0.0469	0.0256	0.0115	0.0036	0.0005
	2	0.3675	0.3456	0.3105	0.2646	0.2109	0.1536	0.0975	0.0486	0.0135
	3	0.2995	0.3456	0.3845	0.4116	0.4219	0.4096	0.3685	0.2916	0.1715
	4	0.0915	0.1296	0.1785	0.2401	0.3164	0.4096	0.5220	0.6561	0.8145
5	0	0.0185	0.0102	0.0053	0.0024	0.0010	0.0003	0.0001	0.0000	0.0000
	1	0.1128	0.0768	0.0488	0.0284	0.0146	0.0064	0.0022	0.0005	0.0000
	2	0.2757	0.2304	0.1811	0.1323	0.0879	0.0512	0.0244	0.0081	0.0011
	3	0.3369	0.3456	0.3364	0.3087	0.2637	0.2048	0.1382	0.0729	0.0214
	4	0.2059	0.2592	0.3124	0.3601	0.3955	0.4096	0.3915	0.3281	0.2036
	5	0.0503	0.0778	0.1160	0.1681	0.2373	0.3277	0.4437	0.5905	0.7738
6	0	0.0083	0.0041	0.0018	0.0007	0.0002	0.0001	0.0000	0.0000	0.0000
	1	0.0609	0.0369	0.0205	0.0102	0.0044	0.0015	0.0004	0.0001	0.0000
	2	0.1861	0.1382	0.0951	0.0595	0.0330	0.0154	0.0055	0.0012	0.0001
	3	0.3032	0.2765	0.2355	0.1852	0.1318	0.0819	0.0415	0.0146	0.0021
	4	0.2780	0.3110	0.3280	0.3241	0.2966	0.2458	0.1762	0.0984	0.0305
	5	0.1359	0.1866	0.2437	0.3025	0.3560	0.3932	0.3993	0.3543	0.2321
	6	0.0277	0.0467	0.0754	0.1176	0.1780	0.2621	0.3771	0.5314	0.7351
7	0	0.0037	0.0016	0.0006	0.0002	0.0001	0.0000	0.0000	0.0000	0.0000
	1	0.0320	0.0172	0.0084	0.0036	0.0013	0.0004	0.0001	0.0000	0.0000
	2	0.1172	0.0774	0.0466	0.0250	0.0115	0.0043	0.0012	0.0002	0.0000
	3	0.2388	0.1935	0.1442	0.0972	0.0577	0.0287	0.0109	0.0026	0.0002
	4	0.2918	0.2903	0.2679	0.2269	0.1730	0.1147	0.0617	0.0230	0.0036
	5	0.2140	0.2613	0.2985	0.3177	0.3115	0.2753	0.2097	0.1240	0.0406
	6	0.0872	0.1306	0.1848	0.2471	0.3115	0.3670	0.3960	0.3720	0.2573
	7	0.0152	0.0280	0.0490	0.0824	0.1335	0.2097	0.3206	0.4783	0.6983
8	0	0.0017	0.0007	0.0002	0.0001	0.0000	0.0000	0.0000	0.0000	0.0000
	1	0.0164	0.0079	0.0033	0.0012	0.0004	0.0001	0.0000	0.0000	0.0000
	2	0.0703	0.0413	0.0217	0.0100	0.0038	0.0011	0.0002	0.0000	0.0000
	3	0.1719	0.1239	0.0808	0.0467	0.0231	0.0092	0.0026	0.0004	0.0000
	4	0.2627	0.2322	0.1875	0.1361	0.0865	0.0459	0.0185	0.0046	0.0004
	5	0.2568	0.2787	0.2786	0.2541	0.2076	0.1468	0.0839	0.0331	0.0054
	6	0.1569	0.2090	0.2587	0.2965	0.3115	0.2936	0.2376	0.1488	0.0515
	7	0.0548	0.0896	0.1373	0.1977	0.2670	0.3355	0.3847	0.3826	0.2793
	8	0.0084	0.0168	0.0319	0.0576	0.1001	0.1678	0.2725	0.4305	0.6634

TABLE 5 BINOMIAL PROBABILITIES (*Continued*)

		p								
n	*x*	0.55	0.60	0.65	0.70	0.75	0.80	0.85	0.90	0.95
9	0	0.0008	0.0003	0.0001	0.0000	0.0000	0.0000	0.0000	0.0000	0.0000
	1	0.0083	0.0035	0.0013	0.0004	0.0001	0.0000	0.0000	0.0000	0.0000
	2	0.0407	0.0212	0.0098	0.0039	0.0012	0.0003	0.0000	0.0000	0.0000
	3	0.1160	0.0743	0.0424	0.0210	0.0087	0.0028	0.0006	0.0001	0.0000
	4	0.2128	0.1672	0.1181	0.0735	0.0389	0.0165	0.0050	0.0008	0.0000
	5	0.2600	0.2508	0.2194	0.1715	0.1168	0.0661	0.0283	0.0074	0.0006
	6	0.2119	0.2508	0.2716	0.2668	0.2336	0.1762	0.1069	0.0446	0.0077
	7	0.1110	0.1612	0.2162	0.2668	0.3003	0.3020	0.2597	0.1722	0.0629
	8	0.0339	0.0605	0.1004	0.1556	0.2253	0.3020	0.3679	0.3874	0.2985
	9	0.0046	0.0101	0.0207	0.0404	0.0751	0.1342	0.2316	0.3874	0.6302
10	0	0.0003	0.0001	0.0000	0.0000	0.0000	0.0000	0.0000	0.0000	0.0000
	1	0.0042	0.0016	0.0005	0.0001	0.0000	0.0000	0.0000	0.0000	0.0000
	2	0.0229	0.0106	0.0043	0.0014	0.0004	0.0001	0.0000	0.0000	0.0000
	3	0.0746	0.0425	0.0212	0.0090	0.0031	0.0008	0.0001	0.0000	0.0000
	4	0.1596	0.1115	0.0689	0.0368	0.0162	0.0055	0.0012	0.0001	0.0000
	5	0.2340	0.2007	0.1536	0.1029	0.0584	0.0264	0.0085	0.0015	0.0001
	6	0.2384	0.2508	0.2377	0.2001	0.1460	0.0881	0.0401	0.0112	0.0010
	7	0.1665	0.2150	0.2522	0.2668	0.2503	0.2013	0.1298	0.0574	0.0105
	8	0.0763	0.1209	0.1757	0.2335	0.2816	0.3020	0.2759	0.1937	0.0746
	9	0.0207	0.0403	0.0725	0.1211	0.1877	0.2684	0.3474	0.3874	0.3151
	10	0.0025	0.0060	0.0135	0.0282	0.0563	0.1074	0.1969	0.3487	0.5987
12	0	0.0001	0.0000	0.0000	0.0000	0.0000	0.0000	0.0000	0.0000	0.0000
	1	0.0010	0.0003	0.0001	0.0000	0.0000	0.0000	0.0000	0.0000	0.0000
	2	0.0068	0.0025	0.0008	0.0002	0.0000	0.0000	0.0000	0.0000	0.0000
	3	0.0277	0.0125	0.0048	0.0015	0.0004	0.0001	0.0000	0.0000	0.0000
	4	0.0762	0.0420	0.0199	0.0078	0.0024	0.0005	0.0001	0.0000	0.0000
	5	0.1489	0.1009	0.0591	0.0291	0.0115	0.0033	0.0006	0.0000	0.0000
	6	0.2124	0.1766	0.1281	0.0792	0.0401	0.0155	0.0040	0.0005	0.0000
	7	0.2225	0.2270	0.2039	0.1585	0.1032	0.0532	0.0193	0.0038	0.0002
	8	0.1700	0.2128	0.2367	0.2311	0.1936	0.1329	0.0683	0.0213	0.0021
	9	0.0923	0.1419	0.1954	0.2397	0.2581	0.2362	0.1720	0.0852	0.0173
	10	0.0339	0.0639	0.1088	0.1678	0.2323	0.2835	0.2924	0.2301	0.0988
	11	0.0075	0.0174	0.0368	0.0712	0.1267	0.2062	0.3012	0.3766	0.3413
	12	0.0008	0.0022	0.0057	0.0138	0.0317	0.0687	0.1422	0.2824	0.5404
15	0	0.0000	0.0000	0.0000	0.0000	0.0000	0.0000	0.0000	0.0000	0.0000
	1	0.0001	0.0000	0.0000	0.0000	0.0000	0.0000	0.0000	0.0000	0.0000
	2	0.0010	0.0003	0.0001	0.0000	0.0000	0.0000	0.0000	0.0000	0.0000
	3	0.0052	0.0016	0.0004	0.0001	0.0000	0.0000	0.0000	0.0000	0.0000
	4	0.0191	0.0074	0.0024	0.0006	0.0001	0.0000	0.0000	0.0000	0.0000
	5	0.0515	0.0245	0.0096	0.0030	0.0007	0.0001	0.0000	0.0000	0.0000
	6	0.1048	0.0612	0.0298	0.0116	0.0034	0.0007	0.0001	0.0000	0.0000
	7	0.1647	0.1181	0.0710	0.0348	0.0131	0.0035	0.0005	0.0000	0.0000
	8	0.2013	0.1771	0.1319	0.0811	0.0393	0.0138	0.0030	0.0003	0.0000
	9	0.1914	0.2066	0.1906	0.1472	0.0917	0.0430	0.0132	0.0019	0.0000
	10	0.1404	0.1859	0.2123	0.2061	0.1651	0.1032	0.0449	0.0105	0.0006
	11	0.0780	0.1268	0.1792	0.2186	0.2252	0.1876	0.1156	0.0428	0.0049

TABLE 5 BINOMIAL PROBABILITIES (*Continued*)

		p								
n	*x*	**0.55**	**0.60**	**0.65**	**0.70**	**0.75**	**0.80**	**0.85**	**0.90**	**0.95**
	12	0.0318	0.0634	0.1110	0.1700	0.2252	0.2501	0.2184	0.1285	0.0307
	13	0.0090	0.0219	0.0476	0.0916	0.1559	0.2309	0.2856	0.2669	0.1348
	14	0.0016	0.0047	0.0126	0.0305	0.0668	0.1319	0.2312	0.3432	0.3658
	15	0.0001	0.0005	0.0016	0.0047	0.0134	0.0352	0.0874	0.2059	0.4633
18	0	0.0000	0.0000	0.0000	0.0000	0.0000	0.0000	0.0000	0.0000	0.0000
	1	0.0000	0.0000	0.0000	0.0000	0.0000	0.0000	0.0000	0.0000	0.0000
	2	0.0001	0.0000	0.0000	0.0000	0.0000	0.0000	0.0000	0.0000	0.0000
	3	0.0009	0.0002	0.0000	0.0000	0.0000	0.0000	0.0000	0.0000	0.0000
	4	0.0039	0.0011	0.0002	0.0000	0.0000	0.0000	0.0000	0.0000	0.0000
	5	0.0134	0.0045	0.0012	0.0002	0.0000	0.0000	0.0000	0.0000	0.0000
	6	0.0354	0.0145	0.0047	0.0012	0.0002	0.0000	0.0000	0.0000	0.0000
	7	0.0742	0.0374	0.0151	0.0046	0.0010	0.0001	0.0000	0.0000	0.0000
	8	0.1248	0.0771	0.0385	0.0149	0.0042	0.0008	0.0001	0.0000	0.0000
	9	0.1694	0.1284	0.0794	0.0386	0.0139	0.0033	0.0004	0.0000	0.0000
	10	0.1864	0.1734	0.1327	0.0811	0.0376	0.0120	0.0022	0.0002	0.0000
	11	0.1657	0.1892	0.1792	0.1376	0.0820	0.0350	0.0091	0.0010	0.0000
	12	0.1181	0.1655	0.1941	0.1873	0.1436	0.0816	0.0301	0.0052	0.0002
	13	0.0666	0.1146	0.1664	0.2017	0.1988	0.1507	0.0787	0.0218	0.0014
	14	0.0291	0.0614	0.1104	0.1681	0.2130	0.2153	0.1592	0.0700	0.0093
	15	0.0095	0.0246	0.0547	0.1046	0.1704	0.2297	0.2406	0.1680	0.0473
	16	0.0022	0.0069	0.0190	0.0458	0.0958	0.1723	0.2556	0.2835	0.1683
	17	0.0003	0.0012	0.0042	0.0126	0.0338	0.0811	0.1704	0.3002	0.3763
	18	0.0000	0.0001	0.0004	0.0016	0.0056	0.0180	0.0536	0.1501	0.3972
20	0	0.0000	0.0000	0.0000	0.0000	0.0000	0.0000	0.0000	0.0000	0.0000
	1	0.0000	0.0000	0.0000	0.0000	0.0000	0.0000	0.0000	0.0000	0.0000
	2	0.0000	0.0000	0.0000	0.0000	0.0000	0.0000	0.0000	0.0000	0.0000
	3	0.0002	0.0000	0.0000	0.0000	0.0000	0.0000	0.0000	0.0000	0.0000
	4	0.0013	0.0003	0.0000	0.0000	0.0000	0.0000	0.0000	0.0000	0.0000
	5	0.0049	0.0013	0.0003	0.0000	0.0000	0.0000	0.0000	0.0000	0.0000
	6	0.0150	0.0049	0.0012	0.0002	0.0000	0.0000	0.0000	0.0000	0.0000
	7	0.0366	0.0146	0.0045	0.0010	0.0002	0.0000	0.0000	0.0000	0.0000
	8	0.0727	0.0355	0.0136	0.0039	0.0008	0.0001	0.0000	0.0000	0.0000
	9	0.1185	0.0710	0.0336	0.0120	0.0030	0.0005	0.0000	0.0000	0.0000
	10	0.1593	0.1171	0.0686	0.0308	0.0099	0.0020	0.0002	0.0000	0.0000
	11	0.1771	0.1597	0.1158	0.0654	0.0271	0.0074	0.0011	0.0001	0.0000
	12	0.1623	0.1797	0.1614	0.1144	0.0609	0.0222	0.0046	0.0004	0.0000
	13	0.1221	0.1659	0.1844	0.1643	0.1124	0.0545	0.0160	0.0020	0.0000
	14	0.0746	0.1244	0.1712	0.1916	0.1686	0.1091	0.0454	0.0089	0.0003
	15	0.0365	0.0746	0.1272	0.1789	0.2023	0.1746	0.1028	0.0319	0.0022
	16	0.0139	0.0350	0.0738	0.1304	0.1897	0.2182	0.1821	0.0898	0.0133
	17	0.0040	0.0123	0.0323	0.0716	0.1339	0.2054	0.2428	0.1901	0.0596
	18	0.0008	0.0031	0.0100	0.0278	0.0669	0.1369	0.2293	0.2852	0.1887
	19	0.0001	0.0005	0.0020	0.0068	0.0211	0.0576	0.1368	0.2702	0.3774
	20	0.0000	0.0000	0.0002	0.0008	0.0032	0.0115	0.0388	0.1216	0.3585

TABLE 6 VALUES OF $e^{-\mu}$

μ	$e^{-\mu}$	μ	$e^{-\mu}$	μ	$e^{-\mu}$
.00	1.0000	2.00	.1353	4.00	.0183
.05	.9512	2.05	.1287	4.05	.0174
.10	.9048	2.10	.1225	4.10	.0166
.15	.8607	2.15	.1165	4.15	.0158
.20	.8187	2.20	.1108	4.20	.0150
.25	.7788	2.25	.1054	4.25	.0143
.30	.7408	2.30	.1003	4.30	.0136
.35	.7047	2.35	.0954	4.35	.0129
.40	.6703	2.40	.0907	4.40	.0123
.45	.6376	2.45	.0863	4.45	.0117
.50	.6065	2.50	.0821	4.50	.0111
.55	.5769	2.55	.0781	4.55	.0106
.60	.5488	2.60	.0743	4.60	.0101
.65	.5220	2.65	.0707	4.65	.0096
.70	.4966	2.70	.0672	4.70	.0091
.75	.4724	2.75	.0639	4.75	.0087
.80	.4493	2.80	.0608	4.80	.0082
.85	.4274	2.85	.0578	4.85	.0078
.90	.4066	2.90	.0550	4.90	.0074
.95	.3867	2.95	.0523	4.95	.0071
1.00	.3679	3.00	.0498	5.00	.0067
1.05	.3499	3.05	.0474	6.00	.0025
1.10	.3329	3.10	.0450	7.00	.0009
1.15	.3166	3.15	.0429	8.00	.000335
1.20	.3012	3.20	.0408	9.00	.000123
				10.00	.000045
1.25	.2865	3.25	.0388		
1.30	.2725	3.30	.0369		
1.35	.2592	3.35	.0351		
1.40	.2466	3.40	.0334		
1.45	.2346	3.45	.0317		
1.50	.2231	3.50	.0302		
1.55	.2122	3.55	.0287		
1.60	.2019	3.60	.0273		
1.65	.1920	3.65	.0260		
1.70	.1827	3.70	.0247		
1.75	.1738	3.75	.0235		
1.80	.1653	3.80	.0224		
1.85	.1572	3.85	.0213		
1.90	.1496	3.90	.0202		
1.95	.1423	3.95	.0193		

TABLE 7 POISSON PROBABILITIES

Entries in the table give the probability of x occurrences for a Poisson process with a mean μ. For example, when $\mu = 2.5$, the probability of four occurrences is .1336.

	μ									
x	**0.1**	**0.2**	**0.3**	**0.4**	**0.5**	**0.6**	**0.7**	**0.8**	**0.9**	**1.0**
0	.9048	.8187	.7408	.6703	.6065	.5488	.4966	.4493	.4066	.3679
1	.0905	.1637	.2222	.2681	.3033	.3293	.3476	.3595	.3659	.3679
2	.0045	.0164	.0333	.0536	.0758	.0988	.1217	.1438	.1647	.1839
3	.0002	.0011	.0033	.0072	.0126	.0198	.0284	.0383	.0494	.0613
4	.0000	.0001	.0002	.0007	.0016	.0030	.0050	.0077	.0111	.0153
5	.0000	.0000	.0000	.0001	.0002	.0004	.0007	.0012	.0020	.0031
6	.0000	.0000	.0000	.0000	.0000	.0000	.0001	.0002	.0003	.0005
7	.0000	.0000	.0000	.0000	.0000	.0000	.0000	.0000	.0000	.0001

	μ									
x	**1.1**	**1.2**	**1.3**	**1.4**	**1.5**	**1.6**	**1.7**	**1.8**	**1.9**	**2.0**
0	.3329	.3012	.2725	.2466	.2231	.2019	.1827	.1653	.1496	.1353
1	.3662	.3614	.3543	.3452	.3347	.3230	.3106	.2975	.2842	.2707
2	.2014	.2169	.2303	.2417	.2510	.2584	.2640	.2678	.2700	.2707
3	.0738	.0867	.0998	.1128	.1255	.1378	.1496	.1607	.1710	.1804
4	.0203	.0260	.0324	.0395	.0471	.0551	.0636	.0723	.0812	.0902
5	.0045	.0062	.0084	.0111	.0141	.0176	.0216	.0260	.0309	.0361
6	.0008	.0012	.0018	.0026	.0035	.0047	.0061	.0078	.0098	.0120
7	.0001	.0002	.0003	.0005	.0008	.0011	.0015	.0020	.0027	.0034
8	.0000	.0000	.0001	.0001	.0001	.0002	.0003	.0005	.0006	.0009
9	.0000	.0000	.0000	.0000	.0000	.0000	.0001	.0001	.0001	.0002

	μ									
x	**2.1**	**2.2**	**2.3**	**2.4**	**2.5**	**2.6**	**2.7**	**2.8**	**2.9**	**3.0**
0	.1225	.1108	.1003	.0907	.0821	.0743	.0672	.0608	.0550	.0498
1	.2572	.2438	.2306	.2177	.2052	.1931	.1815	.1703	.1596	.1494
2	.2700	.2681	.2652	.2613	.2565	.2510	.2450	.2384	.2314	.2240
3	.1890	.1966	.2033	.2090	.2138	.2176	.2205	.2225	.2237	.2240
4	.0992	.1082	.1169	.1254	.1336	.1414	.1488	.1557	.1622	.1680
5	.0417	.0476	.0538	.0602	.0668	.0735	.0804	.0872	.0940	.1008
6	.0146	.0174	.0206	.0241	.0278	.0319	.0362	.0407	.0455	.0504
7	.0044	.0055	.0068	.0083	.0099	.0118	.0139	.0163	.0188	.0216
8	.0011	.0015	.0019	.0025	.0031	.0038	.0047	.0057	.0068	.0081
9	.0003	.0004	.0005	.0007	.0009	.0011	.0014	.0018	.0022	.0027
10	.0001	.0001	.0001	.0002	.0002	.0003	.0004	.0005	.0006	.0008
11	.0000	.0000	.0000	.0000	.0000	.0001	.0001	.0001	.0002	.0002
12	.0000	.0000	.0000	.0000	.0000	.0000	.0000	.0000	.0000	.0001

TABLE 7 POISSON PROBABILITIES (*Continued*)

	μ									
x	**3.1**	**3.2**	**3.3**	**3.4**	**3.5**	**3.6**	**3.7**	**3.8**	**3.9**	**4.0**
0	.0450	.0408	.0369	.0344	.0302	.0273	.0247	.0224	.0202	.0183
1	.1397	.1304	.1217	.1135	.1057	.0984	.0915	.0850	.0789	.0733
2	.2165	.2087	.2008	.1929	.1850	.1771	.1692	.1615	.1539	.1465
3	.2237	.2226	.2209	.2186	.2158	.2125	.2087	.2046	.2001	.1954
4	.1734	.1781	.1823	.1858	.1888	.1912	.1931	.1944	.1951	.1954
5	.1075	.1140	.1203	.1264	.1322	.1377	.1429	.1477	.1522	.1563
6	.0555	.0608	.0662	.0716	.0771	.0826	.0881	.0936	.0989	.1042
7	.0246	.0278	.0312	.0348	.0385	.0425	.0466	.0508	.0551	.0595
8	.0095	.0111	.0129	.0148	.0169	.0191	.0215	.0241	.0269	.0298
9	.0033	.0040	.0047	.0056	.0066	.0076	.0089	.0102	.0116	.0132
10	.0010	.0013	.0016	.0019	.0023	.0028	.0033	.0039	.0045	.0053
11	.0003	.0004	.0005	.0006	.0007	.0009	.0011	.0013	.0016	.0019
12	.0001	.0001	.0001	.0002	.0002	.0003	.0003	.0004	.0005	.0006
13	.0000	.0000	.0000	.0000	.0001	.0001	.0001	.0001	.0002	.0002
14	.0000	.0000	.0000	.0000	.0000	.0000	.0000	.0000	.0000	.0001

	μ									
x	**4.1**	**4.2**	**4.3**	**4.4**	**4.5**	**4.6**	**4.7**	**4.8**	**4.9**	**5.0**
0	.0166	.0150	.0136	.0123	.0111	.0101	.0091	.0082	.0074	.0067
1	.0679	.0630	.0583	.0540	.0500	.0462	.0427	.0395	.0365	.0337
2	.1393	.1323	.1254	.1188	.1125	.1063	.1005	.0948	.0894	.0842
3	.1904	.1852	.1798	.1743	.1687	.1631	.1574	.1517	.1460	.1404
4	.1951	.1944	.1933	.1917	.1898	.1875	.1849	.1820	.1789	.1755
5	.1600	.1633	.1662	.1687	.1708	.1725	.1738	.1747	.1753	.1755
6	.1093	.1143	.1191	.1237	.1281	.1323	.1362	.1398	.1432	.1462
7	.0640	.0686	.0732	.0778	.0824	.0869	.0914	.0959	.1002	.1044
8	.0328	.0360	.0393	.0428	.0463	.0500	.0537	.0575	.0614	.0653
9	.0150	.0168	.0188	.0209	.0232	.0255	.0280	.0307	.0334	.0363
10	.0061	.0071	.0081	.0092	.0104	.0118	.0132	.0147	.0164	.0181
11	.0023	.0027	.0032	.0037	.0043	.0049	.0056	.0064	.0073	.0082
12	.0008	.0009	.0011	.0014	.0016	.0019	.0022	.0026	.0030	.0034
13	.0002	.0003	.0004	.0005	.0006	.0007	.0008	.0009	.0011	.0013
14	.0001	.0001	.0001	.0001	.0002	.0002	.0003	.0003	.0004	.0005
15	.0000	.0000	.0000	.0000	.0001	.0001	.0001	.0001	.0001	.0002

	μ									
x	**5.1**	**5.2**	**5.3**	**5.4**	**5.5**	**5.6**	**5.7**	**5.8**	**5.9**	**6.0**
0	.0061	.0055	.0050	.0045	.0041	.0037	.0033	.0030	.0027	.0025
1	.0311	.0287	.0265	.0244	.0225	.0207	.0191	.0176	.0162	.0149
2	.0793	.0746	.0701	.0659	.0618	.0580	.0544	.0509	.0477	.0446
3	.1348	.1293	.1239	.1185	.1133	.1082	.1033	.0985	.0938	.0892
4	.1719	.1681	.1641	.1600	.1558	.1515	.1472	.1428	.1383	.1339

TABLE 7 POISSON PROBABILITIES (*Continued*)

	μ									
x	5.1	5.2	5.3	5.4	5.5	5.6	5.7	5.8	5.9	6.0
5	.1753	.1748	.1740	.1728	.1714	.1697	.1678	.1656	.1632	.1606
6	.1490	.1515	.1537	.1555	.1571	.1587	.1594	.1601	.1605	.1606
7	.1086	.1125	.1163	.1200	.1234	.1267	.1298	.1326	.1353	.1377
8	.0692	.0731	.0771	.0810	.0849	.0887	.0925	.0962	.0998	.1033
9	.0392	.0423	.0454	.0486	.0519	.0552	.0586	.0620	.0654	.0688
10	.0200	.0220	.0241	.0262	.0285	.0309	.0334	.0359	.0386	.0413
11	.0093	.0104	.0116	.0129	.0143	.0157	.0173	.0190	.0207	.0225
12	.0039	.0045	.0051	.0058	.0065	.0073	.0082	.0092	.0102	.0113
13	.0015	.0018	.0021	.0024	.0028	.0032	.0036	.0041	.0046	.0052
14	.0006	.0007	.0008	.0009	.0011	.0013	.0015	.0017	.0019	.0022
15	.0002	.0002	.0003	.0003	.0004	.0005	.0006	.0007	.0008	.0009
16	.0001	.0001	.0001	.0001	.0001	.0002	.0002	.0002	.0003	.0003
17	.0000	.0000	.0000	.0000	.0000	.0001	.0001	.0001	.0001	.0001

	μ									
x	6.1	6.2	6.3	6.4	6.5	6.6	6.7	6.8	6.9	7.0
0	.0022	.0020	.0018	.0017	.0015	.0014	.0012	.0011	.0010	.0009
1	.0137	.0126	.0116	.0106	.0098	.0090	.0082	.0076	.0070	.0064
2	.0417	.0390	.0364	.0340	.0318	.0296	.0276	.0258	.0240	.0223
3	.0848	.0806	.0765	.0726	.0688	.0652	.0617	.0584	.0552	.0521
4	.1294	.1249	.1205	.1162	.1118	.1076	.1034	.0992	.0952	.0912
5	.1579	.1549	.1519	.1487	.1454	.1420	.1385	.1349	.1314	.1277
6	.1605	.1601	.1595	.1586	.1575	.1562	.1546	.1529	.1511	.1490
7	.1399	.1418	.1435	.1450	.1462	.1472	.1480	.1486	.1489	.1490
8	.1066	.1099	.1130	.1160	.1188	.1215	.1240	.1263	.1284	.1304
9	.0723	.0757	.0791	.0825	.0858	.0891	.0923	.0954	.0985	.1014
10	.0441	.0469	.0498	.0528	.0558	.0588	.0618	.0649	.0679	.0710
11	.0245	.0265	.0285	.0307	.0330	.0353	.0377	.0401	.0426	.0452
12	.0124	.0137	.0150	.0164	.0179	.0194	.0210	.0227	.0245	.0264
13	.0058	.0065	.0073	.0081	.0089	.0098	.0108	.0119	.0130	.0142
14	.0025	.0029	.0033	.0037	.0041	.0046	.0052	.0058	.0064	.0071
15	.0010	.0012	.0014	.0016	.0018	.0020	.0023	.0026	.0029	.0033
16	.0004	.0005	.0005	.0006	.0007	.0008	.0010	.0011	.0013	.0014
17	.0001	.0002	.0002	.0002	.0003	.0003	.0004	.0004	.0005	.0006
18	.0000	.0001	.0001	.0001	.0001	.0001	.0001	.0002	.0002	.0002
19	.0000	.0000	.0000	.0000	.0000	.0000	.0000	.0001	.0001	.0001

	μ									
x	7.1	7.2	7.3	7.4	7.5	7.6	7.7	7.8	7.9	8.0
0	.0008	.0007	.0007	.0006	.0006	.0005	.0005	.0004	.0004	.0003
1	.0059	.0054	.0049	.0045	.0041	.0038	.0035	.0032	.0029	.0027
2	.0208	.0194	.0180	.0167	.0156	.0145	.0134	.0125	.0116	.0107
3	.0492	.0464	.0438	.0413	.0389	.0366	.0345	.0324	.0305	.0286
4	.0874	.0836	.0799	.0764	.0729	.0696	.0663	.0632	.0602	.0573

TABLE 7 POISSON PROBABILITIES (*Continued*)

	μ									
x	**7.1**	**7.2**	**7.3**	**7.4**	**7.5**	**7.6**	**7.7**	**7.8**	**7.9**	**8.0**
5	.1241	.1204	.1167	.1130	.1094	.1057	.1021	.0986	.0951	.0916
6	.1468	.1445	.1420	.1394	.1367	.1339	.1311	.1282	.1252	.1221
7	.1489	.1486	.1481	.1474	.1465	.1454	.1442	.1428	.1413	.1396
8	.1321	.1337	.1351	.1363	.1373	.1382	.1388	.1392	.1395	.1396
9	.1042	.1070	.1096	.1121	.1144	.1167	.1187	.1207	.1224	.1241
10	.0740	.0770	.0800	.0829	.0858	.0887	.0914	.0941	.0967	.0993
11	.0478	.0504	.0531	.0558	.0585	.0613	.0640	.0667	.0695	.0722
12	.0283	.0303	.0323	.0344	.0366	.0388	.0411	.0434	.0457	.0481
13	.0154	.0168	.0181	.0196	.0211	.0227	.0243	.0260	.0278	.0296
14	.0078	.0086	.0095	.0104	.0113	.0123	.0134	.0145	.0157	.0169
15	.0037	.0041	.0046	.0051	.0057	.0062	.0069	.0075	.0083	.0090
16	.0016	.0019	.0021	.0024	.0026	.0030	.0033	.0037	.0041	.0045
17	.0007	.0008	.0009	.0010	.0012	.0013	.0015	.0017	.0019	.0021
18	.0003	.0003	.0004	.0004	.0005	.0006	.0006	.0007	.0008	.0009
19	.0001	.0001	.0001	.0002	.0002	.0002	.0003	.0003	.0003	.0004
20	.0000	.0000	.0001	.0001	.0001	.0001	.0001	.0001	.0001	.0002
21	.0000	.0000	.0000	.0000	.0000	.0000	.0000	.0000	.0001	.0001

	μ									
x	**8.1**	**8.2**	**8.3**	**8.4**	**8.5**	**8.6**	**8.7**	**8.8**	**8.9**	**9.0**
0	.0003	.0003	.0002	.0002	.0002	.0002	.0002	.0002	.0001	.0001
1	.0025	.0023	.0021	.0019	.0017	.0016	.0014	.0013	.0012	.0011
2	.0100	.0092	.0086	.0079	.0074	.0068	.0063	.0058	.0054	.0050
3	.0269	.0252	.0237	.0222	.0208	.0195	.0183	.0171	.0160	.0150
4	.0544	.0517	.0491	.0466	.0443	.0420	.0398	.0377	.0357	.0337
5	.0882	.0849	.0816	.0784	.0752	.0722	.0692	.0663	.0635	.0607
6	.1191	.1160	.1128	.1097	.1066	.1034	.1003	.0972	.0941	.0911
7	.1378	.1358	.1338	.1317	.1294	.1271	.1247	.1222	.1197	.1171
8	.1395	.1392	.1388	.1382	.1375	.1366	.1356	.1344	.1332	.1318
9	.1256	.1269	.1280	.1290	.1299	.1306	.1311	.1315	.1317	.1318
10	.1017	.1040	.1063	.1084	.1104	.1123	.1140	.1157	.1172	.1186
11	.0749	.0776	.0802	.0828	.0853	.0878	.0902	.0925	.0948	.0970
12	.0505	.0530	.0555	.0579	.0604	.0629	.0654	.0679	.0703	.0728
13	.0315	.0334	.0354	.0374	.0395	.0416	.0438	.0459	.0481	.0504
14	.0182	.0196	.0210	.0225	.0240	.0256	.0272	.0289	.0306	.0324
15	.0098	.0107	.0116	.0126	.0136	.0147	.0158	.0169	.0182	.1094
16	.0050	.0055	.0060	.0066	.0072	.0079	.0086	.0093	.0101	.0109
17	.0024	.0026	.0029	.0033	.0036	.0040	.0044	.0048	.0053	.0058
18	.0011	.0012	.0014	.0015	.0017	.0019	.0021	.0024	.0026	.0029
19	.0005	.0005	.0006	.0007	.0008	.0009	.0010	.0011	.0012	.0014
20	.0002	.0002	.0002	.0003	.0003	.0004	.0004	.0005	.0005	.0006
21	.0001	.0001	.0001	.0001	.0001	.0002	.0002	.0002	.0002	.0003
22	.0000	.0000	.0000	.0000	.0001	.0001	.0001	.0001	.0001	.0001

TABLE 7 POISSON PROBABILITIES (*Continued*)

	μ									
x	**9.1**	**9.2**	**9.3**	**9.4**	**9.5**	**9.6**	**9.7**	**9.8**	**9.9**	**10**
0	.0001	.0001	.0001	.0001	.0001	.0001	.0001	.0001	.0001	.0000
1	.0010	.0009	.0009	.0008	.0007	.0007	.0006	.0005	.0005	.0005
2	.0046	.0043	.0040	.0037	.0034	.0031	.0029	.0027	.0025	.0023
3	.0140	.0131	.0123	.0115	.0107	.0100	.0093	.0087	.0081	.0076
4	.0319	.0302	.0285	.0269	.0254	.0240	.0226	.0213	.0201	.0189
5	.0581	.0555	.0530	.0506	.0483	.0460	.0439	.0418	.0398	.0378
6	.0881	.0851	.0822	.0793	.0764	.0736	.0709	.0682	.0656	.0631
7	.1145	.1118	.1091	.1064	.1037	.1010	.0982	.0955	.0928	.0901
8	.1302	.1286	.1269	.1251	.1232	.1212	.1191	.1170	.1148	.1126
9	.1317	.1315	.1311	.1306	.1300	.1293	.1284	.1274	.1263	.1251
10	.1198	.1210	.1219	.1228	.1235	.1241	.1245	.1249	.1250	.1251
11	.0991	.1012	.1031	.1049	.1067	.1083	.1098	.1112	.1125	.1137
12	.0752	.0776	.0799	.0822	.0844	.0866	.0888	.0908	.0928	.0948
13	.0526	.0549	.0572	.0594	.0617	.0640	.0662	.0685	.0707	.0729
14	.0342	.0361	.0380	.0399	.0419	.0439	.0459	.0479	.0500	.0521
15	.0208	.0221	.0235	.0250	.0265	.0281	.0297	.0313	.0330	.0347
16	.0118	.0127	.0137	.0147	.0157	.0168	.0180	.0192	.0204	.0217
17	.0063	.0069	.0075	.0081	.0088	.0095	.0103	.0111	.0119	.0128
18	.0032	.0035	.0039	.0042	.0046	.0051	.0055	.0060	.0065	.0071
19	.0015	.0017	.0019	.0021	.0023	.0026	.0028	.0031	.0034	.0037
20	.0007	.0008	.0009	.0010	.0011	.0012	.0014	.0015	.0017	.0019
21	.0003	.0003	.0004	.0004	.0005	.0006	.0006	.0007	.0008	.0009
22	.0001	.0001	.0002	.0002	.0002	.0002	.0003	.0003	.0004	.0004
23	.0000	.0001	.0001	.0001	.0001	.0001	.0001	.0001	.0002	.0002
24	.0000	.0000	.0000	.0000	.0000	.0000	.0000	.0001	.0001	.0001

	μ									
x	**11**	**12**	**13**	**14**	**15**	**16**	**17**	**18**	**19**	**20**
0	.0000	.0000	.0000	.0000	.0000	.0000	.0000	.0000	.0000	.0000
1	.0002	.0001	.0000	.0000	.0000	.0000	.0000	.0000	.0000	.0000
2	.0010	.0004	.0002	.0001	.0000	.0000	.0000	.0000	.0000	.0000
3	.0037	.0018	.0008	.0004	.0002	.0001	.0000	.0000	.0000	.0000
4	.0102	.0053	.0027	.0013	.0006	.0003	.0001	.0001	.0000	.0000
5	.0224	.0127	.0070	.0037	.0019	.0010	.0005	.0002	.0001	.0001
6	.0411	.0255	.0152	.0087	.0048	.0026	.0014	.0007	.0004	.0002
7	.0646	.0437	.0281	.0174	.0104	.0060	.0034	.0018	.0010	.0005
8	.0888	.0655	.0457	.0304	.0194	.0120	.0072	.0042	.0024	.0013
9	.1085	.0874	.0661	.0473	.0324	.0213	.0135	.0083	.0050	.0029
10	.1194	.1048	.0859	.0663	.0486	.0341	.0230	.0150	.0095	.0058
11	.1194	.1144	.1015	.0844	.0663	.0496	.0355	.0245	.0164	.0106
12	.1094	.1144	.1099	.0984	.0829	.0661	.0504	.0368	.0259	.0176
13	.0926	.1056	.1099	.1060	.0956	.0814	.0658	.0509	.0378	.0271
14	.0728	.0905	.1021	.1060	.1024	.0930	.0800	.0655	.0514	.0387

TABLE 7 POISSON PROBABILITIES (*Continued*)

	μ									
x	11	12	13	14	15	16	17	18	19	20
15	.0534	.0724	.0885	.0989	.1024	.0992	.0906	.0786	.0650	.0516
16	.0367	.0543	.0719	.0866	.0960	.0992	.0963	.0884	.0772	.0646
17	.0237	.0383	.0550	.0713	.0847	.0934	.0963	.0936	.0863	.0760
18	.0145	.0256	.0397	.0554	.0706	.0830	.0909	.0936	.0911	.0844
19	.0084	.0161	.0272	.0409	.0557	.0699	.0814	.0887	.0911	.0888
20	.0046	.0097	.0177	.0286	.0418	.0559	.0692	.0798	.0866	.0888
21	.0024	.0055	.0109	.0191	.0299	.0426	.0560	.0684	.0783	.0846
22	.0012	.0030	.0065	.0121	.0204	.0310	.0433	.0560	.0676	.0769
23	.0006	.0016	.0037	.0074	.0133	.0216	.0320	.0438	.0559	.0669
24	.0003	.0008	.0020	.0043	.0083	.0144	.0226	.0328	.0442	.0557
25	.0001	.0004	.0010	.0024	.0050	.0092	.0154	.0237	.0336	.0446
26	.0000	.0002	.0005	.0013	.0029	.0057	.0101	.0164	.0246	.0343
27	.0000	.0001	.0002	.0007	.0016	.0034	.0063	.0109	.0173	.0254
28	.0000	.0000	.0001	.0003	.0009	.0019	.0038	.0070	.0117	.0181
29	.0000	.0000	.0001	.0002	.0004	.0011	.0023	.0044	.0077	.0125
30	.0000	.0000	.0000	.0001	.0002	.0006	.0013	.0026	.0049	.0083
31	.0000	.0000	.0000	.0000	.0001	.0003	.0007	.0015	.0030	.0054
32	.0000	.0000	.0000	.0000	.0001	.0001	.0004	.0009	.0018	.0034
33	.0000	.0000	.0000	.0000	.0000	.0001	.0002	.0005	.0010	.0020
34	.0000	.0000	.0000	.0000	.0000	.0000	.0001	.0002	.0006	.0012
35	.0000	.0000	.0000	.0000	.0000	.0000	.0000	.0001	.0003	.0007
36	.0000	.0000	.0000	.0000	.0000	.0000	.0000	.0001	.0002	.0004
37	.0000	.0000	.0000	.0000	.0000	.0000	.0000	.0000	.0001	.0002
38	.0000	.0000	.0000	.0000	.0000	.0000	.0000	.0000	.0000	.0001
39	.0000	.0000	.0000	.0000	.0000	.0000	.0000	.0000	.0000	.0001

TABLE 8 T_L VALUES FOR THE MANN-WHITNEY-WILCOXON TEST

Reject the hypothesis of identical populations if the sum of the ranks for the n_1 items is *less* than the value T_L shown in the following table or if the sum of the ranks for the n_1 items is *greater* than the value T_U where

$$T_U = n_1(n_1 + n_2 + 1) - T_L$$

$\alpha = .10$		n_2								
		2	**3**	**4**	**5**	**6**	**7**	**8**	**9**	**10**
	2	3	3	3	4	4	4	5	5	5
	3	6	7	7	8	9	9	10	11	11
	4	10	11	12	13	14	15	16	17	18
	5	16	17	18	20	21	22	24	25	27
n_1	6	22	24	25	27	29	30	32	34	36
	7	29	31	33	35	37	40	42	44	46
	8	38	40	42	45	47	50	52	55	57
	9	47	50	52	55	58	61	64	67	70
	10	57	60	63	67	70	73	76	80	83

$\alpha = .05$		n_2								
		2	**3**	**4**	**5**	**6**	**7**	**8**	**9**	**10**
	2	3	3	3	3	3	3	4	4	4
	3	6	6	6	7	8	8	9	9	10
	4	10	10	11	12	13	14	15	15	16
	5	15	16	17	18	19	21	22	23	24
n_1	6	21	23	24	25	27	28	30	32	33
	7	28	30	32	34	35	37	39	41	43
	8	37	39	41	43	45	47	50	52	54
	9	46	48	50	53	56	58	61	63	66
	10	56	59	61	64	67	70	73	76	79

Appendix C: Summation Notation

Summations

Definition

$$\sum_{i=1}^{n} x_i = x_1 + x_2 + \cdots + x_n \qquad \textbf{(C.1)}$$

Example for $x_1 = 5, x_2 = 8, x_3 = 14$:

$$\begin{aligned}\sum_{i=1}^{3} x_i &= x_1 + x_2 + x_3 \\ &= 5 + 8 + 14 \\ &= 27\end{aligned}$$

Result 1

For a constant c:

$$\sum_{i=1}^{n} c = \underbrace{(c + c + \cdots + c)}_{n \text{ times}} = nc \qquad \textbf{(C.2)}$$

Example for $c = 5, n = 10$:

$$\sum_{i=1}^{10} 5 = 10(5) = 50$$

Example for $c = \bar{x}$:

$$\sum_{i=1}^{n} \bar{x} = n\bar{x}$$

Result 2

$$\begin{aligned}\sum_{i=1}^{n} cx_i &= cx_1 + cx_2 + \cdots + cx_n \\ &= c(x_1 + x_2 + \cdots + x_n) = c\sum_{i=1}^{n} x_i \qquad \textbf{(C.3)}\end{aligned}$$

Example for $x_1 = 5, x_2 = 8, x_3 = 14, c = 2$:

$$\sum_{i=1}^{3} 2x_i = 2\sum_{i=1}^{3} x_i = 2(27) = 54$$

Result 3

$$\sum_{i=1}^{n} (ax_i + by_i) = a\sum_{i=1}^{n} x_i + b\sum_{i=1}^{n} y_i \qquad \textbf{(C.4)}$$

Example for $x_1 = 5, x_2 = 8, x_3 = 14, a = 2, y_1 = 7, y_2 = 3, y_3 = 8, b = 4$:

$$\begin{aligned}\sum_{i=1}^{3}(2x_i + 4y_i) &= 2\sum_{i=1}^{3}x_i + 4\sum_{i=1}^{3}y_i \\ &= 2(27) + 4(18) \\ &= 54 + 72 \\ &= 126\end{aligned}$$

Double Summations

Consider the following data involving the variable x_{ij}, where i is the subscript denoting the row position and j is the subscript denoting the column position:

		Column		
		1	**2**	**3**
Row	**1**	$x_{11} = 10$	$x_{12} = 8$	$x_{13} = 6$
	2	$x_{21} = 7$	$x_{22} = 4$	$x_{23} = 12$

Definition

$$\sum_{i=1}^{n}\sum_{j=1}^{m}x_{ij} = (x_{11} + x_{12} + \cdots + x_{1m}) + (x_{21} + x_{22} + \cdots + x_{2m}) + (x_{31} + x_{32} + \cdots + x_{3m}) + \cdots + (x_{n1} + x_{n2} + \cdots + x_{nm}) \quad \textbf{(C.5)}$$

Example:

$$\begin{aligned}\sum_{i=1}^{2}\sum_{j=1}^{3}x_{ij} &= x_{11} + x_{12} + x_{13} + x_{21} + x_{22} + x_{23} \\ &= 10 + 8 + 6 + 7 + 4 + 12 \\ &= 47\end{aligned}$$

Definition

$$\sum_{i=1}^{n}x_{ij} = x_{1j} + x_{2j} + \cdots + x_{nj} \quad \textbf{(C.6)}$$

Example:

$$\begin{aligned}\sum_{i=1}^{2}x_{i2} &= x_{12} + x_{22} \\ &= 8 + 4 \\ &= 12\end{aligned}$$

Shorthand Notation

Sometimes when a summation is for all values of the subscript, we use the following shorthand notations:

$$\sum_{i=1}^{n}x_i = \sum x_i \quad \textbf{(C.7)}$$

$$\sum_{i=1}^{n}\sum_{j=1}^{m}x_{ij} = \sum\sum x_{ij} \quad \textbf{(C.8)}$$

$$\sum_{i=1}^{n}x_{ij} = \sum_{i}x_{ij} \quad \textbf{(C.9)}$$

Appendix D: Self-Test Solutions and Answers to Even-Numbered Exercises

Chapter 1

2. a. 9
b. 4
c. Qualitative: country and room rate
Quantitative: number of rooms and overall score
d. Country is nominal; room rate is ordinal; number of rooms is ratio; overall score is interval

3. a. Average number of rooms = 808/9 = 89.78, or approximately 90 rooms
b. Average overall score = 732.1/9 = 81.3
c. 2 of 9 are located in England; approximately 22%
d. 4 of 9 have a room rate of $$; approximately 44%

4. a. 10
b. All brands of minisystems manufactured
c. $314
d. $314

6. Questions a, c, and d provide quantitative data
Questions b and e provide qualitative data

8. a. 1005
b. Qualitative
c. Percentages
d. Approximately 291

10. a. Quantitative; ratio
b. Qualitative; nominal
c. Qualitative; ordinal
d. Quantitative; ratio
e. Qualitative; nominal

12. a. All visitors to Hawaii
b. Yes
c. First and fourth questions provide quantitative data
Second and third questions provide qualitative data

13. a. Earnings in billions of dollars are quantitative data
b. Time series for 1997 to 2005
c. Earnings for Volkswagen
d. Earnings are relatively low in 1997 to 1999, excellent growth occurs in 2000 and 2001, and decline happens in 2003 to 2005; the decline in earnings suggests the $600 million projected earnings for 2006 is reasonable
e. In July 2001, the earnings tread was positive; Volkswagen would have been a promising investment in 2001
f. Be careful when projecting time series data into the future, because trends in past data may or may not continue

14. a. Graph with a time series line for each manufacturer
b. Toyota surpasses General Motors in 2006 to become the leading auto manufacturer
c. A bar graph would show cross-sectional data for 2007; bar heights would be GM 8.8, Ford 7.9, DC 4.6, and Toyota 9.6

16. a. Product taste tests and test marketing
b. Specially designed statistical studies

18. a. 36%
b. 189
c. Qualitative

20. a. 43% of managers were bullish or very bullish, and 21% of managers expected health care to be the leading industry over the next 12 months
b. The average 12-month return estimate is 11.2% for the population of investment managers
c. The sample average of 2.5 years is an estimate of how long the population of investment managers think it will take to resume sustainable growth

22. a. All registered voters in California
b. Registered voters contacted by the Policy Institute
c. Too time consuming and costly to reach the entire population

24. a. Correct
b. Incorrect
c. Correct
d. Incorrect
e. Incorrect

Chapter 2

2. a. .20
b. 40
c/d.

Class	Frequency	Percent Frequency
A	44	22
B	36	18
C	80	40
D	40	20
Total	200	100

3. a. $360° \times 58/120 = 174°$
b. $360° \times 42/120 = 126°$

c.

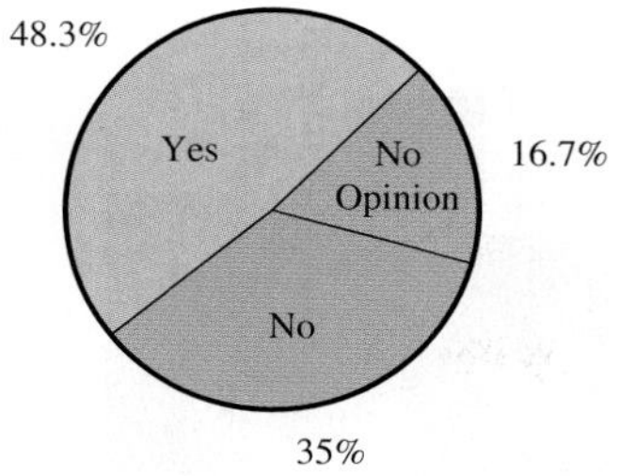

d.

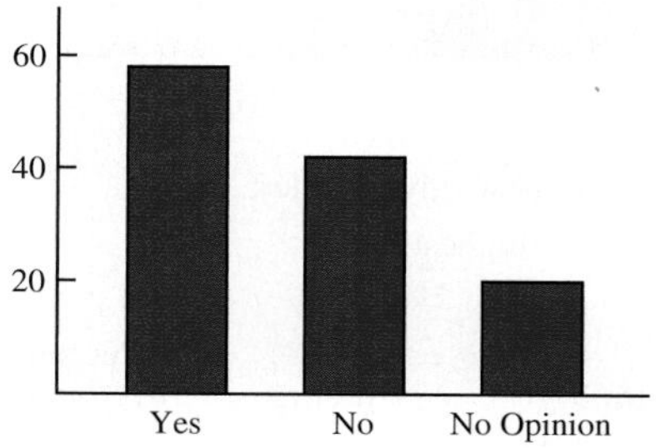

4. a. Qualitative

b.

TV Show	Frequency	Percent Frequency
CSI	18	36
ER	11	22
Friends	15	30
Raymond	6	12
Total	50	100

d. CSI had the largest; Friends was second

6. a.

Network	Frequency	Percent Frequency
ABC	15	30
CBS	17	34
FOX	1	2
NBC	17	34

b. CBS and NBC tied for first; ABC is close with 15

7.

Rating	Frequency	Relative Frequency
Outstanding	19	.38
Very good	13	.26
Good	10	.20
Average	6	.12
Poor	2	.04

Management should be pleased with these results: 64% of the ratings are very good to outstanding, and 84% of the ratings are good or better; comparing these ratings to previous results will show whether the restaurant is making improvements in its customers' ratings of food quality

8. a.

Position	Frequency	Relative Frequency
P	17	.309
H	4	.073
1	5	.091
2	4	.073
3	2	.036
S	5	.091
L	6	.109
C	5	.091
R	7	.127
Totals	55	1.000

b. Pitcher

c. 3rd base

d. Right field

e. Infielders 16 to outfielders 18

10. a. The data are qualitative; they provide quality classifications

b.

Rating	Frequency	Relative Frequency
1 star	0	.000
2 star	3	.167
3 star	3	.167
4 star	10	.556
5 star	2	.111
	18	1.000

d. Very good overall, with 10 4-star ratings and 12 (66.7%) 4-star or 5-star ratings

12.

Class	Cumulative Frequency	Cumulative Relative Frequency
≤ 19	10	.20
≤ 29	24	.48
≤ 39	41	.82
≤ 49	48	.96
≤ 59	50	1.00

14. b/c.

Class	Frequency	Percent Frequency
6.0–7.9	4	20
8.0–9.9	2	10
10.0–11.9	8	40
12.0–13.9	3	15
14.0–15.9	3	15
Totals	20	100

15. a/b.

Waiting Time	Frequency	Relative Frequency
0–4	4	.20
5–9	8	.40
10–14	5	.25
15–19	2	.10
20–24	1	.05
Totals	20	1.00

c/d.

Waiting Time	Cumulative Frequency	Cumulative Relative Frequency
≤4	4	.20
≤9	12	.60
≤14	17	.85
≤19	19	.95
≤24	20	1.00

e. 12/20 = .60

16. a. Adjusted Gross Income

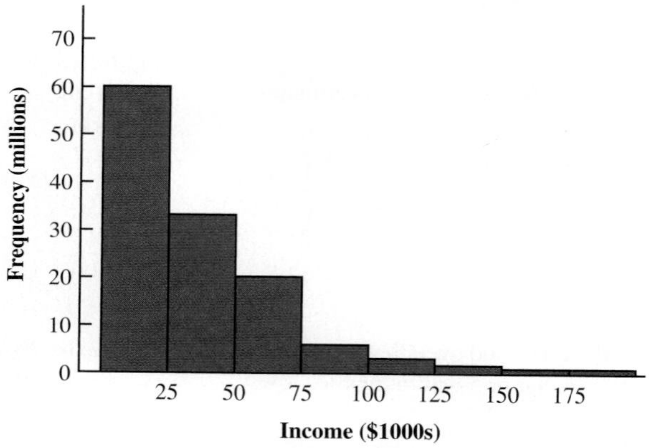

Histogram is skewed to the right

b. Exam Scores

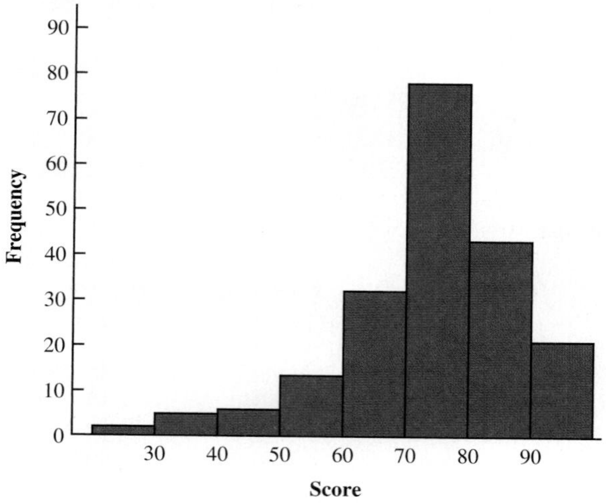

Histogram is skewed to the left

c.

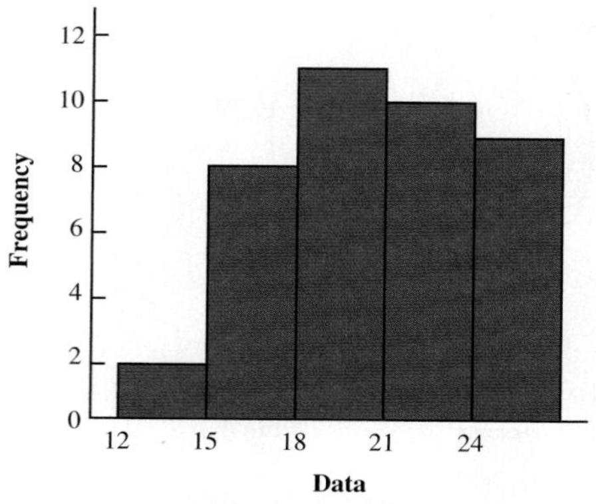

Histogram skewed slightly to the left

18. a. Lowest \$180; highest \$2050

b.

Spending	Frequency	Percent Frequency
\$0–249	3	12
250–499	6	24
500–749	5	20
750–999	5	20
1000–1249	3	12
1250–1499	1	4
1500–1749	0	0
1750–1999	1	4
2000–2249	1	4
Total	25	100

c. The distribution shows a positive skewness

d. Majority (64%) of consumers spend between \$250 and \$1000; the middle value is about \$750; and two high spenders are above \$1750

20. a.

Price	Frequency	Percent Frequency
30–39.99	7	35
40–49.99	5	25
50–59.99	2	10
60–69.99	3	15
70–79.99	3	15
Total	20	100

c. Fleetwood Mac, Harper/Johnson

22.

5	7 8
6	4 5 8
7	0 2 2 5 5 6 8
8	0 2 3 5

23. Leaf unit = .1

6	3
7	5 5 7
8	1 3 4 8
9	3 6
10	0 4 5
11	3

24. Leaf unit = 10

11	6
12	0 2
13	0 6 7
14	2 2 7
15	5
16	0 2 8
17	0 2 3

25.

9	8 9
10	2 4 6 6
11	4 5 7 8 8 9
12	2 4 5 7
13	1 2
14	4
15	1

26. a.

1	0 3 7 7
2	4 5 5
3	0 0 5 5 9
4	0 0 0 5 5 8
5	0 0 0 4 5 5

b.

0	5 7
1	0 1 1 3 4
1	5 5 5 8
2	0 0 0 0 0 0
2	5 5
3	0 0 0
3	6
4	
4	
5	
5	
6	3

28. a.

2	14
2	67
3	011123
3	5677
4	003333344
4	6679
5	00022
5	5679
6	14
6	6
7	2

b. 40–44 with 9

c. 43 with 5

d. 10%; relatively small participation in the race

29. a.

		y: 1	2	Total
x	A	5	0	5
	B	11	2	13
	C	2	10	12
	Total	18	12	30

b.

		y: 1	2	Total
x	A	100.0	0.0	100.0
	B	84.6	15.4	100.0
	C	16.7	83.3	100.0

c.

		y: 1	2
x	A	27.8	0.0
	B	61.1	16.7
	C	11.1	83.3
	Total	100.0	100.0

d. *A* values are always in $y = 1$
B values are most often in $y = 1$
C values are most often in $y = 2$

30. a.

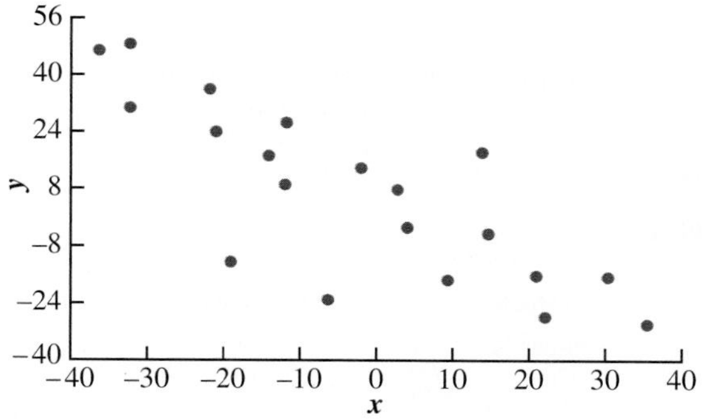

b. A negative relationship between *x* and *y*; *y* decreases as *x* increases

32. a.

Education Level	Household Income ($1000s) Under 25	25.0–49.9	50.0–74.9	75.0–99.9	100 or more	Total
Not H.S. Graduate	32.70	14.82	8.27	5.02	2.53	15.86
H.S. Graduate	35.74	35.56	31.48	25.39	14.47	30.78
Some College	21.17	29.77	30.25	29.82	22.26	26.37
Bachelor's Degree	7.53	14.43	20.56	25.03	33.88	17.52
Beyond Bach. Deg.	2.86	5.42	9.44	14.74	26.86	9.48
Total	100.00	100.00	100.00	100.00	100.00	100.00

15.86% of the heads of households did not graduate from high school

b. 26.86%, 39.72%

c. Positive relationship between income and education level

34. a.

Sales/Margins/ROE	EPS Rating 0–19	20–39	40–59	60–79	80–100	Total
A				1	8	9
B		1	4	5	2	12
C	1		1	2	3	7
D	3	1		1		5
E		2	1			3
Total	4	4	6	9	13	36

b.

Sales/Margins/ROE	EPS Rating 0–19	20–39	40–59	60–79	80–100	Total
A				11.11	88.89	100
B		8.33	33.33	41.67	16.67	100
C	14.29		14.29	28.57	42.86	100
D	60.00	20.00		20.00		100
E		66.67	33.33			100

Higher EPS ratings seem to be associated with higher ratings on Sales/Margins/ROE

36. b. No apparent relationship

38. a.

Vehicle	Frequency	Percent Frequency
Accord	6	12
Camry	7	14
F-Series	14	28
Ram	10	20
Silverado	13	26

b. Ford F-Series and the Toyota Camry

40. a.

Response	Frequency	Percent Frequency
Accuracy	16	16
Approach shots	3	3
Mental approach	17	17
Power	8	8
Practice	15	15
Putting	10	10
Short game	24	24
Strategic decisions	7	7
Total	100	100

b. Poor short game, poor mental approach, lack of accuracy, and limited practice

42. a.

SAT Score	Frequency
750–849	2
850–949	5
950–1049	10
1050–1149	5
1150–1249	3
Total	25

b. Nearly symmetrical

c. 40% of the scores fall between 950 and 1049
A score below 750 or above 1249 is unusual
The average is near or slightly above 1000

44. a.

Population	Frequency	Percent Frequency
0.0–2.4	17	34
2.5–4.9	12	24
5.0–7.4	9	18
7.5–9.9	4	8
10.0–12.4	3	6
12.5–14.9	1	2
15.0–17.4	1	2
17.5–19.9	1	2
20.0–22.4	0	0
22.5–24.9	1	2
25.0–27.4	0	0
27.5–29.9	0	0
30.0–32.4	0	0
32.5–34.9	0	0
35.0–37.4	1	2
Total	50	100

c. High positive skewness

d. 17 (34%) with population less than 2.5 million
29 (58%) with population less than 5 million
8 (16%) with population greater than 10 million
Largest 35.9 million (California)
Smallest .5 million (Wyoming)

46. a. High Temperatures

1	
2	
3	0
4	1 2 2 5
5	2 4 5
6	0 0 0 1 2 2 5 6 8
7	0 7
8	4

b. Low Temperatures

1	1
2	1 2 6 7 9
3	1 5 6 8 9
4	0 3 3 6 7
5	0 0 4
6	5
7	
8	

c. The most frequent range for high is in 60s (9 of 20) with only one low temperature above 54
High temperatures range mostly from 41 to 68, while low temperatures range mostly from 21 to 47
Low was 11; high was 84

d.

High Temp	Frequency	Low Temp	Frequency
10–19	0	10–19	1
20–29	0	20–29	5
30–39	1	30–39	5
40–49	4	40–49	5
50–59	3	50–59	3
60–69	9	60–69	1
70–79	2	70–79	0
80–89	1	80–89	0
Total	20	Total	20

48. a.

	Satisfaction Score						
Occupation	30–39	40–49	50–59	60–69	70–79	80–89	Total
Cabinetmaker			2	4	3	1	10
Lawyer	1	5	2	1	1		10
Physical Therapist			5	2	1	2	10
Systems Analyst		2	1	4	3		10
Total	1	7	10	11	8	3	40

b.

	Satisfaction Score						
Occupation	30–39	40–49	50–59	60–69	70–79	80–89	Total
Cabinetmaker			20	40	30	10	100
Lawyer	10	50	20	10	10		100
Physical Therapist			50	20	10	20	100
Systems Analyst		20	10	40	30		100

c. Cabinetmakers seem to have the highest job satisfaction scores; lawyers seem to have the lowest

50. a. Row totals: 247; 54; 82; 121
Column totals: 149; 317; 17; 7; 14

b.

Year	Freq.	Fuel	Freq.
1973 or before	247	Elect.	149
1974–79	54	Nat. Gas	317
1980–86	82	Oil	17
1987–91	121	Propane	7
Total	504	Other	14
		Total	504

c. Crosstabulation of column percentages

	Fuel Type				
Year Constructed	Elect.	Nat. Gas	Oil	Propane	Other
1973 or before	26.9	57.7	70.5	71.4	50.0
1974–1979	16.1	8.2	11.8	28.6	0.0
1980–1986	24.8	12.0	5.9	0.0	42.9
1987–1991	32.2	22.1	11.8	0.0	7.1
Total	100.0	100.0	100.0	100.0	100.0

d. Crosstabulation of row percentages.

	Fuel Type					
Year Constructed	Elect.	Nat. Gas	Oil	Propane	Other	Total
1973 or before	16.2	74.1	4.9	2.0	2.8	100.0
1974–1979	44.5	48.1	3.7	3.7	0.0	100.0
1980–1986	45.1	46.4	1.2	0.0	7.3	100.0
1987–1991	39.7	57.8	1.7	0.0	0.8	100.0

52. a. Crosstabulation of market value and profit

	Profit ($1000s)				
Market Value ($1000s)	0–300	300–600	600–900	900–1200	Total
0–8000	23	4			27
8000–16,000	4	4	2	2	12
16,000–24,000		2	1	1	4
24,000–32,000		1	2	1	4
32,000–40,000		2	1		3
Total	27	13	6	4	50

b. Crosstabulation of row percentages

	Profit ($1000s)				
Market Value ($1000s)	0–300	300–600	600–900	900–1200	Total
0–8000	85.19	14.81	0.00	0.00	100
8000–16,000	33.33	33.33	16.67	16.67	100
16,000–24,000	0.00	50.00	25.00	25.00	100
24,000–32,000	0.00	25.00	50.00	25.00	100
32,000–40,000	0.00	66.67	33.33	0.00	100

c. A positive relationship is indicated between profit and market value; as profit goes up, market value goes up

54. b. A positive relationship is demonstrated between market value and stockholders' equity

Chapter 3

2. 16, 16.5

3. Arrange data in order: 15, 20, 25, 25, 27, 28, 30, 34

$i = \frac{20}{100}(8) = 1.6$; round up to position 2

20th percentile = 20

$i = \frac{25}{100}(8) = 2$; use positions 2 and 3

$25\text{th percentile} = \frac{20 + 25}{2} = 22.5$

$i = \frac{65}{100}(8) = 5.2$; round up to position 6

65th percentile = 28

$i = \frac{75}{100}(8) = 6$; use positions 6 and 7

$75\text{th percentile} = \frac{28 + 30}{2} = 29$

4. 59.73, 57, 53

6. a. Marketing: 36.3, 35.5, 34.2
Accounting: 45.7, 44.7, no mode

b. Marketing: 34.2, 39.5
Accounting: 40.95, 49.8

c. Accounting salaries are approximately \$9000 higher

8. a. $\bar{x} = \frac{\Sigma x_i}{n} = \frac{695}{20} = 34.75$

Mode = 25 (appears three times)

b. Data in order: 18, 20, 25, 25, 25, 26, 27, 27, 28, 33, 36, 37, 40, 40, 42, 45, 46, 48, 53, 54

Median (10th and 11th positions)

$\frac{33 + 36}{2} = 34.5$

At-home workers are slightly younger

c. $i = \frac{25}{100}(20) = 5$; use positions 5 and 6

$Q_1 = \frac{25 + 26}{2} = 25.5$

$i = \frac{75}{100}(20) = 15$; use positions 15 and 16

$Q_3 = \frac{42 + 45}{2} = 43.5$

d. $i = \frac{32}{100}(20) = 6.4$; round up to position 7

32nd percentile = 27
At least 32% of the people are 27 or younger

10. a. 76, 76

b. 39, 37.5

c. Yes; emergency wait time is too long

12. Disney: 3321, 255.5, 253, 169, 325
Pixar: 3231, 538.5, 505, 363, 631
Pixar films generate approximately twice as much box office revenue per film

14. 16, 4

15. Range = 34 − 15 = 19
Arrange data in order: 15, 20, 25, 25, 27, 28, 30, 34

$i = \frac{25}{100}(8) = 2$; $Q_1 = \frac{20 + 25}{2} = 22.5$

$i = \frac{75}{100}(8) = 6$; $Q_3 = \frac{28 + 30}{2} = 29$

$\text{IQR} = Q_3 - Q_1 = 29 - 22.5 = 6.5$

$\bar{x} = \frac{\Sigma x_i}{n} = \frac{204}{8} = 25.5$

x_i	$(x_i - \bar{x})$	$(x_i - \bar{x})^2$
27	1.5	2.25
25	−.5	.25
20	−5.5	30.25
15	−10.5	110.25
30	4.5	20.25
34	8.5	72.25
28	2.5	6.25
25	−.5	.25
		242.00

$s^2 = \frac{\Sigma(x_i - \bar{x})^2}{n - 1} = \frac{242}{8 - 1} = 34.57$

$s = \sqrt{34.57} = 5.88$

16. a. Range = 190 − 168 = 22

b. $\bar{x} = \frac{\Sigma x_i}{n} = \frac{1068}{6} = 178$

$s^2 = \frac{\Sigma(x_i - \bar{x})^2}{n - 1}$

$= \frac{4^2 + (-10)^2 + 6^2 + 12^2 + (-8)^2 + (-4)^2}{6 - 1}$

$= \frac{376}{5} = 75.2$

c. $s = \sqrt{75.2} = 8.67$

d. $\frac{s}{\bar{x}}(100) = \frac{8.67}{178}(100\%) = 4.87\%$

18. a. 38, 97, 9.85

b. Eastern shows more variation

20. *Dawson:* range = 2, s = .67
Clark: range = 8, s = 2.58

22. a. 45.05, 23.98; 57.50, 11.475

b. 190.67, 13.81; 140.63, 11.86

c. 38.02%; 57.97%

d. Variability greater for broker-assisted trades

24. *Quarter-milers:* s = .0564, Coef. of Var. = 5.8%
Milers: s = .1295, Coef. of Var. = 2.9%

26. .20, 1.50, 0, −.50, −2.20

27. Chebyshev's theorem: *at least* $(1 - 1/z^2)$

a. $z = \frac{40 - 30}{5} = 2$; $1 - \frac{1}{(2)^2} = .75$

b. $z = \frac{45 - 30}{5} = 3$; $1 - \frac{1}{(3)^2} = .89$

c. $z = \frac{38 - 30}{5} = 1.6$; $1 - \frac{1}{(1.6)^2} = .61$

d. $z = \frac{42 - 30}{5} = 2.4$; $1 - \frac{1}{(2.4)^2} = .83$

e. $z = \dfrac{48 - 30}{5} = 3.6;\ 1 - \dfrac{1}{(3.6)^2} = .92$

28. a. 95%
b. Almost all
c. 68%

29. a. $z = 2$ standard deviations

$1 - \dfrac{1}{z^2} = 1 - \dfrac{1}{2^2} = \dfrac{3}{4}$; at least 75%

b. $z = 2.5$ standard deviations

$1 - \dfrac{1}{z^2} = 1 - \dfrac{1}{2.5^2} = .84$; at least 84%

c. $z = 2$ standard deviations
Empirical rule: 95%

30. a. 68%
b. 81.5%
c. 2.5%

32. a. −.67
b. 1.50
c. Neither an outlier
d. Yes; $z = 8.25$

34. a. 76.5, 7
b. 16%, 2.5%
c. 12.2, 7.89; no

36. 15, 22.5, 26, 29, 34

38. Arrange data in order: 5, 6, 8, 10, 10, 12, 15, 16, 18

$i = \dfrac{25}{100}(9) = 2.25$; round up to position 3

$Q_1 = 8$
Median (5th position) = 10

$i = \dfrac{75}{100}(9) = 6.75$; round up to position 7

$Q_3 = 15$
5-number summary: 5, 8, 10, 15, 18

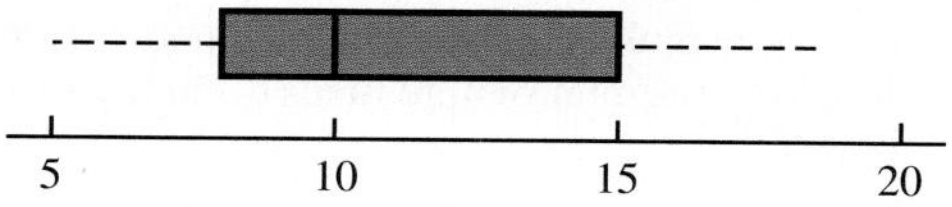

40. a. 619, 725, 1016, 1699, 4450
b. Limits: 0, 3160
c. Yes
d. No

41. a. Arrange data in order low to high

$i = \dfrac{25}{100}(21) = 5.25$; round up to 6th position

$Q_1 = 1872$
Median (11th position) = 4019

$i = \dfrac{75}{100}(21) = 15.75$; round up to 16th position

$Q_3 = 8305$
5-number summary: 608, 1872, 4019, 8305, 14138

b. IQR $= Q_3 - Q_1 = 8305 - 1872 = 6433$
Lower limit: $1872 - 1.5(6433) = -7777.5$
Upper limit: $8305 + 1.5(6433) = 17{,}955$

c. No; data are within limits
d. 41,138 > 27,604; 41,138 would be an outlier; data value would be reviewed and corrected
e.

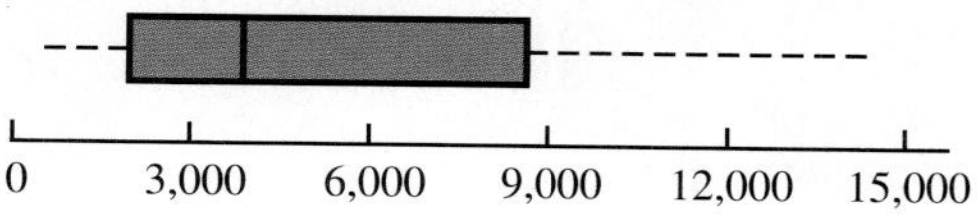

42. a. 66
b. 30, 49, 66, 88, 208
c. Yes; upper limit = 146.5

44. a. 18.2, 15.35
b. 11.7, 23.5
c. 3.4, 11.7, 15.35, 23.5, 41.3
d. Yes; Alger Small Cap 41.3

45. b. There appears to be a negative linear relationship between x and y

c.

x_i	y_i	$x_i - \bar{x}$	$y_i - \bar{y}$	$(x_i - \bar{x})(y_i - \bar{y})$
4	50	−4	4	−16
6	50	−2	4	−8
11	40	3	−6	−18
3	60	−5	14	−70
16	30	8	−16	−128
40	230	0	0	−240

$\bar{x} = 8;\ \bar{y} = 46$

$$s_{xy} = \frac{\Sigma(x_i - \bar{x})(y_i - \bar{y})}{n - 1} = \frac{-240}{4} = -60$$

The sample covariance indicates a negative linear association between x and y

d. $r_{xy} = \dfrac{s_{xy}}{s_x s_y} = \dfrac{-60}{(5.43)(11.40)} = -.969$

The sample correlation coefficient of −.969 is indicative of a strong negative linear relationship

46. b. There appears to be a positive linear relationship between x and y
c. $s_{xy} = 26.5$
d. $r_{xy} = .693$

48. −.91; negative relationship

50. b. .9098
c. Strong positive linear relationship; no

52. a. 3.69
b. 3.175

53. a.

f_i	M_i	$f_i M_i$
4	5	20
7	10	70
9	15	135
5	20	100
25		325

$$\bar{x} = \frac{\Sigma f_i M_i}{n} = \frac{325}{25} = 13$$

b.

f_i	M_i	$(M_i - \bar{x})$	$(M_i - \bar{x})^2$	$f_i(M_i - \bar{x})^2$
4	5	−8	64	256
7	10	−3	9	63
9	15	2	4	36
5	20	7	49	245
25				600

$$s^2 = \frac{\Sigma f_i(M_i - \bar{x})^2}{n - 1} = \frac{600}{25 - 1} = 25$$

$$s = \sqrt{25} = 5$$

54. a.

Grade x_i	Weight w_i
4 (A)	9
3 (B)	15
2 (C)	33
1 (D)	3
0 (F)	0
	60 credit hours

$$\bar{x} = \frac{\Sigma w_i x_i}{\Sigma w_i} = \frac{9(4) + 15(3) + 33(2) + 3(1)}{9 + 15 + 33 + 3}$$

$$= \frac{150}{60} = 2.5$$

b. Yes

56. 3.49, .94

58. a. 1800, 1351
b. 387, 1710
c. 7280, 1323
d. 3,675,303, 1917
e. 9271.01, 96.29
f. High positive skewness
g. Using a box plot: 4135 and 7450 are outliers

60. a. 2.3, 1.85
b. 1.90, 1.38
c. Altria Group 5%
d. −.51, below mean
e. 1.02, above mean
f. No

62. a. $670
b. $456
c. $z = 3$; yes
d. Save time and prevent a penalty cost

64. a. 215.9
b. 55%
c. 175.0, 628.3
d. 48.8, 175.0, 215.9, 628.3, 2325.0
e. Yes, any price over 1308.25
f. 482.1; prefer median

66. b. .9856, strong positive relationship

68. a. 817
b. 833

70. a. 60.68
b. $s^2 = 31.23$; $s = 5.59$

Chapter 4

2. $\binom{6}{3} = \frac{6!}{3!3!} = \frac{6\cdot5\cdot4\cdot3\cdot2\cdot1}{(3\cdot2\cdot1)(3\cdot2\cdot1)} = 20$

ABC	ACE	BCD	BEF
ABD	ACF	BCE	CDE
ABE	ADE	BCF	CDF
ABF	ADF	BDE	CEF
ACD	AEF	BDF	DEF

4. b. (H,H,H), (H,H,T), (H,T,H), (H,T,T), (T,H,H), (T,H,T), (T,T,H), (T,T,T)
c. ⅛

6. $P(E_1) = .40$, $P(E_2) = .26$, $P(E_3) = .34$
The relative frequency method was used

8. a. 4: Commission Positive—Council Approves
Commission Positive—Council Disapproves
Commission Negative—Council Approves
Commission Negative—Council Disapproves

9. $\binom{50}{4} = \frac{50!}{4!46!} = \frac{50\cdot49\cdot48\cdot47}{4\cdot3\cdot2\cdot1} = 230{,}300$

10. a. Use the relative frequency approach
$P(\text{California}) = 1{,}434/2{,}374 = .60$
b. Number not from four states
$= 2{,}374 - 1{,}434 - 390 - 217 - 112$
$= 221$

$P(\text{Not from 4 states}) = 221/2{,}374 = .09$
c. $P(\text{Not in early stages}) = 1 - .22 = .78$
d. Estimate of number of Massachusetts companies in early stage of development $= (.22)390 \approx 86$
e. If we assume the size of the awards did not differ by state, we can multiply the probability an award went to Colorado by the total venture funds disbursed to get an estimate

Estimate of Colorado funds $= (112/2374)(\$32.4)$
$= \$1.53$ billion

Authors' Note: The actual amount going to Colorado was $1.74 billion

12. a. 3,478,761
b. 1/3,478,761
c. 1/146,107,962

14. a. ¼
b. ½
c. ¾

15. a. S = {ace of clubs, ace of diamonds, ace of hearts, ace of spades}
b. S = {2 of clubs, 3 of clubs, . . . , 10 of clubs, J of clubs, Q of clubs, K of clubs, A of clubs}

c. There are 12; jack, queen, or king in each of the four suits
d. For (a): 4/52 = 1/13 = .08
For (b): 13/52 = 1/4 = .25
For (c): 12/52 = .23

16. a. 36
c. $\frac{1}{6}$
d. $\frac{5}{18}$
e. No; $P(\text{odd}) = P(\text{even}) = \frac{1}{2}$
f. Classical

17. a. (4, 6), (4, 7), (4, 8)
b. .05 + .10 + .15 = .30
c. (2, 8), (3, 8), (4, 8)
d. .05 + .05 + .15 = .25
e. .15

18. a. $P(0) = .05$
b. $P(4 \text{ or } 5) = .20$
c. $P(0, 1, \text{or } 2) = .55$

20. a. .108
b. .096
c. .434

22. a. .40, .40, .60
b. .80, yes
c. $A^c = \{E_3, E_4, E_5\}$; $C^c = \{E_1, E_4\}$;
$P(A^c) = .60$; $P(C^c) = .40$
d. (E_1, E_2, E_5); .60
e. .80

23. a. $P(A) = P(E_1) + P(E_4) + P(E_6)$
$= .05 + .25 + .10 = .40$
$P(B) = P(E_2) + P(E_4) + P(E_7)$
$= .20 + .25 + .05 = .50$
$P(C) = P(E_2) + P(E_3) + P(E_5) + P(E_7)$
$= .20 + .20 + .15 + .05 = .60$
b. $A \cup B = \{E_1, E_2, E_4, E_6, E_7\}$;
$P(A \cup B) = P(E_1) + P(E_2) + P(E_4) + P(E_6) + P(E_7)$
$= .05 + .20 + .25 + .10 + .05$
$= .65$
c. $A \cap B = \{E_4\}$; $P(A \cap B) = P(E_4) = .25$
d. Yes, they are mutually exclusive
e. $B^c = \{E_1, E_3, E_5, E_6\}$;
$P(B^c) = P(E_1) + P(E_3) + P(E_5) + P(E_6)$
$= .05 + .20 + .15 + .10$
$= .50$

24. a. .05
b. .70

26. a. .30, .23
b. .17
c. .64

28. Let B = rented a car for business reasons
P = rented a car for personal reasons
a. $P(B \cup P) = P(B) + P(P) - P(B \cap P)$
$= .540 + .458 - .300$
$= .698$
b. $P(\text{Neither}) = 1 - .698 = .302$

30. a. $P(A \mid B) = \dfrac{P(A \cap B)}{P(B)} = \dfrac{.40}{.60} = .6667$
b. $P(B \mid A) = \dfrac{P(A \cap B)}{P(A)} = \dfrac{.40}{.50} = .80$
c. No, because $P(A \mid B) \neq P(A)$

32. a.

	Yes	No	Total
18 to 34	.375	.085	.46
35 and older	.475	.065	.54
Total	.850	.150	1.00

b. 46% 18 to 34; 54% 35 and older
c. .15
d. .1848
e. .1204
f. .5677
g. Higher probability of No for 18 to 34

33. a.

	Reason for Applying			
	Quality	**Cost/ Convenience**	**Other**	**Total**
Full-time	.218	.204	.039	.461
Part-time	.208	.307	.024	.539
Total	.426	.511	.063	1.000

b. A student is most likely to cite cost or convenience as the first reason (probability = .511); school quality is the reason cited by the second largest number of students (probability = .426)
c. $P(\text{quality} \mid \text{full-time}) = .218/.461 = .473$
d. $P(\text{quality} \mid \text{part-time}) = .208/.539 = .386$
e. For independence, we must have $P(A)P(B) = P(A \cap B)$; from the table

$P(A \cap B) = .218$, $P(A) = .461$, $P(B) = .426$
$P(A)P(B) = (.461)(.426) = .196$

Because $P(A)P(B) \neq P(A \cap B)$, the events are not independent

34. a. .44
b. .15
c. .136
d. .106
e. .0225
f. .0025

36. a. .7921
b. .9879
c. .0121
d. .3364, .8236, .1764
Don't foul Reggie Miller

38. a. .70
b. .30
c. .67, .33

d. .20, .10
e. .40
f. .20
g. No; $P(S \mid M) \neq P(S)$

39. a. Yes, because $P(A_1 \cap A_2) = 0$
b. $P(A_1 \cap B) = P(A_1)P(B \mid A_1) = .40(.20) = .08$
$P(A_2 \cap B) = P(A_2)P(B \mid A_2) = .60(.05) = .03$
c. $P(B) = P(A_1 \cap B) + P(A_2 \cap B) = .08 + .03 = .11$
d. $P(A_1 \mid B) = \frac{.08}{.11} = .7273$
$P(A_2 \mid B) = \frac{.03}{.11} = .2727$

40. a. .10, .20, .09
b. .51
c. .26, .51, .23

42. M = missed payment
D_1 = customer defaults
D_2 = customer does not default
$P(D_1) = .05, P(D_2) = .95, P(M \mid D_2) = .2, P(M \mid D_1) = 1$
a. $P(D_1 \mid M) = \frac{P(D_1)P(M \mid D_1)}{P(D_1)P(M \mid D_1) + P(D_2)P(M \mid D_2)}$
$= \frac{(.05)(1)}{(.05)(1) + (.95)(.2)}$
$= \frac{.05}{.24} = .21$
b. Yes, the probability of default is greater than .20

44. a. .47, .53, .50, .45
b. .4963
c. .4463
d. 47%, 53%

46. a. .68
b. 52
c. 10

48. a. 315
b. .29
c. No
d. Republicans

50. a. .76
b. .24

52. b. .2022
c. .4618
d. .4005

54. a. .49
b. .44
c. .54
d. No
e. Yes

56. a. .25
b. .125
c. .0125
d. .10
e. No

58. 3.44%

60. a. .40
b. .67

Chapter 5

1. a. Head, Head (H, H)
Head, Tail (H, T)
Tail, Head (T, H)
Tail, Tail (T, T)
b. x = number of heads on two coin tosses
c.

Outcome	Values of x
(H, H)	2
(H, T)	1
(T, H)	1
(T, T)	0

d. Discrete; it may assume 3 values: 0, 1, and 2

2. a. x = time in minutes to assemble product
b. Any positive value: $x > 0$
c. Continuous

3. Let Y = position is offered
N = position is not offered
a. $S = \{(Y, Y, Y), (Y, Y, N), (Y, N, Y), (Y, N, N), (N, Y, Y), (N, Y, N), (N, N, Y), (N, N, N)\}$
b. Let N = number of offers made; N is a discrete random variable
c.

Experimental Outcome	(Y, Y, Y)	(Y, Y, N)	(Y, N, Y)	(Y, N, N)	(N, Y, Y)	(N, Y, N)	(N, N, Y)	(N, N, N)
Value of N	3	2	2	1	2	1	1	0

4. $x = 0, 1, 2, \ldots, 12$

6. a. 0, 1, 2, . . . , 20; discrete
b. 0, 1, 2, . . . ; discrete
c. 0, 1, 2, . . . , 50; discrete
d. $0 \leq x \leq 8$; continuous
e. $x > 0$; continuous

7. a. $f(x) \geq 0$ for all values of x
$\Sigma f(x) = 1$; therefore, it is a valid probability distribution
b. Probability $x = 30$ is $f(30) = .25$
c. Probability $x \leq 25$ is $f(20) + f(25) = .20 + .15 = .35$
d. Probability $x > 30$ is $f(35) = .40$

8. a.

x	$f(x)$
1	3/20 = .15
2	5/20 = .25
3	8/20 = .40
4	4/20 = .20
Total	1.00

b.

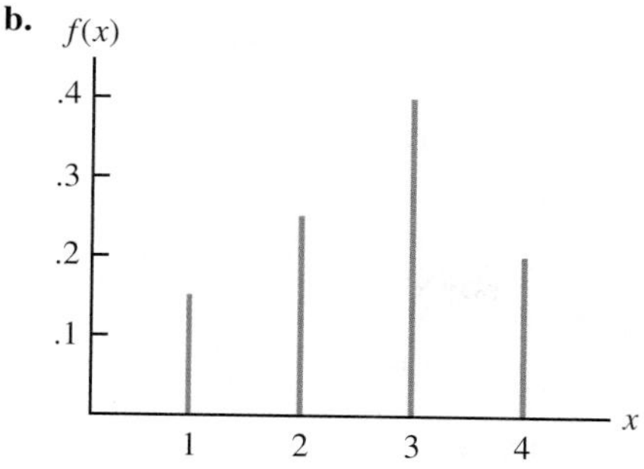

c. $f(x) \geq 0$ for $x = 1, 2, 3, 4$
$\Sigma f(x) = 1$

10. a.

x	1	2	3	4	5
$f(x)$	.05	.09	.03	.42	.41

b.

x	1	2	3	4	5
$f(x)$	.04	.10	.12	.46	.28

c. .83
d. .28
e. Senior executives are more satisfied

12. a. Yes
b. .65

14. a. .05
b. .70
c. .40

16. a.

y	$f(y)$	$yf(y)$
2	.20	.4
4	.30	1.2
7	.40	2.8
8	.10	.8
Totals	1.00	5.2

$E(y) = \mu = 5.2$

b.

y	$y - \mu$	$(y - \mu)^2$	$f(y)$	$(y - \mu)^2 f(y)$
2	−3.20	10.24	.20	2.048
4	−1.20	1.44	.30	.432
7	1.80	3.24	.40	1.296
8	2.80	7.84	.10	.784
			Total	4.560

$\text{Var}(y) = 4.56$

$\sigma = \sqrt{4.56} = 2.14$

18. a/b.

x	$f(x)$	$xf(x)$	$x - \mu$	$(x - \mu)^2$	$(x - \mu)^2 f(x)$
0	0.04	0.00	−1.84	3.39	0.12
1	0.34	0.34	−0.84	0.71	0.24
2	0.41	0.82	0.16	0.02	0.01
3	0.18	0.53	1.16	1.34	0.24
4	0.04	0.15	2.16	4.66	0.17
Total	1.00	1.84 ↑ $E(x)$			0.79 ↑ $\text{Var}(x)$

c/d.

y	$f(y)$	$yf(y)$	$y - \mu$	$(y - \mu)^2$	$y - \mu^2 f(y)$
0	0.00	0.00	−2.93	8.58	0.01
1	0.03	0.03	−1.93	3.72	0.12
2	0.23	0.45	−0.93	0.86	0.20
3	0.52	1.55	0.07	0.01	0.00
4	0.22	0.90	1.07	1.15	0.26
Total	1.00	2.93 ↑ $E(y)$			0.59 ↑ $\text{Var}(y)$

e. The number of bedrooms in owner-occupied houses is greater than in renter-occupied houses; the expected number of bedrooms is $2.93 - 1.84 = 1.09$ greater, and the variability in the number of bedrooms is less for the owner-occupied houses

20. a. 430
b. −90; concern is to protect against the expense of a big accident

22. a. 445
b. $1250 loss

24. a. Medium: 145; large: 140
b. Medium: 2725; large: 12,400

25. a.

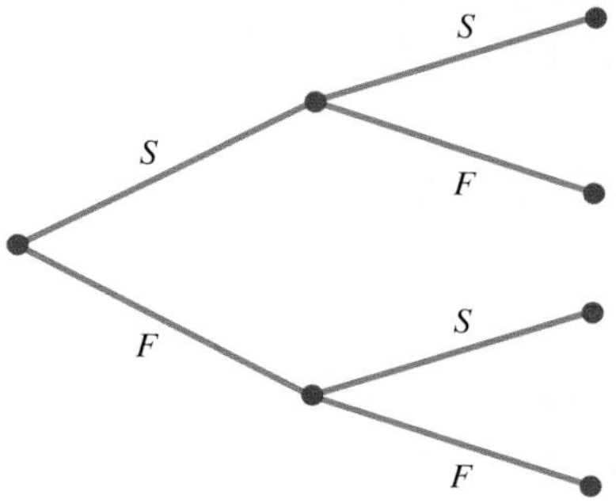

b. $f(1) = \binom{2}{1}(.4)^1(.6)^1 = \frac{2!}{1!1!}(.4)(.6) = .48$

c. $f(0) = \binom{2}{0}(.4)^0(.6)^2 = \frac{2!}{0!2!}(1)(.36) = .36$

d. $f(2) = \binom{2}{2}(.4)^2(.6)^0 = \frac{2!}{2!0!}(.16)(.1) = .16$

e. $P(x \geq 1) = f(1) + f(2) = .48 + .16 = .64$
f. $E(x) = np = 2(.4) = .8$
$\text{Var}(x) = np(1 - p) = 2(.4)(.6) = .48$
$\sigma = \sqrt{.48} = .6928$

26. a. $f(0) = .3487$
b. $f(2) = .1937$
c. .9298
d. .6513
e. 1
f. $\sigma^2 = .9000, \sigma = .9487$

28. a. .2789
b. .4181
c. .0733

30. a. Probability of a defective part being produced must be .03 for each part selected; parts must be selected independently
b. Let D = defective
G = not defective

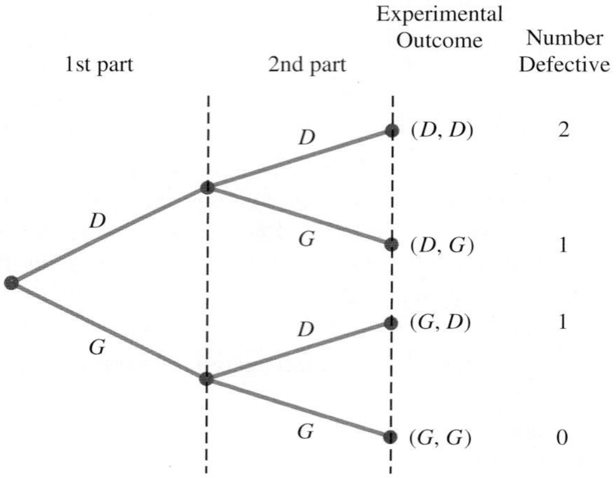

c. Two outcomes result in exactly one defect
d. $P(\text{no defects}) = (.97)(.97) = .9409$
$P(\text{1 defect}) = 2(.03)(.97) = .0582$
$P(\text{2 defects}) = (.03)(.03) = .0009$

32. a. .90
b. .99
c. .999
d. Yes

34. a. .2262
b. .8355

38. a. $f(x) = \dfrac{3^x e^{-3}}{x!}$
b. .2241
c. .1494
d. .8008

39. a. $f(x) = \dfrac{2^x e^{-2}}{x!}$
b. $\mu = 6$ for 3 time periods
c. $f(x) = \dfrac{6^x e^{-6}}{x!}$
d. $f(2) = \dfrac{2^2 e^{-2}}{2!} = \dfrac{4(.1353)}{2} = .2706$
e. $f(6) = \dfrac{6^6 e^{-6}}{6!} = .1606$
f. $f(5) = \dfrac{4^5 e^{-4}}{5!} = .1563$

40. a. $\mu = 48(5/60) = 4$
$f(3) = \dfrac{4^3 e^{-4}}{3!} = \dfrac{(64)(.0183)}{6} = .1952$
b. $\mu = 48(15/60) = 12$
$f(10) = \dfrac{12^{10} e^{-12}}{10!} = .1048$
c. $\mu = 48(5/60) = 4$; expect four callers to be waiting after 5 minutes
$f(0) = \dfrac{4^0 e^{-4}}{0!} = .0183$; the probability none will be waiting after 5 minutes is .0183
d. $\mu = 48(3/60) = 2.4$
$f(0) = \dfrac{2.4^0 e^{-2.4}}{0!} = .0907$; the probability of no interruptions in 3 minutes is .0907

42. a. $f(0) = \dfrac{7^0 e^{-7}}{0!} = e^{-7} = .0009$
b. probability $= 1 - [f(0) + f(1)]$
$f(1) = \dfrac{7^1 e^{-7}}{1!} = 7e^{-7} = .0064$
probability $= 1 - [.0009 + .0064] = .9927$
c. $\mu = 3.5$
$f(0) = \dfrac{3.5^0 e^{-3.5}}{0!} = e^{-3.5} = .0302$
probability $= 1 - f(0) = 1 - .0302 = .9698$
d.
$$\begin{aligned}\text{probability} &= 1 - [f(0) + f(1) + f(2) + f(3) + f(4)] \\ &= 1 - [.0009 + .0064 + .0223 + .0521 + .0912] \\ &= .8271\end{aligned}$$

44. a. $\mu = 1.25$
b. .2865
c. .3581
d. .3554

46. a. $f(1) = \dfrac{\dbinom{3}{1}\dbinom{10-3}{4-1}}{\dbinom{10}{4}} = \dfrac{\left(\dfrac{3!}{1!2!}\right)\left(\dfrac{7!}{3!4!}\right)}{\dfrac{10!}{4!6!}}$
$= \dfrac{(3)(35)}{210} = .50$
b. $f(2) = \dfrac{\dbinom{3}{2}\dbinom{10-3}{2-2}}{\dbinom{10}{2}} = \dfrac{(3)(1)}{45} = .067$
c. $f(0) = \dfrac{\dbinom{3}{0}\dbinom{10-3}{2-0}}{\dbinom{10}{2}} = \dfrac{(1)(21)}{45} = .4667$

d. $f(2) = \dfrac{\binom{3}{2}\binom{10-3}{4-2}}{\binom{10}{4}} = \dfrac{(3)(21)}{210} = .30$

48. a. .5250
b. .1833

50. $N = 60, n = 10$
a. $r = 20, x = 0$

$$f(0) = \frac{\binom{20}{0}\binom{40}{10}}{\binom{60}{10}} = \frac{(1)\left(\frac{40!}{10!30!}\right)}{\frac{60!}{10!50!}}$$
$$= \left(\frac{40!}{10!30!}\right)\left(\frac{10!50!}{60!}\right)$$
$$= \frac{40\cdot39\cdot38\cdot37\cdot36\cdot35\cdot34\cdot33\cdot32\cdot31}{60\cdot59\cdot58\cdot57\cdot56\cdot55\cdot54\cdot53\cdot52\cdot51}$$
$$\approx .01$$

b. $r = 20, x = 1$

$$f(1) = \frac{\binom{20}{1}\binom{40}{9}}{\binom{60}{10}} = 20\left(\frac{40!}{9!31!}\right)\left(\frac{10!50!}{60!}\right)$$
$$\approx .07$$

c. $1 - f(0) - f(1) = 1 - .08 = .92$
d. Same as the probability one will be from Hawaii; in part (b) it was equal to approximately .07

52. a. .5333
b. .6667
c. .7778
d. $n = 7$

54. a.

x	1	2	3	4	5
$f(x)$	.24	.21	.10	.21	.24

b. 3.00, 2.34
c. Bonds: $E(x) = 1.36$, $\text{Var}(x) = .23$
Stocks: $E(x) = 4$, $\text{Var}(x) = 1$

56. a. .0596
b. .3585
c. 100
d. 9.75

58. a. .9510
b. .0480
c. .0490

60. a. 240
b. 12.96
c. 12.96

62. .1912

64. a. .2240
b. .5767

66. a. .4667
b. .4667
c. .0667

Chapter 6

1. a.

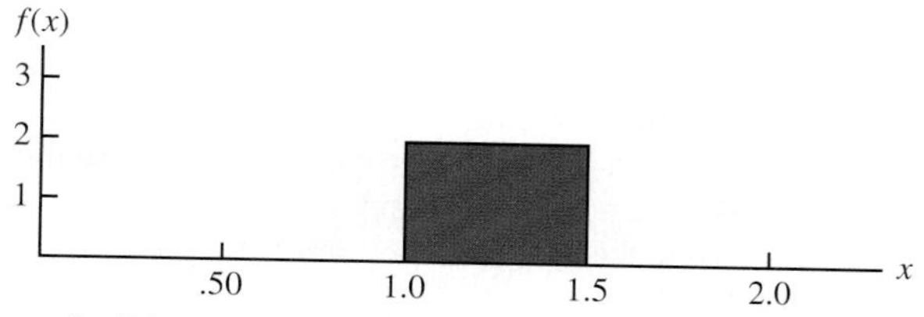

b. $P(x = 1.25) = 0$; the probability of any single point is zero because the area under the curve above any single point is zero
c. $P(1.0 \leq x \leq 1.25) = 2(.25) = .50$
d. $P(1.20 < x < 1.5) = 2(.30) = .60$

2. b. .50
c. .60
d. 15
e. 8.33

4. a.

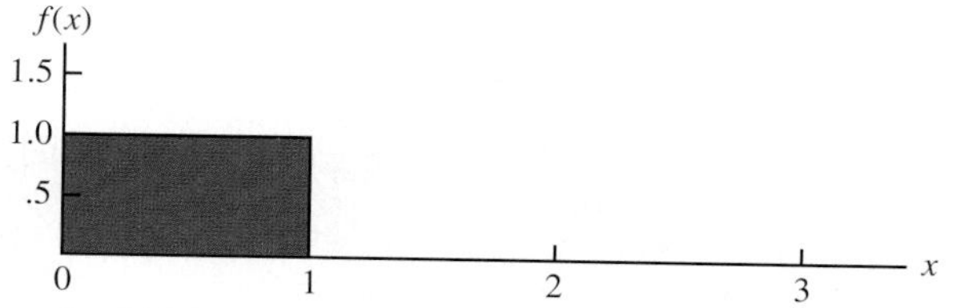

b. $P(.25 < x < .75) = 1(.50) = .50$
c. $P(x \leq .30) = 1(.30) = .30$
d. $P(x > .60) = 1(.40) = .40$

6. a. .40
b. .64
c. .68

10. a. .9332
b. .8413
c. .0919
d. .4938

12. a. .2967
b. .4418
c. .3300
d. .5910
e. .8849
f. .2389

13. a. $P(-1.98 \leq z \leq .49) = P(z \leq .49) - P(z < -1.98) = .6879 - .0239 = .6640$
b. $P(.52 \leq z \leq 1.22) = P(z \leq 1.22) - P(z < .52) = .8888 - .6985 = .1903$
c. $P(-1.75 \leq z \leq -1.04) = P(z \leq -1.04) - P(z < -1.75) = .1492 - .0401 = .1091$

14. a. $z = 1.96$
b. $z = 1.96$
c. $z = .61$
d. $z = 1.12$
e. $z = .44$
f. $z = .44$

15. a. The z-value corresponding to a cumulative probability of .2119 is $z = -.80$

b. Compute $.9030/2 = .4515$; the cumulative probability of $.5000 + .4515 = .9515$ corresponds to $z = 1.66$

c. Compute $.2052/2 = .1026$; z corresponds to a cumulative probability of $.5000 + .1026 = .6026$, so $z = .26$

d. The z-value corresponding to a cumulative probability of .9948 is $z = 2.56$

e. The area to the left of z is $1 - .6915 = .3085$, so $z = -.50$

16. a. $z = 2.33$

b. $z = 1.96$

c. $z = 1.645$

d. $z = 1.28$

18. $\mu = 30$ and $\sigma = 8.2$

a. At $x = 40$, $z = \dfrac{40 - 30}{8.2} = 1.22$

$P(z \leq 1.22) = .8888$
$P(x \geq 40) = 1.000 - .8888 = .1112$

b. At $x = 20$, $z = \dfrac{20 - 30}{8.2} = -1.22$

$P(z \leq -1.22) = .1112$
$P(x \leq 20) = .1112$

c. A z-value of 1.28 cuts off an area of approximately 10% in the upper tail

$x = 30 + 8.2(1.28)$
$= 40.50$

A stock price of \$40.50 or higher will put a company in the top 10%

20. a. .0885

b. 12.51%

c. 93.8 hours or more

22. a. .7193

b. \$35.59

c. .0233

24. a. 200, 26.04

b. .2206

c. .1251

d. 242.84 million

26. a. $\mu = np = 100(.20) = 20$

$\sigma^2 = np(1 - p) = 100(.20)(.80) = 16$

$\sigma = \sqrt{16} = 4$

b. Yes, because $np = 20$ and $n(1 - p) = 80$

c. $P(23.5 \leq x \leq 24.5)$

$z = \dfrac{24.5 - 20}{4} = 1.13 \qquad P(z \leq 1.13) = .8708$

$z = \dfrac{23.5 - 20}{4} = .88 \qquad P(z \leq .88) = .8106$

$P(23.5 \leq x \leq 24.5) = P(.88 \leq z \leq 1.13)$
$= .8708 - .8106 = .0602$

d. $P(17.5 \leq x \leq 22.5)$

$z = \dfrac{22.5 - 20}{4} = .63 \qquad P(z \leq .63) = .7357$

$z = \dfrac{17.5 - 20}{4} = -.63 \qquad P(z \leq -.63) = .2643$

$P(17.5 \leq x \leq 22.5) = P(-.63 \leq z \leq .63)$
$= .7357 - .2643 = .4714$

e. $P(x \leq 15.5)$

$z = \dfrac{15.5 - 20}{4} = -1.13 \qquad P(z \leq -1.13) = .1292$

$P(x \leq 15.5) = P(z \leq -1.13) = .1292$

28. a. In answering this part, we assume the exact numbers of Democrats and Republicans in the group are unknown

$\mu = np = 250(.47) = 117.5$
$\sigma^2 = np(1 - p) = 250(.47)(.53) = 62.275$
$\sigma = \sqrt{62.275} = 7.89$

Half the group is 125 people, so we want to find $P(x \geq 124.5)$

At $x = 124.5$, $z = \dfrac{124.5 - 117.5}{7.89} = .89$

$P(z \geq .89) = 1 - .8133 = .1867$
So $P(x \geq 124.5) = .1867$

We estimate a probability of .1867 that at least half the group is in favor of the proposal

b. For Republicans: $np = 150(.64) = 96$
For Democrats: $np = 100(.29) = 29$
Expected number in favor $= 96 + 29 = 125$

c. From part (b), we see that we can expect just as many in favor of the proposal as opposed

30. a. 220

b. .0392

c. .8962

32. a. .5276

b. .3935

c. .4724

d. .1341

33. a. $P(x \leq x_0) = 1 - e^{-x_0/3}$

b. $P(x \leq 2) = 1 - e^{-2/3} = 1 - .5134 = .4866$

c. $P(x \geq 3) = 1 - P(x \leq 3) = 1 - (1 - e^{-3/3})$
$= e^{-1} = .3679$

d. $P(x \leq 5) = 1 - e^{-5/3} = 1 - .1889 = .8111$

e. $P(2 \leq x \leq 5) = P(x \leq 5) - P(x \leq 2)$
$= .8111 - .4866 = .3245$

34. a. .5624

b. .1915

c. .2461

d. .2259

35. a.

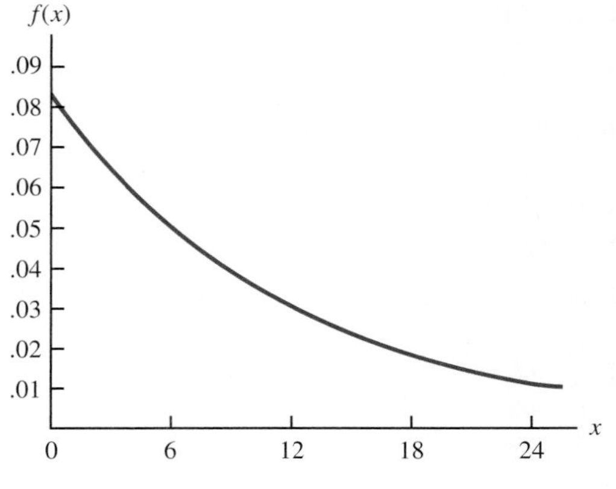

b. $P(x \leq 12) = 1 - e^{-12/12} = 1 - .3679 = .6321$
c. $P(x \leq 6) = 1 - e^{-6/12} = 1 - .6065 = .3935$
d. $P(x \geq 30) = 1 - P(x < 30)$
$= 1 - (1 - e^{-30/12})$
$= .0821$

36. a. 50 hours
b. .3935
c. .1353

38. a. $f(x) = 5.5e^{-5.5x}$
b. .2528
c. .6002

40. a. \$3780 or less
b. 19.22%
c. \$8167.50

42. a. 3229
b. .2244
c. \$12,382 or more

44. a. .0228
b. \$50

46. a. 38.3%
b. 3.59% better, 96.41% worse
c. 38.21%

48. $\mu = 19.23$ ounces

50. a. Lose \$240
b. .1788
c. .3557
d. .0594

52. a. 1/7 minute
b. $7e^{-7x}$
c. .0009
d. .2466

54. a. 2 minutes
b. .2212
c. .3935
d. .0821

Chapter 7

1. a. AB, AC, AD, AE, BC, BD, BE, CD, CE, DE
b. With 10 samples, each has a 1/10 probability
c. E and C because 8 and 0 do not apply; 5 identifies E; 7 does not apply; 5 is skipped because E is already in the sample; 3 identifies C; 2 is not needed because the sample of size 2 is complete

2. 22, 147, 229, 289

3. 459, 147, 385, 113, 340, 401, 215, 2, 33, 348

4. a. Bell South, LSI Logic, General Electric
b. 120

6. 2782, 493, 825, 1807, 289

8. Maryland, Iowa, Florida State, Virginia, Pittsburgh, Oklahoma

10. a. finite; **b.** infinite; **c.** infinite; **d.** infinite; **e.** finite

11. a. $\bar{x} = \dfrac{\Sigma x_i}{n} = \dfrac{54}{6} = 9$

b. $s = \sqrt{\dfrac{\Sigma(x_i - \bar{x})^2}{n - 1}}$

$\Sigma(x_i - \bar{x})^2 = (-4)^2 + (-1)^2 + 1^2 + (-2)^2 + 1^2 + 5^2 = 48$

$s = \sqrt{\dfrac{48}{6 - 1}} = 3.1$

12. a. .50
b. .3667

13. a. $\bar{x} = \dfrac{\Sigma x_i}{n} = \dfrac{465}{5} = 93$

b.

	x_i	$(x_i - \bar{x})$	$(x_i - \bar{x})^2$
	94	+1	1
	100	+7	49
	85	−8	64
	94	+1	1
	92	−1	1
Totals	465	0	116

$s = \sqrt{\dfrac{\Sigma(x_i - \bar{x})^2}{n - 1}} = \sqrt{\dfrac{116}{4}} = 5.39$

14. a. .45
b. .15
c. .45

16. a. .10
b. 20
c. .72

18. a. 200
b. 5
c. Normal with $E(\bar{x}) = 200$ and $\sigma_{\bar{x}} = 5$
d. The probability distribution of $\bar{x}$

19. a. The sampling distribution is normal with
$E(\bar{x}) = \mu = 200$
$\sigma_{\bar{x}} = \sigma/\sqrt{n} = 50/\sqrt{100} = 5$
For ±5, $195 \leq \bar{x} \leq 205$
Using the standard normal probability table:
At $\bar{x} = 205$, $z = \dfrac{\bar{x} - \mu}{\sigma_{\bar{x}}} = \dfrac{5}{5} = 1$
$P(z \leq 1) = .8413$
At $\bar{x} = 195$, $z = \dfrac{\bar{x} - \mu}{\sigma_{\bar{x}}} = \dfrac{-5}{5} = -1$
$P(z < -1) = .1587$
$P(195 \leq \bar{x} \leq 205) = .8413 - .1587 = .6826$

b. For ±10, $190 \leq \bar{x} \leq 210$
Using the standard normal probability table:
At $\bar{x} = 210$, $z = \dfrac{\bar{x} - \mu}{\sigma_{\bar{x}}} = \dfrac{10}{5} = 2$
$P(z \leq 2) = .9772$

At $\bar{x} = 190$, $z = \dfrac{\bar{x} - \mu}{\sigma_{\bar{x}}} = \dfrac{-10}{5} = -2$

$P(z < -2) = .0228$

$P(190 \le \bar{x} \le 210) = .9722 - .0228 = .9544$

20. 3.54, 2.50, 2.04, 1.77

$\sigma_{\bar{x}}$ decreases as n increases

22. a. Normal with $E(\bar{x}) = 51{,}800$ and $\sigma_{\bar{x}} = 516.40$

b. $\sigma_{\bar{x}}$ decreases to 365.15

c. $\sigma_{\bar{x}}$ decreases as n increases

23. a.

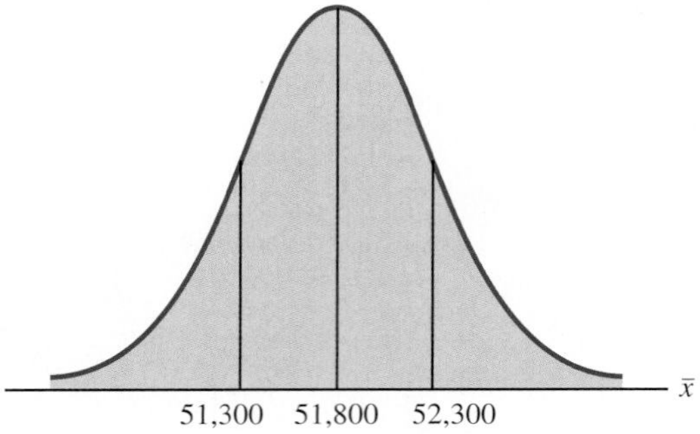

$$\sigma_{\bar{x}} = \frac{\sigma}{\sqrt{n}} = \frac{4000}{\sqrt{60}} = 516.40$$

At $\bar{x} = 52{,}300$, $z = \dfrac{52{,}300 - 51{,}800}{516.40} = .97$

$P(\bar{x} \le 52{,}300) = P(z \le .97) = .8340$

At $\bar{x} = 51{,}300$, $z = \dfrac{51{,}300 - 51{,}800}{516.40} = -.97$

$P(\bar{x} < 51{,}300) = P(z < -.97) = .1660$

$P(51{,}300 \le \bar{x} \le 52{,}300) = .8340 - .1660 = .6680$

b. $\sigma_{\bar{x}} = \dfrac{\sigma}{\sqrt{n}} = \dfrac{4000}{\sqrt{120}} = 365.15$

At $\bar{x} = 52{,}300$, $z = \dfrac{52{,}300 - 51{,}800}{365.15} = 1.37$

$P(\bar{x} \le 52{,}300) = P(z \le 1.37) = .9147$

At $\bar{x} = 51{,}300$, $z = \dfrac{51{,}300 - 51{,}800}{365.15} = -1.37$

$P(\bar{x} < 51{,}300) = P(z < -1.37) = .0853$

$P(51{,}300 \le \bar{x} \le 52{,}300) = .9147 - .0853 = .8294$

24. a. Normal with $E(\bar{x}) = 4260$ and $\sigma_{\bar{x}} = 127.28$

b. .95

c. .5704

26. a. .4246, .5284, .6922, .9586

b. Higher probability the sample mean will be close to population mean

28. a. Normal with $E(\bar{x}) = 95$ and $\sigma_{\bar{x}} = 2.56$

b. .7580

c. .8502

d. Part (c), larger sample size

30. a. $n/N = .01$; no

b. 1.29, 1.30; little difference

c. .8764

32. a. $E(\bar{p}) = .40$

$$\sigma_{\bar{p}} = \sqrt{\frac{p(1-p)}{n}} = \sqrt{\frac{(.40)(.60)}{200}} = .0346$$

Within ±.03 means $.37 \le \bar{p} \le .43$

$$z = \frac{\bar{p} - p}{\sigma_{\bar{p}}} = \frac{.03}{.0346} = .87$$

$P(.37 \le \bar{p} \le .43) = P(-.87 \le z \le .87)$
$= .8078 - .1922$
$= .6156$

b. $z = \dfrac{\bar{p} - p}{\sigma_{\bar{p}}} = \dfrac{.05}{.0346} = 1.44$

$P(.35 \le \bar{p} \le .45) = P(-1.44 \le z \le 1.44)$
$= .9251 - .0749$
$= .8502$

34. a. .6156

b. .7814

c. .9488

d. .9942

e. Higher probability with larger n

35. a.

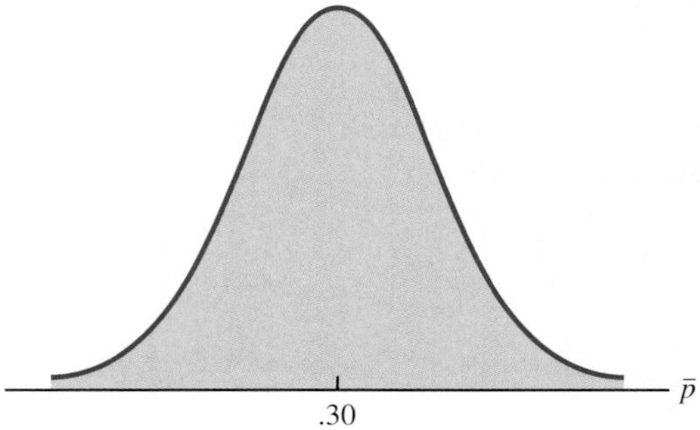

$$\sigma_{\bar{p}} = \sqrt{\frac{p(1-p)}{n}} = \sqrt{\frac{.30(.70)}{100}} = .0458$$

The normal distribution is appropriate because $np = 100(.30) = 30$ and $n(1 - p) = 100(.70) = 70$ are both greater than 5

b. $P(.20 \le \bar{p} \le .40) = ?$

$$z = \frac{.40 - .30}{.0458} = 2.18$$

$P(.20 \le \bar{p} \le .40) = P(-2.18 \le z \le 2.18)$
$= .9854 - .0146$
$= .9708$

c. $P(.25 \le \bar{p} \le .35) = ?$

$$z = \frac{.35 - .30}{.0458} = 1.09$$

$P(.25 \le \bar{p} \le .35) = P(-1.09 \le z \le 1.09)$
$= .8621 - .1379$
$= .7242$

36. a. Normal with $E(\bar{p}) = .66$ and $\sigma_{\bar{p}} = .0273$

b. .8584

c. .9606

d. Yes, standard error is smaller in part (c)

e. .9616, the probability is larger because the increased sample size reduces the standard error

38. a. Normal with $E(\bar{p}) = .56$ and $\sigma_{\bar{p}} = .0248$
b. .5820
c. .8926

40. a. Normal with $E(\bar{p}) = .76$ and $\sigma_{\bar{p}} = .0214$
b. .8384
c. .9452

42. 112, 145, 73, 324, 293, 875, 318, 618

44. a. Normal with $E(\bar{x}) = 115.50$ and $\sigma_{\bar{x}} = 5.53$
b. .9298
c. $z = -2.80$, .0026

46. a. 707
b. .50
c. .8414
d. .9544

48. a. 625
b. .7888

50. a. Normal with $E(\bar{p}) = .28$ and $\sigma_{\bar{p}} = .0290$
b. .8324
c. .5098

52. a. .8882
b. .0233

54. a. 48
b. Normal, $E(\bar{p}) = .25$, $\sigma_{\bar{p}} = .0625$
c. .2119

Chapter 8

2. Use $\bar{x} \pm z_{\alpha/2}(\sigma/\sqrt{n})$
a. $32 \pm 1.645(6/\sqrt{50})$
32 ± 1.4; 30.6 to 33.4
b. $32 \pm 1.96(6/\sqrt{50})$
32 ± 1.66; 30.34 to 33.66
c. $32 \pm 2.576(6/\sqrt{50})$
32 ± 2.19; 29.81 to 34.19

4. 54

5. a. $1.96\sigma/\sqrt{n} = 1.96(5/\sqrt{49}) = 1.40$
b. 24.80 ± 1.40; 23.40 to 26.20

6. 8.1 to 8.9

8. a. Population is at least approximately normal
b. 3.1
c. 4.1

10. a. \$113,638 to \$124,672
b. \$112,581 to \$125,729
c. \$110,515 to \$127,795
d. Width increases as confidence level increases

12. a. 2.179
b. −1.676
c. 2.457
d. −1.708 and 1.708
e. −2.014 and 2.014

13. a. $\bar{x} = \dfrac{\Sigma x_i}{n} = \dfrac{80}{8} = 10$

b. $s = \sqrt{\dfrac{\Sigma(x_i - \bar{x})^2}{n-1}} = \sqrt{\dfrac{84}{7}} = 3.464$

c. $t_{.025}\left(\dfrac{s}{\sqrt{n}}\right) = 2.365\left(\dfrac{3.46}{\sqrt{8}}\right) = 2.9$

d. $\bar{x} \pm t_{.025}\left(\dfrac{s}{\sqrt{n}}\right)$
10 ± 2.9 (7.1 to 12.9)

14. a. 21.5 to 23.5
b. 21.3 to 23.7
c. 20.9 to 24.1
d. A larger margin of error and a wider interval

15. $\bar{x} \pm t_{\alpha/2}(s/\sqrt{n})$
90% confidence: $df = 64$ and $t_{.05} = 1.669$
$19.5 \pm 1.669\left(\dfrac{5.2}{\sqrt{65}}\right)$
19.5 ± 1.08 (18.42 to 20.58)
95% confidence: $df = 64$ and $t_{.025} = 1.998$
$19.5 \pm 1.998\left(\dfrac{5.2}{\sqrt{65}}\right)$
19.5 ± 1.29 (18.21 to 20.79)

16. a. 1.69
b. 47.31 to 50.69
c. Fewer hours and higher cost for United

18. a. 3.8
b. .84
c. 2.96 to 4.64
d. Larger n next time

20. $\bar{x} = 22$; 21.48 to 22.52

22. a. 3.35
b. 2.40 to 4.30

24. a. Planning value of $\sigma = \dfrac{\text{Range}}{4} = \dfrac{36}{4} = 9$

b. $n = \dfrac{z_{.025}^2\sigma^2}{E^2} = \dfrac{(1.96)^2(9)^2}{(3)^2} = 34.57$; use $n = 35$

c. $n = \dfrac{(1.96)^2(9)^2}{(2)^2} = 77.79$; use $n = 78$

25. a. Use $n = \dfrac{z_{\alpha/2}^2\sigma^2}{E^2}$

$n = \dfrac{(1.96)^2(6.84)^2}{(1.5)^2} = 79.88$; use $n = 80$

b. $n = \dfrac{(1.645)^2(6.84)^2}{(2)^2} = 31.65$; use $n = 32$

26. a. 18
b. 35
c. 97

28. a. 343
b. 487
c. 840
d. n gets larger; no to 99% confidence

30. 81

31. a. $\bar{p} = \frac{100}{400} = .25$

b. $\sqrt{\frac{\bar{p}(1 - \bar{p})}{n}} = \sqrt{\frac{.25(.75)}{400}} = .0217$

c. $\bar{p} \pm z_{.025}\sqrt{\frac{\bar{p}(1 - \bar{p})}{n}}$

$.25 \pm 1.96(.0217)$

$.25 \pm .0424$; .2076 to .2924

32. a. .6733 to .7267
b. .6682 to .7318

34. 1068

35. a. $\bar{p} = \frac{281}{611} = .4599$ (46%)

b. $z_{.05}\sqrt{\frac{\bar{p}(1 - \bar{p})}{n}} = 1.645\sqrt{\frac{.4599(1 - .4599)}{611}} = .0332$

c. $\bar{p} \pm .0332$
$.4599 \pm .0332$ (.4267 to .4931)

36. a. .23
b. .1716 to .2884

38. a. .1790
b. .0738, .5682 to .7158
c. 354

39. a. $n = \frac{z^2_{.025}\, p^*(1 - p^*)}{E^2} = \frac{(1.96)^2(.156)(1 - .156)}{(.03)^2}$

$= 562$

b. $n = \frac{z^2_{.005} p^*(1 - p^*)}{E^2} = \frac{(2.576)^2(.156)(1 - .156)}{(.03)^2}$

$= 970.77$; use 971

40. .0267 (.8333 to .8867)

42. a. .0442
b. 601, 1068, 2401, 9604

44. a. 4.00
b. \$29.77 to \$37.77

46. a. 998
b. \$24,479 to \$26,455
c. \$93.5 million
d. Yes; \$21.4 (30%) over *Lost World*

48. a. 14 minutes
b. 13.38 to 14.62
c. 32 per day
d. Staff reduction

50. 37

52. 176

54. a. .5420
b. .0508
c. .4912 to .5928

56. a. .8273
b. .7957 to .8589

58. a. 1267
b. 1509

60. a. .3101
b. .2898 to .3304
c. 8219; no, this sample size is unnecessarily large

Chapter 9

2. a. $H_0: \mu \leq 14$
$H_a: \mu > 14$
b. No evidence that the new plan increases sales
c. The research hypothesis $\mu > 14$ is supported; the new plan increases sales

4. a. $H_0: \mu \geq 220$
$H_a: \mu < 220$

5. a. Rejecting $H_0: \mu \leq 56.2$ when it is true
b. Accepting $H_0: \mu \leq 56.2$ when it is false

6. a. $H_0: \mu \leq 1$
$H_a: \mu > 1$
b. Claiming $\mu > 1$ when it is not true
c. Claiming $\mu \leq 1$ when it is not true

8. a. $H_0: \mu \geq 220$
$H_a: \mu < 220$
b. Claiming $\mu < 220$ when it is not true
c. Claiming $\mu \geq 220$ when it is not true

10. a. $z = \frac{\bar{x} - \mu_0}{\sigma/\sqrt{n}} = \frac{26.4 - 25}{6/\sqrt{40}} = 1.48$
b. Using normal table with $z = 1.48$: p-value $= 1.0000 - .9306 = .0694$
c. p-value $> .01$, do not reject H_0
d. Reject H_0 if $z \geq 2.33$
$1.48 < 2.33$, do not reject H_0

11. a. $z = \frac{\bar{x} - \mu_0}{\sigma/\sqrt{n}} = \frac{14.15 - 15}{3/\sqrt{50}} = -2.00$
b. p-value $= 2(.0228) = .0456$
c. p-value $\leq .05$, reject H_0
d. Reject H_0 if $z \leq -1.96$ or $z \geq 1.96$
$-2.00 \leq -1.96$, reject H_0

12. a. .1056; do not reject H_0
b. .0062; reject H_0
c. ≈ 0; reject H_0
d. .7967; do not reject H_0

14. a. .3844; do not reject H_0
b. .0074; reject H_0
c. .0836; do not reject H_0

15. a. $H_0: \mu \geq 1056$
$H_a: \mu < 1056$
b. $z = \frac{\bar{x} - \mu_0}{\sigma/\sqrt{n}} = \frac{910 - 1056}{1600/\sqrt{400}} = -1.83$
p-value $= .0336$
c. p-value $\leq .05$, reject H_0; the mean refund of "last-minute" filers is less than \$1056

d. Reject H_0 if $z \leq -1.645$
$-1.83 \leq -1.645$; reject H_0

16. a. H_0: $\mu \leq 895$
H_a: $\mu > 895$
b. .1170
c. Do not reject H_0
d. Withhold judgment; collect more data

18. a. H_0: $\mu = 4.1$
H_a: $\mu \neq 4.1$
b. -2.21, .0272
c. Reject H_0

20. a. H_0: $\mu \geq 32.79$
H_a: $\mu < 32.79$
b. -2.73
c. .0032
d. Reject H_0

22. a. H_0: $\mu = 8$
H_a: $\mu \neq 8$
b. .1706
c. Do not reject H_0
d. 7.83 to 8.97; yes

24. a. $t = \dfrac{\bar{x} - \mu_0}{s/\sqrt{n}} = \dfrac{17 - 18}{4.5/\sqrt{48}} = -1.54$
b. Degrees of freedom $= n - 1 = 47$
Area in lower tail is between .05 and .10
p-value (two-tail) is between .10 and .20
Exact p-value = .1303
c. p-value $> .05$; do not reject H_0
d. With $df = 47$, $t_{.025} = 2.012$
Reject H_0 if $t \leq -2.012$ or $t \geq 2.012$
$t = -1.54$; do not reject H_0

26. a. Between .02 and .05; exact p-value = .0397; reject H_0
b. Between .01 and .02; exact p-value = .0125; reject H_0
c. Between .10 and .20; exact p-value = .1285; do not reject H_0

27. a. H_0: $\mu \geq 238$
H_a: $\mu < 238$
b. $t = \dfrac{\bar{x} - \mu_0}{s/\sqrt{n}} = \dfrac{231 - 238}{80/\sqrt{100}} = -.88$
Degrees of freedom $= n - 1 = 99$
p-value is between .10 and .20
Exact p-value = .1905
c. p-value $> .05$; do not reject H_0
Cannot conclude mean weekly benefit in Virginia is less than the national mean
d. $df = 99$, $t_{.05} = -1.66$
Reject H_0 if $t \leq -1.66$
$-.88 > -1.66$; do not reject H_0

28. a. H_0: $\mu \leq 3530$
H_a: $\mu > 3530$
b. Between .005 and .01
Exact p-value = .0072
c. Reject H_0

30. a. H_0: $\mu = 600$
H_a: $\mu \neq 600$
b. Between .20 and .40
Exact p-value = .2491
c. Do not reject H_0
d. A larger sample size

32. a. H_0: $\mu = 10{,}192$
H_a: $\mu \neq 10{,}192$
b. Between .02 and .05
Exact p-value = .0304
c. Reject H_0

34. a. H_0: $\mu = 2$
H_a: $\mu \neq 2$
b. 2.2
c. .52
d. Between .20 and .40
Exact p-value = .2535
e. Do not reject H_0

36. a. $z = \dfrac{\bar{p} - p_0}{\sqrt{\dfrac{p_0(1 - p_0)}{n}}} = \dfrac{.68 - .75}{\sqrt{\dfrac{.75(1 - .75)}{300}}} = -2.80$
p-value = .0026
p-value $\leq .05$; reject H_0
b. $z = \dfrac{.72 - .75}{\sqrt{\dfrac{.75(1 - .75)}{300}}} = -1.20$
p-value = .1151
p-value $> .05$; do not reject H_0
c. $z = \dfrac{.70 - .75}{\sqrt{\dfrac{.75(1 - .75)}{300}}} = -2.00$
p-value = .0228
p-value $\leq .05$; reject H_0
d. $z = \dfrac{.77 - .75}{\sqrt{\dfrac{.75(1 - .75)}{300}}} = .80$
p-value = .7881
p-value $> .05$; do not reject H_0

38. a. H_0: $p = .64$
H_a: $p \neq .64$
b. $\bar{p} = 52/100 = .52$
$z = \dfrac{\bar{p} - p_0}{\sqrt{\dfrac{p_0(1 - p_0)}{n}}} = \dfrac{.52 - .64}{\sqrt{\dfrac{.64(1 - .64)}{100}}} = -2.50$
p-value = 2(.0062) = .0124
c. p-value $\leq .05$; reject H_0
Proportion differs from the reported .64
d. Yes, because $\bar{p} = .52$ indicates that fewer believe the supermarket brand is as good as the name brand

40. a. .2702
b. H_0: $p \leq .22$
H_a: $p > .22$
p-value ≈ 0; reject H_0
c. Helps evaluate the effectiveness of commercials

42. H_0: $p \leq .24$
H_a: $p > .24$
p-value = .0023; reject H_0

44. a. H_0: $p \leq .51$
H_a: $p > .51$
b. $\bar{p} = .58$, p-value = .0026
c. Reject H_0

46.

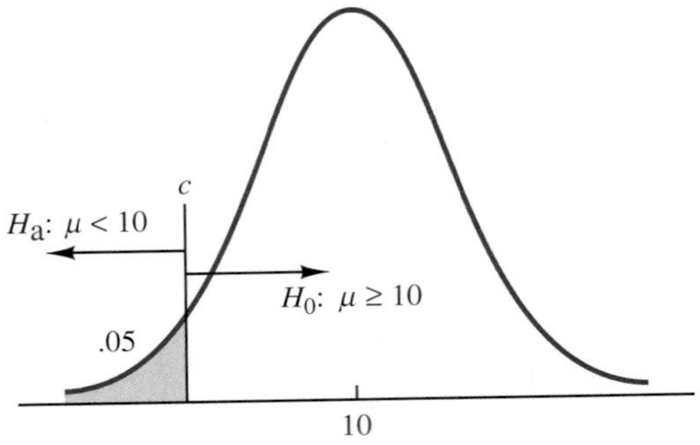

$$c = 10 - 1.645(5/\sqrt{120}) = 9.25$$
Reject H_0 if $\bar{x} < 9.25$

a. When $\mu = 9$,
$$z = \frac{9.25 - 9}{5/\sqrt{120}} = .55$$
$$P(\text{Reject } H_0) = (1.0000 - .7088) = .2912$$
b. Type II error
c. When $\mu = 8$,
$$z = \frac{9.25 - 8}{5/\sqrt{120}} = 2.74$$
$$\beta = (1.0000 - .9969) = .0031$$

48. a. Concluding $\mu \leq 15$ when it is not true
b. .2676
c. .0179

49. a. H_0: $\mu \geq 25$
H_a: $\mu < 25$
Reject H_0 if $z < -2.05$
$$z = \frac{\bar{x} - \mu_0}{\sigma/\sqrt{n}} = \frac{\bar{x} - 25}{3/\sqrt{30}} = -2.05$$
Solve for $\bar{x} = 23.88$
Decision Rule: Accept H_0 if $\bar{x} > 23.88$
Reject H_0 if $\bar{x} \leq 23.88$
b. For $\mu = 23$,
$$z = \frac{23.88 - 23}{3/\sqrt{30}} = 1.61$$
$$\beta = 1.0000 - .9463 = .0537$$
c. For $\mu = 24$,
$$z = \frac{23.88 - 24}{3/\sqrt{30}} = -.22$$
$$\beta = 1.0000 - .4129 = .5871$$
d. The Type II error cannot be made in this case; note that when $\mu = 25.5$, H_0 is true; the Type II error can only be made when H_0 is false

50. a. Concluding $\mu = 28$ when it is not true
b. .0853, .6179, .6179, .0853
c. .9147

52. .1151, .0015
Increasing n reduces β

54. $n = \dfrac{(z_\alpha + z_\beta)^2\sigma^2}{(\mu_0 - \mu_a)^2} = \dfrac{(1.645 + 1.28)^2(5)^2}{(10 - 9)^2} = 214$

56. 109

57. At $\mu_0 = 400$, $\alpha = .02$; $z_{.02} = 2.05$
At $\mu_a = 385$, $\beta = .10$; $z_{.10} = 1.28$
With $\sigma = 30$,
$$n = \frac{(z_\alpha + z_\beta)^2\sigma^2}{(\mu_0 - \mu_a)^2} = \frac{(2.05 + 1.28)^2(30)^2}{(400 - 385)^2} = 44.4 \text{ or } 45$$

58. 324

60. a. H_0: $\mu = 16$
H_a: $\mu \neq 16$
b. .0286; reject H_0
Readjust line
c. .2186; do not reject H_0
Continue operation
d. $z = 2.19$; reject H_0
$z = -1.23$; do not reject H_0
Yes, same conclusion

62. a. H_0: $\mu \leq 119{,}155$
H_a: $\mu > 119{,}155$
b. .0047
c. Reject H_0

64. $t = -.93$
p-value between .20 and .40
Exact p-value = .3596
Do not reject H_0

66. $t = 2.26$
p-value between .01 and .025
Exact p-value = .0155
Reject H_0

68. a. H_0: $p \leq .50$
H_a: $p > .50$
b. .64
c. .0026; reject H_0

70. a. H_0: $p \leq .80$
H_a: $p > .80$
b. .84
c. .0418
d. Reject H_0

72. H_0: $p \geq .90$
H_a: $p < .90$
p-value = .0808
Do not reject H_0

74. a. H_0: $\mu \leq 72$
H_a: $\mu > 72$
b. .2912
c. .7939
d. 0, because H_0 is true

76. a. 45
b. .0192, .2358, .7291, .7291, .2358, .0192

Chapter 10

1. a. $\bar{x}_1 - \bar{x}_2 = 13.6 - 11.6 = 2$
b. $z_{\alpha/2} = z_{.05} = 1.645$

$$\bar{x}_1 - \bar{x}_2 \pm 1.645\sqrt{\frac{\sigma_1^2}{n_1} + \frac{\sigma_2^2}{n_2}}$$

$$2 \pm 1.645\sqrt{\frac{(2.2)^2}{50} + \frac{(3)^2}{35}}$$

$2 \pm .98$ (1.02 to 2.98)
c. $z_{\alpha/2} = z_{.05} = 1.96$

$$2 \pm 1.96\sqrt{\frac{(2.2)^2}{50} + \frac{(3)^2}{35}}$$

2 ± 1.17 (.83 to 3.17)

2. a. $$z = \frac{(\bar{x}_1 - \bar{x}_2) - D_0}{\sqrt{\frac{\sigma_1^2}{n_1} + \frac{\sigma_2^2}{n_2}}} = \frac{(25.2 - 22.8) - 0}{\sqrt{\frac{(5.2)^2}{40} + \frac{(6)^2}{50}}} = 2.03$$
b. p-value $= 1.0000 - .9788 = .0212$
c. p-value $\leq .05$; reject H_0

4. a. $\bar{x}_1 - \bar{x}_2 = 2.04 - 1.72 = .32$
b. $$z_{.025}\sqrt{\frac{\sigma_1^2}{n_1} + \frac{\sigma_2^2}{n_2}} = 1.96\sqrt{\frac{(.10)^2}{40} + \frac{(.08)^2}{35}} = .04$$
c. $.32 \pm .04$ (.28 to .36)

6. p-value $= .015$
Reject H_0; an increase

8. a. 1.08
b. .2802
c. Do not reject H_0; cannot conclude a difference exists

9. a. $\bar{x}_1 - \bar{x}_2 = 22.5 - 20.1 = 2.4$
b. $$df = \frac{\left(\frac{s_1^2}{n_1} + \frac{s_2^2}{n_2}\right)^2}{\frac{1}{n_1 - 1}\left(\frac{s_1^2}{n_1}\right)^2 + \frac{1}{n_2 - 1}\left(\frac{s_2^2}{n_2}\right)^2}$$

$$= \frac{\left(\frac{2.5^2}{20} + \frac{4.8^2}{30}\right)^2}{\frac{1}{19}\left(\frac{2.5^2}{20}\right)^2 + \frac{1}{29}\left(\frac{4.8^2}{30}\right)^2} = 45.8$$
c. $df = 45$, $t_{.025} = 2.014$

$$t_{.025}\sqrt{\frac{s_1^2}{n_1} + \frac{s_2^2}{n_2}} = 2.014\sqrt{\frac{2.5^2}{20} + \frac{4.8^2}{30}} = 2.1$$
d. 2.4 ± 2.1 (.3 to 4.5)

10. a. $$t = \frac{(\bar{x}_1 - \bar{x}_2) - 0}{\sqrt{\frac{s_1^2}{n_1} + \frac{s_2^2}{n_2}}} = \frac{(13.6 - 10.1) - 0}{\sqrt{\frac{5.2^2}{35} + \frac{8.5^2}{40}}} = 2.18$$
b. $$df = \frac{\left(\frac{s_1^2}{n_1} + \frac{s_2^2}{n_2}\right)^2}{\frac{1}{n_1 - 1}\left(\frac{s_1^2}{n_1}\right)^2 + \frac{1}{n_2 - 1}\left(\frac{s_2^2}{n_2}\right)^2}$$

$$= \frac{\left(\frac{5.2^2}{35} + \frac{8.5^2}{40}\right)^2}{\frac{1}{34}\left(\frac{5.2^2}{35}\right)^2 + \frac{1}{39}\left(\frac{8.5^2}{40}\right)^2} = 65.7$$

Use $df = 65$
c. $df = 65$, area in tail is between .01 and .025;
two-tailed p-value is between .02 and .05
Exact p-value $= .0329$
d. p-value $\leq .05$; reject H_0

12. a. $\bar{x}_1 - \bar{x}_2 = 22.5 - 18.6 = 3.9$ miles
b. $$df = \frac{\left(\frac{s_1^2}{n_1} + \frac{s_2^2}{n_2}\right)^2}{\frac{1}{n_1 - 1}\left(\frac{s_1^2}{n_1}\right)^2 + \frac{1}{n_2 - 1}\left(\frac{s_2^2}{n_2}\right)^2}$$

$$= \frac{\left(\frac{8.4^2}{50} + \frac{7.4^2}{40}\right)^2}{\frac{1}{49}\left(\frac{8.4^2}{50}\right)^2 + \frac{1}{39}\left(\frac{7.4^2}{40}\right)^2} = 87.1$$

Use $df = 87$, $t_{.025} = 1.988$

$$3.9 \pm 1.988\sqrt{\frac{8.4^2}{50} + \frac{7.4^2}{40}}$$

3.9 ± 3.3 (.6 to 7.2)

14. a. H_0: $\mu_1 - \mu_2 = 0$
H_a: $\mu_1 - \mu_2 \neq 0$
b. 2.18
c. Using t table, p-value is between .02 and .05
Exact p-value $= .03$
d. Reject H_0; mean ages differ

16. a. H_0: $\mu_1 - \mu_2 \leq 0$
H_a: $\mu_1 - \mu_2 > 0$
b. 38
c. $t = 1.80$, $df = 25$
Using t table, p-value is between .025 and .05
Exact p-value $= .0420$
d. Reject H_0; conclude higher mean score if college grad

18. a. H_0: $\mu_1 - \mu_2 \geq 120$
H_a: $\mu_1 - \mu_2 < 120$
b. -2.10
Using t table, p-value is between .01 and .025
Exact p-value $= .0195$
c. 32 to 118
d. Larger sample size

19. a. 1, 2, 0, 0, 2
b. $\bar{d} = \Sigma d_i/n = 5/5 = 1$
c. $$s_d = \sqrt{\frac{\Sigma(d_i - \bar{d})^2}{n - 1}} = \sqrt{\frac{4}{5 - 1}} = 1$$
d. $$t = \frac{\bar{d} - \mu}{s_d/\sqrt{n}} = \frac{1 - 0}{1/\sqrt{5}} = 2.24$$

$df = n - 1 = 4$
Using t table, p-value is between .025 and .05
Exact p-value $= .0443$
p-value $\leq .05$; reject H_0

20. a. 3, −1, 3, 5, 3, 0, 1
b. 2
c. 2.08
d. 2
e. .07 to 3.93

21. $H_0: \mu_d \leq 0$
$H_a: \mu_d > 0$
$\bar{d} = .625$
$s_d = 1.30$

$$t = \frac{\bar{d} - \mu_d}{s_d/\sqrt{n}} = \frac{.625 - 0}{1.30/\sqrt{8}} = 1.36$$

$df = n - 1 = 7$
Using t table, p-value is between .10 and .20
Exact p-value = .1080
p-value > .05; do not reject H_0

22. \$.10 to \$.32

24. $t = 1.32$
Using t table, p-value is greater than .10
Exact p-value = .1142
Do not reject H_0

26. a. $t = -.60$
Using t table, p-value is greater than .40
Exact p-value = .5633
Do not reject H_0
b. −.103
c. .39; larger sample size

28. a. $\bar{p}_1 - \bar{p}_2 = .48 - .36 = .12$

b. $$\bar{p}_1 - \bar{p}_2 \pm z_{.05}\sqrt{\frac{\bar{p}_1(1 - \bar{p}_1)}{n_1} + \frac{\bar{p}_2(1 - \bar{p}_2)}{n_2}}$$

$$.12 \pm 1.645\sqrt{\frac{.48(1 - .48)}{400} + \frac{.36(1 - .36)}{300}}$$

.12 ± .0614 (.0586 to .1814)

c. $$.12 \pm 1.96\sqrt{\frac{.48(1 - .48)}{400} + \frac{.36(1 - .36)}{300}}$$

.12 ± .0731 (.0469 to .1931)

29. a. $$\bar{p} = \frac{n_1\bar{p}_1 + n_2\bar{p}_2}{n_1 + n_2} = \frac{200(.22) + 300(.16)}{200 + 300} = .1840$$

$$z = \frac{\bar{p}_1 - \bar{p}_2}{\sqrt{\bar{p}(1 - \bar{p})\left(\frac{1}{n_1} + \frac{1}{n_2}\right)}}$$

$$= \frac{.22 - .16}{\sqrt{.1840(1 - .1840)\left(\frac{1}{200} + \frac{1}{300}\right)}} = 1.70$$

p-value = 1.0000 − .9554 = .0446
b. p-value ≤ .05; reject H_0

30. $\bar{p}_1 = .55$, $\bar{p}_2 = .48$
.07 ± .0691

32. a. $H_0: p_w \leq p_m$
$H_a: p_w > p_m$
b. $\bar{p}_w = .3699$
c. $\bar{p}_m = .3400$
d. p-value = .1093
Do not reject H_0

34. a. .803
b. .849
c. $H_0: p_1 - p_2 \geq 0$
$H_a: p_1 - p_2 < 0$
d. p-value = .0055
Reject H_0

36. a. $H_0: p_1 - p_2 = 0$
$H_a: p_1 - p_2 \neq 0$
b. .13
c. p-value = .0404

38. a. $H_0: \mu_1 - \mu_2 = 0$
$H_a: \mu_1 - \mu_2 \neq 0$
$z = 2.79$
p-value = .0052
Reject H_0

40. a. $H_0: \mu_1 - \mu_2 \leq 0$
$H_a: \mu_1 - \mu_2 > 0$
b. $t = .60$, $df = 57$
Using t table, p-value is greater than .20
Exact p-value = .2754
Do not reject H_0

42. a. 15 (or \$15,000)
b. 9.81 to 20.19
c. 11.5%

44. a. p-value ≈ 0, reject H_0
b. .0468 to .1332

46. a. 163, 66
b. .0804 to .2196
c. Yes

Chapter 11

2. $s^2 = 25$
a. With 19 degrees of freedom, $\chi^2_{.05} = 30.144$ and $\chi^2_{.95} = 10.117$

$$\frac{19(25)}{30.144} \leq \sigma^2 \leq \frac{19(25)}{10.117}$$

$$15.76 \leq \sigma^2 \leq 46.95$$

b. With 19 degrees of freedom, $\chi^2_{.025} = 32.852$ and $\chi^2_{.975} = 8.907$

$$\frac{19(25)}{32.852} \leq \sigma^2 \leq \frac{19(25)}{8.907}$$

$$14.46 \leq \sigma^2 \leq 53.33$$

c. $3.8 \leq \sigma \leq 7.3$

4. a. .22 to .71
b. .47 to .84

6. a. .2205, 47.95, 6.92
b. 5.27 to 10.11

8. a. .00845
b. .092
c. .0042 to .0244
.065 to .156

9. H_0: $\sigma^2 \le .0004$
H_a: $\sigma^2 > .0004$

$$\chi^2 = \frac{(n-1)s^2}{\sigma_0^2} = \frac{(30-1)(.0005)}{.0004} = 36.25$$

From table with 29 degrees of freedom, p-value is greater than .10
p-value $> .05$; do not reject H_0
The product specification does not appear to be violated

10. H_0: $\sigma^2 \le 331.24$
H_a: $\sigma^2 > 331.24$
$\chi^2 = 52.07$, $df = 35$
p-value between .025 and .05
Reject H_0

12. a. .8106
b. $\chi^2 = 9.49$
p-value greater than .20
Do not reject H_0

14. a. $F = 2.4$
p-value between .025 and .05
Reject H_0
b. $F_{.05} = 2.2$; reject H_0

15. a. Larger sample variance is s_1^2

$$F = \frac{s_1^2}{s_2^2} = \frac{8.2}{4} = 2.05$$

Degrees of freedom: 20, 25
From table, area in tail is between .025 and .05
p-value for two-tailed test is between .05 and .10
p-value $> .05$; do not reject H_0
b. For a two-tailed test:
$F_{\alpha/2} = F_{.025} = 2.30$
Reject H_0 if $F \ge 2.30$
$2.05 < 2.30$; do not reject H_0

16. $F = 2.63$
p-value less than .01
Reject H_0

17. a. Population 1 is 4-year-old automobiles
H_0: $\sigma_1^2 \le \sigma_2^2$
H_a: $\sigma_1^2 > \sigma_2^2$

b. $$F = \frac{s_1^2}{s_2^2} = \frac{170^2}{100^2} = 2.89$$

Degrees of freedom: 25, 24
From tables, p-value is less than .01
p-value $\le .01$; reject H_0
Conclude that 4-year-old automobiles have a larger variance in annual repair costs compared to 2-year-old automobiles, which is expected because older automobiles are more likely to have more expensive repairs that lead to greater variance in the annual repair costs

18. $F = 3.54$
p-value between .10 and .20
Do not reject H_0

20. $F = 5.29$
p-value ≈ 0
Reject H_0

22. a. $F = 4$
p-value less than .01
Reject H_0

24. 10.72 to 24.68

26. a. $\chi^2 = 27.44$
p-value between .01 and .025
Reject H_0
b. .00012 to .00042

28. $\chi^2 = 31.50$
p-value between .05 and .10
Reject H_0

30. a. $n = 15$
b. 6.25 to 11.13

32. $F = 1.39$
Do not reject H_0

34. $F = 2.08$
p-value between .05 and .10
Reject H_0

Chapter 12

1. a. Expected frequencies: $e_1 = 200(.40) = 80$
$e_2 = 200(.40) = 80$
$e_3 = 200(.20) = 40$

Actual frequencies: $f_1 = 60, f_2 = 120, f_3 = 20$

$$\chi^2 = \frac{(60-80)^2}{80} + \frac{(120-80)^2}{80} + \frac{(20-40)^2}{40}$$

$$= \frac{400}{80} + \frac{1600}{80} + \frac{400}{40}$$

$$= 5 + 20 + 10 = 35$$

Degrees of freedom: $k - 1 = 2$
$\chi^2 = 35$ shows p-value is less than .005
p-value $\le .01$; reject H_0
b. Reject H_0 if $\chi^2 \ge 9.210$
$\chi^2 = 35$; reject H_0

2. $\chi^2 = 15.33$, $df = 3$
p-value less than .005
Reject H_0

3. H_0: $p_{ABC} = .29, p_{CBS} = .28, p_{NBC} = .25, p_{IND} = .18$
H_a: The proportions are not
$p_{ABC} = .29, p_{CBS} = .28, p_{NBC} = .25, p_{IND} = .18$
Expected frequencies: $300(.29) = 87$, $300(.28) = 84$
$300(.25) = 75$, $300(.18) = 54$
$e_1 = 87, e_2 = 84, e_3 = 75, e_4 = 54$

Actual frequencies: $f_1 = 95, f_2 = 70, f_3 = 89, f_4 = 46$

$$\chi^2 = \frac{(95 - 87)^2}{87} + \frac{(70 - 84)^2}{84} + \frac{(89 - 75)^2}{75} + \frac{(46 - 54)^2}{54} = 6.87$$

Degrees of freedom: $k - 1 = 3$
$\chi^2 = 6.87$, p-value between .05 and .10
Do not reject H_0

4. $\chi^2 = 29.51$, $df = 5$
p-value is less than .005
Reject H_0

6. a. $\chi^2 = 12.21$, $df = 3$
p-value is between .005 and .01
Conclude difference for 2003
b. 21%, 30%, 15%, 34%
Increased use of debit card
c. 51%

8. $\chi^2 = 16.31$, $df = 3$
p-value less than .005
Reject H_0

9. H_0: The column variable is independent of the row variable

H_a: The column variable is not independent of the row variable

Expected frequencies:

	A	B	C
P	28.5	39.9	45.6
Q	21.5	30.1	34.4

$$\chi^2 = \frac{(20 - 28.5)^2}{28.5} + \frac{(44 - 39.9)^2}{39.9} + \frac{(50 - 45.6)^2}{45.6} + \frac{(30 - 21.5)^2}{21.5} + \frac{(26 - 30.1)^2}{30.1} + \frac{(30 - 34.4)^2}{34.4}$$
$$= 7.86$$

Degrees of freedom: $(2 - 1)(3 - 1) = 2$
$\chi^2 = 7.86$, p-value between .01 and .025
Reject H_0

10. $\chi^2 = 19.77$, $df = 4$
p-value less than .005
Reject H_0

11. H_0: Type of ticket purchased is independent of the type of flight

H_a: Type of ticket purchased is not independent of the type of flight

Expected frequencies:

$e_{11} = 35.59$ $e_{12} = 15.41$
$e_{21} = 150.73$ $e_{22} = 65.27$
$e_{31} = 455.68$ $e_{32} = 197.32$

Ticket	Flight	Observed Frequency (f_i)	Expected Frequency (e_i)	$(f_i - e_i)^2/e_i$
First	Domestic	29	35.59	1.22
First	International	22	15.41	2.82
Business	Domestic	95	150.73	20.61
Business	International	121	65.27	47.59
Full-fare	Domestic	518	455.68	8.52
Full-fare	International	135	197.32	19.68
Totals		920		$\chi^2 = 100.43$

Degrees of freedom: $(3 - 1)(2 - 1) = 2$
$\chi^2 = 100.43$, p-value is less than .005
Reject H_0

12. a. $\chi^2 = 7.95$, $df = 3$
p-value is between .025 and .05
Reject H_0
b. 18 to 24 use most

14. a. $\chi^2 = 10.60$, $df = 4$
p-value is between .025 and .05
Reject H_0; not independent
b. Higher negative effect on grades as hours increase

16. a. $\chi^2 = 7.85$, $df = 3$
p-value is between .025 and .05
Reject H_0
b. Pharmaceutical, 98.6%

18. $\chi^2 = 3.01$, $df = 2$
p-value is greater than .10
Do not reject H_0; 63.3%

20. First estimate μ from the sample data (sample size = 120)

$$\mu = \frac{0(39) + 1(30) + 2(30) + 3(18) + 4(3)}{120}$$
$$= \frac{156}{120} = 1.3$$

Therefore, we use Poisson probabilities with $\mu = 1.3$ to compute expected frequencies

x	Observed Frequency	Poisson Probability	Expected Frequency	Difference $(f_i - e_i)$
0	39	.2725	32.70	6.30
1	30	.3543	42.51	−12.51
2	30	.2303	27.63	2.37
3	18	.0998	11.98	6.02
4 or more	3	.0431	5.16	−2.17

$$\chi^2 = \frac{(6.30)^2}{32.70} + \frac{(-12.51)^2}{42.51} + \frac{(2.37)^2}{27.63} + \frac{(6.02)^2}{11.98} + \frac{(-2.17)^2}{5.16} = 9.04$$

Degrees of freedom: $5 - 1 - 1 = 3$
$\chi^2 = 9.04$, p-value is between .025 and .05
Reject H_0; not a Poisson distribution

21. With $n = 30$ we will use six classes with .1667 of the probability associated with each class

$$\bar{x} = 22.8,\ s = 6.27$$

The z values that create 6 intervals, each with probability .1667 are $-.98$, $-.43$, 0, .43, .98

z	Cutoff Value of x
−.98	$22.8 - .98(6.27) = 16.66$
−.43	$22.8 - .43(6.27) = 20.11$
0	$22.8 + .00(6.27) = 22.80$
.43	$22.8 + .43(6.27) = 25.49$
.98	$22.8 + .98(6.27) = 28.94$

Interval	Observed Frequency	Expected Frequency	Difference
less than 16.66	3	5	−2
16.66–20.11	7	5	2
20.11–22.80	5	5	0
22.80–25.49	7	5	2
25.49–28.94	3	5	−2
28.94 and up	5	5	0

$$\chi^2 = \frac{(-2)^2}{5} + \frac{(2)^2}{5} + \frac{(0)^2}{5} + \frac{(2)^2}{5} + \frac{(-2)^2}{5} + \frac{(0)^2}{5}$$

$$= \frac{16}{5} = 3.20$$

Degrees of freedom: $6 - 2 - 1 = 3$
$\chi^2 = 3.20$, p-value greater than .10
Do not reject H_0
Assumption of a normal distribution is not rejected

22. $\chi^2 = 4.30$, $df = 2$
p-value greater than .10
Do not reject H_0

24. $\chi^2 = 2.8$, $df = 3$
p-value greater than .10
Do not reject H_0

26. $\chi^2 = 8.04$, $df = 3$
p-value between .025 and .05
Reject H_0

28. $\chi^2 = 4.64$, $df = 2$
p-value between .05 and .10
Do not reject H_0

30. $\chi^2 = 42.53$, $df = 4$
p-value is less than .005
Reject H_0

32. $\chi^2 = 23.37$, $df = 3$
p-value is less than .005
Reject H_0

34. a. $\chi^2 = 12.86$, $df = 2$
p-value is less than .005
Reject H_0

b. 66.9, 30.3, 2.9
54.0, 42.0, 4.0

36. $\chi^2 = 6.17$, $df = 6$
p-value is greater than .10
Do not reject H_0

38. $\chi^2 = 7.75$, $df = 3$
p-value is between .05 and .10
Do not reject H_0

Chapter 13

1. a. $\bar{\bar{x}} = (156 + 142 + 134)/3 = 144$

$$\text{SSTR} = \sum_{j=1}^{k} n_j(\bar{x}_j - \bar{\bar{x}})^2$$
$$= 6(156 - 144)^2 + 6(142 - 144)^2 + 6(134 - 144)^2$$
$$= 1488$$

b. $\text{MSTR} = \dfrac{\text{SSTR}}{k - 1} = \dfrac{1488}{2} = 744$

c. $s_1^2 = 164.4$, $s_2^2 = 131.2$, $s_3^2 = 110.4$

$$\text{SSE} = \sum_{j=1}^{k} (n_j - 1)s_j^2$$
$$= 5(164.4) + 5(131.2) + 5(110.4)$$
$$= 2030$$

d. $\text{MSE} = \dfrac{\text{SSE}}{n_T - k} = \dfrac{2030}{18 - 3} = 135.3$

e.

Source of Variation	Sum of Squares	Degrees of Freedom	Mean Square	F	p-value
Treatments	1488	2	744	5.50	.0162
Error	2030	15	135.3		
Total	3518	17			

f. $F = \dfrac{\text{MSTR}}{\text{MSE}} = \dfrac{744}{135.3} = 5.50$

From the F table (2 numerator degrees of freedom and 15 denominator), p-value is between .01 and .025

Using Excel or Minitab, the p-value corresponding to $F = 5.50$ is .0162

Because p-value $\leq \alpha = .05$, we reject the hypothesis that the means for the three treatments are equal

2.

Source of Variation	Sum of Squares	Degrees of Freedom	Mean Square	F	p-value
Treatments	300	4	75	14.07	.0000
Error	160	30	5.33		
Total	460	34			

4.

Source of Variation	Sum of Squares	Degrees of Freedom	Mean Square	F	p-value
Treatments	150	2	75	4.80	.0233
Error	250	16	15.63		
Total	400	18			

Reject H_0 because p-value $\leq \alpha = .05$

6. Because p-value $= .0082$ is less than $\alpha = .05$, we reject the null hypothesis that the means of the three treatments are equal

8. $\bar{\bar{x}} = (79 + 74 + 66)/3 = 73$

$$\text{SSTR} = \sum_{j=1}^{k} n_j(\bar{x}_j - \bar{\bar{x}})^2 = 6(79 - 73)^2 + 6(74 - 73)^2 + 6(66 - 73)^2 = 516$$

$$\text{MSTR} = \frac{\text{SSTR}}{k - 1} = \frac{516}{2} = 258$$

$$s_1^2 = 34 \qquad s_2^2 = 20 \qquad s_3^2 = 32$$

$$\text{SSE} = \sum_{j=1}^{k} (n_j - 1)s_j^2 = 5(34) + 5(20) + 5(32) = 430$$

$$\text{MSE} = \frac{\text{SSE}}{n_T - k} = \frac{430}{18 - 3} = 28.67$$

$$F = \frac{\text{MSTR}}{\text{MSE}} = \frac{258}{28.67} = 9.00$$

Source of Variation	Sum of Squares	Degrees of Freedom	Mean Square	F	p-value
Treatments	516	2	258	9.00	.003
Error	430	15	28.67		
Total	946	17			

Using F table (2 numerator degrees of freedom and 15 denominator), p-value is less than .01

Using Excel or Minitab, the p-value corresponding to $F = 9.00$ is .003

Because p-value $\leq \alpha = .05$, we reject the null hypothesis that the means for the three plants are equal; in other words, analysis of variance supports the conclusion that the population mean examination scores at the three NCP plants are not equal

10. p-value $= .0000$

Because p-value $\leq \alpha = .05$, we reject the null hypothesis that the means for the three groups are equal

12. p-value $= .0003$

Because p-value $\leq \alpha = .05$, we reject the null hypothesis that the mean miles per gallon ratings are the same for the three automobiles

13. a. $\bar{\bar{x}} = (30 + 45 + 36)/3 = 37$

$$\text{SSTR} = \sum_{j=1}^{k} n_j(\bar{x}_j - \bar{\bar{x}})^2 = 5(30 - 37)^2 + 5(45 - 37)^2 + 5(36 - 37)^2 = 570$$

$$\text{MSTR} = \frac{\text{SSTR}}{k - 1} = \frac{570}{2} = 285$$

$$\text{SSE} = \sum_{j=1}^{k} (n_j - 1)s_j^2 = 4(6) + 4(4) + 4(6.5) = 66$$

$$\text{MSE} = \frac{\text{SSE}}{n_T - k} = \frac{66}{15 - 3} = 5.5$$

$$F = \frac{\text{MSTR}}{\text{MSE}} = \frac{285}{5.5} = 51.82$$

Using F table (2 numerator degrees of freedom and 12 denominator), p-value is less than .01

Using Excel or Minitab, the p-value corresponding to $F = 51.82$ is .0000

Because p-value $\leq \alpha = .05$, we reject the null hypothesis that the means of the three populations are equal

b. $\text{LSD} = t_{\alpha/2}\sqrt{\text{MSE}\left(\frac{1}{n_i} + \frac{1}{n_j}\right)}$

$$= t_{.025}\sqrt{5.5\left(\frac{1}{5} + \frac{1}{5}\right)}$$

$$= 2.179\sqrt{2.2} = 3.23$$

$|\bar{x}_1 - \bar{x}_2| = |30 - 45| = 15 > \text{LSD}$; significant difference
$|\bar{x}_1 - \bar{x}_3| = |30 - 36| = 6 > \text{LSD}$; significant difference
$|\bar{x}_2 - \bar{x}_3| = |45 - 36| = 9 > \text{LSD}$; significant difference

c. $\bar{x}_1 - \bar{x}_2 \pm t_{\alpha/2}\sqrt{\text{MSE}\left(\frac{1}{n_1} + \frac{1}{n_2}\right)}$

$$(30 - 45) \pm 2.179\sqrt{5.5\left(\frac{1}{5} + \frac{1}{5}\right)}$$

$$-15 \pm 3.23 = -18.23 \text{ to } -11.77$$

14. a. Significant; p-value $= .0106$

b. LSD $= 15.34$

1 and 2; significant
1 and 3; not significant
2 and 3; significant

15. a.

	Manufacturer 1	Manufacturer 2	Manufacturer 3
Sample Mean	23	28	21
Sample Variance	6.67	4.67	3.33

$$\bar{\bar{x}} = (23 + 28 + 21)/3 = 24$$

$$\text{SSTR} = \sum_{j=1}^{k} n_j(\bar{x}_j - \bar{\bar{x}})^2 = 4(23 - 24)^2 + 4(28 - 24)^2 + 4(21 - 24)^2 = 104$$

$$\text{MSTR} = \frac{\text{SSTR}}{k - 1} = \frac{104}{2} = 52$$

$$\text{SSE} = \sum_{j=1}^{k} (n_j - 1)s_j^2 = 3(6.67) + 3(4.67) + 3(3.33) = 44.01$$

$$\text{MSE} = \frac{\text{SSE}}{n_T - k} = \frac{44.01}{12 - 3} = 4.89$$

$$F = \frac{\text{MSTR}}{\text{MSE}} = \frac{52}{4.89} = 10.63$$

Using F table (2 numerator degrees of freedom and 9 denominator), p-value is less than .01

Using Excel or Minitab, the p-value corresponding to $F = 10.63$ is .0043

Because p-value $\leq \alpha = .05$, we reject the null hypothesis that the mean time needed to mix a batch of material is the same for each manufacturer.

b. $\text{LSD} = t_{\alpha/2}\sqrt{\text{MSE}\left(\frac{1}{n_1} + \frac{1}{n_3}\right)}$

$= t_{.025}\sqrt{4.89\left(\frac{1}{4} + \frac{1}{4}\right)}$

$= 2.262\sqrt{2.45} = 3.54$

Since $|\bar{x}_1 - \bar{x}_3| = |23 - 21| = 2 < 3.54$, there does not appear to be any significant difference between the means for manufacturer 1 and manufacturer 3.

16. $\bar{x}_1 - \bar{x}_2 \pm \text{LSD}$
$23 - 28 \pm 3.54$
$-5 \pm 3.54 = -8.54$ to -1.46

18. a. Significant; p-value = .0000
b. Significant; $2.3 > \text{LSD} = 1.19$

20. a. Significant; p-value = .042
b. LSD = 5.74; significant difference between small and large

21. ***Treatment Means***

$\bar{x}_{\cdot 1} = 13.6, \quad \bar{x}_{\cdot 2} = 11.0, \quad \bar{x}_{\cdot 3} = 10.6$

Block Means

$\bar{x}_{1\cdot} = 9,\ \bar{x}_{2\cdot} = 7.67,\ \bar{x}_{3\cdot} = 15.67,\ \bar{x}_{4\cdot} = 18.67,\ \bar{x}_{5\cdot} = 7.67$

Overall Mean

$\bar{\bar{x}} = 176/15 = 11.73$

Step 1

$$\text{SST} = \sum_i \sum_j (x_{ij} - \bar{\bar{x}})^2$$
$$= (10 - 11.73)^2 + (9 - 11.73)^2 + \cdots + (8 - 11.73)^2$$
$$= 354.93$$

Step 2

$$\text{SSTR} = b \sum_j (\bar{x}_{\cdot j} - \bar{\bar{x}})^2$$
$$= 5[(13.6 - 11.73)^2 + (11.0 - 11.73)^2 + (10.6 - 11.73)^2] = 26.53$$

Step 3

$$\text{SSBL} = k \sum_j (\bar{x}_{i\cdot} - \bar{\bar{x}})^2$$
$$= 3[(9 - 11.73)^2 + (7.67 - 11.73)^2 + (15.67 - 11.73)^2 + (18.67 - 11.73)^2 + (7.67 - 11.73)^2] = 312.32$$

Step 4

$$\text{SSE} = \text{SST} - \text{SSTR} - \text{SSBL}$$
$$= 354.93 - 26.53 - 312.32 = 16.08$$

Source of Variation	Sum of Squares	Degrees of Freedom	Mean Square	F	p-value
Treatments	26.53	2	13.27	6.60	.0203
Blocks	312.32	4	78.08		
Error	16.08	8	2.01		
Total	354.93	14			

From the F table (2 numerator degrees of freedom and 8 denominator), p-value is between .01 and .025

Actual p-value = .0203

Because p-value $\leq \alpha = .05$, we reject the null hypothesis that the means of the three treatments are equal

22.

Source of Variation	Sum of Squares	Degrees of Freedom	Mean Square	F	p-value
Treatments	310	4	77.5	17.69	.0005
Blocks	85	2	42.5		
Error	35	8	4.38		
Total	430	14			

Significant; p-value $\leq \alpha = .05$

24. p-value = .0453

Because p-value $\leq \alpha = .05$, we reject the null hypothesis that the mean tune-up times are the same for both analyzers

26. Significant; p-value = .0000

28. *Step 1*

$$\text{SST} = \sum_i \sum_j \sum_k (x_{ijk} - \bar{\bar{x}})^2$$
$$= (135 - 111)^2 + (165 - 111)^2 + \cdots + (136 - 111)^2 = 9028$$

Step 2

$$\text{SSA} = br \sum_i (\bar{x}_{j\cdot} - \bar{\bar{x}})^2$$
$$= 3(2)[(104 - 111)^2 + (118 - 111)^2] = 588$$

Step 3

$$\text{SSB} = ar \sum_j (\bar{x}_{\cdot j} - \bar{\bar{x}})^2$$
$$= 2(2)[(130 - 111)^2 + (97 - 111)^2 + (106 - 111)^2]$$
$$= 2328$$

Step 4

$$\text{SSAB} = r \sum_i \sum_j (\bar{x}_{ij} - \bar{x}_{i\cdot} - \bar{x}_{\cdot j} + \bar{\bar{x}})^2$$
$$= 2[(150 - 104 - 130 + 111)^2 + (78 - 104 - 97 + 111)^2 + \cdots + (128 - 118 - 106 + 111)^2] = 4392$$

Step 5

$$\text{SSE} = \text{SST} - \text{SSA} - \text{SSB} - \text{SSAB}$$
$$= 9028 - 588 - 2328 - 4392 = 1720$$

Source of Variation	Sum of Squares	Degrees of Freedom	Mean Square	F	p-value
Factor A	588	1	588	2.05	.2022
Factor B	2328	2	1164	4.06	.0767
Interaction	4392	2	2196	7.66	.0223
Error	1720	6	286.67		
Total	9028	11			

Factor A: $F = 2.05$

Using F table (1 numerator degree of freedom and 6 denominator), p-value is greater than .10

Using Excel or Minitab, the p-value corresponding to $F = 2.05$ is .2022

Because p-value $> \alpha = .05$, Factor A is not significant

Factor B: $F = 4.06$

Using F table (2 numerator degrees of freedom and 6 denominator), p-value is between .05 and .10

Using Excel or Minitab, the p-value corresponding to $F = 4.06$ is .0767

Because p-value $> \alpha = .05$, Factor B is not significant

Interaction: $F = 7.66$

Using F table (2 numerator degrees of freedom and 6 denominator), p-value is between .01 and .025

Using Excel or Minitab, the p-value corresponding to $F = 7.66$ is .0223

Because p-value $\le \alpha = .05$, interaction is significant

30. Design: p-value $= .0104$; significant
Size: p-value $= .1340$; not significant
Interaction: p-value $= .2519$; not significant

32. Gender: p-value $= .0001$; significant
Occupation: p-value $= .0001$; significant
Interaction: p-value $= .0106$; significant

34. Significant; p-value $= .0134$

36. Significant; p-value $= .046$

38. Not significant; p-value $= .2455$

40. a. Significant; p-value $= .0175$

42. Significant; p-value $= .004$

44. Type of machine (p-value $= .0226$) is significant; type of loading system (p-value $= .7913$) and interaction (p-value $= .0671$) are not significant

Chapter 14

1. a.

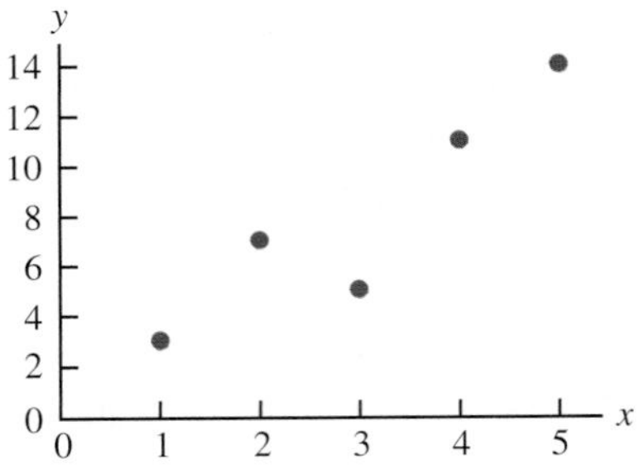

b. There appears to be a positive linear relationship between x and y

c. Many different straight lines can be drawn to provide a linear approximation of the relationship between x and y; in part (d) we will determine the equation of a straight line that "best" represents the relationship according to the least squares criterion

d. Summations needed to compute the slope and y-intercept:

$$\bar{x} = \frac{\Sigma x_i}{n} = \frac{15}{5} = 3, \quad \bar{y} = \frac{\Sigma y_i}{n} = \frac{40}{5} = 8,$$

$$\Sigma(x_i - \bar{x})(y_i - \bar{y}) = 26, \quad \Sigma(x_i - \bar{x})^2 = 10$$

$$b_1 = \frac{\Sigma(x_i - \bar{x})(y_i - \bar{y})}{\Sigma(x_i - \bar{x})^2} = \frac{26}{10} = 2.6$$

$$b_0 = \bar{y} - b_1\bar{x} = 8 - (2.6)(3) = 0.2$$

$$\hat{y} = 0.2 - 2.6x$$

e. $\hat{y} = .2 + 2.6x = .2 + 2.6(4) = 10.6$

2. b. There appears to be a negative linear relationship between x and y

d. $\hat{y} = 68 - 3x$

e. 38

4. a.

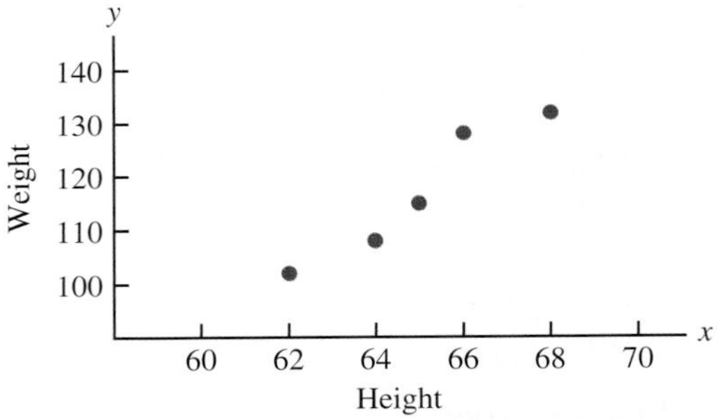

b. There appears to be a positive linear relationship between height and weight

c. Many different straight lines can be drawn to provide a linear approximation of the relationship between height and weight; in part (d) we will determine the equation of a straight line that "best" represents the relationship according to the least squares criterion

d. Summations needed to compute the slope and y-intercept:

$$\bar{x} = \frac{\Sigma x_i}{n} = \frac{325}{5} = 65, \quad \bar{y} = \frac{\Sigma y_i}{n} = \frac{585}{5} = 117,$$

$$\Sigma(x_i - \bar{x})(y_i - \bar{y}) = 110, \quad \Sigma(x_i - \bar{x})^2 = 20$$

$$b_1 = \frac{\Sigma(x_i - \bar{x})(y_i - \bar{y})}{\Sigma(x_i - \bar{x})^2} = \frac{110}{20} = 5.5$$

$$b_0 = \bar{y} - b_1\bar{x} = 117 - (5.5)(65) = -240.5$$

$$\hat{y} = -240.5 + 5.5x$$

e. $\hat{y} = -240.5 + 5.5(63) = 106$
The estimate of weight is 106 pounds

6. c. $\hat{y} = -10.1641 + .1843x$

e. 11.95 or approximately $12,000

8. c. $\hat{y} = 490.21 + 204.24x$

d. 1307

10. c. $\hat{y} = 359.2668 - 5.2772x$
d. $254

12. c. $\hat{y} = -8129.4439 + 22.4443x$
d. $8704

14. b. $\hat{y} = 28.30 - .0415x$
c. 26.2

15. a. $\hat{y}_i = .2 + 2.6x_i$ and $\bar{y} = 8$

x_i	y_i	$\hat{y}_i$	$y_i - \hat{y}_i$	$(y_i - \hat{y}_i)^2$	$y_i - \bar{y}$	$(y_i - \bar{y})^2$
1	3	2.8	.2	.04	−5	25
2	7	5.4	1.6	2.56	−1	1
3	5	8.0	−3.0	9.00	−3	9
4	11	10.6	.4	.16	3	9
5	14	13.2	.8	.64	6	36
				SSE = 12.40		SST = 80

SSR = SST − SSE = 80 − 12.4 = 67.6

b. $r^2 = \dfrac{\text{SSR}}{\text{SST}} = \dfrac{67.6}{80} = .845$

The least squares line provided a good fit; 84.5% of the variability in y has been explained by the least squares line

c. $r_{xy} = \sqrt{.845} = +.9192$

16. a. SSE = 230, SST = 1850, SSR = 1620
b. $r^2 = .876$
c. $r_{xy} = -.936$

18. a. The estimated regression equation and the mean for the dependent variable:

$\hat{y} = 1790.5 + 581.1x, \quad \bar{y} = 3650$

The sum of squares due to error and the total sum of squares:

$\text{SSE} = \Sigma(y_i - \hat{y}_i)^2 = 85{,}135.14$

$\text{SST} = \Sigma(y_i - \bar{y})^2 = 335{,}000$

Thus, SSR = SST − SSE

= 335,000 − 85,135.14 = 249,864.86

b. $r^2 = \dfrac{\text{SSR}}{\text{SST}} = \dfrac{249{,}864.86}{335{,}000} = .746$

The least squares line accounted for 74.6% of the total sum of squares

c. $r_{xy} = \sqrt{.746} = +.8637$

20. a. $\hat{y} = 12.0169 + .0127x$
b. $r^2 = .4503$
c. 53

22. a. $\hat{y} = -745.480627 + 117.917320x$
b. $r^2 = .7071$
c. $r_{xy} = +.84$

23. a. $s^2 = \text{MSE} = \dfrac{\text{SSE}}{n-2} = \dfrac{12.4}{3} = 4.133$

b. $s = \sqrt{\text{MSE}} = \sqrt{4.133} = 2.033$

c. $\Sigma(x_i - \bar{x})^2 = 10$

$$s_{b_1} = \frac{s}{\sqrt{\Sigma(x_i - \bar{x})^2}} = \frac{2.033}{\sqrt{10}} = .643$$

d. $t = \dfrac{b_1 - \beta_1}{s_{b_1}} = \dfrac{2.6 - 0}{.643} = 4.044$

From the t table (3 degrees of freedom), area in tail is between .01 and .025

p-value is between .02 and .05

Using Excel or Minitab, the p-value corresponding to $t = 4.04$ is .0272

Because p-value $\leq \alpha$, we reject H_0: $\beta_1 = 0$

e. $\text{MSR} = \dfrac{\text{SSR}}{1} = 67.6$

$$F = \frac{\text{MSR}}{\text{MSE}} = \frac{67.6}{4.133} = 16.36$$

From the F table (1 numerator degree of freedom and 3 denominator), p-value is between .025 and .05

Using Excel or Minitab, the p-value corresponding to $F = 16.36$ is .0272

Because p-value $\leq \alpha$, we reject H_0: $\beta_1 = 0$

Source of Variation	Sum of Squares	Degrees of Freedom	Mean Square	F	p-value
Regression	67.6	1	67.6	16.36	.0272
Error	12.4	3	4.133		
Total	80	4			

24. a. 76.6667
b. 8.7560
c. .6526
d. Significant; p-value = .0193
e. Significant; p-value = .0193

26. a. $s^2 = \text{MSE} = \dfrac{\text{SSE}}{n-2} = \dfrac{85{,}135.14}{4} = 21{,}283.79$

$s = \sqrt{\text{MSE}} = \sqrt{21{,}283.79} = 145.89$

$\Sigma(x_i - \bar{x})^2 = .74$

$$s_{b_1} = \frac{s}{\sqrt{\Sigma(x_i - \bar{x})^2}} = \frac{145.89}{\sqrt{.74}} = 169.59$$

$$t = \frac{b_1 - \beta_1}{s_{b_1}} = \frac{581.08 - 0}{169.59} = 3.43$$

From the t table (4 degrees of freedom), area in tail is between .01 and .025

p-value is between .02 and .05

Using Excel or Minitab, the p-value corresponding to $t = 3.43$ is .0266

Because p-value $\leq \alpha$, we reject H_0: $\beta_1 = 0$

b. $\text{MSR} = \dfrac{\text{SSR}}{1} = \dfrac{249{,}864.86}{1} = 249{,}864.86$

$$F = \frac{\text{MSR}}{\text{MSE}} = \frac{249{,}864.86}{21{,}283.79} = 11.74$$

From the F table (1 numerator degree of freedom and 4 denominator), p-value is between .025 and .05

Using Excel or Minitab, the p-value corresponding to $F = 11.74$ is .0266

Because p-value $\leq \alpha$, we reject H_0: $\beta_1 = 0$

c.

Source of Variation	Sum of Squares	Degrees of Freedom	Mean Square	F	p-value
Regression	29,864.86	1	29,864.86	11.74	.0266
Error	85,135.14	4	21,283.79		
Total	335,000	5			

28. They are related; p-value = .000

30. Significant; p-value = .002

32. a. $s = 2.033$

$\bar{x} = 3,\ \Sigma(x_i - \bar{x})^2 = 10$

$$s_{\hat{y}_p} = s\sqrt{\frac{1}{n} + \frac{(x_p - \bar{x})^2}{\Sigma(x_i - \bar{x})^2}}$$

$$= 2.033\sqrt{\frac{1}{5} + \frac{(4-3)^2}{10}} = 1.11$$

b. $\hat{y} = .2 + 2.6x = .2 + 2.6(4) = 10.6$

$\hat{y}_p \pm t_{\alpha/2}s_{\hat{y}_p}$

$10.6 \pm 3.182(1.11)$

10.6 ± 3.53, or 7.07 to 14.13

c. $$s_{\text{ind}} = s\sqrt{1 + \frac{1}{n} + \frac{(x_p - \bar{x})^2}{\Sigma(x_i - \bar{x})^2}}$$

$$= 2.033\sqrt{1 + \frac{1}{5} + \frac{(4-3)^2}{10}} = 2.32$$

d. $\hat{y}_p \pm t_{\alpha/2}s_{\text{ind}}$

$10.6 \pm 3.182(2.32)$

10.6 ± 7.38, or 3.22 to 17.98

34. Confidence interval: 8.65 to 21.15

Prediction interval: −4.50 to 41.30

35. a. $s = 145.89,\ \bar{x} = 3.2,\ \Sigma(x_i - \bar{x})^2 = .74$

$\hat{y} = 1790.5 + 581.1x = 1790.5 + 581.1(3)$

$= 3533.8$

$$s_{\hat{y}_p} = s\sqrt{\frac{1}{n} + \frac{(x_p - \bar{x})^2}{\Sigma(x_i - \bar{x})^2}}$$

$$= 145.89\sqrt{\frac{1}{6} + \frac{(3-3.2)^2}{.74}} = 68.54$$

$\hat{y}_p \pm t_{\alpha/2}s_{\hat{y}_p}$

$3533.8 \pm 2.776(68.54)$

3533.8 ± 190.27, or \$3343.53 to \$3724.07

b. $$s_{\text{ind}} = s\sqrt{1 + \frac{1}{n} + \frac{(x_p - \bar{x})^2}{\Sigma(x_i - \bar{x})^2}}$$

$$= 145.89\sqrt{1 + \frac{1}{6} + \frac{(3-3.2)^2}{.74}} = 161.19$$

$\hat{y}_p \pm t_{\alpha/2}s_{\text{ind}}$

$3533.8 \pm 2.776(161.19)$

3533.8 ± 447.46, or \$3086.34 to \$3981.26

36. a. \$201

b. 167.25 to 234.65

c. 108.75 to 293.15

38. a. \$5046.67

b. \$3815.10 to \$6278.24

c. Not out of line

40. a. 9

b. $\hat{y} = 20.0 + 7.21x$

c. 1.3626

d. SSE = SST − SSR = 51,984.1 − 41,587.3 = 10,396.8

MSE = 10,396.8/7 = 1485.3

$$F = \frac{\text{MSR}}{\text{MSE}} = \frac{41{,}587.3}{1485.3} = 28.0$$

From the F table (1 numerator degree of freedom and 7 denominator), p-value is less than .01

Using Excel or Minitab, the p-value corresponding to $F = 28.0$ is .0011

Because p-value $\leq \alpha = .05$, we reject H_0: $\beta_1 = 0$

e. $\hat{y} = 20.0 + 7.21(50) = 380.5$, or \$380,500

42. a. $\hat{y} = 80.0 + 50.0x$

b. 30

c. Significant; p-value = .000

d. \$680,000

44. b. Yes

c. $\hat{y} = 37.1 - .779x$

d. Significant; p-value = 0.003

e. $r^2 = .434$; not a good fit

f. \$12.27 to \$22.90

g. \$17.47 to \$39.05

45. a. $\bar{x} = \frac{\Sigma x_i}{n} = \frac{70}{5} = 14,\ \bar{y} = \frac{\Sigma y_i}{n} = \frac{76}{5} = 15.2,$

$\Sigma(x_i - \bar{x})(y_i - \bar{y}) = 200,\ \Sigma(x_i - \bar{x})^2 = 126$

$$b_1 = \frac{\Sigma(x_i - \bar{x})(y_i - \bar{y})}{\Sigma(x_i - \bar{x})^2} = \frac{200}{126} = 1.5873$$

$b_0 = \bar{y} - b_1\bar{x} = 15.2 - (1.5873)(14) = -7.0222$

$\hat{y} = -7.02 + 1.59x$

b.

x_i	y_i	$\hat{y}_i$	$y_i - \hat{y}_i$
6	6	2.52	3.48
11	8	10.47	−2.47
15	12	16.83	−4.83
18	20	21.60	−1.60
20	30	24.78	5.22

c.

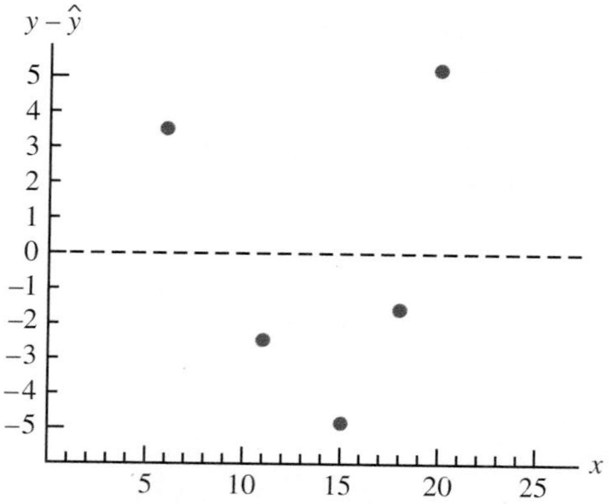

With only five observations, it is difficult to determine whether the assumptions are satisfied; however, the plot does suggest curvature in the residuals, which would indicate that the error term assumptions are not satisfied; the scatter diagram for these data also indicates that the underlying relationship between x and y may be curvilinear

d. $s^2 = 23.78$

$$h_i = \frac{1}{n} + \frac{(x_i - \bar{x})^2}{\Sigma(x_i - \bar{x})^2}$$

$$= \frac{1}{5} + \frac{(x_i - 14)^2}{126}$$

x_i	h_i	$s_{y_i - \hat{y}_i}$	$y_i - \hat{y}_i$	Standardized Residuals
6	.7079	2.64	3.48	1.32
11	.2714	4.16	−2.47	−.59
15	.2079	4.34	−4.83	−1.11
18	.3270	4.00	−1.60	−.40
20	.4857	3.50	5.22	1.49

e. The plot of the standardized residuals against $\hat{y}$ has the same shape as the original residual plot; as stated in part (c), the curvature observed indicates that the assumptions regarding the error term may not be satisfied

46. a. $\hat{y} = 2.32 + .64x$

b. No; the variance does not appear to be the same for all values of x

47. a. Let x = advertising expenditures and y = revenue

$\hat{y} = 29.4 + 1.55x$

b. SST = 1002, SSE = 310.28, SSR = 691.72

$$\text{MSR} = \frac{\text{SSR}}{1} = 691.72$$

$$\text{MSE} = \frac{\text{SSE}}{n-2} = \frac{310.28}{5} = 62.0554$$

$$F = \frac{\text{MSR}}{\text{MSE}} = \frac{691.72}{62.0554} = 11.15$$

From the F table (1 numerator degree of freedom and 5 denominator), p-value is between .01 and .025

Using Excel or Minitab, p-value = .0206

Because p-value $\leq \alpha = .05$, we conclude that the two variables are related

c.

x_i	y_i	$\hat{y}_i = 29.40 + 1.55x_i$	$y_i - \hat{y}_i$
1	19	30.95	−11.95
2	32	32.50	−.50
4	44	35.60	8.40
6	40	38.70	1.30
10	52	44.90	7.10
14	53	51.10	1.90
20	54	60.40	−6.40

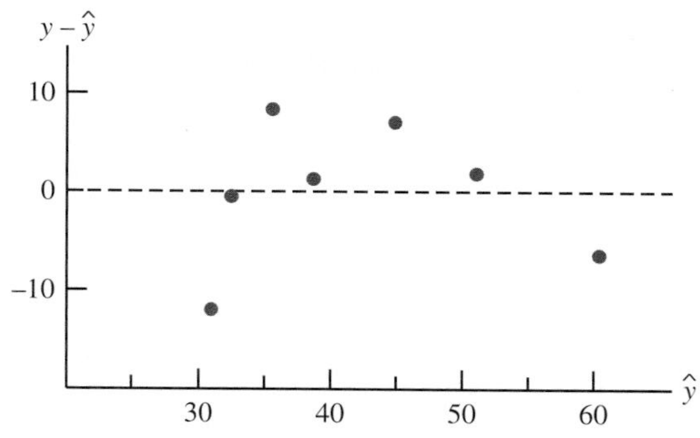

d. The residual plot leads us to question the assumption of a linear relationship between x and y; even though the relationship is significant at the $\alpha = .05$ level, it would be extremely dangerous to extrapolate beyond the range of the data

48. b. Yes

50. a. Using Minitab, we obtained the estimated regression equation $\hat{y} = 66.1 + .402x$; a portion of the Minitab output is shown in Figure D14.50; the fitted values and standardized residuals are shown:

x_i	y_i	$\hat{y}_i$	Standardized Residuals
135	145	120.41	2.11
110	100	110.35	−1.08
130	120	118.40	.14
145	120	124.43	−.38
175	130	136.50	−.78
160	130	130.47	−.04
120	110	114.38	−.41

b.

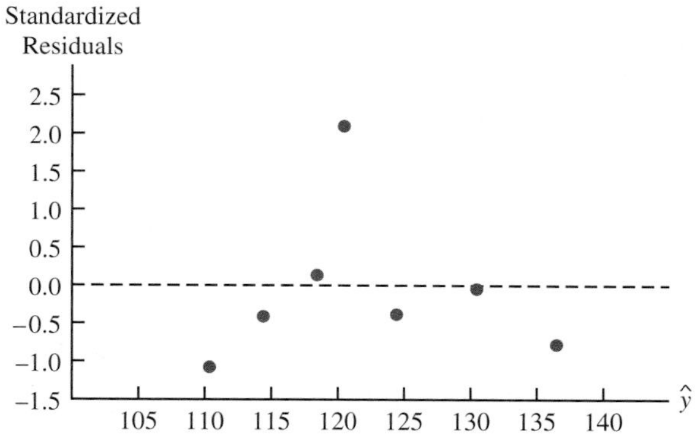

The standardized residual plot indicates that the observation $x = 135$, $y = 145$ may be an outlier; note that this observation has a standardized residual of 2.11

FIGURE D14.50

```
The regression equation is
Y = 66.1 + 0.402 X

Predictor        Coef    SE Coef       T        p
Constant        66.10      32.06    2.06    0.094
X              0.4023     0.2276    1.77    0.137

S = 12.62     R-sq = 38.5%     R-sq(adj) = 26.1%

Analysis of Variance

SOURCE            DF        SS        MS      F        p
Regression         1     497.2     497.2   3.12    0.137
Residual Error     5     795.7     159.1
Total              6    1292.9

Unusual Observations
Obs     X        Y       Fit    SE Fit    Residual    St Resid
  1   135   145.00    120.42      4.87       24.58       2.11R

R denotes an observation with a large standardized residual
```

FIGURE D14.52

```
The regression equation is
Shipment = 4.09 + 0.196 Media$

Predictor        Coef    SE Coef       T        p
Constant        4.089      2.168    1.89    0.096
Media$        0.19552    0.03635    5.38    0.000

S = 5.044     R-Sq = 78.3%     R-Sq(adj) = 75.6%

Analysis of Variance
Source            DF        SS        MS       F        p
Regression         1    735.84    735.84   28.93    0.000
Residual Error     8    203.51     25.44
Total              9    939.35

Unusual Observations
Obs   Media$   Shipment     Fit   SE Fit   Residual   St Resid
  1      120      36.30   27.55     3.30       8.75      2.30R
R denotes an observation with a large standardized residual
```

c. The scatter diagram is shown:

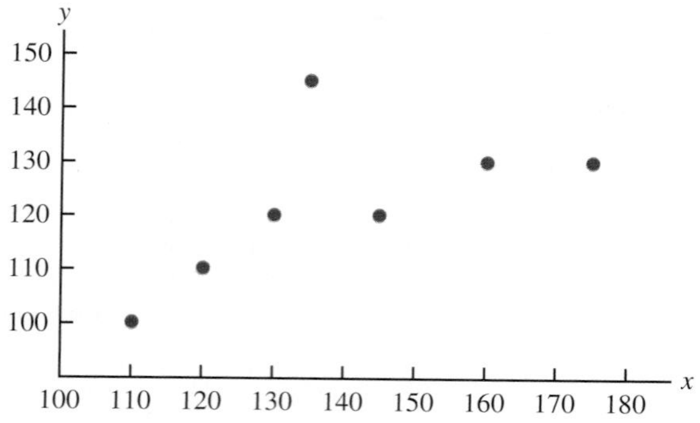

The scatter diagram also indicates that the observation $x = 135$, $y = 145$ may be an outlier; the implication is that for simple linear regression outliers can be identified by looking at the scatter diagram

52. a. A portion of the Minitab output is shown in Figure D14.52

b. Minitab identifies observation 1 as having a large standardized residual; thus, we would consider observation 1 to be an outlier

54. a. $\hat{y} = 707 + .00482x$

b. Observation 6 is an influential observation

58. a. $\hat{y} = 9.26 + .711x$

b. Significant; p-value $= .001$

c. $r^2 = .744$; good fit
d. \$13.53

60. b. $\hat{y} = -182.11 + 133428$ DJIA
c. Significant; p-value = .000
d. Excellent fit; $r^2 = .956$
e. 1286

62. a. $\hat{y} = 22.2 - .148x$
b. Significant relationship; p-value = .028
c. Good fit; $r^2 = .739$
d. 12.294 to 17.271

64. a. $\hat{y} = 220 + 132x$
b. Significant; p-value = .000
c. $r^2 = .873$; very good fit
d. \$559.50 to \$933.90

66. a. Market beta = .95
b. Significant; p-value = .029
c. $r^2 = .470$; not a good fit
d. Texas Instruments has a higher risk

68. b. There appears to be a positive linear relationship between the two variables
c. $\hat{y} = 9.37 + 1.2875$ Top Five (%)
d. Significant; p-value = .000
e. $r^2 = .741$; good fit
f. $r_{xy} = .86$

Chapter 15

2. a. The estimated regression equation is
$\hat{y} = 45.06 + 1.94x_1$
An estimate of y when $x_1 = 45$ is
$\hat{y} = 45.06 + 1.94(45) = 132.36$
b. The estimated regression equation is
$\hat{y} = 85.22 + 4.32x_2$
An estimate of y when $x_2 = 15$ is
$\hat{y} = 85.22 + 4.32(15) = 150.02$
c. The estimated regression equation is
$\hat{y} = -18.37 + 2.01x_1 + 4.74x_2$
An estimate of y when $x_1 = 45$ and $x_2 = 15$ is
$\hat{y} = -18.37 + 2.01(45) + 4.74(15) = 143.18$

4. a. \$255,000

5. a. The Minitab output is shown in Figure D15.5a
b. The Minitab output is shown in Figure D15.5b
c. It is 1.60 in part (a) and 2.29 in part (b); in part (a) the coefficient is an estimate of the change in revenue due to a one-unit change in television advertising expenditures; in part (b) it represents an estimate of the change in revenue due to a one-unit change in television advertising expenditures when the amount of newspaper advertising is held constant
d. Revenue = 83.2 + 2.29(3.5) + 1.30(1.8) = 93.56 or \$93,560

6. a. Proportion Won = .354 + .000888 HR
b. Proportion Won = .865 − .0837 ERA
c. Proportion Won = .709 + .00140 HR − .103 ERA

8. a. Return = 247 − 32.8 Safety + 34.6 ExpRatio
b. 70.2

10. a. PCT = −1.22 + 3.96 FG%
b. Increase of 1% in FG% will increase PCT by .04
c. PCT = −1.23 + 4.82 FG% − 2.59 Opp 3 Pt% + .0344 Opp TO
d. Increase FG%; decrease Opp 3 Pt%; increase Opp TO
e. .638

12. a. $R^2 = \dfrac{SSR}{SST} = \dfrac{14{,}052.2}{15{,}182.9} = .926$

b. $R_a^2 = 1 - (1 - R^2)\dfrac{n-1}{n-p-1}$

$= 1 - (1 - .926)\dfrac{10-1}{10-2-1} = .905$

c. Yes; after adjusting for the number of independent variables in the model, we see that 90.5% of the variability in y has been accounted for

14. a. .75 **b.** .68

FIGURE D15.5a

```
The regression equation is
Revenue = 88.6 + 1.60 TVAdv

Predictor      Coef    SE Coef       T        p
Constant     88.638      1.582   56.02    0.000
TVAdv        1.6039     0.4778    3.36    0.015

S = 1.215    R-sq = 65.3%    R-sq(adj) = 59.5%

Analysis of Variance

SOURCE            DF       SS       MS        F       p
Regression         1   16.640   16.640    11.27   0.015
Residual Error     6    8.860    1.477
Total              7   25.500
```

FIGURE D15.5b

```
The regression equation is
Revenue = 83.2 + 2.29 TVAdv + 1.30 NewsAdv

Predictor        Coef    SE Coef        T        p
Constant       83.230      1.574    52.88    0.000
TVAdv          2.2902     0.3041     7.53    0.001
NewsAdv        1.3010     0.3207     4.06    0.010

S = 0.6426      R-sq = 91.9%       R-sq(adj) = 88.7%

Analysis of Variance

SOURCE            DF        SS        MS        F        p
Regression         2    23.435    11.718    28.38    0.002
Residual Error     5     2.065     0.413
Total              7    25.500
```

15. a. $R^2 = \dfrac{\text{SSR}}{\text{SST}} = \dfrac{23.435}{25.5} = .919$

$R_a^2 = 1 - (1 - R^2)\dfrac{n - 1}{n - p - 1}$

$= 1 - (1 - .919)\dfrac{8 - 1}{8 - 2 - 1} = .887$

b. Multiple regression analysis is preferred because both R^2 and R_a^2 show an increased percentage of the variability of y explained when both independent variables are used

16. a. No, $R^2 = .153$

b. Better fit with multiple regression

18. a. $R^2 = .564$, $R_a^2 = .511$

b. The fit is not very good

19. a. $\text{MSR} = \dfrac{\text{SSR}}{p} = \dfrac{6216.375}{2} = 3108.188$

$\text{MSE} = \dfrac{\text{SSE}}{n - p - 1} = \dfrac{507.75}{10 - 2 - 1} = 72.536$

b. $F = \dfrac{\text{MSR}}{\text{MSE}} = \dfrac{3108.188}{72.536} = 42.85$

From the F table (2 numerator degrees of freedom and 7 denominator), p-value is less than .01

Using Excel or Minitab the p-value corresponding to $F = 42.85$ is .0001

Because p-value $\leq \alpha$, the overall model is significant

c. $t = \dfrac{b_1}{s_{b_1}} = \dfrac{.5906}{.0813} = 7.26$

p-value = .0002

Because p-value $\leq \alpha$, β_1 is significant

d. $t = \dfrac{b_2}{s_{b_2}} = \dfrac{.4980}{.0567} = 8.78$

p-value = .0001

Because p-value $\leq \alpha$, β_2 is significant

20. a. Significant; p-value = .000

b. Significant; p-value = .000

c. Significant; p-value = .002

22. a. SSE = 4000, $s^2 = 571.43$, MSR = 6000

b. Significant; p-value = .008

23. a. $F = 28.38$

p-value = .002

Because p-value $\leq \alpha$, there is a significant relationship

b. $t = 7.53$

p-value = .001

Because p-value $\leq \alpha$, β_1 is significant and x_1 should not be dropped from the model

c. $t = 4.06$

p-value = .010

Because p-value $\leq \alpha$, β_2 is significant and x_2 should not be dropped from the model

24. a. Significant relationship; p-value = .000

b. HR: Reject H_0: $\beta_1 = 0$; p-value = .000
ERA: Reject H_0: $\beta_2 = 0$; p-value = .000

26. a. Significant; p-value = .000

b. All significant; p-values are all $< \alpha = .05$

28. a. Using Minitab, the 95% confidence interval is 132.16 to 154.15

b. Using Minitab, the 95% prediction interval is 111.15 at 175.17

29. a. See Minitab output in Figure D15.5b.

$\hat{y} = 83.230 + 2.2902(3.5) + 1.3010(1.8) = 93.588$ or \$93,588

b. Minitab results: 92.840 to 94.335, or \$92,840 to \$94,335

c. Minitab results: 91.774 to 95.401, or \$91,774 to \$95,401

30. a. 46.758 to 50.646
b. 44.815 to 52.589

32. a. $E(y) = \beta_0 + \beta_1 x_1 + \beta_2 x_2$

where $x_2 = \begin{cases} 0 \text{ if level 1} \\ 1 \text{ if level 2} \end{cases}$

b. $E(y) = \beta_0 + \beta_1 x_1 + \beta_2(0) = \beta_0 + \beta_1 x_1$
c. $E(y) = \beta_0 + \beta_1 x_1 + \beta_2(1) = \beta_0 + \beta_1 x_1 + \beta_2$
d. $\beta_2 = E(y \mid \text{level 2}) - E(y \mid \text{level 1})$
β_1 is the change in $E(y)$ for a 1-unit change in x_1 holding x_2 constant

34. a. $15,300
b. $\hat{y} = 10.1 - 4.2(2) + 6.8(8) + 15.3(0) = 56.1$
Sales prediction: $56,100
c. $\hat{y} = 10.1 - 4.2(1) + 6.8(3) + 15.3(1) = 41.6$
Sales prediction: $41,600

36. a. $\hat{y} = 1.86 + 0.291$ Months $+ 1.10$ Type $- 0.609$ Person
b. Significant; p-value $= .002$
c. Person is not significant; p-value $= .167$

38. a. $\hat{y} = -91.8 + 1.08$ Age $+ .252$ Pressure $+ 8.74$ Smoker
b. Significant; p-value $= .01$
c. 95% prediction interval is 21.35 to 47.18 or a probability of .2135 to .4718; quit smoking and begin some type of treatment to reduce his blood pressure

39. a. The Minitab output is shown in Figure D15.39
b. Minitab provides the following values:

x_i	y_i	$\hat{y}_i$	Standardized Residual
1	3	2.8	.16
2	7	5.4	.94
3	5	8.0	−1.65
4	11	10.6	.24
5	14	13.2	.62

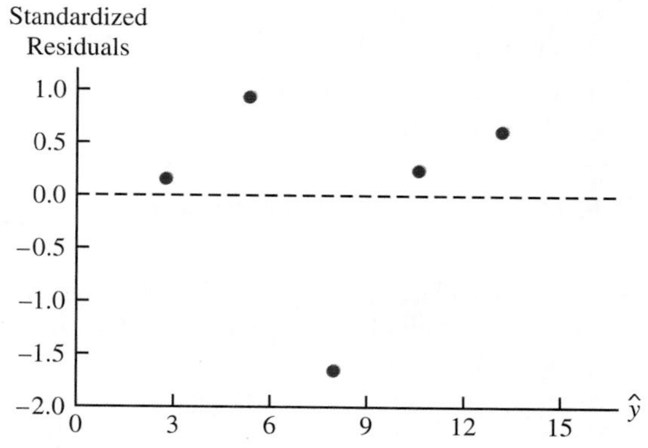

The point (3,5) does not appear to follow the trend of the remaining data; however, the value of the standardized residual for this point, −1.65, is not large enough for us to conclude that (3,5) is an outlier

c. Minitab provides the following values:

x_i	y_i	Studentized Deleted Residual
1	3	.13
2	7	.91
3	5	−4.42
4	11	.19
5	14	.54

$t_{.025} = 4.303$ ($n - p - 2 = 5 - 1 - 2 = 2$ degrees of freedom)
Because the studentized deleted residual for (3,5) is $-4.42 < -4.303$, we conclude that the 3rd observation is an outlier

40. a. $\hat{y} = -53.3 + 3.11x$
b. −1.94, −.12, 1.79, .40, −1.90; no

FIGURE D15.39

```
The regression equation is
Y = 0.20 + 2.60 X

Predictor        Coef    SE Coef       T        p
Constant        0.200      2.132    0.09    0.931
X              2.6000     0.6429    4.04    0.027

S = 2.033      R-sq = 84.5%      R-sq(adj) = 79.3%

Analysis of Variance
SOURCE              DF        SS        MS        F        p
Regression           1    67.600    67.600    16.35    0.027
Residual Error       3    12.400     4.133
Total                4    80.000
```

c. .38, .28, .22, .20, .92; no
d. .60, .00, .26, .03, 11.09; yes, the fifth observation

41. a. The Minitab output appears in Figure D15.5b; the estimated regression equation is

Revenue = 83.2 + 2.29 TVAdv + 1.30 NewsAdv

b. Minitab provides the following values:

$\hat{y}_i$	Standardized Residual	$\hat{y}_i$	Standardized Residual
96.63	−1.62	94.39	1.10
90.41	−1.08	94.24	−.40
94.34	1.22	94.42	−1.12
92.21	−.37	93.35	1.08

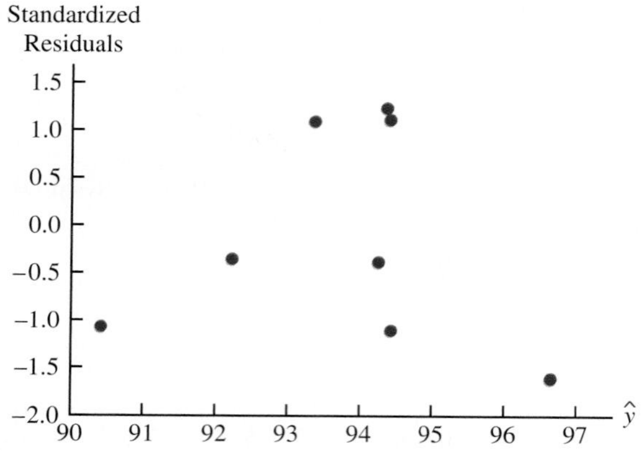

With relatively few observations, it is difficult to determine whether any of the assumptions regarding ϵ have been violated; for instance, an argument could be made that there does not appear to be any pattern in the plot; alternatively, an argument could be made that there is a curvilinear pattern in the plot

c. The values of the standardized residuals are greater than −2 and less than +2; thus, using this test, there are no outliers

As a further check for outliers, we used Minitab to compute the following studentized deleted residuals:

Observation	Studentized Deleted Residual	Observation	Studentized Deleted Residual
1	−2.11	5	1.13
2	−1.10	6	−.36
3	1.31	7	−1.16
4	−.33	8	1.10

$t_{.025} = 2.776$ ($n - p - 2 = 8 - 2 - 2 = 4$ degrees of freedom)

Because none of the studentized deleted residuals are less than −2.776 or greater than 2.776, we conclude that there are no outliers in the data

d. Minitab provides the following values:

Observation	h_i	D_i
1	.63	1.52
2	.65	.70
3	.30	.22
4	.23	.01
5	.26	.14
6	.14	.01
7	.66	.81
8	.13	.06

The critical leverage value is

$$\frac{3(p+1)}{n} = \frac{3(2+1)}{8} = 1.125$$

Because none of the values exceed 1.125, we conclude that there are no influential observations; however, using Cook's distance measure, we see that $D_1 > 1$ (rule of thumb critical value); thus, we conclude that the first observation is influential

Final conclusion: observation 1 is an influential observation

42. b. Unusual trend
c. No outliers
d. Observation 2 is an influential observation

44. a. $E(y) = \dfrac{e^{\beta_0+\beta_1 x}}{1 + e^{\beta_0+\beta_1 x}}$

b. Estimate of the probability that a customer who does not have a Simmons credit card will make a purchase
c. $\hat{g}(x) = -0.9445 + 1.0245x$
d. .28 for customers who do not have a Simmons credit card
.52 for customers who have a Simmons credit card
e. Estimated odds ratio = 2.79

46. a. $E(y) = \dfrac{e^{\beta_0+\beta_1 x}}{1 + e^{\beta_0+\beta_1 x}}$

b. $E(y) = \dfrac{e^{-2.6355+0.22018x}}{1 + e^{-2.6355+0.22018x}}$

c. Significant; p-value = .0002
d. .39
e. $1200
f. Estimated odds ratio = 1.25

48. a. $E(y) = \dfrac{e^{\beta_0+\beta_1 x}}{1 + e^{\beta_0+\beta_1 x}}$

b. $\hat{g}(x) = -2.805 + 1.1492x$
c. .86
d. Estimated odds ratio = 3.16

50. b. 67.39

52. a. $\hat{y} = -1.41 + .0235x_1 + .00486x_2$
b. Significant; p-value = .0001
c. $R^2 = .937$; $R_a^2 = 9.19$; good fit
d. Both significant

54. a. Score = 50.6 + 1.56 RecRes
b. $r^2 = .431$; not a good fit

c. Score = 33.5 + 1.90 RecRes + 2.61 Afford
Significant
R_a^2 = .784; much better fit

56. a. CityMPG = 24.1 − 2.10 Displace
Significant; p-value = .000
b. CityMPG = 26.4 − 2.44 Displace − 1.20 Drive4
c. Significant; p-value = .016
d. CityMPG = 33.3 − 4.15 Displace − 1.24 Drive4 + 2.16 EightCyl
e. Significant overall and individually

Chapter 16

1. a. The Minitab output is shown in Figure D16.1a
b. Because the p-value corresponding to $F = 6.85$ is $.059 > \alpha = .05$, the relationship is not significant
c.

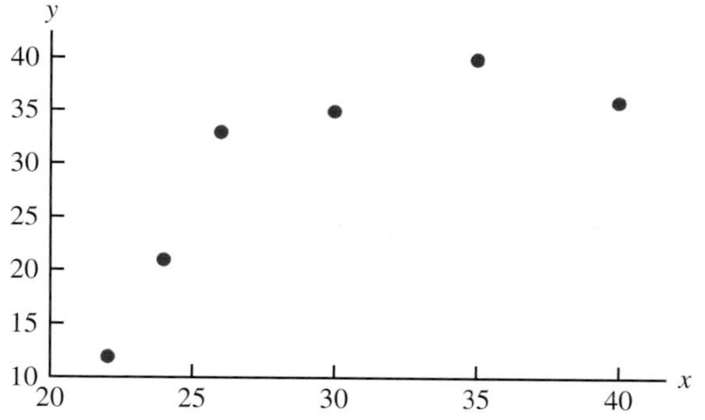

The scatter diagram suggests that a curvilinear relationship may be appropriate
d. The Minitab output is shown in Figure D16.1d
e. Because the p-value corresponding to $F = 25.68$ is $.013 < \alpha = .05$, the relationship is significant

f. $\hat{y} = -168.88 + 12.187(25) - .17704(25)^2 = 25.145$

2. a. $\hat{y} = 9.32 + .424x$; p-value = .117 indicates a weak relationship between x and y
b. $\hat{y} = -8.10 + 2.41x - .0480x^2$
R_a^2 = .932; a good fit
c. 20.965

4. a. $\hat{y} = 943 + 8.71x$
b. Significant; p-value = $.005 < \alpha = .01$

5. a. The Minitab output is shown in Figure D16.5a
b. Because the p-value corresponding to $F = 73.15$ is $.003 < \alpha = .01$, the relationship is significant; we would reject H_0: $\beta_1 = \beta_2 = 0$
c. See Figure D16.5c

6. b. No, the relationship appears to be curvilinear
c. Several possible models; e.g.,
$\hat{y} = 2.90 - .185x + .00351x^2$

8. a. It appears that a simple linear regression model is not appropriate
b. Price = 33829 − 4571 Rating + 154 Rating Sq
c. logPrice = −10.2 + 10.4 logRating
d. Part (c); higher percentage of variability is explained

10. a. Significant; p-value = .000
b. Significant; p-value = .000

11. a. SSE = 1805 − 1760 = 45

$$F = \frac{\text{MSR}}{\text{MSE}} = \left(\frac{1760/4}{45/25}\right) = 244.44$$

Because p-value = .000 the relationship is significant
b. SSE(x_1, x_2, x_3, x_4) = 45
c. SSE(x_2, x_3) = 1805 − 1705 = 100
d. $F = \dfrac{(100 - 45)/2}{1.8} = 15.28 \qquad F_{.05} = 3.39$
Because p-value = .000, x_1 and x_2 are significant

FIGURE D16.1a

```
The regression equation is
Y = - 6.8 + 1.23 X

Predictor      Coef   SE Coef       T       p
Constant      -6.77     14.17   -0.48   0.658
X            1.2296    0.4697    2.62   0.059

S = 7.269      R-sq = 63.1%     R-sq(adj) = 53.9%

Analysis of Variance

SOURCE            DF        SS        MS       F        p
Regression         1    362.13    362.13    6.85    0.059
Residual Error     4    211.37     52.84
Total              5    573.50
```

FIGURE D16.1d

```
The regression equation is
Y = - 169 + 12.2 X - 0.177 XSQ

Predictor        Coef     SE Coef        T        p
Constant      -168.88       39.79    -4.74    0.024
X              12.187       2.663     4.58    0.020
XSQ          -0.17704     0.04290    -4.13    0.026

S = 3.248     R-sq = 94.5%     R-sq(adj) = 90.8%

Analysis of Variance

SOURCE            DF       SS        MS        F       p
Regression         2   541.85    270.92    25.68   0.013
Residual Error     3    31.65     10.55
Total              5   573.50
```

FIGURE D16.5a

```
The regression equation is
Y = 433 + 37.4 X -0.383 XSQ

Predictor        Coef     SE Coef        T        p
Constant        432.6       141.2     3.06    0.055
X              37.429       7.807     4.79    0.017
XSQ           -0.3829      0.1036    -3.70    0.034

S = 15.83     R-sq = 98.0%     R-sq(adj) = 96.7%

Analysis of Variance

SOURCE            DF       SS        MS        F       p
Regression         2    36643     18322    73.15   0.003
Residual Error     3      751       250
Total              5    37395
```

FIGURE D16.5c

```
    Fit   Stdev.Fit            95% C.I.              95% P.I.
1302.01        9.93   (1270.41, 1333.61)    (1242.55, 1361.47)
```

12. a. The Minitab output is shown in Figure D16.12a

b. The Minitab output is shown in Figure D16.12b

c. $F = \dfrac{[\text{SSE(reduced)} - \text{SSE(full)}]/(\text{\# extra terms})}{\text{MSE(full)}}$

$= \dfrac{(7.2998 - 4.3240)/2}{.1663} = 8.95$

The p-value associated with $F = 8.95$ (2 numerator degrees of freedom and 26 denominator) is .001; with a p-value $< \alpha = .05$, the addition of the two independent variables is significant

14. a. $\hat{y} = -111 + 1.32 \text{ Age} + .296 \text{ Pressure}$

b. $\hat{y} = -123 + 1.51 \text{ Age} + .448 \text{ Pressure} + 8.87 \text{ Smoker} - .00276 \text{ AgePress}$

c. Significant; p-value $= .000$

16. a. Weeks $= -8.9 + 1.51$ Age

b. Weeks $= -.07 + 1.73$ Age $- 2.7$ Manager $- 15.1$ Head $- 17.4$ Sales

c. Same as part (b)

d. Same as part (b)

e. Weeks $= 13.1 + 1.64$ Age $- 9.76$ Married $- 19.4$ Head $- 29.0$ Manager $- 19.0$ Sales

FIGURE D16.12a

```
The regression equation is
Scoring Avg. = 46.3 + 14.1 Putting Avg.

Predictor         Coef    SE Coef     T       p
Constant        46.277      6.026   7.68   0.000
Putting Avg.    14.103      3.356   4.20   0.000

S = 0.510596    R-Sq = 38.7%    R-Sq(adj) = 36.5%

Analysis of Variance

SOURCE           DF       SS        MS       F        p
Regression        1   4.6036    4.6036   17.66   0.0000
Residual Error   28   7.2998    0.2607
Total            29  11.9035
```

FIGURE D16.12b

```
The regression equation is
Scoring Avg. = 59.0 - 10.3 Greens in Reg.
  + 11.4 Putting Avg - 1.81 Sand Saves

Predictor            Coef    SE Coef       T       p
Constant           59.022      5.774   10.22   0.000
Greens in Reg.    -10.281      2.877   -3.57   0.001
Putting Avg.       11.413      2.760    4.14   0.000
Sand Saves        -1.8130     0.9210   -1.97   0.060

S = 0.407808      R-Sq = 63.7%      R-Sq(adj) = 59.5%

Analysis of Variance

Source           DF       SS       MS       F       p
Regression        3   7.5795   2.5265   15.19   0.000
Residual Error   26   4.3240   0.1663
Total            29  11.9035
```

18. a. RPG = −4.05 + 27.6 OBP

b. A variety of models will provide a good fit; the five-variable model identified using Minitab's Stepwise Regression procedure with Alpha-to-Enter = .10 and Alpha-to-Remove = .10 follows:

RPG = −.0909 + 32.2 OBP + .109 HR − 21.5 AVG + .244 3B − .0223 BB

20.

x_1	x_2	x_3	**Treatment**
0	0	0	A
1	0	0	B
0	1	0	C
0	0	1	D

$E(y) = \beta_0 + \beta_1 x_1 + \beta_2 x_2 + \beta_3 x_3$

22. Factor A: $x_1 = 0$ if level 1 and 1 if level 2

Factor B:

x_2	x_3	**Level**
0	0	1
1	0	2
0	1	3

$E(y) = \beta_0 + \beta_1 x_1 + \beta_2 x_2 + \beta_3 x_1 x_2 + \beta_4 x_1 x_3$

24. a. Not significant at the .05 level of significance; p-value = .093

b. 139

26. Overall significant; p-value = .029

Individually, none of the variables are significant at the .05 level of significance. A larger sample size would be helpful.

28. $d = 1.60$; test is inconclusive

30. a. Let ExS denote the interaction between expense ratio and safety rating
Perform% = 23.3 + 222 Expense% − 28.9 ExS
b. R-Sq (adj) = 65.3%; not bad
c. 25.8 or approximately 26%

32. a. AUDELAY = 63.0 + 11.1 INDUS; no significant positive autocorrelation

34. Significant differences between comfort levels for the three types of browsers; p-value = .034.

Chapter 17

1. a.

Item	Price Relative
A	103 = (7.75/7.50)(100)
B	238 = (1500/630)(100)

b. $I_{2006} = \frac{7.75 + 1500.00}{7.50 + 630.00}(100) = \frac{1507.75}{637.50}(100) = 237$

c. $I_{2006} = \frac{7.75(1500) + 1500.00(2)}{7.50(1500) + 630.00(2)}(100)$

$= \frac{14{,}625.00}{12{,}510.00}(100) = 117$

d. $I_{2006} = \frac{7.75(1800) + 1500.00(1)}{7.50(1800) + 630.00(1)}(100)$

$= \frac{15{,}450.00}{14{,}130.00}(100) = 109$

2. a. 32%
b. $8.14

3. a. Price relatives for A = (6.00/5.45)100 = 110
B = (5.95/5.60)100 = 106
C = (6.20/5.50)100 = 113

b. $I_{2006} = \frac{6.00 + 5.95 + 6.20}{5.45 + 5.60 + 5.50}(100) = 110$

c. $I_{2006} = \frac{6.00(150) + 5.95(200) + 6.20(120)}{5.45(150) + 5.60(200) + 5.50(120)}(100)$

$= 109$

9% increase over the two-year period

4. $I_{2006} = 122$

6.

Item	Price Relative	Base Period Price	Base Period Usage	Weight	Weighted Price Relative
A	150	22.00	20	440	66,000
B	90	5.00	50	250	22,500
C	120	14.00	40	560	67,200
			Totals	1250	155,700

$I = \frac{155{,}700}{1250} = 125$

7. a. Price relatives for A = (3.95/2.50)100 = 158
B = (9.90/8.75)100 = 113
C = (.95/.99)100 = 96

b.

Item	Price Relative	Base Price	Quantity	Weight $P_{i0}Q_i$	Weighted Price Relative
A	158	2.50	25	62.5	9,875
B	113	8.75	15	131.3	14,837
C	96	.99	60	59.4	5,702
			Totals	253.2	30,414

$I = \frac{30{,}414}{253.2} = 120$

Cost of raw materials is up 20% for the chemical

8. $I = 105$; portfolio is up 5%

10. a. Deflated 1996 wages: $\frac{\$11.86}{154.9}(100) = \$7.66$

Deflated 2006 wages: $\frac{\$16.47}{198.7}(100) = \$8.29$

b. $\frac{16.47}{11.86}(100) = 138.9$; the percentange increase in actual wages is 38.9%

c. $\frac{8.29}{7.66}(100) = 108.2$; the change in real wages is an increase of 8.2%

12. a. 2420, 2449, 2242
Manufacturing shipments decreased slightly in constant dollars
b. 3032, 3057, 2822
c. PPI

14. $I = \frac{300(18.00) + 400(4.90) + 850(15.00)}{350(18.00) + 220(4.90) + 730(15.00)}(100)$

$= \frac{20{,}110}{18{,}328}(100) = 110$

15. $I = \frac{95(1200) + 75(1800) + 50(2000) + 70(1500)}{120(1200) + 86(1800) + 35(2000) + 60(1500)}(100)$

$= 99$

Quantities are down slightly

16. $I = 83$

18. a. 151, 197, 143, 178
b. $I = 170$

20. $I_{\text{Jan}} = 73.5$, $I_{\text{Mar}} = 70.1$

22. $I = 86.2$

24. $36,082; $32,528; $27,913; $34,387; $40,551; $42,651; $46,458; $56,324

26. $I = 143$; quantity is up 43%

Chapter 18

1. a.

Week	Time Series Value	Forecast	Forecast Error	Squared Forecast Error
1	8			
2	13			
3	15			
4	17	12	5	25
5	16	15	1	1
6	9	16	−7	49
			Total	75

Forecast for week 7 is (17 + 16 + 9)/3 = 14

b. MSE = 75/3 = 25

c.

Week (t)	Time Series Value (Y_t)	Forecast F_t	Forecast Error $Y_t - F_t$	Squared Error $(Y_t - F_t)^2$
1	8			
2	13	8.00	5.00	25.00
3	15	9.00	6.00	36.00
4	17	10.20	6.80	46.24
5	16	11.56	4.44	19.71
6	9	12.45	−3.45	11.90
Total				138.85

Forecast for week 7 is .2(9) + .8(12.45) = 11.76

d. For the $\alpha = .2$ exponential smoothing forecast

$$\text{MSE} = \frac{138.85}{5} = 27.77$$

Because the three-week moving average has a smaller MSE, it appears to provide the better forecasts

e.

Week (t)	Time Series Value (Y_t)	Forecast F_t	Forecast Error $Y_t - F_t$	Squared Error $(Y_t - F_t)^2$
1	8			
2	13	8.0	5.0	25.00
3	15	10.0	5.0	25.00
4	17	12.0	5.0	25.00
5	16	14.0	2.0	4.00
6	9	14.8	−5.8	33.64
			Total	112.64

$$\text{MSE} = \frac{112.64}{5} = 22.53$$

A smoothing constant of .4 appears to provide the better forecasts; for week 7 the forecast using $\alpha = .4$ is .4(9) + .6(14.8) = 12.48

2. a.

Week	Four-Week	Five-Week
10	19.00	18.80
11	20.00	19.20
12	18.75	19.00

b. 9.65, 7.41

c. Five weeks

4. Weeks 10, 11, and 12: 18.48, 18.63, 18.27
MSE = 9.25; $\alpha = .2$ is better

6. a. MSE (three-month) = 1.24
MSE ($\alpha = .2$) = 3.55
Use three-month moving averages

b. 83.3

8. a.

Month	Time Series Value	Three-Month Moving Average Forecast	(Error)^2	$\alpha = .2$ Forecast	(Error)^2
1	240				
2	350			240.00	12,100.00
3	230			262.00	1,024.00
4	260	273.33	177.69	255.60	19.36
5	280	280.00	0.00	256.48	553.19
6	320	256.67	4,010.69	261.18	3,459.79
7	220	286.67	4,444.89	272.95	2,803.70
8	310	273.33	1,344.69	262.36	2,269.57
9	240	283.33	1,877.49	271.89	1,016.97
10	310	256.67	2,844.09	265.51	1,979.36
11	240	286.67	2,178.09	274.41	1,184.05
12	230	263.33	1,110.89	267.53	1,408.50
Totals			17,988.52		27,818.49

MSE (three-month) = 17,988.52/9 = 1998.72

MSE ($\alpha = .2$) = 27,818.49/11 = 2528.95

Based on the preceding MSE values, the three-month moving average appears better; however, exponential smoothing was penalized by including month 2, which was difficult for any method to forecast

Using only the errors for months 4–12, the MSE for exponential smoothing is revised to

MSE($\alpha = .2$) = 14,694.49/9 = 1632.72

Thus, exponential smoothing was better considering months 4–12

b. Using exponential smoothing,

$$F_{13} = \alpha Y_{12} + (1 - \alpha)F_{12}$$
$$= .20(230) + .80(267.53) = 260$$

10. c. Use $\alpha = .3$; $F_{11} = 7.57$

12. $\Sigma t = 15$, $\Sigma t^2 = 55$, $\Sigma Y_t = 55$, $\Sigma tY_t = 186$

$$b_1 = \frac{\Sigma tY_t - (\Sigma t\, \Sigma Y_t)/n}{\Sigma t^2 - (\Sigma t)^2/n}$$

$$= \frac{186 - (15)(55)/5}{55 - (15)^2/5} = 2.1$$

$$b_0 = \bar{Y} - b_1\bar{t} = 11 - 2.1(3) = 4.7$$

$$T_t = 4.7 + 2.1t$$

$$T_6 = 4.7 + 2.1(6) = 17.3$$

14. $\Sigma t = 21, \Sigma t^2 = 91, \Sigma Y_t = 117.1, \Sigma tY_t = 403.7$

$$b_1 = \frac{\Sigma tY_t - (\Sigma t\, \Sigma Y_t)/n}{\Sigma t^2 - (\Sigma t)^2/n}$$

$$= \frac{403.7 - (21)(117.1)/6}{91 - (21)^2/6} = -.3514$$

$$b_0 = \bar{Y} - b_1\bar{t} = 19.5167 - (-.3514)(3.5) = 20.7466$$

$$T_t = 20.7466 - .3514t$$

Enrollment appears to be decreasing by about 351 students per year

16. Consider a nonlinear trend

18. a. Rural: $T_t = -4 + 5.2t$
Urban: $T_t = 2.3 + 6.9t$
Suburban: $T_t = 1.4 + 7.4t$

b. 5.2%, 6.9%, 7.4%

c. 27.2%, 43.7%, 45.8%

20. a. $T_t = 1997.6 + 397.545t$

b. $T_{11} = 6371, T_{12} = 6768$

22. a.

Year	Quarter	Y_t	Four-Quarter Moving Average	Centered Moving Average
1	1	4		
	2	2		
			3.50	
	3	3		3.750
			4.00	
	4	5		4.125
			4.25	
2	1	6		4.500
			4.75	
	2	3		5.000
			5.25	
	3	5		5.375
			5.50	
	4	7		5.875
			6.25	
3	1	7		6.375
			6.50	
	2	6		6.625
			6.75	
	3	6		
	4	8		

b.

Year	Quarter	Y_t	Centered Moving Average	Seasonal–Irregular Component
1	1	4		
	2	2		
	3	3	3.750	.8000
	4	5	4.125	1.2121
2	1	6	4.500	1.3333
	2	3	5.000	.6000
	3	5	5.375	.9302
	4	7	5.875	1.1915
3	1	7	6.375	1.0980
	2	6	6.625	.9057
	3	6		
	4	8		

Quarter	Seasonal–Irregular Component Values	Seasonal Index
1	1.3333, 1.0980	1.2157
2	.6000, .9057	.7529
3	.8000, .9302	.8651
4	1.2121, 1.1915	1.2018
	Total	4.0355

$$\text{Adjustment for seasonal index} = \frac{4}{4.0355} = .9912$$

Quarter	Adjusted Seasonal Index
1	1.2050
2	.7463
3	.8575
4	1.1912

24. Adjusted seasonal indexes: 0.707, 0.777, 0.827, 0.966, 1.016, 1.305, 1.494, 1.225, 0.976, 0.986, 0.936, 0.787
Note: adjustment = 0.996

26. a. Yes

b. 12–4: 166,761.13
4–8: 146,052.99

28. a. .3 is better

b. 18.41

30. 20.26

32. a. $\alpha = .5$

b. $T_t = 244.778 + 22.088t$

c. Trend projection; smaller MSE

34. $T_8 = 252.28, T_9 = 259.10$

36. a. Yes

b. $T_t = -5 + 15t$

38. a. Linear trend appears to be appropriate

b. $T_t = 6.4564 + .5345t$

c. .5345 million
d. 12.87 million

40. b. Adjusted seasonal indexes: 0.899, 1.362, 1.118, 0.621
Note: adjustment = 1.0101
c. Quarter 2; seems reasonable

42. a. $T_t = 6.329 + 1.055t$
b. 36.92, 37.98, 39.03, 40.09
c. 33.23, 51.65, 43.71, 24.86

Chapter 19

1. Binomial probabilities for $n = 10, p = .50$

x	Probability	x	Probability
0	.0010	6	.2051
1	.0098	7	.1172
2	.0439	8	.0439
3	.1172	9	.0098
4	.2051	10	.0010
5	.2461		

Number of plus signs = 7

$$P(x \geq 7) = P(7) + P(8) + P(9) + P(10)$$
$$= .1172 + .0439 + .0098 + .0010$$
$$= .1719$$

p-value = 2(.1719) = .3438
p-value > .05; do not reject H_0
No indication difference exists

2. $n = 27$ cases in which a value different from 150 is obtained
Use normal approximation with $\mu = np = .5(27) = 13.5$ and $\sigma = \sqrt{.25n} = \sqrt{.25(27)} = 2.6$
Use $x = 22$ as the number of plus signs and obtain the following test statistic:

$$z = \frac{x - \mu}{\sigma} = \frac{22 - 13.5}{2.6} = 3.27$$

Largest table value $z = 3.09$
Area in tail = 1.0000 − .9990 = .001
For $z = 3.27$, p-value less than .001
p-value ≤ .01; reject H_0 and conclude median > 150

4. We need to determine the number of "better" responses and the number of "worse" responses; the sum of the two is the sample size used for the study

$$n = .34(1253) + .29(1253) = 789.4$$

Use the large-sample test and the normal distribution; the value of $n = 789.4$ need not be integer.

Use $\mu = .5n = .5(789.4) = 394.7$
$\sigma = \sqrt{.25n} = \sqrt{.25(789.4)} = 14.05$

Let p = proportion of adults who feel children will have a better future

H_0: $p \leq .50$
H_a: $p > .50$

$$x = .34(1253) = 426.0$$

$$z = \frac{x - \mu}{\sigma} = \frac{426.0 - 394.7}{14.05} = 2.23$$

p-value = 1.0000 − .9871 = .0129
Reject H_0 and conclude that more adults feel their children will have a better future

6. $z = 2.32$
p-value = .0204
Reject H_0

8. $z = 3.76$
p-value ≈ 0
Reject H_0

10. $z = 1.27$
p-value = .2040
Do not reject H_0

12. H_0: The populations are identical
H_a: The populations are not identical

Additive 1	Additive 2	Difference	Absolute Value	Rank	Signed Rank
20.12	18.05	2.07	2.07	9	+9
23.56	21.77	1.79	1.79	7	+7
22.03	22.57	−.54	.54	3	−3
19.15	17.06	2.09	2.09	10	+10
21.23	21.22	.01	.01	1	+1
24.77	23.80	.97	.97	4	+4
16.16	17.20	−1.04	1.04	5	−5
18.55	14.98	3.57	3.57	12	+12
21.87	20.03	1.84	1.84	8	+8
24.23	21.15	3.08	3.08	11	+11
23.21	22.78	.43	.43	2	+2
25.02	23.70	1.32	1.32	6	+6
					$T = 62$

$$\mu_T = 0$$

$$\sigma_T = \sqrt{\frac{n(n+1)(2n+1)}{6}} = \sqrt{\frac{12(13)(25)}{6}} = 25.5$$

$$z = \frac{T - \mu_T}{\sigma_T} = \frac{62 - 0}{25.5} = 2.43$$

p-value = 2(1.0000 − .9925) = .0150
Reject H_0 and conclude that there is a significant difference between the additives

13.

Without Relaxant	With Relaxant	Difference	Rank of Absolute Difference	Signed Rank
15	10	5	9	+9
12	10	2	3	+3
22	12	10	10	+10
8	11	−3	6.5	−6.5
10	9	1	1	+1
7	5	2	3	+3
8	10	−2	3	−3
10	7	3	6.5	+6.5
14	11	3	6.5	+6.5
9	6	3	6.5	+6.5
				$T = 36$

$\mu_T = 0$

$$\sigma_T = \sqrt{\frac{n(n+1)(2n+1)}{6}} = \sqrt{\frac{10(11)(21)}{6}} = 19.62$$

$$z = \frac{T - \mu_T}{\sigma_T} = \frac{36}{19.62} = 1.83$$

p-value $= 1.0000 - .9664 = .0336$

Reject H_0 and conclude there is a significant difference in favor of the relaxant

14. $z = 2.29$
p-value $= .0220$
Reject H_0

16. $z = -1.48$
p-value $= .1388$
Do not reject H_0

18. Rank the combined samples and find rank sum for each sample; this is a small-sample test because $n_1 = 7$ and $n_2 = 9$

Additive 1		Additive 2	
MPG	**Rank**	**MPG**	**Rank**
17.3	2	18.7	8.5
18.4	6	17.8	4
19.1	10	21.3	15
16.7	1	21.0	14
18.2	5	22.1	16
18.6	7	18.7	8.5
17.5	3	19.8	11
	34	20.7	13
		20.2	12
			102

$T = 34$

With $\alpha = .05$, $n_1 = 7$, and $n_2 = 9$

$T_L = 41$ and $T_U = 7(7 + 9 + 1) - 41 = 78$

Because $T = 34 < 41$, reject H_0 and conclude that there is a significant difference in gasoline mileage

19. a.

Public Accountant	Rank	Financial Planner	Rank
45.2	5	44.0	2
53.8	19	44.2	3
51.3	16	48.1	10
53.2	18	50.9	15
49.2	13	46.9	8.5
50.0	14	48.6	11
45.9	6	44.7	4
54.5	20	48.9	12
52.0	17	46.8	7
46.9	8.5	43.9	1
	136.5		73.5

$$\mu_T = \frac{1}{2}n_1(n_1 + n_2 + 1) = \frac{1}{2}(10)(10 + 10 + 1) = 105$$

$$\sigma_T = \sqrt{\frac{1}{12}n_1 n_2(n_1 + n_2 + 1)} = \sqrt{\frac{1}{12}(10)(10)(10 + 10 + 1)}$$

$= 13.23$

$T = 136.5$

$$z = \frac{136.5 - 105}{13.23} = 2.38$$

p-value $= 2(1.0000 - .9913) = .0174$

Reject H_0 and conclude that salaries differ significantly for the two professions

b. Public Accountant $50,200
Financial Planner $46,700

20. a. Men 49.9, Women 35.4
b. $T = 36$, $T_L = 37$
Reject H_0

22. $z = 2.77$
p-value $= .0056$
Reject H_0

24. $z = -.25$
p-value $= .8026$
Do not reject H_0

26. Rankings:

Product A	Product B	Product C
4	11	7
8	14	2
10	15	1
3	12	6
9	13	5
34	65	21

$$W = \frac{12}{(15)(16)}\left[\frac{(34)^2}{5} + \frac{(65)^2}{5} + \frac{(21)^2}{5}\right] - 3(15 + 1)$$

$= 58.22 - 48 = 10.22 \quad (df = 2)$

p-value is between .005 and .01

Reject H_0 and conclude the ratings for the products differ

28. Rankings:

Swimming	Tennis	Cycling
8	9	5
4	14	1
11	13	3
6	10	7
12	15	2
41	61	18

$$W = \frac{12}{15(15 + 1)}\left[\frac{41^2}{5} + \frac{61^2}{5} + \frac{18^2}{5}\right] - 3(15 + 1)$$

$= 9.26 \quad (df = 2)$

p-value is between .005 and .01

Reject H_0 and conclude that activities differ

30. $W = 8.03$; $df = 3$
p-value is between .025 and .05
Reject H_0

32. a. $\Sigma d_i^2 = 52$

$$r_s = 1 - \frac{6\Sigma d_i^2}{n(n^2 - 1)} = 1 - \frac{6(52)}{10(99)} = .68$$

b. $\sigma_{r_s} = \sqrt{\frac{1}{n-1}} = \sqrt{\frac{1}{9}} = .33$

$z = \frac{r_s - 0}{\sigma_{r_s}} = \frac{.68}{.33} = 2.05$

p-value $= 2(1.0000 - .9798) = .0404$

Reject H_0 and conclude that significant rank correlation exists

34. $\Sigma d_i^2 = 250$

$r_s = 1 - \frac{6\Sigma d_i^2}{n(n^2-1)} = 1 - \frac{6(250)}{11(120)} = -.136$

$\sigma_{r_s} = \sqrt{\frac{1}{n-1}} = \sqrt{\frac{1}{10}} = .32$

$z = \frac{r_s - 0}{\sigma_{r_s}} = \frac{-.136}{.32} = -.43$

p-value $= 2(.3336) = .6672$

Do not reject H_0; we cannot conclude that there is a significant relationship between the rankings

36. $r_s = -.71$, $z = -2.13$
p-value $= .0332$
Reject H_0

38. $z = -3.17$
p-value is less than .002
Reject H_0

40. $z = -2.59$
p-value $= .0096$
Reject H_0

42. $z = -2.97$
p-value $= .003$
Reject H_0

44. $W = 12.61$; $df = 2$
p-value is between .01 and .025
Reject H_0

46. $r_s = .76$, $z = 2.83$
p-value $= .0046$
Reject H_0

Chapter 20

2. a. 5.42
b. UCL = 6.09, LCL = 4.75

4. *R chart:*
UCL $= \bar{R}D_4 = 1.6(1.864) = 2.98$
LCL $= \bar{R}D_3 = 1.6(.136) = .22$
$\bar{x}$ chart:
UCL $= \bar{\bar{x}} + A_2\bar{R} = 28.5 + .373(1.6) = 29.10$
LCL $= \bar{\bar{x}} - A_2\bar{R} = 28.5 - .373(1.6) = 27.90$

6. 20.01, .082

8. a. .0470
b. UCL = .0989, LCL = −0.0049 (use LCL = 0)
c. $\bar{p} = .08$; in control
d. UCL = 14.826, LCL = −0.726 (use LCL = 0)
Process is out of control if more than 14 defective
e. In control with 12 defective
f. np chart

10. $f(x) = \frac{n!}{x!(n-x)!}p^x(1-p)^{n-x}$

When $p = .02$, the probability of accepting the lot is

$f(0) = \frac{25!}{0!(25-0)!}(.02)^0(1-.02)^{25} = .6035$

When $p = .06$, the probability of accepting the lot is

$f(0) = \frac{25!}{0!(25-0)!}(.06)^0(1-.06)^{25} = .2129$

12. $p_0 = .02$; producer's risk = .0599
$p_0 = .06$; producer's risk = .3396
Producer's risk decreases as the acceptance number c is increased

14. $n = 20$, $c = 3$

16. a. 95.4
b. UCL = 96.07, LCL = 94.73
c. No

18.

	***R* Chart**	**$\bar{x}$ Chart**
UCL	4.23	6.57
LCL	0	4.27

Estimate of standard deviation = .86

20.

	***R* Chart**	**$\bar{x}$ Chart**
UCL	.1121	3.112
LCL	0	3.051

22. a. UCL = .0817, LCL = −.0017 (use LCL = 0)

24. a. .03
b. $\beta = .0802$

Chapter 21

1. a.

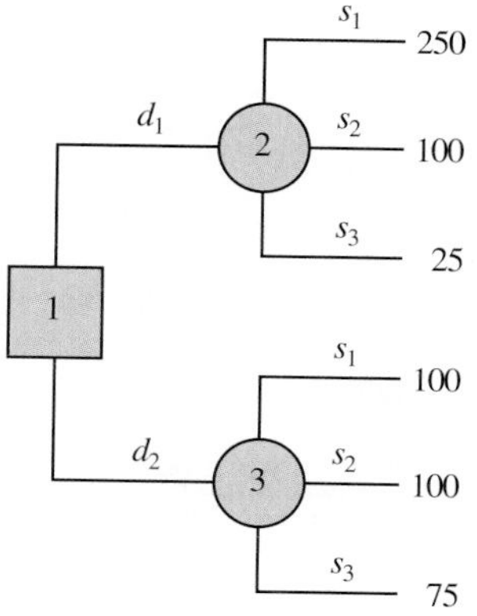

b. EV(d_1) = .65(250) + .15(100) + .20(25) = 182.5
EV(d_2) = .65(100) + .15(100) + .20(75) = 95
The optimal decision is d_1

2. a. d_1; EV(d_1) = 11.3
b. d_4; EV(d_4) = 9.5

3. a. EV(own staff) = .2(650) + .5(650) + .3(600)
= 635
EV(outside vendor) = .2(900) + .5(600)
+ .3(300) = 570
EV(combination) = .2(800) + .5(650) + .3(500)
= 635
Optimal decision: hire an outside vendor with an expected cost of $570,000
b. EVwPI = .2(650) + .5(600) + .3(300)
= 520
EVPI = |520 − 570| = 50, or $50,000

4. b. Discount; EV = 565
c. Full Price; EV = 670

6. c. Chardonnay only; EV = 42.5
d. Both grapes; EV = 46.4
e. Both grapes; EV = 39.6

8. a.

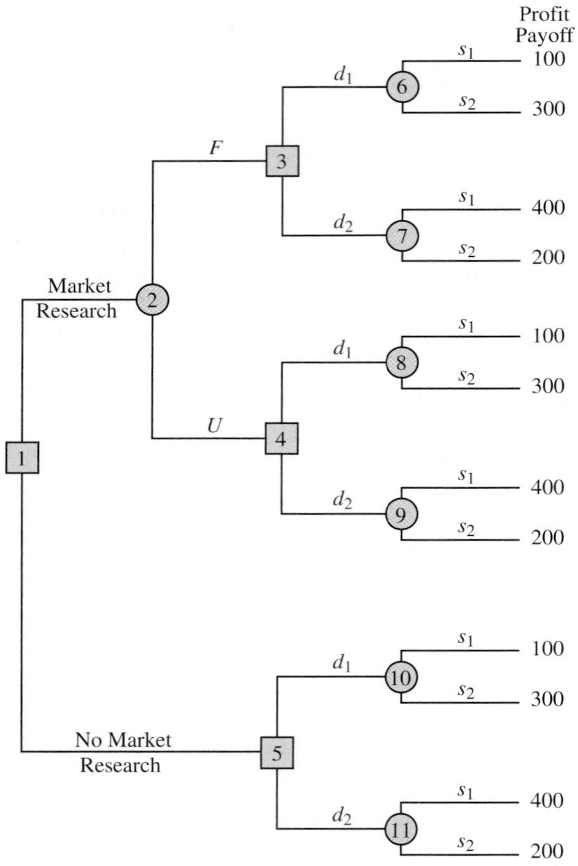

b. EV (node 6) = .57(100) + .43(300) = 186
EV (node 7) = .57(400) + .43(200) = 314
EV (node 8) = .18(100) + .82(300) = 264
EV (node 9) = .18(400) + .82(200) = 236
EV (node 10) = .40(100) + .60(300) = 220
EV (node 11) = .40(400) + .60(200) = 280

EV (node 3) = Max(186,314) = 314 d_2
EV (node 4) = Max(264,236) = 264 d_1
EV (node 5) = Max(220,280) = 280 d_2

EV (node 2) = .56(314) + .44(264) = 292
EV (node 1) = Max(292,280) = 292

∴ Market Research
If Favorable, decision d_2
If Unfavorable, decision d_1

10. a. 5000 − 200 − 2000 − 150 = 2650
3000 − 200 − 2000 − 150 = 650

b. Expected values at nodes

8: 2350	5: 2350	9: 1100
6: 1150	10: 2000	7: 2000
4: 1870	3: 2000	2: 1560
1: 1560		

c. Cost would have to decrease by at least $130,000

12. b. d_1, 1250
c. 1700
d. If N, d_1
If U, d_2; 1666

14.

State of Nature	$P(s_j)$	$P(I \mid s_j)$	$P(I \cap s_j)$	$P(s_j \mid I)$
s_1	.2	.10	.020	.1905
s_2	.5	.05	.025	.2381
s_3	.3	.20	.060	.5714
	1.0		$P(I)$ = .105	1.0000

16. a. .695, .215, .090
.98, .02
.79, .21
.00, 1.00
c. If C, Expressway
If O, Expressway
If R, Queen City
26.6 minutes

Appendix E: Using Excel Functions

Excel provides a wealth of functions for data management and statistical analysis. If we know what function is needed, and how to use it, we can simply enter the function into the appropriate worksheet cell. However, if we are not sure what functions are available to accomplish a task or are not sure how to use a particular function, Excel can provide assistance.

Finding the Right Excel Function

*In earlier versions of Excel, the **Paste Function** dialog box serves the same purpose as the **Insert Function** dialog box in Excel 2003.*

To identify the functions available in Excel, select the **Insert** menu and then choose **Function** from the list of options. Alternatively, select the f_x button on the formula bar. Either approach provides the **Insert Function** dialog box shown in Figure 1.

The **Search for a function** box at the top of the Insert Function dialog box enables us to type a brief description of what we want to do. After doing so and clicking **Go**, Excel will search for and display, in the **Select a function** box, the functions that may accomplish our task. In many situations, however, we may want to browse through an entire category of functions to see what is available. For this task, the **Or select a category** box is helpful. It contains a drop-down list of several categories of functions provided by Excel. Figure 1 shows that we selected the **Statistical** category. As a result, Excel's statistical functions

FIGURE 1 INSERT FUNCTION DIALOG BOX

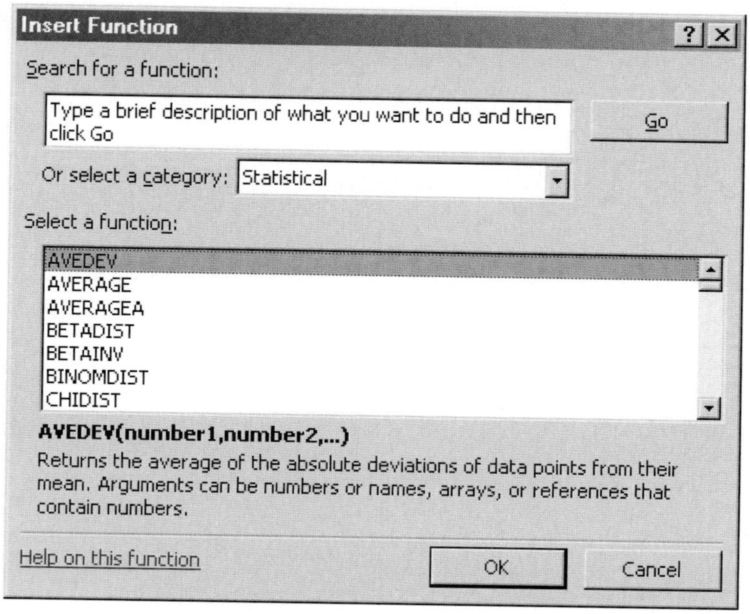

appear in alphabetic order in the Select a function box. We see the AVEDEV function listed first, followed by the AVERAGE function, and so on.

The AVEDEV function is highlighted in Figure 1, indicating it is the function currently selected. The proper syntax for the function and a brief description of the function appear below the Select a function box. We can scroll through the list in the Select a function box to display the syntax and a brief description for each of the statistical functions available. For instance, scrolling down farther, we select the COUNTIF function, as shown in Figure 2. Note that COUNTIF is now highlighted, and that immediately below the Select a function box we see **COUNTIF(range,criteria)**, which indicates that the COUNTIF function contains two arguments, range and criteria. In addition, we see that the description of the COUNTIF function is "Counts the number of cells within a range that meet the given condition."

*In earlier versions of Excel, a similar dialog box will appear. It serves the same purpose as the **Function Arguments** dialog box in Excel 2003.*

If the function selected (highlighted) is the one we want to use, we click **OK**; the **Function Arguments** dialog box then appears. The Function Arguments dialog box for the COUNTIF function is shown in Figure 3. This dialog box assists in creating the appropriate arguments for the function selected. When finished entering the arguments, we click **OK**; Excel then inserts the function into a worksheet cell.

Inserting a Function into a Worksheet Cell

We will now show how to use the Insert Function and Function Arguments dialog boxes to select a function, develop its arguments, and insert the function into a worksheet cell.

In Section 2.1, we used Excel's COUNTIF function to construct a frequency distribution for soft drink purchases. Figure 4 displays an Excel worksheet containing the soft drink

FIGURE 2 DESCRIPTION OF THE COUNTIF FUNCTION IN THE INSERT FUNCTION DIALOG BOX

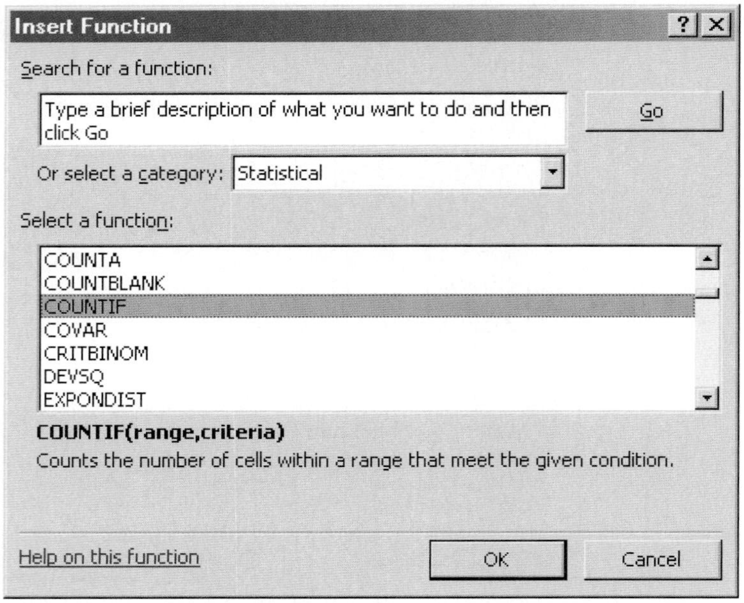

FIGURE 3 FUNCTION ARGUMENTS DIALOG BOX FOR THE COUNTIF FUNCTION

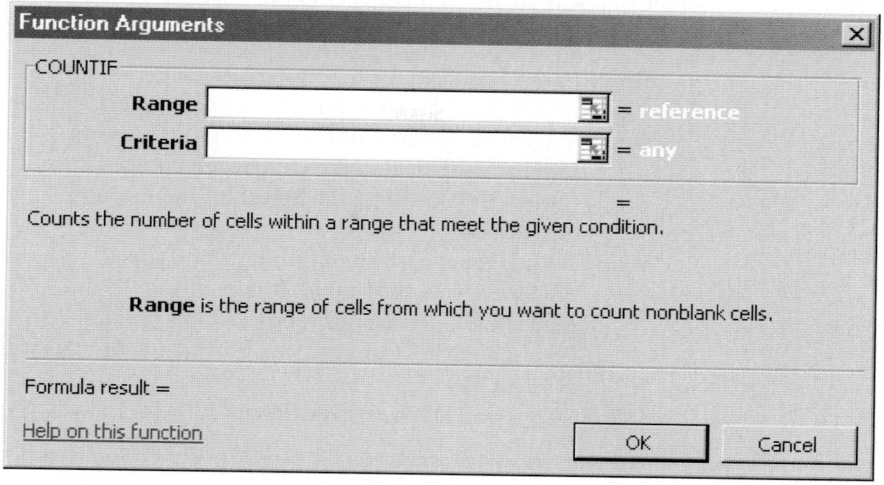

FIGURE 4 EXCEL WORKSHEET WITH SOFT DRINK DATA AND LABELS FOR THE FREQUENCY DISTRIBUTION WE WOULD LIKE TO CONSTRUCT

CD file
SoftDrink

Note: Rows 11–44 are hidden.

	A	B	C	D	E
1	**Brand Purchased**		**Soft Drink**	**Frequency**	
2	Coke Classic		Coke Classic		
3	Diet Coke		Diet Coke		
4	Pepsi		Dr. Pepper		
5	Diet Coke		Pepsi		
6	Coke Classic		Sprite		
7	Coke Classic				
8	Dr. Pepper				
9	Diet Coke				
10	Pepsi				
45	Pepsi				
46	Pepsi				
47	Pepsi				
48	Coke Classic				
49	Dr. Pepper				
50	Pepsi				
51	Sprite				
52					

data and labels for the frequency distribution we would like to construct. We see that the frequency of Coke Classic purchases will go into cell D2, the frequency of Diet Coke purchases will go into cell D3, and so on. Suppose we want to use the COUNTIF function to compute the frequencies for these cells and would like some assistance from Excel.

Step 1. Select cell D2
Step 2. Click f_x on the formula bar (or select **Insert** and then choose **Function**)
Step 3. When the **Insert Function** dialog box appears:
Select **Statistical** in the **Or select a category box**
Select **COUNTIF** in the **Select a function box**
Click **OK**
Step 4. When the **Function Arguments** box appears (see Figure 5):
Enter $A$2:$A$51 in the **Range** box
Enter C2 in the **Criteria** box (At this point, the value of the function will appear on the next-to-last line of the dialog box. Its value is 19.)
Click **OK**
Step 5. Copy cell D2 to cells D3:D6

The worksheet then appears as in Figure 6. The formula worksheet is in the background; the value worksheet appears in the foreground. The formula worksheet shows that the COUNTIF function was inserted into cell D2. We copied the contents of cell D2 into cells D3:D6. The value worksheet shows the proper class frequencies as computed.

We illustrated the use of Excel's capability to provide assistance in using the COUNTIF function. The procedure is similar for all Excel functions. This capability is especially helpful if you do not know what function to use or forget the proper name and/or syntax for a function.

FIGURE 5 COMPLETED FUNCTION ARGUMENTS DIALOG BOX FOR THE COUNTIF FUNCTION

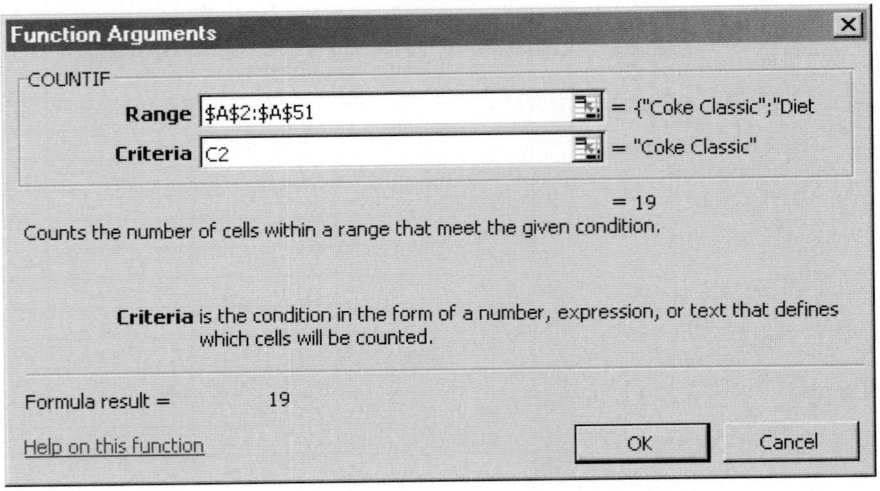

FIGURE 6 EXCEL WORKSHEET SHOWING THE USE OF EXCEL'S COUNTIF FUNCTION TO CONSTRUCT A FREQUENCY DISTRIBUTION

	A	B	C	D	E
1	**Brand Purchased**		**Soft Drink**	**Frequency**	
2	Coke Classic		Coke Classic	=COUNTIF($A$2:$A$51,C2)	
3	Diet Coke		Diet Coke	=COUNTIF($A$2:$A$51,C3)	
4	Pepsi		Dr. Pepper	=COUNTIF($A$2:$A$51,C4)	
5	Diet Coke		Pepsi	=COUNTIF($A$2:$A$51,C5)	
6	Coke Classic		Sprite	=COUNTIF($A$2:$A$51,C6)	
7	Coke Classic				
8	Dr. Pepper				
9	Diet Coke				
10	Pepsi				
45	Pepsi				
46	Pepsi				
47	Pepsi				
48	Coke Classic				
49	Dr. Pepper				
50	Pepsi				
51	Sprite				
52					

Note: Rows 11–44 are hidden.

	A	B	C	D	E
1	**Brand Purchased**		**Soft Drink**	**Frequency**	
2	Coke Classic		Coke Classic	19	
3	Diet Coke		Diet Coke	8	
4	Pepsi		Dr. Pepper	5	
5	Diet Coke		Pepsi	13	
6	Coke Classic		Sprite	5	
7	Coke Classic				
8	Dr. Pepper				
9	Diet Coke				
10	Pepsi				
45	Pepsi				
46	Pepsi				
47	Pepsi				
48	Coke Classic				
49	Dr. Pepper				
50	Pepsi				
51	Sprite				
52					

Appendix F: Computing p-Values Using Minitab and Excel

Here we describe how Minitab and Excel can be used to compute p-values for the z, t, χ^2, and F statistics that are used in hypothesis tests. As discussed in the text, only approximate p-values for the t, χ^2, and F statistics can be obtained by using tables. This appendix is helpful to a person who has computed the test statistic by hand, or by other means, and wishes to use computer software to compute the exact p-value.

Using Minitab

Minitab can be used to provide the cumulative probability associated with the z, t, χ^2, and F test statistics. So the lower tail p-value is obtained directly. The upper tail p-value is computed by subtracting the lower tail p-value from 1. The two-tailed p-value is obtained by doubling the smaller of the lower and upper tail p-values.

The z Test Statistic. We use the Hilltop Coffee lower tail hypothesis test in Section 9.3 as an illustration; the value of the test statistic is $z = -2.67$. The Minitab steps used to compute the cumulative probability corresponding to $z = -2.67$ follow.

Step 1. Select the **Calc** menu
Step 2. Choose **Probability Distributions**
Step 3. Choose **Normal**
Step 4. When the Normal Distribution dialog box appears:
Select **Cumulative probability**
Enter 0 in the **Mean** box
Enter 1 in the **Standard deviation** box
Select **Input Constant**
Enter -2.67 in the **Input Constant** box
Click **OK**

Minitab provides the cumulative probability of .0038. This cumulative probability is the lower tail p-value used for the Hilltop Coffee hypothesis test.

For an upper tail test, the p-value is computed from the cumulative probability provided by Minitab as follows:

$$p\text{-value} = 1 - \text{cumulative probability}$$

For instance, the upper tail p-value corresponding to a test statistic of $z = -2.67$ is $1 - .0038 = .9962$. The two-tailed p-value corresponding to a test statistic of $z = -2.67$ is 2 times the minimum of the upper and lower tail p-values; that is, the two-tailed p-value corresponding to $z = -2.67$ is $2(.0038) = .0076$.

The t Test Statistic. We use the Heathrow Airport example from Section 9.4 as an illustration; the value of the test statistic is $t = 1.84$ with 59 degrees of freedom. The Minitab steps used to compute the cumulative probability corresponding to $t = 1.84$ follow.

Step 1. Select the **Calc** menu
Step 2. Choose **Probability Distributions**

Step 3. Choose **t**
Step 4. When the t Distribution dialog box appears:
Select **Cumulative probability**
Enter 59 in the **Degrees of freedom** box
Select **Input Constant**
Enter 1.84 in the **Input Constant** box
Click **OK**

Minitab provides a cumulative probability of .9646, and hence the lower tail p-value = .9646. The Heathrow Airport example is an upper tail test; the upper tail p-value is 1 − .9646 = .0354. In the case of a two-tailed test, we would use the minimum of .9646 and .0354 to compute p-value = 2(.0354) = .0708.

The χ^2 Test Statistic. We use the St. Louis Metro Bus example from Section 11.1 as an illustration; the value of the test statistic is $\chi^2 = 28.18$ with 23 degrees of freedom. The Minitab steps used to compute the cumulative probability corresponding to $\chi^2 = 28.18$ follow.

Step 1. Select the **Calc** menu
Step 2. Choose **Probability Distributions**
Step 3. Choose **Chi-Square**
Step 4. When the Chi-Square Distribution dialog box appears:
Select **Cumulative probability**
Enter 23 in the **Degrees of freedom** box
Select **Input Constant**
Enter 28.18 in the **Input Constant** box
Click **OK**

Minitab provides a cumulative probability of .7909, which is the lower tail p-value. The upper tail p-value = 1 − the cumulative probability, or 1 − .7909 = .2091. The two-tailed p-value is 2 times the minimum of the lower and upper tail p-values. Thus, the two-tailed p-value is 2(.2091) = .4182. The St. Louis Metro Bus example involved an upper tail test, so we use p-value = .2091.

The F Test Statistic. We use the Dullus County Schools example from Section 11.2 as an illustration; the test statistic is $F = 2.40$ with 25 numerator degrees of freedom and 15 denominator degrees of freedom. The Minitab steps to compute the cumulative probability corresponding to $F = 2.40$ follow.

Step 1. Select the **Calc** menu
Step 2. Choose **Probability Distributions**
Step 3. Choose **F**
Step 4. When the F Distribution dialog box appears:
Select **Cumulative probability**
Enter 25 in the **Numerator degrees of freedom** box
Enter 15 in the **Denominator degrees of freedom** box
Select **Input Constant**
Enter 2.40 in the **Input Constant** box
Click **OK**

Minitab provides the cumulative probability and hence a lower tail p-value = .9594. The upper tail p-value is 1 − .9594 = .0406. Because the Dullus County Schools example is a two-tailed test, the minimum of .9594 and .0406 is used to compute p-value = 2(.0406) = .0812.

Using Excel

CD file

p-Value

Excel functions and formulas can be used to compute p-values associated with the z, t, χ^2, and F test statistics. We provide a template in the data file entitled p-Value for use in computing these p-values. Using the template, it is only necessary to enter the value of the test statistic and, if necessary, the appropriate degrees of freedom. Refer to Figure F.1 as we describe how the template is used. For users interested in the Excel functions and formulas being used, just click on the appropriate cell in the template.

The z Test Statistic. We use the Hilltop Coffee lower tail hypothesis test in Section 9.3 as an illustration; the value of the test statistic is $z = -2.67$. To use the p-value template for this hypothesis test, simply enter -2.67 into cell B6 (see Figure F.1). After doing so, p-values for all three types of hypothesis tests will appear. For Hilltop Coffee, we would use the lower tail p-value $= .0038$ in cell B9. For an upper tail test, we would use the p-value in cell B10, and for a two-tailed test we would use the p-value in cell B11.

The t Test Statistic. We use the Heathrow Airport example from Section 9.4 as an illustration; the value of the test statistic is $t = 1.84$ with 59 degrees of freedom. To use the p-value template for this hypothesis test, enter 1.84 into cell E6 and enter 59 into cell E7 (see Figure F.1). After doing so, p-values for all three types of hypothesis tests will appear. The

FIGURE F.1 EXCEL WORKSHEET FOR COMPUTING p-VALUES

	A	B	C	D	E
1	**Computing *p*-Values**				
2					
3					
4	**Using the Test Statistic *z***			**Using the Test Statistic *t***	
5					
6	**Enter *z* -->**	−2.67		**Enter *t* -->**	1.84
7				***df* -->**	59
8					
9	***p*-value (Lower Tail)**	0.0038		***p*-value (Lower Tail)**	0.9646
10	***p*-value (Upper Tail)**	0.9962		***p*-value (Upper Tail)**	0.0354
11	***p*-value (Two Tail)**	0.0076		***p*-value (Two Tail)**	0.0708
12					
13					
14					
15					
16	**Using the Test Statistic Chi Square**			**Using the Test Statistic *F***	
17					
18	**Enter Chi Square -->**	28.18		**Enter *F* -->**	2.40
19	**df -->**	23		**Numerator df -->**	25
20				**Denominator df -->**	15
21					
22	***p*-value (Lower Tail)**	0.7909		***p*-value (Lower Tail)**	0.9594
23	***p*-value (Upper Tail)**	0.2091		***p*-value (Upper Tail)**	0.0406
24	***p*-value (Two Tail)**	0.4181		***p*-value (Two Tail)**	0.0812

Heathrow Airport example involves an upper tail test, so we would use the upper tail p-value = .0354 provided in cell E10 for the hypothesis test.

The χ^2 Test Statistic. We use the St. Louis Metro Bus example from Section 11.1 as an illustration; the value of the test statistic is $\chi^2 = 28.18$ with 23 degrees of freedom. To use the p-value template for this hypothesis test, enter 28.18 into cell B18 and enter 23 into cell B19 (see Figure F.1). After doing so, p-values for all three types of hypothesis tests will appear. The St. Louis Metro Bus example involves an upper tail test, so we would use the upper tail p-value = .2091 provided in cell B23 for the hypothesis test.

The F Test Statistic. We use the Dullus County Schools example from Section 11.2 as an illustration; the test statistic is $F = 2.40$ with 25 numerator degrees of freedom and 15 denominator degrees of freedom. To use the p-value template for this hypothesis test, enter 2.40 into cell E18, enter 25 into cell E19, and enter 15 into cell B20 (see Figure F.1). After doing so, p-values for all three types of hypothesis tests will appear. The Dullus County Schools example involves a two-tailed test, so we would use the two-tailed p-value = .0812 provided in cell E24 for the hypothesis test.

Index

Note: Chapter 22 can be found on the CD-ROM included with this book. Index entries found in this chapter are denoted by chapter number 22, hyphen, and page number.

Page numbers followed by a **n** indicate a footnote.

C

D

E

F

G

H

I

N

Q

R

S

T

Example for $x_1 = 5, x_2 = 8, x_3 = 14, a = 2, y_1 = 7, y_2 = 3, y_3 = 8, b = 4$:

$$\begin{aligned}\sum_{i=1}^{3}(2x_i + 4y_i) &= 2\sum_{i=1}^{3}x_i + 4\sum_{i=1}^{3}y_i \\ &= 2(27) + 4(18) \\ &= 54 + 72 \\ &= 126\end{aligned}$$

Double Summations

Consider the following data involving the variable x_{ij}, where i is the subscript denoting the row position and j is the subscript denoting the column position:

		Column		
		1	**2**	**3**
Row	**1**	$x_{11} = 10$	$x_{12} = 8$	$x_{13} = 6$
	2	$x_{21} = 7$	$x_{22} = 4$	$x_{23} = 12$

Definition

$$\sum_{i=1}^{n}\sum_{j=1}^{m}x_{ij} = (x_{11} + x_{12} + \cdots + x_{1m}) + (x_{21} + x_{22} + \cdots + x_{2m}) + (x_{31} + x_{32} + \cdots + x_{3m}) + \cdots + (x_{n1} + x_{n2} + \cdots + x_{nm}) \quad \textbf{(C.5)}$$

Example:

$$\begin{aligned}\sum_{i=1}^{2}\sum_{j=1}^{3}x_{ij} &= x_{11} + x_{12} + x_{13} + x_{21} + x_{22} + x_{23} \\ &= 10 + 8 + 6 + 7 + 4 + 12 \\ &= 47\end{aligned}$$

Definition

$$\sum_{i=1}^{n}x_{ij} = x_{1j} + x_{2j} + \cdots + x_{nj} \quad \textbf{(C.6)}$$

Example:

$$\begin{aligned}\sum_{i=1}^{2}x_{i2} &= x_{12} + x_{22} \\ &= 8 + 4 \\ &= 12\end{aligned}$$

Shorthand Notation

Sometimes when a summation is for all values of the subscript, we use the following shorthand notations:

$$\sum_{i=1}^{n}x_i = \sum x_i \quad \textbf{(C.7)}$$

$$\sum_{i=1}^{n}\sum_{j=1}^{m}x_{ij} = \sum\sum x_{ij} \quad \textbf{(C.8)}$$

$$\sum_{i=1}^{n}x_{ij} = \sum_{i}x_{ij} \quad \textbf{(C.9)}$$

Statistics for Business and Economics Data Disk

Chapter 1

BWS&P	Table 1.1
Hotel	Table 1.6
Minisystems	Table 1.7
Norris	Table 1.5
Shadow02	Exercise 25

Chapter 2

ApTest	Table 2.8
Audit	Table 2.4
AutoData	Exercise 38
Broker	Exercise 26
CEOs	Exercise 9
CityTemp	Exercise 46
Computer	Exercise 21
Concerts	Exercise 20
Crosstab	Exercise 29
DivYield	Exercise 41
Fortune	Exercise 51
Frequency	Exercise 11
Golf	Exercise 40
Holiday	Exercise 18
IBD	Exercise 34
Major	Exercise 39
Marathon	Exercise 28
Movies	Case Problem 2
Names	Exercise 5
Networks	Exercise 6
NFL	Exercise 37
OccupSat	Exercise 48
PelicanStores	Case Problem 1
Population	Exercies 44
PriceShare	Exercise 17
Restaurant	Table 2.9
RevEmps	Exercise 49
SATScores	Exercise 42
Scatter	Exercise 30
Shadow	Exercise 43
SoftDrink	Table 2.1
Stereo	Table 2.12
TVMedia	Exercise 4

Chapter 3

Ages	Exersice 59
Asian	Case Problem 3
BASalary	Exercise 6
Baseball	Exercise 42
Beer	Exercise 65
Broker	Exercises 7 & 22
Disney	Exercise 12
Homes	Exercise 64
Hotels	Exercise 5
Movies	Case Problem 2
Mutual	Exercise 44
NCAA	Exercise 34
PCs	Exercise 49
PelicanStores	Case Problem 1
Penalty	Exercise 62
Property	Exercise 40
Speakers	Exercise 35
StartSalary	Table 3.1
Stereo	Table 3.7
StockMarket	Exercise 50
Temperature	Exercise 51
Visa	Exercise 58

Chapter 4

Judge	Case Problem

Chapter 6

Volume	Exercise 24

Chapter 7

EAI	Section 7.1
MetAreas	Table 7.6
MutualFund	Exercise 14

Chapter 8

ActTemps	Exercise 49
Alcohol	Exercise 21
Auto	Case Problem 3
FastFood	Exercise 18
Flights	Exercise 48
GulfProp	Case Problem 2
Interval p	Appendix 8.2
JobSatisfaction	Exercise 37
Lloyd's	Section 8.1
Miami	Exercise 17
NewBalance	Table 8.3
Nielsen	Exercise 6
NYSEStocks	Exercise 47
OpenEndFunds	Exercise 22
Professional	Case Problem 1
Program	Exercise 20
Scheer	Table 8.4
TeeTimes	Section 8.4

Chapter 9

AirRating	Section 9.4
BLS	Case Problem 2
Coffee	Section 9.3
Diamonds	Exercise 29
Drowsy	Exercise 44
Eagle	Exercise 43
Fowle	Exercise 21
Gasoline	Exercise 67
GolfTest	Section 9.3
Hyp Sigma Known	Appendix 9.2
Hyp Sigma Unknown	Appendix 9.2
Hypothesis p	Appendix 9.2
Orders	Section 9.4
Quality	Case Problem 1
RentalRates	Exercise 16
UsedCars	Exercise 32
WomenGolf	Section 9.5

Chapter 10

AirFare	Exercise 24
Cargo	Exercise 13
CheckAcct	Section 10.2
Digital	Exercise 39
Earnings	Exercise 26
Earnings2005	Exercise 22
ExamScores	Section 10.1
Florida	Exercise 42
Golf	Case Problem
Matched	Table 10.2
Mortgage	Exercise 6
Mutual	Exercise 40
SAT	Exercise 18
SATVerbal	Exercise 16
SoftwareTest	Table 10.1
TaxPrep	Section 10.4
TVRadio	Exercise 25

Chapter 11

Bags	Exercise 19
BusTimes	Section 11.1
Return	Exercise 6
SchoolBus	Section 11.2
Training	Case Problem
Travel	Exercise 25

Chapter 12

Chemline	Table 12.10
FitTest	Appendix 12.2
Independence	Appendix 12.2
NYReform	Case Problem

Chapter 13

AirTraf	Table 13.5
Assembly	Exercise 38
AudJudg	Exercise 10
Browsing	Exercise 39
Chemitech	Table 13.1
Exer6	Exercise 6
Funds	Exercise 36
GMAT	Table 13.10
Grocery	Exercise 41
JobSalary	Exercise 37
Medical1	Case Problem 1
Medical2	Case Problem 1
NCP	Table 13.4
Paint	Exercise 11
Salaries	Exercise 32
SalesSalary	Case Problem 2
SatisJob	Exercise 35
Ships	Exercise 20
Snow	Exercise 27
Vitamins	Exercise 25

Chapter 14

Absent	Exercise 63
ADRs	Exercise 49
AgeCost	Exercise 64
Airport	Exercise 11
Alumni	Case Problem 3
Armand's	Table 14.1
Beer	Exercise 52
Beta	Case Problem 1
Boats	Exercise 5
Boots	Exercise 27
Cars	Exercises 7 & 19
CEO	Exercise 54
DJIAS&P500	Exercise 60
HoursPts	Exercise 65
Hydration1	Exercise 43
Hydration2	Exercise 53
IPO	Exercise 58
IRSAudit	Exercise 67
Jensen	Exercise 61
JetSki	Exercise 12
JobSat	Exercise 68
MktBeta	Exercise 66
MLB	Case Problem 4
MtnBikes	Exercise 8
OffRates	Exercise 44
Options	Exercise 59
PlasmaTV	Exercises 20 & 31
Printers	Exercises 22 & 30
Safety	Case Problem 2
Salaries	Exercise 14
Sales	Exercise 9
SleepingBags	Exercises 10, 28, & 36
VPSalary	Exercise 6

Chapter 15

Alumni	Case Problem 3
Auto2	Exercise 42
Backpack	Exercise 7
Bank	Exercise 46
Boats	Exercises 9, 17, & 30
Brokers	Exercise 25
Butler	Tables 15.1 & 15.2
Chocolate	Exercise 48
Consumer	Case Problem 1
Enquirer	Case Problem 2
Exer2	Exercise 2
Football	Exercise 37
ForFunds	Exercise 8
FuelEcon	Exercise 56
HomeValue	Exercise 54
Johnson	Table 15.6
Lakeland	Exercise 47
LPGA	Exercise 43
MLB	Exercises 6, 16, & 24
NBA	Exercises 10, 18, & 26
NFLStats	Case Problem 4
Repair	Exercise 35
Showtime	Exercises 5, 15, & 41
Simmons	Table 15.11
SportsCar	Exercise 31
Stroke	Exercise 38
Treadmills	Exercise 55
Trucks	Exercise 57

Chapter 16

Audit	Exercise 31
Browsing	Exercise 34
Cars	Case Problem 2
ClassicCars	Exercise 8
ColorPrinter	Exercise 29
Cravens	Table 16.5
GradRate	Case Problem 3
IBM	Exercise 27
Layoffs	Exercise 16
LightRail	Exercise 9
LPGATour	Exercises 12 & 13
LPGATour2	Exercise 17
Monitors	Exercise 7
MPG	Table 16.4
MutFunds	Exercise 30
NFL	Exercise 15
PGATour	Case Problem 1
Resale	Exercise 35
Reynolds	Table 16.1
Stroke	Exercises 14 & 19
Tyler	Table 16.2
Yankees	Exercise 18

Chapter 18

AcctBal	Exercise 35
AptExp	Exercise 24
Bicycle	Table 18.6
Broadband	Exercise 18
CDSales	Exercise 32
Gasoline	Table 18.1
IBM	Exercise 27
MfgCap	Exercise 11
Pollution	Exercise 25
Power	Exercise 26
TVSales	Table 18.7
Vintage	Case Problem 1

Chapter 19

Annual	Exercise 11

Chapter 20

Coffee	Exercise 20
Jensen	Table 20.2
Tires	Exercise 7

Chapter 21

PDC Tree	Appendix 21.1

Appendix F

p-Value	Appendix F

CHAPTER 4

Decision Analysis

CONTENTS

Decision analysis can be used to develop an optimal strategy when a decision maker is faced with several decision alternatives and an uncertain or risk-filled pattern of future events. For example, Ohio Edison used decision analysis to choose the best type of particulate control equipment for coal-fired generating units when it faced future uncertainties concerning sulfur content requirements, construction costs, and so on. The State of North Carolina used decision analysis in evaluating whether to implement a medical screening test to detect metabolic disorders in newborns. Thus, decision analysis repeatedly proves its value in decision making. The Q.M. in Action, Decision Analysis at Eastman Kodak, describes how the use of decision analysis added approximately $1 billion in value.

Even when a careful decision analysis has been conducted, the uncertain future events make the final consequence uncertain. In some cases, the selected decision alternative may provide good or excellent results. In other cases, a relatively unlikely future event may occur causing the selected decision alternative to provide only fair or even poor results. The risk associated with any decision alternative is a direct result of the uncertainty associated with the final consequence. A good decision analysis includes risk analysis. Through risk analysis the decision maker is provided with probability information about the favorable as well as the unfavorable consequences that may occur.

Q.M. IN ACTION

DECISION ANALYSIS AT EASTMAN KODAK*

Clemen and Kwit conducted a study to determine the value of decision analysis at the Eastman Kodak company. The study involved an analysis of 178 decision analysis projects over a 10-year period. The projects involved a variety of applications including strategy development, vendor selection, process analysis, new-product brainstorming, product-portfolio selection, and emission-reduction analysis. These projects required 14,372 hours of analyst time and the involvement of many other individuals at Kodak over the 10-year period. The shortest projects took less than 20 hours, and the longest projects took almost a year to complete.

Most decision analysis projects are one-time activities, which makes it difficult to measure the value added to the corporation. Clemen and Kwit used detailed records that were available and some innovative approaches to develop estimates of the incremental dollar value generated by the decision analysis projects. Their conservative estimate of the average value per project was $6.65 million and their optimistic estimate of the average value per project was $16.35 million. Their analysis led to the conclusion that all projects taken together added more than $1 billion in value to Eastman Kodak. Using these estimates, Clemen and Kwit concluded that decision analysis returned substantial value to the company. Indeed, they concluded that the value added by the projects was at least 185 times the cost of the analysts' time.

In addition to the monetary benefits, the authors point out that decision analysis adds value by facilitating discussion among stakeholders, promoting careful thinking about strategies, providing a common language for discussing the elements of a decision problem, and speeding implementation by helping to build consensus among decision makers. In commenting on the value of decision analysis at Eastman Kodak, Nancy L. S. Sousa said, "As General Manager, New Businesses, VP Health Imaging, Eastman Kodak, I encourage all of the business planners to use the decision and risk principles and processes as part of evaluating new business opportunities. The processes have clearly led to better decisions about entry and exit of businesses."

Although measuring the value of a particular decision analysis project can be difficult, it would be difficult to dispute the success that decision analysis had at Kodak.

*Based on Robert T. Clemen and Robert C. Kwit, "The Value of Decision Analysis at Eastman Kodak Company," *Interfaces* (September/October 2001): 74–92.

We begin the study of decision analysis by considering problems that involve reasonably few decision alternatives and reasonably few possible future events. Influence diagrams and payoff tables are introduced to provide a structure for the decision problem and to illustrate the fundamentals of decision analysis. We then introduce decision trees to show the sequential nature of decision problems. Decision trees are used to analyze more complex problems and to identify an optimal sequence of decisions, referred to as an optimal decision strategy. Sensitivity analysis shows how changes in various aspects of the problem affect the recommended decision alternative.

4.1 PROBLEM FORMULATION

The first step in the decision analysis process is problem formulation. We begin with a verbal statement of the problem. We then identify the **decision alternatives,** the uncertain future events, referred to as **chance events,** and the **consequences** associated with each decision alternative and each chance event outcome. Let us begin by considering a construction project of the Pittsburgh Development Corporation.

Pittsburgh Development Corporation (PDC) purchased land that will be the site of a new luxury condominium complex. The location provides a spectacular view of downtown Pittsburgh and the Golden Triangle where the Allegheny and Monongahela rivers meet to form the Ohio River. PDC plans to price the individual condominium units between $300,000 and $1,400,000.

PDC commissioned preliminary architectural drawings for three different projects: one with 30 condominiums, one with 60 condominiums, and one with 90 condominiums. The financial success of the project depends upon the size of the condominium complex and the chance event concerning the demand for the condominiums. The statement of the PDC decision problem is to select the size of the new luxury condominium project that will lead to the largest profit given the uncertainty concerning the demand for the condominiums.

Given the statement of the problem, it is clear that the decision is to select the best size for the condominium complex. PDC has the following three decision alternatives:

$$d_1 = \text{a small complex with 30 condominiums}$$
$$d_2 = \text{a medium complex with 60 condominiums}$$
$$d_3 = \text{a large complex with 90 condominiums}$$

A factor in selecting the best decision alternative is the uncertainty associated with the chance event concerning the demand for the condominiums. When asked about the possible demand for the condominiums, PDC's president acknowledged a wide range of possibilities, but decided that it would be adequate to consider two possible chance event outcomes: a strong demand and a weak demand.

In decision analysis, the possible outcomes for a chance event are referred to as the **states of nature.** The states of nature are defined so that one and only one of the possible states of nature will occur. For the PDC problem, the chance event concerning the demand for the condominiums has two states of nature:

$$s_1 = \text{strong demand for the condominiums}$$
$$s_2 = \text{weak demand for the condominiums}$$

Management must first select a decision alternative (complex size), then a state of nature follows (demand for the condominiums), and finally a consequence will occur. In this case, the consequence is PDC's profit.

Influence Diagrams

An **influence diagram** is a graphical device that shows the relationships among the decisions, the chance events, and the consequences for a decision problem. The **nodes** in an influence diagram represent the decisions, chance events, and consequences. Rectangles or squares depict **decision nodes,** circles or ovals depict **chance nodes,** and diamonds depict **consequence nodes.** The lines connecting the nodes, referred to as *arcs,* show the direction of influence that the nodes have on one another. Figure 4.1 shows the influence diagram for the PDC problem. The complex size is the decision node, demand is the chance node, and profit is the consequence node. The arcs connecting the nodes show that both the complex size and the demand influence PDC's profit.

Payoff Tables

Given the three decision alternatives and the two states of nature, which complex size should PDC choose? To answer this question, PDC will need to know the consequence associated with each decision alternative and each state of nature. In decision analysis, we refer to the consequence resulting from a specific combination of a decision alternative and a state of nature as a **payoff.** A table showing payoffs for all combinations of decision alternatives and states of nature is a **payoff table.**

Payoffs can be expressed in terms of profit, cost, time, distance, or any other measure appropriate for the decision problem being analyzed.

Because PDC wants to select the complex size that provides the largest profit, profit is used as the consequence. The payoff table with profits expressed in millions of dollars is shown in Table 4.1. Note, for example, that if a medium complex is built and demand turns out to be strong, a profit of \$14 million will be realized. We will use the notation V_{ij} to denote the payoff associated with decision alternative i and state of nature j. Using Table 4.1, $V_{31} = 20$ indicates a payoff of \$20 million occurs if the decision is to build a large complex (d_3) and the strong demand state of nature (s_1) occurs. Similarly, $V_{32} = -9$ indicates a loss of \$9 million if the decision is to build a large complex (d_3) and the weak demand state of nature (s_2) occurs.

Decision Trees

A **decision tree** provides a graphical representation of the decision-making process. Figure 4.2 presents a decision tree for the PDC problem. Note that the decision tree shows the natural or logical progression that will occur over time. First, PDC must make a decision

FIGURE 4.1 INFLUENCE DIAGRAM FOR THE PDC PROJECT

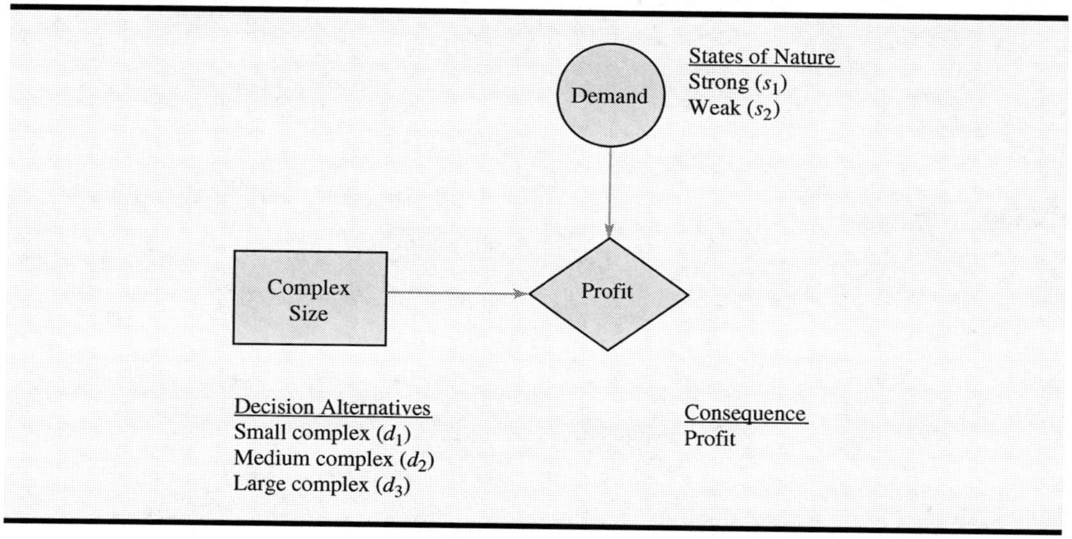

TABLE 4.1 PAYOFF TABLE FOR THE PDC CONDOMINIUM PROJECT (PAYOFFS IN $ MILLIONS)

	State of Nature	
Decision Alternative	**Strong Demand s_1**	**Weak Demand s_2**
Small complex, d_1	8	7
Medium complex, d_2	14	5
Large complex, d_3	20	−9

regarding the size of the condominium complex (d_1, d_2, or d_3). Then, after the decision is implemented, either state of nature s_1 or s_2 will occur. The number at each end point of the tree indicates the payoff associated with a particular sequence. For example the topmost payoff of 8 indicates that an $8 million profit is anticipated if PDC constructs a small condominium complex (d_1) and demand turns out to be strong (s_1). The next payoff of 7 indicates an anticipated profit of $7 million if PDC constructs a small condominium complex (d_1) and demand turns out to be weak (s_2). Thus, the decision tree shows graphically the sequences of decision alternatives and states of nature that provide the six possible payoffs for PDC.

If you have a payoff table, you can develop a decision tree. Try Problem 1(a).

The decision tree in Figure 4.2 shows four nodes, numbered 1–4. Squares are used to depict decision nodes and circles are used to depict chance nodes. Thus, node 1 is a decision node, and nodes 2, 3, and 4 are chance nodes. The **branches,** which connect the nodes, leaving the decision node correspond to the decision alternatives. The branches leaving each chance node correspond to the states of nature. The payoffs are shown at the end of the states-of-nature branches. We now turn to the question: How can the decision maker use the information in the payoff table or the decision tree to select the best decision alternative? Several approaches may be used.

FIGURE 4.2 DECISION TREE FOR THE PDC CONDOMINIUM PROJECT (PAYOFFS IN $ MILLIONS)

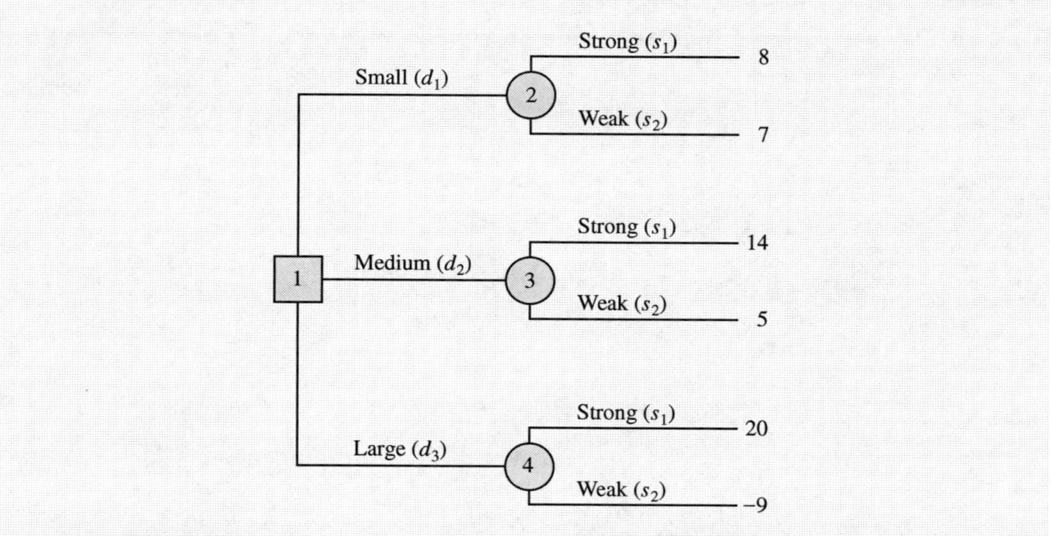

NOTES AND COMMENTS

1. Experts in problem solving agree that the first step in solving a complex problem is to decompose it into a series of smaller subproblems. Decision trees provide a useful way to show how a problem can be decomposed and the sequential nature of the decision process.

2. People often view the same problem from different perspectives. Thus, the discussion regarding the development of a decision tree may provide additional insight about the problem.

4.2 DECISION MAKING WITHOUT PROBABILITIES

Many people think of a good decision as one in which the consequence is good. However, in some instances, a good, well-thought-out decision may still lead to a bad or undesirable consequence.

In this section we consider approaches to decision making that do not require knowledge of the probabilities of the states of nature. These approaches are appropriate in situations in which the decision maker has little confidence in his or her ability to assess the probabilities, or in which a simple best-case and worst-case analysis is desirable. Because different approaches sometimes lead to different decision recommendations, the decision maker needs to understand the approaches available and then select the specific approach that, according to the decision maker's judgment, is the most appropriate.

Optimistic Approach

The **optimistic approach** evaluates each decision alternative in terms of the *best* payoff that can occur. The decision alternative that is recommended is the one that provides the best possible payoff. For a problem in which maximum profit is desired, as in the PDC problem, the optimistic approach would lead the decision maker to choose the alternative corresponding to the largest profit. For problems involving minimization, this approach leads to choosing the alternative with the smallest payoff.

For a maximization problem, the optimistic approach often is referred to as the maximax approach; for a minimization problem, the corresponding terminology is minimin.

To illustrate the optimistic approach, we use it to develop a recommendation for the PDC problem. First, we determine the maximum payoff for each decision alternative; then we select the decision alternative that provides the overall maximum payoff. These steps systematically identify the decision alternative that provides the largest possible profit. Table 4.2 illustrates these steps.

Because 20, corresponding to d_3, is the largest payoff, the decision to construct the large condominium complex is the recommended decision alternative using the optimistic approach.

Conservative Approach

The **conservative approach** evaluates each decision alternative in terms of the *worst* payoff that can occur. The decision alternative recommended is the one that provides the best of the worst possible payoffs. For a problem in which the output measure is profit, as in the PDC problem, the conservative approach would lead the decision maker to choose the alternative that maximizes the minimum possible profit that could be obtained. For problems involving minimization, this approach identifies the alternative that will minimize the maximum payoff.

For a maximization problem, the conservative approach is often referred to as the maximin approach; for a minimization problem, the corresponding terminology is minimax.

To illustrate the conservative approach, we use it to develop a recommendation for the PDC problem. First, we identify the minimum payoff for each of the decision alternatives; then we select the decision alternative that maximizes the minimum payoff. Table 4.3 illustrates these steps for the PDC problem.

Because 7, corresponding to d_1, yields the maximum of the minimum payoffs, the decision alternative of a small condominium complex is recommended. This decision approach is considered conservative because it identifies the worst possible payoffs and then recommends the decision alternative that avoids the possibility of extremely "bad" payoffs.

TABLE 4.2 MAXIMUM PAYOFF FOR EACH PDC DECISION ALTERNATIVE

Decision Alternative	Maximum Payoff	
Small complex, d_1	8	
Medium complex, d_2	14	
Large complex, d_3	20	← Maximum of the maximum payoff values

In the conservative approach, PDC is guaranteed a profit of at least \$7 million. Although PDC may make more, it *cannot* make less than \$7 million.

Minimax Regret Approach

The **minimax regret approach** to decision making is neither purely optimistic nor purely conservative. Let us illustrate the minimax regret approach by showing how it can be used to select a decision alternative for the PDC problem.

Suppose that PDC constructs a small condominium complex (d_1) and demand turns out to be strong (s_1). Table 4.1 showed that the resulting profit for PDC would be \$8 million. However, given that the strong demand state of nature (s_1) has occurred, we realize that the decision to construct a large condominium complex (d_3), yielding a profit of \$20 million, would have been the best decision. The difference between the payoff for the best decision alternative (\$20 million) and the payoff for the decision to construct a small condominium complex (\$8 million) is the **opportunity loss,** or **regret,** associated with decision alternative d_1 when state of nature s_1 occurs; thus, for this case, the opportunity loss or regret is \$20 million − \$8 million = \$12 million. Similarly, if PDC makes the decision to construct a medium condominium complex (d_2) and the strong demand state of nature (s_1) occurs, the opportunity loss, or regret, associated with d_2 would be \$20 million − \$14 million = \$6 million.

In general the following expression represents the opportunity loss, or regret.

$$R_{ij} = |V_j^* - V_{ij}| \tag{4.1}$$

where

R_{ij} = the regret associated with decision alternative d_i and state of nature s_j
V_j^* = the payoff value* corresponding to the best decision for the state of nature s_j
V_{ij} = the payoff corresponding to decision alternative d_i and state of nature s_j

TABLE 4.3 MINIMUM PAYOFF FOR EACH PDC DECISION ALTERNATIVE

Decision Alternative	Minimum Payoff	
Small complex, d_1	7	← Maximum of the minimum payoff values
Medium complex, d_2	5	
Large complex, d_3	−9	

*In maximization problems, V_j^* will be the largest entry in column j of the payoff table. In minimization problems, V_j^* will be the smallest entry in column j of the payoff table.

TABLE 4.4 OPPORTUNITY LOSS, OR REGRET, TABLE FOR THE PDC CONDOMINIUM PROJECT ($ MILLIONS)

	State of Nature	
Decision Alternative	Strong Demand s_1	Weak Demand s_2
Small complex, d_1	12	0
Medium complex, d_2	6	2
Large complex, d_3	0	16

Note the role of the absolute value in equation (4.1). For minimization problems, the best payoff, V_j^*, is the smallest entry in column j. Because this value always is less than or equal to V_{ij}, the absolute value of the difference between V_j^* and V_{ij} ensures that the regret is always the magnitude of the difference.

Using equation (4.1) and the payoffs in Table 4.1, we can compute the regret associated with each combination of decision alternative d_i and state of nature s_j. Because the PDC problem is a maximization problem, V_j^* will be the largest entry in column j of the payoff table. Thus, to compute the regret, we simply subtract each entry in a column from the largest entry in the column. Table 4.4 shows the opportunity loss, or regret, table for the PDC problem.

The next step in applying the minimax regret approach is to list the maximum regret for each decision alternative; Table 4.5 shows the results for the PDC problem. Selecting the decision alternative with the *minimum* of the *maximum* regret values—hence, the name *minimax regret*—yields the minimax regret decision. For the PDC problem, the alternative to construct the medium condominium complex, with a corresponding maximum regret of $6 million, is the recommended minimax regret decision.

For practice in developing a decision recommendation using the optimistic, conservative, and minimax regret approaches, try Problem 1 (part b).

Note that the three approaches discussed in this section provide different recommendations, which in itself isn't bad. It simply reflects the difference in decision-making philosophies that underlie the various approaches. Ultimately, the decision maker will have to choose the most appropriate approach and then make the final decision accordingly. The main criticism of the approaches discussed in this section is that they do not consider any information about the probabilities of the various states of nature. In the next section we discuss an approach that utilizes probability information in selecting a decision alternative.

4.3 DECISION MAKING WITH PROBABILITIES

In many decision-making situations, we can obtain probability assessments for the states of nature. When such probabilities are available, we can use the **expected value approach** to identify the best decision alternative. Let us first define the expected value of a decision alternative and then apply it to the PDC problem.

TABLE 4.5 MAXIMUM REGRET FOR EACH PDC DECISION ALTERNATIVE

Decision Alternative	Maximum Regret	
Small complex, d_1	12	
Medium complex, d_2	6	← Minimum of the maximum regret
Large complex, d_3	16	

Let

$$N = \text{the number of states of nature}$$
$$P(s_j) = \text{the probability of state of nature } s_j$$

Because one and only one of the N states of nature can occur, the probabilities must satisfy two conditions:

$$P(s_j) \geq 0 \qquad \text{for all states of nature} \tag{4.2}$$

$$\sum_{j=1}^{N} P(s_j) = P(s_1) + P(s_2) + \cdots + P(s_N) = 1 \tag{4.3}$$

The **expected value (EV)** of decision alternative d_i is defined as follows:

$$\text{EV}(d_i) = \sum_{j=1}^{N} P(s_j)V_{ij} \tag{4.4}$$

In words, the expected value of a decision alternative is the sum of weighted payoffs for the decision alternative. The weight for a payoff is the probability of the associated state of nature and therefore the probability that the payoff will occur. Let us return to the PDC problem to see how the expected value approach can be applied.

PDC is optimistic about the potential for the luxury high-rise condominium complex. Suppose that this optimism leads to an initial subjective probability assessment of 0.8 that demand will be strong (s_1) and a corresponding probability of 0.2 that demand will be weak (s_2). Thus, $P(s_1) = 0.8$ and $P(s_2) = 0.2$. Using the payoff values in Table 4.1 and equation (4.4), we compute the expected value for each of the three decision alternatives as follows:

$$\text{EV}(d_1) = 0.8(8) + 0.2(7) = 7.8$$
$$\text{EV}(d_2) = 0.8(14) + 0.2(5) = 12.2$$
$$\text{EV}(d_3) = 0.8(20) + 0.2(-9) = 14.2$$

Thus, using the expected value approach, we find that the large condominium complex, with an expected value of \$14.2 million, is the recommended decision.

Can you now use the expected value approach to develop a decision recommendation? Try Problem 5.

The calculations required to identify the decision alternative with the best expected value can be conveniently carried out on a decision tree. Figure 4.3 shows the decision tree for the PDC problem with state-of-nature branch probabilities. Working backward through the decision tree, we first compute the expected value at each chance node. That is, at each chance node, we weight each possible payoff by its probability of occurrence. By doing so, we obtain the expected values for nodes 2, 3, and 4, as shown in Figure 4.4.

Because the decision maker controls the branch leaving decision node 1 and because we are trying to maximize the expected profit, the best decision alternative at node 1 is d_3. Thus, the decision tree analysis leads to a recommendation of d_3 with an expected value of \$14.2 million. Note that this recommendation is also obtained with the expected value approach in conjunction with the payoff table.

Computer software packages are available to help in constructing more complex decision trees. See Appendix 4.1.

Other decision problems may be substantially more complex than the PDC problem, but if a reasonable number of decision alternatives and states of nature are present, you can use the decision tree approach outlined here. First, draw a decision tree consisting of deci-

FIGURE 4.3 PDC DECISION TREE WITH STATE-OF-NATURE BRANCH PROBABILITIES

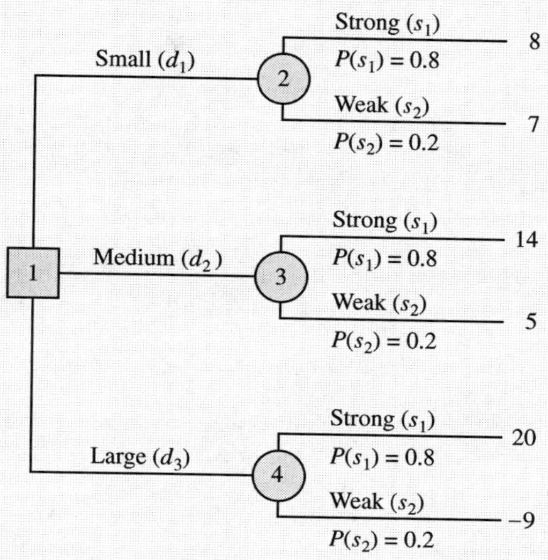

sion nodes, chance nodes, and branches that describe the sequential nature of the problem. If you use the expected value approach, the next step is to determine the probabilities for each of the states of nature and compute the expected value at each chance node. Then select the decision branch leading to the chance node with the best expected value. The decision alternative associated with this branch is the recommended decision.

The Q.M. in Action, Early Detection of High-Risk Worker Disability Claims, describes how the Workers' Compensation Board of British Columbia used a decision tree and expected cost to help determine whether a short-term disability claim should be considered a high-risk or a low-risk claim.

FIGURE 4.4 APPLYING THE EXPECTED VALUE APPROACH USING A DECISION TREE

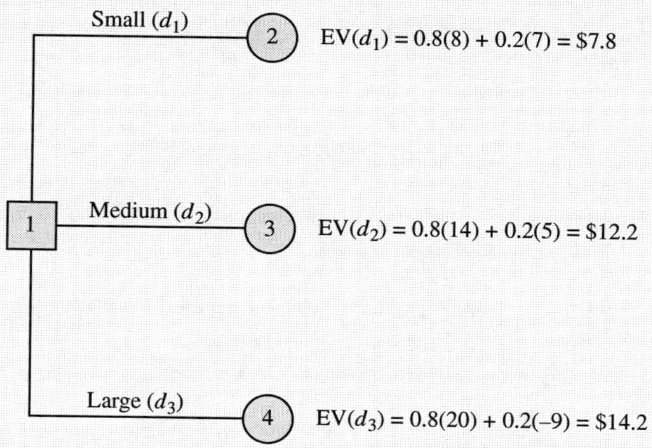

Q.M. IN ACTION

EARLY DETECTION OF HIGH-RISK WORKER DISABILITY CLAIMS*

The Workers' Compensation Board of British Columbia (WCB) helps workers and employers maintain safe workplaces and helps injured workers obtain disability income and return to work safely. The funds used to make the disability compensation payments are obtained from assessments levied on employers. In return, employers receive protection from lawsuits arising from work-related injuries. In recent years, the WCB spent more than $1 billion on worker compensation and rehabilitation.

A short-term disability claim occurs when a worker suffers an injury or illness that results in temporary absence from work. Whenever a worker fails to recover completely from a short-term disability, the claim is reclassified as a long-term disability claim and more expensive long-term benefits are paid.

The WCB wanted a systematic way to identify short-term disability claims that posed a high financial risk of being converted to the more expensive long-term disability claims. If a short-term disability claim could be classified as high risk early in the process, a WCB management team could intervene and monitor the claim and the recovery process more closely. As a result, WCB could improve the management of the high-risk claims and reduce the cost of any subsequent long-term disability claims.

The WCB used a decision analysis approach to classify each new short-term disability claim as being either a high-risk claim or a low-risk claim. A decision tree consisting of two decision nodes and two states-of-nature nodes was developed. The two decision alternatives were: (1) Classify the new short-term claim as high-risk and intervene; (2) Classify the new short-term claim as low-risk and do not intervene. The two states of nature were: (1) The short-term claim converts to a long-term claim; (2) The short-term claim does not convert to a long-term claim. The characteristics of each new short-term claim were used to determine the probabilities for the states of nature. The payoffs were the disability claim costs associated with each decision alternative and each state-of-nature outcome. The objective of minimizing the expected cost determined whether a new short-term claim should be classified as high-risk.

Implementation of the decision analysis model improved the practice of claim management for the Workers' Compensation Board. Early intervention on the high-risk claims saved an estimated $4.7 million per year.

*Based on E. Urbanovich, E. Young, M. Puterman, and S. Fattedad, "Early Detection of High-Risk Claims at the Workers' Compensation Board of British Columbia," *Interfaces* (July/August 2003): 15–26.

Expected Value of Perfect Information

Suppose that PDC has the opportunity to conduct a market research study that would help evaluate buyer interest in the condominium project and provide information that management could use to improve the probability assessments for the states of nature. To determine the potential value of this information, we begin by supposing that the study could provide *perfect information* regarding the states of nature; that is, we assume for the moment that PDC could determine with certainty, prior to making a decision, which state of nature is going to occur. To make use of this perfect information, we will develop a decision strategy that PDC should follow once it knows which state of nature will occur. A decision strategy is simply a decision rule that specifies the decision alternative to be selected after new information becomes available.

To help determine the decision strategy for PDC, we reproduced PDC's payoff table as Table 4.6. Note that, if PDC knew for sure that state of nature s_1 would occur, the best decision alternative would be d_3, with a payoff of $20 million. Similarly, if PDC knew for sure that state of nature s_2 would occur, the best decision alternative would be d_1, with a payoff of $7 million. Thus, we can state PDC's optimal decision strategy when the perfect information becomes available as follows:

If s_1, select d_3 and receive a payoff of $20 million.
If s_2, select d_1 and receive a payoff of $7 million.

TABLE 4.6 PAYOFF TABLE FOR THE PDC CONDOMINIUM PROJECT ($ MILLIONS)

	State of Nature	
Decision Alternative	**Strong Demand s_1**	**Weak Demand s_2**
Small complex, d_1	8	7
Medium complex, d_2	14	5
Large complex, d_3	20	−9

What is the expected value for this decision strategy? To compute the expected value with perfect information, we return to the original probabilities for the states of nature: $P(s_1) = 0.8$, and $P(s_2) = 0.2$. Thus, there is a 0.8 probability that the perfect information will indicate state of nature s_1 and the resulting decision alternative d_3 will provide a $20 million profit. Similarly, with a 0.2 probability for state of nature s_2, the optimal decision alternative d_1 will provide a $7 million profit. Thus, from equation (4.4), the expected value of the decision strategy that uses perfect information is

$$0.8(20) + 0.2(7) = 17.4$$

We refer to the expected value of $17.4 million as the *expected value with perfect information* (EVwPI).

Earlier in this section we showed that the recommended decision using the expected value approach is decision alternative d_3, with an expected value of $14.2 million. Because this decision recommendation and expected value computation were made without the benefit of perfect information, $14.2 million is referred to as the *expected value without perfect information* (EVwoPI).

It would be worth $3.2 million for PDC to learn the level of market acceptance before selecting a decision alternative.

The expected value with perfect information is $17.4 million, and the expected value without perfect information is $14.2; therefore, the expected value of the perfect information (EVPI) is $17.4 − $14.2 = $3.2 million. In other words, $3.2 million represents the additional expected value that can be obtained if perfect information were available about the states of nature.

Generally speaking, a market research study will not provide "perfect" information; however, if the market research study is a good one, the information gathered might be worth a sizable portion of the $3.2 million. Given the EVPI of $3.2 million, PDC might seriously consider a market survey as a way to obtain more information about the states of nature.

In general, the **expected value of perfect information (EVPI)** is computed as follows:

$$\text{EVPI} = |\text{EVwPI} - \text{EVwoPI}| \qquad (4.5)$$

where

EVPI = expected value of perfect information
EVwPI = expected value *with* perfect information about the states of nature
EVwoPI = expected value *without* perfect information about the states of nature

For practice in determining the expected value of perfect information, try Problem 14.

Note the role of the absolute value in equation (4.5). For minimization problems the expected value with perfect information is always less than or equal to the expected value without perfect information. In this case, EVPI is the magnitude of the difference between EVwPI and EVwoPI, or the absolute value of the difference as shown in equation (4.5).

NOTES AND COMMENTS

We restate the *opportunity loss,* or *regret,* table for the PDC problem (see Table 4.4) as follows.

	State of Nature	
	Strong Demand	**Weak Demand**
Decision Alternative	s_1	s_2
Small complex, d_1	12	0
Medium complex, d_2	6	2
Large complex, d_3	0	16

Using $P(s_1)$, $P(s_2)$, and the opportunity loss values, we can compute the *expected opportunity loss* (EOL) for each decision alternative. With $P(s_1) = 0.8$ and $P(s_2) = 0.2$, the expected opportunity loss for each of the three decision alternatives is

$$\begin{aligned} \text{EOL}(d_1) &= 0.8(12) + 0.2(0) = 9.6 \\ \text{EOL}(d_2) &= 0.8(6) + 0.2(2) = 5.2 \\ \text{EOL}(d_3) &= 0.8(0) + 0.2(16) = 3.2 \end{aligned}$$

Regardless of whether the decision analysis involves maximization or minimization, the *minimum* expected opportunity loss always provides the best decision alternative. Thus, with $\text{EOL}(d_3) = 3.2$, d_3 is the recommended decision. In addition, the minimum expected opportunity loss always is *equal to the expected value of perfect information.* That is, EOL(best decision) = EVPI; for the PDC problem, this value is \$3.2 million.

4.4 RISK ANALYSIS AND SENSITIVITY ANALYSIS

Risk analysis helps the decision maker recognize the difference between the expected value of a decision alternative and the payoff that may actually occur. **Sensitivity analysis** also helps the decision maker by describing how changes in the state-of-nature probabilities and/or changes in the payoffs affect the recommended decision alternative.

Risk Analysis

A decision alternative and a state of nature combine to generate the payoff associated with a decision. The **risk profile** for a decision alternative shows the possible payoffs along with their associated probabilities.

Let us demonstrate risk analysis and the construction of a risk profile by returning to the PDC condominium construction project. Using the expected value approach, we identified the large condominium complex (d_3) as the best decision alternative. The expected value of \$14.2 million for d_3 is based on a 0.8 probability of obtaining a \$20 million profit and a 0.2 probability of obtaining a \$9 million loss. The 0.8 probability for the \$20 million payoff and the 0.2 probability for the −\$9 million payoff provide the risk profile for the large complex decision alternative. This risk profile is shown graphically in Figure 4.5.

Sometimes a review of the risk profile associated with an optimal decision alternative may cause the decision maker to choose another decision alternative even though the expected value of the other decision alternative is not as good. For example, the risk profile for the medium complex decision alternative (d_2) shows a 0.8 probability for a \$14 million payoff and 0.2 probability for a \$5 million payoff. Because no probability of a loss is associated with decision alternative d_2, the medium complex decision alternative would be judged less risky than the large complex decision alternative. As a result, a decision maker might prefer the less-risky medium complex decision alternative even though it has an expected value of \$2 million less than the large complex decision alternative.

Sensitivity Analysis

Sensitivity analysis can be used to determine how changes in the probabilities for the states of nature or changes in the payoffs affect the recommended decision alternative. In many cases, the probabilities for the states of nature and the payoffs are based on subjective

FIGURE 4.5 RISK PROFILE FOR THE LARGE COMPLEX DECISION ALTERNATIVE FOR THE PDC CONDOMINIUM PROJECT

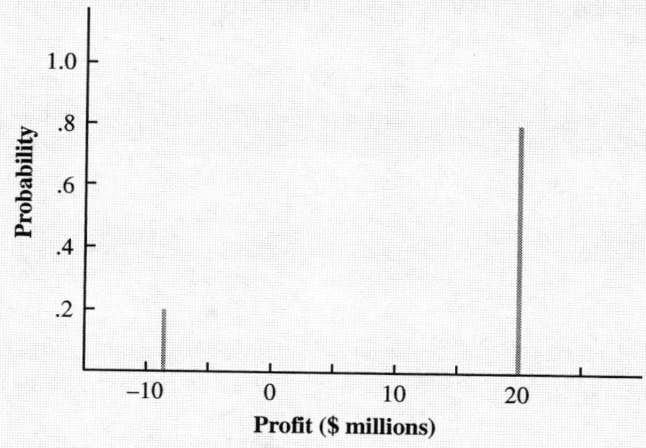

assessments. Sensitivity analysis helps the decision maker understand which of these inputs are critical to the choice of the best decision alternative. If a small change in the value of one of the inputs causes a change in the recommended decision alternative, the solution to the decision analysis problem is sensitive to that particular input. Extra effort and care should be taken to make sure the input value is as accurate as possible. On the other hand, if a modest to large change in the value of one of the inputs does not cause a change in the recommended decision alternative, the solution to the decision analysis problem is not sensitive to that particular input. No extra time or effort would be needed to refine the estimated input value.

One approach to sensitivity analysis is to select different values for the probabilities of the states of nature and the payoffs and then resolve the decision analysis problem. If the recommended decision alternative changes, we know that the solution is sensitive to the changes made. For example, suppose that in the PDC problem the probability for a strong demand is revised to 0.2 and the probability for a weak demand is revised to 0.8. Would the recommended decision alternative change? Using $P(s_1) = 0.2$, $P(s_2) = 0.8$, and equation (4.4), the revised expected values for the three decision alternatives are

$$\begin{aligned} EV(d_1) &= 0.2(8) + 0.8(7) = 7.2 \\ EV(d_2) &= 0.2(14) + 0.8(5) = 6.8 \\ EV(d_3) &= 0.2(20) + 0.8(-9) = -3.2 \end{aligned}$$

With these probability assessments the recommended decision alternative is to construct a small condominium complex (d_1), with an expected value of \$7.2 million. The probability of strong demand is only 0.2, so constructing the large condominium complex (d_3) is the least preferred alternative, with an expected value of −\$3.2 million (a loss).

Computer software packages for decision analysis make it easy to calculate these revised scenarios.

Thus, when the probability of strong demand is large, PDC should build the large complex; when the probability of strong demand is small, PDC should build the small complex. Obviously, we could continue to modify the probabilities of the states of nature and learn even more about how changes in the probabilities affect the recommended decision alternative. The drawback to this approach is the numerous calculations required to evaluate the effect of several possible changes in the state-of-nature probabilities.

For the special case of two states of nature, a graphical procedure can be used to determine how changes for the probabilities of the states of nature affect the recommended decision alternative. To demonstrate this procedure, we let p denote the probability of state of nature s_1; that is, $P(s_1) = p$. With only two states of nature in the PDC problem, the probability of state of nature s_2 is

$$P(s_2) = 1 - P(s_1) = 1 - p$$

Using equation (4.4) and the payoff values in Table 4.1, we determine the expected value for decision alternative d_1 as follows:

$$\begin{aligned} EV(d_1) &= P(s_1)(8) + P(s_2)(7) \\ &= p(8) + (1 - p)(7) \\ &= 8p + 7 - 7p = p + 7 \end{aligned} \tag{4.6}$$

Repeating the expected value computations for decision alternatives d_2 and d_3, we obtain expressions for the expected value of each decision alternative as a function of p:

$$EV(d_2) = 9p + 5 \tag{4.7}$$

$$EV(d_3) = 29p - 9 \tag{4.8}$$

Thus, we have developed three equations that show the expected value of the three decision alternatives as a function of the probability of state of nature s_1.

We continue by developing a graph with values of p on the horizontal axis and the associated EVs on the vertical axis. Because equations (4.6), (4.7), and (4.8) are linear equations, the graph of each equation is a straight line. For each equation, we can obtain the line by identifying two points that satisfy the equation and drawing a line through the points. For instance, if we let $p = 0$ in equation (4.6), $EV(d_1) = 7$. Then, letting $p = 1$, $EV(d_1) = 8$. Connecting these two points, (0,7) and (1,8), provides the line labeled $EV(d_1)$ in Figure 4.6. Similarly, we obtain the lines labeled $EV(d_2)$ and $EV(d_3)$; these lines are the graphs of equations (4.7) and (4.8), respectively.

Figure 4.6 shows how the recommended decision changes as p, the probability of the strong demand state of nature (s_1), changes. Note that for small values of p, decision alternative d_1 (small complex) provides the largest expected value and is thus the recommended decision. When the value of p increases to a certain point, decision alternative d_2 (medium complex) provides the largest expected value and is the recommended decision. Finally, for large values of p, decision alternative d_3 (large complex) becomes the recommended decision.

The value of p for which the expected values of d_1 and d_2 are equal is the value of p corresponding to the intersection of the $EV(d_1)$ and the $EV(d_2)$ lines. To determine this value, we set $EV(d_1) = EV(d_2)$ and solve for the value of p:

$$\begin{aligned} p + 7 &= 9p + 5 \\ 8p &= 2 \\ p &= \frac{2}{8} = 0.25 \end{aligned}$$

FIGURE 4.6 EXPECTED VALUE FOR THE PDC DECISION ALTERNATIVES AS A FUNCTION OF p

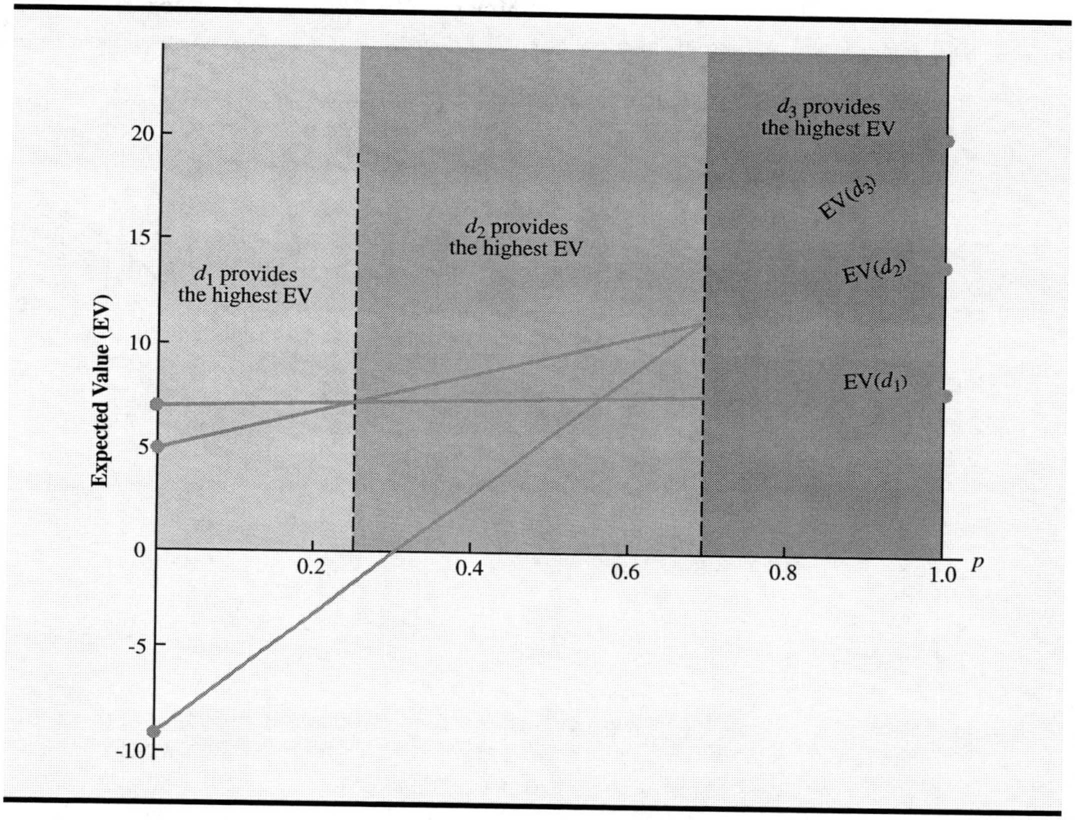

Graphical sensitivity analysis shows how changes in the probabilities for the states of nature affect the recommended decision alternative. Try Problem 8.

Hence, when $p = 0.25$, decision alternatives d_1 and d_2 provide the same expected value. Repeating this calculation for the value of p corresponding to the intersection of the EV(d_2) and EV(d_3) lines, we obtain $p = 0.70$.

Using Figure 4.6, we can conclude that decision alternative d_1 provides the largest expected value for $p \leq 0.25$, decision alternative d_2 provides the largest expected value for $0.25 \leq p \leq 0.70$, and decision alternative d_3 provides the largest expected value for $p \geq 0.70$. Because p is the probability of state of nature s_1 and $(1 - p)$ is the probability of state of nature s_2, we now have the sensitivity analysis information that tells us how changes in the state-of-nature probabilities affect the recommended decision alternative.

Sensitivity analysis calculations can also be made for the values of the payoffs. In the original PDC problem, the expected values for the three decision alternatives were as follows: EV(d_1) = 7.8, EV(d_2) = 12.2, and EV(d_3) = 14.2. Decision alternative d_3 (large complex) was recommended. Note that decision alternative d_2 with EV(d_2) = 12.2 was the second best decision alternative. Decision alternative d_3 will remain the optimal decision alternative as long as EV(d_3) is greater than or equal to the expected value of the second best decision alternative. Thus, decision alternative d_3 will remain the optimal decision alternative as long as

$$\text{EV}(d_3) \geq 12.2 \tag{4.9}$$

Let

$$S = \text{the payoff of decision alternative } d_3 \text{ when demand is strong}$$
$$W = \text{the payoff of decision alternative } d_3 \text{ when demand is weak}$$

Using $P(s_1) = 0.8$ and $P(s_2) = 0.2$, the general expression for EV(d_3) is

$$\text{EV}(d_3) = 0.8S + 0.2W \tag{4.10}$$

Assuming that the payoff for d_3 stays at its original value of −\$9 million when demand is weak, the large complex decision alternative will remain optimal as long as

$$\text{EV}(d_3) = 0.8S + 0.2(-9) \geq 12.2 \tag{4.11}$$

Solving for S, we have

$$\begin{aligned} 0.8S - 1.8 &\geq 12.2 \\ 0.8S &\geq 14 \\ S &\geq 17.5 \end{aligned}$$

Recall that when demand is strong, decision alternative d_3 has an estimated payoff of \$20 million. The preceding calculation shows that decision alternative d_3 will remain optimal as long as the payoff for d_3 when demand is strong is at least \$17.5 million.

Assuming that the payoff for d_3 when demand is strong stays at its original value of \$20 million, we can make a similar calculation to learn how sensitive the optimal solution is with regard to the payoff for d_3 when demand is weak. Returning to the expected value calculation of equation (4.10), we know that the large complex decision alternative will remain optimal as long as

$$\text{EV}(d_3) = 0.8(20) + 0.2W \geq 12.2 \tag{4.12}$$

Solving for W, we have

$$\begin{aligned} 16 + 0.2W &\geq 12.2 \\ 0.2W &\geq -3.8 \\ W &\geq -19 \end{aligned}$$

Recall that when demand is weak, decision alternative d_3 has an estimated payoff of −\$9 million. The preceding calculation shows that decision alternative d_3 will remain optimal as long as the payoff for d_3 when demand is weak is at least −\$19 million.

Based on this sensitivity analysis, we conclude that the payoffs for the large complex decision alternative (d_3) could vary considerably and d_3 would remain the recommended decision alternative. Thus, we conclude that the optimal solution for the PDC decision problem is not particularly sensitive to the payoffs for the large complex decision alternative.

Sensitivity analysis can assist management in deciding whether more time and effort should be spent obtaining better estimates of payoffs and probabilities.

We note, however, that this sensitivity analysis has been conducted based on only one change at a time. That is, only one payoff was changed and the probabilities for the states of nature remained $P(s_1) = 0.8$ and $P(s_2) = 0.2$. Note that similar sensitivity analysis calculations can be made for the payoffs associated with the small complex decision alternative d_1 and the medium complex decision alternative d_2. However, in these cases, decision alternative d_3 remains optimal only if the changes in the payoffs for decision alternatives d_1 and d_2 meet the requirements that $\text{EV}(d_1) \leq 14.2$ and $\text{EV}(d_2) \leq 14.2$.

NOTES AND COMMENTS

1. Some decision analysis software automatically provide the risk profiles for the optimal decision alternative. These packages also allow the user to obtain the risk profiles for other decision alternatives. After comparing the risk profiles, a decision maker may decide to select a decision alternative with a good risk profile even though the expected value of the decision alternative is not as good as the optimal decision alternative.
2. A *tornado diagram,* a graphical display, is particularly helpful when several inputs combine to determine the value of the optimal solution. By varying each input over its range of values, we obtain information about how each input affects the value of the optimal solution. To display this information, a bar is constructed for the input with the width of the bar showing how the input affects the value of the optimal solution. The widest bar corresponds to the input that is most sensitive. The bars are arranged in a graph with the widest bar at the top, resulting in a graph that has the appearance of a tornado.

4.5 DECISION ANALYSIS WITH SAMPLE INFORMATION

In applying the expected value approach, we showed how probability information about the states of nature affects the expected value calculations and thus the decision recommendation. Frequently, decision makers have preliminary or **prior probability** assessments for the states of nature that are the best probability values available at that time. However, to make the best possible decision, the decision maker may want to seek additional information about the states of nature. This new information can be used to revise or update the prior probabilities so that the final decision is based on more accurate probabilities for the states of nature. Most often, additional information is obtained through experiments designed to provide **sample information** about the states of nature. Raw material sampling, product testing, and market research studies are examples of experiments (or studies) that may enable management to revise or update the state-of-nature probabilities. These revised probabilities are called **posterior probabilities.**

Let us return to the PDC problem and assume that management is considering a six-month market research study designed to learn more about potential market acceptance of the PDC condominium project. Management anticipates that the market research study will provide one of the following two results:

1. Favorable report: A significant number of the individuals contacted express interest in purchasing a PDC condominium.
2. Unfavorable report: Very few of the individuals contacted express interest in purchasing a PDC condominium.

Influence Diagram

By introducing the possibility of conducting a market research study, the PDC problem becomes more complex. The influence diagram for the expanded PDC problem is shown in Figure 4.7. Note that the two decision nodes correspond to the research study and the

FIGURE 4.7 INFLUENCE DIAGRAM FOR THE PDC PROBLEM WITH SAMPLE INFORMATION

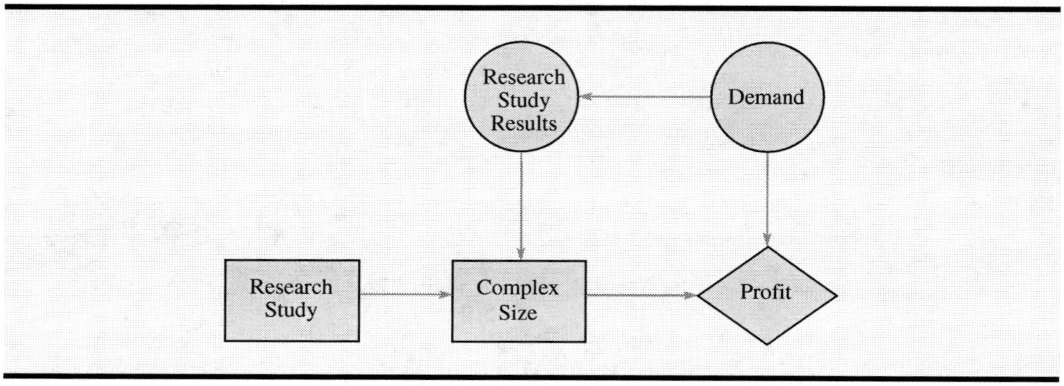

complex-size decisions. The two chance nodes correspond to the research study results and demand for the condominiums. Finally, the consequence node is the profit. From the arcs of the influence diagram, we see that demand influences both the research study results and profit. Although demand is currently unknown to PDC, some level of demand for the condominiums already exists in the Pittsburgh area. If existing demand is strong, the research study is likely to find a significant number of individuals who express an interest in purchasing a condominium. However, if the existing demand is weak, the research study is more likely to find a significant number of individuals who express little interest in purchasing a condominium. In this sense, existing demand for the condominiums will influence the research study results, and clearly, demand will have an influence upon PDC's profit.

The arc from the research study decision node to the complex-size decision node indicates that the research study decision precedes the complex-size decision. No arc spans from the research study decision node to the research study results node, because the decision to conduct the research study does not actually influence the research study results. The decision to conduct the research study makes the research study results available, but it does not influence the results of the research study. Finally, the complex-size node and the demand node both influence profit. Note that if a stated cost to conduct the research study were given, the decision to conduct the research study would also influence profit. In such a case, we would need to add an arc from the research study decision node to the profit node to show the influence that the research study cost would have on profit.

Decision Tree

The decision tree for the PDC problem with sample information shows the logical sequence for the decisions and the chance events in Figure 4.8.

First, PDC's management must decide whether the market research should be conducted. If it is conducted, PDC's management must be prepared to make a decision about the size of the condominium project if the market research report is favorable and, possibly, a different decision about the size of the condominium project if the market research report is unfavorable. In Figure 4.8, the squares are decision nodes and the circles are chance nodes. At each decision node, the branch of the tree that is taken is based on the decision made. At

FIGURE 4.8 THE PDC DECISION TREE INCLUDING THE MARKET RESEARCH STUDY

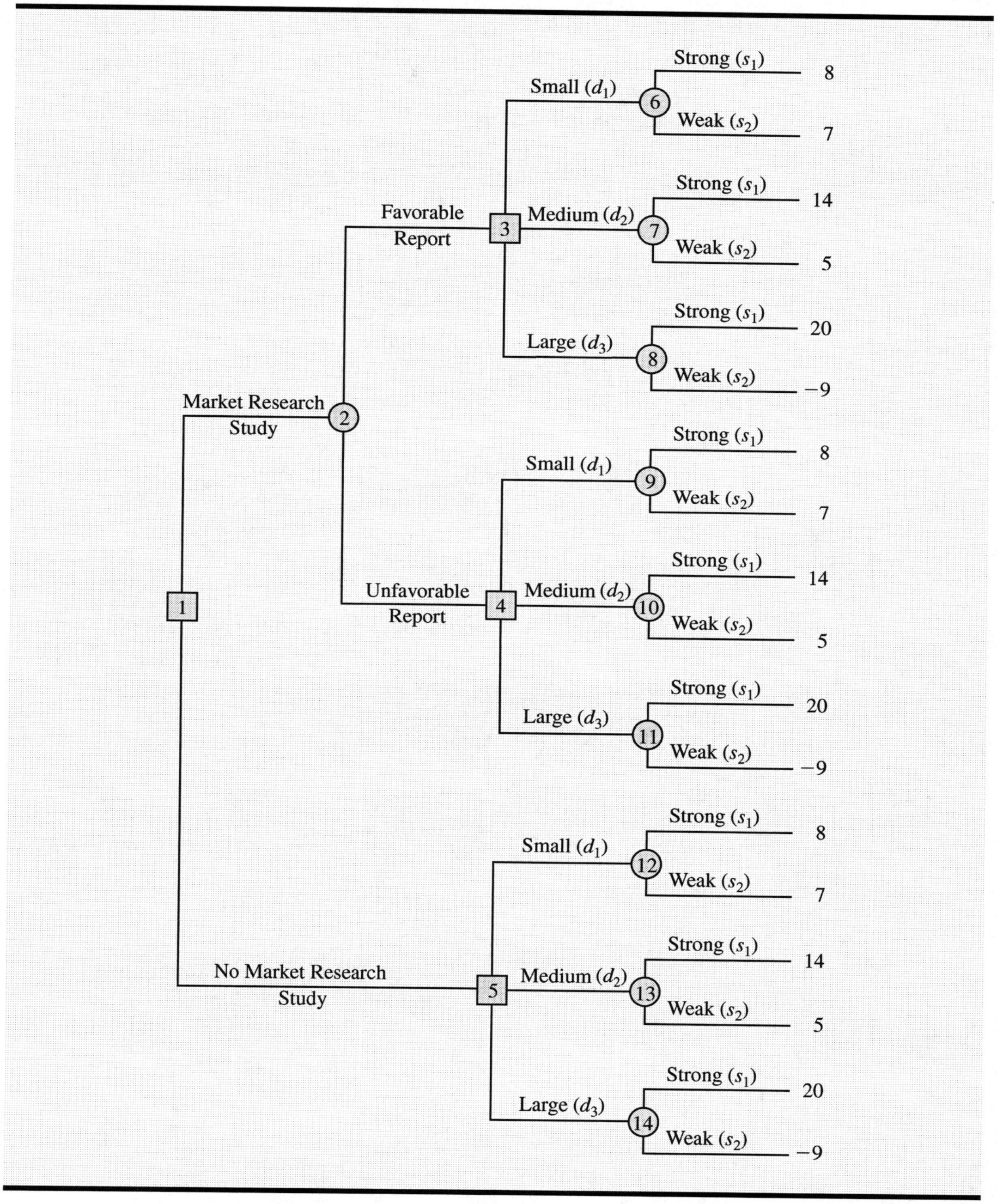

each chance node, the branch of the tree that is taken is based on probability or chance. For example, decision node 1 shows that PDC must first make the decision of whether to conduct the market research study. If the market research study is undertaken, chance node 2 indicates that both the favorable report branch and the unfavorable report branch are not under PDC's control and will be determined by chance. Node 3 is a decision node, indicating that PDC must make the decision to construct the small, medium, or large complex if the market research report is favorable. Node 4 is a decision node showing that PDC must make the decision to construct the small, medium, or large complex if the market research report is unfavorable. Node 5 is a decision node indicating that PDC must make the decision to construct the small, medium, or large complex if the market research is not undertaken. Nodes 6 to 14 are chance nodes indicating that the strong demand or weak demand state-of-nature branches will be determined by chance.

We explain in Section 4.6 how these probabilities can be developed.

Analysis of the decision tree and the choice of an optimal strategy requires that we know the branch probabilities corresponding to all chance nodes. PDC has developed the following branch probabilities.

If the market research study is undertaken

$$P(\text{Favorable report}) = 0.77$$
$$P(\text{Unfavorable report}) = 0.23$$

If the market research report is favorable

$$P(\text{Strong demand given a favorable report}) = 0.94$$
$$P(\text{Weak demand given a favorable report}) = 0.06$$

If the market research report is unfavorable

$$P(\text{Strong demand given an unfavorable report}) = 0.35$$
$$P(\text{Weak demand given an unfavorable report}) = 0.65$$

If the market research report is not undertaken, the prior probabilities are applicable.

$$P(\text{Strong demand}) = 0.80$$
$$P(\text{Weak demand}) = 0.20$$

The branch probabilities are shown on the decision tree in Figure 4.9.

Decision Strategy

A **decision strategy** is a sequence of decisions and chance outcomes where the decisions chosen depend on the yet to be determined outcomes of chance events.

The approach used to determine the optimal decision strategy is based on a backward pass through the decision tree using the following steps:

1. At chance nodes, compute the expected value by multiplying the payoff at the end of each branch by the corresponding branch probabilities.
2. At decision nodes, select the decision branch that leads to the best expected value. This expected value becomes the expected value at the decision node.

FIGURE 4.9 THE PDC DECISION TREE WITH BRANCH PROBABILITIES

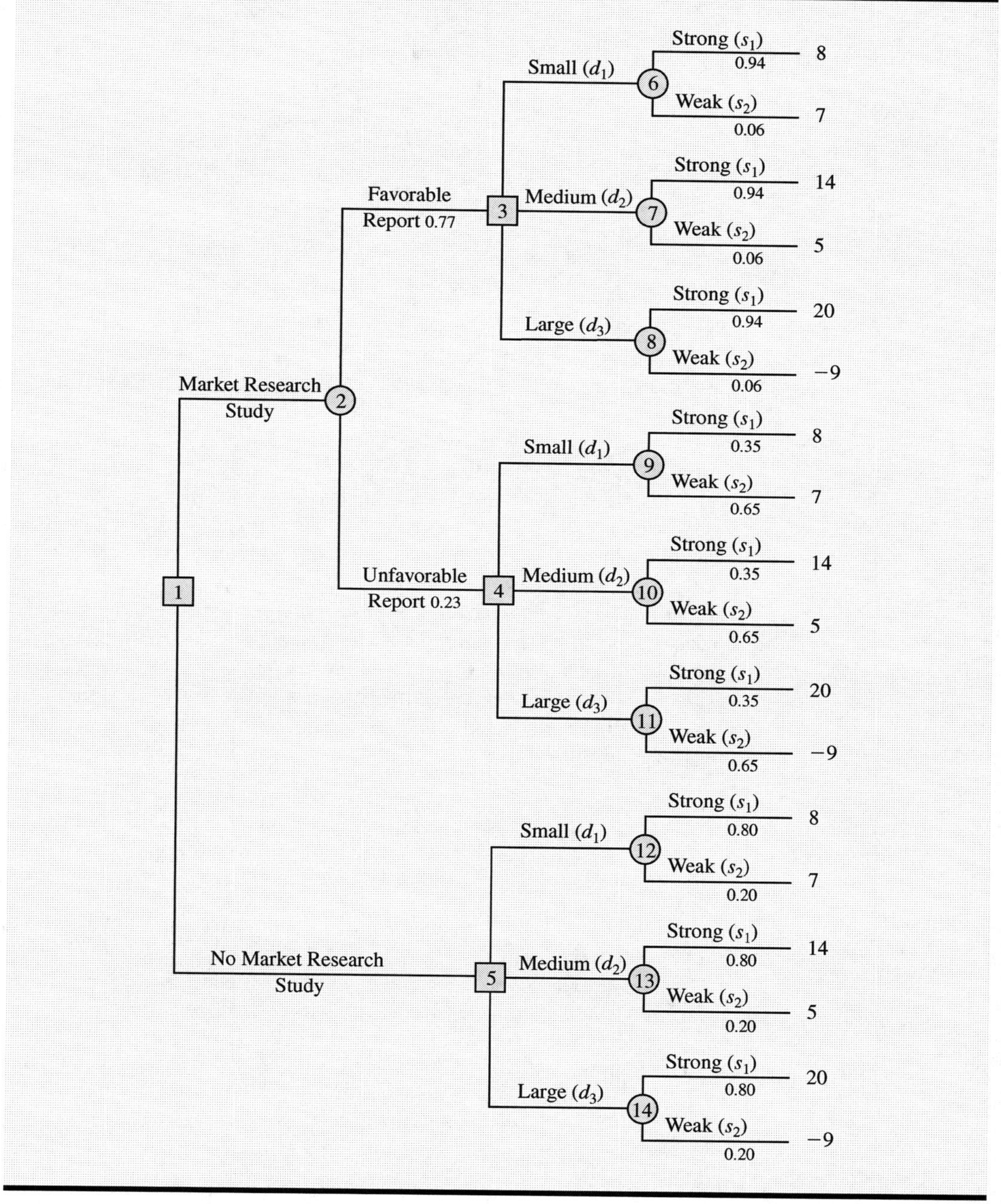

Starting the backward pass calculations by computing the expected values at chance nodes 6 to 14 provides the following results.

$$
\begin{aligned}
EV(\text{Node } 6) &= 0.94(8) + 0.06(7) = 7.94 \\
EV(\text{Node } 7) &= 0.94(14) + 0.06(5) = 13.46 \\
EV(\text{Node } 8) &= 0.94(20) + 0.06(-9) = 18.26 \\
EV(\text{Node } 9) &= 0.35(8) + 0.65(7) = 7.35 \\
EV(\text{Node } 10) &= 0.35(14) + 0.65(5) = 8.15 \\
EV(\text{Node } 11) &= 0.35(20) + 0.65(-9) = 1.15 \\
EV(\text{Node } 12) &= 0.80(8) + 0.20(7) = 7.80 \\
EV(\text{Node } 13) &= 0.80(14) + 0.20(5) = 12.20 \\
EV(\text{Node } 14) &= 0.80(20) + 0.20(-9) = 14.20
\end{aligned}
$$

Figure 4.10 shows the reduced decision tree after computing expected values at these chance nodes.

Next, move to decision nodes 3, 4, and 5. For each of these nodes, we select the decision alternative branch that leads to the best expected value. For example, at node 3 we have the choice of the small complex branch with EV(Node 6) = 7.94, the medium complex branch with EV(Node 7) = 13.46, and the large complex branch with EV(Node 8) = 18.26. Thus, we select the large complex decision alternative branch and the expected value at node 3 becomes EV(Node 3) = 18.26.

For node 4, we select the best expected value from nodes 9, 10, and 11. The best decision alternative is the medium complex branch that provides EV(Node 4) = 8.15. For node 5, we select the best expected value from nodes 12, 13, and 14. The best decision alternative is the large complex branch that provides EV(Node 5) = 14.20. Figure 4.11 shows the reduced decision tree after choosing the best decisions at nodes 3, 4, and 5.

The expected value at chance node 2 can now be computed as follows:

$$
\begin{aligned}
EV(\text{Node } 2) &= 0.77EV(\text{Node } 3) + 0.23EV(\text{Node } 4) \\
&= 0.77(18.26) + 0.23(8.15) = 15.93
\end{aligned}
$$

This calculation reduces the decision tree to one involving only the two decision branches from node 1 (see Figure 4.12).

Finally, the decision can be made at decision node 1 by selecting the best expected values from nodes 2 and 5. This action leads to the decision alternative to conduct the market research study, which provides an overall expected value of 15.93.

The optimal decision for PDC is to conduct the market research study and then carry out the following decision strategy:

If the market research is favorable, construct the large condominium complex.

If the market research is unfavorable, construct the medium condominium complex.

Problem 16 will test your ability to develop an optimal decision strategy.

The analysis of the PDC decision tree describes the methods that can be used to analyze more complex sequential decision problems. First, draw a decision tree consisting of decision and chance nodes and branches that describe the sequential nature of the problem. Determine the probabilities for all chance outcomes. Then, by working backward through the tree, compute expected values at all chance nodes and select the best decision branch at all decision nodes. The sequence of optimal decision branches determines the optimal decision strategy for the problem.

FIGURE 4.10 PDC DECISION TREE AFTER COMPUTING EXPECTED VALUES AT CHANCE NODES 6 TO 14

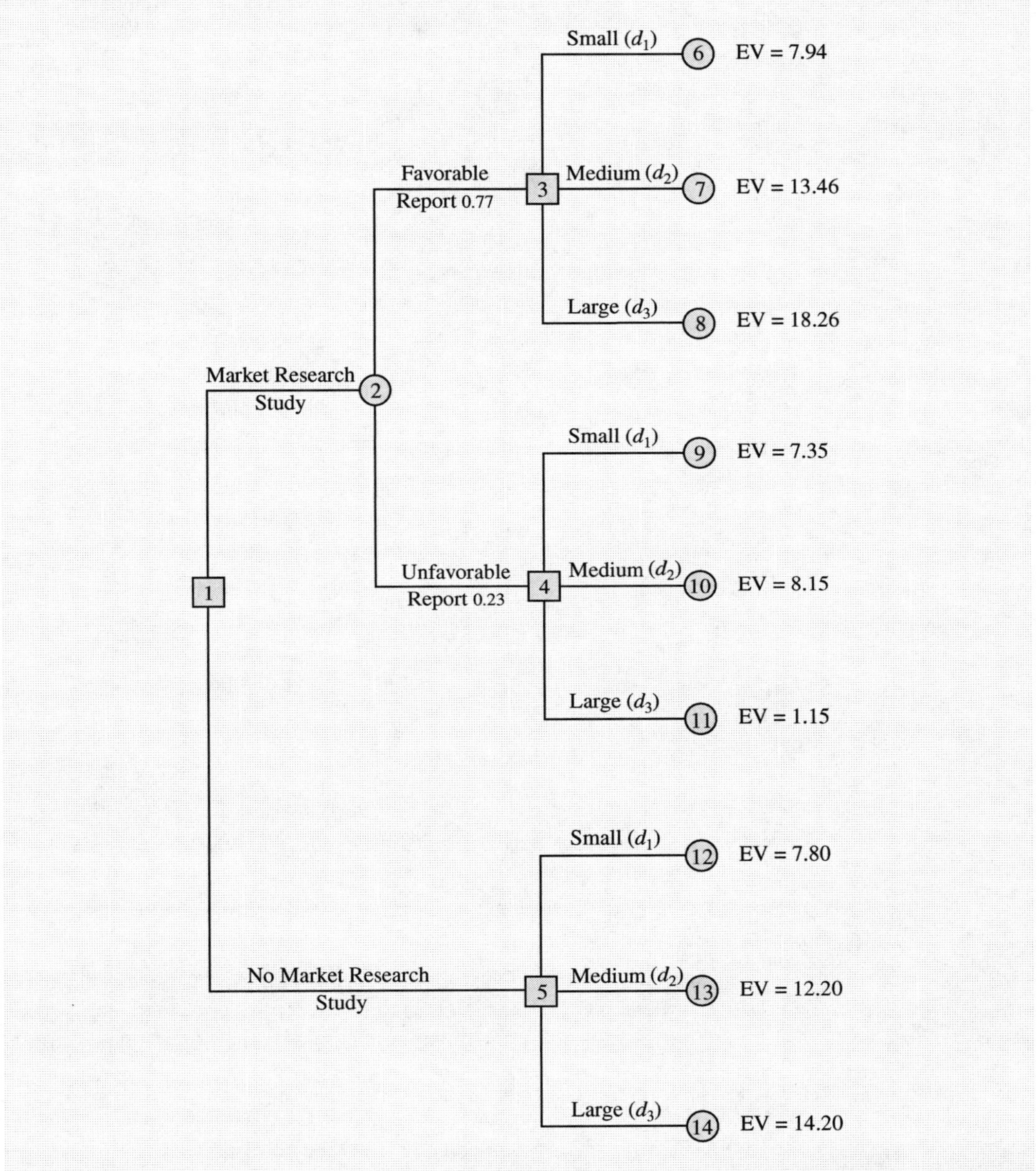

FIGURE 4.11 PDC DECISION TREE AFTER CHOOSING BEST DECISIONS AT NODES 3, 4, AND 5

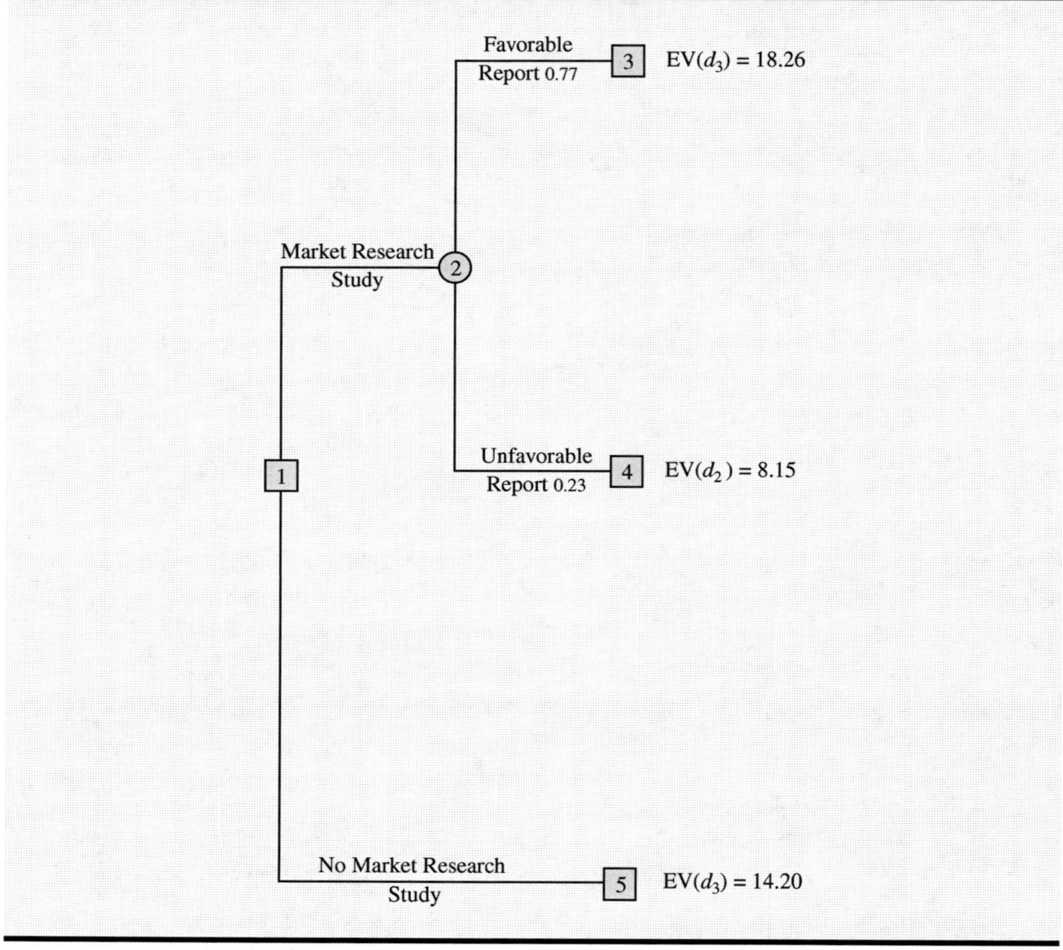

The Q.M. in Action, New Drug Decision Analysis at Bayer Pharmaceuticals, describes how an extension of the decision analysis principles presented in this section enabled Bayer to make decisions about the development and marketing of a new drug.

Risk Profile

Figure 4.13 provides a reduced decision tree showing only the sequence of decision alternatives and chance events for the PDC optimal decision strategy. By implementing the optimal decision strategy, PDC will obtain one of the four payoffs shown at the terminal branches of the decision tree. Recall that a risk profile shows the possible payoffs with their associated probabilities. Thus, in order to construct a risk profile for the optimal decision strategy we will need to compute the probability for each of the four payoffs.

Note that each payoff results from a sequence of branches leading from node 1 to the payoff. For instance, the payoff of $20 million is obtained by following the upper branch from node 1, the upper branch from node 2, the lower branch from node 3, and the upper branch from node 8. The probability of following that sequence of branches can be found by multiplying the probabilities for the branches from the chance nodes in the sequence.

FIGURE 4.12 PDC DECISION TREE REDUCED TO TWO DECISION BRANCHES

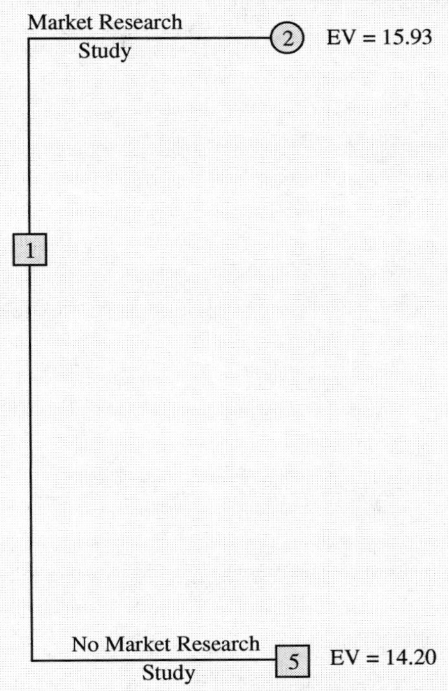

Q.M. IN ACTION

NEW DRUG DECISION ANALYSIS AT BAYER PHARMACEUTICALS*

Drug development in the United States requires substantial investment and is very risky. It takes nearly 15 years to research and develop a new drug. The Bayer Biological Products (BP) group used decision analysis to evaluate the potential for a new blood-clot-busting drug. An influence diagram was used to describe the complex structure of the decision analysis process. Six key yes-or-no decision nodes were identified: (1) begin preclinical development, (2) begin testing in humans, (3) continue development into phase 3, (4) continue development into phase 4, (5) file a license application with the FDA, and (6) launch the new drug into the marketplace. More than 50 chance nodes appeared in the influence diagram. The chance nodes showed how uncertainties—related to factors such as direct labor costs, process development costs, market share, tax rate, and pricing—affected the outcome. Net present value provided the consequence and the decision-making criterion.

Probability assessments were made concerning both the technical risk and market risk at each stage of the process. The resulting sequential decision tree had 1955 possible paths that led to different net present value outcomes. Cost inputs, judgments of potential outcomes, and the assignment of probabilities helped evaluate the project's potential contribution. Sensitivity analysis was used to identify key variables that would require special attention by the project team and management during the drug development process. Application of decision analysis principles allowed Bayer to make good decisions about how to develop and market the new drug.

*Based on Jeffrey S. Stonebraker, "How Bayer Makes Decisions to Develop New Drugs," *Interfaces,* no. 6 (November/December 2002): 77–90.

FIGURE 4.13 PDC DECISION TREE SHOWING ONLY BRANCHES ASSOCIATED WITH OPTIMAL DECISION STRATEGY

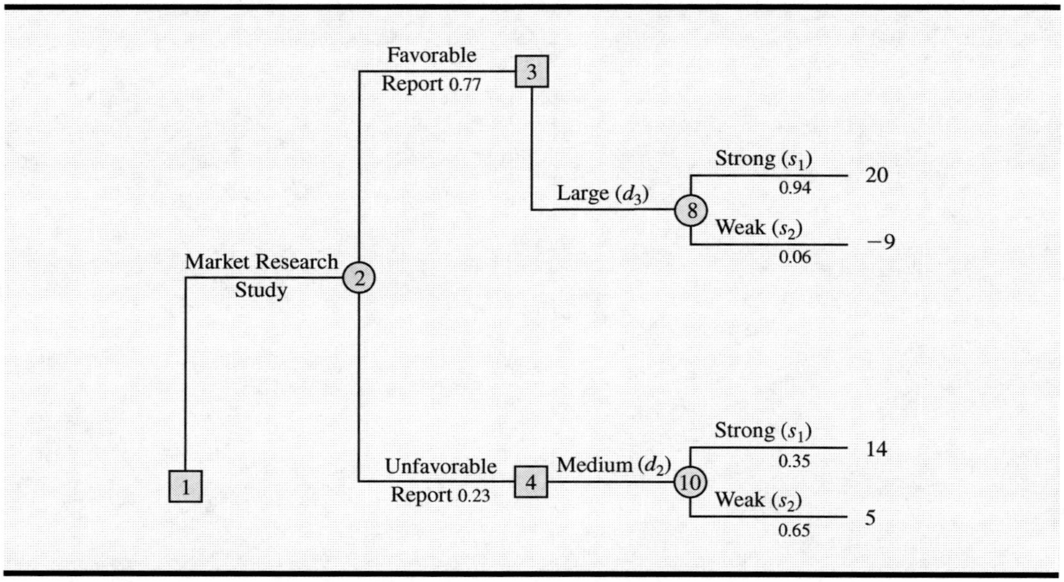

Thus, the probability of the \$20 million payoff is (0.77)(0.94) = 0.72. Similarly, the probabilities for each of the other payoffs are obtained by multiplying the probabilities for the branches from the chance nodes leading to the payoffs. Doing so, we find the probability of the −\$9 million payoff is (0.77)(0.06) = 0.05; the probability of the \$14 million payoff is (0.23)(0.35) = 0.08; and the probability of the \$5 million payoff is (0.23)(0.65) = 0.15. The following table showing the probability distribution for the payoffs for the PDC optimal decision strategy is the tabular representation of the risk profile for the optimal decision strategy.

Payoff (\$ millions)	**Probability**
−9	0.05
5	0.15
14	0.08
20	0.72
	1.00

Figure 4.14 provides a graphical representation of the risk profile. Comparing Figures 4.5 and 4.14, we see that the PDC risk profile is changed by the strategy to conduct the market research study. In fact, the use of the market research study lowered the probability of the \$9 million loss from 0.20 to 0.05. PDC's management would most likely view that change as a significant reduction in the risk associated with the condominium project.

Expected Value of Sample Information

In the PDC problem, the market research study is the sample information used to determine the optimal decision strategy. The expected value associated with the market research study is \$15.93. In Section 4.3 we showed that the best expected value if the market research study

FIGURE 4.14 RISK PROFILE FOR PDC CONDOMINIUM PROJECT WITH SAMPLE INFORMATION SHOWING PAYOFFS ASSOCIATED WITH OPTIMAL DECISION STRATEGY

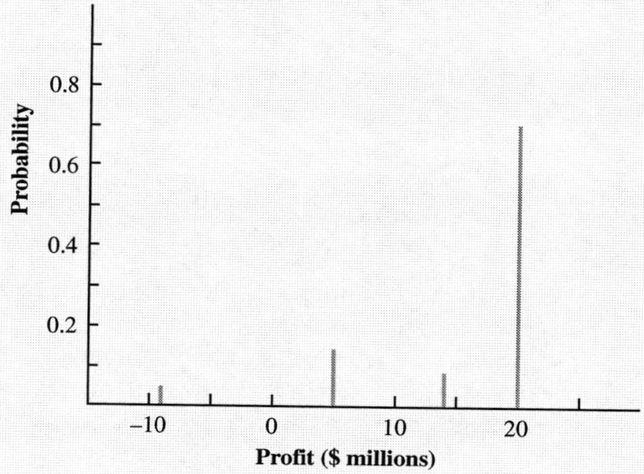

The EVSI = $1.73 million suggests PDC should be willing to pay up to $1.73 million to conduct the market research study.

is *not* undertaken is $14.20. Thus, we can conclude that the difference, $15.93 − $14.20 = $1.73, is the **expected value of sample information (EVSI).** In other words, conducting the market research study adds $1.73 million to the PDC expected value. In general, the expected value of sample information is as follows:

$$\text{EVSI} = |\text{EVwSI} - \text{EVwoSI}| \tag{4.13}$$

where

EVSI = expected value of sample information
EVwSI = expected value *with* sample information about the states of nature
EVwoSI = expected value *without* sample information about the states of nature

Note the role of the absolute value in equation (4.13). For minimization problems the expected value with sample information is always less than or equal to the expected value without sample information. In this case, EVSI is the magnitude of the difference between EVwSI and EVwoSI; thus, by taking the absolute value of the difference as shown in equation (4.13), we can handle both the maximization and minimization cases with one equation.

Efficiency of Sample Information

In Section 4.3 we showed that the expected value of perfect information (EVPI) for the PDC problem is $3.2 million. We never anticipated that the market research report would obtain perfect information, but we can use an **efficiency** measure to express the value of the market research information. With perfect information having an efficiency rating of 100 percent, the efficiency rating E for sample information is computed as follows.

$$E = \frac{\text{EVSI}}{\text{EVPI}} \times 100 \tag{4.14}$$

For the PDC problem,

$$E = \frac{1.73}{3.2} \times 100 = 54.1\%$$

In other words, the information from the market research study is 54.1 percent as efficient as perfect information.

Low efficiency ratings for sample information might lead the decision maker to look for other types of information. However, high efficiency ratings indicate that the sample information is almost as good as perfect information and that additional sources of information would not yield significantly better results.

4.6 COMPUTING BRANCH PROBABILITIES

In Section 4.5 the branch probabilities for the PDC decision tree chance nodes were specified in the problem description. No computations were required to determine these probabilities. In this section we show how **Bayes' theorem** can be used to compute branch probabilities for decision trees.

The PDC decision tree is shown again in Figure 4.15. Let

F = Favorable market research report
U = Unfavorable market research report
s_1 = Strong demand (state of nature 1)
s_2 = Weak demand (state of nature 2)

At chance node 2, we need to know the branch probabilities $P(F)$ and $P(U)$. At chance nodes 6, 7, and 8, we need to know the branch probabilities $P(s_1 \mid F)$, the probability of state of nature 1 given a favorable market research report, and $P(s_2 \mid F)$, the probability of state of nature 2 given a favorable market research report. $P(s_1 \mid F)$ and $P(s_2 \mid F)$ are referred to as *posterior probabilities* because they are conditional probabilities based on the outcome of the sample information. At chance nodes 9, 10, and 11, we need to know the branch probabilities $P(s_1 \mid U)$ and $P(s_2 \mid U)$; note that these are also posterior probabilities, denoting the probabilities of the two states of nature *given* that the market research report is unfavorable. Finally, at chance nodes 12, 13, and 14, we need the probabilities for the states of nature, $P(s_1)$ and $P(s_2)$, if the market research study is not undertaken.

In making the probability computations, we need to know PDC's assessment of the probabilities for the two states of nature, $P(s_1)$ and $P(s_2)$, which are the prior probabilities as discussed earlier. In addition, we must know the **conditional probability** of the market research outcomes (the sample information) *given* each state of nature. For example, we need to know the conditional probability of a favorable market research report given that the state of nature is strong demand for the PDC project; note that this conditional probability of F given state of nature s_1 is written $P(F \mid s_1)$. To carry out the probability calculations, we will need conditional probabilities for all sample outcomes given all states of

FIGURE 4.15 THE PDC DECISION TREE

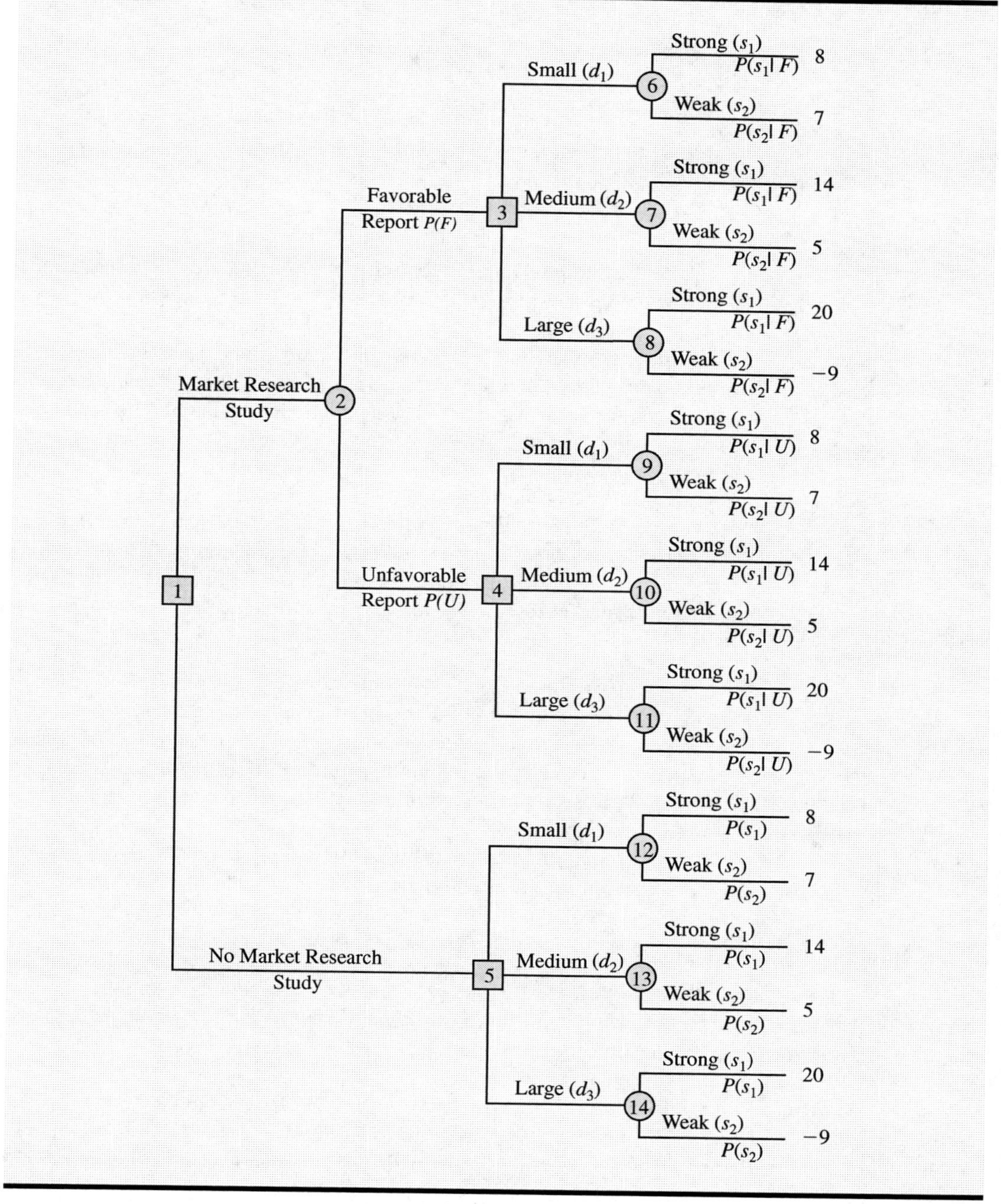

nature, that is, $P(F \mid s_1)$, $P(F \mid s_2)$, $P(U \mid s_1)$, and $P(U \mid s_2)$. In the PDC problem, we assume that the following assessments are available for these conditional probabilities.

	Market Research	
State of Nature	Favorable, F	Unfavorable, U
Strong demand, s_1	$P(F \mid s_1) = 0.90$	$P(U \mid s_1) = 0.10$
Weak demand, s_2	$P(F \mid s_2) = 0.25$	$P(U \mid s_2) = 0.75$

Note that the preceding probability assessments provide a reasonable degree of confidence in the market research study. If the true state of nature is s_1, the probability of a favorable market research report is 0.90, and the probability of an unfavorable market research report is 0.10. If the true state of nature is s_2, the probability of a favorable market research report is 0.25, and the probability of an unfavorable market research report is 0.75. The reason for a 0.25 probability of a potentially misleading favorable market research report for state of nature s_2 is that when some potential buyers first hear about the new condominium project, their enthusiasm may lead them to overstate their real interest in it. A potential buyer's initial favorable response can change quickly to a "no thank you" when later faced with the reality of signing a purchase contract and making a down payment.

In the following discussion, we present a tabular approach as a convenient method for carrying out the probability computations. The computations for the PDC problem based on a favorable market research report (F) are summarized in Table 4.7. The steps used to develop this table are as follows.

Step 1. In column 1 enter the states of nature. In column 2 enter the *prior probabilities* for the states of nature. In column 3 enter the *conditional probabilities* of a favorable market research report (F) given each state of nature.

Step 2. In column 4 compute the **joint probabilities** by multiplying the prior probability values in column 2 by the corresponding conditional probability values in column 3.

Step 3. Sum the joint probabilities in column 4 to obtain the probability of a favorable market research report, $P(F)$.

Step 4. Divide each joint probability in column 4 by $P(F) = 0.77$ to obtain the revised or *posterior probabilities,* $P(s_1 \mid F)$ and $P(s_2 \mid F)$.

Table 4.7 shows that the probability of obtaining a favorable market research report is $P(F) = 0.77$. In addition, $P(s_1 \mid F) = 0.94$ and $P(s_2 \mid F) = 0.06$. In particular, note that a

TABLE 4.7 BRANCH PROBABILITIES FOR THE PDC CONDOMINIUM PROJECT BASED ON A FAVORABLE MARKET RESEARCH REPORT

States of Nature s_j	Prior Probabilities $P(s_j)$	Conditional Probabilities $P(F \mid s_j)$	Joint Probabilities $P(F \cap s_j)$	Posterior Probabilities $P(s_j \mid F)$
s_1	0.8	0.90	0.72	0.94
s_2	0.2	0.25	0.05	0.06
	1.0		$P(F) = 0.77$	1.00

TABLE 4.8 BRANCH PROBABILITIES FOR THE PDC CONDOMINIUM PROJECT BASED ON AN UNFAVORABLE MARKET RESEARCH REPORT

States of Nature s_j	Prior Probabilities $P(s_j)$	Conditional Probabilities $P(U \mid s_j)$	Joint Probabilities $P(U \cap s_j)$	Posterior Probabilities $P(s_j \mid U)$
s_1	0.8	0.10	0.08	0.35
s_2	0.2	0.75	0.15	0.65
	1.0		$P(U) = 0.23$	1.00

favorable market research report will prompt a revised or posterior probability of 0.94 that the market demand of the condominium will be strong, s_1.

The tabular probability computation procedure must be repeated for each possible sample information outcome. Thus, Table 4.8 shows the computations of the branch probabilities of the PDC problem based on an unfavorable market research report. Note that the probability of obtaining an unfavorable market research report is $P(U) = 0.23$. If an unfavorable report is obtained, the posterior probability of a strong market demand, s_1, is 0.35 and of a weak market demand, s_2, is 0.65. The branch probabilities from Tables 4.7 and 4.8 were shown on the PDC decision tree in Figure 4.9.

Problem 23 asks you to compute the posterior probabilities.

The discussion in this section shows an underlying relationship between the probabilities on the various branches in a decision tree. To assume different prior probabilities, $P(s_1)$ and $P(s_2)$, without determining how these changes would alter $P(F)$ and $P(U)$, as well as the posterior probabilities $P(s_1 \mid F)$, $P(s_2 \mid F)$, $P(s_1 \mid U)$, and $P(s_2 \mid U)$, would be inappropriate.

The Q.M. in Action, Medical Screening Test at Duke University Medical Center, shows how posterior probability information and decision analysis helped management understand the risks and costs associated with a new screening procedure.

Q.M. IN ACTION

MEDICAL SCREENING TEST AT DUKE UNIVERSITY MEDICAL CENTER*

A medical screening test developed at the Duke University Medical Center involved using blood samples from newborns to screen for metabolic disorders. A positive test result indicated that a deficiency was present, while a negative test result indicated that a deficiency was not present. However, it was understood that the screening test was not a perfect predictor; that is, false-positive test results as well as false-negative test results were possible. A false-positive test result meant that the test detected a deficiency when in fact no deficiency was present. This case resulted in unnecessary further testing as well as unnecessary worry for the parents of the newborn. A false-negative test result meant that the test did not detect the presence of an existing deficiency. Using probability and decision analysis, a research team analyzed the role and value of the screening test.

A decision tree with six nodes, 13 branches, and eight outcomes was used to model the screening test procedure. A decision node with the decision branches Test and No Test was placed at the start of the decision tree. Chance nodes and branches were used to describe the possible sequences of a positive test result, a negative test result, a deficiency present, and a deficiency not present.

The particular deficiency in question was rare, occurring at a rate of one case for every 250,000 newborns. Thus, the prior probability of a deficiency was $1/250{,}000 = 0.000004$. Based on judgments about the probabilities of false-positive and false-negative test results, Bayes' theorem was used to calculate the posterior probability that a newborn with a positive test result actually had a deficiency.

(continued)

This posterior probability was 0.074. Thus, while a positive test result increased the probability the newborn had a deficiency from 0.000004 to 0.074, the probability that the newborn had a deficiency was still relatively low (0.074).

The probability information was helpful to doctors in reassuring worried parents that even though further testing was recommended, the chances were greater than 90% that a deficiency was not present. After the assignment of costs to the eight possible outcomes, decision analysis showed that the decision alternative to conduct the test provided the optimal decision strategy. The expected cost criterion established the expected cost to be approximately $6 per test. Decision analysis helped provide a realistic understanding of the risks and costs associated with the screening test.

*Based on James E. Smith and Robert L. Winkler, "Casey's Problem: Interpreting and Evaluating a New Test," *Interfaces* 29, no. 3 (May/June 1999): 63–76.

SUMMARY

Decision analysis can be used to determine a recommended decision alternative or an optimal decision strategy when a decision maker is faced with an uncertain and risk-filled pattern of future events. The goal of decision analysis is to identify the best decision alternative or the optimal decision strategy given information about the uncertain events and the possible consequences or payoffs. The uncertain future events are called chance events and the outcomes of the chance events are called states of nature.

We showed how influence diagrams, payoff tables, and decision trees could be used to structure a decision problem and describe the relationships among the decisions, the chance events, and the consequences. We presented three approaches to decision making without probabilities: the optimistic approach, the conservative approach, and the minimax regret approach. When probability assessments are provided for the states of nature, the expected value approach can be used to identify the recommended decision alternative or decision strategy.

In cases where sample information about the chance events is available, a sequence of decisions has to be made. First we must decide whether to obtain the sample information. If the answer to this decision is yes, an optimal decision strategy based on the specific sample information must be developed. In this situation, decision trees and the expected value approach can be used to determine the optimal decision strategy.

Even though the expected value approach can be used to obtain a recommended decision alternative or optimal decision strategy, the payoff that actually occurs will usually have a value different from the expected value. A risk profile provides a probability distribution for the possible payoffs and can assist the decision maker in assessing the risks associated with different decision alternatives. Finally, sensitivity analysis can be conducted to determine the effect changes in the probabilities for the states of nature and changes in the values of the payoffs have on the recommended decision alternative.

Decision analysis has been widely used in practice. The Q.M. in Action, Investing in a Transmission System at Oglethorpe Power, describes the use of decision analysis to decide whether to invest in a major transmission system between Georgia and Florida.

Q.M. IN ACTION

INVESTING IN A TRANSMISSION SYSTEM AT OGLETHORPE POWER*

Oglethorpe Power Corporation (OPC) provides wholesale electrical power to consumer-owned cooperatives in the state of Georgia. Florida Power Corporation proposed that OPC join in the building of a major transmission line from Georgia to Florida. Deciding whether to become involved in the building of the transmission line was a major decision for OPC because it would involve the commitment of substantial OPC resources. OPC worked with Applied Decision Analysis, Inc., to conduct a comprehensive decision analysis of the problem.

In the problem formulation step, three decisions were identified: (1) build a transmission line from Georgia to Florida; (2) upgrade existing transmission facilities; and (3) who would control the new facilities. Oglethorpe was faced with five chance events: (1) construction costs, (2) competition, (3) demand in Florida, (4) OPC's share of the operation, and (5) pricing. The consequence or payoff was measured in terms of dollars saved. The influence diagram for the problem had three decision nodes, five chance nodes, a consequence node, and several intermediate nodes that described intermediate calculations. The decision tree for the problem had more than 8000 paths from the starting node to the terminal branches.

An expected value analysis of the decision tree provided an optimal decision strategy for OPC. However, the risk profile for the optimal decision strategy showed that the recommended strategy was very risky and had a significant probability of increasing OPC's cost rather than providing a savings. The risk analysis led to the conclusion that more information about the competition was needed in order to reduce OPC's risk. Sensitivity analysis involving various probabilities and payoffs showed that the value of the optimal decision strategy was stable over a reasonable range of input values. The final recommendation from the decision analysis was that OPC should begin negotiations with Florida Power Corporation concerning the building of the new transmission line.

*Based on Adam Borison, "Oglethorpe Power Corporation Decides About Investing in a Major Transmission System," *Interfaces* (March/April 1995): 25–36.

GLOSSARY

Decision alternatives Options available to the decision maker.

Chance event An uncertain future event affecting the consequence, or payoff, associated with a decision.

Consequence The result obtained when a decision alternative is chosen and a chance event occurs. A measure of the consequence is often called a payoff.

States of nature The possible outcomes for chance events that affect the payoff associated with a decision alternative.

Influence diagram A graphical device that shows the relationship among decisions, chance events, and consequences for a decision problem.

Node An intersection or junction point of an influence diagram or a decision tree.

Decision nodes Nodes indicating points where a decision is made.

Chance nodes Nodes indicating points where an uncertain event will occur.

Consequence nodes Nodes of an influence diagram indicating points where a payoff will occur.

Payoff A measure of the consequence of a decision such as profit, cost, or time. Each combination of a decision alternative and a state of nature has an associated payoff (consequence).

Payoff table A tabular representation of the payoffs for a decision problem.

Decision tree A graphical representation of the decision problem that shows the sequential nature of the decision-making process.

Branch Lines showing the alternatives from decision nodes and the outcomes from chance nodes.

Optimistic approach An approach to choosing a decision alternative without using probabilities. For a maximization problem, it leads to choosing the decision alternative corresponding to the largest payoff; for a minimization problem, it leads to choosing the decision alternative corresponding to the smallest payoff.

Conservative approach An approach to choosing a decision alternative without using probabilities. For a maximization problem, it leads to choosing the decision alternative that maximizes the minimum payoff; for a minimization problem, it leads to choosing the decision alternative that minimizes the maximum payoff.

Minimax regret approach An approach to choosing a decision alternative without using probabilities. For each alternative, the maximum regret is computed, which leads to choosing the decision alternative that minimizes the maximum regret.

Opportunity loss, or regret The amount of loss (lower profit or higher cost) from not making the best decision for each state of nature.

Expected value approach An approach to choosing a decision alternative based on the expected value of each decision alternative. The recommended decision alternative is the one that provides the best expected value.

Expected value (EV) For a chance node, it is the weighted average of the payoffs. The weights are the state-of-nature probabilities.

Expected value of perfect information (EVPI) The expected value of information that would tell the decision maker exactly which state of nature is going to occur (i.e., perfect information).

Risk analysis The study of the possible payoffs and probabilities associated with a decision alternative or a decision strategy.

Sensitivity analysis The study of how changes in the probability assessments for the states of nature or changes in the payoffs affect the recommended decision alternative.

Risk profile The probability distribution of the possible payoffs associated with a decision alternative or decision strategy.

Prior probabilities The probabilities of the states of nature prior to obtaining sample information.

Sample information New information obtained through research or experimentation that enables an updating or revision of the state-of-nature probabilities.

Posterior (revised) probabilities The probabilities of the states of nature after revising the prior probabilities based on sample information.

Decision strategy A strategy involving a sequence of decisions and chance outcomes to provide the optimal solution to a decision problem.

Expected value of sample information (EVSI) The difference between the expected value of an optimal strategy based on sample information and the "best" expected value without any sample information.

Efficiency The ratio of EVSI to EVPI as a percentage; perfect information is 100% efficient.

Bayes' theorem A theorem that enables the use of sample information to revise prior probabilities.

Conditional probabilities The probability of one event given the known outcome of a (possibly) related event.

Joint probabilities The probabilities of both sample information and a particular state of nature occurring simultaneously.

PROBLEMS

SELF test

1. The following payoff table shows profit for a decision analysis problem with two decision alternatives and three states of nature.

Decision Alternative	State of Nature s_1	s_2	s_3
d_1	250	100	25
d_2	100	100	75

   a. Construct a decision tree for this problem.
   b. If the decision maker knows nothing about the probabilities of the three states of nature, what is the recommended decision using the optimistic, conservative, and minimax regret approaches?

2. Suppose that a decision maker faced with four decision alternatives and four states of nature develops the following profit payoff table.

Decision Alternative	State of Nature s_1	s_2	s_3	s_4
d_1	14	9	10	5
d_2	11	10	8	7
d_3	9	10	10	11
d_4	8	10	11	13

   a. If the decision maker knows nothing about the probabilities of the four states of nature, what is the recommended decision using the optimistic, conservative, and minimax regret approaches?
   b. Which approach do you prefer? Explain. Is establishing the most appropriate approach before analyzing the problem important for the decision maker? Explain.
   c. Assume that the payoff table provides *cost* rather than profit payoffs. What is the recommended decision using the optimistic, conservative, and minimax regret approaches?

SELF test

3. Southland Corporation's decision to produce a new line of recreational products resulted in the need to construct either a small plant or a large plant. The best selection of plant size depends on how the marketplace reacts to the new product line. To conduct an analysis, marketing management has decided to view the possible long-run demand as either low, medium, or high. The following payoff table shows the projected profit in millions of dollars:

Plant Size	Long-Run Demand Low	Medium	High
Small	150	200	200
Large	50	200	500

a. What is the decision to be made, and what is the chance event for Southland's problem?
b. Construct an influence diagram.
c. Construct a decision tree.
d. Recommend a decision based on the use of the optimistic, conservative, and minimax regret approaches.

4. Amy Lloyd is interested in leasing a new Saab and has contacted three automobile dealers for pricing information. Each dealer offered Amy a closed-end 36-month lease with no down payment due at the time of signing. Each lease includes a monthly charge and a mileage allowance. Additional miles receive a surcharge on a per-mile basis. The monthly lease cost, the mileage allowance, and the cost for additional miles follow:

Dealer	Monthly Cost	Mileage Allowance	Cost per Additional Mile
Forno Saab	$299	36,000	$0.15
Midtown Motors	$310	45,000	$0.20
Hopkins Automotive	$325	54,000	$0.15

Amy decided to choose the lease option that will minimize her total 36-month cost. The difficulty is that Amy is not sure how many miles she will drive over the next three years. For purposes of this decision she believes it is reasonable to assume that she will drive 12,000 miles per year, 15,000 miles per year, or 18,000 miles per year. With this assumption Amy estimated her total costs for the three lease options. For example, she figures that the Forno Saab lease will cost her $10,764 if she drives 12,000 miles per year, $12,114 if she drives 15,000 miles per year, or $13,464 if she drives 18,000 miles per year.

a. What is the decision, and what is the chance event?
b. Construct a payoff table for Amy's problem.
c. If Amy has no idea which of the three mileage assumptions is most appropriate, what is the recommended decision (leasing option) using the optimistic, conservative, and minimax regret approaches?
d. Suppose that the probabilities that Amy drives 12,000, 15,000, and 18,000 miles per year are 0.5, 0.4, and 0.1, respectively. What option should Amy choose using the expected value approach?
e. Develop a risk profile for the decision selected in part (d). What is the most likely cost, and what is its probability?
f. Suppose that after further consideration, Amy concludes that the probabilities that she will drive 12,000, 15,000, and 18,000 miles per year are 0.3, 0.4, and 0.3, respectively. What decision should Amy make using the expected value approach?

SELF test

5. The following profit payoff table was presented in Problem 1. Suppose that the decision maker obtained the probability assessments $P(s_1) = 0.65$, $P(s_2) = 0.15$, and $P(s_3) = 0.20$. Use the expected value approach to determine the optimal decision.

	State of Nature		
Decision Alternative	s_1	s_2	s_3
d_1	250	100	25
d_2	100	100	75

6. Investment Advisors estimated the stock market returns for four market segments: computers, financial, manufacturing, and pharmaceuticals. Annual return projections vary depending on whether the general economic conditions are improving, stable, or declining. The anticipated annual return percentages for each market segment under each economic condition are as follows:

	Economic Condition		
Market Segment	**Improving**	**Stable**	**Declining**
Computers	10	2	−4
Financial	8	5	−3
Manufacturing	6	4	−2
Pharmaceuticals	6	5	−1

a. Assume that an individual investor wants to select one market segment for a new investment. A forecast shows stable to declining economic conditions with the following probabilities: improving (0.2), stable (0.5), and declining (0.3). What is the preferred market segment for the investor, and what is the expected return percentage?

b. At a later date, a revised forecast shows a potential for an improvement in economic conditions. New probabilities are as follows: improving (0.4), stable (0.4), and declining (0.2). What is the preferred market segment for the investor based on these new probabilities? What is the expected return percentage?

SELF test

7. Hudson Corporation is considering three options for managing its data processing operation: continuing with its own staff, hiring an outside vendor to do the managing (referred to as *outsourcing*), or using a combination of its own staff and an outside vendor. The cost of the operation depends on future demand. The annual cost of each option (in thousands of dollars) depends on demand as follows.

	Demand		
Staffing Options	**High**	**Medium**	**Low**
Own staff	650	650	600
Outside vendor	900	600	300
Combination	800	650	500

a. If the demand probabilities are 0.2, 0.5, and 0.3, which decision alternative will minimize the expected cost of the data processing operation? What is the expected annual cost associated with that recommendation?

b. Construct a risk profile for the optimal decision in part (a). What is the probability of the cost exceeding $700,000?

SELF test

8. The following payoff table shows the profit for a decision problem with two states of nature and two decision alternatives.

	State of Nature	
Decision Alternative	s_1	s_2
d_1	10	1
d_2	4	3

a. Use graphical sensitivity analysis to determine the range of probabilities of state of nature s_1 for which each of the decision alternatives has the largest expected value.
b. Suppose $P(s_1) = 0.2$ and $P(s_2) = 0.8$. What is the best decision using the expected value approach?
c. Perform sensitivity analysis on the payoffs for decision alternative d_1. Assume the probabilities are as given in part (b) and find the range of payoffs under states of nature s_1 and s_2 that will keep the solution found in part (b) optimal. Is the solution more sensitive to the payoff under state of nature s_1 or s_2?

9. Myrtle Air Express decided to offer direct service from Cleveland to Myrtle Beach. Management must decide between a full-price service using the company's new fleet of jet aircraft and a discount service using smaller capacity commuter planes. It is clear that the best choice depends on the market reaction to the service Myrtle Air offers. Management developed estimates of the contribution to profit for each type of service based upon two possible levels of demand for service to Myrtle Beach: strong and weak. The following table shows the estimated quarterly profits (in thousands of dollars).

	Demand for Service	
Service	**Strong**	**Weak**
Full price	\$960	−\$490
Discount	\$670	\$320

a. What is the decision to be made, what is the chance event, and what is the consequence for this problem? How many decision alternatives are there? How many outcomes are there for the chance event?
b. If nothing is known about the probabilities of the chance outcomes, what is the recommended decision using the optimistic, conservative, and minimax regret approaches?
c. Suppose that management of Myrtle Air Express believes that the probability of strong demand is 0.7 and the probability of weak demand is 0.3. Use the expected value approach to determine an optimal decision.
d. Suppose that the probability of strong demand is 0.8 and the probability of weak demand is 0.2. What is the optimal decision using the expected value approach?
e. Use graphical sensitivity analysis to determine the range of demand probabilities for which each of the decision alternatives has the largest expected value.

10. Video Tech is considering marketing one of two new video games for the coming holiday season: Battle Pacific or Space Pirates. Battle Pacific is a unique game and appears to have no competition. Estimated profits (in thousands of dollars) under high, medium, and low demand are as follows:

		Demand	
Battle Pacific	**High**	**Medium**	**Low**
Profit	\$1000	\$700	\$300
Probability	0.2	0.5	0.3

Video Tech is optimistic about its Space Pirates game. However, the concern is that profitability will be affected by a competitor's introduction of a video game viewed as similar to Space Pirates. Estimated profits (in thousands of dollars) with and without competition are as follows:

Space Pirates With Competition	High	Demand Medium	Low
Profit	$800	$400	$200
Probability	0.3	0.4	0.3

Space Pirates Without Competition	High	Demand Medium	Low
Profit	$1600	$800	$400
Probability	0.5	0.3	0.2

a. Develop a decision tree for the Video Tech problem.
b. For planning purposes, Video Tech believes there is a 0.6 probability that its competitor will produce a new game similar to Space Pirates. Given this probability of competition, the director of planning recommends marketing the Battle Pacific video game. Using expected value, what is your recommended decision?
c. Show a risk profile for your recommended decision.
d. Use sensitivity analysis to determine what the probability of competition for Space Pirates would have to be for you to change your recommended decision alternative.

11. For the Pittsburgh Development Corporation problem in Section 4.3, the decision alternative to build the large condominium complex was found to be optimal using the expected value approach. In Section 4.4 we conducted a sensitivity analysis for the payoffs associated with this decision alternative. We found that the large complex remained optimal as long as the payoff for the strong demand was greater than or equal to $17.5 million and as long as the payoff for the weak demand was greater than or equal to −$19 million.
    a. Consider the medium complex decision. How much could the payoff under strong demand increase and still keep decision alternative d_3 the optimal solution?
    b. Consider the small complex decision. How much could the payoff under strong demand increase and still keep decision alternative d_3 the optimal solution?

12. The distance from Potsdam to larger markets and limited air service have hindered the town in attracting new industry. Air Express, a major overnight delivery service, is considering establishing a regional distribution center in Potsdam. However, Air Express will not establish the center unless the length of the runway at the local airport is increased. Another candidate for new development is Diagnostic Research, Inc. (DRI), a leading producer of medical testing equipment. DRI is considering building a new manufacturing plant. Increasing the length of the runway is not a requirement for DRI, but the planning commission feels that doing so will help convince DRI to locate their new plant in Potsdam. Assuming that the town lengthens the runway, the Potsdam planning commission believes that the probabilities shown in the following table are applicable.

	DRI Plant	No DRI Plant
Air Express Center	.30	.10
No Air Express Center	.40	.20

For instance, the probability that Air Express will establish a distribution center and DRI will build a plant is .30.

The estimated annual revenue to the town, after deducting the cost of lengthening the runway, is as follows:

	DRI Plant	No DRI Plant
Air Express Center	$600,000	$150,000
No Air Express Center	$250,000	−$200,000

If the runway expansion project is not conducted, the planning commission assesses the probability DRI will locate their new plant in Potsdam at 0.6; in this case, the estimated annual revenue to the town will be $450,000. If the runway expansion project is not conducted and DRI does not locate in Potsdam, the annual revenue will be $0 since no cost will have been incurred and no revenues will be forthcoming.

a. What is the decision to be made, what is the chance event, and what is the consequence?
b. Compute the expected annual revenue associated with the decision alternative to lengthen the runway.
c. Compute the expected annual revenue associated with the decision alternative to not lengthen the runway.
d. Should the town elect to lengthen the runway? Explain.
e. Suppose that the probabilities associated with lengthening the runway were as follows:

	DRI Plant	No DRI Plant
Air Express Center	.40	.10
No Air Express Center	.30	.20

What effect, if any, would this change in the probabilities have on the recommended decision?

13. Seneca Hill Winery recently purchased land for the purpose of establishing a new vineyard. Management is considering two varieties of white grapes for the new vineyard: Chardonnay and Riesling. The Chardonnay grapes would be used to produce a dry Chardonnay wine, and the Riesling grapes would be used to produce a semi-dry Riesling wine. It takes approximately four years from the time of planting before new grapes can be harvested. This length of time creates a great deal of uncertainty concerning future demand and makes the decision concerning the type of grapes to plant difficult. Three possibilities are being considered: Chardonnay grapes only; Riesling grapes only; and both Chardonnay and Riesling grapes. Seneca management decided that for planning purposes it would be adequate to consider only two demand possibilities for each type of wine: strong or weak. With two possibilities for each type of wine it was necessary to assess four probabilities. With the help of some forecasts in industry publications management made the following probability assessments.

	Riesling Demand	
Chardonnay Demand	**Weak**	**Strong**
Weak	0.05	0.50
Strong	0.25	0.20

Revenue projections show an annual contribution to profit of $20,000 if Seneca Hill only plants Chardonnay grapes and demand is weak for Chardonnay wine, and $70,000 if they only plant Chardonnay grapes and demand is strong for Chardonnay wine. If they only plant Riesling grapes, the annual profit projection is $25,000 if demand is weak for Riesling grapes and $45,000 if demand is strong for Riesling grapes. If Seneca plants both types of grapes, the annual profit projections are shown in the following table.

	Riesling Demand	
Chardonnay Demand	**Weak**	**Strong**
Weak	$22,000	$40,000
Strong	$26,000	$60,000

a. What is the decision to be made, what is the chance event, and what is the consequence? Identify the alternatives for the decisions and the possible outcomes for the chance events.
b. Develop a decision tree.
c. Use the expected value approach to recommend which alternative Seneca Hill Winery should follow in order to maximize expected annual profit.
d. Suppose management is concerned about the probability assessments when demand for Chardonnay wine is strong. Some believe it is likely for Riesling demand to also be strong in this case. Suppose the probability of strong demand for Chardonnay and weak demand for Riesling is 0.05 and that the probability of strong demand for Chardonnay and strong demand for Riesling is 0.40. How does this change the recommended decision? Assume that the probabilities when Chardonnay demand is weak are still 0.05 and 0.50.
e. Other members of the management team expect the Chardonnay market to become saturated at some point in the future, causing a fall in prices. Suppose that the annual profit projections fall to $50,000 when demand for Chardonnay is strong and Chardonnay grapes only are planted. Using the original probability assessments, determine how this change would affect the optimal decision.

SELF test

14. The following profit payoff table was presented in Problems 1 and 5.

	State of Nature		
Decision Alternative	s_1	s_2	s_3
d_1	250	100	25
d_2	100	100	75

The probabilities for the states of nature are $P(s_1) = 0.65$, $P(s_2) = 0.15$, and $P(s_3) = 0.20$.
a. What is the optimal decision strategy if perfect information were available?
b. What is the expected value for the decision strategy developed in part (a)?
c. Using the expected value approach, what is the recommended decision without perfect information? What is its expected value?
d. What is the expected value of perfect information?

15. The Lake Placid Town Council decided to build a new community center to be used for conventions, concerts, and other public events, but considerable controversy surrounds the appropriate size. Many influential citizens want a large center that would be a showcase for the area. But the mayor feels that if demand does not support such a center, the com-

munity will lose a large amount of money. To provide structure for the decision process, the council narrowed the building alternatives to three sizes: small, medium, and large. Everybody agreed that the critical factor in choosing the best size is the number of people who will want to use the new facility. A regional planning consultant provided demand estimates under three scenarios: worst case, base case, and best case. The worst-case scenario corresponds to a situation in which tourism drops significantly; the base-case scenario corresponds to a situation in which Lake Placid continues to attract visitors at current levels; and the best-case scenario corresponds to a significant increase in tourism. The consultant has provided probability assessments of 0.10, 0.60, and 0.30 for the worst-case, base-case, and best-case scenarios, respectively.

The town council suggested using net cash flow over a five-year planning horizon as the criterion for deciding on the best size. The following projections of net cash flow (in thousands of dollars) for a five-year planning horizon have been developed. All costs, including the consultant's fee, have been included.

	Demand Scenario		
Center Size	Worst Case	Base Case	Best Case
Small	400	500	660
Medium	−250	650	800
Large	−400	580	990

a. What decision should Lake Placid make using the expected value approach?
b. Construct risk profiles for the medium and large alternatives. Given the mayor's concern over the possibility of losing money and the result of part (a), which alternative would you recommend?
c. Compute the expected value of perfect information. Do you think it would be worth trying to obtain additional information concerning which scenario is likely to occur?
d. Suppose the probability of the worst-case scenario increases to 0.2, the probability of the base-case scenario decreases to 0.5, and the probability of the best-case scenario remains at 0.3. What effect, if any, would these changes have on the decision recommendation?
e. The consultant has suggested that an expenditure of $150,000 on a promotional campaign over the planning horizon will effectively reduce the probability of the worst-case scenario to zero. If the campaign can be expected to also increase the probability of the best-case scenario to 0.4, is it a good investment?

SELF test

16. Consider a variation of the PDC decision tree shown in Figure 4.9. The company must first decide whether to undertake the market research study. If the market research study is conducted, the outcome will either be favorable (F) or unfavorable (U). Assume there are only two decision alternatives d_1 and d_2 and two states of nature s_1 and s_2. The payoff table showing profit is as follows:

	State of Nature	
Decision Alternative	s_1	s_2
d_1	100	300
d_2	400	200

a. Show the decision tree.
b. Using the following probabilities, what is the optimal decision strategy?

$$P(F) = 0.56 \quad P(s_1 \mid F) = 0.57 \quad P(s_1 \mid U) = 0.18 \quad P(s_1) = 0.40$$
$$P(U) = 0.44 \quad P(s_2 \mid F) = 0.43 \quad P(s_2 \mid U) = 0.82 \quad P(s_2) = 0.60$$

17. Hemmingway, Inc., is considering a \$5 million research and development (R&D) project. Profit projections appear promising, but Hemmingway's president is concerned because the probability that the R&D project will be successful is only 0.50. Secondly, the president knows that even if the project is successful, it will require that the company build a new production facility at a cost of \$20 million in order to manufacture the product. If the facility is built, uncertainty remains about the demand and thus uncertainty about the profit that will be realized. Another option is that if the R&D project is successful, the company could sell the rights to the product for an estimated \$25 million. Under this option, the company would not build the \$20 million production facility.

The decision tree is shown in Figure 4.16. The profit projection for each outcome is shown at the end of the branches. For example, the revenue projection for the high demand outcome is \$59 million. However, the cost of the R&D project (\$5 million) and the cost of the production facility (\$20 million) show the profit of this outcome to be \$59 − \$5 − \$20 = \$34 million. Branch probabilities are also shown for the chance events.

a. Analyze the decision tree to determine whether the company should undertake the R&D project. If it does, and if the R&D project is successful, what should the company do? What is the expected value of your strategy?
b. What must the selling price be for the company to consider selling the rights to the product?
c. Develop a risk profile for the optimal strategy.

FIGURE 4.16 DECISION TREE FOR HEMMINGWAY, INC.

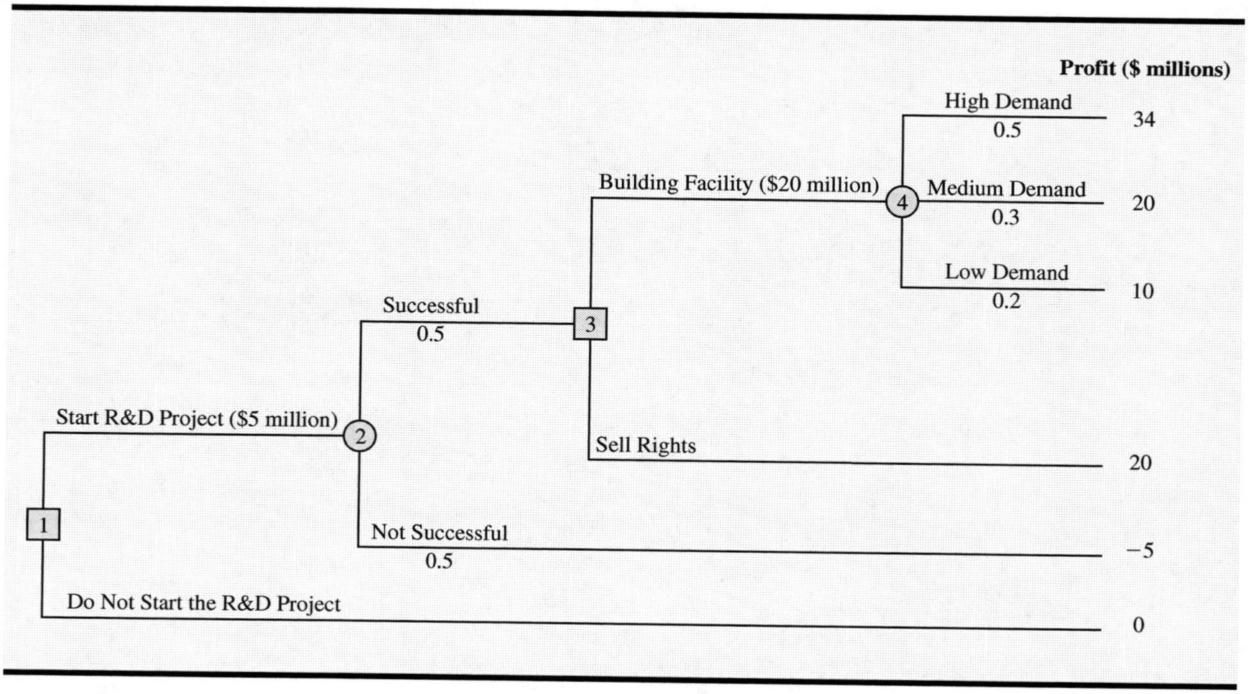

18. Dante Development Corporation is considering bidding on a contract for a new office building complex. Figure 4.17 shows the decision tree prepared by one of Dante's analysts. At node 1, the company must decide whether to bid on the contract. The cost of preparing the bid is $200,000. The upper branch from node 2 shows that the company has a 0.8 probability of winning the contract if it submits a bid. If the company wins the bid, it will have to pay $2,000,000 to become a partner in the project. Node 3 shows that the company will then consider doing a market research study to forecast demand for the office units prior to beginning construction. The cost of this study is $150,000. Node 4 is a chance node showing the possible outcomes of the market research study.

    Nodes 5, 6, and 7 are similar in that they are the decision nodes for Dante to either build the office complex or sell the rights in the project to another developer. The decision to build the complex will result in an income of $5,000,000 if demand is high and $3,000,000 if demand is moderate. If Dante chooses to sell its rights in the project to another developer, income from the sale is estimated to be $3,500,000. The probabilities shown at nodes 4, 8, and 9 are based on the projected outcomes of the market research study.

    a. Verify Dante's profit projections shown at the ending branches of the decision tree by calculating the payoffs of $2,650,000 and $650,000 for first two outcomes.
    b. What is the optimal decision strategy for Dante, and what is the expected profit for this project?
    c. What would the cost of the market research study have to be before Dante would change its decision about the market research study?
    d. Develop a risk profile for Dante.

19. Hale's TV Productions is considering producing a pilot for a comedy series in the hope of selling it to a major television network. The network may decide to reject the series, but it may also decide to purchase the rights to the series for either one or two years. At this point

FIGURE 4.17 DECISION TREE FOR THE DANTE DEVELOPMENT CORPORATION

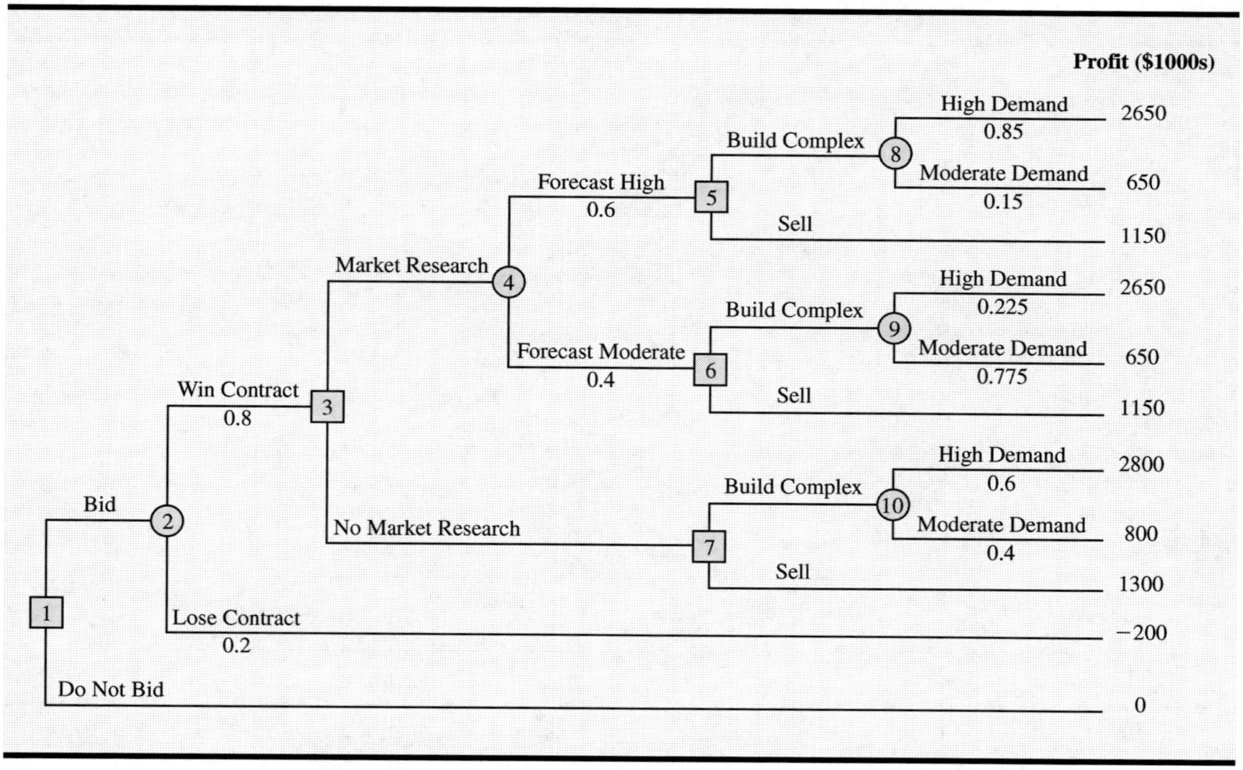

in time, Hale may either produce the pilot and wait for the network's decision or transfer the rights for the pilot and series to a competitor for \$100,000. Hale's decision alternatives and profits (in thousands of dollars) are as follows:

	State of Nature		
Decision Alternative	**Reject, s_1**	**1 Year, s_2**	**2 Years, s_3**
Produce pilot, d_1	−100	50	150
Sell to competitor, d_2	100	100	100

The probabilities for the states of nature are $P(s_1) = 0.20$, $P(s_2) = 0.30$, and $P(s_3) = 0.50$. For a consulting fee of \$5000, an agency will review the plans for the comedy series and indicate the overall chances of a favorable network reaction to the series. Assume that the agency review will result in a favorable (F) or an unfavorable (U) review and that the following probabilities are relevant.

$$P(F) = 0.69 \qquad P(s_1 \mid F) = 0.09 \qquad P(s_1 \mid U) = 0.45$$
$$P(U) = 0.31 \qquad P(s_2 \mid F) = 0.26 \qquad P(s_2 \mid U) = 0.39$$
$$P(s_3 \mid F) = 0.65 \qquad P(s_3 \mid U) = 0.16$$

a. Construct a decision tree for this problem.
b. What is the recommended decision if the agency opinion is not used? What is the expected value?
c. What is the expected value of perfect information?
d. What is Hale's optimal decision strategy assuming the agency's information is used?
e. What is the expected value of the agency's information?
f. Is the agency's information worth the \$5000 fee? What is the maximum that Hale should be willing to pay for the information?
g. What is the recommended decision?

20. Embassy Publishing Company received a six-chapter manuscript for a new college textbook. The editor of the college division is familiar with the manuscript and estimated a 0.65 probability that the textbook will be successful. If successful, a profit of \$750,000 will be realized. If the company decides to publish the textbook and it is unsuccessful, a loss of \$250,000 will occur.

Before making the decision to accept or reject the manuscript, the editor is considering sending the manuscript out for review. A review process provides either a favorable (F) or unfavorable (U) evaluation of the manuscript. Past experience with the review process suggests probabilities $P(F) = 0.7$ and $P(U) = 0.3$ apply. Let s_1 = the textbook is successful, and s_2 = the textbook is unsuccessful. The editor's initial probabilities of s_1 and s_2 will be revised based on whether the review is favorable or unfavorable. The revised probabilities are as follows.

$$P(s_1 \mid F) = 0.75 \qquad P(s_1 \mid U) = 0.417$$
$$P(s_2 \mid F) = 0.25 \qquad P(s_2 \mid U) = 0.583$$

a. Construct a decision tree assuming that the company will first make the decision of whether to send the manuscript out for review and then make the decision to accept or reject the manuscript.
b. Analyze the decision tree to determine the optimal decision strategy for the publishing company.
c. If the manuscript review costs \$5000, what is your recommendation?
d. What is the expected value of perfect information? What does this EVPI suggest for the company?

21. A real estate investor has the opportunity to purchase land currently zoned residential. If the county board approves a request to rezone the property as commercial within the next year, the investor will be able to lease the land to a large discount firm that wants to open a new store on the property. However, if the zoning change is not approved, the investor will have to sell the property at a loss. Profits (in thousands of dollars) are shown in the following payoff table.

	State of Nature	
	Rezoning Approved	**Rezoning Not Approved**
Decision Alternative	s_1	s_2
Purchase, d_1	600	−200
Do not purchase, d_2	0	0

a. If the probability that the rezoning will be approved is 0.5, what decision is recommended? What is the expected profit?

b. The investor can purchase an option to buy the land. Under the option, the investor maintains the rights to purchase the land anytime during the next three months while learning more about possible resistance to the rezoning proposal from area residents. Probabilities are as follows.

Let H = High resistance to rezoning
L = Low resistance to rezoning

$P(H) = 0.55$	$P(s_1 \mid H) = 0.18$	$P(s_2 \mid H) = 0.82$
$P(L) = 0.45$	$P(s_1 \mid L) = 0.89$	$P(s_2 \mid L) = 0.11$

What is the optimal decision strategy if the investor uses the option period to learn more about the resistance from area residents before making the purchase decision?

c. If the option will cost the investor an additional $10,000, should the investor purchase the option? Why or why not? What is the maximum that the investor should be willing to pay for the option?

22. Lawson's Department Store faces a buying decision for a seasonal product for which demand can be high, medium, or low. The purchaser for Lawson's can order 1, 2, or 3 lots of the product before the season begins but cannot reorder later. Profit projections (in thousands of dollars) are shown.

	State of Nature		
	High Demand	**Medium Demand**	**Low Demand**
Decision Alternative	s_1	s_2	s_3
Order 1 lot, d_1	60	60	50
Order 2 lots, d_2	80	80	30
Order 3 lots, d_3	100	70	10

a. If the prior probabilities for the three states of nature are 0.3, 0.3, and 0.4, respectively, what is the recommended order quantity?

b. At each preseason sales meeting, the vice president of sales provides a personal opinion regarding potential demand for this product. Because of the vice president's enthusiasm and optimistic nature, the predictions of market conditions have always been either "excellent" (E) or "very good" (V). Probabilities are as follows.

$P(E) = 0.70$	$P(s_1 \mid E) = 0.34$	$P(s_1 \mid V) = 0.20$
$P(V) = 0.30$	$P(s_2 \mid E) = 0.32$	$P(s_2 \mid V) = 0.26$
	$P(s_3 \mid E) = 0.34$	$P(s_3 \mid V) = 0.54$

What is the optimal decision strategy?

c. Use the efficiency of sample information and discuss whether the firm should consider a consulting expert who could provide independent forecasts of market conditions for the product.

SELF test

23. Suppose that you are given a decision situation with three possible states of nature: s_1, s_2, and s_3. The prior probabilities are $P(s_1) = 0.2$, $P(s_2) = 0.5$, and $P(s_3) = 0.3$. With sample information I, $P(I \mid s_1) = 0.1$, $P(I \mid s_2) = 0.05$, and $P(I \mid s_3) = 0.2$. Compute the revised or posterior probabilities: $P(s_1 \mid I)$, $P(s_2 \mid I)$, and $P(s_3 \mid I)$.

24. To save on expenses, Rona and Jerry agreed to form a carpool for traveling to and from work. Rona preferred to use the somewhat longer but more consistent Queen City Avenue. Although Jerry preferred the quicker expressway, he agreed with Rona that they should take Queen City Avenue if the expressway had a traffic jam. The following payoff table provides the one-way time estimate in minutes for traveling to or from work.

	State of Nature	
Decision Alternative	Expressway Open s_1	Expressway Jammed s_2
Queen City Avenue, d_1	30	30
Expressway, d_2	25	45

Based on their experience with traffic problems, Rona and Jerry agreed on a 0.15 probability that the expressway would be jammed.

In addition, they agreed that weather seemed to affect the traffic conditions on the expressway. Let

C = clear
O = overcast
R = rain

The following conditional probabilities apply.

$P(C \mid s_1) = 0.8$	$P(O \mid s_1) = 0.2$	$P(R \mid s_1) = 0.0$
$P(C \mid s_2) = 0.1$	$P(O \mid s_2) = 0.3$	$P(R \mid s_2) = 0.6$

a. Use Bayes' theorem for probability revision to compute the probability of each weather condition and the conditional probability of the expressway open s_1 or jammed s_2 given each weather condition.
b. Show the decision tree for this problem.
c. What is the optimal decision strategy, and what is the expected travel time?

25. The Gorman Manufacturing Company must decide whether to manufacture a component part at its Milan, Michigan, plant or purchase the component part from a supplier. The resulting profit is dependent upon the demand for the product. The following payoff table shows the projected profit (in thousands of dollars).

	State of Nature		
	Low Demand	**Medium Demand**	**High Demand**
Decision Alternative	s_1	s_2	s_3
Manufacture, d_1	−20	40	100
Purchase, d_2	10	45	70

The state-of-nature probabilities are $P(s_1) = 0.35$, $P(s_2) = 0.35$, and $P(s_3) = 0.30$.

a. Use a decision tree to recommend a decision.
b. Use EVPI to determine whether Gorman should attempt to obtain a better estimate of demand.
c. A test market study of the potential demand for the product is expected to report either a favorable (F) or unfavorable (U) condition. The relevant conditional probabilities are as follows:

$$P(F \mid s_1) = 0.10 \qquad P(U \mid s_1) = 0.90$$
$$P(F \mid s_2) = 0.40 \qquad P(U \mid s_2) = 0.60$$
$$P(F \mid s_3) = 0.60 \qquad P(U \mid s_3) = 0.40$$

What is the probability that the market research report will be favorable?
d. What is Gorman's optimal decision strategy?
e. What is the expected value of the market research information?
f. What is the efficiency of the information?

Case Problem 1 PROPERTY PURCHASE STRATEGY

Glenn Foreman, president of Oceanview Development Corporation, is considering submitting a bid to purchase property that will be sold by sealed bid at a county tax foreclosure. Glenn's initial judgment is to submit a bid of \$5 million. Based on his experience, Glenn estimates that a bid of \$5 million will have a 0.2 probability of being the highest bid and securing the property for Oceanview. The current date is June 1. Sealed bids for the property must be submitted by August 15. The winning bid will be announced on September 1.

If Oceanview submits the highest bid and obtains the property, the firm plans to build and sell a complex of luxury condominiums. However, a complicating factor is that the property is currently zoned for single-family residences only. Glenn believes that a referendum could be placed on the voting ballot in time for the November election. Passage of the referendum would change the zoning of the property and permit construction of the condominiums.

The sealed-bid procedure requires the bid to be submitted with a certified check for 10% of the amount bid. If the bid is rejected, the deposit is refunded. If the bid is accepted, the deposit is the down payment for the property. However, if the bid is accepted and the bidder does not follow through with the purchase and meet the remainder of the financial obligation within six months, the deposit will be forfeited. In this case, the county will offer the property to the next highest bidder.

To determine whether Oceanview should submit the \$5 million bid, Glenn conducted some preliminary analysis. This preliminary work provided an assessment of 0.3 for the probability that the referendum for a zoning change will be approved and resulted in the following estimates of the costs and revenues that will be incurred if the condominiums are built.

Cost and Revenue Estimates	
Revenue from condominium sales	\$15,000,000
Cost	
Property	\$5,000,000
Construction expenses	\$8,000,000

If Oceanview obtains the property and the zoning change is rejected in November, Glenn believes that the best option would be for the firm not to complete the purchase of the property. In this case, Oceanview would forfeit the 10 percent deposit that accompanied the bid.

Because the likelihood that the zoning referendum will be approved is such an important factor in the decision process, Glenn suggested that the firm hire a market research service to conduct a survey of voters. The survey would provide a better estimate of the likelihood that the referendum for a zoning change would be approved. The market research firm that Oceanview Development has worked with in the past has agreed to do the study for \$15,000. The results of the study will be available August 1, so that Oceanview will have this information before the August 15 bid deadline. The results of the survey will be either a prediction that the zoning change will be approved or a prediction that the zoning change will be rejected. After considering the record of the market research service in previous studies conducted for Oceanview, Glenn developed the following probability estimates concerning the accuracy of the market research information.

$$P(A \mid s_1) = 0.9 \qquad P(N \mid s_1) = 0.1$$
$$P(A \mid s_2) = 0.2 \qquad P(N \mid s_2) = 0.8$$

where

A = prediction of zoning change approval
N = prediction that zoning change will not be approved
s_1 = the zoning change is approved by the voters
s_2 = the zoning change is rejected by the voters

Managerial Report

Perform an analysis of the problem facing the Oceanview Development Corporation, and prepare a report that summarizes your findings and recommendations. Include the following items in your report:

1. A decision tree that shows the logical sequence of the decision problem
2. A recommendation regarding what Oceanview should do if the market research information is not available
3. A decision strategy that Oceanview should follow if the market research is conducted
4. A recommendation as to whether Oceanview should employ the market research firm, along with the value of the information provided by the market research firm

Include the details of your analysis as an appendix to your report.

Case Problem 2 LAWSUIT DEFENSE STRATEGY

John Campbell, an employee of Manhattan Construction Company, claims to have injured his back as a result of a fall while repairing the roof at one of the Eastview apartment buildings. He filed a lawsuit against Doug Reynolds, the owner of Eastview Apartments, asking for damages of $1,500,000. John claims that the roof had rotten sections and that his fall could have been prevented if Mr. Reynolds had told Manhattan Construction about the problem. Mr. Reynolds notified his insurance company, Allied Insurance, of the lawsuit. Allied must defend Mr. Reynolds and decide what action to take regarding the lawsuit.

Some depositions and a series of discussions took place between both sides. As a result, John Campbell offered to accept a settlement of $750,000. Thus, one option is for Allied to pay John $750,000 to settle the claim. Allied is also considering making John a counteroffer of $400,000 in the hope that he will accept a lesser amount to avoid the time and cost of going to trial. Allied's preliminary investigation shows that John's case is strong; Allied is concerned that John may reject their counteroffer and request a jury trial. Allied's lawyers spent some time exploring John's likely reaction if they make a counteroffer of $400,000.

The lawyers concluded that it is adequate to consider three possible outcomes to represent John's possible reaction to a counteroffer of $400,000: (1) John will accept the counteroffer and the case will be closed; (2) John will reject the counteroffer and elect to have a jury decide the settlement amount; or (3) John will make a counteroffer to Allied of $600,000. If John does make a counteroffer, Allied decided that they will not make additional counteroffers. They will either accept John's counteroffer of $600,000 or go to trial.

If the case goes to a jury trial, Allied considers three outcomes possible: (1) the jury may reject John's claim and Allied will not be required to pay any damages; (2) the jury will find in favor of John and award him $750,000 in damages; or (3) the jury will conclude that John has a strong case and award him the full amount of $1,500,000.

Key considerations as Allied develops its strategy for disposing of the case are the probabilities associated with John's response to an Allied counteroffer of $400,000 and the probabilities associated with the three possible trial outcomes. Allied's lawyers believe the probability that John will accept a counteroffer of $400,000 is 0.10, the probability that John will reject a counteroffer of $400,000 is 0.40, and the probability that John will, himself, make a counteroffer to Allied of $600,000 is 0.50. If the case goes to court, they believe that the probability the jury will award John damages of $1,500,000 is 0.30, the probability that the jury will award John damages of $750,000 is 0.50, and the probability that the jury will award John nothing is 0.20.

Managerial Report

Perform an analysis of the problem facing Allied Insurance and prepare a report that summarizes your findings and recommendations. Be sure to include the following items:

1. A decision tree
2. A recommendation regarding whether Allied should accept John's initial offer to settle the claim for $750,000
3. A decision strategy that Allied should follow if they decide to make John a counteroffer of $400,000
4. A risk profile for your recommended strategy

Appendix 4.1 DECISION ANALYSIS WITH TREEPLAN

Tutorial 9: Decision Analysis Using TreePlan

TreePlan* is an Excel add-in that can be used to develop decision trees for decision analysis problems. The software package is provided on the CD that accompanies this text. Instructions for installing TreePlan are included with the software. A manual contain-

*TreePlan was developed by Professor Michael R. Middleton at the University of San Francisco and modified for use by Professor James E. Smith at Duke University. The TreePlan Web site is www.treeplan.com.

FIGURE 4.18 PDC DECISION TREE

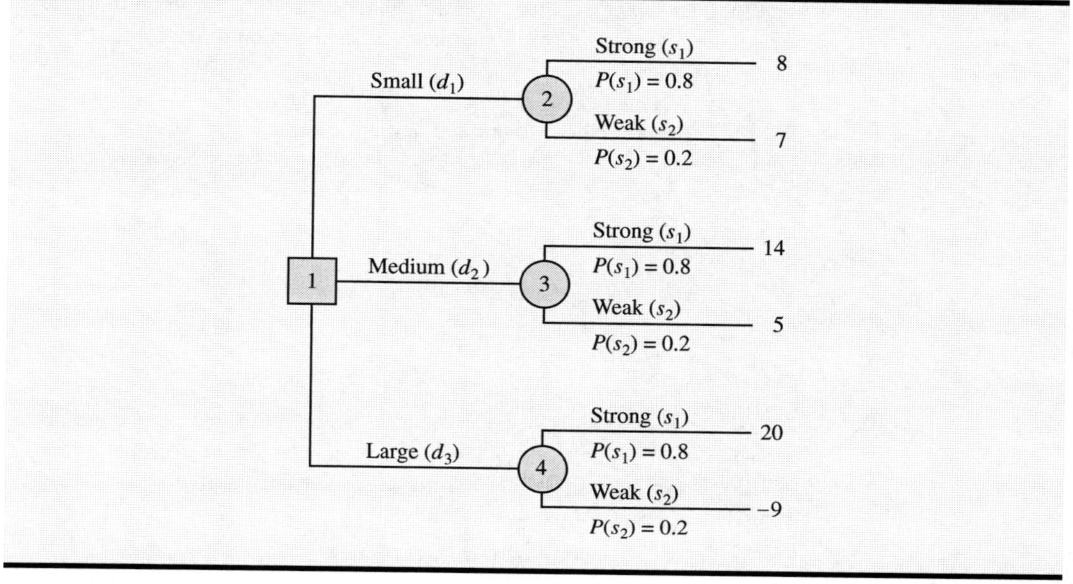

ing additional information on starting and using TreePlan is also included on the CD. In this appendix, we show how to use TreePlan to build a decision tree and solve the PDC problem presented in Section 4.3. The decision tree for the PDC problem is shown in Figure 4.18.

Getting Started: An Initial Decision Tree

We begin by assuming that TreePlan has been installed and an Excel workbook is open. To build a TreePlan version of the PDC decision tree proceed as follows:

Step 1. Select cell A1
Step 2. Select the **Tools** menu and choose **Decision Tree**
Step 3. When the **TreePlan New** dialog box appears:
Click **New Tree**

A decision tree with one decision node and two branches appears as follows:

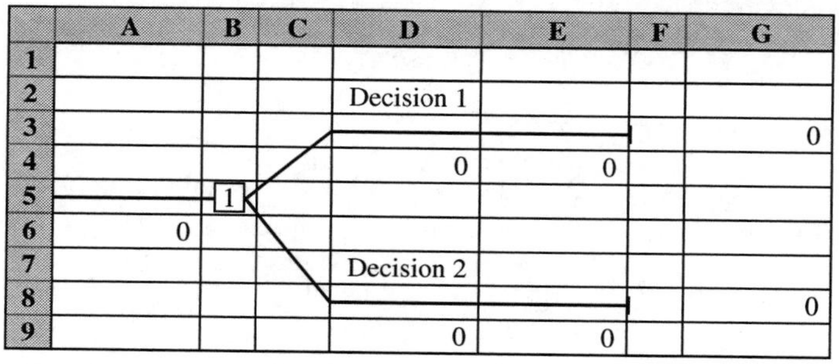

Adding a Branch

The PDC problem has three decision alternatives (small, medium, and large condominium complexes), so we must add another decision branch to the tree.

Step 1. Select cell B5
Step 2. Select the **Tools** menu and choose **Decision Tree**
Step 3. When the **TreePlan Decision** dialog box appears:
Select **Add branch**
Click **OK**

A revised tree with three decision branches now appears in the Excel worksheet.

Naming the Decision Alternatives

The decision alternatives can be named by selecting the cells containing the labels Decision 1, Decision 2, and Decision 3, and then entering the corresponding PDC names Small, Medium, and Large. After naming the alternatives, the PDC tree with three decision branches appears as follows:

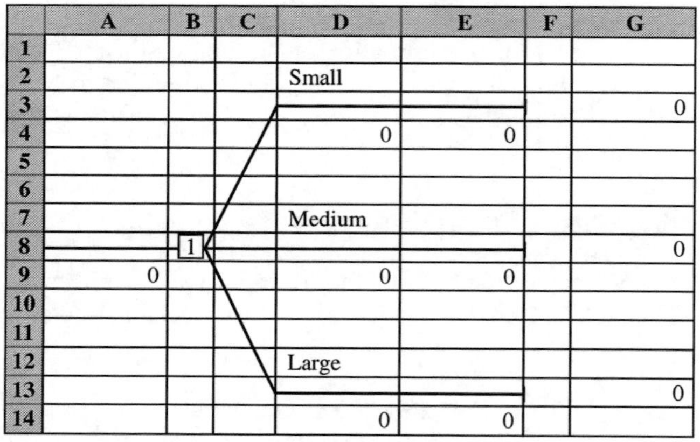

Adding Chance Nodes

The chance event for the PDC problem is the demand for the condominiums, which may be either strong or weak. Thus, a chance node with two branches must be added at the end of each decision alternative branch.

Step 1. Select cell F3
Step 2. Select the **Tools** menu and choose **Decision Tree**
Step 3. When the **TreePlan Terminal** dialog box appears:
Select **Change to event node**
Select **Two** in the **Branches** section
Click **OK**

The tree now appears as follows:

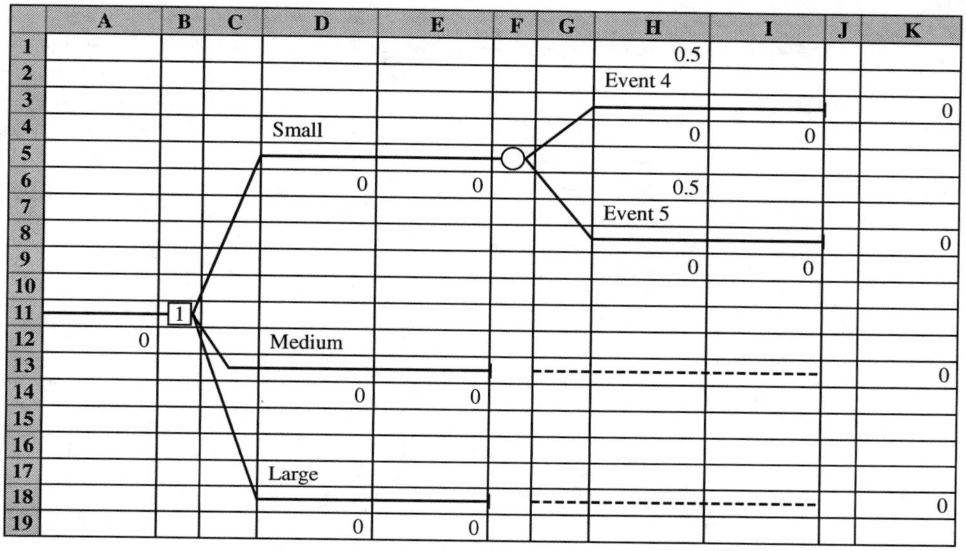

We next select the cells containing Event 4 and Event 5 and rename them Strong and Weak to provide the proper names for the PDC states of nature. After doing so we can copy the subtree for the chance node in cell F5 to the other two decision branches to complete the structure of the PDC decision tree.

Step 1. Select cell F5
Step 2. Select the **Tools** menu and choose **Decision Tree**
Step 3. When the **TreePlan Event** dialog box appears:
  Select **Copy subtree**
  Click **OK**
Step 4. Select cell F13
Step 5. Select the **Tools** menu and choose **Decision Tree**
Step 6. When the **TreePlan Terminal** dialog box appears:
  Select **Paste subtree**
  Click **OK**

This copy/paste procedure places a chance node at the end of the Medium decision branch. Repeating the same copy/paste procedure for the Large decision branch completes the structure of the PDC decision tree as shown in Figure 4.19.

Inserting Probabilities and Payoffs

TreePlan provides the capability of inserting probabilities and payoffs into the decision tree. In Figure 4.19, we see that TreePlan automatically assigned an equal probability 0.5 to each of the chance outcomes. For PDC, the probability of strong demand is 0.8 and the

FIGURE 4.19 THE PDC DECISION TREE DEVELOPED BY TREEPLAN

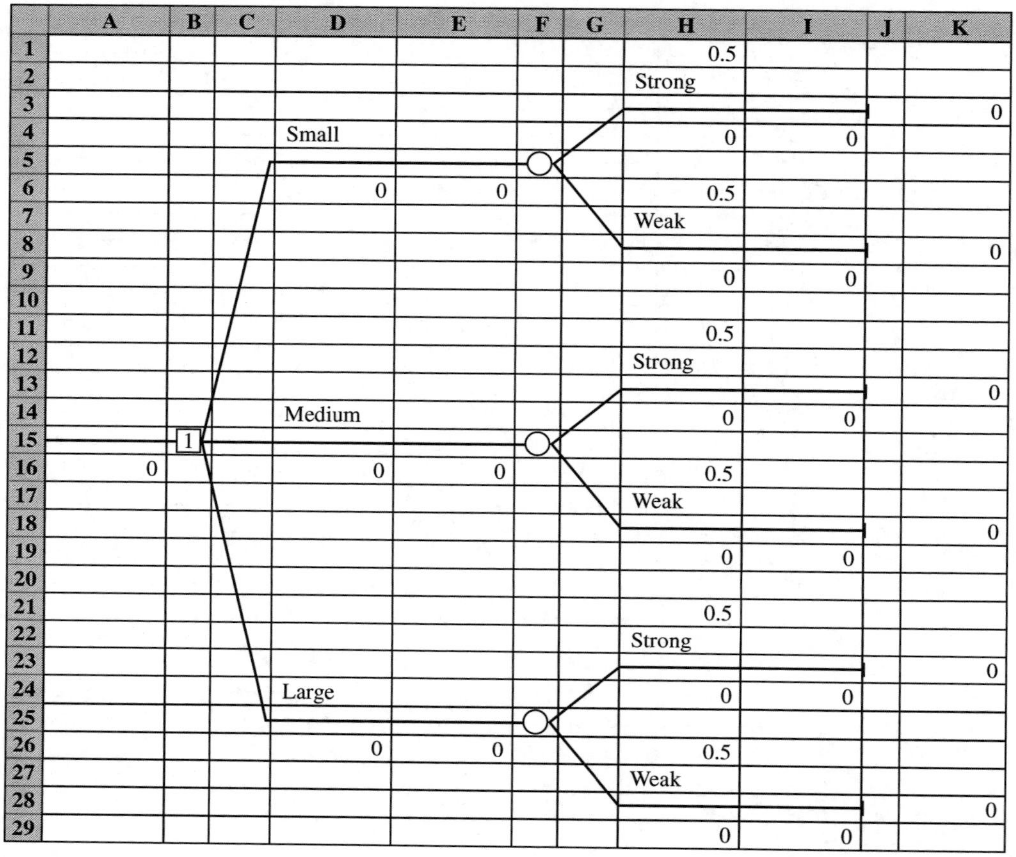

probability of weak demand is 0.2. We can select cells H1, H6, H11, H16, H21, and H26 and insert the appropriate probabilities. The payoffs for the chance outcomes are inserted in cells H4, H9, H14, H19, H24, and H29. After inserting the PDC probabilities and payoffs, the PDC decision tree appears as shown in Figure 4.20.

Note that the payoffs also appear in the right-hand margin of the decision tree. The payoffs in the right margin are computed by a formula that adds the payoffs on all of the branches leading to the associated terminal node. For the PDC problem, no payoffs are associated with the decision alternatives branches so we leave the default values of zero in cells D6, D16, and D24. The PDC decision tree is now complete.

Interpreting the Result

When probabilities and payoffs are inserted, TreePlan automatically makes the backward pass computations necessary to determine the optimal solution. Optimal decisions are identified by the number in the corresponding decision node. In the PDC decision tree in Figure 4.20, cell B15 contains the decision node. Note that a 3 appears in this node, which tells us that decision alternative branch 3 provides the optimal decision. Thus, decision analysis recommends PDC construct the Large condominium complex. The expected value of this

FIGURE 4.20 THE PDC DECISION TREE WITH BRANCH PROBABILITIES AND PAYOFFS

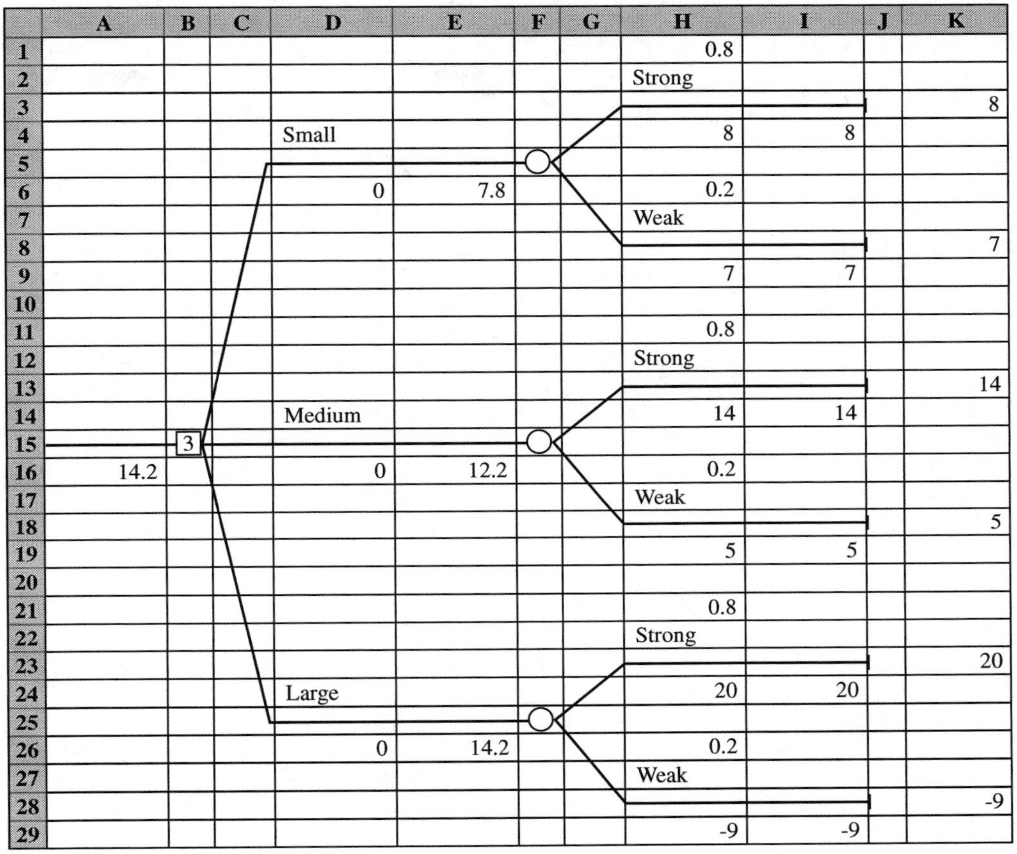

decision appears at the beginning of the tree in cell A16. Thus, we see the optimal expected value is $14.2 million. The expected values of the other decision alternatives are displayed at the end of the corresponding decision branch. Thus, referring to cells E6 and E16, we see that the expected value of the Small complex is $7.8 million and the expected value of the Medium complex is $12.2 million.

Other Options

TreePlan defaults to a maximization objective. If you would like a minimization objective, follow these steps:

Step 1. Select the **Tools** menu and choose **Decision Tree**
Step 2. Select **Options**
Step 3. Choose **Minimize (costs)**
Click **OK**

In using a TreePlan decision tree, we can modify probabilities and payoffs and quickly observe the impact of the changes on the optimal solution. Using this "what if" type of sensitivity analysis, we can identify changes in probabilities and payoffs that would change the optimal decision. Also, because TreePlan is an Excel add-in, most of Excel's capabilities are available. For instance, we could use boldface to highlight the name of the optimal decision alternative on the final decision tree solution. A variety of other options TreePlan provides is contained in the TreePlan manual on the CD that accompanies this text. Computer software packages such as TreePlan make it easier to do a thorough analysis of a decision problem.

CHAPTER 5

Utility and Game Theory

CONTENTS

The decision analysis situations presented in Chapter 4 often expressed consequences or payoffs in terms of monetary values. With probability information available about the outcomes of the chance events, we defined the optimal decision alternative as the one that provided the best expected monetary value. However, in some situations the decision alternative with the best expected monetary value may not be the preferred alternative. A decision maker may also wish to consider intangible factors such as risk, image, or other nonmonetary criteria in order to evaluate the decision alternatives. When monetary value does not necessarily lead to the most preferred decision, expressing the value (or worth) of a consequence in terms of its utility will permit the use of expected utility to identify the most desirable decision alternative. The discussion of utility and its application in decision analysis is presented in the first part of this chapter.

In the last part of this chapter, we introduce the topic of game theory. Game theory is the study of developing optimal strategies where two or more decision makers, usually called players, compete as adversaries. Game theory can be viewed as a relative of decision analysis. A key difference, however, is that each player selects a decision strategy not by considering the possible outcomes of a chance event, but by considering the possible strategies selected by one or more competing players.

We note here that utility and game theory are separable topics. Either or both may be studied, and it is not required that you cover one topic before the other.

5.1 THE MEANING OF UTILITY

Utility is a measure of the total worth of a particular outcome; it reflects the decision maker's attitude toward a collection of factors such as profit, loss, and risk. Researchers have found that as long as the monetary value of payoffs stays within a range that the decision maker considers reasonable, selecting the decision alternative with the best expected monetary value usually leads to selection of the most preferred decision. However, when the payoffs become extreme, most decision makers are not satisfied with the decision that simply provides the best expected monetary value.

As an example of a situation in which utility can help in selecting the best decision alternative, let us consider the problem faced by Swofford, Inc., a relatively small real estate investment firm located in Atlanta, Georgia. Swofford currently has two investment opportunities that require approximately the same cash outlay. The cash requirements necessary prohibit Swofford from making more than one investment at this time. Consequently, three possible decision alternatives may be considered.

The three decision alternatives, denoted d_1, d_2, and d_3, are

$$d_1 = \text{make investment A}$$
$$d_2 = \text{make investment B}$$
$$d_3 = \text{do not invest}$$

The monetary payoffs associated with the investment opportunities depend on the investment decision and on the direction of the real estate market during the next six months (the chance event). Real estate prices will go up, remain stable, or go down. Thus the Swofford states of nature, denoted by s_1, s_2, and s_3, are

$$s_1 = \text{real estate prices go up}$$
$$s_2 = \text{real estate prices remain stable}$$
$$s_3 = \text{real estate prices go down}$$

TABLE 5.1 PAYOFF TABLE FOR SWOFFORD, INC.

	State of Nature		
Decision Alternative	Prices Up s_1	Prices Stable s_2	Prices Down s_3
Investment A, d_1	\$30,000	\$20,000	−\$50,000
Investment B, d_2	\$50,000	−\$20,000	−\$30,000
Do not invest, d_3	0	0	0

Using the best information available, Swofford has estimated the profits, or payoffs, associated with each decision alternative and state-of-nature combination. The resulting payoff table is shown in Table 5.1.

The best estimate of the probability that real estate prices will go up is 0.3; the best estimate of the probability that prices will remain stable is 0.5; and the best estimate of the probability that prices will go down is 0.2. Thus the expected values for the three decision alternatives are

$$\begin{aligned}
\text{EV}(d_1) &= 0.3(30{,}000) + 0.5(20{,}000) + 0.2(-50{,}000) = 9000 \\
\text{EV}(d_2) &= 0.3(50{,}000) + 0.5(-20{,}000) + 0.2(-30{,}000) = -1000 \\
\text{EV}(d_3) &= 0.3(0) + 0.5(0) + 0.2(0) = 0
\end{aligned}$$

Using the expected value approach, the optimal decision is to select investment A with an expected monetary value of \$9000. Is it really the best decision alternative? Let us consider some other relevant factors that relate to Swofford's capability for absorbing the loss of \$50,000 if investment A is made and prices actually go down.

Actually, Swofford's current financial position is weak. This condition is partly reflected in Swofford's ability to make only one investment. More important, however, the firm's president believes that, if the next investment results in a substantial loss, Swofford's future will be in jeopardy. Although the expected value approach leads to a recommendation for d_1, do you think the firm's president would prefer this decision? We suspect that the president would select d_2 or d_3 to avoid the possibility of incurring a \$50,000 loss. In fact, a reasonable conclusion is that, if a loss of even \$30,000 could drive Swofford out of business, the president would select d_3, believing that both investments A and B are too risky for Swofford's current financial position.

The way we resolve Swofford's dilemma is first to determine Swofford's utility for the various monetary outcomes. Recall that the utility of any outcome is the total worth of that outcome, taking into account all risks and consequences involved. If the utilities for the various consequences are assessed correctly, the decision alternative with the highest expected utility is the most preferred, or best, alternative. In the next section we show how to determine the utility of the monetary outcomes so that the alternative with the highest expected utility can be identified.

5.2 UTILITY AND DECISION MAKING

The procedure we use to establish utility values for the payoffs in Swofford's situation requires that we first assign a utility value to the best and worst possible payoffs. Any values will work as long as the utility assigned to the best payoff is greater than the utility assigned

Utility values of 0 and 1 could have been selected here; we selected 0 and 10 in order to avoid any possible confusion between the utility value for a payoff and the probability p.

to the worst payoff. In this case, \$50,000 is the best payoff and −\$50,000 is the worst. Suppose, then, that we arbitrarily make assignments to these two payoffs as follows:

$$\text{Utility of } -\$50{,}000 = U(-50{,}000) = 0$$
$$\text{Utility of } \$50{,}000 = U(50{,}000) = 10$$

Let us now determine the utility associated with every other payoff.

Consider the process of establishing the utility of a payoff of \$30,000. First we ask Swofford's president to state a preference between a guaranteed \$30,000 payoff and an opportunity to engage in the following **lottery,** or bet:

Lottery: Swofford obtains a payoff of \$50,000 with probability p and a payoff of −\$50,000 with probability $(1 - p)$.

p is often referred to as the indifference probability.

Obviously, if p is very close to 1, Swofford's president would prefer the lottery to the guaranteed payoff of \$30,000 because the firm would virtually ensure itself a payoff of \$50,000. If p is very close to 0, Swofford's president would clearly prefer the guarantee of \$30,000. In any event, as p changes continuously from 0 to 1, the preference for the guaranteed payoff of \$30,000 will change at some point into a preference for the lottery. At this value of p, Swofford's president would have no greater preference for the guaranteed payoff of \$30,000 than for the lottery. For example, let us assume that when $p = 0.95$, Swofford's president is indifferent between the guaranteed payoff of \$30,000 and the lottery. For this value of p, we can compute the utility of a \$30,000 payoff as follows:

$$\begin{aligned} U(30{,}000) &= pU(50{,}000) + (1 - p)U(-50{,}000) \\ &= 0.95(10) + (0.05)(0) \\ &= 9.5 \end{aligned}$$

Obviously, if we had started with a different assignment of utilities for a payoff of \$50,000 and −\$50,000, the result would have been a different utility for \$30,000. For example, if we had started with an assignment of 100 for \$50,000 and 10 for −\$50,000, the utility of a \$30,000 payoff would be

$$\begin{aligned} U(30{,}000) &= 0.95(100) + 0.05(10) \\ &= 95 + 0.5 \\ &= 95.5 \end{aligned}$$

Hence, we must conclude that the utility assigned to each payoff is not unique but merely depends on the initial choice of utilities for the best and worst payoffs. We will discuss utility choice further at the end of the section. For now, however, we will continue to use a value of 10 for the utility of \$50,000 and a value of 0 for the utility of −\$50,000.

Before computing the utility for the other payoffs, let us consider the significance of Swofford's president assigning a utility of 9.5 to a payoff of \$30,000. Clearly, when $p = 0.95$, the expected value of the lottery is

$$\begin{aligned} \text{EV(lottery)} &= 0.95(\$50{,}000) + 0.05(-\$50{,}000) \\ &= \$47{,}500 - \$2{,}500 \\ &= \$45{,}000 \end{aligned}$$

Although the expected value of the lottery when $p = 0.95$ is \$45,000, Swofford's president would just as soon take a guaranteed payoff of \$30,000. Thus, Swofford's president is tak-

The difference between the expected value of the lottery and the guaranteed payoff can be viewed as the risk premium the decision maker is willing to pay.

ing a conservative, or risk-avoiding, viewpoint. A decision maker who would choose a guaranteed payoff over a lottery with a better expected payoff is a **risk avoider.** The president would rather have $30,000 for certain than risk anything greater than a 5% chance of incurring a loss of $50,000. In other words the difference between the EV of $45,000 and the guaranteed payoff of $30,000 is the risk premium that Swofford's president would be willing to pay to avoid the 5% chance of losing $50,000.

To compute the utility associated with a payoff of −$20,000, we must ask Swofford's president to state a preference between a guaranteed −$20,000 payoff and an opportunity to engage again in the following lottery:

Lottery: Swofford obtains a payoff of $50,000 with probability p and a payoff of −$50,000 with probability $(1 - p)$

Note that this lottery is exactly the same as the one we used to establish the utility of a payoff of $30,000. In fact, we use this lottery to establish the utility for any monetary value in the Swofford payoff table. We need to determine the value of p that would make the president indifferent between a guaranteed payoff of −$20,000 and the lottery. For example, we might begin by asking the president to choose between a certain loss of $20,000 and the lottery with a payoff of $50,000 with probability $p = 0.90$ and a payoff of −$50,000 with probability $(1 - p) = 0.10$. What answer do you think we would get? Surely, with this high probability of obtaining a payoff of $50,000, the president would elect the lottery. Next, we might ask whether $p = 0.85$ would result in indifference between the loss of $20,000 for certain and the lottery. Again the president might prefer the lottery. Suppose that we continue until we get to $p = 0.55$, at which point the president is indifferent between the payoff of −$20,000 and the lottery. That is, for any value of p less than 0.55, the president would take a loss of $20,000 for certain rather than risk the potential loss of $50,000 with the lottery; and for any value of p above 0.55, the president would choose the lottery. Thus, the utility assigned to a payoff of −$20,000 is

$$\begin{aligned} U(-\$20{,}000) &= pU(50{,}000) + (1 - p)U(-\$50{,}000) \\ &= 0.55(10) + 0.45(0) \\ &= 5.5 \end{aligned}$$

Again let us compare the significance of this assignment to the expected value approach. When $p = 0.55$, the expected value of the lottery is

$$\begin{aligned} \text{EV(lottery)} &= 0.55(\$50{,}000) + 0.45(-\$50{,}000) \\ &= \$27{,}500 - \$22{,}500 \\ &= \$5{,}000 \end{aligned}$$

Thus, Swofford's president would just as soon absorb a loss of $20,000 for certain as take the lottery, even though the expected value of the lottery is $5000. Once again this preference demonstrates the conservative, or risk-avoiding, point of view of Swofford's president.

In these two examples we computed the utility for the monetary payoffs of $30,000 and −$20,000. We can determine the utility for any monetary payoff M in a similar fashion. First, we must find the probability p for which the decision maker is indifferent between a guaranteed payoff of M and a lottery with a payoff of $50,000 with probability p and −$50,000 with probability $(1 - p)$. The utility of M is then computed as follows:

$$\begin{aligned} U(M) &= pU(\$50{,}000) + (1 - p)U(-\$50{,}000) \\ &= p(10) + (1 - p)0 \\ &= 10p \end{aligned}$$

TABLE 5.2 UTILITY OF MONETARY PAYOFFS FOR SWOFFORD, INC.

Monetary Value	Indifference Value of p	Utility Value
$ 50,000	Does not apply	10.0
30,000	0.95	9.5
20,000	0.90	9.0
0	0.75	7.5
−20,000	0.55	5.5
−30,000	0.40	4.0
−50,000	Does not apply	0

Using this procedure we developed utility values for the rest of the payoffs in Swofford's problem. The results are presented in Table 5.2.

Now that we have determined the utility value of each of the possible monetary values, we can write the original payoff table in terms of utility values. Table 5.3 shows the utility for the various outcomes in the Swofford problem. The notation we use for the entries in the utility table is U_{ij}, which denotes the utility associated with decision alternative d_i and state of nature s_j. Using this notation, we see that $U_{23} = 4.0$.

The Expected Utility Approach

We can now apply the expected value computations introduced in Chapter 4 to the utilities in Table 5.3 in order to select an optimal decision alternative for Swofford, Inc. However, because utility values represent such a special case of expected value, we will refer to the expected value when applied to utility values as the **expected utility (EU).** Thus, the expected utility approach requires the analyst to compute the expected utility for each decision alternative and then select the alternative yielding the highest expected utility. With N possible states of nature, the expected utility of a decision alternative d_i is given by

$$\text{EU}(d_i) = \sum_{j=1}^{N} P(s_j)U_{ij} \tag{5.1}$$

The expected utility for each of the decision alternatives in the Swofford problem is

$$\begin{aligned}
\text{EU}(d_1) &= 0.3(9.5) + 0.5(9.0) + 0.2(0) = 7.35 \\
\text{EU}(d_2) &= 0.3(10) + 0.5(5.5) + 0.2(4.0) = 6.55 \\
\text{EU}(d_3) &= 0.3(7.5) + 0.5(7.5) + 0.2(7.5) = 7.50
\end{aligned}$$

TABLE 5.3 UTILITY TABLE FOR SWOFFORD, INC.

	State of Nature		
Decision Alternative	Prices Up s_1	Prices Stable s_2	Prices Down s_3
Investment A, d_1	9.5	9.0	0
Investment B, d_2	10.0	5.5	4.0
Do not invest, d_3	7.5	7.5	7.5

Can you use the expected utility approach to determine the optimal decision? Try Problem 1.

Note that the optimal decision using the expected utility approach is d_3, do not invest. The ranking of alternatives according to the president's utility assignments and the associated monetary values are as follows.

Ranking of Decision Alternatives	Expected Utility	Expected Monetary Value
Do not invest	7.50	0
Investment A	7.35	9000
Investment B	6.55	−1000

Note that although investment A had the highest expected monetary value of $9000, the analysis indicates that Swofford should decline this investment. The rationale behind not selecting investment A is that the 0.20 probability of a $50,000 loss was considered to involve a serious risk by Swofford's president. The seriousness of this risk and its associated impact on the company were not adequately reflected by the expected monetary value of investment A. We assessed the utility for each payoff to assess this risk adequately.

NOTES AND COMMENTS

In the Swofford problem we have been using a utility of 10 for the best payoff and 0 for the worst. The choice of values could have been anything, and we might have chosen 1 for the utility of the best payoff and 0 for the utility of the worst. Had we made this choice, the utility for any monetary value M would have been the value of p at which the decision maker was indifferent between a guaranteed payoff of M and a lottery in which the best payoff is obtained with probability p and the worst payoff is obtained with probability $(1 - p)$. Thus, the utility for any monetary value would have been equal to the probability of earning the best payoff. Often this choice is made because of the ease in computation. We chose not to do so to emphasize the distinction between the utility values and the indifference probabilities for the lottery.

Summary of Steps for Determining the Utility of Money

Before considering other aspects of utility, let us summarize the steps involved in determining the utility for a monetary value and using it within the decision analysis framework. The following steps state in general terms the procedure used to solve the Swofford, Inc., investment problem.

Step 1. Develop a payoff table using monetary values.

Step 2. Identify the best and worst payoff values in the table and assign each a utility value, with $U(\text{best payoff}) > U(\text{worst payoff})$.

Step 3. For every other monetary value M in the original payoff table, do the following to determine its utility value.

a. Define the lottery: The best payoff is obtained with probability p and the worst payoff is obtained with probability $(1 - p)$.

b. Determine the value of p such that the decision maker is indifferent between a guaranteed payoff of M and the lottery defined in step 3(a).

c. Calculate the utility of M as follows:

$$U(M) = pU(\text{best payoff}) + (1 - p)U(\text{worst payoff})$$

Step 4. Convert the payoff table from monetary values to utility values.

Step 5. Apply the expected utility approach to the utility table developed in step 4 and select the decision alternative with the highest expected utility.

NOTES AND COMMENTS

The procedure we described for determining the utility of monetary consequences can also be used to develop a utility measure for nonmonetary consequences. Assign the best consequence a utility of 10 and the worst a utility of 0. Then create a lottery with a probability of p for the best consequence and $(1 - p)$ for the worst consequence. For each of the other consequences, find the value of p that makes the decision maker indifferent between the lottery and the consequence. Then calculate the utility of the consequence in question as follows:

$$U(\text{consequence}) = pU(\text{best consequence}) + (1 - p)U(\text{worst consequence})$$

5.3 UTILITY: OTHER CONSIDERATIONS

In this section, we describe how a risk-avoiding decision maker and a risk-taking decision maker differ in their assessment of utility. Expected utility is then used to show how a risk-avoiding decision maker and a risk-taking decision maker may prefer different decision alternatives for the same decision problem. We close this section by comparing expected monetary value and expected utility as criteria for decision making.

Risk Avoiders Versus Risk Takers

The financial position of Swofford, Inc., was such that the firm's president evaluated investment opportunities from a conservative, or risk-avoiding, point of view. However, if the firm had a surplus of cash and a stable future, Swofford's president might have been looking for investment alternatives that, although perhaps risky, contained a potential for substantial profit. That type of behavior would have made the president a risk taker.

A **risk taker** is a decision maker who would choose a lottery over a better guaranteed payoff. In this section we analyze the decision problem faced by Swofford from the point of view of a decision maker who would be classified as a risk taker. We then compare the conservative, or risk-avoiding, point of view of Swofford's president with the behavior of a decision maker who is a risk taker.

For the decision problem facing Swofford, Inc., and using the general procedure for developing utilities as discussed in Section 5.2, a risk taker might express the utility for the various payoffs shown in Table 5.4. As before, $U(50{,}000) = 10$ and $U(-50{,}000) = 0$. Note the difference in behavior reflected in Table 5.4 and Table 5.2. That is, in determining the value of p at which the decision maker is indifferent between a guaranteed payoff of M and a lottery in which \$50,000 is obtained with probability p and −\$50,000 with

TABLE 5.4 REVISED UTILITY VALUES FOR SWOFFORD, INC., ASSUMING A RISK TAKER

Monetary Value	Indifference Value of p	Utility Value
\$ 50,000	Does not apply	10.0
30,000	0.50	5.0
20,000	0.40	4.0
0	0.25	2.5
−20,000	0.15	1.5
−30,000	0.10	1.0
−50,000	Does not apply	0

TABLE 5.5 PAYOFF TABLE FOR SWOFFORD, INC.

	State of Nature		
Decision Alternative	Prices Up s_1	Prices Stable s_2	Prices Down s_3
Investment A, d_1	\$30,000	\$20,000	−\$50,000
Investment B, d_2	\$50,000	−\$20,000	−\$30,000
Do not invest, d_3	0	0	0

probability $(1 - p)$, the risk taker is willing to accept a greater risk of incurring a loss of \$50,000 in order to gain the opportunity to realize a profit of \$50,000.

To help develop the utility table for the risk taker, we have reproduced the Swofford, Inc., payoff table in Table 5.5. Using these payoffs and the risk taker's utility values given in Table 5.4, we can write the risk taker's utility table as shown in Table 5.6. Using the state-of-nature probabilities $P(s_1) = 0.3$, $P(s_2) = 0.5$, and $P(s_3) = 0.2$, the expected utility for each decision alternative is

$$\begin{aligned} \text{EU}(d_1) &= 0.3(5.0) + 0.5(4.0) + 0.2(0) = 3.50 \\ \text{EU}(d_2) &= 0.3(10) + 0.5(1.5) + 0.2(1.0) = 3.95 \\ \text{EU}(d_3) &= 0.3(2.5) + 0.5(2.5) + 0.2(2.5) = 2.50 \end{aligned}$$

What is the recommended decision? Perhaps somewhat to your surprise, the analysis recommends investment B, with the highest expected utility of 3.95. Recall that this investment has a −\$1000 expected monetary value. Why is it now the recommended decision? Remember that the decision maker in this revised problem is a risk taker. Thus, although the expected value of investment B is negative, utility analysis has shown that this decision maker is enough of a risk taker to prefer investment B and its potential for the \$50,000 profit.

The expected utility values give the following order of preference of the decision alternatives for the risk taker and the associated expected monetary values.

Ranking of Decision Alternatives	Expected Utility	Expected Monetary Value
Investment B	3.95	−\$1000
Investment A	3.50	\$9000
Do not invest	2.50	0

TABLE 5.6 UTILITY TABLE OF A RISK TAKER FOR SWOFFORD, INC.

	State of Nature		
Decision Alternative	Prices Up s_1	Prices Stable s_2	Prices Down s_3
Investment A, d_1	5.0	4.0	0
Investment B, d_2	10.0	1.5	1.0
Do not invest, d_3	2.5	2.5	2.5

Comparing the utility analysis for a risk taker with the more conservative preferences of the president of Swofford, Inc., who is a risk avoider, we see that, even with the same decision problem, different attitudes toward risk can lead to different recommended decisions. The utility values established by Swofford's president indicated that the firm should not invest at this time, whereas the utilities established by the risk taker showed a preference for investment B. Note that both of these decisions differ from the best expected monetary value decision, which was investment A.

We can obtain another perspective of the difference between behaviors of a risk avoider and a risk taker by developing a graph that depicts the relationship between monetary value and utility. We use the horizontal axis of the graph to represent monetary values and the vertical axis to represent the utility associated with each monetary value. Now, consider the data in Table 5.2, with a utility value corresponding to each monetary value for the original Swofford, Inc., problem. These values can be plotted on a graph such as that in Figure 5.1, and a curve can be drawn through the observed points. The resulting curve is the **utility function for money** for Swofford's president. Recall that these points reflected the conservative, or risk-avoiding, nature of Swofford's president. Hence, we refer to the curve in Figure 5.1 as a utility function for a risk avoider. Using the data in Table 5.4, developed for a risk taker, we can plot these points on a graph such as that in Figure 5.2. The resulting curve depicts the utility function for a risk taker.

By looking at the utility functions of Figures 5.1 and 5.2, we can begin to generalize about the utility functions for risk avoiders and risk takers. Although the exact shape of the utility function will vary from one decision maker to another, we can see the general shape of these two types of utility functions. The utility function for a risk avoider shows a diminishing marginal return for money. For example, the increase in utility going from a monetary value of −\$30,000 to \$0 is 7.5 − 4.0 = 3.5, whereas the increase in utility in going from \$0 to \$30,000 is only 9.5 − 7.5 = 2.0. However, the utility function for a risk taker shows an increasing marginal return for money. For example, in Figure 5.2, the increase in utility in going from −\$30,000 to \$0 is 2.5 − 1.0 = 1.5, whereas the increase in utility in going from \$0 to \$30,000

FIGURE 5.1 UTILITY FUNCTION FOR MONEY FOR THE RISK AVOIDER

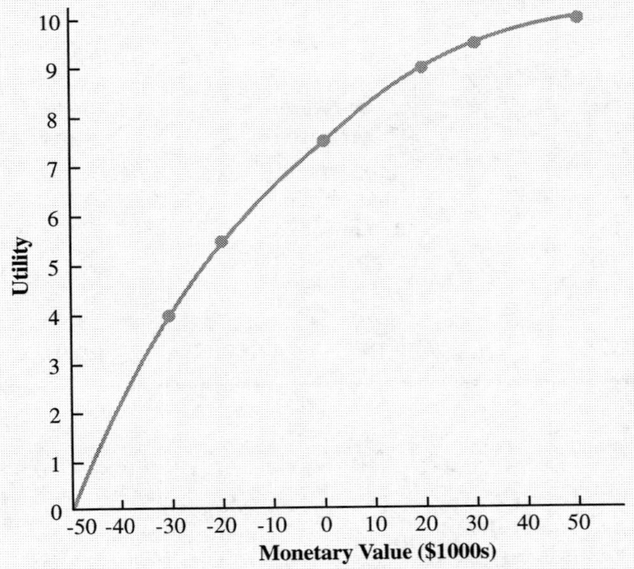

FIGURE 5.2 UTILITY FUNCTION FOR MONEY FOR THE RISK TAKER

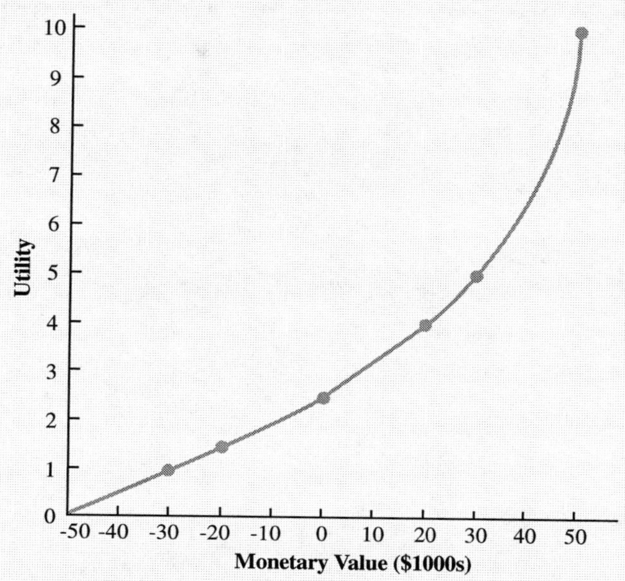

is 5.0 − 2.5 = 2.5. Note also that in either case the utility function is always increasing; that is, more money leads to more utility. All utility functions possess this property.

We concluded that the utility function for a risk avoider shows a diminishing marginal return for money and that the utility function for a risk taker shows an increasing marginal return. When the marginal return for money is neither decreasing nor increasing but remains constant, the corresponding utility function describes the behavior of a decision maker who is neutral to risk. The following characteristics are associated with a **risk-neutral decision maker.**

1. The utility function can be drawn as a straight line connecting the "best" and the "worst" points.
2. The expected utility approach and the expected value approach applied to monetary payoffs result in the same action.

Try Problem 5 for practice in plotting the utility function for risk-avoider, risk-taker, and risk-neutral decision makers.

Figure 5.3 depicts the utility function of a risk-neutral decision maker using the Swofford, Inc., problem data. For comparison purposes, we also show the utility functions for the cases where the decision maker is either a risk taker or a risk avoider.

Expected Monetary Value Versus Expected Utility

In many decision-making problems, expected monetary value and expected utility will lead to identical recommendations. In fact, this result will always be true if the decision maker is risk neutral. In general, if the decision maker is almost risk neutral over the range of payoffs (from lowest to highest) for a particular decision problem, the decision alternative with the best expected monetary value leads to selection of the most preferred decision alternative. The trick lies in recognizing the range of monetary values over which a decision maker's utility function is risk neutral.

Generally, when the payoffs for a particular decision-making problem fall into a reasonable range—the best is not too good and the worst is not too bad—decision makers tend to express preferences in agreement with the expected monetary value approach. Thus, we

FIGURE 5.3 UTILITY FUNCTIONS FOR RISK-AVOIDER, RISK-TAKER, AND RISK-NEUTRAL DECISION MAKERS

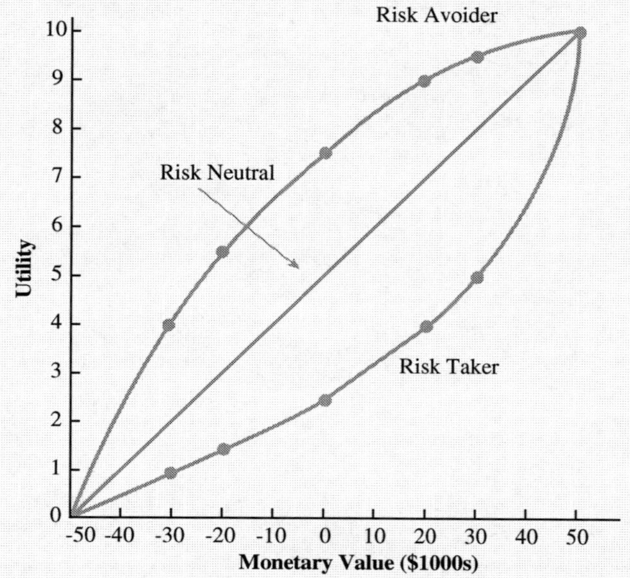

suggest asking the decision maker to consider the best and worst possible payoffs for a problem and assess their reasonableness. If the decision maker believes that they are in the reasonable range, the decision alternative with the best expected monetary value can be used. However, if the payoffs appear unreasonably large or unreasonably small (for example, a huge loss) and if the decision maker believes that monetary values do not adequately reflect her or his true preferences for the payoffs, a utility analysis of the problem should be considered.

Unfortunately, determination of the appropriate utilities is not a trivial task. As we have shown, measuring utility requires a degree of subjectivity on the part of the decision maker, and different decision makers will have different utility functions. This aspect of utility often causes decision makers to feel uncomfortable about using the expected utility approach. However, if you encounter a decision situation in which you are convinced that monetary value is not the sole measure of performance, and if you agree that a quantitative analysis of the decision problem is desirable, you should recommend that utility analysis be considered.

5.4 INTRODUCTION TO GAME THEORY

Until 1944, when Von Neumann and Morgenstern published the book Theory of Games and Economic Behavior, *the literature on decisions involving risk consisted primarily of applications involving the use of probability in gambling.*

In decision analysis, a single decision maker seeks to select an optimal decision alternative after considering the possible outcomes of one or more chance events. In **game theory,** two or more decision makers are called players, and they compete as adversaries against each other. Each player selects a strategy independently without knowing in advance the strategy of the other player or players. The combination of the competing strategies provides the value of the game to the players. Game theory applications have been developed for situations in which the competing players are teams, companies, political candidates, armies, and contract bidders.

In this section, we describe **two-person, zero-sum games.** *Two-person* means that two competing players take part in the game. *Zero-sum* means that the gain (or loss) for one player is equal to the corresponding loss (gain) for the other player. As a result, the gain and loss balance out so that the game results in the sum of zero. What one player wins, the other player loses. Let us demonstrate a two-person, zero-sum game and its solution by considering two companies competing for market share.

Competing for Market Share

Suppose that two companies are the only manufacturers of a particular product; they compete against each other for market share. In planning a marketing strategy for the coming year, each company is considering three strategies designed to take market share from the other company. The three strategies, assumed to be the same for both companies, are as follows:

Strategy 1 Increase advertising

Strategy 2 Provide quantity discounts

Strategy 3 Extend product warranty

A payoff table showing the percentage gain in the market share for Company A expected for each combination of strategies follows. The notations a_1, a_2, and a_3 identify the three strategies for Company A; the notations b_1, b_2, and b_3 identify the three strategies for Company B. It is a zero-sum game because any gain in market share for Company A is a loss in market share for Company B.

		Company B		
		Increase Advertising b_1	**Quantity Discounts** b_2	**Extend Warranty** b_3
Company A	**Increase Advertising,** a_1	4	3	2
	Quantity Discounts, a_2	−1	4	1
	Extend Warranty, a_3	5	−2	0

In interpreting the entries in the table we see that if Company A increases advertising (a_1) and Company B increases advertising (b_1), Company A will come out ahead with an increase in market share of 4%. On the other hand, if Company A provides quantity discounts (a_2) and Company B increases advertising (b_1), Company A is projected to lose 1% of market share to Company B. Company A is seeking payoff values that show relatively large increases in its market share. Company B is seeking payoff values that show decreases or small increases in Company A's market share, and thus better results for Company B.

This game involving market share meets the requirements of a two-person, zero-sum game. The two companies are the two players and the zero-sum occurs because the gain in market share for Company A is the same as the loss in market share for Company B. Due to the planning horizon, each company must select a strategy before knowing the other company's strategy. What are the optimal strategies for the two companies?

The logic of game theory assumes that each company or player has the same information and will select a strategy that provides the best possible outcome from its point of view. Suppose Company A selects strategy a_1. Market share increases of 4%, 3%, or 2% are possible depending upon Company B's strategy. If Company B believes that Company A will use strategy a_1, then Company B will employ strategy b_3. Under the assumption that Company B will select the strategy that is best for it, Company A analyzes the game by protecting itself against the actions of Company B. In doing so, Company A identifies the minimum possible payoff for each of its actions. This payoff is the minimum value in each row of the payoff matrix. These row minimums are computed in the payoff table as follows:

		Company B			
		Increase Advertising b_1	Quantity Discounts b_2	Extend Warranty b_3	Minimum
Company A	Increase Advertising, a_1	4	3	2	(2)
	Quantity Discounts, a_2	−1	4	1	−1
	Extend Warranty, a_3	5	−2	0	−2

Maximum of row minimums

Considering the entries in the Minimum column, we see that Company A can be guaranteed an increase in market share of at least 2 percent by selecting the strategy that provides the *maximum of the row minimums* (strategy a_1). Thus, Company A follows a *maximin* procedure and selects strategy a_1 as its best strategy.

Let us now look at the payoff table from the point of view of the other player, Company B. The entries in the payoff table represent losses in market share. Consider what happens to Company B if strategy b_1 is selected. Market share decreases of 4%, –1%, and 5% are possible. Under the assumption that Company A will select the strategy that is best for it, Company B knows that if it selects strategy b_1, a loss in market share of as much as 5% could be incurred. Thus, Company B analyzes the game by considering the maximum value in each column, which provides the maximum decrease in its market share for each Company A strategy. These column maximums are computed as follows:

		Company B			
		Increase Advertising b_1	Quantity Discounts b_2	Extend Warranty b_3	Minimum
Company A	Increase Advertising, a_1	4	3	2	(2)
	Quantity Discounts, a_2	−1	4	1	−1
	Extend Warranty, a_3	5	−2	0	−2
	Maximum	5	4	(2)	

Minimum of column maximums

Maximum of row minimums

By considering the entries in the Maximum row, Company B can be guaranteed a decrease in market share of no more than 2% by selecting the strategy that provides the *minimum of the column maximums* (strategy b_3). Thus, Company B follows a *minimax* procedure and selects strategy b_3 as its best strategy. Under strategy b_3 Company B knows that Company A cannot gain more than 2% in market share.

Identifying a Pure Strategy

Whenever, the maximum of the row minimums *equals* the minimum of the column maximums, the players cannot improve their outcomes by changing strategies. The game is said to have a **saddle point.** With a saddle point, the optimal strategies and the value of the game cannot be improved by either player changing strategies. Thus, a **pure strategy** has been identified as being optimal for both players. The requirement for a pure strategy is as follows:

$$\text{Maximum(Row minimums)} = \text{Minimum(Column maximums)}$$

That is, the maximin value for Player A equals the minimax value for Player B. In this example, the solution to the game is for Company A to increase its advertising (strategy a_1) and Company B to extend its product warranty (strategy b_3). The value of the game shows that this optimal solution will increase Company A's market share by 2% and decrease Company B's market share by 2%.

With a pure strategy, neither player can improve its position by changing to a different strategy. In our marketing example, the pure strategy for Company A is a_1. When Company B selects its pure strategy b_3 the value of the game shows an increase in Company A's market share of 2%. Note that if Company B tries to change its pure strategy from b_3, Company A's market share will increase 4% if b_1 is selected or will increase 3% if b_2 is selected. Company B must stay with its pure strategy b_3 to obtain its best result. Similarly note that if Company A tries to change its pure strategy from a_1, Company A's market share will increase only 1% if a_2 is selected or will not increase at all if a_3 is selected. Company A must stay with its pure strategy a_1 in order to keep its 2% increase in market share. Thus, even if one of the players discovered in advance the opponent's strategy, no advantage could be gained by switching to a different strategy.

If a pure strategy exists, it is the optimal solution for the game.

When a pure strategy is optimal for a two-person, zero-sum game the following steps will find the optimal strategy for each player.

Step 1. Compute the minimum payoff for each row (Player A).

Step 2. For Player A, select the strategy that provides the *maximum* of the row minimums.

Step 3. Compute the maximum payoff for each column (Player B).

Step 4. For Player B select the strategy that provides the *minimum* of the column maximums.

Step 5. If the maximin value (step 2) equals the minimax value (step 4), an optimal pure strategy exists for both players. The optimal strategy for Player A is identified in step 2, and the optimal strategy for Player B is identified in step 4. The value of the game is given by the value at the saddle point where the optimal strategies for both players intersect.

If in step 5 the maximin value for Player A does not equal the minimax value for Player B, a pure strategy is not optimal for the two-person, zero-sum game. In this case, a *mixed strategy* is best. We show when it is necessary to employ a mixed strategy in the next section.

5.5 MIXED STRATEGY GAMES

Consider the two-person, zero-sum game that occurs in a football game. The two competing players are the two football teams. On each play, the game is zero-sum because the yardage gained by one team is equal to the yardage lost by the other team. As usual in game theory, each team must select its strategy before knowing the strategy selected by the other team. In this example, let Team A be the team on offense trying to gain yardage and Team B be the team on defense trying to keep the yardage gained by Team A to a minimum. We define the offensive strategies for Team A as follows:

$$a_1 = \text{running play}$$
$$a_2 = \text{passing play}$$

The defensive strategies for Team B are as follows:

$$b_1 = \text{run defense}$$
$$b_2 = \text{pass defense}$$

The payoff table shows the yardage gained by Team A depending upon the strategies selected by the two teams.

		Team B	
		Run defense b_1	**Pass defense** b_2
Team A	**Run,** a_1	1	6
	Pass, a_2	15	0

Applying the five-step procedure used to identify a pure strategy, the row minimums and the column maximums are as follows:

		Team B		
		Run defense b_1	**Pass defense** b_2	**Minimum**
Team A	**Run,** a_1	1	6	(1)
	Pass, a_2	15	0	0
	Maximum	15	(6)	

The maximum of the row minimums is 1 and the minimum of the column maximums is 6. Because these values are not equal, the two-person, zero-sum game does not have an optimal pure strategy. In this case, a **mixed strategy** solution is best. With a mixed strategy, the optimal solution for each player is to randomly select among the alternative strategies. In the football example, then, the offensive Team A will mix up or vary its selection of running (a_1) and passing (a_2) plays, while the defensive Team B will mix up or vary its selection of a run defense (b_1) and a pass defense (b_2).

When you think about a football game, it becomes clear that a pure strategy such as Team A always selecting a running play would not work. Team B would recognize Team A's pure strategy and would always be prepared with a run defense. Thus, a Team A mixed strategy of sometimes running and sometimes passing would make sense. When a mixed strategy solution is needed, game theory will determine the optimal probabilities for each strategy for each player. That is, the game theory solution of the football example will tell the offensive team the optimal probabilities for a running play and a passing play. At the same time, the solution will tell the defensive team the optimal probabilities for a run defense and a pass defense. The following discussion shows how to calculate these mixed strategy probabilities.

Let

$$p = \text{the probability Team A selects a running play}$$
$$(1 - p) = \text{the probability Team A selects a passing play}$$

When a mixed strategy solution exists, we seek to determine the probability p for Team A such that Team B cannot improve its result by changing its defensive strategy. First assume that Team B selects a run defense as shown in column b_1. If Team A selects a running play with probability p and a passing play with probability $(1 - p)$, the expected value of the yardage gain for Team A is computed as follows:

If Team B selects b_1:

$$\text{EV(Yardage)} = 1p + 15(1 - p)$$

If Team B selects its pass defense as shown in column b_2, the expected value of the yardage gain for Team A will be as follows:

If Team B selects b_2:

$$\text{EV(Yardage)} = 6p + 0(1 - p) = 6p$$

To guarantee that Team B cannot change its strategy and decrease the expected value of the yardage gained by Team A, we set the two expected values equal and solve for the value of p.

$$\begin{aligned} 1p + 15(1 - p) &= 6p \\ 1p + 15 - 15p &= 6p \\ 20p &= 15 \\ p &= 15/20 = .75 \end{aligned}$$

With $p = .75$, $(1 - p) = 1 - .75 = .25$. This result tells Team A it should select a running play with a .75 probably and a passing play with a .25 probability. The expected value of the yardage gained, which is the *value of the game,* is

$$\text{EV(Yardage)} = 1p + 15(1 - p) = 1(.75) + 15(.25) = 4.5 \text{ yards per play}$$

Now let us consider the optimal probabilities for Team B. Let

$$\begin{aligned} q &= \text{the probability Team B selects a run defense} \\ (1 - q) &= \text{the probability Team B selects a pass defense} \end{aligned}$$

Using the same logic we used for computing Team A's optimal probabilities, we want to determine the value of q such that Team A cannot increase the expected value of the yardage gained by changing its offensive strategy. We first compute the expected value of the yardage for Team B for the following two cases:

If Team A selects a_1:

$$\text{EV(Yardage)} = 1q + 6(1 - q)$$

If Team A selects a_2:

$$\text{EV(Yardage)} = 15q + 0(1 - q) = 15q$$

To guarantee that Team A cannot change its strategy and affect the expected value of the yardage for Team B, we set the two expected values equal and solve for the value of q as follows:

$$\begin{aligned} 1q + 6(1 - q) &= 15q \\ 1q + 6 - 6q &= 15q \\ 20q &= 6 \\ q &= 6/20 = .30 \end{aligned}$$

With $q = .30$, $(1 - q) = 1 - .30 = .70$. This result tells Team B that it should select a run defense with a .30 probably and a pass defense with a .70 probability. The expected yardage gained, which is the value of the game, will remain 4.5 yards per play.

Thus, we have the optimal mixed strategy solution for the football game example. Any 2×2 two-person, zero-sum mixed strategy game can be solved algebraically as shown in this example. If a larger two-person, zero-sum game involves a mixed strategy, solving it is a bit more complicated.

A Larger Mixed Strategy Game

Consider the following two-person, zero-sum game.

		Player B		
		b_1	b_2	b_3
Player A	a_1	0	−1	2
	a_2	5	4	−3
	a_3	2	3	−4

Following the usual procedure for identifying a pure strategy, we compute the row minimums and the column maximums.

		Player B			
		b_1	b_2	b_3	**Minimum**
Player A	a_1	0	−1	2	(−1)
	a_2	5	4	−3	−3
	a_3	2	3	−4	−4
	Maximum	5	4	(2)	

The maximum of the row minimums is −1 and the minimum of the column maximums is 2. Because the maximin and minimax values are not equal, the two-person, zero-sum game does not have an optimal pure strategy. However, with a problem larger than 2×2, we cannot use the algebraic solution for the mixed strategy probabilities as we did in the previous example.

If a game larger than 2×2 requires a mixed strategy, we first look for dominated strategies in order to reduce the size of the game. A **dominated strategy** exists if another strategy *is at least as good* regardless of what the opponent does. For example, consider strategies a_2 and a_3. The payoff table shows that in column b_1, $5 > 2$, in column b_2, $4 > 3$, and in column b_3, $-3 > -4$. Thus, regardless of what Player B does, Player A will always prefer the higher values of strategy a_2 compared to strategy a_3. Thus, strategy a_3 is dominated by strategy a_2 and thus strategy a_3 can be dropped from consideration by Player A. Eliminating dominated strategies from the game reduces its size. After eliminating a_3, the reduced game becomes

		Player B		
		b_1	b_2	b_3
Player A	a_1	0	−1	2
	a_2	5	4	−3

Next we look for more dominated strategies. Player A finds no other dominated strategies. However, consider strategies b_1 and b_2 for Player B. Remember that Player B is interested in smaller values. The payoff table shows that in row a_1, $-1 < 0$ and in row a_2, $4 < 5$. Thus, regardless of what Player A does, Player B would always prefer the smaller values of strategy b_2 compared to strategy b_1. Thus, strategy b_1 is dominated by strategy b_2 and can be eliminated from the game. With this dominated strategy eliminated, the reduced game becomes

		Player B	
		b_1	b_3
Player A	a_1	−1	2
	a_2	4	−3

Problem 14 at the end of the chapter will ask you to find the optimal probabilities for this example.

By successively eliminating dominated strategies, we reduce the game to a 2 × 2 game. The algebraic solution procedure described earlier in this section can now be used to identify the optimal probabilities for the mixed strategy solution.

Identifying and eliminating dominated strategies may reduce the game to a 2 × 2 game. If so, an algebraic procedure may be used to determine the mixed strategy solution.

Finally, it is important to realize that no hard-and-fast rule identifies dominated strategies. Basically, the analyst must make pairwise comparisons of the decision strategies in an attempt to identify dominated strategies. The goal is to identify and eliminate dominated strategies sequentially in order to reduce the game to a 2 × 2 game so that an algebraic solution procedure can be used to solve for the mixed strategy probabilities.

Summary of Steps for Solving Two-Person, Zero-Sum Games

The following summary shows the steps used to solve two-person, zero-sum games.

1. Use the maximin procedure for Player A and the minimax procedure for Player B to determine whether a pure strategy solution exists. (See previous steps for identifying a pure strategy.) If a pure strategy exists, it is the optimal solution.
2. If a pure strategy does not exist and the game is larger than 2 × 2, identify a dominated strategy to eliminate a row or column. Develop the reduced payoff table and continue to use dominance to eliminate as many additional rows and columns as possible.
3. If the reduced game is 2 × 2, solve for the optimal mixed strategy probabilities algebraically.

If the game cannot be reduced to a 2 × 2 game, a linear programming model can be used to solve for the optimal mixed strategy probabilities. The formulation of a linear programming model to solve these larger game theory problems is beyond the scope of this text.

Extensions

In 1994, John Harsanui, John Nash, and Reinhard Selten received the Nobel Prize in Economics for their work on noncooperative game theory.

We presented the basic model for two-person, zero-sum games. However, game theory models extend beyond two-person, zero-sum games. One extension is a two-person, constant-sum game that occurs when the payoffs for the strategies chosen sum to a constant other than zero. In addition, game theory can be extended to include more general n-person games. Cooperative games where players are allowed preplay communications is another variation. Finally, some game theory models allow an infinite number of strategies to be available for the players.

SUMMARY

In this chapter we showed how utility could be used in decision-making situations in which monetary value did not provide an adequate measure of the payoffs. Utility is a measure of the total worth of a consequence. As such, utility takes into account the decision maker's assessment of all aspects of a consequence including profit, loss, risk, and perhaps additional nonmonetary factors. The examples showed how the use of expected utility can lead to decision recommendations that differ from those based on expected monetary value.

A decision maker's judgment must be used to establish the utility for each consequence. We presented a step-by-step procedure to determine a decision maker's utility for monetary payoffs. We also discussed how conservative, risk-avoiding decision makers assess utility differently from more aggressive, risk-taking decision makers. If the decision maker is risk neutral, we showed that the solution using expected utility is identical to the solution using expected monetary value.

We presented an introduction to game theory by describing how to solve two-person, zero-sum games. In these games, the two players end up with the sum of the gain (loss) to one player and the loss (gain) to the other player always equal to zero. We described the steps that can be used to determine whether a two-person, zero-sum game results in an optimal pure strategy. If a pure strategy is optimal, a saddle point determines the value of the game. If an optimal pure strategy does not exist for a two-person, zero-sum 2×2 game, we showed how to identify an optimal mixed strategy. With a mixed strategy, each player uses probability to select a strategy for each play of the game. We showed how dominance could be used to reduce the size of mixed strategy games. If the elimination of dominated strategies can reduce a larger game to a 2×2 game, an algebraic solution procedure can be used to find a solution. If the game cannot be reduced to a 2×2 game, a linear programming model is needed to determine the optimal mixed strategy solution.

GLOSSARY

Utility A measure of the total worth of a consequence reflecting a decision maker's attitude toward considerations such as profit, loss, and risk.

Lottery A hypothetical investment alternative with a probability p of obtaining the best payoff and a probability of $(1 - p)$ of obtaining the worst payoff.

Risk avoider A decision maker who would choose a guaranteed payoff over a lottery with a better expected payoff.

Expected utility (EU) The weighted average of the utilities associated with a decision alternative. The weights are the state-of-nature probabilities.

Risk taker A decision maker who would choose a lottery over a better guaranteed payoff.

Utility function for money A curve that depicts the relationship between monetary value and utility.

Risk-neutral decision maker A decision maker who is neutral to risk. For this decision maker the decision alternative with the best expected monetary value is identical to the alternative with the highest expected utility.

Game theory The study of decision situations in which two or more players compete as adversaries. The combination of strategies chosen by the players determines the value of the game to each player.

Two-person, zero-sum game A game with two players in which the gain to one player is equal to the loss to the other player.

Saddle point A condition that exists when pure strategies are optimal for both players in a two-person, zero-sum game. The saddle point occurs at the intersection of the optimal strategies for the players, and the value of the saddle point is the value of the game.

Pure strategy A game solution that provides a single best strategy for each player.

Mixed strategy A game solution in which the player randomly selects the strategy to play from among several strategies with positive probabilities. The solution to the mixed strategy game identifies the probabilities that each player should use to randomly select the strategy to play.

Dominated strategy A strategy is dominated if another strategy is at least as good for every strategy that the opposing player may employ. A dominated strategy will never be selected by the player and as such, can be eliminated in order to reduce the size of the game.

PROBLEMS

SELF test

1. A firm has three investment alternatives. Payoffs are in thousands of dollars.

	Economic Conditions		
Decision Alternative	**Up s_1**	**Stable s_2**	**Down s_3**
Investment A, d_1	100	25	0
Investment B, d_2	75	50	25
Investment C, d_3	50	50	50
Probabilities	0.40	0.30	0.30

a. Using the expected value approach, which decision is preferred?

b. For the lottery having a payoff of \$100,000 with probability p and \$0 with probability $(1 - p)$, two decision makers expressed the following indifference probabilities. Find the most preferred decision for each decision maker using the expected utility approach.

	Indifference Probability (p)	
Profit	**Decision Maker A**	**Decision Maker B**
\$75,000	0.80	0.60
\$50,000	0.60	0.30
\$25,000	0.30	0.15

c. Why don't decision makers A and B select the same decision alternative?

2. Alexander Industries is considering purchasing an insurance policy for its new office building in St. Louis, Missouri. The policy has an annual cost of \$10,000. If Alexander Industries doesn't purchase the insurance and minor fire damage occurs, a cost of \$100,000 is anticipated; the cost if major or total destruction occurs is \$200,000. The costs, including the state-of-nature probabilities, are as follows.

	Damage		
Decision Alternative	**None s_1**	**Minor s_2**	**Major s_3**
Purchase insurance, d_1	10,000	10,000	10,000
Do not purchase insurance, d_2	0	100,000	200,000
Probabilities	0.96	0.03	0.01

a. Using the expected value approach, what decision do you recommend?
b. What lottery would you use to assess utilities? (Note: Because the data are costs, the best payoff is \$0.)
c. Assume that you found the following indifference probabilities for the lottery defined in part (b). What decision would you recommend?

Cost	Indifference Probability
10,000	$p = 0.99$
100,000	$p = 0.60$

d. Do you favor using expected value or expected utility for this decision problem? Why?

3. In a certain state lottery, a lottery ticket costs \$2. In terms of the decision to purchase or not to purchase a lottery ticket, suppose that the following payoff table applies.

	State of Nature	
Decision Alternatives	Win s_1	Lose s_2
Purchase lottery ticket, d_1	300,000	−2
Do not purchase lottery ticket, d_2	0	0

a. A realistic estimate of the chances of winning are 1 in 250,000. Use the expected value approach to recommend a decision.
b. If a particular decision maker assigns an indifference probability of 0.000001 to the \$0 payoff, would this individual purchase a lottery ticket? Use expected utility to justify your answer.

4. Two different routes accommodate travel between two cities. Route A normally takes 60 minutes, and route B normally takes 45 minutes. If traffic problems are encountered on route A, the travel time increases to 70 minutes; traffic problems on route B increase travel time to 90 minutes. The probability of a delay is 0.20 for route A and 0.30 for route B.
a. Using the expected value approach, what is the recommended route?
b. If utilities are to be assigned to the travel times, what is the appropriate lottery? (Note: The smaller times should reflect higher utilities.)
c. Use the lottery of part (b) and assume that the decision maker expresses indifference probabilities of

$p = 0.80$ for 60 minutes
$p = 0.60$ for 70 minutes

What route should this decision maker select? Is the decision maker a risk taker or a risk avoider?

SELF test

5. Three decision makers have assessed utilities for the following decision problem (payoff in dollars).

	State of Nature		
Decision Alternative	s_1	s_2	s_3
d_1	20	50	−20
d_2	80	100	−100

The indifference probabilities are as follows.

	Indifference Probability (p)		
Payoff	**Decision Maker A**	**Decision Maker B**	**Decision Maker C**
100	1.00	1.00	1.00
80	0.95	0.70	0.90
50	0.90	0.60	0.75
20	0.70	0.45	0.60
−20	0.50	0.25	0.40
−100	0.00	0.00	0.00

a. Plot the utility function for money for each decision maker.
b. Classify each decision maker as a risk avoider, a risk taker, or risk neutral.
c. For the payoff of 20, what is the premium that the risk avoider will pay to avoid risk? What is the premium that the risk taker will pay to have the opportunity of the high payoff?

6. In Problem 5, if $P(s_1) = 0.25$, $P(s_2) = 0.50$, and $P(s_3) = 0.25$, find a recommended decision for each of the three decision makers. (Note: For the same decision problem, different utilities can lead to different decisions.)

7. Suppose that the point spread for a particular sporting event is 10 points and that with this spread you are convinced you would have a 0.60 probability of winning a bet on your team. However, the local bookie will accept only a $1000 bet. Assuming that such bets are legal, would you bet on your team? (Disregard any commission charged by the bookie.) Remember that *you* must pay losses out of your own pocket. Your payoff table is as follows.

	State of Nature	
Decision Alternatives	**You Win**	**You Lose**
Bet	1000	−1000
Don't bet	0	0

a. What decision does the expected value approach recommend?
b. What is *your* indifference probability for the $0 payoff? (Although this choice isn't easy, be as realistic as possible. It is required for an analysis that reflects your attitude toward risk.)
c. What decision would you make based on the expected utility approach? In this case are you a risk taker or risk avoider?
d. Would other individuals assess the same utility values you do? Explain.
e. If your decision in part (c) was to place the bet, repeat the analysis assuming a minimum bet of $10,000.

8. A Las Vegas roulette wheel has 38 different numerical values. If an individual bets on one number and wins, the payoff is 35 to 1.
a. Show a payoff table for a $10 bet on one number for decision alternatives of bet and do not bet.
b. What is the recommended decision using the expected value approach?
c. Do the Las Vegas casinos want risk-taking or risk-avoiding customers? Explain.
d. What range of utility values would a decision maker have to assign to the $0 payoff in order to have expected utility justify a decision to place the $10 bet?

9. A new product has the following profit projections and associated probabilities.

Profit	Probability
$150,000	0.10
$100,000	0.25
$ 50,000	0.20
0	0.15
−$ 50,000	0.20
−$100,000	0.10

a. Use the expected value approach to decide whether to market the new product.
b. Because of the high dollar values involved, especially the possibility of a $100,000 loss, the marketing vice president has expressed some concern about the use of the expected value approach. As a consequence, if a utility analysis is performed, what is the appropriate lottery?
c. Assume that the following indifference probabilities are assigned. Do the utilities reflect the behavior of a risk taker or a risk avoider?

Profit	Indifference Probability (p)
$100,000	0.95
$ 50,000	0.70
0	0.50
−$ 50,000	0.25

d. Use expected utility to make a recommended decision.
e. Should the decision maker feel comfortable with the final decision recommended by the analysis?

10. A television network has been receiving low ratings for its programs. Currently, management is considering two alternatives for the Monday night 8:00 P.M.–9:00 P.M. time slot: a western with a well-known star, or a musical variety with a relatively unknown husband-and-wife team. The percentages of viewing audience estimates depend on the degree of program acceptance. The relevant data are as follows.

	Percentage of Viewing Audience	
Program Acceptance	Western	Musical Variety
High	30%	40%
Moderate	25%	20%
Poor	20%	15%

The probabilities associated with program acceptance levels are as follows.

	Probability	
Program Acceptance	Western	Musical Variety
High	0.30	0.30
Moderate	0.60	0.40
Poor	0.10	0.30

a. Using the expected value approach, which program should the network choose?
b. For a utility analysis, what is the appropriate lottery?
c. Based on the lottery in part (b), assume that the network's program manager has assigned the following indifference probabilities. Based on the use of utility measures, which program would you recommend? Is the manager a risk taker or a risk avoider?

Percentage of Audience	Indifference Probability (p)
30%	0.40
25%	0.30
20%	0.10

SELF test

11. Consider the following two-person, zero-sum game. Identify the pure strategy. What is the value of the game?

		Player B		
		b_1	b_2	b_3
Player A	a_1	8	5	7
	a_2	2	4	10

12. Two television stations in a market compete with each other for viewing audience. Local programming options for the 5:00 P.M. weekday time slot include a sitcom rerun, an early news program, or a home improvement show. Assume that each station has the same three programming options and must make its preseason program selection before knowing what the other television station will do. The viewing audience changes in thousands of viewers for Station A are as follows.

		Station B		
		Sitcom b_1	**News** b_2	**Home Improvement** b_3
Station A	**Sitcom,** a_1	10	−5	3
	News, a_2	8	8	6
	Home Improvement, a_3	4	7	3

Determine the optimal programming strategy for each station. What is the value of the game?

13. Two Indiana state senate candidates must decide what city to visit the day before the November election. The same four cities, Indianapolis, Evansville, Fort Wayne, and South Bend are available for both candidates. These cities are listed as strategies 1 to 4 for each candidate. Travel plans must be made in advance, so the candidates must decide which city to visit prior to knowing the other candidate's plans. Values in the following table show thousands of voters for the Republican candidate based on the strategies selected by the two candidates. What city should each candidate visit, and what is the value of the game?

		Democrat Candidate			
		Indianapolis b_1	**Evansville** b_2	**Fort Wayne** b_3	**South Bend** b_4
Republican Candidate	**Indianapolis,** a_1	0	−15	−8	20
	Evansville, a_2	30	−5	5	−10
	Fort Wayne, a_3	10	−25	0	20
	South Bend, a_4	20	20	10	15

SELF test

14. In Section 5.5, we showed the following two-person, zero-sum game had a mixed strategy.

		Player B		
		b_1	b_2	b_3
Player A	a_1	0	−1	2
	a_2	5	4	−3
	a_3	2	3	−4

a. Use dominance to reduce the game to a 2 × 2 game. What strategies are dominated?
b. Determine the optimal mixed strategy solution.
c. What is the value of the game?

15. In a gambling game, Player A and Player B both have a \$1 and a \$5 bill. Each player selects one of the bills without the other player knowing the bill selected. Simultaneously they both reveal the bills selected. If the bills do not match, Player A wins Player B's bill. If the bills match, Player B wins Player A's bill.
    a. Develop the game theory table for this game. The values should be expressed as the gains (or losses) for Player A.
    b. Is there a pure strategy? Why or why not?
    c. Determine the optimal strategies and the value of this game. Does the game favor one player over the other?
    d. Suppose Player B decides to deviate from the optimal strategy and begins playing each bill 50% of the time. What should Player A do to improve Player A's winnings? Comment on why it is important to follow an optimal game theory strategy.

16. Two companies compete for a share of the soft drink market. Each worked with an advertising agency in order to develop alternative advertising strategies for the coming year. A variety of television advertisements, product promotions, in-store displays, and so on provides four different strategies for each company. The following table summarizes the projected change in market share for Company A once the two companies select their advertising strategy for the coming year. What is the optimal solution to this game for each of the players? What is the value of the game?

		Company B			
		b_1	b_2	b_3	b_4
Company A	a_1	3	0	2	4
	a_2	2	−2	1	0
	a_3	4	2	5	6
	a_4	−2	6	−1	0

CHAPTER 14

Waiting Line Models

CONTENTS

Recall the last time that you had to wait at a supermarket checkout counter, for a teller at your local bank, or to be served at a fast-food restaurant. In these and many other waiting line situations, the time spent waiting is undesirable. Adding more checkout clerks, bank tellers, or servers is not always the most economical strategy for improving service, so businesses need to determine ways to keep waiting times within tolerable limits.

Models have been developed to help managers understand and make better decisions concerning the operation of waiting lines. In management science terminology, a waiting line is also known as a **queue,** and the body of knowledge dealing with waiting lines is known as **queueing theory.** In the early 1900s, A. K. Erlang, a Danish telephone engineer, began a study of the congestion and waiting times occurring in the completion of telephone calls. Since then, queueing theory has grown far more sophisticated with applications in a wide variety of waiting line situations.

Waiting line models consist of mathematical formulas and relationships that can be used to determine the **operating characteristics** (performance measures) for a waiting line. Operating characteristics of interest include the following:

1. The probability that no units are in the system
2. The average number of units in the waiting line
3. The average number of units in the system (the number of units in the waiting line plus the number of units being served)
4. The average time a unit spends in the waiting line
5. The average time a unit spends in the system (the waiting time plus the service time)
6. The probability that an arriving unit has to wait for service

Managers who have such information are better able to make decisions that balance desirable service levels against the cost of providing the service.

The Q.M. in Action, ATM Waiting Times at Citibank, describes how a waiting line model was used to help determine the number of automatic teller machines (ATMs) to place at New York City banking centers. A waiting line model prompted the creation of a new kind of line and a chief line director to implement first-come, first-served queue discipline at Whole Foods Market in the Chelsea neighborhood of New York City. In addition, a waiting line model helped the New Haven, Connecticut, fire department develop policies to improve response time for both fire and medical emergencies.

Q.M. IN ACTION

ATM WAITING TIMES AT CITIBANK*

The waiting line model used at Citibank is discussed in Section 14.3.

The New York City franchise of U.S. Citibanking operates more than 250 banking centers. Each center provides one or more automatic teller machines (ATMs) capable of performing a variety of banking transactions. At each center, a waiting line is formed by randomly arriving customers who seek service at one of the ATMs.

In order to make decisions on the number of ATMs to have at selected banking center locations, management needed information about potential waiting times and general customer service. Waiting line operating characteristics such as average number of customers in the waiting line, average time a customer spends waiting, and the probability that an arriving customer has to wait would help management determine the number of ATMs to recommend at each banking center.

For example, one busy Midtown Manhattan center had a peak arrival rate of 172 customers per hour. A multiple-channel waiting line model with six ATMs showed that 88% of the customers would have to wait, with an average wait time between

(*continued*)

six and seven minutes. This level of service was judged unacceptable. Expansion to seven ATMs was recommended for this location based on the waiting line model's projection of acceptable waiting times. Use of the waiting line model provided guidelines for making incremental ATM decisions at each banking center location.

*Based on information provided by Stacey Karter of Citibank.

14.1 STRUCTURE OF A WAITING LINE SYSTEM

To illustrate the basic features of a waiting line model, we consider the waiting line at the Burger Dome fast-food restaurant. Burger Dome sells hamburgers, cheeseburgers, french fries, soft drinks, and milk shakes, as well as a limited number of specialty items and dessert selections. Although Burger Dome would like to serve each customer immediately, at times more customers arrive than can be handled by the Burger Dome food service staff. Thus, customers wait in line to place and receive their orders.

Burger Dome is concerned that the methods currently used to serve customers are resulting in excessive waiting times. Management wants to conduct a waiting line study to help determine the best approach to reduce waiting times and improve service.

Single-Channel Waiting Line

In the current Burger Dome operation, a server takes a customer's order, determines the total cost of the order, takes the money from the customer, and then fills the order. Once the first customer's order is filled, the server takes the order of the next customer waiting for service. This operation is an example of a **single-channel waiting line.** Each customer entering the Burger Dome restaurant must pass through the *one* channel—one order-taking and order-filling station—to place an order, pay the bill, and receive the food. When more customers arrive than can be served immediately, they form a waiting line and wait for the order-taking and order-filling station to become available. A diagram of the Burger Dome single-channel waiting line is shown in Figure 14.1.

Distribution of Arrivals

Defining the arrival process for a waiting line involves determining the probability distribution for the number of arrivals in a given period of time. For many waiting line situations, the arrivals occur *randomly and independently* of other arrivals, and we cannot predict

FIGURE 14.1 THE BURGER DOME SINGLE-CHANNEL WAITING LINE

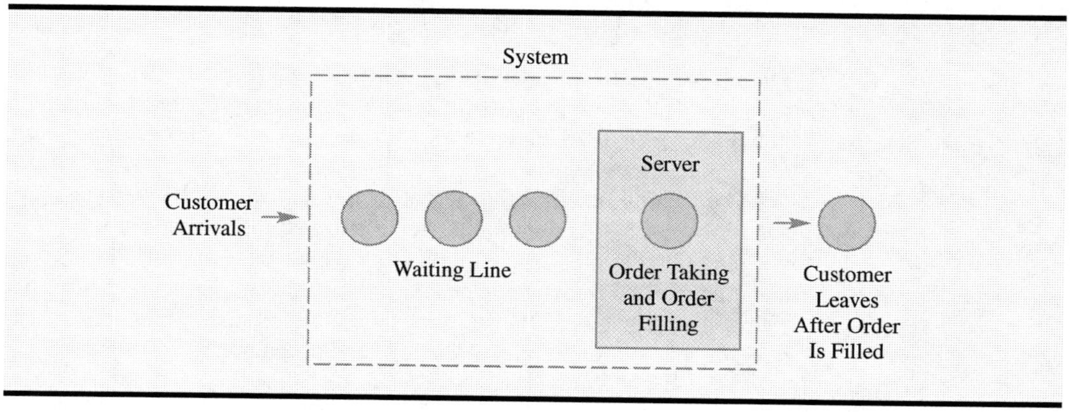

when an arrival will occur. In such cases, quantitative analysts have found that the **Poisson probability distribution** provides a good description of the arrival pattern.

The Poisson probability function provides the probability of x arrivals in a specific time period. The probability function is as follows.[1]

$$P(x) = \frac{\lambda^x e^{-\lambda}}{x!} \quad \text{for } x = 0, 1, 2, \ldots \tag{14.1}$$

where

$$\begin{aligned} x &= \text{the number of arrivals in the time period} \\ \lambda &= \text{the } \textit{mean} \text{ number of arrivals per time period} \\ e &= 2.71828 \end{aligned}$$

The mean number of arrivals per time period, λ, is called the **arrival rate.** Values of $e^{-\lambda}$ can be found using a calculator or by using Appendix D.

Suppose that Burger Dome analyzed data on customer arrivals and concluded that the arrival rate is 45 customers per hour. For a one-minute period, the arrival rate would be $\lambda =$ 45 customers/60 minutes = 0.75 customers per minute. Thus, we can use the following Poisson probability function to compute the probability of x customer arrivals during a one-minute period:

$$P(x) = \frac{\lambda^x e^{-\lambda}}{x!} = \frac{0.75^x e^{-0.75}}{x!} \tag{14.2}$$

Thus, the probabilities of 0, 1, and 2 customer arrivals during a one-minute period are

$$P(0) = \frac{(0.75)^0 e^{-0.75}}{0!} = e^{-0.75} = 0.4724$$

$$P(1) = \frac{(0.75)^1 e^{-0.75}}{1!} = 0.75e^{-0.75} = 0.75(0.4724) = 0.3543$$

$$P(2) = \frac{(0.75)^2 e^{-0.75}}{2!} = \frac{(0.75)^2 e^{-0.75}}{2!} = \frac{(0.5625)(0.4724)}{2} = 0.1329$$

The probability of no customers in a one-minute period is 0.4724, the probability of one customer in a one-minute period is 0.3543, and the probability of two customers in a one-minute period is 0.1329. Table 14.1 shows the Poisson probabilities for customer arrivals during a one-minute period.

The waiting line models that will be presented in Sections 14.2 and 14.3 use the Poisson probability distribution to describe the customer arrivals at Burger Dome. In practice, you should record the actual number of arrivals per time period for several days or weeks and compare the frequency distribution of the observed number of arrivals to the Poisson probability distribution to determine whether the Poisson probability distribution provides a reasonable approximation of the arrival distribution.

---

[1]The term $x!$, *x factorial,* is defined as $x! = x(x-1)(x-2)\ldots(2)(1)$. For example $4! = (4)(3)(2)(1) = 24$. For the special case of $x = 0$, $0! = 1$ by definition.

TABLE 14.1 POISSON PROBABILITIES FOR THE NUMBER OF CUSTOMER ARRIVALS AT A BURGER DOME RESTAURANT DURING A ONE-MINUTE PERIOD ($\lambda = 0.75$)

Number of Arrivals	Probability
0	0.4724
1	0.3543
2	0.1329
3	0.0332
4	0.0062
5 or more	0.0010

Distribution of Service Times

The service time is the time a customer spends at the service facility once the service has started. At Burger Dome, the service time starts when a customer begins to place the order with the food server and continues until the customer receives the order. Service times are rarely constant. At Burger Dome, the number of items ordered and the mix of items ordered vary considerably from one customer to the next. Small orders can be handled in a matter of seconds, but large orders may require more than two minutes.

Quantitative analysts have found that if the probability distribution for the service time can be assumed to follow an **exponential probability distribution,** formulas are available for providing useful information about the operation of the waiting line. Using an exponential probability distribution, the probability that the service time will be less than or equal to a time of length t is

$$P(\text{service time} \leq t) = 1 - e^{-\mu t} \quad (14.3)$$

where

μ = the *mean* number of units that can be served per time period
e = 2.71828

The mean number of units that can be served per time period, μ, is called the **service rate.**

A property of the exponential probability distribution is that there is a 0.6321 probability that the random variable takes on a value less than its mean. In waiting line applications, the exponential probability distribution indicates that approximately 63 percent of the service times are less than the mean service time and approximately 37 percent of the service times are greater than the mean service time.

Suppose that Burger Dome studied the order-taking and order-filling process and found that the single food server can process an average of 60 customer orders per hour. On a one-minute basis, the service rate would be μ = 60 customers/60 minutes = 1 customer per minute. For example, with $\mu = 1$, we can use equation (14.3) to compute probabilities such as the probability an order can be processed in ½ minute or less, 1 minute or less, and 2 minutes or less. These computations are

$$P(\text{service time} \leq 0.5 \text{ min.}) = 1 - e^{-1(0.5)} = 1 - 0.6065 = 0.3935$$
$$P(\text{service time} \leq 1.0 \text{ min.}) = 1 - e^{-1(1.0)} = 1 - 0.3679 = 0.6321$$
$$P(\text{service time} \leq 2.0 \text{ min.}) = 1 - e^{-1(2.0)} = 1 - 0.1353 = 0.8647$$

Thus, we would conclude that there is a 0.3935 probability that an order can be processed in ½ minute or less, a 0.6321 probability that it can be processed in 1 minute or less, and a 0.8647 probability that it can be processed in 2 minutes or less.

In several waiting line models presented in this chapter, we assume that the probability distribution for the service time follows an exponential probability distribution. In practice, you should collect data on actual service times to determine whether the exponential probability distribution is a reasonable approximation of the service times for your application.

Queue Discipline

In describing a waiting line system, we must define the manner in which the waiting units are arranged for service. For the Burger Dome waiting line, and in general for most customer-oriented waiting lines, the units waiting for service are arranged on a **first-come, first-served** basis; this approach is referred to as an **FCFS** queue discipline. However, some situations call for different queue disciplines. For example, when people wait for an elevator, the last one on the elevator is often the first one to complete service (i.e., the first to leave the elevator). Other types of queue disciplines assign priorities to the waiting units and then serve the unit with the highest priority first. In this chapter we consider only waiting lines based on a first-come, first-served queue discipline. The Q.M. in Action, The Serpentine Line and an FCFS Queue Discipline at Whole Foods Market, describes how an FCFS queue discipline is used at a supermarket.

Q.M. IN ACTION

THE SERPENTINE LINE AND AN FCFS QUEUE DISCIPLINE AT WHOLE FOODS MARKET*

The Whole Foods Market in the Chelsea neighborhood of New York City employs a chief line director to implement a first-come, first-served (FCFS) queue discipline. Companies such as Wendy's, American Airlines, and Chemical Bank were among the first to employ serpentine lines to implement an FCFS queue discipline. Such lines are commonplace today. We see them at banks, amusement parks, and fast-food outlets. The line is called *serpentine* because of the way it winds around. When a customer gets to the front of the line, the customer then goes to the first available server. People like serpentine lines because they prevent people who join the line later from being served ahead of an earlier arrival.

As popular as serpentine lines have become, supermarkets have not employed them because of a lack of space. At the typical supermarket, a separate line forms at each checkout counter. When ready to check out a person picks one of the checkout counters and stays in that line until receiving service. Sometimes a person joining another checkout line later will receive service first, which tends to upset people. Manhattan's Whole Foods Market solved this problem by creating a new kind of line and employing a chief line director to direct the first person in line to the next available checkout counter.

The waiting line at the Whole Foods Market is actually three parallel lines. Customers join the shortest line and follow a rotation when they reach the front of the line. For instance, if the first customer in line 1 is sent to a checkout counter, the next customer sent to a checkout counter is the first person in line 2, then the first person in line 3, and so on. This way an FCFS queue discipline is implemented without a long, winding serpentine line.

The Whole Foods Market's customers seem to really like the system and the line director, Bill Jones, has become something of a celebrity. Children point to him on the street and customers invite him over for dinner.

*Based on Ian Parker, "Mr. Next," *The New Yorker* (January 13, 2003).

Steady-State Operation

When the Burger Dome restaurant opens in the morning, no customers are in the restaurant. Gradually, activity builds up to a normal or steady state. The beginning or start-up period is referred to as the **transient period.** The transient period ends when the system reaches the normal or **steady-state operation.** Waiting line models describe the steady-state operating characteristics of a waiting line.

14.2 SINGLE-CHANNEL WAITING LINE MODEL WITH POISSON ARRIVALS AND EXPONENTIAL SERVICE TIMES

Waiting line models are often based on assumptions such as Poisson arrivals and exponential service times. When applying any waiting line model, data should be collected on the actual system to ensure that the assumptions of the model are reasonable.

In this section we present formulas that can be used to determine the steady-state operating characteristics for a single-channel waiting line. The formulas are applicable if the arrivals follow a Poisson probability distribution and the service times follow an exponential probability distribution. As these assumptions apply to the Burger Dome waiting line problem introduced in Section 14.1, we show how formulas can be used to determine Burger Dome's operating characteristics and thus provide management with helpful decision-making information.

The mathematical methodology used to derive the formulas for the operating characteristics of waiting lines is rather complex. However, our purpose in this chapter is not to provide the theoretical development of waiting line models, but rather to show how the formulas that have been developed can provide information about operating characteristics of the waiting line. Readers interested in the mathematical development of the formulas can consult the specialized texts listed in Appendix E at the end of the text.

Operating Characteristics

The following formulas can be used to compute the steady-state operating characteristics for a single-channel waiting line with Poisson arrivals and exponential service times, where

λ = the mean number of arrivals per time period (the arrival rate)

μ = the mean number of services per time period (the service rate)

Equations (14.4) through (14.10) do not provide formulas for optimal conditions. Rather, these equations provide information about the steady-state operating characteristics of a waiting line.

1. The probability that no units are in the system:

$$P_0 = 1 - \frac{\lambda}{\mu} \tag{14.4}$$

2. The average number of units in the waiting line:

$$L_q = \frac{\lambda^2}{\mu(\mu - \lambda)} \tag{14.5}$$

3. The average number of units in the system:

$$L = L_q + \frac{\lambda}{\mu} \tag{14.6}$$

4. The average time a unit spends in the waiting line:

$$W_q = \frac{L_q}{\lambda} \tag{14.7}$$

5. The average time a unit spends in the system:

$$W = W_q + \frac{1}{\mu} \qquad (14.8)$$

6. The probability that an arriving unit has to wait for service:

$$P_w = \frac{\lambda}{\mu} \qquad (14.9)$$

7. The probability of n units in the system:

$$P_n = \left(\frac{\lambda}{\mu}\right)^n P_0 \qquad (14.10)$$

The values of the arrival rate λ and the service rate μ are clearly important components in determining the operating characteristics. Equation (14.9) shows that the ratio of the arrival rate to the service rate, λ/μ, provides the probability that an arriving unit has to wait because the service facility is in use. Hence, λ/μ is referred to as the *utilization factor* for the service facility.

The operating characteristics presented in equations (14.4) through (14.10) are applicable only when the service rate μ is *greater than* the arrival rate λ—in other words, when $\lambda/\mu < 1$. If this condition does not exist, the waiting line will continue to grow without limit because the service facility does not have sufficient capacity to handle the arriving units. Thus, in using equations (14.4) through (14.10), we must have $\mu > \lambda$.

Operating Characteristics for the Burger Dome Problem

Recall that for the Burger Dome problem we had an arrival rate of $\lambda = 0.75$ customers per minute and a service rate of $\mu = 1$ customer per minute. Thus, with $\mu > \lambda$, equations (14.4) through (14.10) can be used to provide operating characteristics for the Burger Dome single-channel waiting line:

$$P_0 = 1 - \frac{\lambda}{\mu} = 1 - \frac{0.75}{1} = 0.25$$

$$L_q = \frac{\lambda^2}{\mu(\mu - \lambda)} = \frac{0.75^2}{1(1 - 0.75)} = 2.25 \text{ customers}$$

$$L = L_q = \frac{\lambda}{\mu} + 2.25 + \frac{0.75}{1} = 3 \text{ customers}$$

$$W_q = \frac{L_q}{\lambda} = \frac{2.25}{0.75} = 3 \text{ minutes}$$

$$W = W_q + \frac{1}{\mu} = 3 + \frac{1}{1} = 4 \text{ minutes}$$

$$P_w = \frac{\lambda}{\mu} = \frac{0.75}{1} = 0.75$$

Problem 5 asks you to compute the operating characteristics for a single-channel waiting line application.

Equation (14.10) can be used to determine the probability of any number of customers in the system. Applying it provides the probability information in Table 14.2.

Managers' Use of Waiting Line Models

The results of the single-channel waiting line for Burger Dome show several important things about the operation of the waiting line. In particular, customers wait an average of three minutes before beginning to place an order, which appears somewhat long for a business based on fast service. In addition, the facts that the average number of customers waiting in line is 2.25 and that 75% of the arriving customers have to wait for service are indicators that something should be done to improve the waiting line operation. Table 14.2 shows a 0.1335 probability that seven or more customers are in the Burger Dome system at one time. This condition indicates a fairly high probability that Burger Dome will experience some long waiting lines if it continues to use the single-channel operation.

If the operating characteristics are unsatisfactory in terms of meeting company standards for service, Burger Dome's management should consider alternative designs or plans for improving the waiting line operation.

Improving the Waiting Line Operation

Waiting line models often indicate when improvements in operating characteristics are desirable. However, the decision of how to modify the waiting line configuration to improve the operating characteristics must be based on the insights and creativity of the analyst.

After reviewing the operating characteristics provided by the waiting line model, Burger Dome's management concluded that improvements designed to reduce waiting times are desirable. To make improvements in the waiting line operation, analysts often focus on ways to improve the service rate. Generally, service rate improvements are obtained by making either or both of the following changes:

1. Increase the service rate by making a creative design change or by using new technology.
2. Add one or more service channels so that more customers can be served simultaneously.

Assume that in considering alternative 1, Burger Dome's management decides to employ an order filler who will assist the order taker at the cash register. The customer begins the service process by placing the order with the order taker. As the order is placed, the order taker

TABLE 14.2 THE PROBABILITY OF n CUSTOMERS IN THE SYSTEM FOR THE BURGER DOME WAITING LINE PROBLEM

Number of Customers	Probability
0	0.2500
1	0.1875
2	0.1406
3	0.1055
4	0.0791
5	0.0593
6	0.0445
7 or more	0.1335

announces the order over an intercom system, and the order filler begins filling the order. When the order is completed, the order taker handles the money, while the order filler continues to fill the order. With this design, Burger Dome's management estimates the service rate can be increased from the current 60 customers per hour to 75 customers per hour. Thus, the service rate for the revised system is $\mu = 75$ customers/60 minutes $= 1.25$ customers per minute. For $\lambda = 0.75$ customers per minute and $\mu = 1.25$ customers per minute, equations (14.4) through (14.10) can be used to provide the new operating characteristics for the Burger Dome waiting line. These operating characteristics are summarized in Table 14.3.

The information in Table 14.3 indicates that all operating characteristics have improved because of the increased service rate. In particular, the average time a customer spends in the waiting line has been reduced from 3 to 1.2 minutes and the average time a customer spends in the system has been reduced from 4 to 2 minutes. Are any other alternatives available that Burger Dome can use to increase the service rate? If so, and if the mean service rate μ can be identified for each alternative, equations (14.4) through (14.10) can be used to determine the revised operating characteristics and any improvements in the waiting line system. The added cost of any proposed change can be compared to the corresponding service improvements to help the manager determine whether the proposed service improvements are worthwhile.

Problem 11 asks you to determine whether a change in the service rate will meet the company's service guideline for its customers.

As mentioned previously, another option often available is to add one or more service channels so that more customers can be served simultaneously. The extension of the single-channel waiting line model to the multiple-channel waiting line model is the topic of the next section.

Excel Solution of Waiting Line Model

Waiting line models are easily implemented with the aid of worksheets. The Excel worksheet for the Burger Dome single-channel waiting line is shown in Figure 14.2. The formula worksheet is in the background; the value worksheet is in the foreground. The arrival rate and the service rate are entered in cells B7 and B8. The formulas for the waiting line's operating characteristics are placed in cells C13 to C18. The worksheet shows the same values for the operating characteristics that we obtained earlier. Modifications in the waiting line design can be evaluated by entering different arrival rates and/or service rates into cells B7 and B8. The new operating characteristics of the waiting line will be shown immediately.

The Management Scientist software also has a waiting line module that can be used to solve the waiting line problems in this chapter.

The Excel worksheet in Figure 14.2 is a template that can be used with any single-channel waiting line model with Poisson arrivals and exponential service times. This worksheet and similar Excel worksheets for the other waiting line models presented in this chapter are available on the CD that accompanies this text.

TABLE 14.3 OPERATING CHARACTERISTICS FOR THE BURGER DOME SYSTEM WITH THE SERVICE RATE INCREASED TO $\mu = 1.25$ CUSTOMERS PER MINUTE

Probability of no customers in the system	0.400
Average number of customers in the waiting line	0.900
Average number of customers in the system	1.500
Average time in the waiting line	1.200 minutes
Average time in the system	2.000 minutes
Probability that an arriving customer has to wait	0.600
Probability that seven or more customers are in the system	0.028

FIGURE 14.2 WORKSHEET FOR THE BURGER DOME SINGLE-CHANNEL WAITING LINE

	A	B	C	D
1	**Single-Channel Waiting Line Model**			
2				
3	**Assumptions**			
4	**Poisson Arrivals**			
5	**Exponential Service Times**			
6				
7	Arrival Rate	0.75		
8	Service Rate	1		
9				
10				
11	**Operating Characteristics**			
12				
13	Probability that no customers are in the system, Po		=1-B7/B8	
14	Average number of customers in the waiting line, Lq		=B7^2/(B8*(B8-B7))	
15	Average number of customers in the system, L		=C14+B7/B8	
16	Average time a customer spends in the waiting line, Wq		=C14/B7	
17	Average time a customer spends in the system, W		=C16+1/B8	
18	Probability an arriving customer has to wait, Pw		=B7/B8	
19				

	A	B	C
1	**Single-Channel Waiting Line Model**		
2			
3	**Assumptions**		
4	**Poisson Arrivals**		
5	**Exponential Service Times**		
6			
7	Arrival Rate	0.75	
8	Service Rate	1	
9			
10			
11	**Operating Characteristics**		
12			
13	Probability that no customers are in the system, Po		0.2500
14	Average number of customers in the waiting line, Lq		2.2500
15	Average number of customers in the system, L		3.0000
16	Average time a customer spends in the waiting line, Wq		3.0000
17	Average time a customer spends in the system, W		4.0000
18	Probability an arriving customer has to wait, Pw		0.7500
19			

EXCELfile
Single

NOTES AND COMMENTS

1. The assumption that arrivals follow a Poisson probability distribution is equivalent to the assumption that the time between arrivals has an exponential probability distribution. For example, if the arrivals for a waiting line follow a Poisson probability distribution with a mean of 20 arrivals per hour, the time between arrivals will follow an exponential probability distribution, with a mean time between arrivals of $\frac{1}{20}$ or 0.05 hour.
2. Many individuals believe that whenever the service rate μ is greater than the arrival rate λ, the system should be able to handle or serve all arrivals. However, as the Burger Dome example shows, the variability of arrival times and service times may result in long waiting times even when the service rate exceeds the arrival rate. A contribution of waiting line models is that they can point out undesirable waiting line operating characteristics even when the $\mu > \lambda$ condition appears satisfactory.

14.3 MULTIPLE-CHANNEL WAITING LINE MODEL WITH POISSON ARRIVALS AND EXPONENTIAL SERVICE TIMES

You may be familiar with multiple-channel systems that also have multiple waiting lines. The waiting line model in this section has multiple channels, but only a single waiting line. Operating characteristics for a multiple-channel system are better when a single waiting line, rather than multiple waiting lines, is used.

A **multiple-channel waiting line** consists of two or more service channels that are assumed to be identical in terms of service capability. In the multiple-channel system, arriving units wait in a single waiting line and then move to the first available channel to be served. The single-channel Burger Dome operation can be expanded to a two-channel system by opening a second service channel. Figure 14.3 shows a diagram of the Burger Dome two-channel waiting line.

In this section we present formulas that can be used to determine the steady-state operating characteristics for a multiple-channel waiting line. These formulas are applicable if the following conditions exist.

1. The arrivals follow a Poisson probability distribution.
2. The service time for each channel follows an exponential probability distribution.

FIGURE 14.3 THE BURGER DOME TWO-CHANNEL WAITING LINE

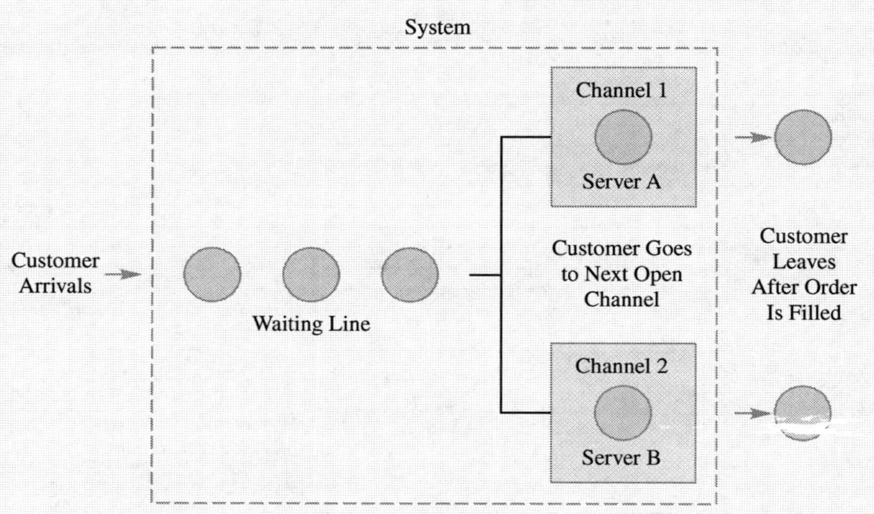

3. The service rate μ is the same for each channel.
4. The arrivals wait in a single waiting line and then move to the first open channel for service.

Operating Characteristics

The following formulas can be used to compute the steady-state operating characteristics for multiple-channel waiting lines, where

$$\lambda = \text{the arrival rate for the system}$$
$$\mu = \text{the service rate for } \textit{each} \text{ channel}$$
$$k = \text{the number of channels}$$

1. The probability that no units are in the system:

$$P_0 = \frac{1}{\displaystyle\sum_{n=0}^{k-1} \frac{(\lambda/\mu)^n}{n!} + \frac{(\lambda/\mu)^k}{k!}\left(\frac{k\mu}{k\mu - \lambda}\right)} \tag{14.11}$$

2. The average number of units in the waiting line:

$$L_q = \frac{(\lambda/\mu)^k \lambda\mu}{(k-1)!(k\mu - \lambda)^2} P_0 \tag{14.12}$$

3. The average number of units in the system:

$$L = L_q + \frac{\lambda}{\mu} \tag{14.13}$$

4. The average time a unit spends in the waiting line:

$$W_q = \frac{L_q}{\lambda} \tag{14.14}$$

5. The average time a unit spends in the system:

$$W = W_q + \frac{1}{\mu} \tag{14.15}$$

6. The probability that an arriving unit has to wait for service:

$$P_w = \frac{1}{k!}\left(\frac{\lambda}{\mu}\right)^k \left(\frac{k\mu}{k\mu - \lambda}\right) P_0 \tag{14.16}$$

7. The probability of n units in the system:

$$P_n = \frac{(\lambda/\mu)^n}{n!} P_0 \quad \text{for } n \leq k \tag{14.17}$$

$$P_n = \frac{(\lambda/\mu)^n}{k!k^{(n-k)}} P_0 \quad \text{for } n > k \tag{14.18}$$

Because μ is the service rate for each channel, $k\mu$ is the service rate for the multiple-channel system. As was true for the single-channel waiting line model, the formulas for the operating characteristics of multiple-channel waiting lines can be applied only in situations where the service rate for the system is greater than the arrival rate for the system; in other words, the formulas are applicable only if $k\mu$ is greater than λ.

Some expressions for the operating characteristics of multiple-channel waiting lines are more complex than their single-channel counterparts. However, equations (14.11) through (14.18) provide the same information as provided by the single-channel model. To help simplify the use of the multiple-channel equations, Table 14.4 contains values of P_0 for selected values of λ/μ and k. The values provided in the table correspond to cases where $k\mu > \lambda$, and hence the service rate is sufficient to process all arrivals.

TABLE 14.4 VALUES OF P_0 FOR MULTIPLE-CHANNEL WAITING LINES WITH POISSON ARRIVALS AND EXPONENTIAL SERVICE TIMES

	Number of Channels (k)			
Ratio λ/μ	2	3	4	5
0.15	0.8605	0.8607	0.8607	0.8607
0.20	0.8182	0.8187	0.8187	0.8187
0.25	0.7778	0.7788	0.7788	0.7788
0.30	0.7391	0.7407	0.7408	0.7408
0.35	0.7021	0.7046	0.7047	0.7047
0.40	0.6667	0.6701	0.6703	0.6703
0.45	0.6327	0.6373	0.6376	0.6376
0.50	0.6000	0.6061	0.6065	0.6065
0.55	0.5686	0.5763	0.5769	0.5769
0.60	0.5385	0.5479	0.5487	0.5488
0.65	0.5094	0.5209	0.5219	0.5220
0.70	0.4815	0.4952	0.4965	0.4966
0.75	0.4545	0.4706	0.4722	0.4724
0.80	0.4286	0.4472	0.4491	0.4493
0.85	0.4035	0.4248	0.4271	0.4274
0.90	0.3793	0.4035	0.4062	0.4065
0.95	0.3559	0.3831	0.3863	0.3867
1.00	0.3333	0.3636	0.3673	0.3678
1.20	0.2500	0.2941	0.3002	0.3011
1.40	0.1765	0.2360	0.2449	0.2463
1.60	0.1111	0.1872	0.1993	0.2014
1.80	0.0526	0.1460	0.1616	0.1646
2.00		0.1111	0.1304	0.1343
2.20		0.0815	0.1046	0.1094
2.40		0.0562	0.0831	0.0889
2.60		0.0345	0.0651	0.0721
2.80		0.0160	0.0521	0.0581
3.00			0.0377	0.0466
3.20			0.0273	0.0372
3.40			0.0186	0.0293
3.60			0.0113	0.0228
3.80			0.0051	0.0174
4.00				0.0130
4.20				0.0093
4.40				0.0063
4.60				0.0038
4.80				0.0017

Operating Characteristics for the Burger Dome Problem

To illustrate the multiple-channel waiting line model, we return to the Burger Dome fast-food restaurant waiting line problem. Suppose that management wants to evaluate the desirability of opening a second order-processing station so that two customers can be served simultaneously. Assume a single waiting line with the first customer in line moving to the first available server. Let us evaluate the operating characteristics for this two-channel system.

We use equations (14.12) through (14.18) for the $k = 2$ channel system. For an arrival rate of $\lambda = 0.75$ customers per minute and a service rate of $\mu = 1$ customer per minute for each channel, we obtain the operating characteristics:

EXCELfile
Multiple

$$P_0 = 0.4545 \quad \text{(from Table 14.4 with } \lambda/\mu = 0.75\text{)}$$

$$L_q = \frac{(0.75/1)^2(0.75)(1)}{(2-1)![2(1) - 0.75]^2}(0.4545) = 0.1227 \text{ customer}$$

$$L = L_q + \frac{\lambda}{\mu} = 0.1227 + \frac{0.75}{1} = 0.8727 \text{ customer}$$

$$W_q = \frac{L_q}{\lambda} = \frac{0.1227}{0.75} = 0.1636 \text{ minute}$$

$$W = W_q + \frac{1}{\mu} = 0.1636 + \frac{1}{1} = 1.1636 \text{ minutes}$$

$$P_w = \frac{1}{2!}\left(\frac{0.75}{1}\right)^2\left[\frac{2(1)}{2(1) - 0.75}\right](0.4545) = 0.2045$$

Try Problem 18 for practice in determining the operating characteristics for a two-channel waiting line.

Using equations (14.17) and (14.18), we can compute the probabilities of n customers in the system. The results from these computations are summarized in Table 14.5.

We can now compare the steady-state operating characteristics of the two-channel system to the operating characteristics of the original single-channel system discussed in Section 14.2.

1. The average time a customer spends in the system (waiting time plus service time) is reduced from $W = 4$ minutes to $W = 1.1636$ minutes.
2. The average number of customers in the waiting line is reduced from $L_q = 2.25$ customers to $L_q = 0.1227$ customer.
3. The average time a customer spends in the waiting line is reduced from $W_q = 3$ minutes to $W_q = 0.1636$ minute.
4. The probability that a customer has to wait for service is reduced from $P_w = 0.75$ to $P_w = 0.2045$.

Clearly the two-channel system will significantly improve the operating characteristics of the waiting line. However, adding an order filler at each service station would further increase the service rate and improve the operating characteristics. The final decision regarding the staffing policy at Burger Dome rests with the Burger Dome management. The waiting line study simply provides the operating characteristics that can be anticipated

TABLE 14.5 THE PROBABILITY OF n CUSTOMERS IN THE SYSTEM FOR THE BURGER DOME TWO-CHANNEL WAITING LINE

Number of Customers	Probability
0	0.4545
1	0.3409
2	0.1278
3	0.0479
4	0.0180
5 or more	0.0109

under three configurations: a single-channel system with one employee, a single-channel system with two employees, and a two-channel system with an employee for each channel. After considering these results, what action would you recommend? In this case, Burger Dome adopted the following policy statement: For periods when customer arrivals are expected to average 45 customers per hour, Burger Dome will open two order-processing channels with one employee assigned to each.

By changing the arrival rate λ to reflect arrival rates at different times of the day, and then computing the operating characteristics, Burger Dome's management can establish guidelines and policies that tell the store managers when to schedule service operations with a single channel, two channels, or perhaps even three or more channels.

NOTES AND COMMENTS

The multiple-channel waiting line model is based on a single waiting line. You may have also encountered situations where each of the k channels has its own waiting line. Analysts have shown that the operating characteristics of multiple-channel systems are better if a single waiting line is used. People like them better also; no one who comes in after you can be served ahead of you. Thus, when possible, banks, airline reservation counters, food-service establishments, and other businesses frequently use a single waiting line for a multiple-channel system.

14.4 SOME GENERAL RELATIONSHIPS FOR WAITING LINE MODELS

In Sections 14.2 and 14.3 we presented formulas for computing the operating characteristics for single-channel and multiple-channel waiting lines with Poisson arrivals and exponential service times. The operating characteristics of interest included

$$\begin{aligned} L_q &= \text{the average number of units in the waiting line} \\ L &= \text{the average number of units in the system} \\ W_q &= \text{the average time a unit spends in the waiting line} \\ W &= \text{the average time a unit spends in the system} \end{aligned}$$

John D. C. Little showed that several relationships exist among these four characteristics and that these relationships apply to a variety of different waiting line systems. Two of the relationships, referred to as *Little's flow equations,* are

$$L = \lambda W \tag{14.19}$$

$$L_q = \lambda W_q \tag{14.20}$$

Equation (14.19) shows that the average number of units in the system, L, can be found by multiplying the arrival rate, λ, by the average time a unit spends in the system, W. Equation (14.20) shows that the same relationship holds between the average number of units in the waiting line, L_q, and the average time a unit spends in the waiting line, W_q.

Using equation (14.20) and solving for W_q, we obtain

$$W_q = \frac{L_q}{\lambda} \tag{14.21}$$

Equation (14.21) follows directly from Little's second flow equation. We used it for the single-channel waiting line model in Section 14.2 and the multiple-channel waiting line model in Section 14.3 [see equations (14.7) and (14.14)]. Once L_q is computed for either of these models, equation (14.21) can then be used to compute W_q.

Another general expression that applies to waiting line models is that the average time in the system, W, is equal to the average time in the waiting line, W_q, plus the average service time. For a system with a service rate μ, the mean service time is $1/\mu$. Thus, we have the general relationship

$$W = W_q + \frac{1}{\mu} \tag{14.22}$$

Recall that we used equation (14.22) to provide the average time in the system for both the single- and multiple-channel waiting line models [see equations (14.8) and (14.15)].

The advantage of Little's flow equations is that they show how operating characteristics L, L_q, W, and W_q are related in any waiting line system. Arrivals and service times do not have to follow specific probability distributions for the flow equations to be applicable.

The importance of Little's flow equations is that they apply to *any waiting line model* regardless of whether arrivals follow the Poisson probability distribution and regardless of whether service times follow the exponential probability distribution. For example, in a study of the grocery checkout counters at Murphy's Foodliner, an analyst concluded that arrivals follow the Poisson probability distribution with an arrival rate of 24 customers per hour or $\lambda = 24/60 = 0.40$ customers per minute. However, the analyst found that service times follow a normal probability distribution rather than an exponential probability distribution. The service rate was found to be 30 customers per hour or $\mu = 30/60 = 0.50$ customers per minute. A time study of actual customer waiting times showed that, on average, a customer spends 4.5 minutes in the system (waiting time plus checkout time); that is, $W = 4.5$. Using the waiting line relationships discussed in this section, we can now compute other operating characteristics for this waiting line.

First, using equation (14.22) and solving for W_q, we have

$$W_q = W - \frac{1}{\mu} = 4.5 - \frac{1}{0.50} = 2.5 \text{ minutes}$$

With both W and W_q known, we can use Little's flow equations, (14.19) and (14.20), to compute

$$L = \lambda W = 0.40(4.5) = 1.8 \text{ customers}$$
$$L_q = \lambda W_q = 0.40(2.5) = 1 \text{ customer}$$

The application of Little's flow equations is demonstrated in Problem 25.

The manager of Murphy's Foodliner can now review these operating characteristics to see whether action should be taken to improve the service and to reduce the waiting time and the length of the waiting line.

NOTES AND COMMENTS

In waiting line systems where the length of the waiting line is limited (e.g., a small waiting area), some arriving units will be blocked from joining the waiting line and will be lost. In this case, the blocked or lost arrivals will make the mean number of units entering the system something less than the arrival rate. By defining λ as the mean number of units *joining the system,* rather than the arrival rate, the relationships discussed in this section can be used to determine W, L, W_q, and L_q.

14.5 ECONOMIC ANALYSIS OF WAITING LINES

Frequently, decisions involving the design of waiting lines will be based on a subjective evaluation of the operating characteristics of the waiting line. For example, a manager may decide that an average waiting time of one minute or less and an average of two customers or fewer in the system are reasonable goals. The waiting line models presented in the preceding sections can be used to determine the number of channels that will meet the manager's waiting line performance goals.

On the other hand, a manager may want to identify the cost of operating the waiting line system and then base the decision regarding system design on a minimum hourly or daily operating cost. Before an economic analysis of a waiting line can be conducted, a total cost model, which includes the cost of waiting and the cost of service, must be developed.

To develop a total cost model for a waiting line, we begin by defining the notation to be used:

Waiting cost is based on average number of units in the system. It includes the time spent waiting in line plus the time spent being served.

c_w = the waiting cost per time period for each unit
L = the average number of units in the system
c_s = the service cost per time period for each channel
k = the number of channels
TC = the total cost per time period

The total cost is the sum of the waiting cost and the service cost; that is,

$$TC = c_w L + c_s k \tag{14.23}$$

Adding more channels always improves the operating characteristics of the waiting line and reduces the waiting cost. However, additional channels increase the service cost. An economic analysis of waiting lines attempts to find the number of channels that will minimize total cost by balancing the waiting cost and the service cost.

To conduct an economic analysis of a waiting line, we must obtain reasonable estimates of the waiting cost and the service cost. Of these two costs, the waiting cost is usually the more difficult to evaluate. In the Burger Dome restaurant problem, the waiting cost would be the cost per minute for a customer waiting for service. This cost is not a direct cost to Burger Dome. However, if Burger Dome ignores this cost and allows long waiting lines, customers ultimately will take their business elsewhere. Thus, Burger Dome will experience lost sales and, in effect, incur a cost.

The service cost is generally easier to determine. This cost is the relevant cost associated with operating each service channel. In the Burger Dome problem, this cost would include the server's wages, benefits, and any other direct costs associated with operating the service channel. At Burger Dome, this cost is estimated to be $7 per hour.

To demonstrate the use of equation (14.23), we assume that Burger Dome is willing to assign a cost of $10 per hour for customer waiting time. We use the average number of units in the system, L, as computed in Sections 14.2 and 14.3 to obtain the total hourly cost for the single-channel and two-channel systems:

Single-channel system ($L = 3$ customers)

$$\begin{aligned} TC &= c_w L + c_s k \\ &= 10(3) + 7(1) = \$37.00 \text{ per hour} \end{aligned}$$

Two-channel system ($L = 0.8727$ customer):

$$\begin{aligned} TC &= c_w L + c_s k \\ &= 10(0.8727) + 7(2) = \$22.73 \text{ per hour} \end{aligned}$$

Thus, based on the cost data provided by Burger Dome, the two-channel system provides the most economical operation.

FIGURE 14.4 THE GENERAL SHAPE OF WAITING COST, SERVICE COST, AND TOTAL COST CURVES IN WAITING LINE MODELS

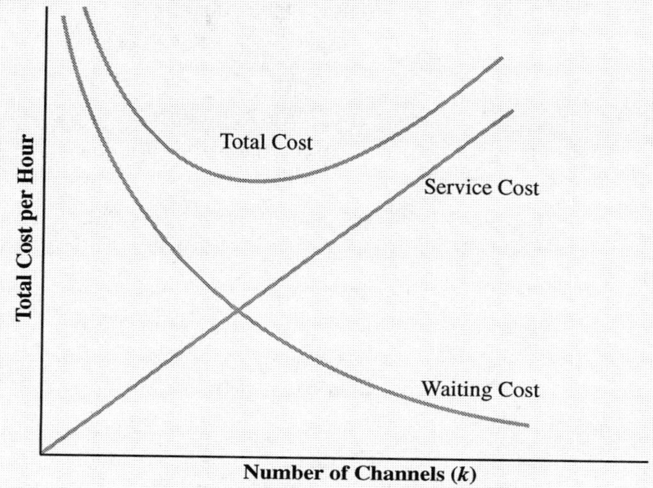

Problem 21 tests your ability to conduct an economic analysis of proposed single-channel and two-channel waiting line systems.

Figure 14.4 shows the general shape of the cost curves in the economic analysis of waiting lines. The service cost increases as the number of channels is increased. However, with more channels, the service is better. As a result, waiting time and cost decrease as the number of channels is increased. The number of channels that will provide a good approximation of the minimum total cost design can be found by evaluating the total cost for several design alternatives.

NOTES AND COMMENTS

1. In dealing with government agencies and utility companies, customers may not be able to take their business elsewhere. In these situations, no lost business occurs when long waiting times are encountered. This condition is one reason that service in such organizations may be poor and that customers in such situations may experience long waiting times.
2. In some instances, the organization providing the service also employs the units waiting for the service. For example, consider the case of a company that owns and operates the trucks used to deliver goods to and from its manufacturing plant. In addition to the costs associated with the trucks waiting to be loaded or unloaded, the firm also pays the wages of the truck loaders and unloaders who operate the service channel. In this case, the cost of having the trucks wait and the cost of operating the service channel are direct expenses to the firm. An economic analysis of the waiting line system is highly recommended for these types of situations.

14.6 OTHER WAITING LINE MODELS

D. G. Kendall suggested a notation that is helpful in classifying the wide variety of different waiting line models that have been developed. The three-symbol Kendall notation is as follows:

$$A/B/k$$

where

A denotes the probability distribution for the arrivals
B denotes the probability distribution for the service time
k denotes the number of channels

Depending on the letter appearing in the A or B position, a variety of waiting line systems can be described. The letters that are commonly used are as follows:

M designates a Poisson probability distribution for the arrivals or an exponential probability distribution for service time
D designates that the arrivals or the service time is deterministic or constant
G designates that the arrivals or the service time has a general probability distribution with a known mean and variance

Using the Kendall notation, the single-channel waiting line model with Poisson arrivals and exponential service times is classified as an $M/M/1$ model. The two-channel waiting line model with Poisson arrivals and exponential service times presented in Section 14.3 would be classified as an $M/M/2$ model.

NOTES AND COMMENTS

In some cases, the Kendall notation is extended to five symbols. The fourth symbol indicates the largest number of units that can be in the system, and the fifth symbol indicates the size of the population. The fourth symbol is used in situations where the waiting line can hold a finite or maximum number of units, and the fifth symbol is necessary when the population of arriving units or customers is finite. When the fourth and fifth symbols of the Kendall notation are omitted, the waiting line system is assumed to have infinite capacity, and the population is assumed to be infinite.

14.7 SINGLE-CHANNEL WAITING LINE MODEL WITH POISSON ARRIVALS AND ARBITRARY SERVICE TIMES

Let us return to the single-channel waiting line model where arrivals are described by a Poisson probability distribution. However, we now assume that the probability distribution for the service times is not an exponential probability distribution. Thus, using the Kendall notation, the waiting line model that is appropriate is an $M/G/1$ model, where G denotes a general or unspecified probability distribution.

When providing input to the M/G/1 model, be consistent in terms of the time period. For example, if λ and μ are expressed in terms of the number of units per hour, the standard deviation of the service time should be expressed in hours. The example that follows uses minutes as the time period for the arrival and service data.

Operating Characteristics for the $M/G/1$ Model

The notation used to describe the operating characteristics for the $M/G/1$ model is

λ = the arrival rate
μ = the service rate
σ = the standard deviation of the service time

Some of the steady-state operating characteristics of the $M/G/1$ waiting line model are as follows:

1. The probability that no units are in the system:

$$P_0 = 1 - \frac{\lambda}{\mu} \tag{14.24}$$

2. The average number of units in the waiting line:

$$L_q = \frac{\lambda^2\sigma^2 + (\lambda/\mu)^2}{2(1 - \lambda/\mu)} \tag{14.25}$$

3. The average number of units in the system:

$$L = L_q + \frac{\lambda}{\mu} \tag{14.26}$$

4. The average time a unit spends in the waiting line:

$$W_q = \frac{L_q}{\lambda} \tag{14.27}$$

5. The average time a unit spends in the system:

$$W = W_q + \frac{1}{\mu} \tag{14.28}$$

6. The probability that an arriving unit has to wait for service:

$$P_w = \frac{\lambda}{\mu} \tag{14.29}$$

Note that the relationships for L, W_q, and W are the same as the relationships used for the waiting line models in Sections 14.2 and 14.3. They are given by Little's flow equations.

Problem 27 provides another application of a single-channel waiting line with Poisson arrivals and arbitrary service times.

An Example Retail sales at Hartlage's Seafood Supply are handled by one clerk. Customer arrivals are random, and the arrival rate is 21 customers per hour or $\lambda = 21/60 = 0.35$ customers per minute. A study of the service process shows that the service time is 2 minutes per customer, with a standard deviation of $\sigma = 1.2$ minutes. The mean time of 2 minutes per customer shows that the clerk has a service rate of $\mu = ½ = 0.50$ customers per minute. The operating characteristics of this $M/G/1$ waiting line system are

EXCELfile
Single-Arbitrary

$$P_0 = 1 - \frac{\lambda}{\mu} = 1 - \frac{0.35}{0.50} = 0.30$$

$$L_q = \frac{(0.35)^2(1.2)^2 + (0.35/0.50)^2}{2(1 - 0.35/0.50)} = 1.1107 \text{ customers}$$

$$L = L_q + \frac{\lambda}{\mu} = 1.1107 + \frac{0.35}{0.50} = 1.8107 \text{ customers}$$

$$W_q = \frac{L_q}{\lambda} = \frac{1.1107}{0.35} = 3.1733 \text{ minutes}$$

$$W = W_q + \frac{1}{\mu} = 3.1733 + \frac{1}{0.50} = 5.1733 \text{ minutes}$$

$$P_w = \frac{\lambda}{\mu} = \frac{0.35}{0.50} = 0.70$$

Hartlage's manager can review these operating characteristics to determine whether scheduling a second clerk appears to be worthwhile.

Constant Service Times

We want to comment briefly on the single-channel waiting line model that assumes random arrivals but constant service times. Such a waiting line can occur in production and manufacturing environments where machine-controlled service times are constant. This waiting line is described by the $M/D/1$ model, with the D referring to the deterministic service times. With the $M/D/1$ model, the average number of units in the waiting line, L_q, can be found by using equation (14.25) with the condition that the standard deviation of the constant service time is $\sigma = 0$. Thus, the expression for the average number of units in the waiting line for the $M/D/1$ waiting line becomes

$$L_q = \frac{(\lambda/\mu)^2}{2(1 - \lambda/\mu)} \tag{14.30}$$

The other expressions presented earlier in this section can be used to determine additional operating characteristics of the $M/D/1$ system.

NOTES AND COMMENTS

Whenever the operating characteristics of a waiting line are unacceptable, managers often try to improve service by increasing the service rate μ. This approach is good, but equation (14.25) shows that the variation in the service times also affects the operating characteristics of the waiting line. Because the standard deviation of service times, σ, appears in the numerator of equation (14.25), a larger variation in service times results in a larger average number of units in the waiting line. Hence, another alternative for improving the service capabilities of a waiting line is to reduce the variation in the service times. Thus, even when the service rate of the service facility cannot be increased, a reduction in σ will reduce the average number of units in the waiting line and improve the operating characteristics of the system.

14.8 MULTIPLE-CHANNEL MODEL WITH POISSON ARRIVALS, ARBITRARY SERVICE TIMES, AND NO WAITING LINE

An interesting variation of the waiting line models discussed so far involves a system in which no waiting is allowed. Arriving units or customers seek service from one of several service channels. If all channels are busy, arriving units are denied access to the system. In waiting line terminology, arrivals occurring when the system is full are **blocked** and are cleared from the system. Such customers may be lost or may attempt a return to the system later.

The specific model considered in this section is based on the following assumptions.

1. The system has k channels.
2. The arrivals follow a Poisson probability distribution, with arrival rate λ.
3. The service times for each channel may have any probability distribution.
4. The service rate μ is the same for each channel.
5. An arrival enters the system only if at least one channel is available. An arrival occurring when all channels are busy is blocked—that is, denied service and not allowed to enter the system.

With G denoting a general or unspecified probability distribution for service times, the appropriate model for this situation is referred to as an $M/G/k$ model with "blocked customers cleared." The question addressed in this type of situation is, How many channels or servers should be used?

A primary application of this model involves the design of telephone and other communication systems where the arrivals are the calls and the channels are the number of telephone or communication lines available. In such a system, the calls are made to one telephone number, with each call automatically switched to an open channel if possible. When all channels are busy, additional calls receive a busy signal and are denied access to the system.

Operating Characteristics for the $M/G/k$ Model with Blocked Customers Cleared

We approach the problem of selecting the best number of channels by computing the steady-state probabilities that j of the k channels will be busy. These probabilities are

$$P_j = \frac{(\lambda/\mu)^j/j!}{\sum_{i=0}^{k} (\lambda/\mu)^i/i!} \tag{14.31}$$

With no waiting allowed, operating characteristics L_q and W_q considered in previous waiting line models are automatically zero regardless of the number of service channels. In this situation, the more important design consideration involves determining how the percentage of blocked customers is affected by the number of service channels.

where

λ = the arrival rate
μ = the service rate for each channel
k = the number of channels
P_j = the probability that j of the k channels are busy for $j = 0, 1, 2, \ldots, k$

The most important probability value is P_k, which is the probability that all k channels are busy. On a percentage basis, P_k indicates the percentage of arrivals that are blocked and denied access to the system.

Another operating characteristic of interest is the average number of units in the system; note that this number is equivalent to the average number of channels in use. Letting L denote the average number of units in the system, we have

$$L = \frac{\lambda}{\mu}(1 - P_k) \qquad (14.32)$$

An Example Microdata Software, Inc., uses a telephone ordering system for its computer software products. Callers place orders with Microdata by using the company's 800 telephone number. Assume that calls to this telephone number arrive at a rate of $\lambda = 12$ calls per hour. The time required to process a telephone order varies considerably from order to order. However, each Microdata sales representative can be expected to handle $\mu = 6$ calls per hour. Currently, the Microdata 800 telephone number has three internal lines or channels, each operated by a separate sales representative. Calls received on the 800 number are automatically transferred to an open line or channel if available.

Whenever all three lines are busy, callers receive a busy signal. In the past, Microdata's management assumed that callers receiving a busy signal would call back later. However, recent research on telephone ordering showed that a substantial number of callers who are denied access do not call back later. These lost calls represent lost revenues for the firm, so Microdata's management requested an analysis of the telephone ordering system. Specifically, management wanted to know the percentage of callers who get busy signals and are blocked from the system. If management's goal is to provide sufficient capacity to handle 90% of the callers, how many telephone lines and sales representatives should Microdata use?

We can demonstrate the use of equation (14.31) by computing P_3, the probability that all three of the currently available telephone lines will be in use and additional callers will be blocked:

EXCELfile
No Waiting

$$P_3 = \frac{(^{12}\!/_6)^3/3!}{(^{12}\!/_6)^0/0! + (^{12}\!/_6)^1/1! + (^{12}\!/_6)^2/2! + (^{12}\!/_6)^3/3!} = \frac{1.3333}{6.3333} = 0.2105$$

With $P_3 = 0.2105$, approximately 21% of the calls, or slightly more than one in five calls, are being blocked. Only 79% of the calls are being handled immediately by the three-line system.

Let us assume that Microdata expands to a four-line system. Then, the probability that all four channels will be in use and that callers will be blocked is

$$P_4 = \frac{(^{12}\!/_6)^4/4!}{(^{12}\!/_6)^0/0! + (^{12}\!/_6)^1/1! + (^{12}\!/_6)^2/2! + (^{12}\!/_6)^3/3! + (^{12}\!/_6)^4/4!} = \frac{0.667}{7} = 0.0952$$

With only 9.52% of the callers blocked, 90.48% of the callers will reach the Microdata sales representatives. Thus, Microdata should expand its order-processing operation to four lines to meet management's goal of providing sufficient capacity to handle at least 90% of the callers. The average number of calls in the four-line system and thus the average number of lines and sales representatives that will be busy is

Problem 30 provides practice in calculating probabilities for multiple-channel systems with no waiting line.

$$L = \frac{\lambda}{\mu}(1 - P_4) = \frac{12}{6}(1 - 0.0952) = 1.8095$$

TABLE 14.6 PROBABILITIES OF BUSY LINES FOR THE MICRODATA FOUR-LINE SYSTEM

Number of Busy Lines	Probability
0	0.1429
1	0.2857
2	0.2857
3	0.1905
4	0.0952

Although an average of fewer than two lines will be busy, the four-line system is necessary to provide the capacity to handle at least 90% of the callers. We used equation (14.31) to calculate the probability that 0, 1, 2, 3, or 4 lines will be busy. These probabilities are summarized in Table 14.6.

As we discussed in Section 14.5, an economic analysis of waiting lines can be used to guide system design decisions. In the Microdata system, the cost of the additional line and additional sales representative should be relatively easy to establish. This cost can be balanced against the cost of the blocked calls. With 9.52% of the calls blocked and $\lambda = 12$ calls per hour, an eight-hour day will have an average of $8(12)(0.0952) = 9.1$ blocked calls. If Microdata can estimate the cost of possible lost sales, the cost of these blocked calls can be established. The economic analysis based on the service cost and the blocked-call cost can assist in determining the optimal number of lines for the system.

NOTES AND COMMENTS

Many of the operating characteristics considered in previous sections are not relevant for the *M/G/k* model with blocked customers cleared. In particular, the average time in the waiting line, W_q, and the average number of units in the waiting line, L_q, are no longer considered because waiting is not permitted in this type of system.

14.9 WAITING LINE MODELS WITH FINITE CALLING POPULATIONS

In previous waiting line models, the arrival rate was constant and independent of the number of units in the system. With a finite calling population, the arrival rate decreases as the number of units in the system increases because, with more units in the system, fewer units are available for arrivals.

For the waiting line models introduced so far, the population of units or customers arriving for service has been considered to be unlimited. In technical terms, when no limit is placed on how many units may seek service, the model is said to have an **infinite calling population.** Under this assumption, the arrival rate λ remains constant regardless of how many units are in the waiting line system. This assumption of an infinite calling population is made in most waiting line models.

In other cases, the maximum number of units or customers that may seek service is assumed to be finite. In this situation, the arrival rate for the system changes, depending on the number of units in the waiting line, and the waiting line model is said to have a **finite calling population.** The formulas for the operating characteristics of the previous waiting line models must be modified to account for the effect of the finite calling population.

The finite calling population model discussed in this section is based on the following assumptions.

1. The arrivals for *each unit* follow a Poisson probability distribution, with arrival rate λ.
2. The service times follow an exponential probability distribution, with service rate μ.
3. The population of units that may seek service is finite.

The arrival rate λ is defined differently for the finite calling population model. Specifically, λ is defined in terms of the arrival rate for each unit.

With a single channel, the waiting line model is referred to as an *M*/*M*/1 model with a finite calling population.

The arrival rate for the *M*/*M*/1 model with a finite calling population is defined in terms of how often *each unit* arrives or seeks service. This situation differs from that for previous waiting line models in which λ denoted the arrival rate for the system. With a finite calling population, the arrival rate for the system varies, depending on the number of units in the system. Instead of adjusting for the changing system arrival rate, in the finite calling population model λ indicates the arrival rate for each unit.

Operating Characteristics for the *M*/*M*/1 Model with a Finite Calling Population

The following formulas are used to determine the steady-state operating characteristics for an *M*/*M*/1 model with a finite calling population, where

$$\begin{aligned} \lambda &= \text{the arrival rate for each unit} \\ \mu &= \text{the service rate} \\ N &= \text{the size of the population} \end{aligned}$$

1. The probability that no units are in the system:

$$P_0 = \frac{1}{\displaystyle\sum_{n=0}^{N} \frac{N!}{(N-n)!}\left(\frac{\lambda}{\mu}\right)^n} \tag{14.33}$$

2. The average number of units in the waiting line:

$$L_q = N - \frac{\lambda + \mu}{\lambda}(1 - P_0) \tag{14.34}$$

3. The average number of units in the system:

$$L = L_q + (1 - P_0) \tag{14.35}$$

4. The average time a unit spends in the waiting line:

$$W_q = \frac{L_q}{(N - L)\lambda} \tag{14.36}$$

5. The average time a unit spends in the system:

$$W = W_q + \frac{1}{\mu} \tag{14.37}$$

6. The probability an arriving unit has to wait for service:

$$P_w = 1 - P_0 \tag{14.38}$$

7. The probability of n units in the system:

$$P_n = \frac{N!}{(N-n)!}\left(\frac{\lambda}{\mu}\right)^n P_0 \quad \text{for } n = 0, 1, \ldots, N \tag{14.39}$$

One of the primary applications of the $M/M/1$ model with a finite calling population is referred to as the *machine repair problem.* In this problem, a group of machines is considered to be the finite population of "customers" that may request repair service. Whenever a machine breaks down, an arrival occurs in the sense that a new repair request is initiated. If another machine breaks down before the repair work has been completed on the first machine, the second machine begins to form a "waiting line" for repair service. Additional breakdowns by other machines will add to the length of the waiting line. The assumption of first-come, first-served indicates that machines are repaired in the order they break down. The $M/M/1$ model shows that one person or one channel is available to perform the repair service. To return the machine to operation, each machine with a breakdown must be repaired by the single-channel operation.

An Example The Kolkmeyer Manufacturing Company uses a group of six identical machines; each machine operates an average of 20 hours between breakdowns. Thus, the arrival rate or request for repair service for each machine is $\lambda = 1/20 = 0.05$ per hour. With randomly occurring breakdowns, the Poisson probability distribution is used to describe the machine breakdown arrival process. One person from the maintenance department provides the single-channel repair service for the six machines. The exponentially distributed service times have a mean of two hours per machine or a service rate of $\mu = 1/2 = 0.50$ machines per hour.

With $\lambda = 0.05$ and $\mu = 0.50$, we use equations (14.33) through (14.38) to compute the operating characteristics for this system. Note that the use of equation (14.33) makes the computations involved somewhat cumbersome. Confirm for yourself that equation (14.33) provides the value of $P_0 = 0.4845$. The computations for the other operating characteristics are

$$L_q = 6 - \left(\frac{0.05 + 0.50}{0.05}\right)(1 - 0.4845) = 0.3297 \text{ machine}$$

$$L = 0.3295 + (1 - 0.4845) = 0.8451 \text{ machine}$$

$$W_q = \frac{0.3295}{(6 - 0.845)0.50} = 1.279 \text{ hours}$$

$$W = 1.279 + \frac{1}{0.50} = 3.279 \text{ hours}$$

$$P_w = 1 - P_0 = 1 - 0.4845 = 0.5155$$

Operating characteristics of an M/M/1 waiting line with a finite calling population are considered in Problem 34.

Finally, equation (14.39) can be used to compute the probabilities of any number of machines being in the repair system.

As with other waiting line models, the operating characteristics provide the manager with information about the operation of the waiting line. In this case, the fact that a machine breakdown waits an average of W_q = 1.279 hours before maintenance begins and the fact that more than 50% of the machine breakdowns must wait for service, P_w = 0.5155, indicates a two-channel system may be needed to improve the machine repair service.

An Excel worksheet template on the CD that accompanies this text or The Management Scientist software may be used to analyze the multiple-channel finite calling population model.

Computations of the operating characteristics of a multiple-channel finite calling population waiting line are more complex than those for the single-channel model. A computer solution is virtually mandatory in this case. The Excel worksheet for the Kolkmeyer two-channel machine repair system is shown in Figure 14.5. With two repair personnel, the average machine breakdown waiting time is reduced to W_q = 0.0834 hours or 5 minutes and only 10%, P_w = 0.1036, of the machine breakdowns wait for service. Thus, the two-channel system significantly improves the machine repair service operation. Ultimately, by considering the cost of machine downtime and the cost of the repair personnel, management can determine whether the improved service of the two-channel system is cost effective.

FIGURE 14.5 WORKSHEET FOR THE KOLKMEYER TWO-CHANNEL MACHINE REPAIR PROBLEM

EXCELfile
Finite

	A	B	C	D
1	**Waiting Line Model with a Finite Calling Population**			
2				
3	**Assumptions**			
4	**Poisson Arrivals**			
5	**Exponential Service Times**			
6	**Finite Calling Population**			
7				
8	Number of Channels	2		
9	Arrival Rate for Each Unit	0.05		
10	Service Rate for Each Channel	0.5		
11	Population Size	6		
12				
13				
14	**Operating Characteristics**			
15				
16	Probability that no machines are in the system, Po		0.5602	
17	Average number of machines in the waiting line, Lq		0.0227	
18	Average number of machines in the system, L		0.5661	
19	Average time a machine spends in the waiting line, Wq		0.0834	
20	Average time a machine spends in the system, W		2.0834	
21	Probability an arriving machine has to wait, Pw		0.1036	
22				

SUMMARY

In this chapter we presented a variety of waiting line models that have been developed to help managers make better decisions concerning the operation of waiting lines. For each model, we presented formulas that could be used to develop operating characteristics or performance measures for the system being studied. The operating characteristics presented include the following:

1. Probability that no units are in the system
2. Average number of units in the waiting line
3. Average number of units in the system
4. Average time a unit spends in the waiting line
5. Average time a unit spends in the system
6. Probability that arriving units will have to wait for service

We also showed how an economic analysis of the waiting line could be conducted by developing a total cost model that includes the cost associated with units waiting for service and the cost required to operate the service facility.

As many of the examples in this chapter show, the most obvious applications of waiting line models are situations in which customers arrive for service such as at a grocery checkout counter, bank, or restaurant. However, with a little creativity, waiting line models can be applied to many different situations such as telephone calls waiting for connections, mail orders waiting for processing, machines waiting for repairs, manufacturing jobs waiting to be processed, and money waiting to be spent or invested. The Q.M. in Action, Improving Productivity at the New Haven Fire Department, describes an application in which a waiting line model helped improve emergency medical response time and also provided a significant savings in operating costs.

The complexity and diversity of waiting line systems found in practice often prevent an analyst from finding an existing waiting line model that fits the specific application being studied. Simulation, the topic discussed in Chapter 15, provides an approach to determining the operating characteristics of such waiting line systems.

Q.M. IN ACTION

IMPROVING PRODUCTIVITY AT THE NEW HAVEN FIRE DEPARTMENT*

The New Haven, Connecticut, Fire Department implemented a reorganization plan with cross-trained fire and medical personnel responding to both fire and medical emergencies. A waiting line model provided the basis for the reorganization by demonstrating that substantial improvements in emergency medical response time could be achieved with only a small reduction in fire protection. Annual savings were reported to be $1.4 million.

The model was based on Poisson arrivals and exponential service times for both fire and medical emergencies. It was used to estimate the average time that a person placing a call would have to wait for the appropriate emergency unit to arrive at the location. Waiting times were estimated by the model's prediction of the average travel time to reach each of the city's 28 census tracts.

The model was first applied to the original system of 16 fire units and 4 emergency medical units that operated independently. It was then applied to the proposed reorganization plan that involved cross-trained department personnel qualified to respond to both fire and medical emergencies. Results from the model demonstrated that average travel times could be reduced under the reorganization plan. Various facility location alternatives also were evaluated. When implemented, the reorganization plan reduced operating cost and improved public safety services.

*Based on A. J. Swersey, L. Goldring, and E. D. Geyer, "Improving Fire Department Productivity: Merging Fire and Emergency Medical Units in New Haven," *Interfaces* 23, no. 1 (January/February 1993): 109–129.

GLOSSARY

Queue A waiting line.

Queueing theory The body of knowledge dealing with waiting lines.

Operating characteristics The performance measures for a waiting line including the probability that no units are in the system, the average number of units in the waiting line, the average waiting time, and so on.

Single-channel waiting line A waiting line with only one service facility.

Poisson probability distribution A probability distribution used to describe the arrival pattern for some waiting line models.

Arrival rate The mean number of customers or units arriving in a given period of time.

Exponential probability distribution A probability distribution used to describe the service time for some waiting line models.

Service rate The mean number of customers or units that can be served by one service facility in a given period of time.

First-come, first-served (FCFS) The queue discipline that serves waiting units on a first-come, first-served basis.

Transient period The start-up period for a waiting line, occurring before the waiting line reaches a normal or steady-state operation.

Steady-state operation The normal operation of the waiting line after it has gone through a start-up or transient period. The operating characteristics of waiting lines are computed for steady-state conditions.

Multiple-channel waiting line A waiting line with two or more parallel service facilities.

Blocked When arriving units cannot enter the waiting line because the system is full. Blocked units can occur when waiting lines are not allowed or when waiting lines have a finite capacity.

Infinite calling population The population of customers or units that may seek service has no specified upper limit.

Finite calling population The population of customers or units that may seek service has a fixed and finite value.

PROBLEMS

1. Willow Brook National Bank operates a drive-up teller window that allows customers to complete bank transactions without getting out of their cars. On weekday mornings, arrivals to the drive-up teller window occur at random, with an arrival rate of 24 customers per hour or 0.4 customer per minute.
   a. What is the mean or expected number of customers that will arrive in a five-minute period?
   b. Assume that the Poisson probability distribution can be used to describe the arrival process. Use the arrival rate in part (a) and compute the probabilities that exactly 0, 1, 2, and 3 customers will arrive during a five-minute period.
   c. Delays are expected if more than three customers arrive during any five-minute period. What is the probability that delays will occur?

2. In the Willow Brook National Bank waiting line system (see Problem 1), assume that the service times for the drive-up teller follow an exponential probability distribution with a service rate of 36 customers per hour or 0.6 customer per minute. Use the exponential probability distribution to answer the following questions.

a. What is the probability the service time is one minute or less?
b. What is the probability the service time is two minutes or less?
c. What is the probability the service time is more than two minutes?

3. Use the single-channel drive-up bank teller operation referred to in Problems 1 and 2 to determine the following operating characteristics for the system.
a. The probability that no customers are in the system
b. The average number of customers waiting
c. The average number of customers in the system
d. The average time a customer spends waiting
e. The average time a customer spends in the system
f. The probability that arriving customers will have to wait for service

4. Use the single-channel drive-up bank teller operation referred to in Problems 1–3 to determine the probabilities of 0, 1, 2, and 3 customers in the system. What is the probability that more than three customers will be in the drive-up teller system at the same time?

SELF test

5. The reference desk of a university library receives requests for assistance. Assume that a Poisson probability distribution with an arrival rate of 10 requests per hour can be used to describe the arrival pattern and that service times follow an exponential probability distribution with a service rate of 12 requests per hour.
a. What is the probability that no requests for assistance are in the system?
b. What is the average number of requests that will be waiting for service?
c. What is the average waiting time in minutes before service begins?
d. What is the average time at the reference desk in minutes (waiting time plus service time)?
e. What is the probability that a new arrival has to wait for service?

6. Movies Tonight is a typical video and DVD movie rental outlet for home viewing customers. During the weeknight evenings, customers arrive at Movies Tonight with an arrival rate of 1.25 customers per minute. The checkout clerk has a service rate of 2 customers per minute. Assume Poisson arrivals and exponential service times.
a. What is the probability that no customers are in the system?
b. What is the average number of customers waiting for service?
c. What is the average time a customer waits for service to begin?
d. What is the probability that an arriving customer will have to wait for service?
e. Do the operating characteristics indicate that the one-clerk checkout system provides an acceptable level of service?

7. Speedy Oil provides a single-channel automobile oil change and lubrication service. Customers provide an arrival rate of 2.5 cars per hour. The service rate is 5 cars per hour. Assume that arrivals follow a Poisson probability distribution and that service times follow an exponential probability distribution.
a. What is the average number of cars in the system?
b. What is the average time that a car waits for the oil and lubrication service to begin?
c. What is the average time a car spends in the system?
d. What is the probability that an arrival has to wait for service?

8. For the Burger Dome single-channel waiting line in Section 14.2, assume that the arrival rate is increased to 1 customer per minute and that the service rate is increased to 1.25 customers per minute. Compute the following operating characteristics for the new system: P_0, L_q, L, W_q, W, and P_w. Does this system provide better or poorer service compared to the original system? Discuss any differences and the reason for these differences.

9. Marty's Barber Shop has one barber. Customers have an arrival rate of 2.2 customers per hour, and haircuts are given with a service rate of 5 per hour. Use the Poisson arrivals and exponential service times model to answer the following questions.
a. What is the probability that no units are in the system?
b. What is the probability that one customer is receiving a haircut and no one is waiting?

c. What is the probability that one customer is receiving a haircut and one customer is waiting?
d. What is the probability that one customer is receiving a haircut and two customers are waiting?
e. What is the probability that more than two customers are waiting?
f. What is the average time a customer waits for service?

10. Trosper Tire Company decided to hire a new mechanic to handle all tire changes for customers ordering a new set of tires. Two mechanics applied for the job. One mechanic has limited experience, can be hired for $14 per hour, and can service an average of three customers per hour. The other mechanic has several years of experience, can service an average of four customers per hour, but must be paid $20 per hour. Assume that customers arrive at the Trosper garage at the rate of two customers per hour.
    a. What are the waiting line operating characteristics using each mechanic, assuming Poisson arrivals and exponential service times?
    b. If the company assigns a customer waiting cost of $30 per hour, which mechanic provides the lower operating cost?

SELF test

11. Agan Interior Design provides home and office decorating assistance to its customers. In normal operation, an average of 2.5 customers arrive each hour. One design consultant is available to answer customer questions and make product recommendations. The consultant averages 10 minutes with each customer.
    a. Compute the operating characteristics of the customer waiting line, assuming Poisson arrivals and exponential service times.
    b. Service goals dictate that an arriving customer should not wait for service more than an average of 5 minutes. Is this goal being met? If not, what action do you recommend?
    c. If the consultant can reduce the average time spent per customer to 8 minutes, what is the mean service rate? Will the service goal be met?

12. Pete's Market is a small local grocery store with only one checkout counter. Assume that shoppers arrive at the checkout lane according to a Poisson probability distribution, with an arrival rate of 15 customers per hour. The checkout service times follow an exponential probability distribution, with a service rate of 20 customers per hour.
    a. Compute the operating characteristics for this waiting line.
    b. If the manager's service goal is to limit the waiting time prior to beginning the checkout process to no more than five minutes, what recommendations would you provide regarding the current checkout system?

13. After reviewing the waiting line analysis of Problem 12, the manager of Pete's Market wants to consider one of the following alternatives for improving service. What alternative would you recommend? Justify your recommendation.
    a. Hire a second person to bag the groceries while the cash register operator is entering the cost data and collecting money from the customer. With this improved single-channel operation, the service rate could be increased to 30 customers per hour.
    b. Hire a second person to operate a second checkout counter. The two-channel operation would have a service rate of 20 customers per hour for each channel.

14. Ocala Software Systems operates a technical support center for its software customers. If customers have installation or use problems with Ocala software products, they may telephone the technical support center and obtain free consultation. Currently, Ocala operates its support center with one consultant. If the consultant is busy when a new customer call arrives, the customer hears a recorded message stating that all consultants are currently busy with other customers. The customer is then asked to hold and a consultant will provide assistance as soon as possible. The customer calls follow a Poisson probability distribution with an arrival rate of five calls per hour. On average, it takes 7.5 minutes for a consultant to answer a customer's questions. The service time follows an exponential probability distribution.

a. What is the service rate in terms of customers per hour?
b. What is the probability that no customers are in the system and the consultant is idle?
c. What is the average number of customers waiting for a consultant?
d. What is the average time a customer waits for a consultant?
e. What is the probability that a customer will have to wait for a consultant?
f. Ocala's customer service department recently received several letters from customers complaining about the difficulty in obtaining technical support. If Ocala's customer service guidelines state that no more than 35% of all customers should have to wait for technical support and that the average waiting time should be two minutes or less, does your waiting line analysis indicate that Ocala is or is not meeting its customer service guidelines? What action, if any, would you recommend?

15. To improve customer service, Ocala Software Systems (see Problem 14) wants to investigate the effect of using a second consultant at its technical support center. What effect would the additional consultant have on customer service? Would two technical consultants enable Ocala to meet its service guidelines with no more than 35% of all customers having to wait for technical support and an average customer waiting time of two minutes or less? Discuss.

16. The new Fore and Aft Marina is to be located on the Ohio River near Madison, Indiana. Assume that Fore and Aft decides to build a docking facility where one boat at a time can stop for gas and servicing. Assume that arrivals follow a Poisson probability distribution, with an arrival rate of 5 boats per hour, and that service times follow an exponential probability distribution, with a service rate of 10 boats per hour. Answer the following questions.
a. What is the probability that no boats are in the system?
b. What is the average number of boats that will be waiting for service?
c. What is the average time a boat will spend waiting for service?
d. What is the average time a boat will spend at the dock?
e. If you were the manager of Fore and Aft Marina, would you be satisfied with the service level your system will be providing? Why or why not?

17. The manager of the Fore and Aft Marina in Problem 16 wants to investigate the possibility of enlarging the docking facility so that two boats can stop for gas and servicing simultaneously. Assume that the arrival rate is 5 boats per hour and that the service rate for each channel is 10 boats per hour.
a. What is the probability that the boat dock will be idle?
b. What is the average number of boats that will be waiting for service?
c. What is the average time a boat will spend waiting for service?
d. What is the average time a boat will spend at the dock?
e. If you were the manager of Fore and Aft Marina, would you be satisfied with the service level your system will be providing? Why or why not?

SELF test

18. All airplane passengers at the Lake City Regional Airport must pass through a security screening area before proceeding to the boarding area. The airport has three screening stations available, and the facility manager must decide how many to have open at any particular time. The service rate for processing passengers at each screening station is 3 passengers per minute. On Monday morning the arrival rate is 5.4 passengers per minute. Assume that processing times at each screening station follow an exponential distribution and that arrivals follow a Poisson distribution.
a. Suppose two of the three screening stations are open on Monday morning. Compute the operating characteristics for the screening facility.
b. Because of space considerations, the facility manager's goal is to limit the average number of passengers waiting in line to 10 or fewer. Will the two-screening-station system be able to meet the manager's goal?
c. What is the average time required for a passenger to pass through security screening?

19. Refer again to the Lake City Regional Airport described in Problem 18. When the security level is raised to high, the service rate for processing passengers is reduced to 2 passengers per minute at each screening station. Suppose the security level is raised to high on Monday morning. The arrival rate is 5.4 passengers per minute.
    a. The facility manager's goal is to limit the average number of passengers waiting in line to 10 or fewer. How many screening stations must be open in order to satisfy the manager's goal?
    b. What is the average time required for a passenger to pass through security screening?

20. A Florida coastal community experiences a population increase during the winter months with seasonal residents arriving from northern states and Canada. Staffing at a local post office is often in a state of change due to the relatively low volume of customers in the summer months and the relatively high volume of customers in the winter months. The service rate of a postal clerk is 0.75 customer per minute. The post office counter has a maximum of three work stations. The target maximum time a customer waits in the system is five minutes.
    a. For a particular Monday morning in November, the anticipated arrival rate is 1.2 customers per minute. What is the recommended staffing for this Monday morning? Show the operating characteristics of the waiting line.
    b. A new population growth study suggests that over the next two years the arrival rate at the postal office during the busy winter months can be expected to be 2.1 customers per minute. Use a waiting line analysis to make a recommendation to the post office manager.

SELF test

21. Refer to the Agan Interior Design situation in Problem 11. Agan's management would like to evaluate two alternatives:
    - Use one consultant with an average service time of 8 minutes per customer.
    - Expand to two consultants, each of whom has an average service time of 10 minutes per customer.

    If the consultants are paid $16 per hour and the customer waiting time is valued at $25 per hour for waiting time prior to service, should Agan expand to the two-consultant system? Explain.

22. A fast-food franchise is considering operating a drive-up window food-service operation. Assume that customer arrivals follow a Poisson probability distribution, with an arrival rate of 24 cars per hour, and that service times follow an exponential probability distribution. Arriving customers place orders at an intercom station at the back of the parking lot and then drive to the service window to pay for and receive their orders. The following three service alternatives are being considered.
    - A single-channel operation in which one employee fills the order and takes the money from the customer. The average service time for this alternative is 2 minutes.
    - A single-channel operation in which one employee fills the order while a second employee takes the money from the customer. The average service time for this alternative is 1.25 minutes.
    - A two-channel operation with two service windows and two employees. The employee stationed at each window fills the order and takes the money for customers arriving at the window. The average service time for this alternative is 2 minutes for each channel.

    Answer the following questions and recommend an alternative design for the fast-food franchise.
    a. What is the probability that no cars are in the system?
    b. What is the average number of cars waiting for service?
    c. What is the average number of cars in the system?
    d. What is the average time a car waits for service?

e. What is the average time in the system?
f. What is the probability that an arriving car will have to wait for service?

23. The following cost information is available for the fast-food franchise in Problem 22.
    - Customer waiting time is valued at $25 per hour to reflect the fact that waiting time is costly to the fast-food business.
    - The cost of each employee is $6.50 per hour.
    - To account for equipment and space, an additional cost of $20 per hour is attributable to each channel.

    What is the lowest-cost design for the fast-food business?

24. Patients arrive at a dentist's office with an arrival rate of 2.8 patients per hour. The dentist can treat patients at a service rate of 3 patients per hour. A study of patient waiting times shows that a patient waits an average of 30 minutes before seeing the dentist.
    a. What are the arrival and service rates in terms of patients per minute?
    b. What is the average number of patients in the waiting room?
    c. If a patient arrives at 10:10 A.M., at what time is the patient expected to leave the office?

SELF test

25. A study of the multiple-channel food-service operation at the Red Birds baseball park shows that the average time between the arrival of a customer at the food-service counter and his or her departure with a filled order is 10 minutes. During the game, customers arrive at the rate of four per minute. The food-service operation requires an average of 2 minutes per customer order.
    a. What is the service rate per channel in terms of customers per minute?
    b. What is the average waiting time in the line prior to placing an order?
    c. On average, how many customers are in the food-service system?

26. Manning Autos operates an automotive service counter. While completing the repair work, Manning mechanics arrive at the company's parts department counter with an arrival rate of four per hour. The parts coordinator spends an average of 6 minutes with each mechanic, discussing the parts the mechanic needs and retrieving the parts from inventory.
    a. Currently, Manning has one parts coordinator. On average, each mechanic waits 4 minutes before the parts coordinator is available to answer questions or retrieve parts from inventory. Find L_q, W, and L for this single-channel parts operation.
    b. A trial period with a second parts coordinator showed that, on average, each mechanic waited only 1 minute before a parts coordinator was available. Find L_q, W, and L for this two-channel parts operation.
    c. If the cost of each mechanic is $20 per hour and the cost of each parts coordinator is $12 per hour, is the one-channel or the two-channel system more economical?

SELF test

27. Gubser Welding, Inc., operates a welding service for construction and automotive repair jobs. Assume that the arrival of jobs at the company's office can be described by a Poisson probability distribution with an arrival rate of two jobs per 8-hour day. The time required to complete the jobs follows a normal probability distribution with a mean time of 3.2 hours and a standard deviation of 2 hours. Answer the following questions, assuming that Gubser uses one welder to complete all jobs.
    a. What is the mean arrival rate in jobs per hour?
    b. What is the mean service rate in jobs per hour?
    c. What is the average number of jobs waiting for service?
    d. What is the average time a job waits before the welder can begin working on it?
    e. What is the average number of hours between when a job is received and when it is completed?
    f. What percentage of the time is Gubser's welder busy?

28. Jobs arrive randomly at a particular assembly plant; assume that the arrival rate is five jobs per hour. Service times (in minutes per job) do not follow the exponential probability distribution. Two proposed designs for the plant's assembly operation are shown.

	Service Time	
Design	Mean	Standard Deviation
A	6.0	3.0
B	6.25	0.6

a. What is the service rate in jobs per hour for each design?
b. For the service rates in part (a), what design appears to provide the best or fastest service rate?
c. What are the standard deviations of the service times in hours?
d. Use the *M/G/*1 model to compute the operating characteristics for each design.
e. Which design provides the best operating characteristics? Why?

29. The Robotics Manufacturing Company operates an equipment repair business where emergency jobs arrive randomly at the rate of three jobs per 8-hour day. The company's repair facility is a single-channel system operated by a repair technician. The service time varies with a mean repair time of 2 hours and a standard deviation of 1.5 hours. The company's cost of the repair operation is $28 per hour. In the economic analysis of the waiting line system, Robotics uses $35 per hour cost for customers waiting during the repair process.
a. What are the arrival rate and service rate in jobs per hour?
b. Show the operating characteristics including the total cost per hour.
c. The company is considering purchasing a computer-based equipment repair system that would enable a constant repair time of 2 hours. For practical purposes, the standard deviation is 0. Because of the computer-based system, the company's cost of the new operation would be $32 per hour. The firm's director of operations said no to the request for the new system because the hourly cost is $4 higher and the mean repair time is the same. Do you agree? What effect will the new system have on the waiting line characteristics of the repair service?
d. Does paying for the computer-based system to reduce the variation in service time make economic sense? How much will the new system save the company during a 40-hour work week?

SELF test

30. A large insurance company maintains a central computing system that contains a variety of information about customer accounts. Insurance agents in a six-state area use telephone lines to access the customer information database. Currently, the company's central computer system allows three users to access the central computer simultaneously. Agents who attempt to use the system when it is full are denied access; no waiting is allowed. Management realizes that with its expanding business, more requests will be made to the central information system. Being denied access to the system is inefficient as well as annoying for agents. Access requests follow a Poisson probability distribution, with a mean of 42 calls per hour. The service rate per line is 20 calls per hour.
a. What is the probability that 0, 1, 2, and 3 access lines will be in use?
b. What is the probability that an agent will be denied access to the system?
c. What is the average number of access lines in use?
d. In planning for the future, management wants to be able to handle $\lambda = 50$ calls per hour; in addition, the probability that an agent will be denied access to the system should be no greater than the value computed in part (b). How many access lines should this system have?

31. Mid-West Publishing Company publishes college textbooks. The company operates an 800 telephone number whereby potential adopters can ask questions about forthcoming

texts, request examination copies of texts, and place orders. Currently, two extension lines are used, with two representatives handling the telephone inquiries. Calls occurring when both extension lines are being used receive a busy signal; no waiting is allowed. Each representative can accommodate an average of 12 calls per hour. The arrival rate is 20 calls per hour.

a. How many extension lines should be used if the company wants to handle 90% of the calls immediately?
b. What is the average number of extension lines that will be busy if your recommendation in part (a) is used?
c. What percentage of calls receive a busy signal for the current telephone system with two extension lines?

32. City Cab, Inc., uses two dispatchers to handle requests for service and to dispatch the cabs. The telephone calls that are made to City Cab use a common telephone number. When both dispatchers are busy, the caller hears a busy signal; no waiting is allowed. Callers who receive a busy signal can call back later or call another cab service. Assume that the arrival of calls follows a Poisson probability distribution, with a mean of 40 calls per hour, and that each dispatcher can handle a mean of 30 calls per hour.
a. What percentage of time are both dispatchers idle?
b. What percentage of time are both dispatchers busy?
c. What is the probability callers will receive a busy signal if two, three, or four dispatchers are used?
d. If management wants no more than 12% of the callers to receive a busy signal, how many dispatchers should be used?

33. Kolkmeyer Manufacturing Company (see Section 14.9) is considering adding two machines to its manufacturing operation. This addition will bring the number of machines to eight. The president of Kolkmeyer asked for a study of the need to add a second employee to the repair operation. The arrival rate is 0.05 machine per hour for each machine, and the service rate for each individual assigned to the repair operation is 0.50 machine per hour.
a. Compute the operating characteristics if the company retains the single-employee repair operation.
b. Compute the operating characteristics if a second employee is added to the machine repair operation.
c. Each employee is paid $20 per hour. Machine downtime is valued at $80 per hour. From an economic point of view, should one or two employees handle the machine repair operation? Explain.

SELF test

34. Five administrative assistants use an office copier. The average time between arrivals for each assistant is 40 minutes, which is equivalent to an arrival rate of $1/40 = 0.025$ arrival per minute. The mean time each assistant spends at the copier is 5 minutes, which is equivalent to a service rate of $\frac{1}{5} = 0.20$ per minute. Use the *M/M/*1 model with a finite calling population to determine the following:
a. The probability that the copier is idle
b. The average number of administrative assistants in the waiting line
c. The average number of administrative assistants at the copier
d. The average time an assistant spends waiting for the copier
e. The average time an assistant spends at the copier
f. During an 8-hour day, how many minutes does an assistant spend at the copier? How much of this time is waiting time?
g. Should management consider purchasing a second copier? Explain.

35. Schips Department Store operates a fleet of 10 trucks. The trucks arrive at random times throughout the day at the store's truck dock to be loaded with new deliveries or to have incoming shipments from the regional warehouse unloaded. Each truck returns to the truck dock for service two times per 8-hour day. Thus, the arrival rate per truck is 0.25

trucks per hour. The service rate is 4 trucks per hour. Using the Poisson arrivals and exponential service times model with a finite calling population of 10 trucks, determine the following operating characteristics:

a. The probability no trucks are at the truck dock
b. The average number of trucks waiting for loading/unloading
c. The average number of trucks in the truck dock area
d. The average waiting time before loading/unloading begins
e. The average waiting time in the system
f. What is the hourly cost of operation if the cost is $50 per hour for each truck and $30 per hour for the truck dock?
g. Consider a two-channel truck dock operation where the second channel could be operated for an additional $30 per hour. How much would the average number of trucks waiting for loading/unloading have to be reduced to make the two-channel truck dock economically feasible?
h. Should the company consider expanding to the two-channel truck dock? Explain.

Case Problem 1 REGIONAL AIRLINES

Regional Airlines is establishing a new telephone system for handling flight reservations. During the 10:00 A.M. to 11:00 A.M. time period, calls to the reservation agent occur randomly at an average of one call every 3.75 minutes. Historical service time data show that a reservation agent spends an average of 3 minutes with each customer. The waiting line model assumptions of Poisson arrivals and exponential service times appear reasonable for the telephone reservation system.

Regional Airlines' management believes that offering an efficient telephone reservation system is an important part of establishing an image as a service-oriented airline. If the system is properly implemented, Regional Airlines will establish good customer relations, which in the long run will increase business. However, if the telephone reservation system is frequently overloaded and customers have difficulty contacting an agent, a negative customer reaction may lead to an eventual loss of business. The cost of a ticket reservation agent is $20 per hour. Thus, management wants to provide good service, but it does not want to incur the cost of overstaffing the telephone reservation operation by using more agents than necessary.

At a planning meeting, Regional's management team agreed that an acceptable customer service goal is to answer at least 85 percent of the incoming calls immediately. During the planning meeting, Regional's vice president of administration pointed out that the data show that the average service rate for an agent is faster than the average arrival rate of the telephone calls. The vice president's conclusion was that personnel costs could be minimized by using one agent and that the single agent should be able to handle the telephone reservations and still have some idle time. The vice president of marketing restated the importance of customer service and expressed support for at least two reservation agents.

The current telephone reservation system design does not allow callers to wait. Callers who attempt to reach a reservation agent when all agents are occupied receive a busy signal and are blocked from the system. A representative from the telephone company suggested that Regional Airlines consider an expanded system that accommodates waiting. In the expanded system, when a customer calls and all agents are busy, a recorded message tells the customer that the call is being held in the order received and that an agent will be available shortly. The customer can stay on the line and listen to background music while waiting for an agent. Regional's management will need more information before switching to the expanded system.

Managerial Report

Prepare a managerial report for Regional Airlines analyzing the telephone reservation system. Evaluate both the system that does not allow waiting and the expanded system that allows waiting. Include the following information in your report.

1. A detailed analysis of the operating characteristics of the reservation system with one agent as proposed by the vice president of administration. What is your recommendation concerning a single-agent system?
2. A detailed analysis of the operating characteristics of the reservation system based on your recommendation regarding the number of agents Regional should use.
3. What appear to be the advantages or disadvantages of the expanded system? Discuss the number of waiting callers the expanded system would need to accommodate.
4. The telephone arrival data presented are for the 10:00 A.M. to 11:00 A.M. time period; however, the arrival rate of incoming calls is expected to change from hour to hour. Describe how your waiting line analysis could be used to develop a ticket agent staffing plan that would enable the company to provide different levels of staffing for the ticket reservation system at different times during the day. Indicate the information that you would need to develop this staffing plan.

Case Problem 2 OFFICE EQUIPMENT, INC.

Office Equipment, Inc. (OEI), leases automatic mailing machines to business customers in Fort Wayne, Indiana. The company built its success on a reputation of providing timely maintenance and repair service. Each OEI service contract states that a service technician will arrive at a customer's business site within an average of three hours from the time that the customer notifies OEI of an equipment problem.

Currently, OEI has 10 customers with service contracts. One service technician is responsible for handling all service calls. A statistical analysis of historical service records indicates that a customer requests a service call at an average rate of one call per 50 hours of operation. If the service technician is available when a customer calls for service, it takes the technician an average of 1 hour of travel time to reach the customer's office and an average of 1.5 hours to complete the repair service. However, if the service technician is busy with another customer when a new customer calls for service, the technician completes the current service call and any other waiting service calls before responding to the new service call. In such cases, once the technician is free from all existing service commitments, the technician takes an average of 1 hour of travel time to reach the new customer's office and an average of 1.5 hours to complete the repair service. The cost of the service technician is $80 per hour. The downtime cost (wait time and service time) for customers is $100 per hour.

OEI is planning to expand its business. Within one year, OEI projects that it will have 20 customers, and within two years, OEI projects that it will have 30 customers. Although OEI is satisfied that one service technician can handle the 10 existing customers, management is concerned about the ability of one technician to meet the average three-hour service call guarantee when the OEI customer base expands. In a recent planning meeting, the marketing manager made a proposal to add a second service technician when OEI reaches 20 customers and to add a third service technician when OEI reaches 30 customers. Before making a final decision, management would like an analysis of OEI service capabilities. OEI is particularly interested in meeting the average three-hour waiting time guarantee at the lowest possible total cost.

Managerial Report

Develop a managerial report summarizing your analysis of the OEI service capabilities. Make recommendations regarding the number of technicians to be used when OEI reaches 20 customers and when OEI reaches 30 customers. Include a discussion of the following in your report.

1. What is the arrival rate for each customer per hour?
2. What is the service rate in terms of the number of customers per hour? Note that the average travel time of 1 hour becomes part of the service time because the time that the service technician is busy handling a service call includes the travel time plus the time required to complete the repair.
3. Waiting line models generally assume that the arriving customers are in the same location as the service facility. Discuss the OEI situation in light of the fact that a service technician travels an average of 1 hour to reach each customer. How should the travel time and the waiting time predicted by the waiting line model be combined to determine the total customer waiting time?
4. OEI is satisfied that one service technician can handle the 10 existing customers. Use a waiting line model to determine the following information:
   - Probability that no customers are in the system
   - Average number of customers in the waiting line
   - Average number of customers in the system
   - Average time a customer waits until the service technician arrives
   - Average time a customer waits until the machine is back in operation
   - Probability that a customer will have to wait more than one hour for the service technician to arrive
   - The number of hours a week the technician is not making service calls
   - The total cost per hour for the service operation

   Do you agree with OEI management that one technician can meet the average three-hour service call guarantee? Explain.
5. What is your recommendation for the number of service technicians to hire when OEI expands to 20 customers? Use the information that you developed in part (4) to justify your answer.
6. What is your recommendation for the number of service technicians to hire when OEI expands to 30 customers? Use the information that you developed in part (4) to justify your answer.
7. What are the annual savings of your recommendation in part (6) compared to the planning committee's proposal that 30 customers will require three service technicians? Assume 250 days of operation per year.

CHAPTER 15

Simulation

CONTENTS

Simulation is one of the most widely used quantitative approaches to decision making. It is a method for learning about a real system by experimenting with a model that represents the system. The simulation model contains the mathematical expressions and logical relationships that describe how to compute the value of the outputs given the values of the inputs. Any simulation model has two inputs: controllable inputs and probabilistic inputs. Figure 15.1 shows a conceptual diagram of a simulation model.

In conducting a **simulation experiment,** an analyst selects the value, or values, for the **controllable inputs.** Then values for the **probabilistic inputs** are randomly generated. The simulation model uses the values of the controllable inputs and the values of the probabilistic inputs to compute the value, or values, of the output. By conducting a series of experiments using a variety of values for the controllable inputs, the analyst learns how values of the controllable inputs affect or change the output of the simulation model. After reviewing the simulation results, the analyst is often able to make decision recommendations for the controllable inputs that will provide the desired output for the real system.

Simulation has been successfully applied in a variety of applications. The following examples are typical.

1. *New Product Development* The objective of this simulation is to determine the probability that a new product will be profitable. A model is developed relating profit (the output measure) to various probabilistic inputs such as demand, parts cost, and labor cost. The only controllable input is whether to introduce the product. A variety of possible values will be generated for the probabilistic inputs, and the resulting profit will be computed. We develop a simulation model for this type of application in Section 15.1.
2. *Airline Overbooking* The objective of this simulation is to determine the number of reservations an airline should accept for a particular flight. A simulation model is developed relating profit for the flight to a probabilistic input, the number of passengers with a reservation who show up and use their reservation, and a controllable input, the number of reservations accepted for the flight. For each selected value for the controllable input, a variety of possible values will be generated for the number of passengers who show up, and the resulting profit can be computed. Similar simulation models are applicable for hotel and car rental reservation systems.
3. *Inventory Policy* The objective of this simulation is to choose an inventory policy that will provide good customer service at a reasonable cost. A model is developed relating two output measures, total inventory cost and the service level, to probabilistic inputs, such as product demand and delivery lead time from vendors, and controllable inputs, such as the order quantity and the reorder point. For each setting of the controllable inputs, a variety of possible values would be generated for the probabilistic inputs, and the resulting cost and service levels would be computed.
4. *Traffic Flow* The objective of this simulation is to determine the effect of installing a left turn signal on the flow of traffic through a busy intersection. A model is devel-

FIGURE 15.1 DIAGRAM OF A SIMULATION MODEL

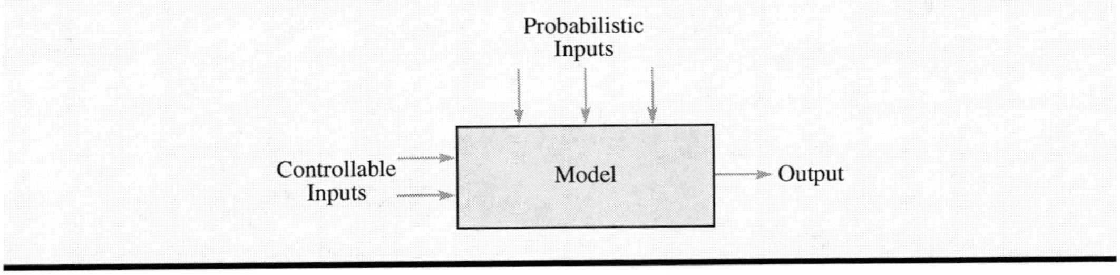

oped relating waiting time for vehicles to get through the intersection to probabilistic inputs such as the number of vehicle arrivals and the fraction that want to make a left turn, and controllable inputs such as the length of time the left turn signal is on. For each setting of the controllable inputs, values would be generated for the probabilistic inputs, and the resulting vehicle waiting times would be computed.

5. *Waiting Lines* The objective of this simulation is to determine the waiting times for customers at a bank's automated teller machine (ATM). A model is developed relating customer waiting times to probabilistic inputs such as customer arrivals and service times, and a controllable input, the number of ATM machines installed. For each value of the controllable input (the number of ATM machines), a variety of values would be generated for the probabilistic inputs and the customer waiting times would be computed. The Q.M. in Action, Call Center Design, describes how simulation of a waiting line system at a call center helped the company balance the service to its customers with the cost of agents providing the service.

Simulation is not an optimization technique. It is a method that can be used to describe or predict how a system will operate given certain choices for the controllable inputs and randomly generated values for the probabilistic inputs. Quantitative analysts often use simulation to determine values for the controllable inputs that are likely to lead to desirable system outputs. In this sense, simulation can be an effective tool in designing a system to provide good performance.

Q.M. IN ACTION

CALL CENTER DESIGN*

A call center is a place where large volumes of calls are made to or received from current or potential customers. More than 60,000 call centers operate in the United States. Saltzman and Mehrotra describe how a simulation model helped make a strategic change in the design of the technical support call center for a major software company. The application used a waiting line simulation model to balance the service to customers calling for assistance with the cost of agents providing the service.

Historically, the software company provided free phone-in technical support, but over time service requests grew to the point where 80% of the callers were waiting between 5 and 10 minutes and abandonment rates were too high. On some days 40% of the callers hung up before receiving service. This service level was unacceptable. As a result, management considered instituting a Rapid Program in which customers would pay a fee for service, but would be guaranteed to receive service within one minute, or the service would be free. Nonpaying customers would continue receiving service but without a guarantee of short service times.

A simulation model was developed to help understand the impact of this new program on the waiting line characteristics of the call center. Data available were used to develop the arrival distribution, the service time distribution, and the probability distribution for abandonment. The key design variables considered were the number of agents (channels) and the percentage of callers subscribing to the Rapid Program. The model was developed using the Arena simulation package.

The simulation results helped the company decide to go ahead with the Rapid Program. Under most of the scenarios considered, the simulation model showed that 95% of the callers in the Rapid Program would receive service within one minute and that free service to the remaining customers could be maintained within acceptable limits. Within nine months, 10% of the software company's customers subscribed to the Rapid Program, generating $2 million in incremental revenue. The company viewed the simulation model as a vehicle for mitigating risk. The model helped evaluate the likely impact of the Rapid Program without experimenting with actual customers.

*Based on Robert M. Saltzman and Vijay Mehrotra, "A Call Center Uses Simulation to Drive Strategic Change," *Interfaces* (May/June 2001): 87–101.

In this chapter we begin by showing how simulation can be used to study the financial risks associated with the development of a new product. We continue with illustrations showing how simulation can be used to establish an effective inventory policy and how simulation can be used to design waiting line systems. Other issues, such as verifying the simulation program, validating the model, and selecting a simulation software package, are discussed in Section 15.4.

15.1 RISK ANALYSIS

Risk analysis is the process of predicting the outcome of a decision in the face of uncertainty. In this section, we describe a problem that involves considerable uncertainty: the development of a new product. We first show how risk analysis can be conducted without using simulation; then, we show how a more comprehensive risk analysis can be conducted with the aid of simulation.

PortaCom Project

PortaCom manufactures personal computers and related equipment. PortaCom's product design group developed a prototype for a new high-quality portable printer. The new printer features an innovative design and has the potential to capture a significant share of the portable printer market. Preliminary marketing and financial analyses provided the following selling price, first-year administrative cost, and first-year advertising cost.

$$\begin{aligned} \text{Selling price} &= \$249 \text{ per unit} \\ \text{Administrative cost} &= \$400{,}000 \\ \text{Advertising cost} &= \$600{,}000 \end{aligned}$$

In the simulation model for the PortaCom problem, the preceding values are constants and are referred to as **parameters** of the model.

The cost of direct labor, the cost of parts, and the first-year demand for the printer are not known with certainty and are considered probabilistic inputs. At this stage of the planning process, PortaCom's best estimates of these inputs are $45 per unit for the direct labor cost, $90 per unit for the parts cost, and 15,000 units for the first-year demand. PortaCom would like an analysis of the first-year profit potential for the printer. Because of PortaCom's tight cash flow situation, management is particularly concerned about the potential for a loss.

What-If Analysis

One approach to risk analysis is called **what-if analysis.** A what-if analysis involves generating values for the probabilistic inputs (direct labor cost, parts cost, and first-year demand) and computing the resulting value for the output (profit). With a selling price of $249 per unit and administrative plus advertising costs equal to $400,000 + $600,000 = $1,000,000, the PortaCom profit model is

$$\text{Profit} = (\$249 - \text{Direct labor cost per unit} - \text{Parts cost per unit})(\text{Demand}) - \$1{,}000{,}000$$

Letting

$$\begin{aligned} c_1 &= \text{direct labor cost per unit} \\ c_2 &= \text{parts cost per unit} \\ x &= \text{first-year demand} \end{aligned}$$

the profit model for the first year can be written as follows:

$$\text{Profit} = (249 - c_1 - c_2)x - 1{,}000{,}000 \qquad (15.1)$$

The PortaCom profit model can be depicted as shown in Figure 15.2.

Recall that PortaCom's best estimates of the direct labor cost per unit, the parts cost per unit, and first-year demand are $45, $90, and 15,000 units, respectively. These values constitute the **base-case scenario** for PortaCom. Substituting these values into equation (15.1) yields the following profit projection:

$$\text{Profit} = (249 - 45 - 90)(15{,}000) - 1{,}000{,}000 = 710{,}000$$

Thus, the base-case scenario leads to an anticipated profit of $710,000.

In risk analysis we are concerned with both the probability of a loss and the magnitude of a loss. Although the base-case scenario looks appealing, PortaCom might be interested in what happens if the estimates of the direct labor cost per unit, parts cost per unit, and first-year demand do not turn out to be as expected under the base-case scenario. For instance, suppose that PortaCom believes that direct labor costs could range from $43 to $47 per unit, parts cost could range from $80 to $100 per unit, and first-year demand could range from 1500 to 28,500 units. Using these ranges, what-if analysis can be used to evaluate a **worst-case scenario** and a **best-case scenario.**

The worst-case value for the direct labor cost is $47 (the highest value), the worst-case value for the parts cost is $100 (the highest value), and the worst-case value for demand is 1500 units (the lowest value). Thus, in the worst-case scenario, $c_1 = 47$, $c_2 = 100$, and $x = 1500$. Substituting these values into equation (15.1) leads to the following profit projection:

$$\text{Profit} = (249 - 47 - 100)(1500) - 1{,}000{,}000 = -847{,}000$$

So, the worst-case scenario leads to a projected loss of $847,000.

The best-case value for the direct labor cost is $43 (the lowest value), the best-case value for the parts cost is $80 (the lowest value), and the best-case value for demand is 28,500 units (the highest value). Substituting these values into equation (15.1) leads to the following profit projection:

Problem 2 will give you practice using what-if analysis.

$$\text{Profit} = (249 - 43 - 80)(28{,}500) - 1{,}000{,}000 = 2{,}591{,}000$$

So, the best-case scenario leads to a projected profit of $2,591,000.

FIGURE 15.2 PORTACOM PROFIT MODEL

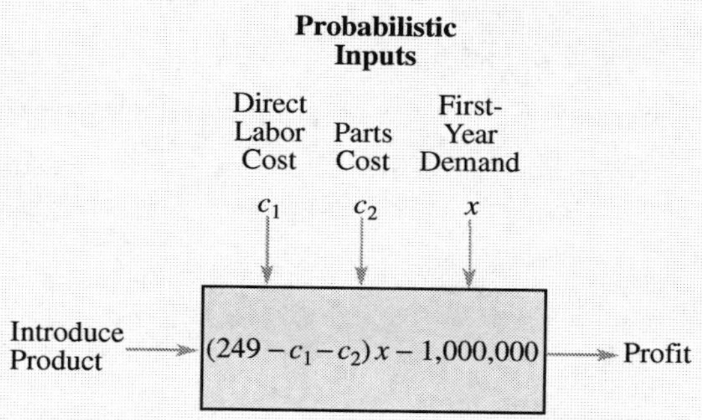

At this point the what-if analysis provides the conclusion that profits can range from a loss of $847,000 to a profit of $2,591,000 with a base-case profit of $710,000. Although the base-case profit of $710,000 is possible, the what-if analysis indicates that either a substantial loss or a substantial profit is possible. Other scenarios that PortaCom might want to consider can also be evaluated. However, the difficulty with what-if analysis is that it does not indicate the likelihood of the various profit or loss values. In particular, we do not know anything about the *probability* of a loss.

Simulation

Using simulation to perform risk analysis for the PortaCom problem is like playing out many what-if scenarios by randomly generating values for the probabilistic inputs. The advantage of simulation is that it allows us to assess the probability of a profit and the probability of a loss.

Using the what-if approach to risk analysis, we selected values for the probabilistic inputs [direct labor cost per unit (c_1), parts cost per unit (c_2), and first-year demand (x)], and then computed the resulting profit. Applying simulation to the PortaCom problem requires generating values for the probabilistic inputs that are representative of what we might observe in practice. To generate such values, we must know the probability distribution for each probabilistic input. Further analysis by PortaCom led to the following probability distributions for the direct labor cost per unit, the parts cost per unit, and first-year demand:

One advantage of simulation is the ability to use probability distributions that are unique to the system being studied.

Direct Labor Cost PortaCom believes that the direct labor cost will range from $43 to $47 per unit and is described by the discrete probability distribution shown in Table 15.1. Thus, we see a 0.1 probability that the direct labor cost will be $43 per unit, a 0.2 probability that the direct labor cost will be $44 per unit, and so on. The highest probability of 0.4 is associated with a direct labor cost of $45 per unit.

Parts Cost This cost depends upon the general economy, the overall demand for parts, and the pricing policy of PortaCom's parts suppliers. PortaCom believes that the parts cost will range from $80 to $100 per unit and is described by the uniform probability distribution shown in Figure 15.3. Costs per unit between $80 and $100 are equally likely.

First-Year Demand PortaCom believes that first-year demand is described by the normal probability distribution shown in Figure 15.4. The mean or expected value of first-year demand is 15,000 units. The standard deviation of 4500 units describes the variability in the first-year demand.

To simulate the PortaCom problem, we must generate values for the three probabilistic inputs and compute the resulting profit. Then, we generate another set of values for the

TABLE 15.1 PROBABILITY DISTRIBUTION FOR DIRECT LABOR COST PER UNIT

Direct Labor Cost per Unit	Probability
$43	0.1
$44	0.2
$45	0.4
$46	0.2
$47	0.1

FIGURE 15.3 UNIFORM PROBABILITY DISTRIBUTION FOR THE PARTS COST PER UNIT

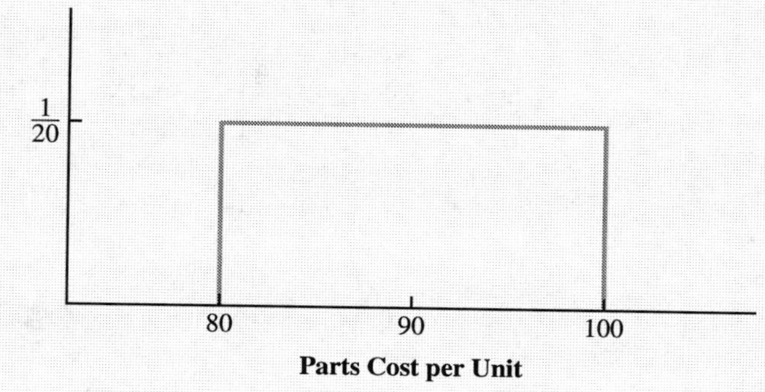

A flowchart provides a graphical representation that helps describe the logic of the simulation model.

probabilistic inputs, compute a second value for profit, and so on. We continue this process until we are satisfied that enough trials have been conducted to describe the probability distribution for profit. This process of generating probabilistic inputs and computing the value of the output is called *simulation*. The sequence of logical and mathematical operations required to conduct a simulation can be depicted with a flowchart. A flowchart for the PortaCom simulation is shown in Figure 15.5.

Following the logic described by the flowchart we see that the model parameters—selling price, administrative cost, and advertising cost—are \$249, \$400,000, and \$600,000, respectively. These values will remain fixed throughout the simulation.

The next three blocks depict the generation of values for the probabilistic inputs. First, a value for the direct labor cost (c_1) is generated. Then a value for the parts cost (c_2) is generated, followed by a value for the first-year demand (x). These probabilistic input values are combined using the profit model given by equation (15.1).

$$\text{Profit} = (249 - c_1 - c_2)x - 1{,}000{,}000$$

The computation of profit completes one trial of the simulation. We then return to the block where we generated the direct labor cost and begin another trial. This process is repeated until a satisfactory number of trials has been generated.

FIGURE 15.4 NORMAL PROBABILITY DISTRIBUTION OF FIRST-YEAR DEMAND

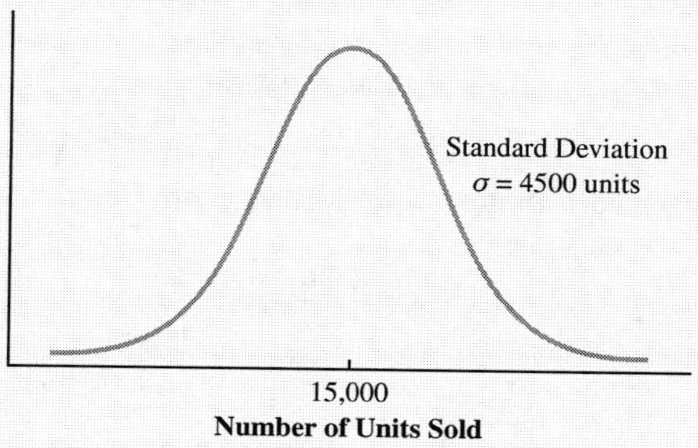

FIGURE 15.5 FLOWCHART FOR THE PORTACOM SIMULATION

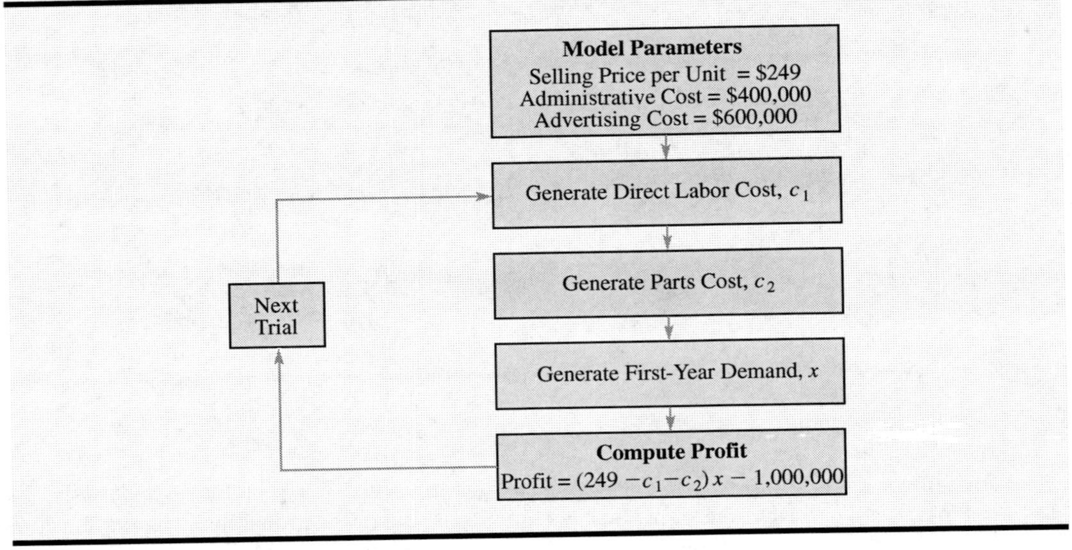

At the end of the simulation, output measures of interest can be developed. For example, we will be interested in computing the average profit and the probability of a loss. For the output measures to be meaningful, the values of the probabilistic inputs must be representative of what is likely to happen when the PortaCom printer is introduced into the market. An essential part of the simulation procedure is the ability to generate representative values for the probabilistic inputs. We now discuss how to generate these values.

Random Numbers and Generating Probabilistic Input Values In the PortaCom simulation, representative values must be generated for the direct labor cost per unit (c_1), the parts cost per unit (c_2), and the first-year demand (x). Random numbers and the probability distributions associated with each probabilistic input are used to generate representative values. To illustrate how to generate these values, we need to introduce the concept of *computer-generated random numbers*.

Computer-generated random numbers[1] are randomly selected decimal numbers from 0 up to, but not including, 1. The computer-generated random numbers are equally likely and are uniformly distributed over the interval from 0 to 1. Computer-generated random numbers can be obtained using built-in functions available in computer simulation packages and spreadsheets. For instance, placing =RAND() in a cell of an Excel worksheet will result in a random number between 0 and 1 being placed into that cell.

Because random numbers are equally likely, quantitative analysts can assign ranges of random numbers to corresponding values of probabilistic inputs so that the probability of any input value to the simulation model is identical to the probability of its occurrence in the real system.

Table 15.2 contains 500 random numbers generated using Excel. These numbers can be viewed as a random sample of 500 values from a uniform probability distribution over the interval from 0 to 1. Let us show how random numbers can be used to generate values for the PortaCom probability distributions. We begin by showing how to generate a value for the direct labor cost per unit. The approach described is applicable for generating values from any discrete probability distribution.

[1]Computer-generated random numbers are called *pseudorandom numbers*. Because they are generated through the use of mathematical formulas, they are not technically random. The difference between random numbers and pseudorandom numbers is primarily philosophical, and we use the term *random numbers* regardless of whether they are generated by a computer.

TABLE 15.2 500 COMPUTER-GENERATED RANDOM NUMBERS

0.6953	0.5247	0.1368	0.9850	0.7467	0.3813	0.5827	0.7893	0.7169	0.8166
0.0082	0.9925	0.6874	0.2122	0.6885	0.2159	0.4299	0.3467	0.2186	0.1033
0.6799	0.1241	0.3056	0.5590	0.0423	0.6515	0.2750	0.8156	0.2871	0.4680
0.8898	0.1514	0.1826	0.0004	0.5259	0.2425	0.8421	0.9248	0.9155	0.9518
0.6515	0.5027	0.9290	0.5177	0.3134	0.9177	0.2605	0.6668	0.1167	0.7870
0.3976	0.7790	0.0035	0.0064	0.0441	0.3437	0.1248	0.5442	0.9800	0.1857
0.0642	0.4086	0.6078	0.2044	0.0484	0.4691	0.7058	0.8552	0.5029	0.3288
0.0377	0.5250	0.7774	0.2390	0.9121	0.5345	0.8178	0.8443	0.4154	0.2526
0.5739	0.5181	0.0234	0.7305	0.0376	0.5169	0.5679	0.5495	0.7872	0.5321
0.5827	0.0341	0.7482	0.6351	0.9146	0.4700	0.7869	0.1337	0.0702	0.4219
0.0508	0.7905	0.2932	0.4971	0.0225	0.4466	0.5118	0.1200	0.0200	0.5445
0.4757	0.1399	0.5668	0.9569	0.7255	0.4650	0.4084	0.3701	0.9446	0.8064
0.6805	0.9931	0.4166	0.1091	0.7730	0.0691	0.9411	0.3468	0.0014	0.7379
0.2603	0.7507	0.6414	0.9907	0.2699	0.4571	0.9254	0.2371	0.8664	0.9553
0.8143	0.7625	0.1708	0.1900	0.2781	0.2830	0.6877	0.0488	0.8635	0.3155
0.5681	0.7854	0.5016	0.9403	0.1078	0.5255	0.8727	0.3815	0.5541	0.9833
0.1501	0.9363	0.3858	0.3545	0.5448	0.0643	0.3167	0.6732	0.6283	0.2631
0.8806	0.7989	0.7484	0.8083	0.2701	0.5039	0.9439	0.1027	0.9677	0.4597
0.4582	0.7590	0.4393	0.4704	0.6903	0.3732	0.6587	0.8675	0.2905	0.3058
0.0785	0.1467	0.3880	0.5274	0.8723	0.7517	0.9905	0.8904	0.8177	0.6660
0.1158	0.6635	0.4992	0.9070	0.2975	0.5686	0.8495	0.1652	0.2039	0.2553
0.2762	0.7018	0.6782	0.4013	0.2224	0.4672	0.5753	0.6219	0.6871	0.9255
0.9382	0.6411	0.7984	0.0608	0.5945	0.3977	0.4570	0.9924	0.8398	0.8361
0.5102	0.7021	0.4353	0.3398	0.8038	0.2260	0.1250	0.1884	0.3432	0.1192
0.2354	0.7410	0.7089	0.2579	0.1358	0.8446	0.1648	0.3889	0.5620	0.6555
0.9082	0.7906	0.7589	0.8870	0.1189	0.7125	0.6324	0.1096	0.5155	0.3449
0.6936	0.0702	0.9716	0.0374	0.0683	0.2397	0.7753	0.2029	0.1464	0.8000
0.4042	0.8158	0.3623	0.6614	0.7954	0.7516	0.6518	0.3638	0.3107	0.2718
0.9410	0.2201	0.6348	0.0367	0.0311	0.0688	0.2346	0.3927	0.7327	0.9994
0.0917	0.2504	0.2878	0.1735	0.3872	0.6816	0.2731	0.3846	0.6621	0.8983
0.8532	0.4869	0.2685	0.6349	0.9364	0.3451	0.4998	0.2842	0.0643	0.6656
0.8980	0.0455	0.8314	0.8189	0.6783	0.8086	0.1386	0.4442	0.9941	0.6812
0.8412	0.8792	0.2025	0.9320	0.7656	0.3815	0.5302	0.8744	0.4584	0.3585
0.5688	0.8633	0.5818	0.0692	0.2543	0.5453	0.9955	0.1237	0.7535	0.5993
0.5006	0.1215	0.8102	0.1026	0.9251	0.6851	0.1559	0.1214	0.2628	0.9374
0.5748	0.4164	0.3427	0.2809	0.8064	0.5855	0.2229	0.2805	0.9139	0.9013
0.1100	0.0873	0.9407	0.8747	0.0496	0.4380	0.5847	0.4183	0.5929	0.4863
0.5802	0.7747	0.1285	0.0074	0.6252	0.7747	0.0112	0.3958	0.3285	0.5389
0.1019	0.6628	0.8998	0.1334	0.2798	0.7351	0.7330	0.6723	0.6924	0.3963
0.9909	0.8991	0.2298	0.2603	0.6921	0.5573	0.8191	0.0384	0.2954	0.0636
0.6292	0.4923	0.0276	0.6734	0.6562	0.4231	0.1980	0.6551	0.3716	0.0507
0.9430	0.2579	0.7933	0.0945	0.3192	0.3195	0.7772	0.4672	0.7070	0.5925
0.9938	0.7098	0.7964	0.7952	0.8947	0.1214	0.8454	0.8294	0.5394	0.9413
0.4690	0.1395	0.0930	0.3189	0.6972	0.7291	0.8513	0.9256	0.7478	0.8124
0.2028	0.3774	0.0485	0.7718	0.9656	0.2444	0.0304	0.1395	0.1577	0.8625
0.6141	0.4131	0.2006	0.2329	0.6182	0.5151	0.6300	0.9311	0.3837	0.7828
0.2757	0.8479	0.7880	0.8492	0.6859	0.8947	0.6246	0.1574	0.4936	0.8077
0.0561	0.0126	0.6531	0.0378	0.4975	0.1133	0.3572	0.0071	0.4555	0.7563
0.1419	0.4308	0.8073	0.4681	0.0481	0.2918	0.2975	0.0685	0.6384	0.0812
0.3125	0.0053	0.9209	0.9768	0.3584	0.0390	0.2161	0.6333	0.4391	0.6991

TABLE 15.3 RANDOM NUMBER INTERVALS FOR GENERATING VALUES OF DIRECT LABOR COST PER UNIT

Direct Labor Cost per Unit	Probability	Interval of Random Numbers
$43	0.1	0.0 but less than 0.1
$44	0.2	0.1 but less than 0.3
$45	0.4	0.3 but less than 0.7
$46	0.2	0.7 but less than 0.9
$47	0.1	0.9 but less than 1.0

An interval of random numbers is assigned to each possible value of the direct labor cost in such a fashion that the probability of generating a random number in the interval is equal to the probability of the corresponding direct labor cost. Table 15.3 shows how this process is done. The interval of random numbers 0.0 but less than 0.1 is associated with a direct labor cost of $43, the interval of random numbers 0.1 but less than 0.3 is associated with a direct labor cost of $44, and so on. With this assignment of random number intervals to the possible values of the direct labor cost, the probability of generating a random number in any interval is equal to the probability of obtaining the corresponding value for the direct labor cost. Thus, to select a value for the direct labor cost, we generate a random number between 0 and 1. If the random number is 0.0 but less than 0.1, we set the direct labor cost equal to $43. If the random number is 0.1 but less than 0.3, we set the direct labor cost equal to $44, and so on.

Try Problem 5 for an opportunity to establish intervals of random numbers and simulate demand from a discrete probability distribution.

Each trial of the simulation requires a value for the direct labor cost. Suppose that on the first trial the random number is 0.9109. From Table 15.3, the simulated value for the direct labor cost is $47 per unit. Suppose that on the second trial the random number is 0.2841. From Table 15.3, the simulated value for the direct labor cost is $44 per unit. Table 15.4 shows the results obtained for the first 10 simulation trials.

Each trial in the simulation requires a value of the direct labor cost, parts cost, and first-year demand. Let us now turn to the issue of generating values for the parts cost. The probability distribution for the parts cost per unit is the uniform distribution shown in Figure 15.3. Because this random variable has a different probability distribution than direct labor cost, we use random numbers in a slightly different way to generate values for parts cost. With

TABLE 15.4 RANDOM GENERATION OF 10 VALUES FOR THE DIRECT LABOR COST PER UNIT

Trial	Random Number	Direct Labor Cost ($)
1	0.9109	47
2	0.2841	44
3	0.6531	45
4	0.0367	43
5	0.3451	45
6	0.2757	44
7	0.6859	45
8	0.6246	45
9	0.4936	45
10	0.8077	46

a uniform probability distribution, the following relationship between the random number and the associated value of the parts cost is used.

$$\text{Parts cost} = a + r(b - a) \tag{15.2}$$

where

r = random number between 0 and 1
a = smallest value for parts cost
b = largest value for parts cost

For PortaCom, the smallest value for the parts cost is \$80, and the largest value is \$100. Applying equation (15.2) with $a = 80$ and $b = 100$ leads to the following formula for generating the parts cost given a random number, r.

$$\text{Parts cost} = 80 + r(100 - 80) = 80 + r20 \tag{15.3}$$

Equation (15.3) generates a value for the parts cost. Suppose that a random number of 0.2680 is obtained. The value for the parts cost is

$$\text{Parts cost} = 80 + 0.2680(20) = 85.36 \text{ per unit}$$

Suppose that a random number of 0.5842 is generated on the next trial. The value for the parts cost is

$$\text{Parts cost} = 80 + 0.5842(20) = 91.68 \text{ per unit}$$

Spreadsheet packages such as Excel have built-in functions that make simulations based on probability distributions such as the normal probability distribution relatively easy.

With appropriate choices of a and b, equation (15.2) can be used to generate values for any uniform probability distribution. Table 15.5 shows the generation of 10 values for the parts cost per unit.

Finally, we need a random number procedure for generating the first-year demand. Because first-year demand is normally distributed with a mean of 15,000 units and a standard deviation of 4500 units (see Figure 15.4), we need a procedure for generating random values

TABLE 15.5 RANDOM GENERATION OF 10 VALUES FOR THE PARTS COST PER UNIT

Trial	Random Number	Parts Cost (\$)
1	0.2680	85.36
2	0.5842	91.68
3	0.6675	93.35
4	0.9280	98.56
5	0.4180	88.36
6	0.7342	94.68
7	0.4325	88.65
8	0.1186	82.37
9	0.6944	93.89
10	0.7869	95.74

from a normal probability distribution. Because of the mathematical complexity, a detailed discussion of the procedure for generating random values from a normal probability distribution is omitted. However, computer simulation packages and spreadsheets include a built-in function that provides randomly generated values from a normal probability distribution. In most cases the user only needs to provide the mean and standard deviation of the normal distribution. For example, using Excel the following formula can be placed into a cell to obtain a value for a probabilistic input that is normally distributed:

=NORMINV(RAND(),Mean,Standard Deviation)

Because the mean for the first-year demand in the PortaCom problem is 15,000 and the standard deviation is 4500, the Excel statement

=NORMINV(RAND(),15000,4500) (15.4)

will provide a normally distributed value for first-year demand. For example, if Excel's RAND() function generates the random number 0.7005, the Excel function shown in equation (15.4) will provide a first-year demand of 17,366 units. If RAND() generates the random number 0.3204, equation (15.4) will provide a first-year demand of 12,900. Table 15.6 shows the results for the first 10 randomly generated values for demand. Note that random numbers less than 0.5 generate first-year demand values below the mean and that random numbers greater than 0.5 generate first-year demand values greater than the mean.

Running the Simulation Model Running the simulation model means implementing the sequence of logical and mathematical operations described in the flowchart in Figure 15.5. The model parameters are $249 per unit for the selling price, $400,000 for the administrative cost, and $600,000 for the advertising cost. Each trial in the simulation involves randomly generating values for the probabilistic inputs (direct labor cost, parts cost, and first-year demand) and computing profit. The simulation is complete when a satisfactory number of trials have been conducted.

Let us compute the profit for the first trial assuming the following probabilistic inputs:

Direct labor cost:	$c_1 = 47$
Parts cost:	$c_2 = 85.36$
First-year demand:	$x = 17{,}366$

TABLE 15.6 RANDOM GENERATION OF 10 VALUES FOR FIRST-YEAR DEMAND

Trial	Random Number	Demand
1	0.7005	17,366
2	0.3204	12,900
3	0.8968	20,686
4	0.1804	10,888
5	0.4346	14,259
6	0.9605	22,904
7	0.5646	15,732
8	0.7334	17,804
9	0.0216	5,902
10	0.3218	12,918

Referring to the flowchart in Figure 15.5, we see that the profit obtained is

$$\begin{aligned}\text{Profit} &= (249 - c_1 - c_2)x - 1{,}000{,}000\\ &= (249 - 47 - 85.36)17{,}366 - 1{,}000{,}000 = 1{,}025{,}570\end{aligned}$$

The first row of Table 15.7 shows the result of this trial of the PortaCom simulation.

The simulated profit for the PortaCom printer if the direct labor cost is $47 per unit, the parts cost is $85.36 per unit, and first-year demand is 17,366 units is $1,025,570. Of course, one simulation trial does not provide a complete understanding of the possible profit and loss. Because other values are possible for the probabilistic inputs, we can benefit from additional simulation trials.

Suppose that on a second simulation trial, random numbers of 0.2841, 0.5842, and 0.3204 are generated for the direct labor cost, the parts cost, and first-year demand, respectively. These random numbers will provide the probabilistic inputs of $44 for the direct labor cost, $91.68 for the parts cost, and 12,900 for first-year demand. These values provide a simulated profit of $461,828 on the second simulation trial (see the second row of Table 15.7).

Repetition of the simulation process with different values for the probabilistic inputs is an essential part of any simulation. Through the repeated trials, management will begin to understand what might happen when the product is introduced into the real world. We have shown the results of 10 simulation trials in Table 15.7. For these 10 cases, we find a profit as high as $1,526,769 for the 6th trial and a loss of $350,131 for the 9th trial. Thus, we see both the possibility of a profit and a loss. Averages for the 10 trials are presented at the bottom of the table. We see that the average profit for the 10 trials is $713,743. The probability of a loss is 0.10, because one of the 10 trials (the 9th) resulted in a loss. We note also that the average values for labor cost, parts cost, and first-year demand are fairly close to their means of $45, $90, and 15,000, respectively.

Simulation of the PortaCom Problem

Using an Excel worksheet, we simulated the PortaCom project 500 times. The worksheet used to carry out the simulation is shown in Figure 15.6. Note that the simulation results for trials 6 through 495 have been hidden so that the results can be shown in a reasonably sized

TABLE 15.7 PORTACOM SIMULATION RESULTS FOR 10 TRIALS

Trial	Direct Labor Cost per Unit ($)	Parts Cost per Unit ($)	Units Sold	Profit ($)
1	47	85.36	17,366	1,025,570
2	44	91.68	12,900	461,828
3	45	93.35	20,686	1,288,906
4	43	98.56	10,888	169,807
5	45	88.36	14,259	648,911
6	44	94.68	22,904	1,526,769
7	45	88.65	15,732	814,686
8	45	82.37	17,804	1,165,501
9	45	93.89	5,902	−350,131
10	46	95.74	12,918	385,585
Total	449	912.64	151,359	7,137,432
Average	$44.90	$91.26	15,136	$713,743

FIGURE 15.6 EXCEL WORKSHEET FOR THE PORTACOM PROBLEM

EXCELfile
PortaCom

	A	B	C	D	E	F
1	**PortaCom Risk Analysis**					
2						
3	Selling Price per Unit		$249			
4	Administrative Cost		$400,000			
5	Advertising Cost		$600,000			
6						
7	**Direct Labor Cost**			**Parts Cost (Uniform Distribution)**		
8	Lower	Upper		Smallest Value	$80	
9	Random No.	Random No.	Cost per Unit	Largest Value	$100	
10	0.0	0.1	$43			
11	0.1	0.3	$44			
12	0.3	0.7	$45	**Demand (Normal Distribution)**		
13	0.7	0.9	$46	Mean	15000	
14	0.9	1.0	$47	Std Deviation	4500	
15						
16						
17	**Simulation Trials**					
18						
19		Direct Labor	Parts	First-Year		
20	Trial	Cost per Unit	Cost per Unit	Demand	Profit	
21	1	47	$85.36	17,366	$1,025,570	
22	2	44	$91.68	12,900	$461,828	
23	3	45	$93.35	20,686	$1,288,906	
24	4	43	$98.56	10,888	$169,807	
25	5	45	$88.36	14,259	$648,911	
516	496	44	$98.67	8,730	($71,739)	
517	497	45	$94.38	19,257	$1,110,952	
518	498	44	$90.85	14,920	$703,118	
519	499	43	$90.37	13,471	$557,652	
520	500	46	$92.50	18,614	$1,056,847	
521						
522			**Summary Statistics**			
523			Mean Profit		$698,457	
524			Standard Deviation		$520,485	
525			Minimum Profit		($785,234)	
526			Maximum Profit		$2,367,058	
527			Number of Losses		51	
528			Probability of Loss		0.1020	
529						

figure. If desired, the rows for these trials can be shown and the simulation results displayed for all 500 trials. The details of the Excel worksheet that provided the PortaCom simulation are described in Appendix 15.1.

Excel worksheets for all simulations presented in this chapter are available on the CD that accompanies this text.

The simulation summary statistics in Figure 15.6 provide information about the risk associated with PortaCom's new printer. The worst result obtained in a simulation of 500 trials is a loss of $785,234, and the best result is a profit of $2,367,058. The mean profit is $698,457. Fifty-one of the trials resulted in a loss; thus, the estimated probability of a loss is 51/500 = 0.1020.

Simulation studies enable an objective estimate of the probability of a loss, which is an important aspect of risk analysis.

A histogram of simulated profit values is shown in Figure 15.7. We note that the distribution of profit values is fairly symmetric with a large number of values in the range of $250,000 to $1,250,000. The probability of a large loss or a large gain is small. Only 3 trials resulted in a loss of more than $500,000, and only 3 trials resulted in a profit greater than $2,000,000. However, the probability of a loss is significant. Forty-eight of the 500 trials resulted in a loss in the $0 to $500,000 range—almost 10 percent. The modal category, the one with the largest number of values, is the range of profits between $750,000 and $1,000,000.

In comparing the simulation approach to risk analysis to the what-if approach, we see that much more information is obtained by using simulation. With the what-if analysis, we learned that the base-case scenario projected a profit of $710,000. The worst-case scenario projected a loss of $847,000, and the best-case scenario projected a profit of $2,591,000. From the 500 trials of the simulation run, we see that the worst- and best-case scenarios, although possible, are unlikely. None of the 500 trials provided a loss as low as the worst-case or a profit as high as the best-case. Indeed, the advantage of simulation for risk analysis is the information it provides on the likely values of the output. We now know the probability of a loss, how the profit values are distributed over their range, and what profit values are most likely.

For practice working through a simulation problem, try Problems 9 and 14.

The simulation results help PortaCom's management better understand the profit/loss potential of the PortaCom portable printer. The 0.1020 probability of a loss may be acceptable to management given a probability of almost 0.80 (see Figure 15.7) that profit will exceed $250,000. On the other hand, PortaCom might want to conduct further market research before deciding whether to introduce the product. In any case, the simulation results should be helpful in reaching an appropriate decision. The Q.M. in Action, Meeting Demand Levels at Pfizer, describes how a simulation model helped find ways to meet increasing demand for a product.

FIGURE 15.7 HISTOGRAM OF SIMULATED PROFIT FOR 500 TRIALS OF THE PORTACOM SIMULATION

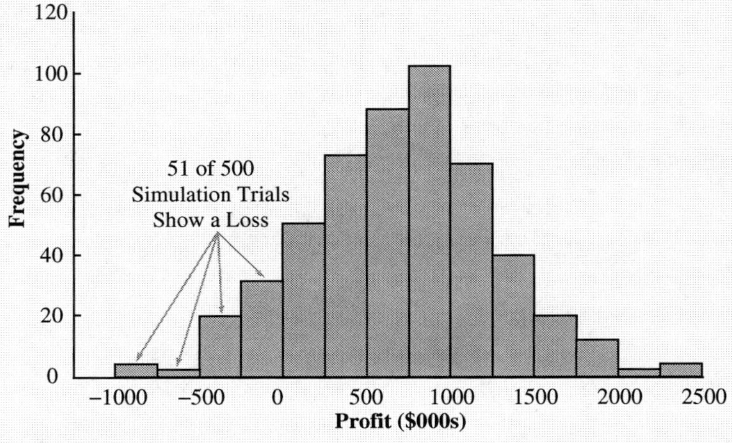

Q.M. IN ACTION

MEETING DEMAND LEVELS AT PFIZER*

Pharmacia & Upjohn's merger with Pfizer created one of the world's largest pharmaceutical firms. Demand for one of Pharmacia & Upjohn's long-standing products remained stable for several years at a level easily satisfied by the company's manufacturing facility. However, changes in market conditions caused an increase in demand to a level beyond the current capacity. A simulation model of the production process was developed to explore ways to increase production to meet the new level of demand in a cost-effective manner.

Simulation results were used to help answer the following questions:

- What is the maximum throughput of the existing facility?
- How can the existing production process be modified to increase throughput?
- How much equipment must be added to the existing facility to meet the increased demand?
- What is the desired size and configuration of the new production process?

The simulation model was able to demonstrate that the existing facilities, with some operating policy improvements, were large enough to satisfy the increased demand for the next several years. Expansion to a new production facility was not necessary. The simulation model also helped determine the number of operators required as the production level increased in the future. This result helped ensure that the proper number of operators would be trained by the time they were needed. The simulation model also provided a way reprocessed material could be used to replace fresh raw materials, resulting in a savings of approximately $3 million per year.

*Based on information provided by David B. Magerlein, James M. Magerlein, and Michael J. Goodrich.

NOTES AND COMMENTS

Appendix 15.2 shows how to perform a simulation of the PortaCom problem using Crystal Ball.

1. The PortaCom simulation model is based on independent trials in which the results for one trial do not affect what happens in subsequent trials. Historically, this type of simulation study was referred to as a *Monte Carlo simulation.* The term *Monte Carlo simulation* was used because early practitioners of simulation saw similarities between the models they were developing and the gambling games played in the casinos of Monte Carlo. Today, many individuals interpret the term *Monte Carlo simulation* more broadly to mean any simulation that involves randomly generating values for the probabilistic inputs.
2. The probability distribution used to generate values for probabilistic inputs in a simulation model is often developed using historical data. For instance, suppose that an analysis of daily sales at a new car dealership for the past 50 days showed that on 2 days no cars were sold, on 5 days one car was sold, on 9 days two cars were sold, on 24 days three cars were sold, on 7 days four cars were sold, and on 3 days five cars were sold. We can estimate the probability distribution of daily demand using the relative frequencies for the observed data. An estimate of the probability that no cars are sold on a given day is 2/50 = 0.04, an estimate of the probability that one car is sold is 5/50 = 0.10, and so on. The estimated probability distribution of daily demand is shown in the table below.
3. Spreadsheet add-in packages such as @RISK® and Crystal Ball® have been developed to make spreadsheet simulation easier. For instance, using Crystal Ball we could simulate the PortaCom new product introduction by first entering the formulas showing the relationships between the probabilistic inputs and the output measure, profit. Then, a probability distribution type is selected for each probabilistic input from among a number of available choices. Crystal Ball will generate random values for each probabilistic input, compute the profit, and repeat the simulation for as many trials as specified. Graphical displays and a variety of descriptive statistics can be easily obtained.

Daily Sales	0	1	2	3	4	5
Probability	0.04	0.10	0.18	0.48	0.14	0.06

15.2 INVENTORY SIMULATION

In this section we describe how simulation can be used to establish an inventory policy for a product that has an uncertain demand. The product is a home ventilation fan distributed by the Butler Electrical Supply Company. Each fan costs Butler \$75 and sells for \$125. Thus Butler realizes a gross profit of \$125 − \$75 = \$50 for each fan sold. Monthly demand for the fan is described by a normal probability distribution with a mean of 100 units and a standard deviation of 20 units.

Butler receives monthly deliveries from its supplier and replenishes its inventory to a level of Q at the beginning of each month. This beginning inventory level is referred to as the replenishment level. If monthly demand is less than the replenishment level, an inventory holding cost of \$15 is charged for each unit that is not sold. However, if monthly demand is greater than the replenishment level, a stock-out occurs and a shortage cost is incurred. Because Butler assigns a goodwill cost of \$30 for each customer turned away, a shortage cost of \$30 is charged for each unit of demand that cannot be satisfied. Management would like to use a simulation model to determine the average monthly net profit resulting from using a particular replenishment level. Management would also like information on the percentage of total demand that will be satisfied. This percentage is referred to as the *service level.*

The controllable input to the Butler simulation model is the replenishment level, Q. The probabilistic input is the monthly demand, D. The two output measures are the average monthly net profit and the service level. Computation of the service level requires that we keep track of the number of fans sold each month and the total demand for fans for each month. The service level will be computed at the end of the simulation run as the ratio of total units sold to total demand. A diagram of the relationship between the inputs and the outputs is shown in Figure 15.8.

When demand is less than or equal to the replenishment level ($D \leq Q$), D units are sold, and an inventory holding cost of \$15 is incurred for each of the $Q - D$ units that remain in inventory. Net profit for this case is computed as follows:

Case 1: $D \leq Q$

$$\begin{aligned} \text{Gross profit} &= \$50D \\ \text{Holding cost} &= \$15(Q - D) \\ \text{Net profit} &= \text{Gross profit} - \text{Holding cost} = \$50D - \$15(Q - D) \end{aligned} \tag{15.5}$$

When demand is greater than the replenishment level ($D >$ Q), Q fans are sold, and a shortage cost of \$30 is imposed for each of the $D - Q$ units of demand not satisfied. Net profit for this case is computed as follows:

Case 2: $D > Q$

$$\begin{aligned} \text{Gross profit} &= \$50Q \\ \text{Shortage cost} &= \$30(D - Q) \\ \text{Net profit} &= \text{Gross profit} - \text{Shortage cost} = \$50Q - \$30(D - Q) \end{aligned} \tag{15.6}$$

Figure 15.9 shows a flowchart that defines the sequence of logical and mathematical operations required to simulate the Butler inventory system. Each trial in the simulation represents one month of operation. The simulation is run for 300 months using a given

FIGURE 15.8 BUTLER INVENTORY SIMULATION MODEL

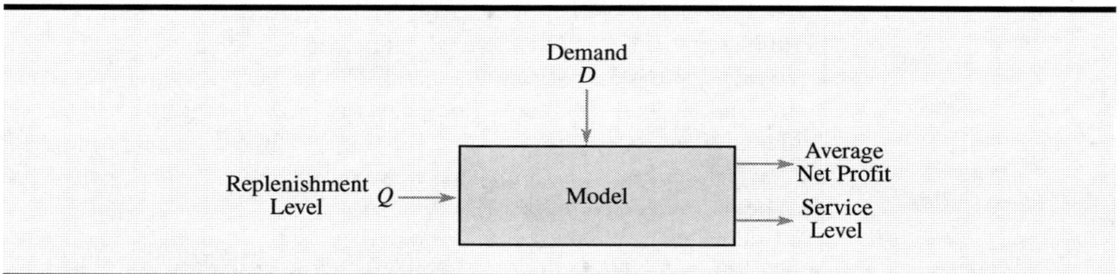

FIGURE 15.9 FLOWCHART FOR THE BUTLER INVENTORY SIMULATION

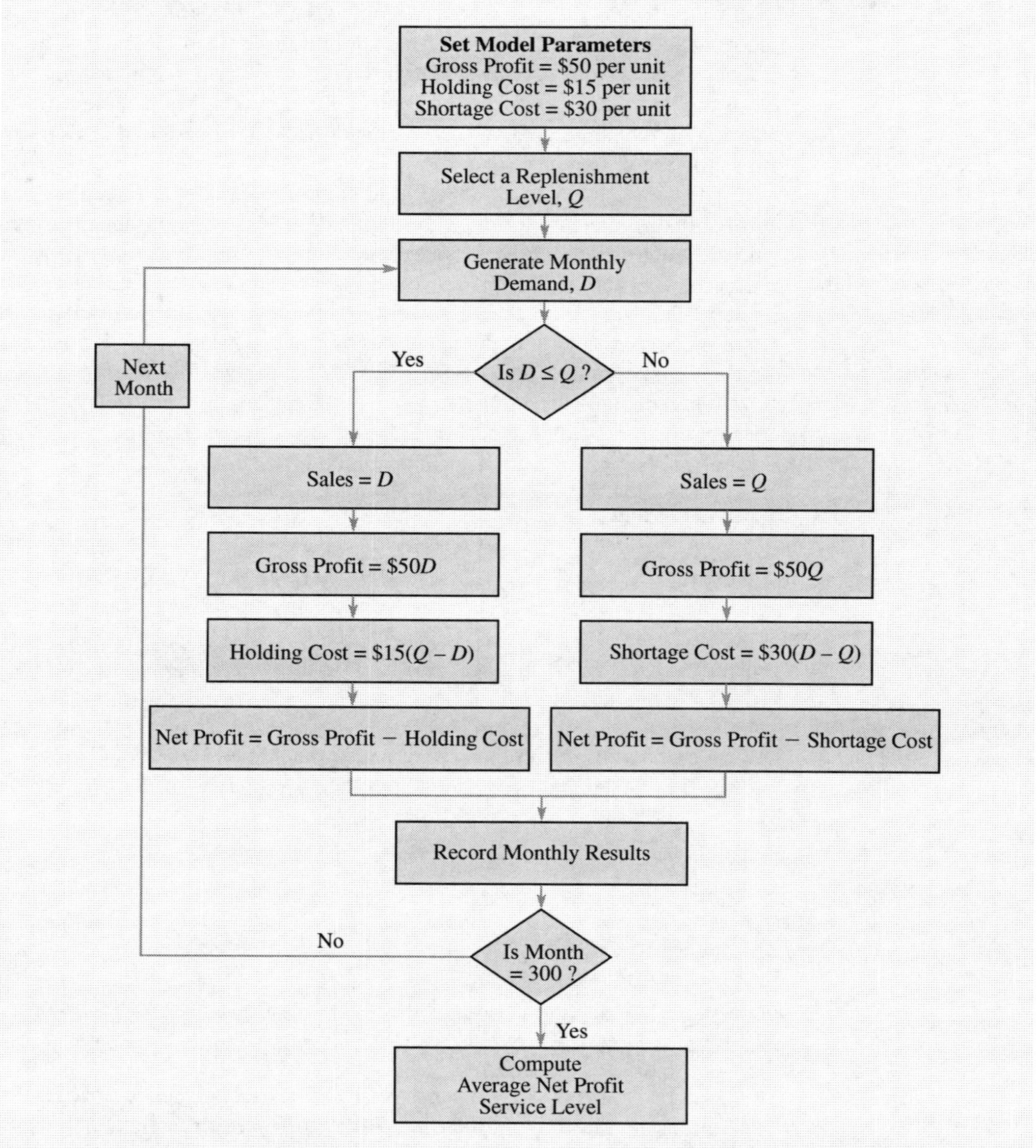

replenishment level, Q. Then, the average profit and service level output measures are computed. Let us describe the steps involved in the simulation by illustrating the results for the first two months of a simulation run using a replenishment level of $Q = 100$.

The first block of the flowchart in Figure 15.9 sets the values of the model parameters: gross profit = \$50 per unit, holding cost = \$15 per unit, and shortage cost = \$30 per unit. The next block shows that a replenishment level of Q is selected; in our illustration, $Q = 100$. Then, a value for monthly demand is generated. Because monthly demand is normally distributed with a mean of 100 units and a standard deviation of 20 units, we can use the Excel function =NORMINV(RAND(),100,20), as described in Section 15.1, to generate a value for monthly demand. Suppose that a value of $D = 79$ is generated on the first trial. This value of demand is then compared with the replenishment level, Q. With the replenishment level set at $Q = 100$, demand is less than the replenishment level, and the left branch of the flowchart is followed. Sales are set equal to demand (79), and gross profit, holding cost, and net profit are computed as follows:

$$\begin{aligned}\text{Gross profit} &= 50D = 50(79) = 3950\\ \text{Holding cost} &= 15(Q - D) = 15(100 - 79) = 315\\ \text{Net profit} &= \text{Gross profit} - \text{Holding cost} = 3950 - 315 = 3635\end{aligned}$$

The values of demand, sales, gross profit, holding cost, and net profit are recorded for the first month. The first row of Table 15.8 summarizes the information for this first trial.

For the second month, suppose that a value of 111 is generated for monthly demand. Because demand is greater than the replenishment level, the right branch of the flowchart is followed. Sales are set equal to the replenishment level (100), and gross profit, shortage cost, and net profit are computed as follows:

$$\begin{aligned}\text{Gross profit} &= 50Q = 50(100) = 5000\\ \text{Shortage cost} &= 30(D - Q) = 30(111 - 100) = 330\\ \text{Net profit} &= \text{Gross profit} - \text{Shortage cost} = 5000 - 330 = 4670\end{aligned}$$

The values of demand, sales, gross profit, holding cost, shortage cost, and net profit are recorded for the second month. The second row of Table 15.8 summarizes the information generated in the second trial.

Results for the first five months of the simulation are shown in Table 15.8. The totals show an accumulated total net profit of \$22,310, which is an average monthly net profit of \$22,310/5 = \$4462. Total unit sales are 472, and total demand is 501. Thus, the service

TABLE 15.8 BUTLER INVENTORY SIMULATION RESULTS FOR FIVE TRIALS WITH $Q = 100$

Month	Demand	Sales	Gross Profit (\$)	Holding Cost (\$)	Shortage Cost (\$)	Net Profit (\$)
1	79	79	3,950	315	0	3,635
2	111	100	5,000	0	330	4,670
3	93	93	4,650	105	0	4,545
4	100	100	5,000	0	0	5,000
5	118	100	5,000	0	540	4,460
Totals	501	472	23,600	420	870	22,310
Average	100	94	\$4,720	\$ 84	\$174	\$4,462

level is 472/501 = 0.942, indicating Butler has been able to satisfy 94.2% of demand during the five-month period.

Simulation of the Butler Inventory Problem

Using Excel, we simulated the Butler inventory operation for 300 months. The worksheet used to carry out the simulation is shown in Figure 15.10. Note that the simulation results for months 6 through 295 have been hidden so that the results can be shown in a reasonably sized figure. If desired, the rows for these months can be shown and the simulation results displayed for all 300 months.

The summary statistics in Figure 15.10 show what can be anticipated over 300 months if Butler operates its inventory system using a replenishment level of 100. The average net profit is $4293 per month. Because 27,917 units of the total demand of 30,181 units were satisfied,

FIGURE 15.10 EXCEL WORKSHEET FOR THE BUTLER INVENTORY PROBLEM

EXCELfile
Butler

	A	B	C	D	E	F	G	H
1	**Butler Inventory**							
2								
3	Gross Profit per Unit		$50					
4	Holding Cost per Unit		$15					
5	Shortage Cost per Unit		$30					
6								
7	**Replenishment Level**		100					
8								
9	**Demand (Normal Distribution)**							
10	Mean	100						
11	Std Deviation	20						
12								
13								
14	**Simulation**							
15								
16	Month	Demand	Sales	Gross Profit	Holding Cost	Shortage Cost	Net Profit	
17	1	79	79	$3,950	$315	$0	$3,635	
18	2	111	100	$5,000	$0	$330	$4,670	
19	3	93	93	$4,650	$105	$0	$4,545	
20	4	100	100	$5,000	$0	$0	$5,000	
21	5	118	100	$5,000	$0	$540	$4,460	
312	296	89	89	$4,450	$165	$0	$4,285	
313	297	91	91	$4,550	$135	$0	$4,415	
314	298	122	100	$5,000	$0	$660	$4,340	
315	299	93	93	$4,650	$105	$0	$4,545	
316	300	126	100	$5,000	$0	$780	$4,220	
317								
318	**Totals**	30,181	27,917		**Summary Statistics**			
319					Mean Profit		$4,293	
320					Standard Deviation		$658	
321					Minimum Profit		($206)	
322					Maximum Profit		$5,000	
323					Service Level		92.5%	
324								

TABLE 15.9 BUTLER INVENTORY SIMULATION RESULTS FOR 300 TRIALS

Replenishment Level	Average Net Profit ($)	Service Level (%)
100	4293	92.5
110	4524	96.5
120	4575	98.6
130	4519	99.6
140	4399	99.9

Simulation allows the user to consider different operating policies and changes to model parameters and then to observe the impact of the changes on output measures such as profit or service level.

the service level is 27,917/30,181 = 92.5%. We are now ready to use the simulation model to consider other replenishment levels that may improve the net profit and the service level.

At this point, we conducted a series of simulation experiments by repeating the Butler inventory simulation with replenishment levels of 110, 120, 130, and 140 units. The average monthly net profits and the service levels are shown in Table 15.9. The highest monthly net profit of $4575 occurs with a replenishment level of $Q = 120$. The associated service level is 98.6 percent. On the basis of these results, Butler selected a replenishment level of $Q = 120$.

Experimental simulation studies, such as this one for Butler's inventory policy, can help identify good operating policies and decisions. Butler's management used simulation to choose a replenishment level of 120 for its home ventilation fan. With the simulation model in place, management can also explore the sensitivity of this decision to some of the model parameters. For instance, we assigned a shortage cost of $30 for any customer demand not met. With this shortage cost, the replenishment level was $Q = 120$ and the service level was 98.6%. If management felt a more appropriate shortage cost was $10 per unit, running the simulation again using $10 as the shortage cost would be a simple matter.

Problem 18 gives you a chance to develop a different simulation model.

We mentioned earlier that simulation is not an optimization technique. Even though we used simulation to choose a replenishment level, it does not guarantee that this choice is optimal. All possible replenishment levels were not tested. Perhaps a manager would like to consider additional simulation runs with replenishment levels of $Q = 115$ and $Q = 125$ to search for an even better inventory policy. Also, we have no guarantee that with another set of 300 randomly generated demand values that the replenishment level with the highest profit would not change. However, with a large number of simulation trials, we should find a good and, at least, near optimal solution. The Q.M. in Action, Petroleum Distribution in the Gulf of Mexico, describes a simulation application for 15 petroleum companies in the state of Florida.

Q.M. IN ACTION

PETROLEUM DISTRIBUTION IN THE GULF OF MEXICO*

Domestic suppliers who operate oil refineries along the Gulf Coast are helping to satisfy Florida's increasing demand for refined petroleum products. Barge fleets, operated either by independent shipping companies or by the petroleum companies themselves, are used to transport more than 20 different petroleum products to 15 Florida petroleum companies. The petroleum products are loaded at refineries in Texas, Louisiana, and Mississippi and are discharged at tank terminals concentrated in Tampa, Port Everglades, and Jacksonville.

Barges operate under three types of contracts between the fleet operator and the client petroleum company:

- The client assumes total control of a barge and uses it for trips between its own refinery and one or more discharging ports.
- The client is guaranteed a certain volume will be moved during the contract period.

(continued)

Schedules vary considerably depending upon the customer's needs and the fleet operator's capabilities.

- The client hires a barge for a single trip.

A simulation model was developed to analyze the complex process of operating barge fleets in the Gulf of Mexico. An appropriate probability distribution was used to simulate requests for shipments by the petroleum companies. Additional probability distributions were used to simulate the travel times depending upon the size and type of barge. Using this information, the simulation model was used to track barge loading times, barge discharge times, barge utilization, and total cost.

Analysts used simulation runs with a variety of what-if scenarios to answer questions about the petroleum distribution system and to make recommendations for improving the efficiency of the operation. Simulation helped determine the following:

- The optimal trade-off between fleet utilization and on-time delivery
- The recommended fleet size
- The recommended barge capacities
- The best service contract structure to balance the trade-off between customer service and delivery cost

Implementation of the simulation-based recommendations demonstrated a significant improvement in the operation and a significant lowering of petroleum distribution costs.

*Based on E. D. Chajakis, "Sophisticated Crude Transportation," *OR/MS Today* (December 1997): 30–34.

15.3 WAITING LINE SIMULATION

The simulation models discussed thus far have been based on independent trials in which the results for one trial do not affect what happens in subsequent trials. In this sense, the system being modeled does not change or evolve over time. Simulation models such as these are referred to as **static simulation models.** In this section, we develop a simulation model of a waiting line system where the state of the system, including the number of customers in the waiting line and whether the service facility is busy or idle, changes or evolves over time. To incorporate time into the simulation model, we use a simulation clock to record the time that each customer arrives for service as well as the time that each customer completes service. Simulation models that must take into account how the system changes or evolves over time are referred to as **dynamic simulation models.** In situations where the arrivals and departures of customers are **events** that occur at *discrete* points in time, the simulation model is also referred to as a **discrete-event simulation model.**

In Chapter 14, we presented formulas that could be used to compute the steady-state operating characteristics of a waiting line, including the average waiting time, the average number of units in the waiting line, the probability of waiting, and so on. In most cases, the waiting line formulas were based on specific assumptions about the probability distribution for arrivals, the probability distribution for service times, the queue discipline, and so on. Simulation, as an alternative for studying waiting lines, is more flexible. In applications where the assumptions required by the waiting line formulas are not reasonable, simulation may be the only feasible approach to studying the waiting line system. In this section we discuss the simulation of the waiting line for the Hammondsport Savings Bank automated teller machine (ATM).

Hammondsport Savings Bank ATM Waiting Line

Hammondsport Savings Bank will open several new branch banks during the coming year. Each new branch is designed to have one automated teller machine (ATM). A concern is that during busy periods several customers may have to wait to use the ATM. This concern prompted the bank to undertake a study of the ATM waiting line system. The bank's vice president wants to determine whether one ATM will be sufficient. The bank established service guidelines for its ATM system stating that the average customer waiting time for an

ATM should be one minute or less. Let us show how a simulation model can be used to study the ATM waiting line at a particular branch.

Customer Arrival Times

One probabilistic input to the ATM simulation model is the arrival times of customers who use the ATM. In waiting line simulations, arrival times are determined by randomly generating the time between two successive arrivals, referred to as the *interarrival time*. For the branch bank being studied, the customer interarrival times are assumed to be uniformly distributed between 0 and 5 minutes as shown in Figure 15.11. With r denoting a random number between 0 and 1, an interarrival time for two successive customers can be simulated by using the formula for generating values from a uniform probability distribution.

$$\text{Interarrival time} = a + r(b - a) \tag{15.7}$$

where

r = random number between 0 and 1
a = minimum interarrival time
b = maximum interarrival time

A uniform probability distribution of interarrival times is used here to illustrate the simulation computations. Actually, any interarrival time probability distribution can be assumed, and the logic of the waiting line simulation model will not change.

For the Hammondsport ATM system, the minimum interarrival time is $a = 0$ minutes, and the maximum interarrival time is $b = 5$ minutes; therefore, the formula for generating an interarrival time is

$$\text{Interarrival time} = 0 + r(5 - 0) = 5r \tag{15.8}$$

Assume that the simulation run begins at time = 0. A random number of $r = 0.2804$ generates an interarrival time of 5(0.2804) = 1.4 minutes for customer 1. Thus, customer 1 arrives 1.4 minutes after the simulation run begins. A second random number of $r = 0.2598$ generates an interarrival time of 5(0.2598) = 1.3 minutes, indicating that customer 2 arrives 1.3 minutes after customer 1. Thus, customer 2 arrives 1.4 + 1.3 = 2.7 minutes after

FIGURE 15.11 UNIFORM PROBABILITY DISTRIBUTION OF INTERARRIVAL TIMES FOR THE ATM WAITING LINE SYSTEM

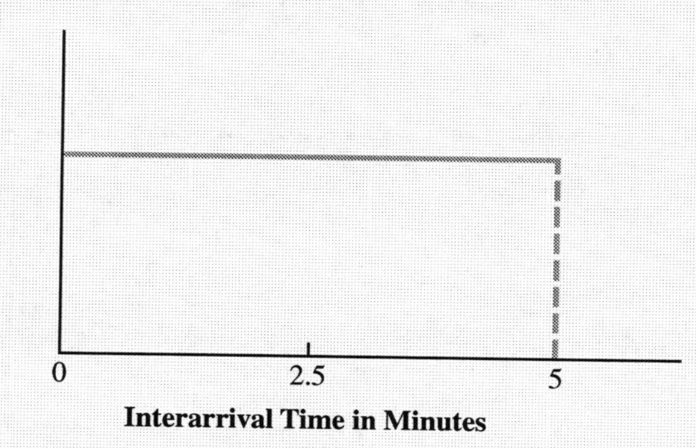

FIGURE 15.12 NORMAL PROBABILITY DISTRIBUTION OF SERVICE TIMES FOR THE ATM WAITING LINE SYSTEM

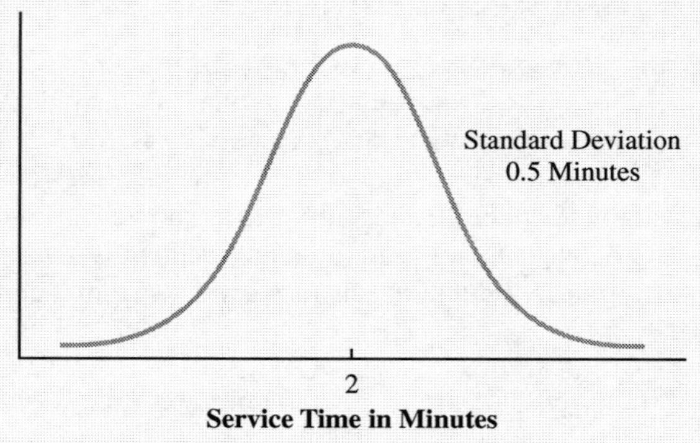

the simulation begins. Continuing, a third random number of $r = 0.9802$ indicates that customer 3 arrives 4.9 minutes after customer 2, which is 7.6 minutes after the simulation begins.

Customer Service Times

Another probabilistic input in the ATM simulation model is the service time, which is the time a customer spends using the ATM machine. Past data from similar ATMs indicate that a normal probability distribution with a mean of 2 minutes and a standard deviation of 0.5 minutes, as shown in Figure 15.12, can be used to describe service times. As discussed in Sections 15.1 and 15.2, values from a normal probability distribution with mean 2 and standard deviation 0.5 can be generated using the Excel function =NORMINV(RAND(),2,0.5). For example, the random number of 0.7257 generates a customer service time of 2.3 minutes.

Simulation Model

The probabilistic inputs to the Hammondsport Savings Bank ATM simulation model are the interarrival time and the service time. The controllable input is the number of ATMs used. The output will consist of various operating characteristics such as the probability of waiting, the average waiting time, the maximum waiting time, and so on. We show a diagram of the ATM simulation model in Figure 15.13.

FIGURE 15.13 HAMMONDSPORT SAVINGS BANK ATM SIMULATION MODEL

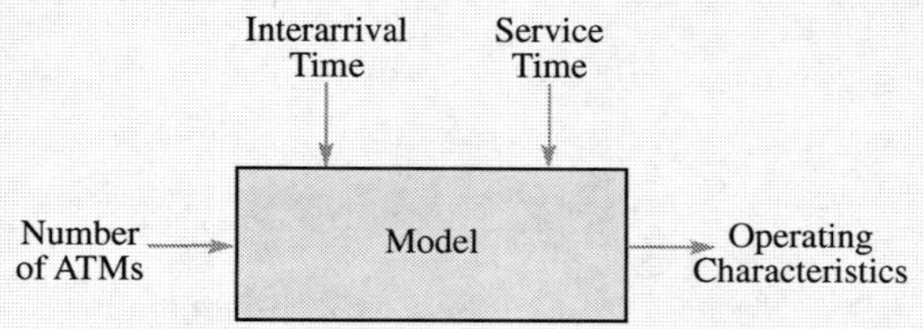

Figure 15.14 shows a flowchart that defines the sequence of logical and mathematical operations required to simulate the Hammondsport ATM system. The flowchart uses the following notation:

IAT = Interarrival time generated
Arrival time (i) = Time at which customer i arrives
Start time (i) = Time at which customer i starts service
Wait time (i) = Waiting time for customer i
ST = Service time generated
Completion time (i) = Time at which customer i completes service
System time (i) = System time for customer i (completion time − arrival time)

FIGURE 15.14 FLOWCHART OF THE HAMMONDSPORT SAVINGS BANK ATM WAITING LINE SIMULATION

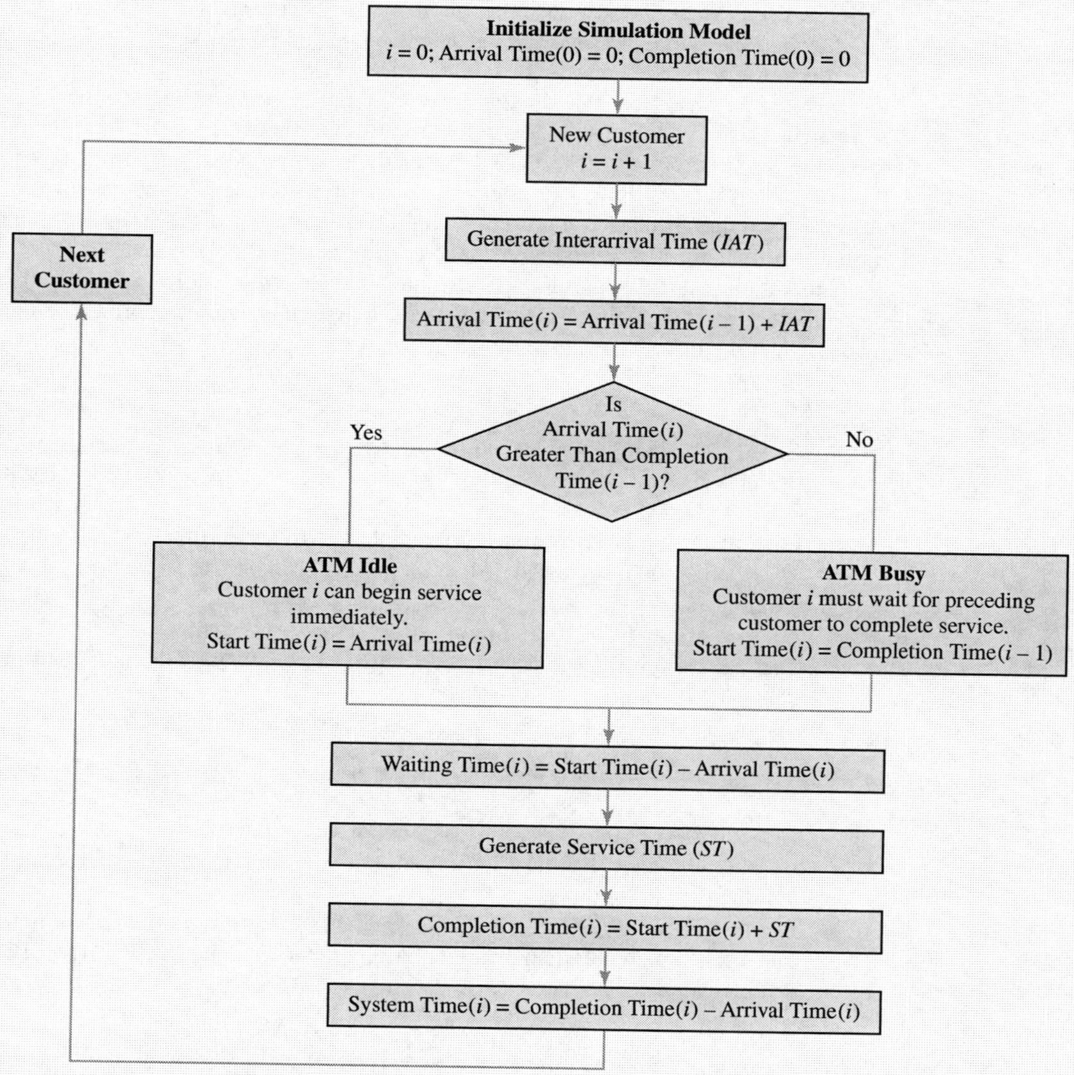

Referring to Figure 15.14, we see that the simulation is initialized in the first block of the flowchart. Then a new customer is created. An interarrival time is generated to determine the time since the preceding customer arrived.[2] The arrival time for the new customer is then computed by adding the interarrival time to the arrival time of the preceding customer.

The decision rule for deciding whether the ATM is idle or busy is the most difficult aspect of the logic in a waiting line simulation model.

The arrival time for the new customer must be compared to the completion time of the preceding customer to determine whether the ATM is idle or busy. If the arrival time of the new customer is greater than the completion time of the preceding customer, the preceding customer will have finished service prior to the arrival of the new customer. In this case, the ATM will be idle, and the new customer can begin service immediately. The service start time for the new customer is equal to the arrival time of the new customer. However, if the arrival time for the new customer is not greater than the completion time of the preceding customer, the new customer arrived before the preceding customer finished service. In this case, the ATM is busy; the new customer must wait to use the ATM until the preceding customer completes service. The service start time for the new customer is equal to the completion time of the preceding customer.

Note that the time the new customer has to wait to use the ATM is the difference between the customer's service start time and the customer's arrival time. At this point, the customer is ready to use the ATM, and the simulation run continues with the generation of the customer's service time. The time at which the customer begins service plus the service time generated determine the customer's completion time. Finally, the total time the customer spends in the system is the difference between the customer's service completion time and the customer's arrival time. At this point, the computations are complete for the current customer, and the simulation continues with the next customer. The simulation is continued until a specified number of customers have been served by the ATM.

Simulation results for the first 10 customers are shown in Table 15.10. We discuss the computations for the first three customers to illustrate the logic of the simulation model and to show how the information in Table 15.10 was developed.

Customer 1

- An interarrival time of $IAT = 1.4$ minutes is generated.
- Because the simulation run begins at time 0, the arrival time for customer 1 is $0 + 1.4 = 1.4$ minutes.
- Customer 1 may begin service immediately with a start time of 1.4 minutes.
- The waiting time for customer 1 is the start time minus the arrival time: $1.4 - 1.4 = 0$ minutes.
- A service time of $ST = 2.3$ minutes is generated for customer 1.
- The completion time for customer 1 is the start time plus the service time: $1.4 + 2.3 = 3.7$ minutes.
- The time in the system for customer 1 is the completion time minus the arrival time: $3.7 - 1.4 = 2.3$ minutes.

Customer 2

- An interarrival time of $IAT = 1.3$ minutes is generated.
- Because the arrival time of customer 1 is 1.4, the arrival time for customer 2 is $1.4 + 1.3 = 2.7$ minutes.
- Because the completion time of customer 1 is 3.7 minutes, the arrival time of customer 2 is not greater than the completion time of customer 1; thus, the ATM is busy when customer 2 arrives.

[2]For the first customer, the interarrival time determines the time since the simulation started. Thus, the first interarrival time determines the time the first customer arrives.

TABLE 15.10 SIMULATION RESULTS FOR 10 ATM CUSTOMERS

Customer	Interarrival Time	Arrival Time	Service Start Time	Waiting Time	Service Time	Completion Time	Time in System
1	1.4	1.4	1.4	0.0	2.3	3.7	2.3
2	1.3	2.7	3.7	1.0	1.5	5.2	2.5
3	4.9	7.6	7.6	0.0	2.2	9.8	2.2
4	3.5	11.1	11.1	0.0	2.5	13.6	2.5
5	0.7	11.8	13.6	1.8	1.8	15.4	3.6
6	2.8	14.6	15.4	0.8	2.4	17.8	3.2
7	2.1	16.7	17.8	1.1	2.1	19.9	3.2
8	0.6	17.3	19.9	2.6	1.8	21.7	4.4
9	2.5	19.8	21.7	1.9	2.0	23.7	3.9
10	1.9	21.7	23.7	2.0	2.3	26.0	4.3
Totals	21.7			11.2	20.9		32.1
Averages	2.17			1.12	2.09		3.21

- Customer 2 must wait for customer 1 to complete service before beginning service. Customer 1 completes service at 3.7 minutes, which becomes the start time for customer 2.
- The waiting time for customer 2 is the start time minus the arrival time: $3.7 - 2.7 = 1$ minute.
- A service time of $ST = 1.5$ minutes is generated for customer 2.
- The completion time for customer 2 is the start time plus the service time: $3.7 + 1.5 = 5.2$ minutes.
- The time in the system for customer 2 is the completion time minus the arrival time: $5.2 - 2.7 = 2.5$ minutes.

Customer 3

- An interarrival time of $IAT = 4.9$ minutes is generated.
- Because the arrival time of customer 2 was 2.7 minutes, the arrival time for customer 3 is $2.7 + 4.9 = 7.6$ minutes.
- The completion time of customer 2 is 5.2 minutes, so the arrival time for customer 3 is greater than the completion time of customer 2. Thus, the ATM is idle when customer 3 arrives.
- Customer 3 begins service immediately with a start time of 7.6 minutes.
- The waiting time for customer 3 is the start time minus the arrival time: $7.6 - 7.6 = 0$ minutes.
- A service time of $ST = 2.2$ minutes is generated for customer 3.
- The completion time for customer 3 is the start time plus the service time: $7.6 + 2.2 = 9.8$ minutes.
- The time in the system for customer 3 is the completion time minus the arrival time: $9.8 - 7.6 = 2.2$ minutes.

Using the totals in Table 15.10, we can compute an average waiting time for the 10 customers of $11.2/10 = 1.12$ minutes, and an average time in the system of $32.1/10 = 3.21$ minutes. Table 15.10 shows that seven of the 10 customers had to wait. The total time for the 10-customer simulation is given by the completion time of the 10th customer: 26.0 minutes. However, at this point, we realize that a simulation for 10 customers is much too short a period to draw any firm conclusions about the operation of the waiting line.

Simulation of the Hammondsport Savings Bank ATM Problem

Using an Excel worksheet, we simulated the operation of the Hammondsport ATM waiting line system for 1000 customers. The worksheet used to carry out the simulation is shown in Figure 15.15. Note that the simulation results for customers 6 through 995 have been hidden so that the results can be shown in a reasonably sized figure. If desired, the rows for these customers can be shown and the simulation results displayed for all 1000 customers.

Ultimately, summary statistics will be collected in order to describe the results of 1000 customers. Before collecting the summary statistics, let us point out that most simulation studies of dynamic systems focus on the operation of the system during its long-run or steady-

EXCELfile
Hammondsport1

FIGURE 15.15 EXCEL WORKSHEET FOR THE HAMMONDSPORT SAVINGS BANK WITH ONE ATM

	A	B	C	D	E	F	G	H	I
1	**Hammondsport Savings Bank with One ATM**								
2									
3	**Interarrival Times (Uniform Distribution)**								
4	Smallest Value	0							
5	Largest Value	5							
6									
7	**Service Times (Normal Distribution)**								
8	Mean	2							
9	Std Deviation	0.5							
10									
11									
12	**Simulation**								
13									
14		Interarrival	Arrival	Service	Waiting	Service	Completion	Time	
15	Customer	Time	Time	Start Time	Time	Time	Time	in System	
16	1	1.4	1.4	1.4	0.0	2.3	3.7	2.3	
17	2	1.3	2.7	3.7	1.0	1.5	5.2	2.5	
18	3	4.9	7.6	7.6	0.0	2.2	9.8	2.2	
19	4	3.5	11.1	11.1	0.0	2.5	13.6	2.5	
20	5	0.7	11.8	13.6	1.8	1.8	15.4	3.6	
1011	996	0.5	2496.8	2498.1	1.3	0.6	2498.7	1.9	
1012	997	0.2	2497.0	2498.7	1.7	2.0	2500.7	3.7	
1013	998	2.7	2499.7	2500.7	1.0	1.8	2502.5	2.8	
1014	999	3.7	2503.4	2503.4	0.0	2.4	2505.8	2.4	
1015	1000	4.0	2507.4	2507.4	0.0	1.9	2509.3	1.9	
1016									
1017		**Summary Statistics**							
1018		Number Waiting			549				
1019		Probability of Waiting			0.6100				
1020		Average Waiting Time			1.59				
1021		Maximum Waiting Time			13.5				
1022		Utilization of ATM			0.7860				
1023		Number Waiting > 1 Min			393				
1024		Probability of Waiting > 1 Min			0.4367				
1025									

state operation. To ensure that the effect of start-up conditions are not included in the steady-state calculations, a dynamic simulation model is usually run for a specified period without collecting any data about the operation of the system. The length of the start-up period can vary depending on the application. For the Hammondsport Savings Bank ATM simulation, we treated the results for the first 100 customers as the start-up period. Thus, the summary statistics shown in Figure 15.15 are for the 900 customers arriving during the steady-state period.

The summary statistics show that 549 of the 900 Hammondsport customers had to wait. This result provides a 549/900 = 0.61 probability that a customer will have to wait for service. In other words, approximately 61% of the customers will have to wait because the ATM is in use. The average waiting time is 1.59 minutes per customer with at least one customer waiting the maximum time of 13.5 minutes. The utilization rate of 0.7860 indicates that the ATM is in use 78.6% of the time. Finally, 393 of the 900 customers had to wait more than 1 minute (43.67% of all customers). A histogram of waiting times for the 900 customers is shown in Figure 15.16. This figure shows that 45 customers (5%) had a waiting time greater than 6 minutes.

The simulation supports the conclusion that the branch will have a busy ATM system. With an average customer wait time of 1.59 minutes, the branch does not satisfy the bank's customer service guideline. This branch is a good candidate for installation of a second ATM.

Simulation with Two ATMs

We extended the simulation model to the case of two ATMs. For the second ATM we also assume that the service time is normally distributed with a mean of 2 minutes and a standard deviation of 0.5 minutes. Table 15.11 shows the simulation results for the first 10 customers. In comparing the two-ATM system results in Table 15.11 with the single ATM simulation results shown in Table 15.10, we see that two additional columns are needed. These two columns show when each ATM becomes available for customer service. We assume that, when a new customer arrives, the customer will be served by the ATM that frees up first. When the simulation begins, the first customer is assigned to ATM 1.

Table 15.11 shows that customer 7 is the first customer who has to wait to use an ATM. We describe how customers 6, 7, and 8 are processed to show how the logic of the simulation run for two ATMs differs from that with a single ATM.

FIGURE 15.16 HISTOGRAM SHOWING THE WAITING TIME FOR 900 ATM CUSTOMERS

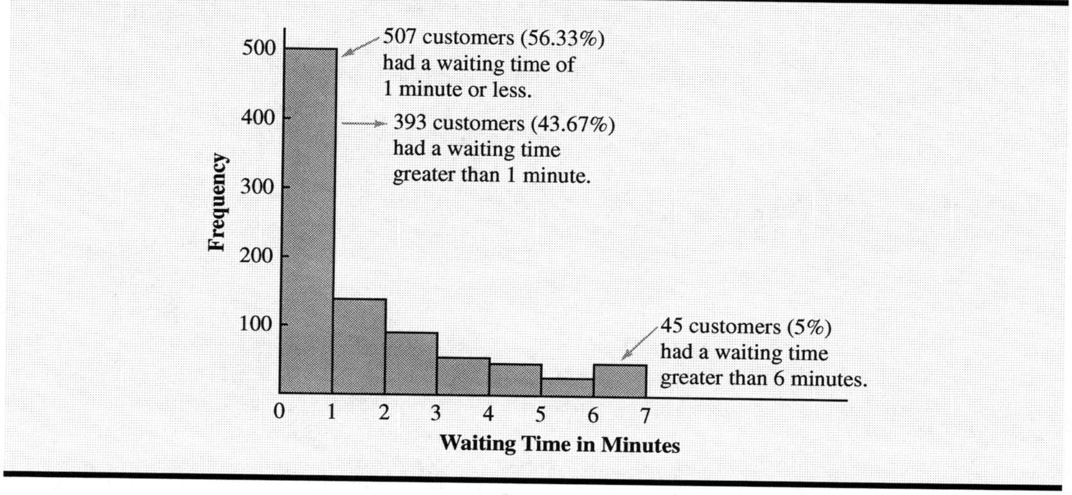

TABLE 15.11 SIMULATION RESULTS FOR 10 CUSTOMERS FOR A TWO-ATM SYSTEM

Customer	Interarrival Time	Arrival Time	Service Start Time	Waiting Time	Service Time	Completion Time	Time in System	Time Available ATM 1	Time Available ATM 2
1	1.7	1.7	1.7	0.0	2.1	3.8	2.1	3.8	0.0
2	0.7	2.4	2.4	0.0	2.0	4.4	2.0	3.8	4.4
3	2.0	4.4	4.4	0.0	1.4	5.8	1.4	5.8	4.4
4	0.1	4.5	4.5	0.0	0.9	5.4	0.9	5.8	5.4
5	4.6	9.1	9.1	0.0	2.2	11.3	2.2	5.8	11.3
6	1.3	10.4	10.4	0.0	1.6	12.0	1.6	12.0	11.3
7	0.6	11.0	11.3	0.3	1.7	13.0	2.0	12.0	13.0
8	0.3	11.3	12.0	0.7	2.2	14.2	2.9	14.2	13.0
9	3.4	14.7	14.7	0.0	2.9	17.6	2.9	14.2	17.6
10	0.1	14.8	14.8	0.0	2.8	17.6	2.8	17.6	17.6
Totals	14.8			1.0	19.8		20.8		
Averages	1.48			0.1	1.98		2.08		

Customer 6

- An interarrival time of 1.3 minutes is generated, and customer 6 arrives 9.1 + 1.3 = 10.4 minutes into the simulation.
- From the customer 5 row, we see that ATM 1 frees up at 5.8 minutes, and ATM 2 will free up at 11.3 minutes into the simulation. Because ATM 1 is free, customer 6 does not wait and begins service on ATM 1 at the arrival time of 10.4 minutes.
- A service time of 1.6 minutes is generated for customer 6. So customer 6 has a completion time of 10.4 + 1.6 = 12.0 minutes.
- The time ATM 1 will next become available is set at 12.0 minutes; the time available for ATM 2 remains 11.3 minutes.

Customer 7

- An interarrival time of 0.6 minute is generated, and customer 7 arrives 10.4 + 0.6 = 11.0 minutes into the simulation.
- From the previous row, we see that ATM 1 will not be available until 12.0 minutes, and ATM 2 will not be available until 11.3 minutes. So customer 7 must wait to use an ATM. Because ATM 2 will free up first, customer 7 begins service on that machine at a start time of 11.3 minutes. With an arrival time of 11.0 and a service start time of 11.3, customer 7 experiences a waiting time of 11.3 − 11.0 = 0.3 minute.
- A service time of 1.7 minutes is generated leading to a completion time of 11.3 + 1.7 = 13.0 minutes.
- The time available for ATM 2 is updated to 13.0 minutes, and the time available for ATM 1 remains at 12.0 minutes.

Customer 8

- An interarrival time of 0.3 minute is generated, and customer 8 arrives 11.0 + 0.3 = 11.3 minutes into the simulation.
- From the previous row, we see that ATM 1 will be the first available. Thus, customer 8 starts service on ATM 1 at 12.0 minutes resulting in a waiting time of 12.0 − 11.3 = 0.7 minute.
- A service time of 2.2 minutes is generated resulting in a completion time of 12.0 + 2.2 = 14.2 minutes and a system time of 0.7 + 2.2 = 2.9 minutes.
- The time available for ATM 1 is updated to 14.2 minutes, and the time available for ATM 2 remains at 13.0 minutes.

From the totals in Table 15.11, we see that the average waiting time for these 10 customers is only 1.0/10 = 0.1 minute. Of course, a much longer simulation will be necessary before any conclusions can be drawn.

Simulation Results with Two ATMs

Worksheets for the Hammondsport one-ATM and two-ATM systems are available on the CD that accompanies this text.

The Excel worksheet that we used to conduct a simulation for 1000 customers using two ATMs is shown in Figure 15.17. Results for the first 100 customers were discarded to account for the start-up period. With two ATMs, the number of customers who had to wait was reduced from 549 to 78. This reduction provides a 78/900 = 0.0867 probability that a customer will have to wait for service when two ATMs are used. The two-ATM system also reduced the average waiting time to 0.07 minute (4.2 seconds) per customer. The maximum waiting time was reduced from 13.5 to 2.9 minutes, and each ATM was in use 40.84% of the time. Finally, only 23 of the 900 customers had to wait more than 1 minute for an ATM to become available. Thus, only 2.56% of customers had to wait more than 1 minute. The simulation results provide evidence that Hammondsport Savings Bank needs to expand to the two-ATM system.

FIGURE 15.17 EXCEL WORKSHEET FOR THE HAMMONDSPORT SAVINGS BANK WITH TWO ATMs

EXCELfile
Hammondsport2

	A	B	C	D	E	F	G	H	I	J	K
1	**Hammondsport Savings Bank with Two ATMs**										
2											
3	**Interarrival Times (Uniform Distribution)**										
4	Smallest Value	0									
5	Largest Value	5									
6											
7	**Service Times (Normal Distribution)**										
8	Mean	2									
9	Std Deviation	0.5									
10											
11											
12	**Simulation**										
13											
14		Interarrival	Arrival	Service	Waiting	Service	Completion	Time	Time Available		
15	Customer	Time	Time	Start Time	Time	Time	Time	in System	ATM 1	ATM 2	
16	1	1.7	1.7	1.7	0.0	2.1	3.8	2.1	3.8	0.0	
17	2	0.7	2.4	2.4	0.0	2.0	4.4	2.0	3.8	4.4	
18	3	2.0	4.4	4.4	0.0	1.4	5.8	1.4	5.8	4.4	
19	4	0.1	4.5	4.5	0.0	0.9	5.4	0.9	5.8	5.4	
20	5	4.6	9.1	9.1	0.0	2.2	11.3	2.2	5.8	11.3	
1011	996	3.3	2483.2	2483.2	0.0	2.2	2485.4	2.2	2485.4	2482.1	
1012	997	4.5	2487.7	2487.7	0.0	1.9	2489.6	1.9	2485.4	2489.6	
1013	998	3.8	2491.5	2491.5	0.0	3.2	2494.7	3.2	2494.7	2489.6	
1014	999	0.0	2491.5	2491.5	0.0	2.4	2493.9	2.4	2494.7	2493.9	
1015	1000	2.6	2494.1	2494.1	0.0	2.8	2496.9	2.8	2494.7	2496.9	
1016											
1017		**Summary Statistics**									
1018		Number Waiting			78						
1019		Probability of Waiting			0.0867						
1020		Average Waiting Time			0.07						
1021		Maximum Waiting Time			2.9						
1022		Utilization of ATMs			0.4084						
1023		Number Waiting > 1 Min			23						
1024		Probability of Waiting > 1 Min			0.0256						
1025											

The simulation models that we developed can now be used to study the ATM operation at other branch banks. In each case, assumptions must be made about the appropriate interarrival time and service time probability distributions. However, once appropriate assumptions have been made, the same simulation models can be used to determine the operating characteristics of the ATM waiting line system. The Q.M. in Action, Preboard Screening at Vancouver International Airport, describes another use of simulation for a queueing system.

Q.M. IN ACTION

PREBOARD SCREENING AT VANCOUVER INTERNATIONAL AIRPORT*

Following the September 11, 2001, terrorist attacks in the United States, long lines at airport security checkpoints became commonplace. In order to reduce passenger waiting time, the Vancouver International Airport Authority teamed up with students and faculty at the University of British Columbia's Centre for Operations Excellence (COE) to build a simulation model of the airport's preboard screening security checkpoints. The goal was to use the simulation model to help achieve acceptable service standards.

Prior to building the simulation model, students from the COE observed the flow of passengers through the screening process and collected data on the service time at each process step. In addition to service time data, passenger demand data provided input to the simulation model. Two triangular probability distributions were used to simulate passenger arrivals at the preboarding facilities. For flights to Canadian destinations a 90-40-20 triangle was used. This distribution assumes that, for each flight, the first passenger will arrive at the screening checkpoint 90 minutes before departure, the last passenger will arrive 20 minutes before departure, and the most likely arrival time is 40 minutes before departure. For international flights a 150-80-20 triangle was used.

Output statistics from the simulation model provided information concerning resource utilization, waiting line lengths and the time passengers spend in the system. The simulation model provided information concerning the number of personnel needed to process 90% of the passengers with a waiting time of 10 minutes or less. Ultimately the airport authority was able to design and staff the preboarding checkpoints in such a fashion that waiting times for 90% of the passengers were a maximum of 10 minutes.

*Based on Derek Atkins et al., "Right on Queue," *OR/MS Today* (April 2003): 26–29.

NOTES AND COMMENTS

1. The ATM waiting line model was based on uniformly distributed interarrival times and normally distributed service times. One advantage of simulation is its flexibility in accommodating a variety of different probability distributions. For instance, if we believe an exponential distribution is more appropriate for interarrival times, the ATM simulation could be repeated by simply changing the way the interarrival times are generated.
2. At the beginning of this section, we defined *discrete-event simulation* as involving a dynamic system that evolves over time. The simulation computations focus on the sequence of events as they occur at discrete points in time. In the ATM waiting line example, customer arrivals and the customer service completions were the discrete events. Referring to the arrival times and completion times in Table 15.10, we see that the first five discrete events for the ATM waiting line simulation were as follows:

Event	Time
Customer 1 arrives	1.4
Customer 2 arrives	2.7
Customer 1 finished	3.7
Customer 2 finished	5.2
Customer 3 arrives	7.6

3. We did not keep track of the number of customers in the ATM waiting line as we carried out the ATM simulation computations on a customer-by-customer basis. However, we can determine the average number of customers in the waiting line from other information in the

simulation output. The following relationship is valid for any waiting line system:

$$\text{Average number in waiting line} = \frac{\text{Total waiting time}}{\text{Total time of simulation}}$$

For the system with one ATM, the 100th customer completed service at 247.8 minutes into the simulation. Thus, the total time of the simulation for the next 900 customers was 2509.3 − 247.8 = 2261.5 minutes. The average waiting time was 1.59 minutes. During the simulation, the 900 customers had a total waiting time of 900(1.59) = 1431 minutes. Therefore, the average number of customers in the waiting line is

$$\begin{aligned}\text{Average number in waiting line} &= 1431/2261.5\\ &= 0.63 \text{ customer}\end{aligned}$$

15.4 OTHER SIMULATION ISSUES

Because simulation is one of the most widely used quantitative analysis techniques, various software tools have been developed to help analysts implement a simulation model on a computer. In this section we comment on the software available and discuss some issues involved in verifying and validating a simulation model. We close the section with a discussion of some of the advantages and disadvantages of using simulation to study a real system.

Computer Implementation

The use of spreadsheets for simulation has grown rapidly in recent years, and third-party software vendors have developed spreadsheet add-ins that make building simulation models on a spreadsheet much easier. These add-in packages provide an easy facility for generating random values from a variety of probability distributions and provide a rich array of statistics describing the simulation output. Two popular spreadsheet add-ins are Crystal Ball from Decisioneering and @RISK from Palisade Corporation. Although spreadsheets can be a valuable tool for some simulation studies, they are generally limited to smaller, less complex systems.

With the growth of simulation applications, both users of simulation and software developers began to realize that computer simulations have many common features: model development, generating values from probability distributions, maintaining a record of what happens during the simulation, and recording and summarizing the simulation output. A variety of special-purpose simulation packages are available, including GPSS®, SIMSCRIPT®, SLAM®, and Arena®. These packages have built-in simulation clocks, simplified methods for generating probabilistic inputs, and procedures for collecting and summarizing the simulation output. Special-purpose simulation packages enable quantitative analysts to simplify the process of developing and implementing the simulation model. Indeed, Arena 6.0 was used to develop the simulation model described in the Q.M. in Action, Preboard Screening at Vancouver International Airport.

The computational and record-keeping aspects of simulation models are assisted by special simulation software packages. The packages ease the tasks of developing a computer simulation model.

Simulation models can also be developed using general-purpose computer programming languages such as BASIC, FORTRAN, PASCAL, C, and C++. The disadvantage of using these languages is that special simulation procedures are not built in. One command in a special-purpose simulation package often performs the computations and record-keeping tasks that would require several BASIC, FORTRAN, PASCAL, C, or C++ statements to duplicate. The advantage of using a general-purpose programming language is that they offer greater flexibility in terms of being able to model more complex systems.

To decide which software to use, an analyst will have to consider the relative merits of a spreadsheet, a special-purpose simulation package, and a general-purpose computer programming language. The goal is to select the method that is easy to use while still providing an adequate representation of the system being studied.

Verification and Validation

An important aspect of any simulation study involves confirming that the simulation model accurately describes the real system. Inaccurate simulation models cannot be expected to provide worthwhile information. Thus, before using simulation results to draw conclusions about a real system, one must take steps to verify and validate the simulation model.

Verification is the process of determining that the computer procedure that performs the simulation calculations is logically correct. Verification is largely a debugging task to make sure that no errors are in the computer procedure that implements the simulation. In some cases, an analyst may compare computer results for a limited number of events with independent hand calculations. In other cases, tests may be performed to verify that the probabilistic inputs are being generated correctly and that the output from the simulation model seems reasonable. The verification step is not complete until the user develops a high degree of confidence that the computer procedure is error free.

Validation is the process of ensuring that the simulation model provides an accurate representation of a real system. Validation requires an agreement among analysts and managers that the logic and the assumptions used in the design of the simulation model accurately reflect how the real system operates. The first phase of the validation process is done prior to, or in conjunction with, the development of the computer procedure for the simulation process. Validation continues after the computer program has been developed with the analyst reviewing the simulation output to see whether the simulation results closely approximate the performance of the real system. If possible, the output of the simulation model is compared to the output of an existing real system to make sure that the simulation output closely approximates the performance of the real system. If this form of validation is not possible, an analyst can experiment with the simulation model and have one or more individuals experienced with the operation of the real system review the simulation output to determine whether it is a reasonable approximation of what would be obtained with the real system under similar conditions.

Verification and validation are not tasks to be taken lightly. They are key steps in any simulation study and are necessary to ensure that decisions and conclusions based on the simulation results are appropriate for the real system.

Advantages and Disadvantages of Using Simulation

The primary advantages of simulation are that it is easy to understand and that the methodology can be used to model and learn about the behavior of complex systems that would be difficult, if not impossible, to deal with analytically. Simulation models are flexible; they can be used to describe systems without requiring the assumptions that are often required by mathematical models. In general, the larger the number of probabilistic inputs a system has, the more likely that a simulation model will provide the best approach for studying the system. Another advantage of simulation is that a simulation model provides a convenient experimental laboratory for the real system. Changing assumptions or operating policies in the simulation model and rerunning it can provide results that help predict how such changes will affect the operation of the real system. Experimenting directly with a real system is often not feasible.

Using simulation, we can ask what-if questions and project how the real system will behave. Although simulation does not guarantee optimality, it will usually provide near-optimal solutions. In addition, simulation models often warn against poor decision strategies by projecting disastrous outcomes such as system failures, large financial losses, and so on.

Simulation is not without some disadvantages. For complex systems, the process of developing, verifying, and validating a simulation model can be time-consuming and expensive. In addition, each simulation run provides only a sample of how the real system will operate. As such, the summary of the simulation data provides only estimates or approximations about the real system. Consequently, simulation does not guarantee an optimal solution. Nonetheless, the danger of obtaining poor solutions is slight if the analyst exercises good judgment in developing the simulation model and if the simulation process is run long enough under a wide variety of conditions so that the analyst has sufficient data to predict how the real system will operate.

SUMMARY

Simulation is a method for learning about a real system by experimenting with a model that represents the system. Some of the reasons simulation is frequently used are

1. It can be used for a wide variety of practical problems.
2. The simulation approach is relatively easy to explain and understand. As a result, management confidence is increased, and acceptance of the results is more easily obtained.
3. Spreadsheet packages now provide another alternative for model implementation, and third-party vendors have developed add-ins that expand the capabilities of the spreadsheet packages.
4. Computer software developers have produced simulation packages that make it easier to develop and implement simulation models for more complex problems.

We first showed how simulation can be used for risk analysis by analyzing a situation involving the development of a new product: the PortaCom printer. We then showed how simulation can be used to select an inventory replenishment level that would provide both a good profit and a good customer service level. Finally, we developed a simulation model for the Hammondsport Savings Bank ATM waiting line system. This model is an example of a dynamic simulation model in which the state of the system changes or evolves over time.

Our approach was to develop a simulation model that contained both controllable inputs and probabilistic inputs. Procedures were developed for randomly generating values for the probabilistic inputs, and a flowchart was developed to show the sequence of logical and mathematical operations that describe the steps of the simulation process. Simulation results were obtained by running the simulation for a suitable number of trials or length of time. Simulation results were obtained and conclusions were drawn about the operation of the real system.

The Q.M. in Action, Netherlands Company Improves Warehouse Order-Picking Efficiency, describes how a simulation model determined the warehouse storage location for 18,000 products and the sequence in which products were retrieved by order-picking personnel.

Q.M. IN ACTION

NETHERLANDS COMPANY IMPROVES WAREHOUSE ORDER-PICKING EFFICIENCY*

As a wholesaler of tools, hardware, and garden equipment, Ankor, based in The Netherlands, warehouses more than 18,000 different products for customers who are primarily retail store chains, do-it-yourself businesses, and garden centers. Warehouse managers store the fastest-moving products on the ends of the aisles on the ground floor, the medium-moving products in the middle section of the aisles on the ground floor, and the slow-moving products on the mezzanine.

When a new order is received, a warehouse order-picker travels to each product location and selects the requested number of units. An average order includes 25 different products, which requires the order-picker to travel to 25 different locations in the warehouse. In order to minimize damage to the products, heavier products are picked first and breakable products are picked last. Order-picking is typically one of the most time-consuming and expensive aspects of operating the warehouse. The company is under continuous pressure to improve the efficiency of this operation.

To increase efficiency, researchers developed a simulation model of the warehouse order-picking system. Using a sequence of 1098 orders received for 27,790 products over a seven-week period, the researchers used the model to simulate the required order-picking times. The researchers, with the help of the model, varied the assignment of products to storage locations and the sequence in which products were retrieved from the storage locations. The model simulated order-picking times for a variety of product storage location alternatives and

(*continued*)

four different routing policies that determined the sequence in which products were picked.

Analysis of the simulation results provided a new storage assignment policy for the warehouse as well as new routing rules for the sequence in which to retrieve products from storage. Implementation of the new storage and routing procedures reduced the average route length of the order-picking operation by 31%. Due to the increased efficiency of the operation, the number of order pickers was reduced by more than 25%, saving the company an estimated €140,00 per year.

*Based on R. Dekker, M. B. M. de Koster, K. J. Roodbergen, and H. van Kalleveen, "Improving Order-Picking Response Time at Ankor's Warehouse," *Interfaces* (July/August 2004): 303–313.

GLOSSARY

Simulation A method for learning about a real system by experimenting with a model that represents the system.

Simulation experiment The generation of a sample of values for the probabilistic inputs of a simulation model and computing the resulting values of the model outputs.

Controllable input Input to a simulation model that is selected by the decision maker.

Probabilistic input Input to a simulation model that is subject to uncertainty. A probabilistic input is described by a probability distribution.

Risk analysis The process of predicting the outcome of a decision in the face of uncertainty.

Parameters Numerical values that appear in the mathematical relationships of a model. Parameters are considered known and remain constant over all trials of a simulation.

What-if analysis A trial-and-error approach to learning about the range of possible outputs for a model. Trial values are chosen for the model inputs (these are the what-ifs) and the value of the output(s) is computed.

Base-case scenario Determining the output given the most likely values for the probabilistic inputs of a model.

Worst-case scenario Determining the output given the worst values that can be expected for the probabilistic inputs of a model.

Best-case scenario Determining the output given the best values that can be expected for the probabilistic inputs of a model.

Static simulation model A simulation model used in situations where the state of the system at one point in time does not affect the state of the system at future points in time. Each trial of the simulation is independent.

Dynamic simulation model A simulation model used in situations where the state of the system affects how the system changes or evolves over time.

Event An instantaneous occurrence that changes the state of the system in a simulation model.

Discrete-event simulation model A simulation model that describes how a system evolves over time by using events that occur at discrete points in time.

Verification The process of determining that a computer program implements a simulation model as it is intended.

Validation The process of determining that a simulation model provides an accurate representation of a real system.

PROBLEMS

Note: Problems 1–12 are designed to give you practice in setting up a simulation model and demonstrating how random numbers can be used to generate values for the probabilistic inputs. These problems, which ask you to provide a small number of simulation trials, can be done with hand calculations. This approach should give you a good understanding of the simulation process, but the simulation results will not be sufficient for you to draw final conclusions or make decisions about the situation. Problems 13–24 are more realistic in that they ask you to generate simulation output(s) for a large number of trials and use the results to draw conclusions about the behavior of the system being studied. These problems require the use of a computer to carry out the simulation computations. The ability to use Excel will be necessary when you attempt Problems 13–24.

1. Consider the PortaCom project discussed in Section 15.1
   a. An engineer on the product development team believes that first-year sales for the new printer will be 20,000 units. Using estimates of $45 per unit for the direct labor cost and $90 per unit for the parts cost, what is the first-year profit using the engineer's sales estimate?
   b. The financial analyst on the product development team is more conservative, indicating that parts cost may well be $100 per unit. In addition, the analyst suggests that a sales volume of 10,000 units is more realistic. Using the most likely value of $45 per unit for the direct labor cost, what is the first-year profit using the financial analyst's estimates?
   c. Why is the simulation approach to risk analysis preferable to generating a variety of what-if scenarios such as those suggested by the engineer and the financial analyst?

SELF test

2. The management of Madeira Manufacturing Company is considering the introduction of a new product. The fixed cost to begin the production of the product is $30,000. The variable cost for the product is expected to be between $16 and $24 with a most likely value of $20 per unit. The product will sell for $50 per unit. Demand for the product is expected to range from 300 to 2100 units, with 1200 units the most likely demand.
   a. Develop the profit model for this product.
   b. Provide the base-case, worst-case, and best-case analyses.
   c. Discuss why simulation would be desirable.
3. Use the random numbers 0.3753, 0.9218, 0.0336, 0.5145, and 0.7000 to generate five simulated values for the PortaCom direct labor cost per unit.
4. To generate leads for new business, Gustin Investment Services offers free financial planning seminars at major hotels in Southwest Florida. Attendance is limited to 25 individuals per seminar. Each seminar costs Gustin $3500, and the average first-year commission for each new account opened is $5000. Historical data collected over the past four years show that the number of new accounts opened at a seminar varies from no accounts opened to a maximum of six accounts opened according to the following probability distribution:

Number of New Accounts Opened	Probability
0	.01
1	.04
2	.10
3	.25
4	.40
5	.15
6	.05

a. Set up intervals of random numbers that can be used to simulate the number of new accounts opened at a seminar.
b. Using the first 10 random numbers in column 9 of Table 15.2, simulate the number of new accounts opened for 10 seminars.
c. Would you recommend that Gustin continue running the seminars?

SELF test

5. The price of a share of a particular stock listed on the New York Stock Exchange is currently \$39. The following probability distribution shows how the price per share is expected to change over a three-month period.

Stock Price Change (\$)	Probability
−2	0.05
−1	0.10
0	0.25
+1	0.20
+2	0.20
+3	0.10
+4	0.10

a. Set up intervals of random numbers that can be used to generate the change in stock price over a three-month period.
b. With the current price of \$39 per share and the random numbers 0.1091, 0.9407, 0.1941, and 0.8083, simulate the price per share for the next four 3-month periods. What is the ending simulated price per share?

6. The Statewide Auto Insurance Company developed the following probability distribution for automobile collision claims paid during the past year.

Payment(\$)	Probability
0	0.83
500	0.06
1,000	0.05
2,000	0.02
5,000	0.02
8,000	0.01
10,000	0.01

a. Set up intervals of random numbers that can be used to generate automobile collision claim payments.
b. Using the first 20 random numbers in column 4 of Table 15.2, simulate the payments for 20 policyholders. How many claims are paid and what is the total amount paid to the policyholders?

7. A variety of routine maintenance checks are made on commercial airplanes prior to each takeoff. A particular maintenance check of an airplane's landing gear requires between 10 and 18 minutes of a maintenance engineer's time. In fact, the exact time required is uniformly distributed over this interval. As part of a larger simulation model designed to determine total on-ground maintenance time for an airplane, we will need to simulate the actual time required to perform this maintenance check on the airplane's landing gear. Using random numbers of 0.1567, 0.9823, 0.3419, 0.5572, and 0.7758, compute the time required for each of five simulated maintenance checks of the airplane's landing gear.

8. Baseball's World Series is a maximum of seven games, with the winner being the first team to win four games. Assume that the Atlanta Braves are in the World Series and that the first two games are to be played in Atlanta, the next three games at the opponent's ball park, and the last two games, if necessary, back in Atlanta. Taking into account the projected starting pitchers for each game and the homefield advantage, the probabilities of Atlanta winning each game are as follows:

Game	1	2	3	4	5	6	7
Probability of Win	0.60	0.55	0.48	0.45	0.48	0.55	0.50

a. Set up random number intervals that can be used to determine the winner of each game. Let the smaller random numbers indicate that Atlanta wins the game. For example, the random number interval "0.00 but less than 0.60" corresponds to Atlanta winning game 1.
b. Use the random numbers in column 6 of Table 15.2 beginning with 0.3813 to simulate the playing of the World Series. Do the Atlanta Braves win the series? How many games are played?
c. Discuss how repeated simulation trials could be used to estimate the overall probability of Atlanta winning the series as well as the most likely number of games in the series.

SELF test

9. A project has four activities (A, B, C, and D) that must be performed sequentially. The probability distributions for the time required to complete each of the activities are as follows:

Activity	**Activity Time (weeks)**	**Probability**
A	5	0.25
	6	0.35
	7	0.25
	8	0.15
B	3	0.20
	5	0.55
	7	0.25
C	10	0.10
	12	0.25
	14	0.40
	16	0.20
	18	0.05
D	8	0.60
	10	0.40

a. Provide the base-case, worst-case, and best-case calculations for the time to complete the project.
b. Use the random numbers 0.1778, 0.9617, 0.6849, and 0.4503 to simulate the completion time of the project in weeks.
c. Discuss how simulation could be used to estimate the probability the project can be completed in 35 weeks or less.

10. Blackjack, or 21, is a popular casino game that begins with each player and the dealer being dealt two cards. The value of each hand is determined by the point total of the cards in the hand. Face cards and 10s count 10 points; aces can be counted as either 1 or 11 points; and all other cards count at their face value. For instance, the value of a hand consisting of a jack and an 8 is 18; the value of a hand consisting of an ace and a two is either 3 or 13

depending on whether the ace is counted as 1 or 11 points. The goal is to obtain a hand with a value of 21, or as close to it as possible without exceeding 21. After the initial deal, each player and the dealer may draw additional cards (called taking a "hit") in order to improve their hand. If a player or the dealer takes a hit and the value of their hand exceeds 21, that person "goes broke" and loses. The dealer's advantage is that each player must decide whether to take a hit before the dealer. If a player takes a hit and goes over 21, the player loses even if the dealer later takes a hit and goes over 21. For this reason, players will often decide not to take a hit when the value of their hand is 12 or greater.

The dealer's hand is dealt with one card up and one card down. The player then decides whether to take a hit based on knowledge of the dealer's up card. A gambling professional determined that when the dealer's up card is a 6, the following probabilities describe the ending value of the dealer's hand.

Value of Hand	17	18	19	20	21	Broke
Probability	0.1654	0.1063	0.1063	0.1017	0.0972	0.4231

a. Set up intervals of random numbers that can be used to simulate the ending value of the dealer's hand when the dealer has a 6 as the up card.

b. Use the random numbers in column 4 of Table 15.2 to simulate the ending value of the dealer's hand for 20 plays of the game.

c. Suppose you are playing blackjack and your hand has a value of 16 for the two cards initially dealt. If you decide to take a hit, the following cards will improve your hand: ace, 2, 3, 4, and 5. Any card with a point count greater than 5 will result in you going broke. Suppose you have a hand with a value of 16 and decide to take a hit. The following probabilities describe the ending value of your hand.

Value of Hand	17	18	19	20	21	Broke
Probability	0.0769	0.0769	0.0769	0.0769	0.0769	0.6155

Use the random numbers in column 5 of Table 15.2 to simulate the ending value of your hand after taking a hit for 20 plays of the game.

d. Use the results of parts (b) and (c) to simulate the result of 20 blackjack hands when the dealer has a 6 up and the player chooses to take a hit with a hand that has a value of 16. How many hands result in the dealer winning, a push (a tie), and the player winning.

e. If the player has a hand with a value of 16 and doesn't take a hit, the only way the player can win is if the dealer goes broke. How many of the hands in part (b) result in the player winning without taking a hit? On the basis of this result and the results in part (d), would you recommend the player take a hit if the player has a hand with a value of 16 and the dealer has a 6 up?

11. Over a five-year period, the quarterly change in the price per share of common stock for a major oil company ranged from −8% to +12%. A financial analyst wants to learn what can be expected for price appreciation of this stock over the next two years. Using the five-year history as a basis, the analyst is willing to assume the change in price for each quarter is uniformly distributed between −8% and 12%. Use simulation to provide information about the price per share for the stock over the coming two-year period (eight quarters).

a. Use two-digit random numbers from column 2 of Table 15.2, beginning with 0.52, 0.99, and so on, to simulate the quarterly price change for each of the eight quarters.

b. If the current price per share is \$80, what is the simulated price per share at the end of the two-year period?

c. Discuss how risk analysis would be helpful in identifying the risk associated with a two-year investment in this stock.

12. The management of Brinkley Corporation is interested in using simulation to estimate the profit per unit for a new product. Probability distributions for the purchase cost, the labor cost, and the transportation cost are as follows:

Purchase Cost ($)	Probability	Labor Cost ($)	Probability	Transportation Cost ($)	Probability
10	0.25	20	0.10	3	0.75
11	0.45	22	0.25	5	0.25
12	0.30	24	0.35		
		25	0.30		

Assume that these are the only costs and that the selling price for the product will be $45 per unit.

a. Provide the base-case, worst-case, and best-case calculations for the profit per unit.
b. Set up intervals of random numbers that can be used to randomly generate the three cost components.
c. Using the random numbers 0.3726, 0.5839, and 0.8275, calculate the profit per unit.
d. Using the random numbers 0.1862, 0.7466, and 0.6171, calculate the profit per unit.
e. Management believes the project may not be profitable if the profit per unit is less than $5. Explain how simulation can be used to estimate the probability the profit per unit will be less than $5.

13. Using the PortaCom Risk Analysis worksheet in Figure 15.6 and on the CD accompanying the text, develop your own worksheet for the PortaCom simulation model.
a. Compute the mean profit, the minimum profit, and the maximum profit.
b. What is your estimate of the probability of a loss?

SELF test

14. Develop a worksheet simulation for the following problem. The management of Madeira Manufacturing Company is considering the introduction of a new product. The fixed cost to begin the production of the product is $30,000. The variable cost for the product is uniformly distributed between $16 and $24 per unit. The product will sell for $50 per unit. Demand for the product is best described by a normal probability distribution with a mean of 1200 units and a standard deviation of 300 units. Develop a spreadsheet simulation similar to Figure 15.6. Use 500 simulation trials to answer the following questions.
a. What is the mean profit for the simulation?
b. What is the probability the project will result in a loss?
c. What is your recommendation concerning the introduction of the product?

15. Use a worksheet to simulate the rolling of dice. Use the VLOOKUP function as described in Appendix 15.1 to select the outcome for each die. Place the number for the first die in column B and the number for the second die in column C. Show the sum in column D. Repeat the simulation for 1000 rolls of the dice. What is your simulation estimate of the probability of rolling a 7?

16. Strassel Investors buys real estate, develops it, and resells it for a profit. A new property is available, and Bud Strassel, the president and owner of Strassel Investors, believes it can be sold for $160,000. The current property owner asked for bids and stated that the property will be sold for the highest bid in excess of $100,000. Two competitors will be submitting bids for the property. Strassel does not know what the competitors will bid, but he assumes for planning purposes that the amount bid by each competitor will be uniformly distributed between $100,000 and $150,000.
a. Develop a worksheet that can be used to simulate the bids made by the two competitors. Strassel is considering a bid of $130,000 for the property. Using a simulation of 1000 trials, what is the estimate of the probability Strassel will be able to obtain the property using a bid of $130,000?

b. How much does Strassel need to bid to be assured of obtaining the property? What is the profit associated with this bid?
c. Use the simulation model to compute the profit for each trial of the simulation run. With maximization of profit as Strassel's objective, use simulation to evaluate Strassel's bid alternatives of \$130,000, \$140,000, or \$150,000. What is the recommended bid, and what is the expected profit?

17. Grear Tire Company has produced a new tire with an estimated mean lifetime mileage of 36,500 miles. Management also believes that the standard deviation is 5000 miles and that tire mileage is normally distributed. Use a worksheet to simulate the miles obtained for a sample of 500 tires.
    a. Use the Excel COUNTIF function to determine the number of tires that last longer than 40,000 miles. What is your estimate of the percentage of tires that will exceed 40,000 miles?
    b. Use COUNTIF to find the number of tires that obtain mileage less than 32,000 miles. Then, find the number with less than 30,000 miles and the number with less than 28,000 miles.
    c. If management would like to advertise a tire mileage guarantee such that approximately no more than 10% of the tires would obtain mileage low enough to qualify for the guarantee, what tire mileage considered in part (b) would you recommend for the guarantee?

SELF test

18. A building contractor is preparing a bid on a new construction project. Two other contractors will be submitting bids for the same project. Based on past bidding practices, bids from the other contractors can be described by the following probability distributions:

Contractor	Probability Distribution of Bid
A	Uniform probability distribution between \$600,000 and \$800,000
B	Normal probability distribution with a mean bid of \$700,000 and a standard deviation of \$50,000

    a. If the building contractor submits a bid of \$750,000, what is the probability the building contractor will obtain the bid? Use a worksheet to simulate 1000 trials of the contract bidding process.
    b. The building contractor is also considering bids of \$775,000 and \$785,000. If the building contractor would like to bid such that the probability of winning the bid is about 0.80, what bid would you recommend? Repeat the simulation process with bids of \$775,000 and \$785,000 to justify your recommendation.

19. Develop your own worksheet for the Butler inventory simulation model shown in Figure 15.10. Suppose that management prefers not to charge for loss of goodwill. Run the Butler inventory simulation model with replenishment levels of 110, 115, 120, and 125. What is your recommendation?

20. In preparing for the upcoming holiday season, Mandrell Toy Company designated a new doll called Freddy. The fixed cost to produce the doll is \$100,000. The variable cost, which includes material, labor, and shipping costs, is \$34 per doll. During the holiday selling season, Mandrell will sell the dolls for \$42 each. If Mandrell overproduces the dolls, the excess dolls will be sold in January through a distributor who has agreed to pay Mandrell \$10 per doll. Demand for new toys during the holiday selling season is extremely uncertain. Forecasts are for expected sales of 60,000 dolls with a standard deviation of 15,000. The normal probability distribution is assumed to be a good description of the demand.
    a. Create a worksheet similar to the inventory worksheet in Figure 15.10. Include columns showing demand, sales, revenue from sales, amount of surplus, revenue from sales of surplus, total cost, and net profit. Use your worksheet to simulate the sales of the Freddy doll using a production quantity of 60,000 units. Using 500 simulation trials, what is the estimate of the mean profit associated with the production quantity of 60,000 dolls?

b. Before making a final decision on the production quantity, management wants an analysis of a more aggressive 70,000 unit production quantity and a more conservative 50,000 unit production quantity. Run your simulation with these two production quantities. What is the mean profit associated with each? What is your recommendation on the production of the Freddy doll?
c. Assuming that Mandrell's management adopts your recommendation, what is the probability of a stock-out and a shortage of the Freddy dolls during the holiday season?

21. South Central Airlines operates a commuter flight between Atlanta and Charlotte. The plane holds 30 passengers, and the airline makes a \$100 profit on each passenger on the flight. When South Central takes 30 reservations for the flight, experience has shown that on average, two passengers do not show up. As a result, with 30 reservations, South Central is averaging 28 passengers with a profit of 28(100) = \$2800 per flight. The airline operations office has asked for an evaluation of an overbooking strategy where they would accept 32 reservations even though the airplane holds only 30 passengers. The probability distribution for the number of passengers showing up when 32 reservations are accepted is as follows.

Passengers Showing Up	Probability
28	0.05
29	0.25
30	0.50
31	0.15
32	0.05

The airline will receive a profit of \$100 for each passenger on the flight up to the capacity of 30 passengers. The airline will incur a cost for any passenger denied seating on the flight. This cost covers added expenses of rescheduling the passenger as well as loss of goodwill, estimated to be \$150 per passenger. Develop a worksheet model that will simulate the performance of the overbooking system. Simulate the number of passengers showing up for each of 500 flights by using the VLOOKUP function. Use the results to compute the profit for each flight.

a. Does your simulation recommend the overbooking strategy? What is the mean profit per flight if overbooking is implemented?
b. Explain how your simulation model could be used to evaluate other overbooking levels such as 31, 33, 34 and for recommending a best overbooking strategy.

22. Develop your own waiting line simulation model for the Hammondsport Savings Bank problem (see Figure 15.14). Assume that a new branch is expected to open with interarrival times uniformly distributed between 0 and 4 minutes. The service times at this branch are anticipated to be normal with a mean of 2 minutes and a standard deviation of 0.5 minute. Simulate the operation of this system for 600 customers using one ATM. What is your assessment of the ability to operate this branch with one ATM? What happens to the average waiting time for customers near the end of the simulation period?

23. The Burger Dome waiting line model in Section 15.1 studies the waiting time of customers at its fast-food restaurant. Burger Dome's single-channel waiting line system has an arrival rate of 0.75 customers per minute and a service rate of 1 customer per minute.

a. Use a worksheet based on Figure 15.15 to simulate the operation of this waiting line. Assuming that customer arrivals follow a Poisson probability distribution, the interarrival times can be simulated with the cell formula $-(1/\lambda)$*LN(RAND()), where $\lambda = 0.75$. Assuming that the service time follows an exponential probability distribution, the service times can be simulated with the cell formula $-\mu$*LN(RAND()), where $\mu = 1$. Run the Burger Dome simulation for 500 customers. The analytical model in

Chapter 14 indicates an average waiting time of 3 minutes per customer. What average waiting time does your simulation model show?

b. One advantage of using simulation is that a simulation model can be altered easily to reflect other assumptions about the probabilistic inputs. Assume that the service time is more accurately described by a normal probability distribution with a mean of 1 minute and a standard deviation of 0.2 minute. This distribution has less service time variability than the exponential probability distribution used in part (a). What is the impact of this change on the average waiting time?

24. Telephone calls come into an airline reservations office randomly at the mean rate of 15 calls per hour. The time between calls follows an exponential distribution with a mean of 4 minutes. When the two reservation agents are busy, a telephone message tells the caller that the call is important and to please wait on the line until the next reservation agent becomes available. The service time for each reservation agent is normally distributed with a mean of 4 minutes and a standard deviation of 1 minute. Use a two-channel waiting line simulation model to evaluate this waiting line system. Use the worksheet design shown in Figure 15.17. The cell formula =−4*LN(RAND()) can be used to generate the interarrival times. Simulate the operation of the telephone reservation system for 600 customers. Discard the first 100 customers, and collect data over the next 500 customers.

a. Compute the mean interarrival time and the mean service time. If your simulation model is operating correctly, both of these should have means of approximately 4 minutes.

b. What is the mean customer waiting time for this system?

c. Use the =COUNTIF function to determine the number of customers who have to wait for a reservation agent. What percentage of the customers have to wait?

Case Problem 1 TRI-STATE CORPORATION

What will your portfolio be worth in 10 years? In 20 years? When you stop working? The Human Resources Department at Tri-State Corporation was asked to develop a financial planning model that would help employees address these questions. Tom Gifford was asked to lead this effort and decided to begin by developing a financial plan for himself. Tom has a degree in business and, at the age of 25, is making $34,000 per year. After two years of contributions to his company's retirement program and the receipt of a small inheritance, Tom has accumulated a portfolio valued at $14,500. Tom plans to work 30 more years and hopes to accumulate a portfolio valued at $1,000,000. Can he do it?

Tom began with a few assumptions about his future salary, his new investment contributions, and his portfolio growth rate. He assumed 5% annual salary growth rate as reasonable and wanted to make new investment contributions at 4% of his salary. After some research on historical stock market performance, Tom decided that a 10% annual portfolio growth rate was reasonable. Using these assumptions, Tom developed the Excel worksheet shown in Figure 15.18. Tom's specific situation and his assumptions are in the top portion of the worksheet (cells D3:D8). The worksheet provides a financial plan for the next five years. In computing the portfolio earnings for a given year, Tom assumed that his new investment contribution would occur evenly throughout the year and thus half of the new investment could be included in the computation of the portfolio earnings for the year. Using Figure 15.18, we see that at age 29, Tom is projected to have a portfolio valued at $32,898.

Tom's plan was to use this worksheet as a template to develop financial plans for the company's employees. The assumptions in cells D3:D8 would be different for each employee, and rows would be added to the worksheet to reflect the number of years appropriate for each employee. After adding another 25 rows to the worksheet, Tom found that he could expect to have a portfolio of $627,937 after 30 years. Tom then took his results to show his boss, Kate Riegle.

Although Kate was pleased with Tom's progress, she voiced several criticisms. One of the criticisms was the assumption of a constant annual salary growth rate. She noted that

FIGURE 15.18 FINANCIAL PLANNING WORKSHEET FOR TOM GIFFORD

EXCEL file
Gifford

	A	B	C	D	E	F	G	H
1	**Financial Analysis - Portfolio Projection**							
2								
3	Age			25				
4	Current Salary			$34,000				
5	Current Portfolio			$14,500				
6	Annual Salary Growth Rate			5%				
7	Annual Investment Rate			4%				
8	Annual Portfolio Growth Rate			10%				
9								
10			Beginning		New	Portfolio	Ending	
11	Year	Age	Portfolio	Salary	Investment	Earnings	Portfolio	
12	1	25	14,500	34,000	1,360	1,518	17,378	
13	2	26	17,378	35,700	1,428	1,809	20,615	
14	3	27	20,615	37,485	1,499	2,136	24,251	
15	4	28	24,251	39,359	1,574	2,504	28,329	
16	5	29	28,329	41,327	1,653	2,916	32,898	
17								

most employees experience some variation in the annual salary growth rate from year to year. In addition, she pointed out that the constant annual portfolio growth rate was unrealistic and that the actual growth rate would vary considerably from year to year. She further suggested that a simulation model for the portfolio projection might allow Tom to account for the random variability in the salary growth rate and the portfolio growth rate.

After some research, Tom and Kate decided to assume that the annual salary growth rate would vary from 0% to 10% and that a uniform probability distribution would provide a realistic approximation. Tri-State's accounting firm suggested that the annual portfolio growth rate could be approximated by a normal probability distribution with a mean of 10% and a standard deviation of 5%. With this information, Tom set off to develop a simulation model that could be used by the company's employees for financial planning.

Managerial Report

Play the role of Tom Gifford and develop a simulation model for financial planning. Write a report for Tom's boss and, at a minimum, include the following:

1. Without considering the random variability in growth rates, extend the worksheet in Figure 15.18 to 30 years. Confirm that by using the constant annual salary growth rate and the constant annual portfolio growth rate, Tom can expect to have a 30-year portfolio of $627,937. What would Tom's annual investment rate have to increase to in order for his portfolio to reach a 30-year, $1,000,000 goal?
2. Incorporate the random variability of the annual salary growth rate and the annual portfolio growth rate into a simulation model. Assume that Tom is willing to use the annual investment rate that predicted a 30-year, $1,000,000 portfolio in part 1. Show how to simulate Tom's 30-year financial plan. Use results from the simulation model to comment on the uncertainty associated with Tom reaching the 30-year, $1,000,000 goal. Discuss the advantages of repeating the simulation numerous times.
3. What recommendations do you have for employees with a current profile similar to Tom's after seeing the impact of the uncertainty in the annual salary growth rate and the annual portfolio growth rate?

4. Assume that Tom is willing to consider working 35 years instead of 30 years. What is your assessment of this strategy if Tom's goal is to have a portfolio worth $1,000,000?
5. Discuss how the financial planning model developed for Tom Gifford can be used as a template to develop a financial plan for any of the company's employees.

Case Problem 2 HARBOR DUNES GOLF COURSE

Harbor Dunes Golf Course was recently honored as one of the top public golf courses in South Carolina. The course, situated on land that was once a rice plantation, offers some of the best views of saltwater marshes available in the Carolinas. Harbor Dunes targets the upper end of the golf market and in the peak spring golfing season, charges green fees of $160 per person and golf cart fees of $20 per person.

Harbor Dunes takes reservations for tee times for groups of four players (foursome) starting at 7:30 each morning. Foursomes start at the same time on both the front nine and the back nine of the course, with a new group teeing off every nine minutes. The process continues with new foursomes starting play on both the front and back nine at noon. To enable all players to complete 18 holes before darkness, the last two afternoon foursomes start their rounds at 1:21 P.M. Under this plan, Harbor Dunes can sell a maximum of 20 afternoon tee times.

Last year Harbor Dunes was able to sell every morning tee time available for every day of the spring golf season. The same result is anticipated for the coming year. Afternoon tee times, however, are generally more difficult to sell. An analysis of the sales data for last year enabled Harbor Dunes to develop the probability distribution of sales for the afternoon tee times as shown in Table 15.12. For the season, Harbor Dunes averaged selling approximately 14 of the 20 available afternoon tee times. The average income from afternoon green fees and cart fees has been $10,240. However, the average of six unused tee times per day resulted in lost revenue.

In an effort to increase the sale of afternoon tee times, Harbor Dunes is considering an idea popular at other golf courses. These courses offer foursomes that play in the morning the option to play another round of golf in the afternoon by paying a reduced fee for the afternoon round. Harbor Dunes is considering two replay options: (1) a green fee of $25 per player plus a cart fee of $20 per player; (2) a green fee of $50 per player plus a cart fee of $20 per player. For option 1, each foursome will generate additional revenues of $180; for option 2, each foursome will generate additional revenues of $280. The key in making a decision as to what option is best depends upon the number of groups that find the option at-

TABLE 15.12 PROBABILITY DISTRIBUTION OF SALES FOR THE AFTERNOON TEE TIMES

Number of Tee Times Sold	Probability
8	0.01
9	0.04
10	0.06
11	0.08
12	0.10
13	0.11
14	0.12
15	0.15
16	0.10
17	0.09
18	0.07
19	0.05
20	0.02

TABLE 15.13 PROBABILITY DISTRIBUTIONS FOR THE NUMBER OF GROUPS REQUESTING A REPLAY

Option 1: $25 per person + Cart Fee		Option 2: $50 per person + Cart Fee	
Number of Foursomes Requesting a Replay	**Probability**	**Number of Foursomes Requesting a Replay**	**Probability**
0	0.01	0	0.06
1	0.03	1	0.09
2	0.05	2	0.12
3	0.05	3	0.17
4	0.11	4	0.20
5	0.15	5	0.13
6	0.17	6	0.11
7	0.15	7	0.07
8	0.13	8	0.05
9	0.09		
10	0.06		

tractive enough to take the replay offer. Working with a consultant who has expertise in statistics and the golf industry, Harbor Dunes developed probability distributions for the number of foursomes requesting a replay for each of the two options. These probability distributions are shown in Table 15.13.

In offering these replay options, Harbor Dunes' first priority will be to sell full-price afternoon advance reservations. If the demand for replay tee times exceeds the number of afternoon tee times available, Harbor Dunes will post a notice that the course is full. In this case, any excess replay requests will not be accepted.

Managerial Report

Develop simulation models for both replay options using Crystal Ball. Run each simulation for 5000 trials. Prepare a report that will help management of Harbor Dunes Golf Course decide which replay option to implement for the upcoming spring golf season. In preparing your report be sure to include the following:

1. Statistical summaries of the revenue expected under each replay option.
2. Your recommendation as to the best replay option.
3. Assuming a 90-day spring golf season, what is the estimate of the added revenue using your recommendation?
4. Discuss any other recommendations you have that might improve the income for Harbor Dunes.

Case Problem 3 COUNTY BEVERAGE DRIVE-THRU

County Beverage Drive-Thru, Inc., operates a chain of beverage supply stores in Northern Illinois. Each store has a single service lane; cars enter at one end of the store and exit at the other end. Customers pick up soft drinks, beer, snacks, and party supplies without getting out of their cars. When a new customer arrives at the store, the customer waits until the preceding customer's order is complete and then drives into the store for service.

Typically, three employees operate each store during peak periods; two clerks take and fill orders, and a third clerk serves as cashier and store supervisor. County Beverage is considering a revised store design in which computerized order-taking and payment are integrated with specialized warehousing equipment. Management hopes that the new design will permit operating each store with one clerk. To determine whether the new design is beneficial, management decided to build a new store using the revised design.

County Beverage's new store will be located near a major shopping center. Based on experience at other locations, management believes that during the peak late afternoon and evening hours, the time between arrivals follows an exponential probability distribution with a mean of six minutes. These peak hours are the most critical time period for the company; most of their profit is generated during these peak hours.

An extensive study of times required to fill orders with a single clerk led to the following probability distribution of service times.

Service Time (minutes)	Probability
2	0.24
3	0.20
4	0.15
5	0.14
6	0.12
7	0.08
8	0.05
9	0.02
Total	1.00

In case customer waiting times prove too long with just a single clerk, County Beverage's management is considering two alternatives: add a second clerk to help with bagging, taking orders, and related tasks, or enlarge the drive-thru area so that two cars can be served at once (a two-channel system). With either of these options, two clerks will be needed. With the two-channel option, service times are expected to be the same for each channel. With the second clerk helping with a single channel, service times will be reduced. The following probability distribution describes service times given that option.

Service Time (minutes)	Probability
1	0.20
2	0.35
3	0.30
4	0.10
5	0.05
Total	1.00

County Beverage's management would like you to develop a spreadsheet simulation model of the new system and use it to compare the operation of the system using the following three designs:

Design	
A	One channel, one clerk
B	One channel, two clerks
C	Two channels, each with one clerk

Management is especially concerned with how long customers have to wait for service. Research has shown that 30% of the customers will wait no longer than 6 minutes and that 90% will wait no longer than 10 minutes. As a guideline, management requires the average waiting time to be less than 1.5 minutes.

Managerial Report

Prepare a report that discusses the general development of the spreadsheet simulation model, and make any recommendations that you have regarding the best store design and staffing plan for County Beverage. One additional consideration is that the design allowing for a two-channel system will cost an additional $10,000 to build.

1. List the information the spreadsheet simulation model should generate so that a decision can be made on the store design and the desired number of clerks.
2. Run the simulation for 1000 customers for each alternative considered. You may want to consider making more than one run with each alternative. [*Note:* Values from an exponential probability distribution with mean μ can be generated in Excel using the following function: $=-\mu$*LN(RAND()).]
3. Be sure to note the number of customers County Beverage is likely to lose due to long customer waiting times with each design alternative.

Appendix 15.1 SIMULATION WITH EXCEL

Excel enables small and moderate-sized simulation models to be implemented relatively easily and quickly. In this appendix we show the Excel worksheets for the three simulation models presented in the chapter.

The PortaCom Simulation Model

Tutorial 7: Simulation Using Basic Excel

We simulated the PortaCom problem 500 times. The worksheet used to carry out the simulation is shown again in Figure 15.19. Note that the simulation results for trials 6 through 495 have been hidden so that the results can be shown in a reasonably sized figure. If desired, the rows for these trials can be shown and the simulation results displayed for all 500 trials. Let us describe the details of the Excel worksheet that provided the PortaCom simulation.

First, the PortaCom data are presented in the first 14 rows of the worksheet. The selling price per unit, administrative cost, and advertising cost parameters are entered directly into cells C3, C4, and C5. The discrete probability distribution for the direct labor cost per unit is shown in a tabular format. Note that the random number intervals are entered first followed by the corresponding cost per unit. For example, 0.0 in cell A10 and 0.1 in cell B10 show that a cost of $43 per unit will be assigned if the random number is in the interval 0.0 but less than 0.1. Thus, approximately 10% of the simulated direct labor costs will be $43 per unit. The uniform probability distribution with a smallest value of $80 in cell E8 and a largest value of $100 in cell E9 describes the parts cost per unit. Finally, a normal probability distribution with a mean of 15,000 units in cell E13 and a standard deviation of 4500 units in cell E14 describes the first-year demand distribution for the product. At this point we are ready to insert the Excel formulas that will carry out each simulation trial.

Simulation information for the first trial appears in row 21 of the worksheet. The cell formulas for row 21 are as follows:

Cell A21	Enter 1 for the first simulation trial
Cell B21	Simulate the direct labor cost per unit* =VLOOKUP(RAND(),$A$10:$C$14,3)
Cell C21	Simulate the parts cost per unit (uniform distribution) =$E$8+($E$9−$E$8)*RAND()

---

*The VLOOKUP function generates a random number using the RAND() function. Then, using the table defined by the region from cells $A$10 to $C$14, the function identifies the row containing the RAND() random number and assigns the corresponding direct labor cost per unit shown in column C.

FIGURE 15.19 WORKSHEET FOR THE PORTACOM PROBLEM

	A	B	C	D	E	F
1	**PortaCom Risk Analysis**					
2						
3	Selling Price per Unit		$249			
4	Administrative Cost		$400,000			
5	Advertising Cost		$600,000			
6						
7	**Direct Labor Cost**			**Parts Cost (Uniform Distribution)**		
8	Lower	Upper		Smallest Value	$80	
9	Random No.	Random No.	Cost per Unit	Largest Value	$100	
10	0.0	0.1	$43			
11	0.1	0.3	$44			
12	0.3	0.7	$45	**Demand (Normal Distribution)**		
13	0.7	0.9	$46	Mean	15000	
14	0.9	1.0	$47	Std Deviation	4500	
15						
16						
17	**Simulation Trials**					
18						
19		Direct Labor	Parts	First-Year		
20	Trial	Cost per Unit	Cost per Unit	Demand	Profit	
21	1	47	$85.36	17,366	$1,025,570	
22	2	44	$91.68	12,900	$461,828	
23	3	45	$93.35	20,686	$1,288,906	
24	4	43	$98.56	10,888	$169,807	
25	5	45	$88.36	14,259	$648,911	
516	496	44	$98.67	8,730	($71,739)	
517	497	45	$94.38	19,257	$1,110,952	
518	498	44	$90.85	14,920	$703,118	
519	499	43	$90.37	13,471	$557,652	
520	500	46	$92.50	18,614	$1,056,847	
521						
522			**Summary Statistics**			
523			Mean Profit		$698,457	
524			Standard Deviation		$520,485	
525			Minimum Profit		($785,234)	
526			Maximum Profit		$2,367,058	
527			Number of Losses		51	
528			Probability of Loss		0.1020	
529						

EXCELfile
PortaCom

Cell D21 Simulate the first-year demand (normal distribution)
=NORMINV(RAND(),$E$13,$E$14)

Cell E21 The profit obtained for the first trial
=($C$3−B21−C21)*D21−$C$4−$C$5

Cells A21:E21 can be copied to A520:E520 in order to provide the 500 simulation trials.

Ultimately, summary statistics will be collected in order to describe the results of the 500 simulated trials. Using the standard Excel functions, the following summary statistics are computed for the 500 simulated profits appearing in cells E21 to E520.

Cell E523 The mean profit per trial = AVERAGE(E21:E520)

Cell E524 The standard deviation of profit = STDEV(E21:E520)

Cell E525 The minimum profit = MIN(E21:E520)

Cell E526 The maximum profit = MAX(E21:E520)

Cell E527 The count of the number of trials where a loss occurred (i.e., profit < $0) = COUNTIF(E21:E520,"<0")

Cell E528 The percentage or probability of a loss based on the 500 trials = E527/500

The F9 key can be used to perform another complete simulation of PortaCom. In this case, the entire worksheet will be recalculated and a set of new simulation results will be provided. Any data summaries, measures, or functions that have been built into the worksheet earlier will be updated automatically.

The Butler Inventory Simulation Model

We simulated the Butler inventory operation for 300 months. The worksheet used to carry out the simulation is shown again in Figure 15.20. Note that the simulation results for months 6 through 295 have been hidden so that the results can be shown in a reasonably sized figure. If desired, the rows for these months can be shown and the simulation results displayed for all 300 months. Let us describe the details of the Excel worksheet that provided the Butler inventory simulation.

First, the Butler inventory data are presented in the first 11 rows of the worksheet. The gross profit per unit, holding cost per unit, and shortage cost per unit data are entered directly into cells C3, C4, and C5. The replenishment level is entered into cell C7, and the mean and standard deviation of the normal probability distribution for demand are entered into cells B10 and B11. At this point we are ready to insert Excel formulas that will carry out each simulation month or trial.

Simulation information for the first month or trial appears in row 17 of the worksheet. The cell formulas for row 17 are as follows:

Cell A17 Enter 1 for the first simulation month

Cell B17 Simulate demand (normal distribution)
=NORMINV(RAND(),$B$10,$B$11)

Next compute the sales, which is equal to demand (cell B17) if demand is less than or equal to the replenishment level, or is equal to the replenishment level (cell C7) if demand is greater than the replenishment level.

Cell C17 Compute sales =IF(B17<=$C$7,B17,$C$7)

Cell D17 Calculate gross profit =$C$3*C17

Cell E17 Calculate the holding cost if demand is less than or equal to the replenishment level
=IF(B17<= $C$7,$C$4*($C$7−B17),0)

Cell F17 Calculate the shortage cost if demand is greater than the replenishment level
=IF(B17>$C$7,$C$5*(B17−$C$7),0)

Cell G17 Calculate net profit =D17−E17−F17

Cells A17:G17 can be copied to cells A316:G316 in order to provide the 300 simulation months.

FIGURE 15.20 WORKSHEET FOR THE BUTLER INVENTORY PROBLEM

	A	B	C	D	E	F	G	H
1	**Butler Inventory**							
2								
3	Gross Profit per Unit		$50					
4	Holding Cost per Unit		$15					
5	Shortage Cost per Unit		$30					
6								
7	**Replenishment Level**		100					
8								
9	**Demand (Normal Distribution)**							
10	Mean	100						
11	Std Deviation	20						
12								
13								
14	**Simulation**							
15								
16	Month	Demand	Sales	Gross Profit	Holding Cost	Shortage Cost	Net Profit	
17	1	79	79	$3,950	$315	$0	$3,635	
18	2	111	100	$5,000	$0	$330	$4,670	
19	3	93	93	$4,650	$105	$0	$4,545	
20	4	100	100	$5,000	$0	$0	$5,000	
21	5	118	100	$5,000	$0	$540	$4,460	
312	296	89	89	$4,450	$165	$0	$4,285	
313	297	91	91	$4,550	$135	$0	$4,415	
314	298	122	100	$5,000	$0	$660	$4,340	
315	299	93	93	$4,650	$105	$0	$4,545	
316	300	126	100	$5,000	$0	$780	$4,220	
317								
318	**Totals**	30,181	27,917		**Summary Statistics**			
319					Mean Profit		$4,293	
320					Standard Deviation		$658	
321					Minimum Profit		($206)	
322					Maximum Profit		$5,000	
323					Service Level		92.5%	
324								

EXCELfile
Butler

Finally, summary statistics will be collected in order to describe the results of the 300 simulated trials. Using the standard Excel functions, the following totals and summary statistics are computed for the 300 months.

Cell B318 Total demand =SUM(B17:B316)

Cell C319 Total sales =SUM(C17:C316)

Cell G319 The mean profit per month =AVERAGE(G17:G316)

Cell G320 The standard deviation of net profit =STDEV(G17:G316)

Cell G321 The minimum net profit =MIN(G17:G316)

Cell G322 The maximum net profit =MAX(G17:G316)

Cell G323 The service level =C318/B318

The Hammondsport ATM Simulation Model

We simulated the operation of the Hammondsport ATM waiting line system for 1000 customers. The worksheet used to carry out the simulation is shown again in Figure 15.21. Note that the simulation results for customers 6 through 995 have been hidden so that the results can be shown in a reasonably sized figure. If desired, the rows for these customers can be shown and the simulation results displayed for all 1000 customers. Let us describe the details of the Excel worksheet that provided the Hammondsport ATM simulation.

The data are presented in the first 9 rows of the worksheet. The interarrival times are described by a uniform distribution with a smallest time of 0 minutes (cell B4) and a largest time of 5 minutes (cell B5). A normal probability distribution with a mean of 2 minutes (cell B8) and a standard deviation of 0.5 minute (cell B9) describes the service time distribution.

FIGURE 15.21 WORKSHEET FOR THE HAMMONDSPORT SAVINGS BANK WITH ONE ATM

EXCELfile
Hammondsport1

	A	B	C	D	E	F	G	H	I
1	**Hammondsport Savings Bank with One ATM**								
2									
3	**Interarrival Times (Uniform Distribution)**								
4	Smallest Value	0							
5	Largest Value	5							
6									
7	**Service Times (Normal Distribution)**								
8	Mean	2							
9	Std Deviation	0.5							
10									
11									
12	**Simulation**								
13									
14		Interarrival	Arrival	Service	Waiting	Service	Completion	Time	
15	Customer	Time	Time	Start Time	Time	Time	Time	in System	
16	1	1.4	1.4	1.4	0.0	2.3	3.7	2.3	
17	2	1.3	2.7	3.7	1.0	1.5	5.2	2.5	
18	3	4.9	7.6	7.6	0.0	2.2	9.8	2.2	
19	4	3.5	11.1	11.1	0.0	2.5	13.6	2.5	
20	5	0.7	11.8	13.6	1.8	1.8	15.4	3.6	
1011	996	0.5	2496.8	2498.1	1.3	0.6	2498.7	1.9	
1012	997	0.2	2497.0	2498.7	1.7	2.0	2500.7	3.7	
1013	998	2.7	2499.7	2500.7	1.0	1.8	2502.5	2.8	
1014	999	3.7	2503.4	2503.4	0.0	2.4	2505.8	2.4	
1015	1000	4.0	2507.4	2507.4	0.0	1.9	2509.3	1.9	
1016									
1017		**Summary Statistics**							
1018		Number Waiting			549				
1019		Probability of Waiting			0.6100				
1020		Average Waiting Time			1.59				
1021		Maximum Waiting Time			13.5				
1022		Utilization of ATM			0.7860				
1023		Number Waiting > 1 Min			393				
1024		Probability of Waiting > 1 Min			0.4367				
1025									

Simulation information for the first customer appears in row 16 of the worksheet. The cell formulas for row 16 are as follows:

Cell A16 Enter 1 for the first customer

Cell B16 Simulate the interarrival time for customer 1 (uniform distribution)
=$B$4+RAND()*($B$5−$B$4)

Cell C16 Compute the arrival time for customer 1 =B16

Cell D16 Compute the start time for customer 1 =C16

Cell E16 Compute the waiting time for customer 1 =D1−C16

Cell F16 Simulate the service time for customer 1 (normal distribution)
=NORMINV(RAND(),$B$8,$B$9)

Cell G16 Compute the completion time for customer 1 =D16+F16

Cell H16 Compute the time in the system for customer 1 =G16−C16

Simulation information for the second customer appears in row 17 of the worksheet. The cell formulas for row 17 are as follows:

Cell A17 Enter 2 for the second customer

Cell B17 Simulate the interarrival time for customer 2 (uniform distribution)
=$B$4+RAND()*($B$5−$B$4)

Cell C17 Compute the arrival time for customer 2 =C16+B17

Cell D17 Compute the start time for customer 2 =IF(C17>G16,C17,G16)

Cell E17 Compute the waiting time for customer 2 =D17−C17

Cell F17 Simulate the service time for customer 2 (normal distribution)
=NORMINV(RAND(),$B$8,$B$9)

Cell G17 Compute the completion time for customer 2 =D17+F17

Cell H17 Compute the time in the system for customer 2 =G17−C17

Cells A17:H17 can be copied to cells A1015:H1015 in order to provide the 1000-customer simulation.

Ultimately, summary statistics will be collected in order to describe the results of 1000 customers. Before collecting the summary statistics, let us point out that most simulation studies of dynamic systems focus on the operation of the system during its long-run or steady-state operation. To ensure that the effect of start-up conditions are not included in the steady-state calculations, a dynamic simulation model is usually run for a specified period without collecting any data about the operation of the system. The length of the start-up period can vary depending on the application. For the Hammondsport Savings Bank ATM simulation, we treated the results for the first 100 customers as the start-up period. The simulation information for customer 100 appears in row 115 of the spreadsheet. Cell G115 shows that the completion time for the 100th customer is 247.8. Thus the length of the start-up period is 247.8 minutes.

Summary statistics are collected for the next 900 customers corresponding to rows 116 to 1015 of the spreadsheet. The following Excel formulas provided the summary statistics.

Cell E1018 Number of customers who had to wait (i.e., waiting time > 0)
=COUNTIF(E116:E1015,">0")

Cell E1019 Probability of waiting =E1018/900

Cell E1020 The average waiting time =AVERAGE(E116:E1015)

Cell E1021 The maximum waiting time =MAX(E116:E1015)

Cell E1022 The utilization of the ATM* =SUM(F116:F1015)/(G1015 − G115)

Cell E1023 The number of customers who had to wait more than 1 minute =COUNTIF(E116:E1015,">1")

Cell E1024 Probability of waiting more than 1 minute =E1023/900

Appendix 15.2 SIMULATION USING CRYSTAL BALL

In Section 15.1 we used simulation to perform risk analysis for the PortaCom problem, and in Appendix 15.1 we showed how to construct the Excel worksheet that provided the simulation results. Developing the worksheet simulation for the PortaCom problem using the basic Excel package was relatively easy. The use of add-ins enable larger and more complex simulation problems to be easily analyzed using spreadsheets. In this appendix, we show how Crystal Ball, an add-in package, can be used to perform the PortaCom simulation. We will run the simulation for 1000 trials here. Instructions for installing and starting Crystal Ball are included with the Crystal Ball software.

Formulating a Crystal Ball Model

We begin by entering the problem data into the top portion of the worksheet. For the PortaCom problem, we must enter the following data: selling price, administrative cost, advertising cost, probability distribution for the direct labor cost per unit, smallest and largest values for the parts cost per unit (uniform distribution), and the mean and standard deviation for first-year demand (normal distribution). These data with appropriate descriptive labels are shown in cells A1:E13 of Figure 15.22.

For the PortaCom problem, the Crystal Ball model contains the following two components: (1) cells for the probabilistic inputs (direct labor cost, parts cost, first-year demand), and (2) a cell containing a formula for computing the value of the simulation model output (profit). In Crystal Ball the cells that contain the values of the probabilistic inputs are called *assumption cells,* and the cells that contain the formulas for the model outputs are referred to as *forecast cells*. The PortaCom problem requires only one output (profit), and thus the Crystal Ball model only contains one forecast cell. In more complex simulation problems more than one forecast cell may be necessary.

The assumption cells may only contain simple numeric values. In this model-building stage, we entered PortaCom's best estimates of the direct labor cost ($45), the parts cost ($90), and the first-year demand (15,000) into cells C21:C23, respectively. The forecast cells in a Crystal Ball model contain formulas that refer to one or more of the assumption cells. Because only one forecast cell in the PortaCom problem corresponds to profit, we entered the following formula into cell C27:

=(C3−C21−C22)*C23−C4−C5

The resulting value of $710,000 is the profit corresponding to the base-case scenario discussed in Section 15.1.

---

*The proportion of time the ATM is in use is equal to the sum of the 900 customer service times in column F divided by the total elapsed time required for the 900 customers to complete service. This total elapsed time is the difference between the completion time of customer 1000 and the completion time of customer 100.

FIGURE 15.22 CRYSTAL BALL WORKSHEET FOR THE PORTACOM PROBLEM

EXCELfile
PortaCom Crystal

	A	B	C	D	E	F
1	**PortaCom Risk Analysis**					
2						
3	Selling Price per Unit		$249			
4	Administrative Cost		$400,000			
5	Advertising Cost		$600,000			
6						
7		**Direct Labor**		**Parts Cost (Uniform Distribution)**		
8		Cost per Unit	Probability	Smallest Value	$80	
9		$43	0.1	Largest Value	$100	
10		$44	0.2			
11		$45	0.4	**Demand (Normal Distribution)**		
12		$46	0.2	Mean	15,000	
13		$47	0.1	Standard Dev	4,500	
14						
15						
16						
17	**Crystal Ball Model**					
18						
19			**Assumption**			
20			**Cells**			
21		**Direct Labor Cost**	$45			
22		**Parts Cost**	$90			
23		**Demand**	15,000			
24						
25			**Forecast**			
26			**Cell**			
27		**Profit**	$710,000			
28						

Defining and Entering Assumptions

We are now ready to define the probability distributions corresponding to each of the assumption cells. We begin by defining the probability distribution for the direct labor cost.

Step 1. Select cell C21
Step 2. Select the **Define** menu
Step 3. Choose **Define Assumption**
Step 4. When the **Distribution Gallery: Cell 21** dialog box appears:
Choose **Custom***
Click **OK**
Step 5. When the **Define Assumption: Cell C21** dialog box appears:
If the  button is to the right of the **Name** box, proceed to Step 6
If the  button is to the right of the **Name** box, click the  button to obtain the  button

*You may have to click **All** and use the scroll bar to see all possible distributions.

Step 6. Choose **Load Data**
Enter B9:C13 in the **Location of data** box
Click **Keep Linked to Spreadsheet**
Click **OK** to terminate the data entry process
Click **OK**

The procedure for defining the probability distribution for the parts cost is similar.

Step 1. Select cell C22
Step 2. Select the **Define** menu
Step 3. Choose **Define Assumption**
Step 4. When the **Distribution Gallery: Cell C22** dialog box appears:
Choose **Uniform** (Use the scroll bar to see all possible distributions.)
Click **OK**
Step 5. When the **Define Assumption: Cell C22** dialog box appears:
Enter =E8 in the **Minimum** box
Enter =E9 in the **Maximum** box
Click **Enter**
Click **OK**

Finally, we perform the following steps to define the probability distribution for first-year demand.

Step 1. Select cell C23
Step 2. Select the **Define** menu
Step 3. Choose **Define Assumption**
Step 4. When the **Distribution Gallery: Cell 23** dialog box appears:
Choose **Normal**
Click **OK**
Step 5. When the **Define Assumption: Cell C23** dialog box appears:
Enter =E12 in the **Mean** box
Enter =E13 in the **Std. Dev.** box
Click **Enter**
Click **OK**

Defining Forecasts

After defining the assumption cells, we are ready to define the forecast cells. The following steps show this process for cell C27, which is the profit forecast cell for the PortaCom problem.

Step 1. Select cell C27
Step 2. Select the **Define** menu
Step 3. Choose **Define Forecast**
Step 4. When the **Define Forecast: Cell C27** dialog box appears:
Profit will appear in the **Name** box
Click **OK**

Setting Run Preferences

We must now make the choices that determine how Crystal Ball runs the simulation. For the PortaCom simulation, we only need to specify the number of trials.

Step 1. Select the **Run** menu
Step 2. Choose **Run Preferences**

Step 3. When the **Run Preferences** dialog box appears:
Make sure the **Trials** tab has been selected
Enter 1000 in the **Number of trials to run:** box
Click **OK**

Running the Simulation

Crystal Ball repeats three steps on each of the 1000 trials of the PortaCom simulation.

1. Values are generated for the three assumption cells according to the defined probability distributions.
2. A new simulated profit (forecast cell) is computed based on the new values in the three assumption cells.
3. The new simulated profit is recorded.

The following steps describe how to begin the simulation.

Step 1. Select the **Run** menu
Step 2. Choose **Start Simulation**

When the run is complete, Crystal Ball displays a Forecast: Profit window, which shows a frequency distribution of the simulated profit values obtained during the simulation run. See Figure 15.23. Other types of charts and output can be displayed. For instance, the following steps describe how to display the descriptive statistics for the simulation run.

Step 1. Select the **View** menu in the **Forecast: Profit** window
Step 2. Choose **Statistics**

FIGURE 15.23 CRYSTAL BALL FREQUENCY CHART FOR THE PORTACOM SIMULATION

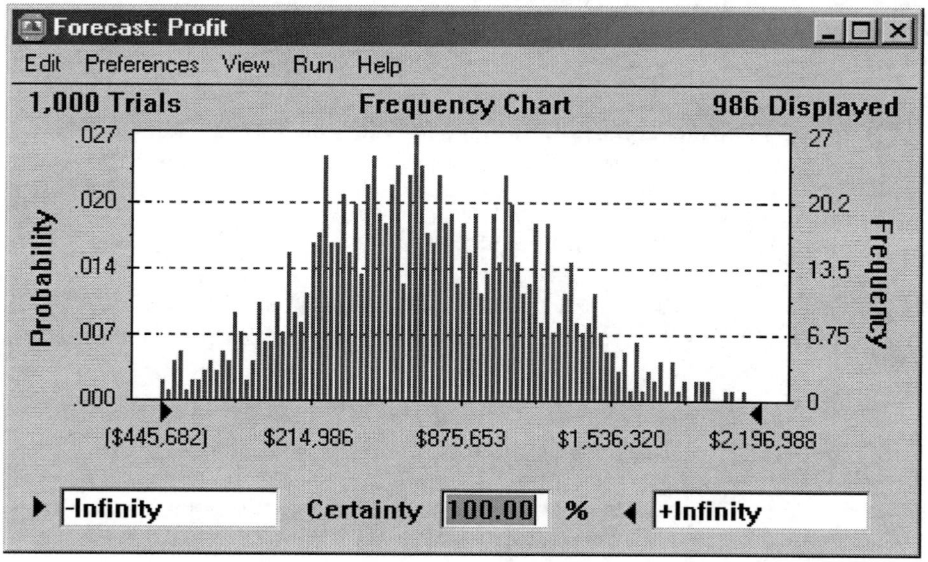

FIGURE 15.24 CRYSTAL BALL STATISTICS FOR THE PORTACOM SIMULATION

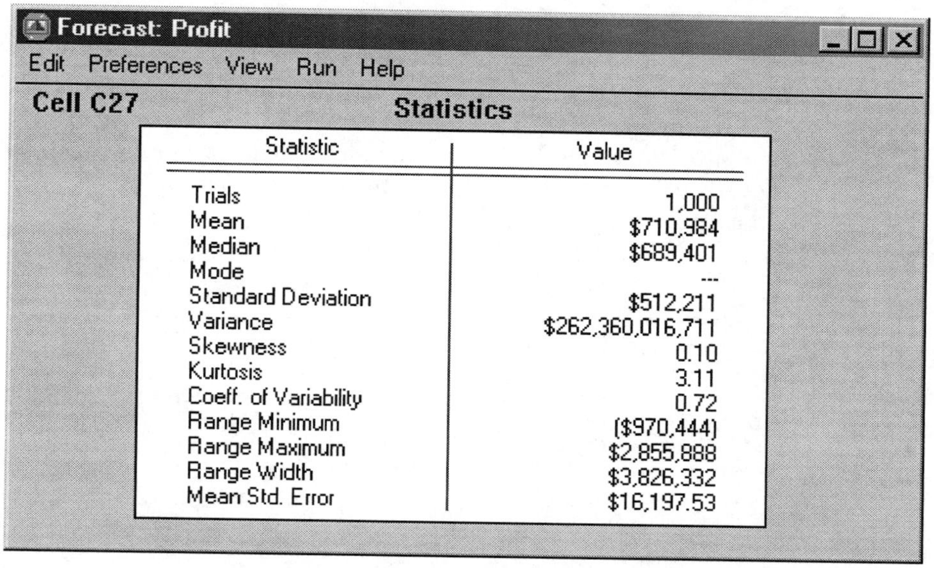

Statistic	Value
Trials	1,000
Mean	$710,984
Median	$689,401
Mode	---
Standard Deviation	$512,211
Variance	$262,360,016,711
Skewness	0.10
Kurtosis	3.11
Coeff. of Variability	0.72
Range Minimum	($970,444)
Range Maximum	$2,855,888
Range Width	$3,826,332
Mean Std. Error	$16,197.53

Figure 15.24 shows the Forecast: Profit window with descriptive statistics. Note that the worst result obtained in this simulation of 1000 trials is a loss of $970,444, and the best result is a profit of $2,855,888. The mean profit is $710,984. These values are similar to the results obtained in Section 15.1. The differences result from the different random numbers used in the two simulations and from the fact that we used 1000 trials with Crystal Ball. If you perform another simulation, your results will differ slightly.

Appendix A Binomial Probabilities

Entries in the following table give the probability of x successes in n trials of a binomial experiment, where p is the probability of a success on one trial. For example, with $n = 6$ trials and $p = 0.40$, the probability of $x = 2$ successes is 0.3110.

		p									
n	x	0.05	0.10	0.15	0.20	0.25	0.30	0.35	0.40	0.45	0.50
1	0	0.9500	0.9000	0.8500	0.8000	0.7500	0.7000	0.6500	0.6000	0.5500	0.5000
	1	0.0500	0.1000	0.1500	0.2000	0.2500	0.3000	0.3500	0.4000	0.4500	0.5000
2	0	0.9025	0.8100	0.7225	0.6400	0.5625	0.4900	0.4225	0.3600	0.3025	0.2500
	1	0.0950	0.1800	0.2550	0.3200	0.3750	0.4200	0.4550	0.4800	0.4950	0.5000
	2	0.0025	0.0100	0.0225	0.0400	0.0625	0.0900	0.1225	0.1600	0.2025	0.2500
3	0	0.8574	0.7290	0.6141	0.5120	0.4219	0.3430	0.2746	0.2160	0.1664	0.1250
	1	0.1354	0.2430	0.3251	0.3840	0.4219	0.4410	0.4436	0.4320	0.4084	0.3750
	2	0.0071	0.0270	0.0574	0.0960	0.1406	0.1890	0.2389	0.2880	0.3341	0.3750
	3	0.0001	0.0010	0.0034	0.0080	0.0156	0.0270	0.0429	0.0640	0.0911	0.1250
4	0	0.8145	0.6561	0.5220	0.4096	0.3164	0.2401	0.1785	0.1296	0.0915	0.0625
	1	0.1715	0.2916	0.3685	0.4096	0.4219	0.4116	0.3845	0.3456	0.2995	0.2500
	2	0.0135	0.0486	0.0975	0.1536	0.2109	0.2646	0.3105	0.3456	0.3675	0.3750
	3	0.0005	0.0036	0.0115	0.0256	0.0469	0.0756	0.1115	0.1536	0.2005	0.2500
	4	0.0000	0.0001	0.0005	0.0016	0.0039	0.0081	0.0150	0.0256	0.0410	0.0625
5	0	0.7738	0.5905	0.4437	0.3277	0.2373	0.1681	0.1160	0.0778	0.0503	0.0312
	1	0.2036	0.3280	0.3915	0.4096	0.3955	0.3602	0.3124	0.2592	0.2059	0.1562
	2	0.0214	0.0729	0.1382	0.2048	0.2637	0.3087	0.3364	0.3456	0.3369	0.3125
	3	0.0011	0.0081	0.0244	0.0512	0.0879	0.1323	0.1811	0.2304	0.2757	0.3125
	4	0.0000	0.0004	0.0022	0.0064	0.0146	0.0284	0.0488	0.0768	0.1128	0.1562
	5	0.0000	0.0000	0.0001	0.0003	0.0010	0.0024	0.0053	0.0102	0.0185	0.0312
6	0	0.7351	0.5314	0.3771	0.2621	0.1780	0.1176	0.0754	0.0467	0.0277	0.0156
	1	0.2321	0.3543	0.3993	0.3932	0.3560	0.3025	0.2437	0.1866	0.1359	0.0938
	2	0.0305	0.0984	0.1762	0.2458	0.2966	0.3241	0.3280	0.3110	0.2780	0.2344
	3	0.0021	0.0146	0.0415	0.0819	0.1318	0.1852	0.2355	0.2765	0.3032	0.3125
	4	0.0001	0.0012	0.0055	0.0154	0.0330	0.0595	0.0951	0.1382	0.1861	0.2344
	5	0.0000	0.0001	0.0004	0.0015	0.0044	0.0102	0.0205	0.0369	0.0609	0.0938
	6	0.0000	0.0000	0.0000	0.0001	0.0002	0.0007	0.0018	0.0041	0.0083	0.0156
7	0	0.6983	0.4783	0.3206	0.2097	0.1335	0.0824	0.0490	0.0280	0.0152	0.0078
	1	0.2573	0.3720	0.3960	0.3670	0.3115	0.2471	0.1848	0.1306	0.0872	0.0547
	2	0.0406	0.1240	0.2097	0.2753	0.3115	0.3177	0.2985	0.2613	0.2140	0.1641
	3	0.0036	0.0230	0.0617	0.1147	0.1730	0.2269	0.2679	0.2903	0.2918	0.2734
	4	0.0002	0.0026	0.0109	0.0287	0.0577	0.0972	0.1442	0.1935	0.2388	0.2734
	5	0.0000	0.0002	0.0012	0.0043	0.0115	0.0250	0.0466	0.0774	0.1172	0.1641
	6	0.0000	0.0000	0.0001	0.0004	0.0013	0.0036	0.0084	0.0172	0.0320	0.0547
	7	0.0000	0.0000	0.0000	0.0000	0.0001	0.0002	0.0006	0.0016	0.0037	0.0078

Binomial Probabilities (*Continued*)

		p									
n	*x*	0.05	0.10	0.15	0.20	0.25	0.30	0.35	0.40	0.45	0.50
8	0	0.6634	0.4305	0.2725	0.1678	0.1001	0.0576	0.0319	0.0168	0.0084	0.0039
	1	0.2793	0.3826	0.3847	0.3355	0.2670	0.1977	0.1373	0.0896	0.0548	0.0312
	2	0.0515	0.1488	0.2376	0.2936	0.3115	0.2965	0.2587	0.2090	0.1569	0.1094
	3	0.0054	0.0331	0.0839	0.1468	0.2076	0.2541	0.2786	0.2787	0.2568	0.2188
	4	0.0004	0.0046	0.0185	0.0459	0.0865	0.1361	0.1875	0.2322	0.2627	0.2734
	5	0.0000	0.0004	0.0026	0.0092	0.0231	0.0467	0.0808	0.1239	0.1719	0.2188
	6	0.0000	0.0000	0.0002	0.0011	0.0038	0.0100	0.0217	0.0413	0.0703	0.1094
	7	0.0000	0.0000	0.0000	0.0001	0.0004	0.0012	0.0033	0.0079	0.0164	0.0312
	8	0.0000	0.0000	0.0000	0.0000	0.0000	0.0001	0.0002	0.0007	0.0017	0.0039
9	0	0.6302	0.3874	0.2316	0.1342	0.0751	0.0404	0.0207	0.0101	0.0046	0.0020
	1	0.2985	0.3874	0.3679	0.3020	0.2253	0.1556	0.1004	0.0605	0.0339	0.0176
	2	0.0629	0.1722	0.2597	0.3020	0.3003	0.2668	0.2162	0.1612	0.1110	0.0703
	3	0.0077	0.0446	0.1069	0.1762	0.2336	0.2668	0.2716	0.2508	0.2119	0.1641
	4	0.0006	0.0074	0.0283	0.0661	0.1168	0.1715	0.2194	0.2508	0.2600	0.2461
	5	0.0000	0.0008	0.0050	0.0165	0.0389	0.0735	0.1181	0.1672	0.2128	0.2461
	6	0.0000	0.0001	0.0006	0.0028	0.0087	0.0210	0.0424	0.0743	0.1160	0.1641
	7	0.0000	0.0000	0.0000	0.0003	0.0012	0.0039	0.0098	0.0212	0.0407	0.0703
	8	0.0000	0.0000	0.0000	0.0000	0.0001	0.0004	0.0013	0.0035	0.0083	0.0176
	9	0.0000	0.0000	0.0000	0.0000	0.0000	0.0000	0.0001	0.0003	0.0008	0.0020
10	0	0.5987	0.3487	0.1969	0.1074	0.0563	0.0282	0.0135	0.0060	0.0025	0.0010
	1	0.3151	0.3874	0.3474	0.2684	0.1877	0.1211	0.0725	0.0403	0.0207	0.0098
	2	0.0746	0.1937	0.2759	0.3020	0.2816	0.2335	0.1757	0.1209	0.0763	0.0439
	3	0.0105	0.0574	0.1298	0.2013	0.2503	0.2668	0.2522	0.2150	0.1665	0.1172
	4	0.0010	0.0112	0.0401	0.0881	0.1460	0.2001	0.2377	0.2508	0.2384	0.2051
	5	0.0001	0.0015	0.0085	0.0264	0.0584	0.1029	0.1536	0.2007	0.2340	0.2461
	6	0.0000	0.0001	0.0012	0.0055	0.0162	0.0368	0.0689	0.1115	0.1596	0.2051
	7	0.0000	0.0000	0.0001	0.0008	0.0031	0.0090	0.0212	0.0425	0.0746	0.1172
	8	0.0000	0.0000	0.0000	0.0001	0.0004	0.0014	0.0043	0.0106	0.0229	0.0439
	9	0.0000	0.0000	0.0000	0.0000	0.0000	0.0001	0.0005	0.0016	0.0042	0.0098
	10	0.0000	0.0000	0.0000	0.0000	0.0000	0.0000	0.0000	0.0001	0.0003	0.0010
12	0	0.5404	0.2824	0.1422	0.0687	0.0317	0.0138	0.0057	0.0022	0.0008	0.0002
	1	0.3413	0.3766	0.3012	0.2062	0.1267	0.0712	0.0368	0.0174	0.0075	0.0029
	2	0.0988	0.2301	0.2924	0.2835	0.2323	0.1678	0.1088	0.0639	0.0339	0.0161
	3	0.0173	0.0853	0.1720	0.2362	0.2581	0.2397	0.1954	0.1419	0.0923	0.0537
	4	0.0021	0.0213	0.0683	0.1329	0.1936	0.2311	0.2367	0.2128	0.1700	0.1208
	5	0.0002	0.0038	0.0193	0.0532	0.1032	0.1585	0.2039	0.2270	0.2225	0.1934
	6	0.0000	0.0005	0.0040	0.0155	0.0401	0.0792	0.1281	0.1766	0.2124	0.2256
	7	0.0000	0.0000	0.0006	0.0033	0.0115	0.0291	0.0591	0.1009	0.1489	0.1934
	8	0.0000	0.0000	0.0001	0.0005	0.0024	0.0078	0.0199	0.0420	0.0762	0.1208
	9	0.0000	0.0000	0.0000	0.0001	0.0004	0.0015	0.0048	0.0125	0.0277	0.0537
	10	0.0000	0.0000	0.0000	0.0000	0.0000	0.0002	0.0008	0.0025	0.0068	0.0161
	11	0.0000	0.0000	0.0000	0.0000	0.0000	0.0000	0.0001	0.0003	0.0010	0.0029
	12	0.0000	0.0000	0.0000	0.0000	0.0000	0.0000	0.0000	0.0000	0.0001	0.0002
15	0	0.4633	0.2059	0.0874	0.0352	0.0134	0.0047	0.0016	0.0005	0.0001	0.0000
	1	0.3658	0.3432	0.2312	0.1319	0.0668	0.0305	0.0126	0.0047	0.0016	0.0005
	2	0.1348	0.2669	0.2856	0.2309	0.1559	0.0916	0.0476	0.0219	0.0090	0.0032

Binomial Probabilities (*Continued*)

		p									
n	*x*	0.05	0.10	0.15	0.20	0.25	0.30	0.35	0.40	0.45	0.50
	3	0.0307	0.1285	0.2184	0.2501	0.2252	0.1700	0.1110	0.0634	0.0318	0.0139
	4	0.0049	0.0428	0.1156	0.1876	0.2252	0.2186	0.1792	0.1268	0.0780	0.0417
	5	0.0006	0.0105	0.0449	0.1032	0.1651	0.2061	0.2123	0.1859	0.1404	0.0916
	6	0.0000	0.0019	0.0132	0.0430	0.0917	0.1472	0.1906	0.2066	0.1914	0.1527
	7	0.0000	0.0003	0.0030	0.0138	0.0393	0.0811	0.1319	0.1771	0.2013	0.1964
	8	0.0000	0.0000	0.0005	0.0035	0.0131	0.0348	0.0710	0.1181	0.1647	0.1964
	9	0.0000	0.0000	0.0001	0.0007	0.0034	0.0116	0.0298	0.0612	0.1048	0.1527
	10	0.0000	0.0000	0.0000	0.0001	0.0007	0.0030	0.0096	0.0245	0.0515	0.0916
	11	0.0000	0.0000	0.0000	0.0000	0.0001	0.0006	0.0024	0.0074	0.0191	0.0417
	12	0.0000	0.0000	0.0000	0.0000	0.0000	0.0001	0.0004	0.0016	0.0052	0.0139
	13	0.0000	0.0000	0.0000	0.0000	0.0000	0.0000	0.0001	0.0003	0.0010	0.0032
	14	0.0000	0.0000	0.0000	0.0000	0.0000	0.0000	0.0000	0.0000	0.0001	0.0005
	15	0.0000	0.0000	0.0000	0.0000	0.0000	0.0000	0.0000	0.0000	0.0000	0.0000
18	0	0.3972	0.1501	0.0536	0.0180	0.0056	0.0016	0.0004	0.0001	0.0000	0.0000
	1	0.3763	0.3002	0.1704	0.0811	0.0338	0.0126	0.0042	0.0012	0.0003	0.0001
	2	0.1683	0.2835	0.2556	0.1723	0.0958	0.0458	0.0190	0.0069	0.0022	0.0006
	3	0.0473	0.1680	0.2406	0.2297	0.1704	0.1046	0.0547	0.0246	0.0095	0.0031
	4	0.0093	0.0700	0.1592	0.2153	0.2130	0.1681	0.1104	0.0614	0.0291	0.0117
	5	0.0014	0.0218	0.0787	0.1507	0.1988	0.2017	0.1664	0.1146	0.0666	0.0327
	6	0.0002	0.0052	0.0301	0.0816	0.1436	0.1873	0.1941	0.1655	0.1181	0.0708
	7	0.0000	0.0010	0.0091	0.0350	0.0820	0.1376	0.1792	0.1892	0.1657	0.1214
	8	0.0000	0.0002	0.0022	0.0120	0.0376	0.0811	0.1327	0.1734	0.1864	0.1669
	9	0.0000	0.0000	0.0004	0.0033	0.0139	0.0386	0.0794	0.1284	0.1694	0.1855
	10	0.0000	0.0000	0.0001	0.0008	0.0042	0.0149	0.0385	0.0771	0.1248	0.1669
	11	0.0000	0.0000	0.0000	0.0001	0.0010	0.0046	0.0151	0.0374	0.0742	0.1214
	12	0.0000	0.0000	0.0000	0.0000	0.0002	0.0012	0.0047	0.0145	0.0354	0.0708
	13	0.0000	0.0000	0.0000	0.0000	0.0000	0.0002	0.0012	0.0045	0.0134	0.0327
	14	0.0000	0.0000	0.0000	0.0000	0.0000	0.0000	0.0002	0.0011	0.0039	0.0117
	15	0.0000	0.0000	0.0000	0.0000	0.0000	0.0000	0.0000	0.0002	0.0009	0.0031
	16	0.0000	0.0000	0.0000	0.0000	0.0000	0.0000	0.0000	0.0000	0.0001	0.0006
	17	0.0000	0.0000	0.0000	0.0000	0.0000	0.0000	0.0000	0.0000	0.0000	0.0001
	18	0.0000	0.0000	0.0000	0.0000	0.0000	0.0000	0.0000	0.0000	0.0000	0.0000
20	0	0.3585	0.1216	0.0388	0.0115	0.0032	0.0008	0.0002	0.0000	0.0000	0.0000
	1	0.3774	0.2702	0.1368	0.0576	0.0211	0.0068	0.0020	0.0005	0.0001	0.0000
	2	0.1887	0.2852	0.2293	0.1369	0.0669	0.0278	0.0100	0.0031	0.0008	0.0002
	3	0.0596	0.1901	0.2428	0.2054	0.1339	0.0716	0.0323	0.0123	0.0040	0.0011
	4	0.0133	0.0898	0.1821	0.2182	0.1897	0.1304	0.0738	0.0350	0.0139	0.0046
	5	0.0022	0.0319	0.1028	0.1746	0.2023	0.1789	0.1272	0.0746	0.0365	0.0148
	6	0.0003	0.0089	0.0454	0.1091	0.1686	0.1916	0.1712	0.1244	0.0746	0.0370
	7	0.0000	0.0020	0.0160	0.0545	0.1124	0.1643	0.1844	0.1659	0.1221	0.0739
	8	0.0000	0.0004	0.0046	0.0222	0.0609	0.1144	0.1614	0.1797	0.1623	0.1201
	9	0.0000	0.0001	0.0011	0.0074	0.0271	0.0654	0.1158	0.1597	0.1771	0.1602
	10	0.0000	0.0000	0.0002	0.0020	0.0099	0.0308	0.0686	0.1171	0.1593	0.1762
	11	0.0000	0.0000	0.0000	0.0005	0.0030	0.0120	0.0336	0.0710	0.1185	0.1602
	12	0.0000	0.0000	0.0000	0.0001	0.0008	0.0039	0.0136	0.0355	0.0727	0.1201
	13	0.0000	0.0000	0.0000	0.0000	0.0002	0.0010	0.0045	0.0146	0.0366	0.0739
	14	0.0000	0.0000	0.0000	0.0000	0.0000	0.0002	0.0012	0.0049	0.0150	0.0370

Binomial Probabilities (*Continued*)

n	x	0.05	0.10	0.15	0.20	0.25	0.30	0.35	0.40	0.45	0.50
	15	0.0000	0.0000	0.0000	0.0000	0.0000	0.0000	0.0003	0.0013	0.0049	0.0148
	16	0.0000	0.0000	0.0000	0.0000	0.0000	0.0000	0.0000	0.0003	0.0013	0.0046
	17	0.0000	0.0000	0.0000	0.0000	0.0000	0.0000	0.0000	0.0000	0.0002	0.0011
	18	0.0000	0.0000	0.0000	0.0000	0.0000	0.0000	0.0000	0.0000	0.0000	0.0002
	19	0.0000	0.0000	0.0000	0.0000	0.0000	0.0000	0.0000	0.0000	0.0000	0.0000
	20	0.0000	0.0000	0.0000	0.0000	0.0000	0.0000	0.0000	0.0000	0.0000	0.0000

Binomial Probabilities (*Continued*)

		p								
n	*x*	0.55	0.60	0.65	0.70	0.75	0.80	0.85	0.90	0.95
2	0	0.2025	0.1600	0.1225	0.0900	0.0625	0.0400	0.0225	0.0100	0.0025
	1	0.4950	0.4800	0.4550	0.4200	0.3750	0.3200	0.2550	0.1800	0.0950
	2	0.3025	0.3600	0.4225	0.4900	0.5625	0.6400	0.7225	0.8100	0.9025
3	0	0.0911	0.0640	0.0429	0.0270	0.0156	0.0080	0.0034	0.0010	0.0001
	1	0.3341	0.2880	0.2389	0.1890	0.1406	0.0960	0.0574	0.0270	0.0071
	2	0.4084	0.4320	0.4436	0.4410	0.4219	0.3840	0.3251	0.2430	0.1354
	3	0.1664	0.2160	0.2746	0.3430	0.4219	0.5120	0.6141	0.7290	0.8574
4	0	0.0410	0.0256	0.0150	0.0081	0.0039	0.0016	0.0005	0.0001	0.0000
	1	0.2005	0.1536	0.1115	0.0756	0.0469	0.0256	0.0115	0.0036	0.0005
	2	0.3675	0.3456	0.3105	0.2646	0.2109	0.1536	0.0975	0.0486	0.0135
	3	0.2995	0.3456	0.3845	0.4116	0.4219	0.4096	0.3685	0.2916	0.1715
	4	0.0915	0.1296	0.1785	0.2401	0.3164	0.4096	0.5220	0.6561	0.8145
5	0	0.0185	0.0102	0.0053	0.0024	0.0010	0.0003	0.0001	0.0000	0.0000
	1	0.1128	0.0768	0.0488	0.0284	0.0146	0.0064	0.0022	0.0005	0.0000
	2	0.2757	0.2304	0.1811	0.1323	0.0879	0.0512	0.0244	0.0081	0.0011
	3	0.3369	0.3456	0.3364	0.3087	0.2637	0.2048	0.1382	0.0729	0.0214
	4	0.2059	0.2592	0.3124	0.3601	0.3955	0.4096	0.3915	0.3281	0.2036
	5	0.0503	0.0778	0.1160	0.1681	0.2373	0.3277	0.4437	0.5905	0.7738
6	0	0.0083	0.0041	0.0018	0.0007	0.0002	0.0001	0.0000	0.0000	0.0000
	1	0.0609	0.0369	0.0205	0.0102	0.0044	0.0015	0.0004	0.0001	0.0000
	2	0.1861	0.1382	0.0951	0.0595	0.0330	0.0154	0.0055	0.0012	0.0001
	3	0.3032	0.2765	0.2355	0.1852	0.1318	0.0819	0.0415	0.0146	0.0021
	4	0.2780	0.3110	0.3280	0.3241	0.2966	0.2458	0.1762	0.0984	0.0305
	5	0.1359	0.1866	0.2437	0.3025	0.3560	0.3932	0.3993	0.3543	0.2321
	6	0.0277	0.0467	0.0754	0.1176	0.1780	0.2621	0.3771	0.5314	0.7351
7	0	0.0037	0.0016	0.0006	0.0002	0.0001	0.0000	0.0000	0.0000	0.0000
	1	0.0320	0.0172	0.0084	0.0036	0.0013	0.0004	0.0001	0.0000	0.0000
	2	0.1172	0.0774	0.0466	0.0250	0.0115	0.0043	0.0012	0.0002	0.0000
	3	0.2388	0.1935	0.1442	0.0972	0.0577	0.0287	0.0109	0.0026	0.0002
	4	0.2918	0.2903	0.2679	0.2269	0.1730	0.1147	0.0617	0.0230	0.0036
	5	0.2140	0.2613	0.2985	0.3177	0.3115	0.2753	0.2097	0.1240	0.0406
	6	0.0872	0.1306	0.1848	0.2471	0.3115	0.3670	0.3960	0.3720	0.2573
	7	0.0152	0.0280	0.0490	0.0824	0.1335	0.2097	0.3206	0.4783	0.6983
8	0	0.0017	0.0007	0.0002	0.0001	0.0000	0.0000	0.0000	0.0000	0.0000
	1	0.0164	0.0079	0.0033	0.0012	0.0004	0.0001	0.0000	0.0000	0.0000
	2	0.0703	0.0413	0.0217	0.0100	0.0038	0.0011	0.0002	0.0000	0.0000
	3	0.1719	0.1239	0.0808	0.0467	0.0231	0.0092	0.0026	0.0004	0.0000
	4	0.2627	0.2322	0.1875	0.1361	0.0865	0.0459	0.0185	0.0046	0.0004
	5	0.2568	0.2787	0.2786	0.2541	0.2076	0.1468	0.0839	0.0331	0.0054
	6	0.1569	0.2090	0.2587	0.2965	0.3115	0.2936	0.2376	0.1488	0.0515
	7	0.0548	0.0896	0.1373	0.1977	0.2670	0.3355	0.3847	0.3826	0.2793
	8	0.0084	0.0168	0.0319	0.0576	0.1001	0.1678	0.2725	0.4305	0.6634

Binomial Probabilities (*Continued*)

		p								
n	*x*	0.55	0.60	0.65	0.70	0.75	0.80	0.85	0.90	0.95
9	0	0.0008	0.0003	0.0001	0.0000	0.0000	0.0000	0.0000	0.0000	0.0000
	1	0.0083	0.0035	0.0013	0.0004	0.0001	0.0000	0.0000	0.0000	0.0000
	2	0.0407	0.0212	0.0098	0.0039	0.0012	0.0003	0.0000	0.0000	0.0000
	3	0.1160	0.0743	0.0424	0.0210	0.0087	0.0028	0.0006	0.0001	0.0000
	4	0.2128	0.1672	0.1181	0.0735	0.0389	0.0165	0.0050	0.0008	0.0000
	5	0.2600	0.2508	0.2194	0.1715	0.1168	0.0661	0.0283	0.0074	0.0006
	6	0.2119	0.2508	0.2716	0.2668	0.2336	0.1762	0.1069	0.0446	0.0077
	7	0.1110	0.1612	0.2162	0.2668	0.3003	0.3020	0.2597	0.1722	0.0629
	8	0.0339	0.0605	0.1004	0.1556	0.2253	0.3020	0.3679	0.3874	0.2985
	9	0.0046	0.0101	0.0207	0.0404	0.0751	0.1342	0.2316	0.3874	0.6302
10	0	0.0003	0.0001	0.0000	0.0000	0.0000	0.0000	0.0000	0.0000	0.0000
	1	0.0042	0.0016	0.0005	0.0001	0.0000	0.0000	0.0000	0.0000	0.0000
	2	0.0229	0.0106	0.0043	0.0014	0.0004	0.0001	0.0000	0.0000	0.0000
	3	0.0746	0.0425	0.0212	0.0090	0.0031	0.0008	0.0001	0.0000	0.0000
	4	0.1596	0.1115	0.0689	0.0368	0.0162	0.0055	0.0012	0.0001	0.0000
	5	0.2340	0.2007	0.1536	0.1029	0.0584	0.0264	0.0085	0.0015	0.0001
	6	0.2384	0.2508	0.2377	0.2001	0.1460	0.0881	0.0401	0.0112	0.0010
	7	0.1665	0.2150	0.2522	0.2668	0.2503	0.2013	0.1298	0.0574	0.0105
	8	0.0763	0.1209	0.1757	0.2335	0.2816	0.3020	0.2759	0.1937	0.0746
	9	0.0207	0.0403	0.0725	0.1211	0.1877	0.2684	0.3474	0.3874	0.3151
	10	0.0025	0.0060	0.0135	0.0282	0.0563	0.1074	0.1969	0.3487	0.5987
12	0	0.0001	0.0000	0.0000	0.0000	0.0000	0.0000	0.0000	0.0000	0.0000
	1	0.0010	0.0003	0.0001	0.0000	0.0000	0.0000	0.0000	0.0000	0.0000
	2	0.0068	0.0025	0.0008	0.0002	0.0000	0.0000	0.0000	0.0000	0.0000
	3	0.0277	0.0125	0.0048	0.0015	0.0004	0.0001	0.0000	0.0000	0.0000
	4	0.0762	0.0420	0.0199	0.0078	0.0024	0.0005	0.0001	0.0000	0.0000
	5	0.1489	0.1009	0.0591	0.0291	0.0115	0.0033	0.0006	0.0000	0.0000
	6	0.2124	0.1766	0.1281	0.0792	0.0401	0.0155	0.0040	0.0005	0.0000
	7	0.2225	0.2270	0.2039	0.1585	0.1032	0.0532	0.0193	0.0038	0.0002
	8	0.1700	0.2128	0.2367	0.2311	0.1936	0.1329	0.0683	0.0213	0.0021
	9	0.0923	0.1419	0.1954	0.2397	0.2581	0.2362	0.1720	0.0852	0.0173
	10	0.0339	0.0639	0.1088	0.1678	0.2323	0.2835	0.2924	0.2301	0.0988
	11	0.0075	0.0174	0.0368	0.0712	0.1267	0.2062	0.3012	0.3766	0.3413
	12	0.0008	0.0022	0.0057	0.0138	0.0317	0.0687	0.1422	0.2824	0.5404
15	0	0.0000	0.0000	0.0000	0.0000	0.0000	0.0000	0.0000	0.0000	0.0000
	1	0.0001	0.0000	0.0000	0.0000	0.0000	0.0000	0.0000	0.0000	0.0000
	2	0.0010	0.0003	0.0001	0.0000	0.0000	0.0000	0.0000	0.0000	0.0000
	3	0.0052	0.0016	0.0004	0.0001	0.0000	0.0000	0.0000	0.0000	0.0000
	4	0.0191	0.0074	0.0024	0.0006	0.0001	0.0000	0.0000	0.0000	0.0000
	5	0.0515	0.0245	0.0096	0.0030	0.0007	0.0001	0.0000	0.0000	0.0000
	6	0.1048	0.0612	0.0298	0.0116	0.0034	0.0007	0.0001	0.0000	0.0000
	7	0.1647	0.1181	0.0710	0.0348	0.0131	0.0035	0.0005	0.0000	0.0000
	8	0.2013	0.1771	0.1319	0.0811	0.0393	0.0138	0.0030	0.0003	0.0000
	9	0.1914	0.2066	0.1906	0.1472	0.0917	0.0430	0.0132	0.0019	0.0000
	10	0.1404	0.1859	0.2123	0.2061	0.1651	0.1032	0.0449	0.0105	0.0006
	11	0.0780	0.1268	0.1792	0.2186	0.2252	0.1876	0.1156	0.0428	0.0049

Binomial Probabilities (*Continued*)

		p								
n	*x*	0.55	0.60	0.65	0.70	0.75	0.80	0.85	0.90	0.95
	12	0.0318	0.0634	0.1110	0.1700	0.2252	0.2501	0.2184	0.1285	0.0307
	13	0.0090	0.0219	0.0476	0.0916	0.1559	0.2309	0.2856	0.2669	0.1348
	14	0.0016	0.0047	0.0126	0.0305	0.0668	0.1319	0.2312	0.3432	0.3658
	15	0.0001	0.0005	0.0016	0.0047	0.0134	0.0352	0.0874	0.2059	0.4633
18	0	0.0000	0.0000	0.0000	0.0000	0.0000	0.0000	0.0000	0.0000	0.0000
	1	0.0000	0.0000	0.0000	0.0000	0.0000	0.0000	0.0000	0.0000	0.0000
	2	0.0001	0.0000	0.0000	0.0000	0.0000	0.0000	0.0000	0.0000	0.0000
	3	0.0009	0.0002	0.0000	0.0000	0.0000	0.0000	0.0000	0.0000	0.0000
	4	0.0039	0.0011	0.0002	0.0000	0.0000	0.0000	0.0000	0.0000	0.0000
	5	0.0134	0.0045	0.0012	0.0002	0.0000	0.0000	0.0000	0.0000	0.0000
	6	0.0354	0.0145	0.0047	0.0012	0.0002	0.0000	0.0000	0.0000	0.0000
	7	0.0742	0.0374	0.0151	0.0046	0.0010	0.0001	0.0000	0.0000	0.0000
	8	0.1248	0.0771	0.0385	0.0149	0.0042	0.0008	0.0001	0.0000	0.0000
	9	0.1694	0.1284	0.0794	0.0386	0.0139	0.0033	0.0004	0.0000	0.0000
	10	0.1864	0.1734	0.1327	0.0811	0.0376	0.0120	0.0022	0.0002	0.0000
	11	0.1657	0.1892	0.1792	0.1376	0.0820	0.0350	0.0091	0.0010	0.0000
	12	0.1181	0.1655	0.1941	0.1873	0.1436	0.0816	0.0301	0.0052	0.0002
	13	0.0666	0.1146	0.1664	0.2017	0.1988	0.1507	0.0787	0.0218	0.0014
	14	0.0291	0.0614	0.1104	0.1681	0.2130	0.2153	0.1592	0.0700	0.0093
	15	0.0095	0.0246	0.0547	0.1046	0.1704	0.2297	0.2406	0.1680	0.0473
	16	0.0022	0.0069	0.0190	0.0458	0.0958	0.1723	0.2556	0.2835	0.1683
	17	0.0003	0.0012	0.0042	0.0126	0.0338	0.0811	0.1704	0.3002	0.3763
	18	0.0000	0.0001	0.0004	0.0016	0.0056	0.0180	0.0536	0.1501	0.3972
20	0	0.0000	0.0000	0.0000	0.0000	0.0000	0.0000	0.0000	0.0000	0.0000
	1	0.0000	0.0000	0.0000	0.0000	0.0000	0.0000	0.0000	0.0000	0.0000
	2	0.0000	0.0000	0.0000	0.0000	0.0000	0.0000	0.0000	0.0000	0.0000
	3	0.0002	0.0000	0.0000	0.0000	0.0000	0.0000	0.0000	0.0000	0.0000
	4	0.0013	0.0003	0.0000	0.0000	0.0000	0.0000	0.0000	0.0000	0.0000
	5	0.0049	0.0013	0.0003	0.0000	0.0000	0.0000	0.0000	0.0000	0.0000
	6	0.0150	0.0049	0.0012	0.0002	0.0000	0.0000	0.0000	0.0000	0.0000
	7	0.0366	0.0146	0.0045	0.0010	0.0002	0.0000	0.0000	0.0000	0.0000
	8	0.0727	0.0355	0.0136	0.0039	0.0008	0.0001	0.0000	0.0000	0.0000
	9	0.1185	0.0710	0.0336	0.0120	0.0030	0.0005	0.0000	0.0000	0.0000
	10	0.1593	0.1171	0.0686	0.0308	0.0099	0.0020	0.0002	0.0000	0.0000
	11	0.1771	0.1597	0.1158	0.0654	0.0271	0.0074	0.0011	0.0001	0.0000
	12	0.1623	0.1797	0.1614	0.1144	0.0609	0.0222	0.0046	0.0004	0.0000
	13	0.1221	0.1659	0.1844	0.1643	0.1124	0.0545	0.0160	0.0020	0.0000
	14	0.0746	0.1244	0.1712	0.1916	0.1686	0.1091	0.0454	0.0089	0.0003
	15	0.0365	0.0746	0.1272	0.1789	0.2023	0.1746	0.1028	0.0319	0.0022
	16	0.0139	0.0350	0.0738	0.1304	0.1897	0.2182	0.1821	0.0898	0.0133
	17	0.0040	0.0123	0.0323	0.0716	0.1339	0.2054	0.2428	0.1901	0.0596
	18	0.0008	0.0031	0.0100	0.0278	0.0669	0.1369	0.2293	0.2852	0.1887
	19	0.0001	0.0005	0.0020	0.0068	0.0211	0.0576	0.1368	0.2702	0.3774
	20	0.0000	0.0000	0.0002	0.0008	0.0032	0.0115	0.0388	0.1216	0.3585

Appendix B Poisson Probabilities

Entries in the following table give the probability of x occurrences for a Poisson process with a mean λ. For example, when $\lambda = 2.5$, the probability of $x = 4$ occurrences is 0.1336.

	λ									
x	0.1	0.2	0.3	0.4	0.5	0.6	0.7	0.8	0.9	1.0
0	0.9048	0.8187	0.7408	0.6703	0.6065	0.5488	0.4966	0.4493	0.4066	0.3679
1	0.0905	0.1637	0.2222	0.2681	0.3033	0.3293	0.3476	0.3595	0.3659	0.3679
2	0.0045	0.0164	0.0333	0.0536	0.0758	0.0988	0.1217	0.1438	0.1647	0.1839
3	0.0002	0.0011	0.0033	0.0072	0.0126	0.0198	0.0284	0.0383	0.0494	0.0613
4	0.0000	0.0001	0.0002	0.0007	0.0016	0.0030	0.0050	0.0077	0.0111	0.0153
5	0.0000	0.0000	0.0000	0.0001	0.0002	0.0004	0.0007	0.0012	0.0020	0.0031
6	0.0000	0.0000	0.0000	0.0000	0.0000	0.0000	0.0001	0.0002	0.0003	0.0005
7	0.0000	0.0000	0.0000	0.0000	0.0000	0.0000	0.0000	0.0000	0.0000	0.0001

	λ									
x	1.1	1.2	1.3	1.4	1.5	1.6	1.7	1.8	1.9	2.0
0	0.3329	0.3012	0.2725	0.2466	0.2231	0.2019	0.1827	0.1653	0.1496	0.1353
1	0.3662	0.3614	0.3543	0.3452	0.3347	0.3230	0.3106	0.2975	0.2842	0.2707
2	0.2014	0.2169	0.2303	0.2417	0.2510	0.2584	0.2640	0.2678	0.2700	0.2707
3	0.0738	0.0867	0.0998	0.1128	0.1255	0.1378	0.1496	0.1607	0.1710	0.1804
4	0.0203	0.0260	0.0324	0.0395	0.0471	0.0551	0.0636	0.0723	0.0812	0.0902
5	0.0045	0.0062	0.0084	0.0111	0.0141	0.0176	0.0216	0.0260	0.0309	0.0361
6	0.0008	0.0012	0.0018	0.0026	0.0035	0.0047	0.0061	0.0078	0.0098	0.0120
7	0.0001	0.0002	0.0003	0.0005	0.0008	0.0011	0.0015	0.0020	0.0027	0.0034
8	0.0000	0.0000	0.0001	0.0001	0.0001	0.0002	0.0003	0.0005	0.0006	0.0009
9	0.0000	0.0000	0.0000	0.0000	0.0000	0.0000	0.0001	0.0001	0.0001	0.0002

	λ									
x	2.1	2.2	2.3	2.4	2.5	2.6	2.7	2.8	2.9	3.0
0	0.1225	0.1108	0.1003	0.0907	0.0821	0.0743	0.0672	0.0608	0.0550	0.0498
1	0.2572	0.2438	0.2306	0.2177	0.2052	0.1931	0.1815	0.1703	0.1596	0.1494
2	0.2700	0.2681	0.2652	0.2613	0.2565	0.2510	0.2450	0.2384	0.2314	0.2240
3	0.1890	0.1966	0.2033	0.2090	0.2138	0.2176	0.2205	0.2225	0.2237	0.2240
4	0.0992	0.1082	0.1169	0.1254	0.1336	0.1414	0.1488	0.1557	0.1622	0.1680
5	0.0417	0.0476	0.0538	0.0602	0.0668	0.0735	0.0804	0.0872	0.0940	0.1008
6	0.0146	0.0174	0.0206	0.0241	0.0278	0.0319	0.0362	0.0407	0.0455	0.0540
7	0.0044	0.0055	0.0068	0.0083	0.0099	0.0118	0.0139	0.0163	0.0188	0.0216

Poisson Probabilities (*Continued*)

	λ									
x	2.1	2.2	2.3	2.4	2.5	2.6	2.7	2.8	2.9	3.0
8	0.0011	0.0015	0.0019	0.0025	0.0031	0.0038	0.0047	0.0057	0.0068	0.0081
9	0.0003	0.0004	0.0005	0.0007	0.0009	0.0011	0.0014	0.0018	0.0022	0.0027
10	0.0001	0.0001	0.0001	0.0002	0.0002	0.0003	0.0004	0.0005	0.0006	0.0008
11	0.0000	0.0000	0.0000	0.0000	0.0000	0.0001	0.0001	0.0001	0.0002	0.0002
12	0.0000	0.0000	0.0000	0.0000	0.0000	0.0000	0.0000	0.0000	0.0000	0.0001

	λ									
x	3.1	3.2	3.3	3.4	3.5	3.6	3.7	3.8	3.9	4.0
0	0.0450	0.0408	0.0369	0.0344	0.0302	0.0273	0.0247	0.0224	0.0202	0.0183
1	0.1397	0.1304	0.1217	0.1135	0.1057	0.0984	0.0915	0.0850	0.0789	0.0733
2	0.2165	0.2087	0.2008	0.1929	0.1850	0.1771	0.1692	0.1615	0.1539	0.1465
3	0.2237	0.2226	0.2209	0.2186	0.2158	0.2125	0.2087	0.2046	0.2001	0.1954
4	0.1734	0.1781	0.1823	0.1858	0.1888	0.1912	0.1931	0.1944	0.1951	0.1954
5	0.1075	0.1140	0.1203	0.1264	0.1322	0.1377	0.1429	0.1477	0.1522	0.1563
6	0.0555	0.0608	0.0662	0.0716	0.0771	0.0826	0.0881	0.0936	0.0989	0.1042
7	0.0246	0.0278	0.0312	0.0348	0.0385	0.0425	0.0466	0.0508	0.0551	0.0595
8	0.0095	0.0111	0.0129	0.0148	0.0169	0.0191	0.0215	0.0241	0.0269	0.0298
9	0.0033	0.0040	0.0047	0.0056	0.0066	0.0076	0.0089	0.0102	0.0116	0.0132
10	0.0010	0.0013	0.0016	0.0019	0.0023	0.0028	0.0033	0.0039	0.0045	0.0053
11	0.0003	0.0004	0.0005	0.0006	0.0007	0.0009	0.0011	0.0013	0.0016	0.0019
12	0.0001	0.0001	0.0001	0.0002	0.0002	0.0003	0.0003	0.0004	0.0005	0.0006
13	0.0000	0.0000	0.0000	0.0000	0.0001	0.0001	0.0001	0.0001	0.0002	0.0002
14	0.0000	0.0000	0.0000	0.0000	0.0000	0.0000	0.0000	0.0000	0.0000	0.0001

	λ									
x	4.1	4.2	4.3	4.4	4.5	4.6	4.7	4.8	4.9	5.0
0	0.0166	0.0150	0.0136	0.0123	0.0111	0.0101	0.0091	0.0082	0.0074	0.0067
1	0.0679	0.0630	0.0583	0.0540	0.0500	0.0462	0.0427	0.0395	0.0365	0.0337
2	0.1393	0.1323	0.1254	0.1188	0.1125	0.1063	0.1005	0.0948	0.0894	0.0842
3	0.1904	0.1852	0.1798	0.1743	0.1687	0.1631	0.1574	0.1517	0.1460	0.1404
4	0.1951	0.1944	0.1933	0.1917	0.1898	0.1875	0.1849	0.1820	0.1789	0.1755
5	0.1600	0.1633	0.1662	0.1687	0.1708	0.1725	0.1738	0.1747	0.1753	0.1755
6	0.1093	0.1143	0.1191	0.1237	0.1281	0.1323	0.1362	0.1398	0.1432	0.1462
7	0.0640	0.0686	0.0732	0.0778	0.0824	0.0869	0.0914	0.0959	0.1002	0.1044
8	0.0328	0.0360	0.0393	0.0428	0.0463	0.0500	0.0537	0.0575	0.0614	0.0653
9	0.0150	0.0168	0.0188	0.0209	0.0232	0.0255	0.0280	0.0307	0.0334	0.0363
10	0.0061	0.0071	0.0081	0.0092	0.0104	0.0118	0.0132	0.0147	0.0164	0.0181
11	0.0023	0.0027	0.0032	0.0037	0.0043	0.0049	0.0056	0.0064	0.0073	0.0082
12	0.0008	0.0009	0.0011	0.0014	0.0016	0.0019	0.0022	0.0026	0.0030	0.0034
13	0.0002	0.0003	0.0004	0.0005	0.0006	0.0007	0.0008	0.0009	0.0011	0.0013
14	0.0001	0.0001	0.0001	0.0001	0.0002	0.0002	0.0003	0.0003	0.0004	0.0005
15	0.0000	0.0000	0.0000	0.0000	0.0001	0.0001	0.0001	0.0001	0.0001	0.0002

Binomial Probabilities (*Continued*)

	λ									
x	5.1	5.2	5.3	5.4	5.5	5.6	5.7	5.8	5.9	6.0
0	0.0061	0.0055	0.0050	0.0045	0.0041	0.0037	0.0033	0.0030	0.0027	0.0025
1	0.0311	0.0287	0.0265	0.0244	0.0225	0.0207	0.0191	0.0176	0.0162	0.0149
2	0.0793	0.0746	0.0701	0.0659	0.0618	0.0580	0.0544	0.0509	0.0477	0.0446
3	0.1348	0.1293	0.1239	0.1185	0.1133	0.1082	0.1033	0.0985	0.0938	0.0892
4	0.1719	0.1681	0.1641	0.1600	0.1558	0.1515	0.1472	0.1428	0.1383	0.1339
5	0.1753	0.1748	0.1740	0.1728	0.1714	0.1697	0.1678	0.1656	0.1632	0.1606
6	0.1490	0.1515	0.1537	0.1555	0.1571	0.1587	0.1594	0.1601	0.1605	0.1606
7	0.1086	0.1125	0.1163	0.1200	0.1234	0.1267	0.1298	0.1326	0.1353	0.1377
8	0.0692	0.0731	0.0771	0.0810	0.0849	0.0887	0.0925	0.0962	0.0998	0.1033
9	0.0392	0.0423	0.0454	0.0486	0.0519	0.0552	0.0586	0.0620	0.0654	0.0688
10	0.0200	0.0220	0.0241	0.0262	0.0285	0.0309	0.0334	0.0359	0.0386	0.0413
11	0.0093	0.0104	0.0116	0.0129	0.0143	0.0157	0.0173	0.0190	0.0207	0.0225
12	0.0039	0.0045	0.0051	0.0058	0.0065	0.0073	0.0082	0.0092	0.0102	0.0113
13	0.0015	0.0018	0.0021	0.0024	0.0028	0.0032	0.0036	0.0041	0.0046	0.0052
14	0.0006	0.0007	0.0008	0.0009	0.0011	0.0013	0.0015	0.0017	0.0019	0.0022
15	0.0002	0.0002	0.0003	0.0003	0.0004	0.0005	0.0006	0.0007	0.0008	0.0009
16	0.0001	0.0001	0.0001	0.0001	0.0001	0.0002	0.0002	0.0002	0.0003	0.0003
17	0.0000	0.0000	0.0000	0.0000	0.0000	0.0001	0.0001	0.0001	0.0001	0.0001

	λ									
x	6.1	6.2	6.3	6.4	6.5	6.6	6.7	6.8	6.9	7.0
0	0.0022	0.0020	0.0018	0.0017	0.0015	0.0014	0.0012	0.0011	0.0010	0.0009
1	0.0137	0.0126	0.0116	0.0106	0.0098	0.0090	0.0082	0.0076	0.0070	0.0064
2	0.0417	0.0390	0.0364	0.0340	0.0318	0.0296	0.0276	0.0258	0.0240	0.0223
3	0.0848	0.0806	0.0765	0.0726	0.0688	0.0652	0.0617	0.0584	0.0552	0.0521
4	0.1294	0.1249	0.1205	0.1162	0.1118	0.1076	0.1034	0.0992	0.0952	0.0912
5	0.1579	0.1549	0.1519	0.1487	0.1454	0.1420	0.1385	0.1349	0.1314	0.1277
6	0.1605	0.1601	0.1595	0.1586	0.1575	0.1562	0.1546	0.1529	0.1511	0.1490
7	0.1399	0.1418	0.1435	0.1450	0.1462	0.1472	0.1480	0.1486	0.1489	0.1490
8	0.1066	0.1099	0.1130	0.1160	0.1188	0.1215	0.1240	0.1263	0.1284	0.1304
9	0.0723	0.0757	0.0791	0.0825	0.0858	0.0891	0.0923	0.0954	0.0985	0.1014
10	0.0441	0.0469	0.0498	0.0528	0.0558	0.0588	0.0618	0.0649	0.0679	0.0710
11	0.0245	0.0265	0.0285	0.0307	0.0330	0.0353	0.0377	0.0401	0.0426	0.0452
12	0.0124	0.0137	0.0150	0.0164	0.0179	0.0194	0.0210	0.0227	0.0245	0.0264
13	0.0058	0.0065	0.0073	0.0081	0.0089	0.0098	0.0108	0.0119	0.0130	0.0142
14	0.0025	0.0029	0.0033	0.0037	0.0041	0.0046	0.0052	0.0058	0.0064	0.0071
15	0.0010	0.0012	0.0014	0.0016	0.0018	0.0020	0.0023	0.0025	0.0029	0.0033
16	0.0004	0.0005	0.0005	0.0006	0.0007	0.0008	0.0010	0.0011	0.0013	0.0014
17	0.0001	0.0002	0.0002	0.0002	0.0003	0.0003	0.0004	0.0004	0.0005	0.0006
18	0.0000	0.0001	0.0001	0.0001	0.0001	0.0001	0.0001	0.0002	0.0002	0.0002
19	0.0000	0.0000	0.0000	0.0000	0.0000	0.0000	0.0000	0.0001	0.0001	0.0001

Poisson Probabilities (*Continued*)

	λ									
x	7.1	7.2	7.3	7.4	7.5	7.6	7.7	7.8	7.9	8.0
0	0.0008	0.0007	0.0007	0.0006	0.0006	0.0005	0.0005	0.0004	0.0004	0.0003
1	0.0059	0.0054	0.0049	0.0045	0.0041	0.0038	0.0035	0.0032	0.0029	0.0027
2	0.0208	0.0194	0.0180	0.0167	0.0156	0.0145	0.0134	0.0125	0.0116	0.0107
3	0.0492	0.0464	0.0438	0.0413	0.0389	0.0366	0.0345	0.0324	0.0305	0.0286
4	0.0874	0.0836	0.0799	0.0764	0.0729	0.0696	0.0663	0.0632	0.0602	0.0573
5	0.1241	0.1204	0.1167	0.1130	0.1094	0.1057	0.1021	0.0986	0.0951	0.0916
6	0.1468	0.1445	0.1420	0.1394	0.1367	0.1339	0.1311	0.1282	0.1252	0.1221
7	0.1489	0.1486	0.1481	0.1474	0.1465	0.1454	0.1442	0.1428	0.1413	0.1396
8	0.1321	0.1337	0.1351	0.1363	0.1373	0.1382	0.1388	0.1392	0.1395	0.1396
9	0.1042	0.1070	0.1096	0.1121	0.1144	0.1167	0.1187	0.1207	0.1224	0.1241
10	0.0740	0.0770	0.0800	0.0829	0.0858	0.0887	0.0914	0.0941	0.0967	0.0993
11	0.0478	0.0504	0.0531	0.0558	0.0585	0.0613	0.0640	0.0667	0.0695	0.0722
12	0.0283	0.0303	0.0323	0.0344	0.0366	0.0388	0.0411	0.0434	0.0457	0.0481
13	0.0154	0.0168	0.0181	0.0196	0.0211	0.0227	0.0243	0.0260	0.0278	0.0296
14	0.0078	0.0086	0.0095	0.0104	0.0113	0.0123	0.0134	0.0145	0.0157	0.0169
15	0.0037	0.0041	0.0046	0.0051	0.0057	0.0062	0.0069	0.0075	0.0083	0.0090
16	0.0016	0.0019	0.0021	0.0024	0.0026	0.0030	0.0033	0.0037	0.0041	0.0045
17	0.0007	0.0008	0.0009	0.0010	0.0012	0.0013	0.0015	0.0017	0.0019	0.0021
18	0.0003	0.0003	0.0004	0.0004	0.0005	0.0006	0.0006	0.0007	0.0008	0.0009
19	0.0001	0.0001	0.0001	0.0002	0.0002	0.0002	0.0003	0.0003	0.0003	0.0004
20	0.0000	0.0000	0.0001	0.0001	0.0001	0.0001	0.0001	0.0001	0.0001	0.0002
21	0.0000	0.0000	0.0000	0.0000	0.0000	0.0000	0.0000	0.0000	0.0001	0.0001

	λ									
x	8.1	8.2	8.3	8.4	8.5	8.6	8.7	8.8	8.9	9.0
0	0.0003	0.0003	0.0002	0.0002	0.0002	0.0002	0.0002	0.0002	0.0001	0.0001
1	0.0025	0.0023	0.0021	0.0019	0.0017	0.0016	0.0014	0.0013	0.0012	0.0011
2	0.0100	0.0092	0.0086	0.0079	0.0074	0.0068	0.0063	0.0058	0.0054	0.0050
3	0.0269	0.0252	0.0237	0.0222	0.0208	0.0195	0.0183	0.0171	0.0160	0.0150
4	0.0544	0.0517	0.0491	0.0466	0.0443	0.0420	0.0398	0.0377	0.0357	0.0337
5	0.0882	0.0849	0.0816	0.0784	0.0752	0.0722	0.0692	0.0663	0.0635	0.0607
6	0.1191	0.1160	0.1128	0.1097	0.1066	0.1034	0.1003	0.0972	0.0941	0.0911
7	0.1378	0.1358	0.1338	0.1317	0.1294	0.1271	0.1247	0.1222	0.1197	0.1171
8	0.1395	0.1392	0.1388	0.1382	0.1375	0.1366	0.1356	0.1344	0.1332	0.1318
9	0.1256	0.1269	0.1280	0.1290	0.1299	0.1306	0.1311	0.1315	0.1317	0.1318
10	0.1017	0.1040	0.1063	0.1084	0.1104	0.1123	0.1140	0.1157	0.1172	0.1186
11	0.0749	0.0776	0.0802	0.0828	0.0853	0.0878	0.0902	0.0925	0.0948	0.0970
12	0.0505	0.0530	0.0555	0.0579	0.0604	0.0629	0.0654	0.0679	0.0703	0.0728
13	0.0315	0.0334	0.0354	0.0374	0.0395	0.0416	0.0438	0.0459	0.0481	0.0504
14	0.0182	0.0196	0.0210	0.0225	0.0240	0.0256	0.0272	0.0289	0.0306	0.0324

Poisson Probabilities (*Continued*)

	λ									
x	8.1	8.2	8.3	8.4	8.5	8.6	8.7	8.8	8.9	9.0
15	0.0098	0.0107	0.0116	0.0126	0.0136	0.0147	0.0158	0.0169	0.0182	0.1094
16	0.0050	0.0055	0.0060	0.0066	0.0072	0.0079	0.0086	0.0093	0.0101	0.0109
17	0.0024	0.0026	0.0029	0.0033	0.0036	0.0040	0.0044	0.0048	0.0053	0.0058
18	0.0011	0.0012	0.0014	0.0015	0.0017	0.0019	0.0021	0.0024	0.0026	0.0029
19	0.0005	0.0005	0.0006	0.0007	0.0008	0.0009	0.0010	0.0011	0.0012	0.0014
20	0.0002	0.0002	0.0002	0.0003	0.0003	0.0004	0.0004	0.0005	0.0005	0.0006
21	0.0001	0.0001	0.0001	0.0001	0.0001	0.0002	0.0002	0.0002	0.0002	0.0003
22	0.0000	0.0000	0.0000	0.0000	0.0001	0.0001	0.0001	0.0001	0.0001	0.0001

	λ									
x	9.1	9.2	9.3	9.4	9.5	9.6	9.7	9.8	9.9	10
0	0.0001	0.0001	0.0001	0.0001	0.0001	0.0001	0.0001	0.0001	0.0001	0.0000
1	0.0010	0.0009	0.0009	0.0008	0.0007	0.0007	0.0006	0.0005	0.0005	0.0005
2	0.0046	0.0043	0.0040	0.0037	0.0034	0.0031	0.0029	0.0027	0.0025	0.0023
3	0.0140	0.0131	0.0123	0.0115	0.0107	0.0100	0.0093	0.0087	0.0081	0.0076
4	0.0319	0.0302	0.0285	0.0269	0.0254	0.0240	0.0226	0.0213	0.0201	0.0189
5	0.0581	0.0555	0.0530	0.0506	0.0483	0.0460	0.0439	0.0418	0.0398	0.0378
6	0.0881	0.0851	0.0822	0.0793	0.0764	0.0736	0.0709	0.0682	0.0656	0.0631
7	0.1145	0.1118	0.1091	0.1064	0.1037	0.1010	0.0982	0.0955	0.0928	0.0901
8	0.1302	0.1286	0.1269	0.1251	0.1232	0.1212	0.1191	0.1170	0.1148	0.1126
9	0.1317	0.1315	0.1311	0.1306	0.1300	0.1293	0.1284	0.1274	0.1263	0.1251
10	0.1198	0.1210	0.1219	0.1228	0.1235	0.1241	0.1245	0.1249	0.1250	0.1251
11	0.0991	0.1012	0.1031	0.1049	0.1067	0.1083	0.1098	0.1112	0.1125	0.1137
12	0.0752	0.0776	0.0799	0.0822	0.0844	0.0866	0.0888	0.0908	0.0928	0.0948
13	0.0526	0.0549	0.0572	0.0594	0.0617	0.0640	0.0662	0.0685	0.0707	0.0729
14	0.0342	0.0361	0.0380	0.0399	0.0419	0.0439	0.0459	0.0479	0.0500	0.0521
15	0.0208	0.0221	0.0235	0.0250	0.0265	0.0281	0.0297	0.0313	0.0330	0.0347
16	0.0118	0.0127	0.0137	0.0147	0.0157	0.0168	0.0180	0.0192	0.0204	0.0217
17	0.0063	0.0069	0.0075	0.0081	0.0088	0.0095	0.0103	0.0111	0.0119	0.0128
18	0.0032	0.0035	0.0039	0.0042	0.0046	0.0051	0.0055	0.0060	0.0065	0.0071
19	0.0015	0.0017	0.0019	0.0021	0.0023	0.0026	0.0028	0.0031	0.0034	0.0027
20	0.0007	0.0008	0.0009	0.0010	0.0011	0.0012	0.0014	0.0015	0.0017	0.0019
21	0.0003	0.0003	0.0004	0.0004	0.0005	0.0006	0.0006	0.0007	0.0008	0.0009
22	0.0001	0.0001	0.0002	0.0002	0.0002	0.0002	0.0003	0.0003	0.0004	0.0004
23	0.0000	0.0001	0.0001	0.0001	0.0001	0.0001	0.0001	0.0001	0.0002	0.0002
24	0.0000	0.0000	0.0000	0.0000	0.0000	0.0000	0.0000	0.0001	0.0001	0.0001

Poisson Probabilities (*Continued*)

	λ									
x	11	12	13	14	15	16	17	18	19	20
0	0.0000	0.0000	0.0000	0.0000	0.0000	0.0000	0.0000	0.0000	0.0000	0.0000
1	0.0002	0.0001	0.0000	0.0000	0.0000	0.0000	0.0000	0.0000	0.0000	0.0000
2	0.0010	0.0004	0.0002	0.0001	0.0000	0.0000	0.0000	0.0000	0.0000	0.0000
3	0.0037	0.0018	0.0008	0.0004	0.0002	0.0001	0.0000	0.0000	0.0000	0.0000
4	0.0102	0.0053	0.0027	0.0013	0.0006	0.0003	0.0001	0.0001	0.0000	0.0000
5	0.0224	0.0127	0.0070	0.0037	0.0019	0.0010	0.0005	0.0002	0.0001	0.0001
6	0.0411	0.0255	0.0152	0.0087	0.0048	0.0026	0.0014	0.0007	0.0004	0.0002
7	0.0646	0.0437	0.0281	0.0174	0.0104	0.0060	0.0034	0.0018	0.0010	0.0005
8	0.0888	0.0655	0.0457	0.0304	0.0194	0.0120	0.0072	0.0042	0.0024	0.0013
9	0.1085	0.0874	0.0661	0.0473	0.0324	0.0213	0.0135	0.0083	0.0050	0.0029
10	0.1194	0.1048	0.0859	0.0663	0.0486	0.0341	0.0230	0.0150	0.0095	0.0058
11	0.1194	0.1144	0.1015	0.0844	0.0663	0.0496	0.0355	0.0245	0.0164	0.0106
12	0.1094	0.1144	0.1099	0.0984	0.0829	0.0661	0.0504	0.0368	0.0259	0.0176
13	0.0926	0.1056	0.1099	0.1060	0.0956	0.0814	0.0658	0.0509	0.0378	0.0271
14	0.0728	0.0905	0.1021	0.1060	0.1024	0.0930	0.0800	0.0655	0.0514	0.0387
15	0.0534	0.0724	0.0885	0.0989	0.1024	0.0992	0.0906	0.0786	0.0650	0.0516
16	0.0367	0.0543	0.0719	0.0866	0.0960	0.0992	0.0963	0.0884	0.0772	0.0646
17	0.0237	0.0383	0.0550	0.0713	0.0847	0.0934	0.0963	0.0936	0.0863	0.0760
18	0.0145	0.0256	0.0397	0.0554	0.0706	0.0830	0.0909	0.0936	0.0911	0.0844
19	0.0084	0.0161	0.0272	0.0409	0.0557	0.0699	0.0814	0.0887	0.0911	0.0888
20	0.0046	0.0097	0.0177	0.0286	0.0418	0.0559	0.0692	0.0798	0.0866	0.0888
21	0.0024	0.0055	0.0109	0.0191	0.0299	0.0426	0.0560	0.0684	0.0783	0.0846
22	0.0012	0.0030	0.0065	0.0121	0.0204	0.0310	0.0433	0.0560	0.0676	0.0769
23	0.0006	0.0016	0.0037	0.0074	0.0133	0.0216	0.0320	0.0438	0.0559	0.0669
24	0.0003	0.0008	0.0020	0.0043	0.0083	0.0144	0.0226	0.0328	0.0442	0.0557
25	0.0001	0.0004	0.0010	0.0024	0.0050	0.0092	0.0154	0.0237	0.0336	0.0446
26	0.0000	0.0002	0.0005	0.0013	0.0029	0.0057	0.0101	0.0164	0.0246	0.0343
27	0.0000	0.0001	0.0002	0.0007	0.0016	0.0034	0.0063	0.0109	0.0173	0.0254
28	0.0000	0.0000	0.0001	0.0003	0.0009	0.0019	0.0038	0.0070	0.0117	0.0181
29	0.0000	0.0000	0.0001	0.0002	0.0004	0.0011	0.0023	0.0044	0.0077	0.0125
30	0.0000	0.0000	0.0000	0.0001	0.0002	0.0006	0.0013	0.0026	0.0049	0.0083
31	0.0000	0.0000	0.0000	0.0000	0.0001	0.0003	0.0007	0.0015	0.0030	0.0054
32	0.0000	0.0000	0.0000	0.0000	0.0001	0.0001	0.0004	0.0009	0.0018	0.0034
33	0.0000	0.0000	0.0000	0.0000	0.0000	0.0001	0.0002	0.0005	0.0010	0.0020
34	0.0000	0.0000	0.0000	0.0000	0.0000	0.0000	0.0001	0.0002	0.0006	0.0012
35	0.0000	0.0000	0.0000	0.0000	0.0000	0.0000	0.0000	0.0001	0.0003	0.0007
36	0.0000	0.0000	0.0000	0.0000	0.0000	0.0000	0.0000	0.0001	0.0002	0.0004
37	0.0000	0.0000	0.0000	0.0000	0.0000	0.0000	0.0000	0.0000	0.0001	0.0002
38	0.0000	0.0000	0.0000	0.0000	0.0000	0.0000	0.0000	0.0000	0.0000	0.0001
39	0.0000	0.0000	0.0000	0.0000	0.0000	0.0000	0.0000	0.0000	0.0000	0.0001

Appendix C Areas for the Standard Normal Distribution

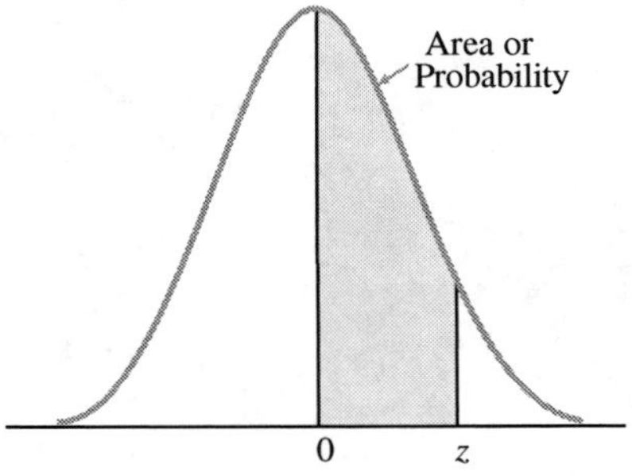

Entries in the following table give the area under the curve between the mean and z standard deviations above the mean. For example, for $z = 1.25$ the area under the curve between the mean and z is 0.3944.

z	**0.00**	**0.01**	**0.02**	**0.03**	**0.04**	**0.05**	**0.06**	**0.07**	**0.08**	**0.09**
0.0	0.0000	0.0040	0.0080	0.0120	0.0160	0.0199	0.0239	0.0279	0.0319	0.0359
0.1	0.0398	0.0438	0.0478	0.0517	0.0557	0.0596	0.0636	0.0675	0.0714	0.0753
0.2	0.0793	0.0832	0.0871	0.0910	0.0948	0.0987	0.1026	0.1064	0.1103	0.1141
0.3	0.1179	0.1217	0.1255	0.1293	0.1331	0.1368	0.1406	0.1443	0.1480	0.1517
0.4	0.1554	0.1591	0.1628	0.1664	0.1700	0.1736	0.1772	0.1808	0.1844	0.1879
0.5	0.1915	0.1950	0.1985	0.2019	0.2054	0.2088	0.2123	0.2157	0.2190	0.2224
0.6	0.2257	0.2291	0.2324	0.2357	0.2389	0.2422	0.2454	0.2486	0.2517	0.2549
0.7	0.2580	0.2611	0.2642	0.2673	0.2704	0.2734	0.2764	0.2794	0.2823	0.2852
0.8	0.2881	0.2910	0.2939	0.2967	0.2995	0.3023	0.3051	0.3078	0.3106	0.3133
0.9	0.3159	0.3186	0.3212	0.3238	0.3264	0.3289	0.3315	0.3340	0.3365	0.3389
1.0	0.3413	0.3438	0.3461	0.3485	0.3508	0.3531	0.3554	0.3577	0.3599	0.3621
1.1	0.3643	0.3665	0.3686	0.3708	0.3729	0.3749	0.3770	0.3790	0.3810	0.3830
1.2	0.3849	0.3869	0.3888	0.3907	0.3925	0.3944	0.3962	0.3980	0.3997	0.4015
1.3	0.4032	0.4049	0.4066	0.4082	0.4099	0.4115	0.4131	0.4147	0.4162	0.4177
1.4	0.4192	0.4207	0.4222	0.4236	0.4251	0.4265	0.4279	0.4292	0.4306	0.4319
1.5	0.4332	0.4345	0.4357	0.4370	0.4382	0.4394	0.4406	0.4418	0.4429	0.4441
1.6	0.4452	0.4463	0.4474	0.4484	0.4495	0.4505	0.4515	0.4525	0.4535	0.4545
1.7	0.4554	0.4564	0.4573	0.4582	0.4591	0.4599	0.4608	0.4616	0.4625	0.4633
1.8	0.4641	0.4649	0.4656	0.4664	0.4671	0.4678	0.4686	0.4693	0.4699	0.4706
1.9	0.4713	0.4719	0.4726	0.4732	0.4738	0.4744	0.4750	0.4756	0.4761	0.4767
2.0	0.4772	0.4778	0.4783	0.4788	0.4793	0.4798	0.4803	0.4808	0.4812	0.4817
2.1	0.4821	0.4826	0.4830	0.4834	0.4838	0.4842	0.4846	0.4850	0.4854	0.4857
2.2	0.4861	0.4864	0.4868	0.4871	0.4875	0.4878	0.4881	0.4884	0.4887	0.4890
2.3	0.4893	0.4896	0.4898	0.4901	0.4904	0.4906	0.4909	0.4911	0.4913	0.4916
2.4	0.4918	0.4920	0.4922	0.4925	0.4927	0.4929	0.4931	0.4932	0.4934	0.4936
2.5	0.4938	0.4940	0.4941	0.4943	0.4945	0.4946	0.4948	0.4949	0.4951	0.4952
2.6	0.4953	0.4955	0.4956	0.4957	0.4959	0.4960	0.4961	0.4962	0.4963	0.4964
2.7	0.4965	0.4966	0.4967	0.4968	0.4969	0.4970	0.4971	0.4972	0.4973	0.4974
2.8	0.4974	0.4975	0.4976	0.4977	0.4977	0.4978	0.4979	0.4979	0.4980	0.4981
2.9	0.4981	0.4982	0.4982	0.4983	0.4984	0.4984	0.4985	0.4985	0.4986	0.4986
3.0	0.4986	0.4987	0.4987	0.4988	0.4988	0.4989	0.4989	0.4989	0.4990	0.4990

Appendix D Values of $e^{-\lambda}$

λ	$e^{-\lambda}$	λ	$e^{-\lambda}$	λ	$e^{-\lambda}$
0.05	0.9512	2.05	0.1287	4.05	0.0174
0.10	0.9048	2.10	0.1225	4.10	0.0166
0.15	0.8607	2.15	0.1165	4.15	0.0158
0.20	0.8187	2.20	0.1108	4.20	0.0150
0.25	0.7788	2.25	0.1054	4.25	0.0143
0.30	0.7408	2.30	0.1003	4.30	0.0136
0.35	0.7047	2.35	0.0954	4.35	0.0129
0.40	0.6703	2.40	0.0907	4.40	0.0123
0.45	0.6376	2.45	0.0863	4.45	0.0117
0.50	0.6065	2.50	0.0821	4.50	0.0111
0.55	0.5769	2.55	0.0781	4.55	0.0106
0.60	0.5488	2.60	0.0743	4.60	0.0101
0.65	0.5220	2.65	0.0707	4.65	0.0096
0.70	0.4966	2.70	0.0672	4.70	0.0091
0.75	0.4724	2.75	0.0639	4.75	0.0087
0.80	0.4493	2.80	0.0608	4.80	0.0082
0.85	0.4274	2.85	0.0578	4.85	0.0078
0.90	0.4066	2.90	0.0550	4.90	0.0074
0.95	0.3867	2.95	0.0523	4.95	0.0071
1.00	0.3679	3.00	0.0498	5.00	0.0067
1.05	0.3499	3.05	0.0474	5.05	0.0064
1.10	0.3329	3.10	0.0450	5.10	0.0061
1.15	0.3166	3.15	0.0429	5.15	0.0058
1.20	0.3012	3.20	0.0408	5.20	0.0055
1.25	0.2865	3.25	0.0388	5.25	0.0052
1.30	0.2725	3.30	0.0369	5.30	0.0050
1.35	0.2592	3.35	0.0351	5.35	0.0047
1.40	0.2466	3.40	0.0334	5.40	0.0045
1.45	0.2346	3.45	0.0317	5.45	0.0043
1.50	0.2231	3.50	0.0302	5.50	0.0041
1.55	0.2122	3.55	0.0287	5.55	0.0039
1.60	0.2019	3.60	0.0273	5.60	0.0037
1.65	0.1920	3.65	0.0260	5.65	0.0035
1.70	0.1827	3.70	0.0247	5.70	0.0033
1.75	0.1738	3.75	0.0235	5.75	0.0032
1.80	0.1653	3.80	0.0224	5.80	0.0030
1.85	0.1572	3.85	0.0213	5.85	0.0029
1.90	0.1496	3.90	0.0202	5.90	0.0027
1.95	0.1423	3.95	0.0193	5.95	0.0026
2.00	0.1353	4.00	0.0183	6.00	0.0025
				7.00	0.0009
				8.00	0.000335
				9.00	0.000123
				10.00	0.000045

Appendix E References and Bibliography

Chapter 1 Introduction

Churchman, C. W., R. L. Ackoff, and E. L. Arnoff. *Introduction to Operations Research.* Wiley, 1957.

Horner, Peter. "The Sabre Story." *OR/MS Today* (June 2000).

Leon, Linda, Z. Przasnyski, and K. C. Seal. "Spreadsheets and OR/MS Models: An End-User Perspective." *Interfaces* (March/April 1996).

Powell, S. G. "Innovative Approaches to Management Science." *OR/MS Today* (October 1996).

Savage, S. "Weighing the Pros and Cons of Decision Technology and Spreadsheets." *OR/MS Today* (February 1997).

Winston, W. L. "The Teachers' Forum: Management Science with Spreadsheets for MBAs at Indiana University." *Interfaces* (March/April 1996).

Chapters 2 and 3 Probability

Anderson, D. R., D. J. Sweeney, and T. A. Williams. *Statistics for Business and Economics,* 7th ed. South-Western, 2005.

Hogg, R. V. and E. A. Tanis. *Probability and Statistical Inference,* 6th ed. Prentice Hall, 2001.

Ross, S. M. *Introduction to Probability Models,* 7th ed. Academic Press, 1993.

Wackerly, D. D., W. Mendenhall, and R. L. Scheaffer. *Mathematical Statistics with Applications,* 6th ed. Duxbury Press, 2002.

Chapters 4 and 5 Decision Analysis and Game Theory

Clemen, R. T. and T. Reilly. *Making Hard Decisions with Decision Tools.* Duxbury Press, 2001.

Davis, Morton D. *Game Theory: A Nontechnical Introduction.* Dover, 1997.

Goodwin, P. and G. Wright. *Decision Analysis for Management Judgment,* 2d ed. Wiley, 1999.

McMillian, John. *Games, Strategies, and Managers.* Oxford University Press, 1992.

Myerson, Roger B. *Game Theory: Analysis of Conflict.* Harvard University Press, 1997.

Osborne, Martin J. *An Introduction to Game Theory.* Oxford University Press, 2004.

Pratt, J. W., H. Raiffa, and R. Schlaiter. *Introduction to Statistical Decision Theory.* MIT Press, 1995.

Raiffa, H. *Decision Analysis.* McGraw-Hill, 1997.

Schlaiter, R. *Analysis of Decisions Under Uncertainty.* Krieger, 1978.

Chapter 6 Forecasting

Bowerman, B. L. and R. T. O'Connell. *Forecasting and Time Series: An Applied Approach,* 3d ed. Duxbury Press, 1993.

Box, G. E. P., G. M. Jenkins, and G. C. Reinsel. *Time Series Analysis: Forecasting and Control,* 3d ed. Prentice Hall, 1994.

Hanke, J. E. and A. G. Reitsch. *Business Forecasting,* 6th ed. Prentice Hall, 1998.

Makridakis, S. G., S. C. Wheelwright, and R. J. Hyndman. *Forecasting: Methods and Applications,* 3d ed. Wiley, 1997.

Wilson, J. H. and B. Keating. *Business Forecasting,* 3d ed. Irwin, 1998.

Chapters 7 to 11 Linear Programming, Transportation, Assignment, Transshipment, Integer Programming Problems

Bazarra, M. S., J. J. Jarvis, and H. D. Sherali. *Linear Programming and Network Flows,* 2d ed. Wiley, 1990.

Dantzig, G. B. *Linear Programming and Extensions.* Princeton University Press, 1963.

Greenberg, H. J. "How to Analyze the Results of Linear Programs—Part 1: Preliminaries." *Interfaces* 23, no. 4 (July/August 1993): 56–67.

Greenberg, H. J. "How to Analyze the Results of Linear Programs—Part 2: Price Interpretation." *Interfaces* 23, no. 5 (September/October 1993): 97–114.

Greenberg, H. J. "How to Analyze the Results of Linear Programs—Part 3: Infeasibility Diagnosis." *Interfaces* 23, no. 6 (November/December 1993): 120–139.

Lillien, G. and A. Rangaswamy. *Marketing Engineering: Computer-Assisted Marketing Analysis and Planning.* Addison-Wesley, 1998.

Nemhauser, G. L. and L. A. Wolsey. *Integer and Combinatorial Optimization.* Wiley, 1988.

Schrage, L. *Optimization Modeling with LINGO,* 4th ed. LINDO Systems Inc., 2000.

Winston, W. L. and S. C. Albright. *Practical Management Science,* 2d ed. Duxbury Press, 2001.

Chapter 12 Project Scheduling: PERT/CPM

Moder, J. J., C. R. Phillips, and E. W. Davis. *Project Management with CPM, PERT and Precedence Diagramming,* 3d ed. Blitz, 1995.

Wiest, J. and F. Levy. *Management Guide to PERT-CPM,* 2d ed. Prentice Hall, 1977.

Chapter 13 Inventory Models

Fogarty, D. W., J. H. Blackstone, and T. R. Hoffman. *Production and Inventory Management,* 2d ed. South-Western, 1990.

Hillier, F., and G. J. Lieberman. *Introduction to Operations Research,* 7th ed. McGraw-Hill, 2000.

Narasimhan, S. L., D. W. McLeavey, and P. B. Lington. *Production Planning and Inventory Control,* 2d ed. Prentice Hall, 1995.

Orlicky, J. and G. W. Plossi. *Orlicky's Material Requirements Planning.* McGraw-Hill, 1994.

Vollmann, T. E., W. L. Berry, and D. C. Whybark. *Manufacturing Planning and Control Systems,* 4th ed. McGraw-Hill, 1997.

Chapter 14 Waiting Line Models

Bunday, B. D. *An Introduction to Queueing Theory.* Wiley, 1996.

Gross, D. and C. M. Harris. *Fundamentals of Queueing Theory,* 3d ed. Wiley, 1997.

Hall, R. W. *Queueing Methods: For Service and Manufacturing.* Prentice Hall, 1991.

Hillier, F. and G. J. Lieberman. *Introduction to Operations Research,* 7th ed. McGraw-Hill, 2000.

Kao, E. P. C. *An Introduction to Stochastic Processes.* Duxbury Press, 1996.

Chapter 15 Simulation

Banks, J., J. S. Carson, and B. L. Nelson. *Discrete-Event System Simulation,* 2d ed. Prentice Hall, 1995.

Fishwick, P. A. *Simulation Model Design and Execution: Building Digital Worlds.* Prentice Hall, 1995.

Harrell, C. R. and K. Tumau. *Simulation Made Easy: A Manager's Guide.* Institute of Industrial Engineers, 1996.

Kelton, W. D., R. P. Sadowski, and D. A. Sadowski. *Simulation with Anema.* McGraw-Hill, 1998.

Law, A. M. and W. D. Kelton. *Simulation Modeling and Analysis,* 3d ed. McGraw-Hill, 1999.

Pidd, M. *Computer Simulation in Management Science,* 4th ed. Wiley, 1998.

Thesen, A. and L. E. Travis. *Simulation for Decision Making.* Wadsworth, 1992.

Chapter 16 Markov Processes

Bharucha-Reid, A. T. *Elements of the Theory of Markov Processes and Their Applications.* Dover, 1997.

Filar, J. A. and K. Vrieze. *Competitive Markov Decision Processes.* Springer-Verlag, 1996.

Norris, J. *Markov Chains.* Cambridge, 1997.

Chapter 17 Multicriteria Decisions

Dyer, J. S. "A Clarification of Remarks on the Analytic Hierarchy Process." *Management Science* 36, no. 3 (March 1990): 274–275.

Dyer, J. S. "Remarks on the Analytic Hierarchy Process." *Management Science* 36, no. 3 (March 1990): 249–258.

Harker, P. T. and L. G. Vargas. "Reply to Remarks on the Analytic Hierarchy Process by J. S. Dyer." *Management Science* 36, no. 3 (March 1990): 269–273.

Keeney, R. L. and H. Raiffa. *Decisions with Multiple Objectives: Preferences and Value Tradeoffs.* Cambridge, 1993.

Saaty, T. *Decision Making for Leaders: The Analytic Hierarchy Process for Decisions in a Complex World.* 3d ed. RWS, 1999.

Saaty, T. *Multicriteria Decision Making,* 2d ed. RWS, 1996.

Saaty, T. L. "An Exposition of the AHP in Reply to the Paper Remarks on the Analytic Hierarchy Process." *Management Science* 36, no. 3 (March 1990): 259–268.

Winkler, R. L. "Decision Modeling and Rational Choice: AHP and Utility Theory." *Management Science* 36, no. 3 (March 1990): 247–248.

Appendix F Self-Test Solutions and Answers to Even-Numbered Problems

Chapter 1

2. Define the problem; identify the alternatives; determine the criteria; evaluate the alternatives; choose an alternative

4. A quantitative approach should be considered because the problem is large, complex, important, new, and repetitive

6. Quicker to formulate, easier to solve, and/or more easily understood

8. a. Max $10x + 5y$

   s.t.

   $$5x + 2y \leq 40$$
   $$x \geq 0,\ y \geq 0$$

   b. Controllable inputs: x and y
   Uncontrollable inputs: profit (10,5), labor-hours (5,2), and labor-hour availability (40)

   c. See Figure 1.8c

   d. $x = 0, y = 20$; Profit $= \$100$ (Solution by trial and error)

   e. Deterministic

10. a. Total units received $= x + y$

   b. Total cost $= 0.20x + 0.25y$

   c. $x + y = 5000$

   d. $x \leq 4000$ Kansas City
   $y \leq 3000$ Minneapolis

   e. Min $0.20x + 0.25y$

   s.t.

   $$\begin{aligned} x + \quad y &= 5000 \\ x \quad\quad &\leq 4000 \\ y &\leq 3000 \\ x, y &\geq 0 \end{aligned}$$

FIGURE 1.8c SOLUTION

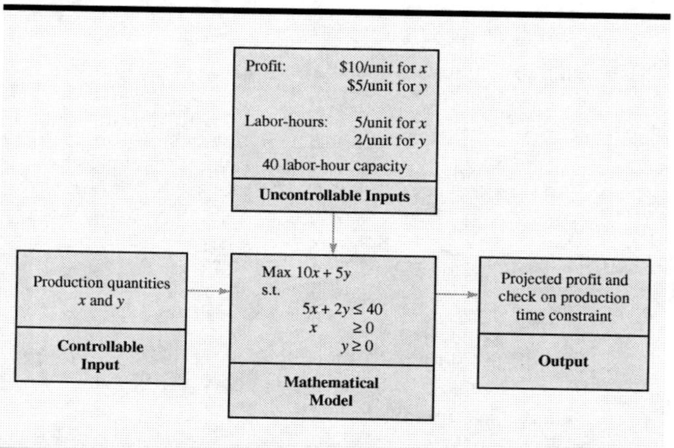

12. a. $TC = 1000 + 30x$

   b. $P = 40x - (1000 + 30x) = 10x - 1000$

   c. Break even when $P = 0$
   Thus $10x - 1000 = 0$

   $$10x = 1000$$
   $$x = 100$$

14. a. 4706

   b. Loss of \$12,000

   c. \$23

   d. \$11,800

16. a. Max $6x + 4y$

   b. $50x + 30y \leq 80{,}000$
   $50x \leq 50{,}000$
   $30y \leq 45{,}000$

Chapter 2

1. a. Record the number of persons waiting at the X-ray department at 9:00 A.M.

   b. The experimental outcomes (sample points) are the number of people waiting: 0, 1, 2, 3, and 4 (*Note:* Although it is theoretically possible for more than four people to be waiting, we use what has actually been observed to define the experimental outcomes.)

   c.

Number Waiting	Probability
0	.10
1	.25
2	.30
3	.20
4	.15
Total	1.00

   d. The relative frequency method

2. a. Choose a person at random, have them taste the four blends of coffee and state their preference

   b. Assign a probability of ¼ to each blend, using the classical method of equally likely outcomes

   c.

Blend	Probability
1	.20
2	.30
3	.35
4	.15
Total	1.00

4. a. Use the relative frequency approach:
$P(\text{California}) = 1{,}434/2{,}374 = .60$
b. Number not from 4 states = 2,374 − 1,434 − 390 − 217 − 112 = 221
$P(\text{Not from 4 States}) = 221/2{,}374 = .09$
c. $P(\text{Not in Early Stages}) = 1 - .22 = .78$
d. Estimate of number of Massachusetts companies in early stage of development = $(.22)390 \approx 86$
e. If we assume the size of the awards did not differ by states, we can multiply the probability an award went to Colorado by the total venture funds disbursed to get an estimate

$$\text{Estimate of Colorado funds} = (112/2374)(\$32.4) = \$1.53 \text{ billion}$$

(*Authors' Note:* The actual amount going to Colorado was $1.74 billion.)

6. a. $P(A) = P(150\text{–}199) + P(200 \text{ and over})$
$$= \frac{26}{100} + \frac{5}{100} = 0.31$$
b. $P(B) = P(\text{less than } 50) + P(50\text{–}99) + P(100\text{–}149) = 0.13 + 0.22 + 0.34 = 0.69$

7. a. $P(A) = 0.40$, $P(B) = 0.40$, $P(C) = 0.60$
b. $P(A \cup B) = P(E_1, E_2, E_3, E_4) = 0.80.$
Yes, $P(A \cup B) = P(A) + P(B)$
c. $A^c = \{E_3, E_4, E_5\}$; $C^c = \{E_1, E_4\}$; $P(A^c) = 0.60$; $P(C^c) = 0.40$
d. $A \cup B^c = \{E_1, E_2, E_5\}$; $P(A \cup B^c) = 0.60$
e. $P(B \cup C) = P(E_2, E_3, E_4, E_5) = 0.80$

8. a. 0.5, 0.4, 0.2
b. 0.70
c. 0.30

10. $P(\text{part-time job or dean's list}) = 0.50$

12. a. $P(A \mid B) = \dfrac{P(A \cap B)}{P(B)} = \dfrac{0.40}{0.60} = 0.6667$
b. $P(B \mid A) = \dfrac{P(A \cap B)}{P(A)} = \dfrac{0.40}{0.50} = 0.80$
c. No, because $P(A \mid B) \neq P(A)$

13. a.

Reason for Applying

	Quality	Cost/ Convenience	Other	Total
Full Time	0.218	0.204	0.039	0.461
Part Time	0.208	0.307	0.024	0.539
Total	0.426	0.511	0.063	1.000

b. A student will most likely cite cost or convenience as the first reason: probability = 0.511; school quality is the first reason cited by the second largest number of students: probability = 0.426

c. $P(\text{Quality} \mid \text{Full Time}) = 0.218/0.461 = 0.473$
d. $P(\text{Quality} \mid \text{Part Time}) = 0.208/0.539 = 0.386$
e. $P(B) = 0.426$ and $P(B \mid A) = 0.473$
Since $P(B) \neq P(B \mid A)$, the events are dependent

14. a. 0.44
b. 0.15
c. 0.0225
d. 0.0025
e. 0.136
f. 0.106

16. a. 0.19
b. 0.71
c. 0.29

18. a. 0.25, 0.40, 0.10
b. 0.25
c. Independent; program does not help

20. a. $P(B \cap A_1) = P(A_1)P(B \mid A_1) = (0.20)(0.50) = 0.10$
$P(B \cap A_2) = P(A_2)P(B \mid A_2) = (0.50)(0.40) = 0.20$
$P(B \cap A_3) = P(A_3)P(B \mid A_3) = (0.30)(0.30) = 0.09$
b. $P(A_2 \mid B) = \dfrac{0.20}{0.10 + 0.20 + 0.09} = 0.51$
c.

Events	$P(A_i)$	$P(B \mid A_i)$	$P(A_i \cap B)$	$P(A_i \mid B)$
A_1	0.20	0.50	0.10	0.26
A_2	0.50	0.40	0.20	0.51
A_3	0.30	0.30	0.09	0.23
	1.00		0.39	1.00

22. a. 0.40
b. 0.67

24. Let: S = small car
S^c = other type of vehicle
F = accident leads to fatality for vehicle occupant

We have $P(S) = .18$, so $P(S^c) = .82$; $P(F \mid S) = .128$ and $P(F \mid S^c) = .05$
Using the tabular form of Bayes' theorem provides:

Events	Prior Probabilities	Conditional Probabilities	Joint Probabilities	Posterior Probabilities
S	.18	.128	.023	.36
S^c	.82	.050	.041	.64
	1.00		.064	1.00

From the posterior probability column, we have $P(S \mid F) = .36$; so, if an accident leads to a fatality, the probability a small car was involved is .36

25. a. P(defective part) = 0.0065 (see below)

Events	$P(A_i)$	$P(D \mid A_i)$	$P(A_i \cap D)$	$P(A_i \mid D)$
Supplier A	0.60	0.0025	0.0015	0.23
Supplier B	0.30	0.0100	0.0030	0.46
Supplier C	0.10	0.0200	0.0020	0.31
	1.00		$P(D)$ = 0.0065	1.00

b. Supplier B (prob. = 0.46) is the most likely source

26. a. $P(D_1 \mid S_1) = 0.2195$, $P(D_2 \mid S_1) = 0.7805$
b. $P(D_1 \mid S_2) = 0.50$, $P(D_2 \mid S_2) = 0.50$
c. $P(D_1 \mid S_3) = 0.8824$, $P(D_2 \mid S_3) = 0.1176$
d. 0.1582 and 0.8418

Chapter 3

1. a. Values: 0, 1, 2, . . . , 20
discrete
b. Values: 0, 1, 2, . . .
discrete
c. Values: 0, 1, 2, . . . , 50
discrete
d. Values: $0 \le x \le 8$
continuous
e. Values: $x \ge 0$
continuous

2. a. 0.05; probability of a $200,000 profit
b. 0.70
c. 0.40

3. a.

x	$f(x)$
1	3/20 = 0.15
2	5/20 = 0.25
3	8/20 = 0.40
4	4/20 = 0.20
	Total 1.00

b.

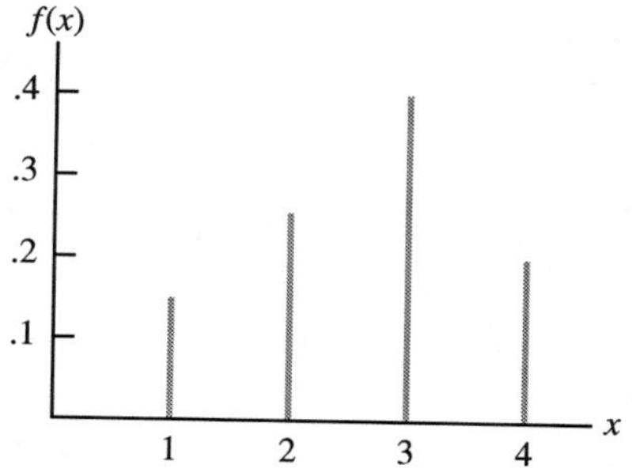

c. $f(x) \ge 0$ *for* $x = 1, 2, 3, 4$
$\Sigma f(x) = 1$

4. a.

x	$f(x)$	$xf(x)$
3	0.25	0.75
6	0.50	3.00
9	0.25	2.25
Totals	1.00	6.00

$E(x) = \mu = 6.00$

b.

x	$x - \mu$	$(x - \mu)^2$	$f(x)$	$(x - \mu)^2 f(x)$
3	−3	9	0.25	2.25
6	0	0	0.50	0.00
9	3	9	0.25	2.25
				4.50

$\text{Var}(x) = \sigma^2 = 4.50$

c. $\sigma = \sqrt{4.50} = 2.12$

6. a.

x	$f(x)$
0	0.04
1	0.34
2	0.41
3	0.18
4+	0.04

b. $E(x) = 1.84$; $\text{Var}(x) = 0.79$

c.

y	$f(y)$
0	0.00
1	0.03
2	0.23
3	0.52
4+	0.22

d. $E(y) = 2.93$; $\text{Var}(y) = 0.59$
e. More bedrooms in owner-occupied houses

8. a. Medium 145; large 140; prefer medium
b. Medium 2725; large 12,400; prefer medium

9. a. $f(1) = \binom{2}{1}(0.4)^1(0.6)^1 = \frac{2!}{1!1!}(0.4)(0.6) = 0.48$
b. $f(0) = \binom{2}{0}(0.4)^0(0.6)^2 = \frac{2!}{0!2!}(1)(0.36) = 0.36$
c. $f(2) = \binom{2}{2}(0.4)^2(0.6)^0 = \frac{2!}{2!0!}(0.16)(1) = 0.16$
d. $P(x \ge 1) = f(1) + f(2) = 0.48 + 0.16 = 0.64$
e. $E(x) = np = 2(0.4) = 0.8$
$\text{Var}(x) = np(1 - p) = 2(0.4)(0.6) = 0.48$
$\sigma = \sqrt{0.48} = 0.6928$

10. a. $f(0) = 0.3487$
b. $f(2) = 0.1937$
c. 0.9298

d. 0.6513
e. 1
f. $\sigma^2 = 0.9000$, $\sigma = 0.9487$

12. a. Probability of a defective part being produced must be 0.03 for each trial; trials must be independent
b. Two outcomes result in exactly one defect
c. $P(\text{no defects}) = (0.97)(0.97) = 0.9409$
$P(1 \text{ defect}) = 2(0.03)(0.97) = 0.0582$
$P(2 \text{ defects}) = (0.03)(0.03) = 0.0009$

14. a. $f(x) = \dfrac{2^x e^{-2}}{x!}$
b. $\mu = 6$ for 3 time periods
c. $f(x) = \dfrac{6^x e^{-6}}{x!}$
d. $f(2) = \dfrac{2^2 e^{-2}}{2!} = \dfrac{4(0.1353)}{2} = 0.2706$
e. $f(6) = \dfrac{6^6 e^{-6}}{6!} = 0.1606$
f. $f(5) = \dfrac{4^5 e^{-4}}{5!} = 0.1563$

16. a. 0.0009
b. 0.9927
c. 0.0302
d. 0.8271

18. a.

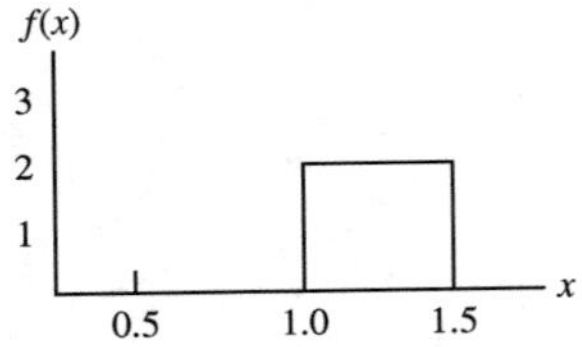

b. $P(x = 1.25) = 0$; the probability of any single point is zero because the area under the curve above any single point is zero
c. $P(1.0 \leq x \leq 1.25) = 2(0.25) = 0.50$
d. $P(1.2 < x < 1.5) = 2(0.30) = 0.60$

20. a.

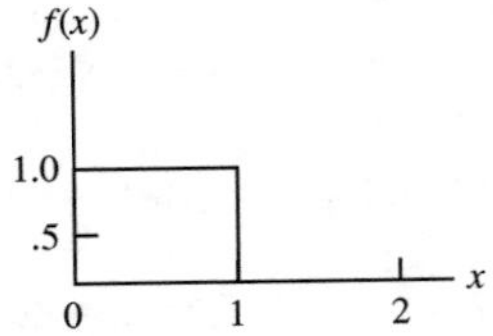

b. 0.50
c. 0.30
d. 0.40

21. a. 0.2967
b. 0.4418
c. $0.5000 - 0.1700 = 0.3300$
d. $0.0910 + 0.5000 = 0.5910$
e. $0.3849 + 0.5000 = 0.8849$
f. $0.5000 - 0.2612 = 0.2388$

22. a. 1.96
b. 0.61
c. 1.12
d. 0.44

23. a. Look in the table for an area of $0.5000 - 0.2119 = 0.2881$; the value we are seeking is below the mean, so the z value must be negative; thus, for an area of 0.2881, $z = -0.80$
b. Look in the table for an area of $0.9030/2 = 0.4515$; $z = 1.66$
c. Look in the table for an area of $0.2052/2 = 0.1026$; $z = 0.26$
d. Look in the table for an area of $0.9948 - 0.5000 = 0.4948$; $z = 2.56$
e. Look in the table for an area of $0.6915 - 0.5000 = 0.1915$; the value we are seeking is below the mean, so the z value must be negative; thus, $z = -0.50$

24. a. 0.3830
b. 0.1056
c. 0.0062
d. 0.1603

26. a. 0.7745
b. 36.32
c. 19%

28. $\mu = 19.23$

29. a. $P(x \leq x_0) = 1 - e^{-x_0/3}$
b. $P(x \leq 2) = 1 - e^{-2/3} = 1 - 0.5134 = 0.4866$
c. $P(x \geq 3) = 1 - P(x \leq 3) = 1 - (1 - e^{-3/3}) = e^{-1} = 0.3679$
d. $P(x \leq 5) = 1 - e^{-5/3} = 1 - 0.1889 = 0.8111$
e. $P(2 \leq x \leq 5) = P(x \leq 5) - P(x \leq 2) = 0.8111 - 0.4866 = 0.3245$

30. a. 0.3935
b. 0.2231
b. 0.3834

31. a.

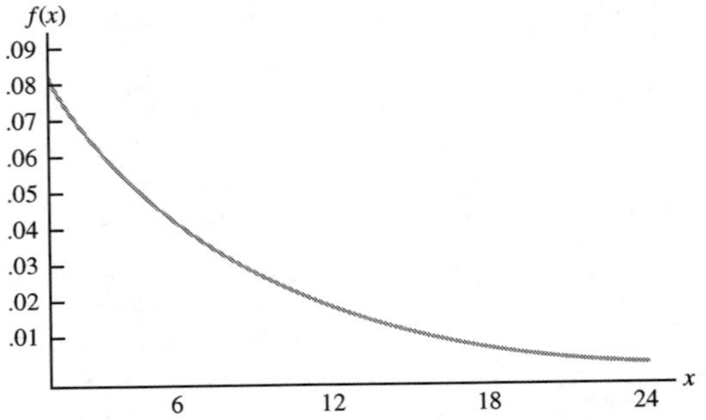

b. $P(x \leq 12) = 1 - e^{-12/12} = 0.6321$
c. $P(x \leq 6) = 1 - e^{-6/12} = 0.3935$
d. $P(x \geq 30) = 1 - P(x < 30) = 1 - (1 - e^{-30/12}) = 0.0821$

32. a. 50 hours
b. 0.3935
c. 0.1353

34. a. 0.5130
b. 0.1655
c. 0.3679

Chapter 4

1. a.

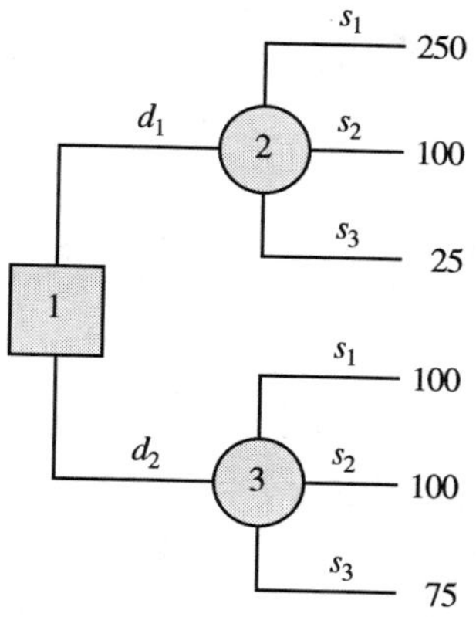

b.

Decision	Maximum Profit	Minimum Profit
d_1	250	25
d_2	100	75

Optimistic approach: Select d_1
Conservative approach: Select d_2

Regret or opportunity loss table:

Decision	s_1	s_2	s_3
d_1	0	0	50
d_2	150	0	0

Maximum regret: 50 for d_1 and 150 for d_2; select d_1

2. a. Optimistic: d_1
Conservative: d_3
Minimax regret: d_3
c. Optimistic: d_1
Conservative: d_2 or d_3
Minimax regret: d_2

3. a. Decision: choose the best plant size from the two alternatives: a small plant and a large plant
Chance event: market demand for the new product line with three possible outcomes (states of nature): low, medium, and high
b. Influence Diagram:

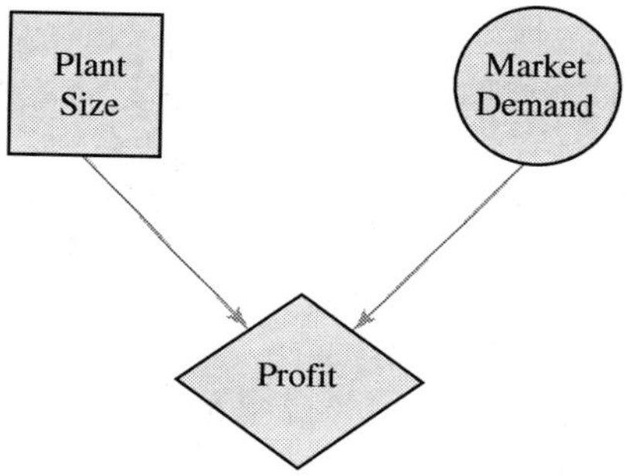

c.

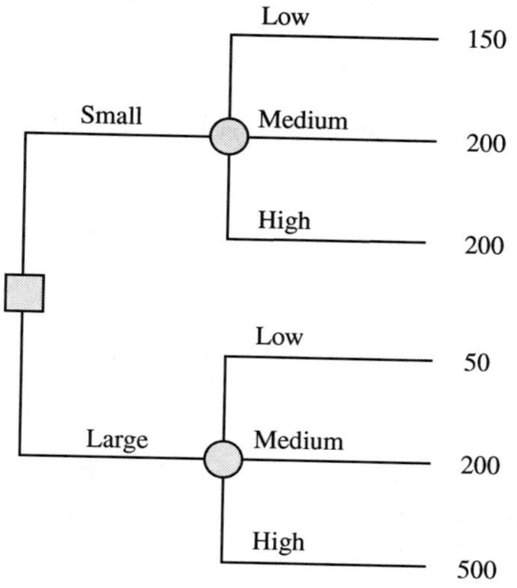

d.

Decision	Maximum Profit	Minimum Profit	Maximum Regret
Small	200	150	300
Large	500	50	100

Optimistic Approach: Large Plant
Conservative Approach: Small Plant
Minimax Regret: Large Plant

4. a. Decision: Which lease option to choose
Chance event: Miles driven
b.

	Annual Miles Driven 12,000	15,000	18,000
Forno	10,764	12,114	13,464
Midtown	11,160	11,160	12,960
Hopkins	11,700	11,700	11,700

c. Optimistic: Forno Saab
Conservative: Hopkins Automotive
Minimax: Hopkins Automotive
d. Midtown Motors
e. Most likely: \$11,160; Probability = 0.9
f. Midtown Motors or Hopkins Automotive

5. a. $EV(d_1) = 0.65(250) + 0.15(100) + 0.20(25) = 182.5$
$EV(d_2) = 0.65(100) + 0.15(100) + 0.20(75) = 95$
The optimal decision is d_1

6. a. Pharmaceuticals; 3.4%
b. Financial; 4.6%

7. a. EV(own staff) $= 0.2(650) + 0.5(650) + 0.3(600)$
$= 635$

EV(outside vendor) = 0.2(900) + 0.5(600) + 0.3(300) = 570

EV(combination) = 0.2(800) + 0.5(650) + 0.3(500) = 635

Optimal decision: hire an outside vendor with an expected cost of $570,000

b.

	Cost	Probability
Own staff	300	0.3
Outside vendor	600	0.5
Combination	900	0.2
		1.0

8. a. $\text{EV}(d_1) = p(10) + (1 - p)(1) = 9p + 1$

$\text{EV}(d_2) = p(4) + (1 - p)(3) = 1p + 3$

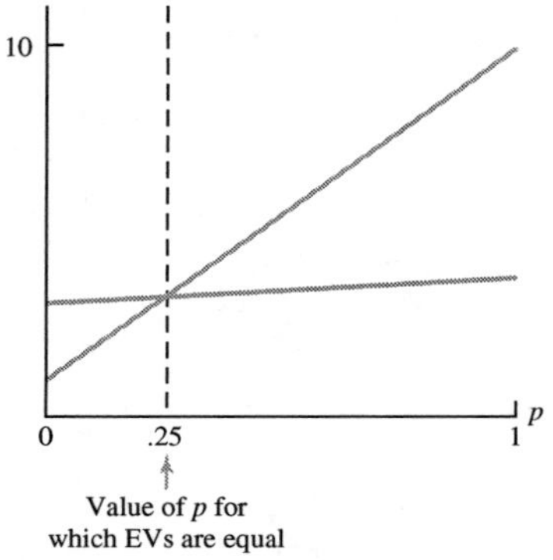

$9p + 1 = 1p + 3$ and hence $p = 0.25$

d_2 is optimal for $p \leq 0.25$, d_1 is optimal for $p \geq 0.25$

b. d_2

c. As long as the payoff for $s_1 \geq 2$, then d_2 is optimal

10. b. Space Pirates

EV = $724,000

$84,000 better than Battle Pacific

c.

$200	0.18
$400	0.32
$800	0.30
$1600	0.20

d. P(Competition) > 0.7273

12. a. Decision: Whether to lengthen the runway

Chance Event: The location decisions of Air Express and DRI

Consequence: Annual revenue

b. $255,000

c. $270,000

d. No

e. Lengthen the runway

14. a. If s_1, then d_1; if s_2, then d_1 or d_2; if s_3, then d_2

b. EVwPI = 0.65(250) + 0.15(100) + 0.20(75) = 192.5

c. From the solution to Problem 5, we know that $\text{EV}(d_1) = 182.5$ and $\text{EV}(d_2) = 95$; thus, recommended decision is d_1; hence, EVwoPI = 182.5

d. EVPI = EVwPI − EVwoPI = 192.5 − 182.5 = 10

16. a.

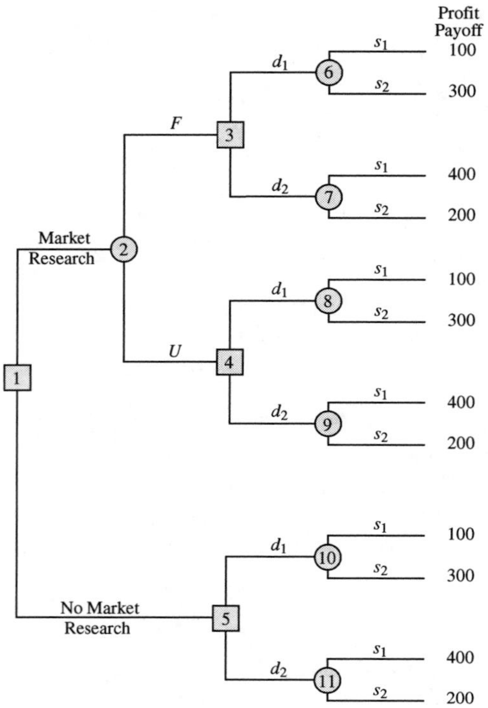

b.
EV (node 6) = 0.57(100) + 0.43(300) = 186
EV (node 7) = 0.57(400) + 0.43(200) = 314
EV (node 8) = 0.18(100) + 0.82(300) = 264
EV (node 9) = 0.18(400) + 0.82(200) = 236
EV (node 10) = 0.40(100) + 0.60(300) = 220
EV (node 11) = 0.40(400) + 0.60(200) = 280

EV (node 3) = Max(186,314) = 314 d_2
EV (node 4) = Max(264,236) = 264 d_1
EV (node 5) = Max(220,280) = 280 d_2

EV (node 2) = 0.56(314) + 0.44(264) = 292
EV (node 1) = Max(292,280) = 292

∴ Market Research
If favorable, decision d_2
If unfavorable, decision d_1

18. a. 5000 − 200 − 2000 − 150 = 2650
3000 − 200 − 2000 − 150 = 650

b. Expected values at nodes

8: 2350	5: 2350	9: 1100
6: 1150	10: 2000	7: 2000
4: 1870	3: 2000	2: 1560
1: 1560		

c. Cost would have to decrease by at least $130,000

d.

Payoff (in millions)	Probability
−$200	0.20
800	0.32
2800	0.48
	1.00

20. b. If Do Not Review, Accept
If Review and F, Accept
If Review and U, Accept
Always Accept
c. Do not review; EVSI = \$0
d. \$87,500; better method of predicting success

22. a. Order 2 lots; \$60,000
b. If E, order 2 lots
If V, order 1 lot
EV = \$60,500
c. EVPI = \$14,000
EVSI = \$500
Efficiency = 3.6%
Yes, use consultant

23.

State of Nature	$P(s_j)$	$P(I/s_j)$	$P(I \cap s_j)$	$P(s_j/I)$
s_1	0.2	0.10	0.020	0.1905
s_2	0.5	0.05	0.025	0.2381
s_3	0.3	0.20	0.060	0.5714
	1.0		$P(I) = 0.105$	1.0000

24. a. 0.695, 0.215, 0.090
0.98, 0.02
0.79, 0.21
0.00, 1.00
c. If C, Expressway
If O, Expressway
If R, Queen City
26.6 minutes

Chapter 5

1. a. $EV(d_1) = 0.40(100) + 0.30(25) + 0.30(0) = 47.5$
$EV(d_2) = 0.40(75) + 0.30(50) + 0.30(25) = 52.5 \} d_2$
$EV(d_3) = 0.40(50) + 0.30(50) + 0.30(50) = 50.0$
b. Using utilities

Decision Maker A	Decision Maker B
$EU(d_1) = 4.9$	$EU(d_1) = 4.45$ Best
$EU(d_2) = 5.9$	$EU(d_2) = 3.75$
$EU(d_3) = 6.0$ Best	$EU(d_3) = 3.00$

c. Difference in attitude toward risk; decision maker A tends to avoid risk, whereas decision maker B tends to take a risk for the opportunity of a large payoff

2. a. d_2; $EV(d_2) = \$5,000$
b. p = probability of a \$0 cost
$1 - p$ = probability of a \$200,000 cost
c. d_1; $EV(d_1) = 9.9$
d. Expected utility approach; it avoids risk of large loss

4. a. Route B; EV = 58.5
b. p = probability of a 45-minute travel time
$1 - p$ = probability of a 90-minute travel time
c. Route A; EV = 7.6; risk-avoider

5. a.

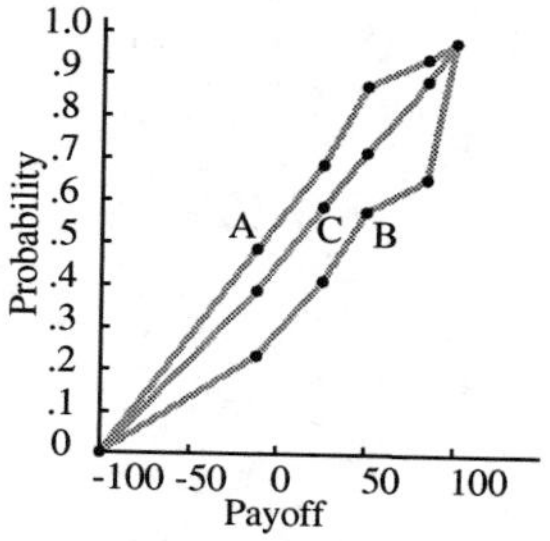

b. A—risk avoider
B—risk taker
C—risk neutral
c. Risk-avoider A, at \$20 payoff $p = 0.70$
∴ EV(Lottery) = 0.70(100) + 0.30(−100) = \$40
∴ Will pay 40 − 20 = \$20
Risk-taker B, at \$20 payoff $p = 0.45$
∴ EV(Lottery) = 0.45(100) + 0.55(−100) = −\$10
∴ Will pay 20 − (−10) = \$30

6. A: d_1; B: d_2; C: d_2

8. a.

	Win	Lose
Bet	350	−10
Do not bet	0	0

b. d_2
c. Risk takers
d. Between 0 and 0.26

10. a. Western; EV = 26%
b. p = probability of a 40% show
$1 - p$ = probability of a 15% show
c. Musical; risk taker

11.

		Player B			
		b_1	b_2	b_3	Minimum
Player A	a_1	8	5	7	(5)
	a_2	2	4	10	2
	Maximum	8	(5)	10	

The maximum of the row minimums is 5 and the minimum of the column maximums is 5. The game has a pure strategy. Player A should take strategy a_1 and Player B should take strategy b_2. The value of the game is 5.

12. Pure Strategy
A: a_2 news program
B: b_3 home improvement
Station A gains 6000

14. a. Strategy a_3 dominated by a_2
Strategy b_1 dominated by b_2

		Player B	
		b_2	b_3
Player A	a_1	−1	2
	a_2	4	−3

b. Let p = probability of a_1
and $(1 - p)$ = probability of a_2
If b_1, EV $= -1p + 4(1 - p)$
If b_2, EV $= 2p - 3(1 - p)$

$$-1p + 4(1 - p) = 2p - 3(1 - p)$$
$$-1p + 4 - 4p = 2p - 3 + 3p$$
$$10p = 7$$
$$p = 0.70$$

$P(a_1) = p = 0.70$
$P(a_2) = 1 - 0.70 = 0.30$

Let q = probability of b_2
and $(1 - q)$ = probability of b_3
If a_1, EV $= -1q + 2(1 - q)$
If a_2, EV $= 4q - 3(1 - q)$

$$-1q + 2(1 - q) = 4q - 3(1 - q)$$
$$-1q + 2 - 2q = 4q - 3 + 3q$$
$$10q = 5$$
$$q = 0.50$$

$P(b_2) = q = 0.50$
$P(b_3) = 1 - 0.50 = 0.50$

c. $-1p + 4(1 - p) = -(0.70) + 4(0.30)$
$= +0.50$

16. A: $P(a_3) = 0.80$, $P(a_4) = 0.20$
B: $P(b_1) = 0.40$, $P(b_2) = 0.60$
Value = 2.8

Chapter 6

1. a.

Month	Time Series Value	3-Month Moving Average Forecast	(Error)²	4-Month Moving Average Forecast	(Error)²
1	9.5				
2	9.3				
3	9.4				
4	9.6	9.40	0.04		
5	9.8	9.43	0.14	9.45	0.12
6	9.7	9.60	0.01	9.53	0.03
7	9.8	9.70	0.01	9.63	0.03
8	10.5	9.77	0.53	9.73	0.59
9	9.9	10.00	0.01	9.95	0.00
10	9.7	10.07	0.14	9.98	0.08
11	9.6	10.03	0.18	9.97	0.14
12	9.6	9.73	0.02	9.92	0.10
		Totals	1.08		1.09

MSE(3-month) = 1.08/9 = 0.12
MSE(4-month) = 1.09/8 = 0.14
Use a three-month moving average.

b. Forecast = (9.7 + 9.6 + 9.6)/3 = 9.63

2. a.

Week	Time Series Value	4-Week Moving Average Forecast	(Error)²	5-Week Moving Average Forecast	(Error)²
1	17				
2	21				
3	19				
4	23				
5	18	20.00	4.00		
6	16	20.25	18.06	19.60	12.96
7	20	19.00	1.00	19.40	0.36
8	18	19.25	1.56	19.20	1.44
9	22	18.00	16.00	19.00	9.00
10	20	19.00	1.00	18.80	1.44
11	15	20.00	25.00	19.20	17.64
12	22	18.75	10.56	19.00	9.00
		Totals	77.18		51.84

b. MSE(4-week) = 77.18/8 = 9.65
MSE(5-week) = 51.84/7 = 7.41

c. For the limited data provided, the five-week moving average provides the smallest MSE

4.

Week	Time Series Value	Forecast	Error	(Error)²
1	17			
2	21	17.00	4.00	16.00
3	19	17.40	1.60	2.56
4	23	17.56	5.44	29.59
5	18	18.10	−0.10	0.01
6	16	18.09	−2.09	4.37
7	20	17.88	2.12	4.49
8	18	18.10	−0.10	0.01
9	22	18.09	3.91	15.29
10	20	18.48	1.52	2.31
11	15	18.63	−3.63	13.18
12	22	18.27	3.73	13.91
			Total	101.72

MSE = 101.72/11 = 9.25
$\alpha = 0.2$ provided a lower MSE
therefore $\alpha = 0.2$ is better than $\alpha = 0.1$

5. a.

Month	Y_t	3-Month Moving Averages Forecast	(Error)²	$\alpha = 2$ Forecast	(Error)²
1	80				
2	82			80.00	4.00

(continued)

Month	Y_t	3-Month Moving Averages Forecast	(Error)^2	$\alpha = 2$ Forecast	(Error)^2
3	84			80.40	12.96
4	83	82.00	1.00	81.12	3.53
5	83	83.00	0.00	81.50	2.25
6	84	83.33	0.45	81.80	4.84
7	85	83.33	2.79	82.24	7.62
8	84	84.00	0.00	82.79	1.46
9	82	84.33	5.43	83.03	1.06
10	83	83.67	0.45	82.83	0.03
11	84	83.00	1.00	82.86	1.30
12	83	83.00	0.00	83.09	0.01
		Totals	11.12		39.06

MSE(3-month) = 11.12/9 = 1.24
MSE(α = 0.2) = 39.06/11 = 3.55
Use a three-month moving average

b. (83 + 84 + 83)/3 = 83.3

6. b. The more recent data receive the greater weight or importance in determining the forecast

8. a. 15.71
b. 15.74
c. 15.51
d. Moving averages; it has the smallest MSE (0.60)

10. a. $\alpha = 0.1$
b. 29.99

12. 3117.01

14. $\sum t = 21; \sum t^2 = 91; \sum Y_t = 117.1;$
$\sum tY_t = 403.7; n = 6$

$$b_1 = \frac{\sum tY_t - (\sum t \sum Y_t)/n}{\sum t^2 - (\sum t)^2/n} = \frac{403.7 - (21)(117.1)/6}{91 - (21)^2/6} = -0.3514$$

$b_0 = \bar{Y} - b_1\bar{t} = 19.5167 - (-.3514)(3.5) = 20.7466$
$T_t = 20.7466 - 0.3514t$

Conclusion: Enrollment appears to be decreasing by an average of approximately 351 students per year

16. a. Linear trend appears to be reasonable
b. $T_t = 19.993 + 1.774t$
Average cost increase of \$1.77 per unit per year

18. a. The graph shows a linear trend
b. $T_t = 60.553 - 1.141t$; 1.14%
c. 48.0%

20. a. A linear trend appears to exist
b. $T_t = -5 + 15t$
Average increase in sales is 15 units per year

22. a. A linear trend appears to be appropriate
b. $T_t = 6.4564 + 0.5345t$
c. 5.345 million
d. 2001–2002 season: $T_{13} = 6.4564 + 0.5345(12) =$ 12.87 million

24. a. Forecast for July is 236.97; forecast for August is 236.97
b. Forecast for July is 278.88; forecast for August is 297.33
c. Not fair; it does not account for upward trend in sales

25. a. Four-quarter moving averages beginning with (1690 + 940 + 2625 + 2500)/4 = 1938.75
Other moving averages are

1966.25	2002.50
1956.25	2052.50
2025.00	2060.00
1990.00	2123.75

b.

Quarter	Seasonal-Irregular Component Values		Seasonal Index	Adjusted Seasonal Index
1	0.904	0.900	0.9020	0.900
2	0.448	0.526	0.4970	0.486
3	1.344	1.453	1.3985	1.396
4	1.275	1.164	1.2195	1.217
		Total	4.0070	

Note: Adjustment for seasonal index = 4.000/4.007 = 0.9983

c. The largest seasonal effect is in the third quarter, which corresponds to the back-to-school demand during July, August, and September of each year

26. 0.707, 0.777, 0.827, 0.966, 1.016, 1.305, 1.494, 1.225, 0.976, 0.986, 0.936, 0.787

28. a. Selected centered moving averages for t = 5, 10, 15, and 20 are 11.125, 18.125, 22.875, and 27.000
b. 0.899, 1.362, 1.118, 0.621
c. Quarter 2, prior to summer boating season

30. a. $T_t = 6.329 + 1.055t$
b. 36.92, 37.98, 39.03, 40.09
c. 33.23, 51.65, 43.71, 24.86

32. a. Yes, there is a seasonal effect; seasonal indexes are 1.696, 1.458, 0.711, 0.326, 0.448, 1.362
b. Forecast for 12–4 is 166,761.13; forecast for 4–8 is 146,052.99

33. a.

Restaurant (i)	x_i	y_i	$x_i y_i$	x_i^2
1	1	19	19	1
2	4	44	176	16
3	6	40	240	36
4	10	52	520	100
5	14	53	742	196
Totals	35	208	1697	349

$$\bar{x} = \frac{35}{5} = 7$$

$$\bar{y} = \frac{208}{5} = 41.6$$

$$b_1 = \frac{\sum x_i y_i - (\sum x_i \sum y_i)/n}{\sum x_i^2 - (\sum x_i)^2/n} = \frac{1697 - (35)(208)/5}{349 - (35)^2/5} = \frac{241}{104} = 2.317$$

$$b_0 = \bar{y} - b_1\bar{x} = 41.6 - 2.317(7) = 25.381$$

$$\hat{y} = 25.381 + 2.317x$$

b. $\hat{y} = 25.381 + 2.317(8) = 43.917$, or \$43,917

34. a. $\hat{y} = 37.666 - 3.222x$

b. \$3444

Chapter 7

1. Parts (a), (b), and (e) are acceptable linear programming relationships
Part (c) is not acceptable because of $-2x_2^2$
Part (d) is not acceptable because of $3\sqrt{x_1}$
Part (f) is not acceptable because of $1x_1x_2$
Parts (c), (d), and (f) could not be found in a linear programming model because they contain nonlinear terms

2. a.

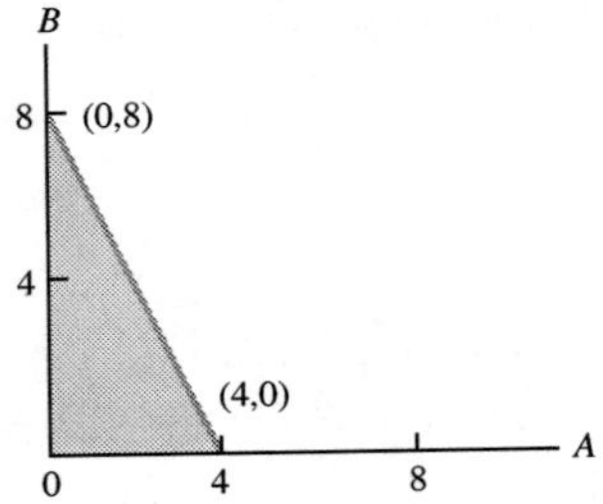

b.

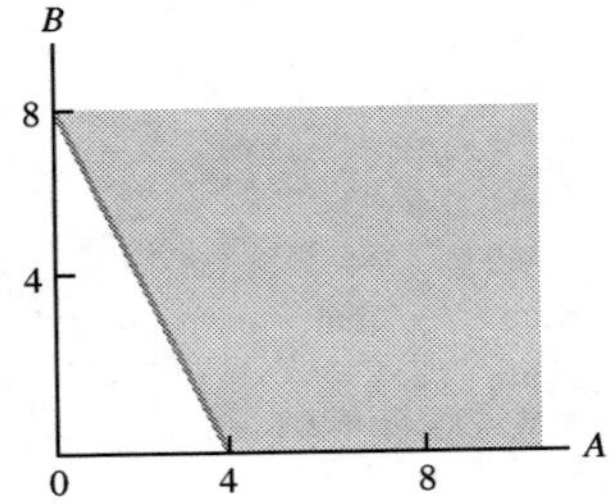

c.

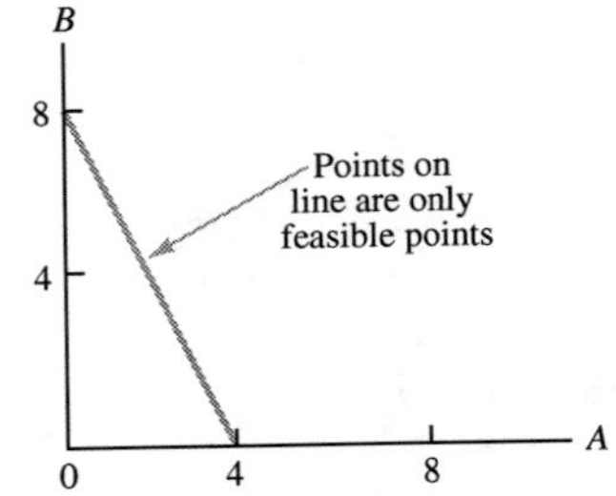

6. $7A + 10B = 420$
$6A + 4B = 420$
$-4A + 7B = 420$

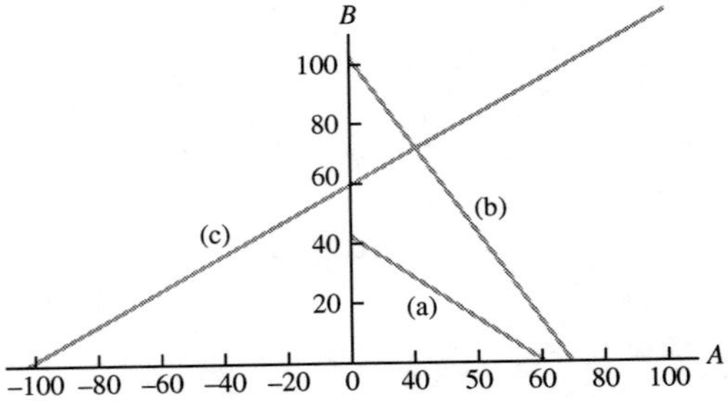

7.

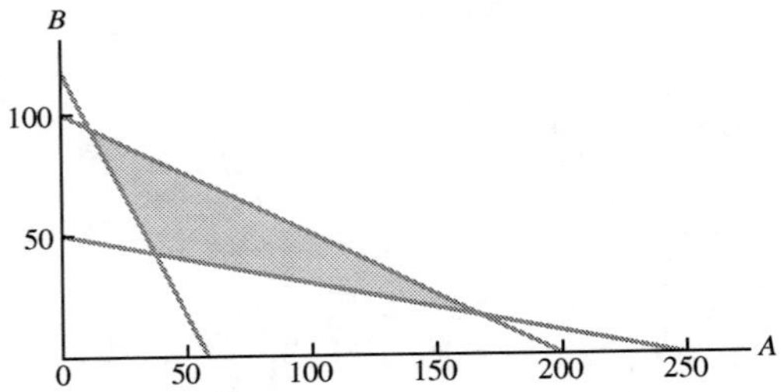

10.

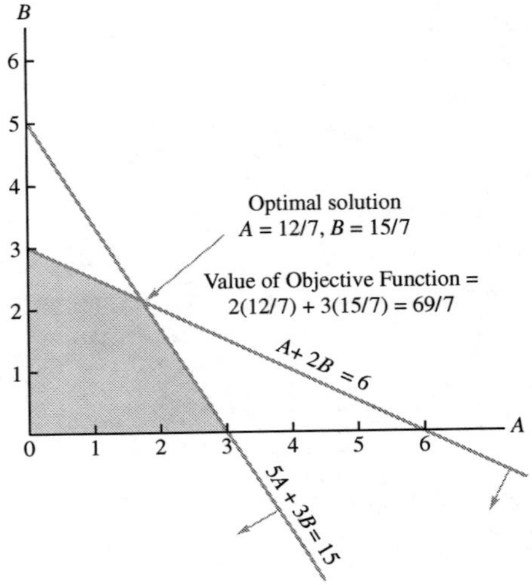

	$A + 2B =$	6	(1)
	$5A + 3B =$	15	(2)
Equation (1) times 5:	$5A + 10B =$	30	(3)

Equation (2) minus equation (3): $-7B = -15$

$B = 15/7$

From equation (1): $A = 6 - 2(15/7)$

$= 6 - 30/7 = 12/7$

12. a. $A = 3, B = 1.5$; Value of optimal solution $= 13.5$
   b. $A = 0, B = 3$; Value of optimal solution $= 18$
   c. four: (0, 0), (4, 0), (3, 1.5), and (0.3)

13. a.

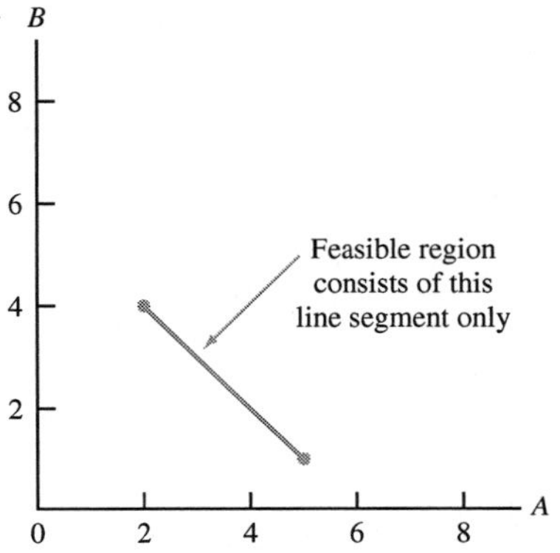

   b. The extreme points are (5,1) and (2,4)
   c.

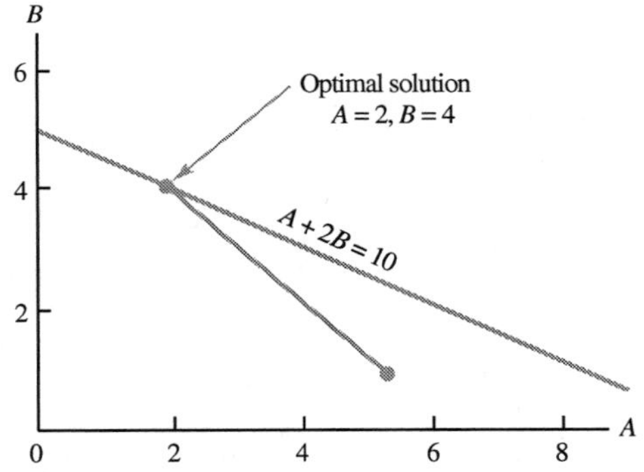

14. a. 540 standard bags, 252 deluxe bags
   b. \$7668
   c. 630, 480, 708, 117
   d. 0, 120, 0, 18

16. a. $3S + 9D$
   b. (0,540)
   c. 90, 150, 348, 0

17. Max $5A + 2B + 0s_1 + 0s_2 + 0s_3$

s.t.

$$\begin{aligned} 1A - 2B + 1s_1 \qquad\qquad &= 420 \\ 2A + 3B - \qquad + 1s_2 \qquad &= 610 \\ 6A - 1B + \qquad\qquad + 1s_3 &= 125 \\ A, B, s_1, s_2, s_3 &\geq 0 \end{aligned}$$

18. b. $A = 18/7, B = 15/7$
   c. 0, 0, 4/7

20. b. $A = 3.43, B = 3.43$
   c. 2.86, 0, 1.43, 0

22. b.

Extreme Point	Coordinates	Profit (\$)
1	(0, 0)	0
2	(1700, 0)	8500
3	(1400, 600)	9400
4	(800, 1200)	8800
5	(0, 1680)	6720

Extreme point 3 generates the highest profit

   c. $A = 1400, C = 600$
   d. Cutting and dyeing constraint and the packaging constraint
   e. $A = 800, C = 1200$; profit $=$ \$9200

24. a. Let R = number of units of regular model

C = number of units of catcher's model

Max $5R + 8C$

$1R + \frac{3}{2}C \leq 900$ Cutting and sewing

$\frac{1}{2}R + \frac{1}{3}C \leq 300$ Finishing

$\frac{1}{8}R + \frac{1}{4}C \leq 100$ Packaging and shipping

$R, C \geq 0$

   b.

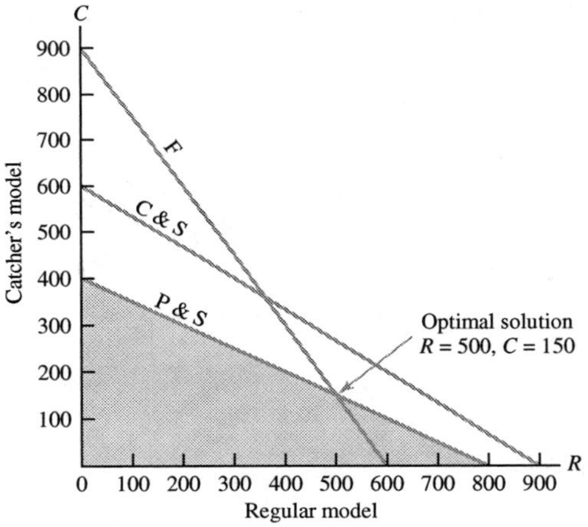

   c. $5(500) + 8(150) = \$3,700$
   d. C & S $1(500) + \frac{3}{2}(150) = 725$

F $\frac{1}{2}(500) + \frac{1}{3}(150) = 300$

P & S $\frac{1}{8}(500) + \frac{1}{4}(150) = 100$

   e.

Department	Capacity	Usage	Slack
Cutting and sewing	900	725	175 hours
Finishing	300	300	0 hours
Packaging and shipping	100	100	0 hours

26. a. Max $50N + 80R$

s.t.

$$\begin{aligned} N + \quad R &= 1000 \\ N \qquad &\geq 250 \\ R &\geq 250 \\ N - \quad 2R &\geq 0 \\ N, R &\geq 0 \end{aligned}$$

   b. $N = 666.67, R = 333.33$; Audience exposure $= 60,000$

28. a. Max $1W + 1.25M$

s.t.

$$5W + 7M \leq 4480$$
$$3W + 1M \leq 2080$$
$$2W + 2M \leq 1600$$
$$W, M \geq 0$$

b. $W = 560$, $M = 240$; Profit = 860

30. a. Max $15E + 18C$

s.t.

$$40E + 25C \leq 50{,}000$$
$$40E \geq 15{,}000$$
$$25C \geq 10{,}000$$
$$25C \leq 25{,}000$$
$$E, C \geq 0$$

c. (375, 400); (1000, 400); (625, 1000); (375, 1000)

d. $E = 625$, $C = 1000$

Total return = $27,375

31.

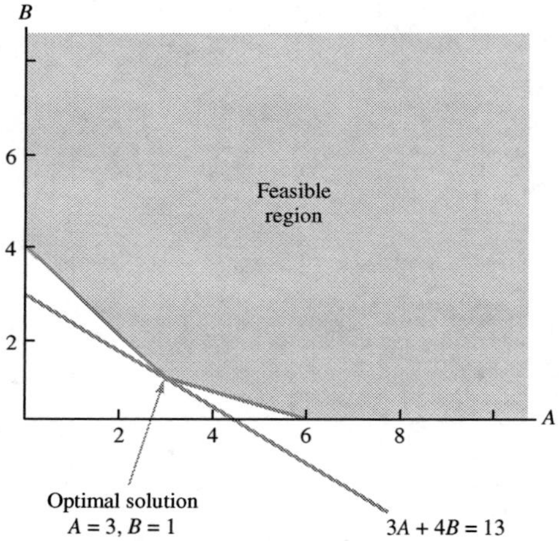

Objective function value = 13

32.

Extreme Points	Objective Function Value	Surplus Demand	Surplus Total Production	Slack Processing Time
(250, 100)	800	125	—	—
(125, 225)	925	—	—	125
(125, 350)	1300	—	125	—

34. a.

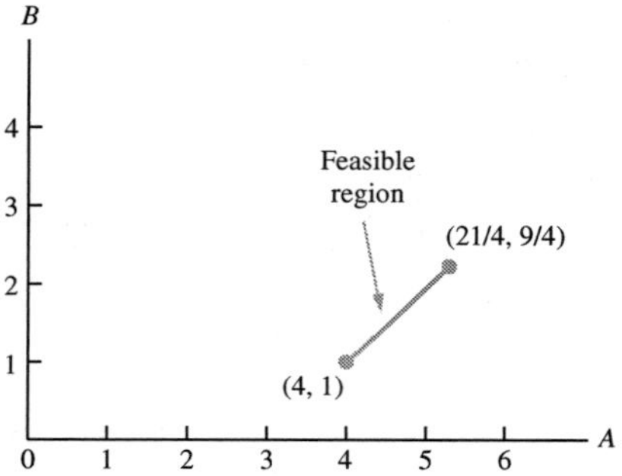

b. There are two extreme points

$(A = 4, B = 1)$ and $(A = 21/4, B = 9/4)$

c. The optimal solution (see part (a)) is $A = 4$, $B = 1$

35. a. Min $6A + 4B + 0s_1 + 0s_2 + 0s_3$

s.t.

$$2A + 1B - s_1 = 12$$
$$1A + 1B - s_2 = 10$$
$$1B + s_3 = 4$$
$$A, B, s_1, s_2, s_3 \geq 0$$

b. The optimal solution is $A = 6$, $B = 4$

c. $s_1 = 4$, $s_2 = 0$, $s_3 = 0$

36. a. Min $10{,}000T + 8{,}000P$

s.t.

$$T \geq 8$$
$$P \geq 10$$
$$T + P \geq 25$$
$$3T + 2P \leq 84$$

c. (15, 10); (21.33, 10); (8, 30); (8, 17)

d. $T = 8$, $P = 17$

Total cost = $216,000

38. a. Min $7.50S + 9.00P$

s.t.

$$0.10S + 0.30P \geq 6$$
$$0.06S + 0.12P \leq 3$$
$$S + P = 30$$
$$S, P \geq 0$$

c. Optional solution is $S = 15$, $P = 15$

d. No

e. Yes

40. $P_1 = 30$, $P_2 = 25$, Cost = $55

42.

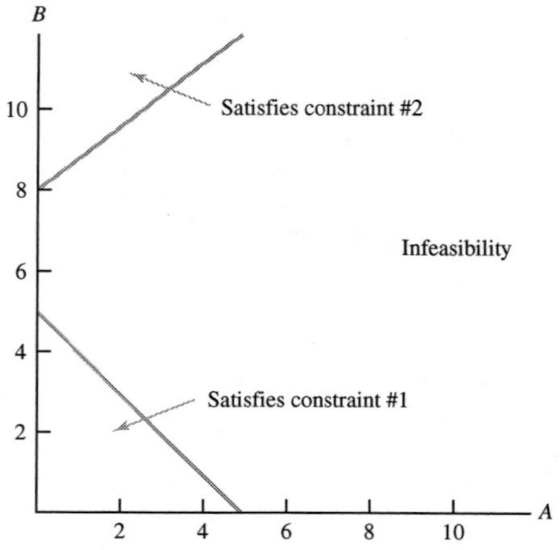

43.

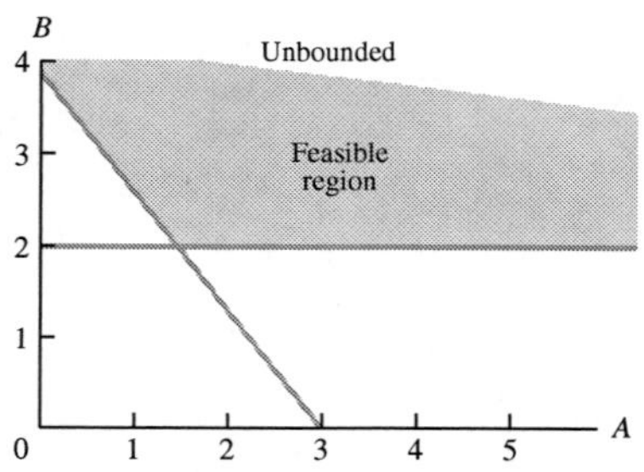

44. a. $A = {}^{30}\!/_{16}, B = {}^{30}\!/_{16}$; Value of optimal solution $= {}^{60}\!/_{16}$
b. $A = 0, B = 3$; Value of optimal solution $= 6$

46. a. 180, 20
b. Alternative optimal solutions
c. 120, 80

48. No feasible solution

50. $M = 65.45, R = 261.82$; Profit = \$45,818

52. $S = 384, O = 80$

54. a. Max $160M_1 + 345M_2$
s.t.

$$\begin{aligned} M_1 &\leq 15 \\ M_2 &\leq 10 \\ M_1 &\geq 5 \\ M_2 &\geq 5 \\ 40M_1 + 50M_2 &\leq 1000 \\ M_1, M_2 &\geq 0 \end{aligned}$$

b. $M_1 = 12.5, M_2 = 10$

Chapter 8

1. a.

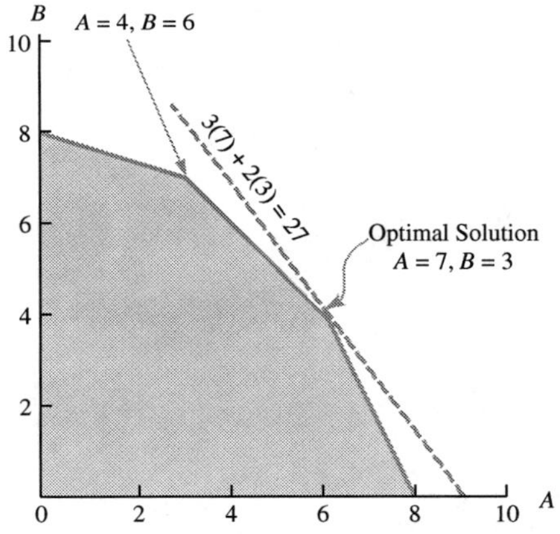

b. The same extreme point, $A = 7$ and $B = 3$, remains optimal; Value of the objective function becomes $5(7) + 2(3) = 41$
c. A new extreme point, $A = 4$ and $B = 6$, becomes optimal; Value of the objective function becomes $3(4) + 4(6) = 36$
d. The objective coefficient range for variable A is 2 to 6; the optimal solution, $A = 7$ and $B = 3$, does not change The objective coefficient range for variable B is 1 to 3; resolve the problem to find the new optimal solution

2. a. The feasible region becomes larger with the new optimal solution of $A = 6.5$ and $B = 4.5$
b. Value of the optimal solution to the revised problem is $3(6.5) + 2(4.5) = 28.5$; the one-unit increase in the right-hand side of constraint 1 improves the value of the optimal solution by $28.5 - 27 = 1.5$, therefore, the dual price for constraint 1 is 1.5
c. The right-hand-side range for constraint 1 is 8 to 11.2; as long as the right-hand side stays within this range, the dual price of 1.5 is applicable
d. The improvement in the value of the optimal solution will be 0.5 for every unit increase in the right-hand side of constraint 2 as long as the right-hand side is between 18 and 30

4. a. $X = 2.5, Y = 2.5$
b. -2
c. 5 to 11
d. -3 between 9 and 18

5. a. Regular glove = 500; Catcher's mitt = 150; Value = 3700
b. The finishing, packaging, and shipping constraints are binding; there is no slack
c. Cutting and sewing = 0
Finishing = 3
Packaging and shipping = 28
Additional finishing time is worth \$3 per unit, and additional packaging and shipping time is worth \$28 per unit
d. In the packaging and shipping department, each additional hour is worth \$28

6. a. 4 to 12
3.33 to 10
b. As long as the profit contribution for the regular glove is between \$4.00 and \$12.00, the current solution is optimal; as long as the profit contribution for the catcher's mitt stays between \$3.33 and \$10.00, the current solution is optimal; the optimal solution is not sensitive to small changes in the profit contributions for the gloves
c. The dual prices for the resources are applicable over the following ranges:

Constraint	Right-Hand-Side Range
Cutting and sewing	725 to No Upper Limit
Finishing	133.33 to 400
Packaging and shipping	75 to 135

d. Amount of increase = (28)(20) = \$560

8. a. More than \$7.00
b. More than \$3.50
c. None

10. a. $S = 4000, M = 10{,}000$, Total risk = 62,000
b.

Variable	Objective Coefficient Range
S	3.75 to No Upper Limit
M	No Lower Limit to 6.4

c. $5(4000) + 4(10{,}000) = \$60{,}000$
d. $60{,}000 / 1{,}200{,}000 = 0.05$ or 5%
e. 0.057 risk units
f. $0.057(100) = 5.7\%$

12. a. $E = 80, S = 120, D = 0$
Profit = $16,440
b. Fan motors and cooling coils
c. Labor hours; 320 hours available
d. Objective function coefficient range of optimality
No Lower Limit to 159
Because $150 is in this range, the optimal solution would not change

13. a. Range of optimality

E 47.5 to 75
S 87 to 126
D No Lower Limit to 159

b.

Model	Profit	Change	Allowable Increase/Decrease	%
E	$ 63	Increase $6(100)	$75 − $63 = $12	$\frac{6}{12}(100) = 50$
S	$ 95	Decrease $2	$95 − $87 = $8	$\frac{2}{8}(100) = 25$
D	$135	Increase $4	$159 − $135 = $24	$\frac{4}{24}(100) = 17$
				92

Because changes are 92% of allowable changes, the optimal solution of $E = 80$, $S = 120$, $D = 0$ will not change
The change in total profit will be

$$\begin{array}{ll} E & 80 \text{ units @ } +\$6 = \$480 \\ S & 120 \text{ units @ } -\$2 = \underline{-240} \\ & \qquad\qquad\qquad \$240 \end{array}$$

$\therefore$ Profit = $16,440 + $240 = $16,680

c. Range of feasibility

Constraint 1 160 to 280
Constraint 2 200 to 400
Constraint 3 2080 to No Upper Limit

d. Yes, Fan motors = 200 + 100 = 300 is outside the range of feasibility; the dual price will change

14. a. Manufacture 100 cases of A and 60 cases of B, and purchase 90 cases of B; Total cost = $2170
b. Demand for A, demand for B, assembly time
c. −12.25, −9.0, 0, .375
d. Assembly time constraint

16. a. 100 suits, 150 sport coats
Profit = $40,900
40 hours of cutting overtime
b. Optimal solution will not change
c. Consider ordering additional material
$34.50 is the maximum price
d. Profit will improve by $875

18. a. The linear programming model is as follows:
Min $30AN + 50AO + 25BN + 40BO$
s.t.

$$\begin{array}{lllll} AN + & AO & & & \geq 50{,}000 \\ & & BN + & BO & \geq 70{,}000 \\ AN & + & BN & & \leq 80{,}000 \\ & AO & + & BO & \leq 60{,}000 \\ \multicolumn{5}{l}{AN, AO, BN, BO \geq 0} \end{array}$$

b. Optimal solution

	New Line	Old Line
Model A	50,000	0
Model B	30,000	40,000

Total cost: $3,850,000

c. The first three constraints are binding
d. Because the dual price is positive, increasing the right-hand side of constraint 3 will *improve* the solution; thus, an increase in capacity for the new production line is desirable
e. Because constraint 4 is not a binding constraint, any increase in the production line capacity of the old production line will have no effect on the optimal solution; thus, increasing the capacity of the old production line results in no benefit
f. The reduced cost for model A made on the old production line is 5; thus, the cost would have to decrease by at least $5 before any units of model A would be produced on the old production line
g. The right-hand-side range for constraint 2 shows a lower limit of 30,000; thus, if the minimum production requirement is reduced 10,000 units to 60,000, the dual price of −40 is applicable; thus, total cost would decrease by 10,000(40) = $400,000

20. a. Max $0.07H + 0.12P + 0.09A$
s.t.

$$\begin{array}{rrrl} H + & P + & A & = 1{,}000{,}000 \\ 0.6H - & 0.4P - & 0.4A & \geq 0 \\ & P - & 0.6A & \leq 0 \\ \multicolumn{4}{l}{H, P, A \geq 0} \end{array}$$

b. H = $400,000, P = $225,000, A = $375,000
Total annual return = $88,750
Annual percentage return = 8.875%
c. No change
d. Increase of $890
e. Increase of $312.50 or 0.031%

22. a. Min $30L + 25D + 18S$
s.t.

$$\begin{array}{rrrl} L + & D + & S & = 100 \\ 0.6L - & 0.4D & & \geq 0 \\ -0.15L - & 0.15D + & 0.85S & \geq 0 \\ -0.25L - & 0.25D + & S & \leq 0 \\ L & & & \leq 50 \\ \multicolumn{4}{l}{L, D, S \geq 0} \end{array}$$

b. $L = 48, D = 72, S = 30$
Total cost = $3780
c. No change
d. No change

24. a. 333.3, 0, 833.3; Risk = 14,666.7; Return = 18,000 or 9%
b. 1000, 0, 0, 2500; Risk = 18,000; Return = 22,000 or 11%
c. $4000

26. a. Let M_1 = units of component 1 manufactured
M_2 = units of component 2 manufactured
M_3 = units of component 3 manufactured
P_1 = units of component 1 purchased
P_2 = units of component 2 purchased
P_3 = units of component 3 purchased

$$
\begin{array}{llll}
\text{Min} & 4.50M_1 + 5.00M_2 + 2.75M_3 + 6.50P_1 + 8.80P_2 + 7.00P_3 & & \\
\text{s.t.} & & & \\
& 2M_1 + 3M_2 + 4M_3 & \le 21{,}600 & \text{Production} \\
& 1M_1 + 1.5M_2 + 3M_3 & \le 15{,}000 & \text{Assembly} \\
& 1.5M_1 + 2M_2 + 5M_3 & \le 18{,}000 & \text{Testing/Packaging} \\
& 1M_1 + 1P_1 & = 6{,}000 & \text{Component 1} \\
& 1M_2 + 1P_2 & = 4{,}000 & \text{Component 2} \\
& 1M_3 + 1P_3 & = 3{,}500 & \text{Component 3} \\
& M_1, M_2, M_3, P_1, P_2, P_3 \ge 0 & &
\end{array}
$$

b.

Source	Component 1	Component 2	Component 3
Manufacture	2000	4000	1400
Purchase	4000		2100

Total Cost $73,550

c. Production: $54.36 per hour
Testing & Packaging: $ 7.50 per hour

d. Dual prices = −$7.969; it would cost Benson $7.969 to add a unit of component 2

28. b. $G = 120{,}000$; $S = 30{,}000$; $M = 150{,}000$
c. 0.15 to 0.60; No Lower Limit to 0.122; 0.02 to 0.20
d. 4668
e. $G = 48{,}000$; $S = 192{,}000$; $M = 60{,}000$
f. The client's risk index and the amount of funds available

30. a. $L = 3, N = 7, W = 5, S = 5$
b. Each additional minute of broadcast time increases cost by $100
c. If local coverage is increased by 1 minute, total cost will increase by $100
d. If the time devoted to local and national news is increased by 1 minute, total cost will increase by $100
e. Increasing the sports by 1 minute will have no effect because the dual price is 0

32. a. Let P_1 = number of PT-100 battery packs produced at the Philippines plant
P_2 = number of PT-200 battery packs produced at the Philippines plant
P_3 = number of PT-300 battery packs produced at the Philippines plant
M_1 = number of PT-100 battery packs produced at the Mexico plant
M_2 = number of PT-200 battery packs produced at the Mexico plant
M_3 = number of PT-300 battery packs produced at the Mexico plant

$$
\begin{array}{lll}
\text{Min} & 1.13P_1 + 1.16P_2 + 1.52P_3 + 1.08M_1 + 1.16M_2 + 1.25M_3 & \\
\text{s.t.} & & \\
& P_1 + M_1 & = 200{,}000 \\
& P_2 + M_2 & = 100{,}000 \\
& P_3 + M_3 & = 150{,}000 \\
& P_1 + P_2 & \le 175{,}000 \\
& M_1 + M_2 & \le 160{,}000 \\
& P_3 & \le 75{,}000 \\
& M_3 & \le 100{,}000 \\
& P_1, P_2, P_3, M_1, M_2, M_3 \ge 0 &
\end{array}
$$

b. The optimal solution is as follows:

	Philippines	Mexico
PT-100	40,000	160,000
PT-200	100,000	0
PT-300	50,000	100,000

Total production and transportation cost is $535,000

c. The range of optimality for the objective function coefficient for P_1 shows a lower limit of $1.08; thus, the production and/or shipping cost would have to decrease by at least 5 cents per unit

d. The range of optimality for the objective function coefficient for M_1 shows a lower limit of $1.11; thus, the production and/or shipping cost would have to decrease by at least 5 cents per unit

Chapter 9

1. a. Let T = number of television advertisements
R = number of radio advertisements
N = number of newspaper advertisements

$$
\begin{array}{llll}
\text{Max} & 100{,}000T + 18{,}000R + 40{,}000N & & \\
\text{s.t.} & & & \\
& 2000T + 300R + 600N & \le 18{,}200 & \text{Budget} \\
& T & \le 10 & \text{Max TV} \\
& R & \le 20 & \text{Max radio} \\
& N & \le 10 & \text{Max news} \\
& -0.5T + 0.5R - 0.5N & \le 0 & \text{Max 50\% radio} \\
& 0.9T - 0.1R - 0.1N & \ge 0 & \text{Min 10\% TV} \\
& T, R, N \ge 0 & &
\end{array}
$$

Solution:		Budget $
	$T = 4$	$ 8000
	$R = 14$	4200
	$N = 10$	6000
		$18,200

Audience = 1,052,000

b. The dual price for the budget constraint is 51.30. Thus, a $100 increase in the budget should provide an increase in audience coverage of approximately 5130. The right-hand-side range for the budget constraint will show that this interpretation is correct.

2. a. $x_1 = 77.89, x_2 = 63.16$, $3284.21
b. Department A $15.79; Department B $47.37
c. $x_1 = 87.21, x_2 = 65.12$, $3341.34
Department A 10 hours; Department B 3.2 hours

4. a. $x_1 = 500, x_2 = 300, x_3 = 200$, \$550
b. \$0.55
c. Aroma, 75; Taste 84.4
d. −\$0.60

6. 50 units of product 1; 0 units of product 2; 300 hours department A; 600 hours department B

8. Schedule 19 officers as follows:
3 begin at 8:00 A.M.; 3 begin at noon; 7 begin at 4:00 P.M.; 4 begin at midnight, 2 begin at 4:00 A.M.

9. a. Decision variables A, P, M, H, and G represent the fraction or proportion of the total investment in each alternative

$$\begin{aligned}
\text{Max} \quad & 0.073A + 0.103P + 0.064M + 0.075H + 0.045G \\
\text{s.t.} \quad & \\
& A + P + M + H + G = 1 \\
& 0.5A + 0.5P - 0.5M - 0.5H \le 0 \\
& -0.5A - 0.5P + 0.5M + 0.5H \le 0 \\
& -0.25M - 0.25H + G \ge 0 \\
& -0.6A + 0.4P \le 0 \\
& A, P, M, H, G \ge 0
\end{aligned}$$

Objective function = 0.079; $A = 0.178$; $P = 0.267$; $M = 0.000$; $H = 0.444$; $G = 0.111$

b. Multiplying A, P, M, H, and G by the \$100,000 invested provides the following

Atlantic Oil	\$ 17,800
Pacific Oil	26,700
Huber Steel	44,400
Government bonds	11,100
	\$100,000

c. 0.079(\$100,000) = \$7900
d. The marginal rate of return is 0.079

10. a. 40.9%, 14.5%, 14.5%, 30.0%
Annual return = 5.4%
b. 0.0%, 36.0%, 36.0%, 28.0%
Annual return = 2.52%
c. 75.0%, 0.0%, 15.0%, 10.0%
Annual return = 8.2%
b. Yes

12.

Week	Buy	Sell	Store
1	80,000	0	100,000
2	0	0	100,000
3	0	100,000	0
4	25,000	0	25,000

14. b.

Quarter	Production	Ending Inventory
1	4000	2100
2	3000	1100
3	2000	100
4	1900	500

15. Let x_{11} = gallons of crude 1 used to produce regular
x_{12} = gallons of crude 1 used to produce high octane
x_{21} = gallons of crude 2 used to produce regular
x_{22} = gallons of crude 2 used to produce high octane

$$\text{Min} \quad 0.10x_{11} + 0.10x_{12} + 0.15x_{21} + 0.15x_{22}$$
s.t.

Each gallon of regular must have at least 40% A

$$\begin{aligned}
x_{11} + x_{21} &= \text{amount of regular produced} \\
0.4(x_{11} + x_{21}) &= \text{amount of A required for regular} \\
0.2x_{11} + 0.50x_{21} &= \text{amount of A in } (x_{11} + x_{21}) \text{ gallons of regular gas} \\
\therefore 0.2x_{11} + 0.50x_{21} &\ge 0.4x_{11} + 0.40x_{21} \\
\therefore -0.2x_{11} + 0.10x_{21} &\ge 0
\end{aligned}$$

Each gallon of high octane can have at most 50% B

$$\begin{aligned}
x_{12} + x_{22} &= \text{amount high octane} \\
0.5(x_{12} + x_{22}) &= \text{amount of B required for high octane} \\
0.60x_{12} + 0.30x_{22} &= \text{amount of B in } (x_{12} + x_{22}) \text{ gallons of high octane} \\
\therefore 0.60x_{12} + 0.30x_{22} &\le 0.5x_{12} + 0.5x_{22} \\
\therefore 0.1x_{12} - 0.2x_{22} &\le 0 \\
x_{11} + x_{21} &\ge 800{,}000 \\
x_{12} + x_{22} &\ge 500{,}000 \\
x_{11}, x_{12}, x_{21}, x_{22} &\ge 0
\end{aligned}$$

Optimal solution: $x_{11} = 266{,}667$, $x_{12} = 333{,}333$, $x_{21} = 533{,}333$, $x_{22} = 166{,}667$
Cost = \$165,000

16. x_i = number of 10-inch rolls processed by cutting alternative i
a. $x_1 = 0, x_2 = 125, x_3 = 500, x_4 = 1500, x_5 = 0, x_6 = 0, x_7 = 0$; 2125 rolls with waste of 750 inches
b. 2500 rolls with no waste; however, 1½-inch size is overproduced by 3000 units

18. a. 5 Super, 2 Regular, and 3 Econo-Tankers
Total cost \$583,000; monthly operating cost \$4650

19. a. Let x_{11} = amount of men's model in month 1
x_{21} = amount of women's model in month 1
x_{12} = amount of men's model in month 2
x_{22} = amount of women's model in month 2
s_{11} = inventory of men's model at end of month 1
s_{21} = inventory of women's model at end of month 1
s_{12} = inventory of men's model at end of month 2
s_{22} = inventory of women's model at end of month 2

$$\text{Min} \quad 120x_{11} + 90x_{21} + 120x_{12} + 90x_{22} + 2.4s_{11} + 1.8s_{21} + 2.4s_{12} + 1.8s_{22}$$
s.t.

$$\left.\begin{aligned}
x_{11} - s_{11} &= 130 \\
x_{21} - s_{21} &= 95 \\
s_{11} + x_{12} - s_{12} &= 200 \\
s_{21} + x_{22} - s_{22} &= 150
\end{aligned}\right\}\text{Satisfy demand}$$

$$\left.\begin{aligned}
s_{12} &\ge 25 \\
s_{22} &\ge 25
\end{aligned}\right\}\text{Ending inventory requirement}$$

Labor-hours: Men's 2.0 + 1.5 = 3.5
Women's 1.6 + 1.0 = 2.6

$$\left.\begin{aligned}
3.5x_{11} + 2.6x_{21} &\ge 900 \\
3.5x_{11} + 2.6x_{21} &\le 1100 \\
3.5x_{11} + 2.6x_{21} - 3.5x_{12} - 2.6x_{22} &\le 100 \\
-3.5x_{11} - 2.6x_{21} + 3.5x_{12} + 2.6x_{22} &\le 100
\end{aligned}\right\}\text{Labor smoothing}$$

$$x_{11}, x_{12}, x_{21}, x_{22}, s_{11}, s_{12}, s_{21}, s_{22} \ge 0$$

Solution: $x_{11} = 193$; $x_{21} = 95$; $x_{12} = 162$; $x_{22} = 175$

Total cost = \$67,156
Inventory levels: $s_{11} = 63$; $s_{12} = 25$; $s_{21} = 0$; $s_{22} = 25$
Labor levels:

Previous	1000 hours
Month 1	922.25 hours
Month 2	1022.25 hours

b. To accommodate the new policy, the right-hand sides of the four labor-smoothing constraints must be changed to 950, 1050, 50, and 50, respectively; the new total cost is \$67,175

20. Produce 10,250 units in March, 10,250 units in April, and 12,000 units in May

22. 5, 515, 887 sq. in. of waste
Machine 3: 492 minutes

24. Investment strategy: 45.8% of A and 100% of B
Objective function = \$4340.40
Savings/Loan schedule

	Period			
	1	2	3	4
Savings	242.11	—	—	341.04
Funds from loan	—	200.00	127.58	—

26. b. Solution does not indicate that General Hospital is relatively inefficient
c. General Hospital

28. c. No; E = 1 indicates that all the resources used by Hospital E are required to produce the outputs of Hospital E
d. Hospital E

30. a. Newark
b. Five ODIFs change: $PMQ = 23$; $POQ = 43$; $NMQ = 56$; $CMQ = 32$; and $COQ = 46$; the allocations for the other ODIFs remain the same as in the original solution
c. Four ODIFs change: $POQ = 45$; $NMQ = 56$; $CMQ = 37$; and $COQ = 44$; the allocations for the other ODIFs remain the same as in the original solution
d. *COY*, with a bid price of \$443

32. c.

Type	Value
Convention/two-night package	36
Convention/Friday only	12
Convention/Saturday only	15
Regular/Two-night package	20
Regular/Friday only	28
Regular/Saturday only	25

d. \$50

Chapter 10

1.

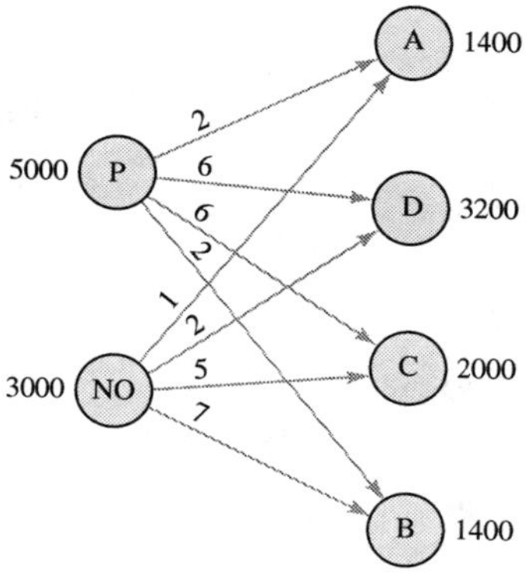

2. a. Let x_{11} = amount shipped from Jefferson City to Des Moines
x_{12} = amount shipped from Jefferson City to Kansas City
⋮
x_{23} = amount shipped from Omaha to St. Louis

$$
\begin{aligned}
\text{Min } & 14x_{11} + 9x_{12} + 7x_{13} + 8x_{21} + 10x_{22} + 5x_{23} \\
\text{s.t.} & \\
& x_{11} + x_{12} + x_{13} \le 30 \\
& x_{21} + x_{22} + x_{23} \le 20 \\
& x_{11} + x_{21} = 25 \\
& x_{12} + x_{22} = 15 \\
& x_{13} + x_{23} = 10 \\
& x_{11}, x_{12}, x_{13}, x_{21}, x_{22}, x_{23} \ge 0
\end{aligned}
$$

b.

Optimal Solution	Amount	Cost
Jefferson City–Des Moines	5	70
Jefferson City–Kansas City	15	135
Jefferson City–St. Louis	10	70
Omaha–Des Moines	20	160
	Total	435

4. b. $x_{12} = 300$, $x_{21} = 100$, $x_{22} = 100$, $x_{23} = 300$, $x_{31} = 100$
Cost = 10,400

6. b.

Seattle–Denver	4000	Seattle–Los Angeles	5000
Columbus–Mobile	4000	New York–Pittsburgh	3000
New York–Mobile	1000	New York–Los Angeles	1000
New York–Washington	3000		

Cost = \$150,000

c.

Seattle–Denver	4000	Seattle–Los Angeles	5000
Columbus–Mobile	5000	New York–Pittsburgh	4000
New York–Los Angeles	1000	New York–Washington	3000

Cost actually decreases by \$9000

8. The network model, the linear programming formulation and the optimal solution are shown. Note that the third constraint corresponds to the dummy origin; the variables x_{31}, x_{32}, x_{33}, and x_{34} are the amounts shipped out of the dummy origin and do not appear in the objective function since they are given a coefficient of zero

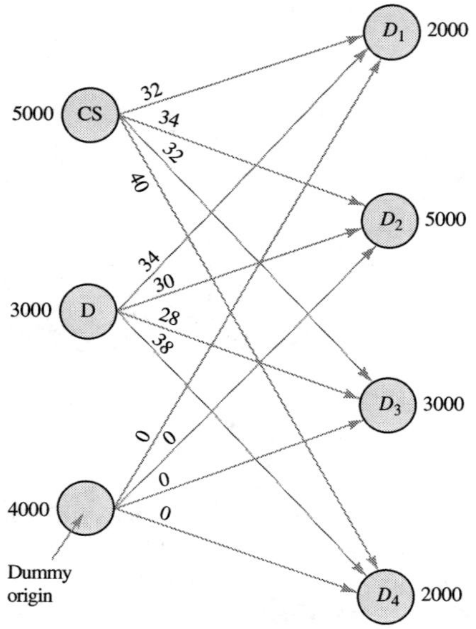

$$
\begin{aligned}
\text{Max } & 32x_{11} + 34x_{12} + 32x_{13} + 40x_{14} + 34x_{21} + 30x_{22} + 28x_{23} + 38x_{24} \\
\text{s.t.} & \\
& x_{11} + x_{12} + x_{13} + x_{14} \le 5000 \\
& x_{21} + x_{22} + x_{23} + x_{24} \le 3000 \\
& x_{31} + x_{32} + x_{33} + x_{34} \le 4000 \\
& x_{11} + x_{21} + x_{31} = 2000 \\
& x_{12} + x_{22} + x_{32} = 5000 \\
& x_{13} + x_{23} + x_{33} = 3000 \\
& x_{14} + x_{24} + x_{34} = 2000 \\
& x_{ij} \ge 0 \quad \text{for all } i, j
\end{aligned}
$$

Optimal Solution	Units	Cost
Clifton Springs-D_2	4,000	\$136,000
Clifton Springs-D_4	1,000	40,000
Danville-D_1	2,000	68,000
Danville-D_4	1,000	38,000
	Total	\$282,000

Customer 2 demand has a shortfall of 1000; customer 3 demand of 3000 is not satisfied

10. 1–A 300; 1–C 1200; 2–A 1200; 3–A 500; 3–B 500

12. a.

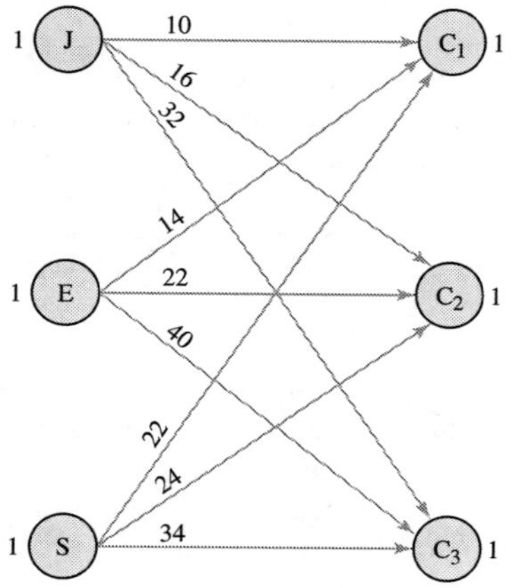

b.

$$
\begin{aligned}
\text{Min } & 10x_{11} + 16x_{12} + 32x_{13} + 14x_{21} + 22x_{22} + 40x_{23} + 22x_{31} + 24x_{32} + 34x_{33} \\
\text{s.t.} & \\
& x_{11} + x_{12} + x_{13} \le 1 \\
& x_{21} + x_{22} + x_{23} \le 1 \\
& x_{31} + x_{32} + x_{33} \le 1 \\
& x_{11} + x_{21} + x_{31} = 1 \\
& x_{12} + x_{22} + x_{32} = 1 \\
& x_{13} + x_{23} + x_{33} = 1 \\
& x_{ij} \ge 0 \quad \text{for all } i, j
\end{aligned}
$$

Solution $x_{12} = 1, x_{21} = 1, x_{33} = 1$; total completion time = 64

14. b.

Green:	Job 1	\$ 26
Brown:	Job 2	34
Red:	Job 3	38
Blue:	Job 4	39
White:	Job 5	25
	Total Cost	\$162

16. b. Toy to 2, Auto Parts to 4, Housewares to 3, Video to 1

18. a. Plano: Kansas City and Dallas
Flagstaff: Los Angeles
Springfield: Chicago, Columbus, and Atlanta
Boulder: Newark and Denver
Cost = \$216,000

b. Nashville

c. Columbus is switched from Springfield to Nashville
Cost = \$227,000

20. A to MS, B to Ph.D., C to MBA, D to undergrad
Maximum total rating = 13.3

22. a.

	Supplier					
Division	1	2	3	4	5	6
1	614	660	534	680	590	630
2	603	639	702	693	693	630
3	865	830	775	850	900	930
4	532	553	511	581	595	553
5	720	648	684	693	657	747

b. Optimal solution:

Supplier 1–Division 2	\$ 603
Supplier 2–Division 5	648
Supplier 3–Division 3	775
Supplier 5–Division 1	590
Supplier 6–Division 4	553
Total	\$3169

23. a.

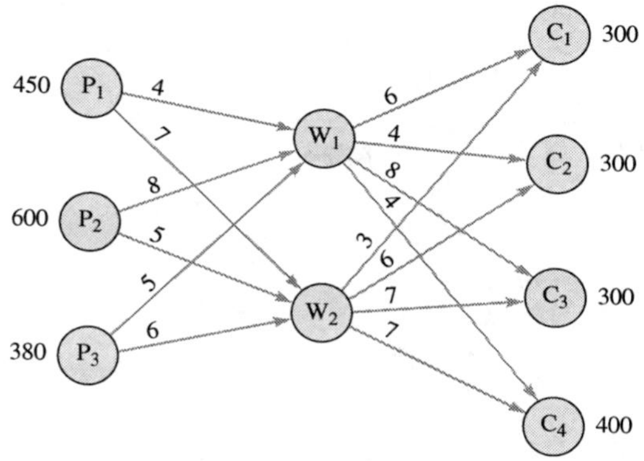

b.

Min $4x_{14}+7x_{15}+8x_{24}+5x_{25}+5x_{34}+6x_{35}+6x_{46}+4x_{47}+8x_{48}+4x_{49}+3x_{56}+6x_{57}+7x_{58}+7x_{59}$

s.t.

$$x_{14}+x_{15} \le 450$$
$$x_{24}+x_{25} \le 600$$
$$x_{34}+x_{35} \le 380$$
$$-x_{14}-x_{24}-x_{34}+x_{46}+x_{47}+x_{48}+x_{49} = 0$$
$$-x_{15}-x_{25}-x_{35}+x_{56}+x_{57}+x_{58}+x_{59} = 0$$
$$x_{46}+x_{56} = 300$$
$$x_{47}+x_{57} = 300$$
$$x_{48}+x_{58} = 300$$
$$x_{49}+x_{59} = 400$$

c.

	Warehouse	
Plant	1	2
1	450	—
2	—	600
3	250	—

Total cost = $11,850

	Customer			
Warehouse	1	2	3	4
1	—	300	—	400
2	300	—	300	—

24. c. $x_{14} = 320, x_{25} = 600, x_{47} = 300, x_{49} = 20, x_{56} = 300, x_{58} = 300, x_{39} = 380$
Cost = $11,220

26. c. Note: Augusta: 1, Tupper Lake: 2, Albany: 3, Portsmouth: 4, Boston: 5, New York: 6, Philadelphia: 7

Variable	Value	Variable	Value
x_{13}	50	x_{36}	0
x_{14}	250	x_{37}	150
x_{23}	100	x_{45}	150
x_{24}	0	x_{46}	100
x_{35}	0	x_{47}	0

Objective function = 4300

28.

Optimal Solution	Units Shipped	Cost
Muncie–Cincinnati	1	6
Cincinnati–Concord	3	84
Brazil–Louisville	6	18
Louisville–Macon	2	88
Louisville–Greenwood	4	136
Xenia–Cincinnati	5	15
Cincinnati–Chatham	3	72
	Total	419

Two rail cars must be held at Muncie until a buyer is found

32. c. Regular-month 1: 275; overtime-month 1: 25; inventory at end of month 1: 150
Regular-month 2: 200; overtime-month 2: 50; inventory at end of month 2: 150
Regular-month 3: 100; overtime-month 3: 50; inventory at end of month 3: 0

Chapter 11

2. a.

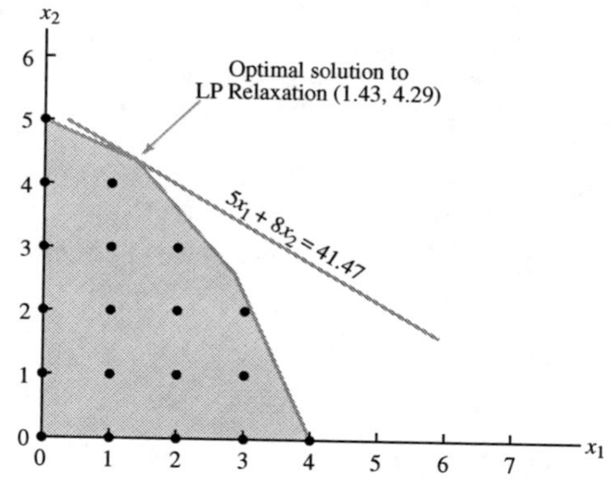

b. The optimal solution to the LP Relaxation is given by $x_1 = 1.43$, $x_2 = 4.29$ with an objective function value of 41.47. Rounding down gives the feasible integer solution $x_1 = 1$, $x_2 = 4$; its value is 37

c.

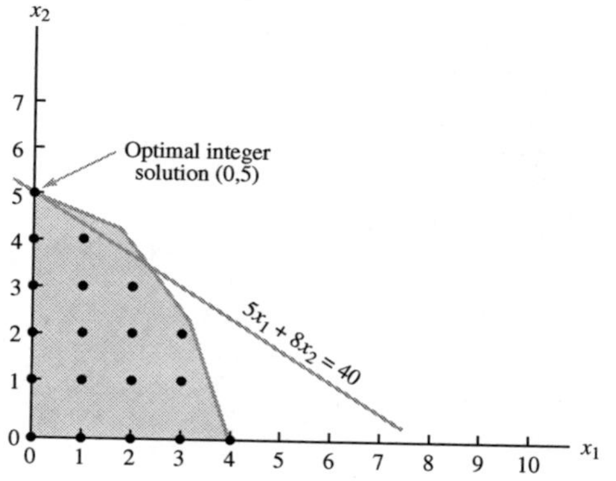

The optimal solution is given by $x_1 = 0$, $x_2 = 5$; its value is 40. It is not the same solution as found by rounding down; it provides a 3-unit increase in the value of the objective function

4. a. $x_1 = 3.67, x_2 = 0$; Value = 36.7
Rounded: $x_1 = 3, x_2 = 0$; Value = 30
Lower bound = 30; Upper bound = 36.7
b. $x_1 = 3, x_2 = 2$; Value = 36
c. Alternative optimal solutions: $x_1 = 0, x_2 = 5$
$x_1 = 2, x_2 = 4$

5. a. The feasible mixed-integer solutions are indicated by the boldface vertical lines in the graph

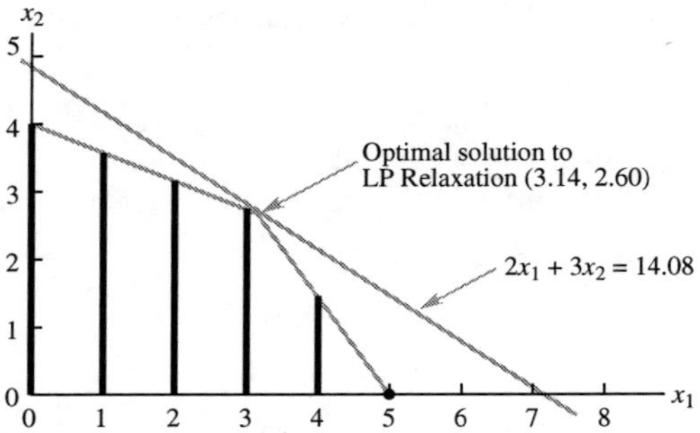

b. The optimal solution to the LP Relaxation is given by $x_1 = 3.14, x_2 = 2.60$; its value is 14.08
Rounding down the value of x_1 to find a feasible mixed-integer solution yields $x_1 = 3, x_2 = 2.60$ with a value of 13.8; this solution is clearly not optimal; with $x_1 = 3$, x_2 can be made larger without violating the constraints
c. The optimal solution to the MILP is given by $x_1 = 3, x_2 = 2.67$; its value is 14 as shown in the following figure

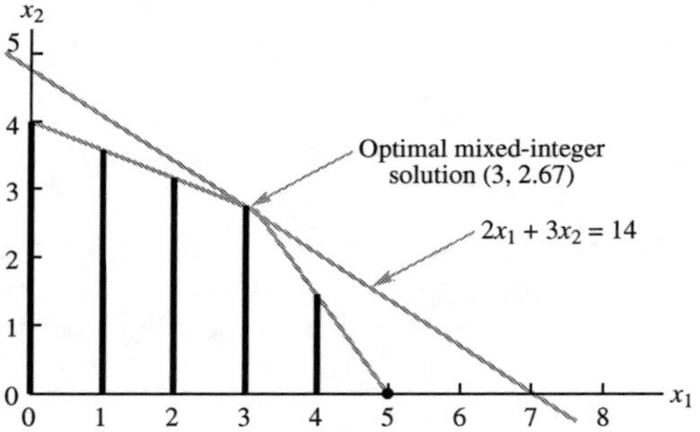

6. b. $x_1 = 1.96, x_2 = 5.48$; Value = 7.44
Rounded: $x_1 = 1.96, x_2 = 5$; Value = 6.96
Lower bound = 6.96; Upper bound = 7.44
c. $x_1 = 1.29, x_2 = 6$; Value = 7.29

7. a. $x_1 + x_3 + x_5 + x_6 = 2$
b. $x_3 - x_5 = 0$
c. $x_1 + x_4 = 1$
d. $x_4 \leq x_1$
$x_4 \leq x_3$
e. $x_4 \leq x_1$
$x_4 \leq x_3$
$x_4 \geq x_1 + x_3 - 1$

8. a. $x_3 = 1, x_4 = 1, x_6 = 1$; Value = 17,500
b. Add $x_1 + x_2 \leq 1$
c. Add $x_3 - x_4 = 0$

10. b. Choose locations B and E

12. a. $P \leq 15 + 15Y_P$
$D \leq 15 + 15Y_D$
$J \leq 15 + 15Y_J$
$Y_P + Y_D + Y_J \leq 1$
b. $P = 15, D = 15, J = 30$
$Y_P = 0, Y_D = 0, Y_J = 1$; Value = 50

13. a. Add the following multiple-choice constraint to the problem
$y_1 + y_2 = 1$
New optimal solution: $y_1 = 1$, $y_3 = 1$, $x_{12} = 10$, $x_{31} = 30, x_{52} = 10, x_{53} = 20$
Value = 940
b. Because one plant is already located in St. Louis, it is only necessary to add the following constraint to the model
$y_3 + y_4 \leq 1$
New optimal solution: $y_4 = 1, x_{42} = 20, x_{43} = 20, x_{51} = 30$
Value = 860

14. b. Modernize plants 1 and 3 or plants 4 and 5
d. Modernize plants 1 and 3

16. b. Use all part-time employees
Bring on as follows: 9:00 A.M.–6, 11:00 A.M.–2, 12:00 noon–6, 1:00 P.M.–1, 3:00 P.M.–6
Cost = \$672
c. Same as in part (b)
d. New solution is to bring on 1 full-time employee at 9:00 A.M., 4 more at 11:00 A.M. and part-time employees as follows:
9:00 A.M.–5, 12:00 noon–5, and 3:00 P.M.–2

18. a. 52, 49, 36, 83, 39, 70, 79, 59
b. Thick crust, cheese blend, chunky sauce, medium sausage. Six of eight consumers will prefer this pizza (75%)

20. a. New objective function: Min $25x_1 + 40x_2 + 40x_3 + 40x_4 + 25x_5$
b. $x_4 = x_5 = 1$; modernize the Ohio and California plants
c. Add the constraint $x_2 + x_3 = 1$
d. $x_1 = x_3 = 1$

22. $x_1 + x_2 + x_3 = 3y_1 + 5y_2 + 7y_3$
$y_1 + y_2 + y_3 = 1$

24. a. $x_{111}, x_{112}, x_{121}$
b. $x_{111} + x_{112} + x_{121} \leq 1$
c. $x_{531} + x_{532} + x_{533} + x_{541} + x_{542} + x_{543} + x_{551} + x_{552} + x_{561} \leq 1$
d. Only two screens are available
e. $x_{213} + x_{222} + x_{231} + x_{422} + x_{431} + x_{531} + x_{532} + x_{533} + x_{631} + x_{632} + x_{633} \leq 2$

Chapter 12

2.

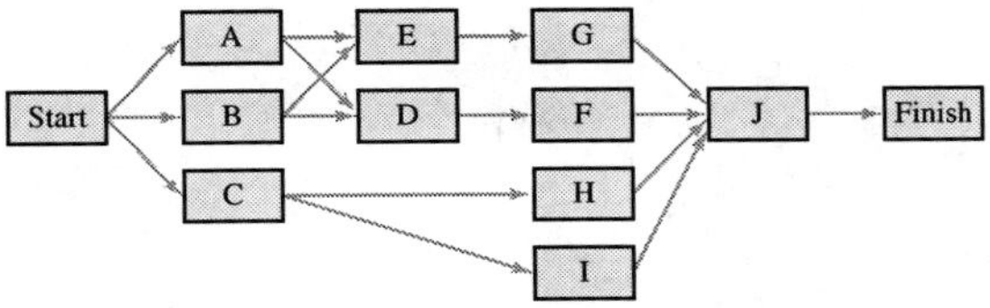

3.

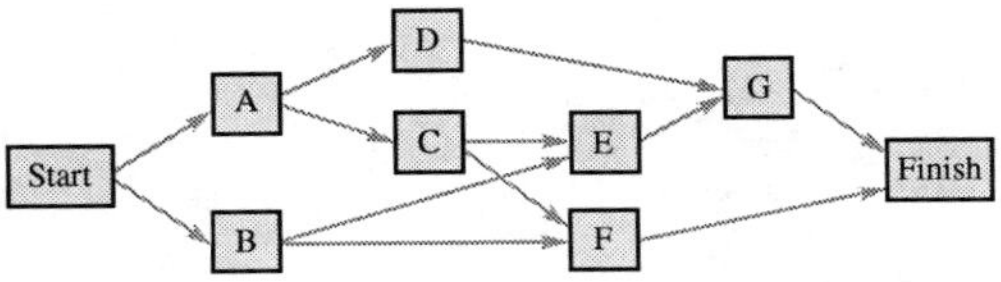

4. a. A–D–G
   b. No; Time = 15 months

6. a. Critial path: A–D–F–H
   b. 22 weeks
   c. No, it is a critical activity
   d. Yes, 2 weeks
   e. Schedule for activity E:

Earliest start	3
Latest start	4
Earliest finish	10
Latest finish	11

8. b. B–C–E–F–H
   d. Yes, time = 49 weeks

10. a.

Activity	Optimistic	Most Probable	Pessimistic	Expected Times	Variance
A	4	5.0	6	5.00	0.11
B	8	9.0	10	9.00	0.11
C	7	7.5	11	8.00	0.44
D	7	9.0	10	8.83	0.25
E	6	7.0	9	7.17	0.25
F	5	6.0	7	6.00	0.11

   b. Critical activities: B–D–F
   Expected project completion time: 9.00 + 8.83 + 6.00 = 23.83
   Variance of projection completion time: 0.11 + 0.25 + 0.11 = 0.47

12. a. A–D–H–I
    b. 25.66 days
    c. 0.2578

13.

Activity	Expected Time	Variance
A	5	0.11
B	3	0.03
C	7	0.11
D	6	0.44
E	7	0.44
F	3	0.11
G	10	0.44
H	8	1.78

From Problem 6, A–D–F–H is the critical path, so $E(T) = 5 + 6 + 3 + 8 = 22$

$\sigma^2 = 0.11 + 0.44 + 0.11 + 1.78 = 2.44$

$$z = \frac{\text{Time} - E(T)}{\sigma} = \frac{\text{Time} - 22}{\sqrt{2.44}}$$

		Area
a. Time = 21:	$z = -0.64$	0.2389

$P(21 \text{ weeks}) = 0.500 - 0.2389 = 0.2611$

		Area
b. Time = 22:	$z = 0$	0.0000

$P(22 \text{ weeks}) = 0.5000$

		Area
c. Time = 25:	$z = +1.92$	0.4726

$P(25 \text{ weeks}) = 0.5000 + 0.4726 = 0.9726$

14. a. A–C–E–G–H
    b. 52 weeks (1 year)
    c. 0.0174
    d. 0.0934
    e. 10 month doubtful
    13 month very likely
    Estimate 12 months (1 year)

16. a.

$E(T)$	Variance
16	3.92
13	2.03
10	1.27

    b. 0.9783, approximately 1.00, approximately 1.00

18. c. A–B–D–G–H–I, 14.17 weeks
    d. 0.0951, yes

20. b. Crash B(1 week), D(2 weeks), E(1 week), F(1 week), G(1 week)
    Total cost = $2427
    c. All activities are critical

21. a.

Activity	Earliest Start	Latest Start	Earliest Finish	Latest Finish	Slack	Critical Activity
A	0	0	3	3	0	Yes
B	0	1	2	3	1	
C	3	3	8	8	0	Yes
D	2	3	7	8	1	
E	8	8	14	14	0	Yes
F	8	10	10	12	2	
G	10	12	12	14	2	

Critical Path: A–C–E

Project completion time $= t_A + t_C + t_E = 3 + 5 + 6 =$ 14 days

b. Total cost = \$8400

22. a.

Activity	Max Crash Days	Crash Cost/Day
A	1	600
B	1	700
C	2	400
D	2	400
E	2	500
F	1	400
G	1	500

$$
\begin{aligned}
\text{Min}\quad & 600Y_A + 700Y_B + 400Y_C + 400Y_D + 500Y_E + 400Y_F + 400Y_G \\
\text{s.t.}\quad & \\
& X_A + Y_A \geq 3 \\
& X_B + Y_B \geq 2 \\
& -X_A + X_C + Y_C \geq 5 \\
& -X_B + X_D + Y_D \geq 5 \\
& -X_C + X_E + Y_E \geq 6 \\
& -X_D + X_E + Y_E \geq 6 \\
& -X_C + X_F + Y_F \geq 2 \\
& -X_D + X_F + Y_F \geq 2 \\
& -X_F + X_G + Y_G \geq 2 \\
& -X_E + X_{FIN} \geq 0 \\
& -X_G + X_{FIN} \geq 0 \\
& X_{FIN} \leq 12 \\
& Y_A \leq 1 \\
& Y_B \leq 1 \\
& Y_C \leq 2 \\
& Y_D \leq 2 \\
& Y_E \leq 2 \\
& Y_F \leq 1 \\
& Y_G \leq 1 \\
& \text{All } X, Y \geq 0
\end{aligned}
$$

b. Solution of the linear programming model in part (a) shows

Activity	Crash	Crashing Cost
C	1 day	\$400
E	1 day	500
	Total	\$900

c. Total cost = Normal cost + Crashing cost
= \$8400 + \$900 = \$9300

24. c. A–B–C–F, 31 weeks
d. Crash A(2 weeks), B(2 weeks), C(1 week), D(1 week), E(1 week)
e. All activities are critical
f. \$112,500

Chapter 13

1. a. $Q^* = \sqrt{\dfrac{2DC_0}{C_h}} = \sqrt{\dfrac{2(3600)(20)}{0.25(3)}} = 438.18$

b. $r = dm = \dfrac{3600}{250}(5) = 72$

c. $T = \dfrac{250Q^*}{D} = \dfrac{250(438.18)}{3600} = 30.43$ days

d. $TC = \dfrac{1}{2}QC_h + \dfrac{D}{Q}C_0$

$= \dfrac{1}{2}(438.18)(0.25)(3) + \dfrac{3600}{438.18}(20) = \$328.63$

2. \$164.32 for each; Total cost = \$328.64

4. a. 1095.45
b. 240
c. 22.82 days
d. \$273.86 for each; Total cost = \$547.72

6. a. 15.95
b. \$2106
c. 15.04
d. 16.62 days

8. $Q^* = 11.73$, use 12
5 classes per year
\$225,200

10. $Q^* = 1414.21$
$T = 28.28$ days
Production runs of 7.07 days

12. a. 1500
b. 4; 3 month cycle time
c. Change to $Q^* = 1500$
d. Savings = \$12,510

13. a. $Q^* = \sqrt{\dfrac{2DC_0}{(1 - D/P)C_h}}$

$= \sqrt{\dfrac{2(7200)(150)}{(1 - 7200/25{,}000)(0.18)(14.50)}} = 1078.12$

b. Number of production runs $= \dfrac{D}{Q^*} = \dfrac{7200}{1078.12} = 6.68$

c. $T = \dfrac{250Q}{D} = \dfrac{250(1078.12)}{7200} = 37.43$ days

d. Production run length $= \dfrac{Q}{P/250}$

$= \dfrac{1078.12}{25{,}000/250} = 10.78$ days

e. Maximum inventory $= \left(1 - \frac{D}{P}\right)Q$

$$= \left(1 - \frac{7200}{25{,}000}\right)(1078.12)$$

$$= 767.62$$

f. Holding cost $= \frac{1}{2}\left(1 - \frac{D}{P}\right)QC_h$

$$= \frac{1}{2}\left(1 - \frac{7200}{25{,}000}\right)(1078.12)(0.18)(14.50)$$

$$= \$1001.74$$

Ordering cost $= \frac{D}{Q}C_0 = \frac{7200}{1078.12}(150) = \$1001.74$

Total cost $= \$2003.48$

g. $r = dm = \left(\frac{D}{250}\right)m = \frac{7200}{250}(15) = 432$

14. New $Q^* = 4509$

15. a. $Q^* = \sqrt{\frac{2DC_0}{C_h}\left(\frac{C_h + C_b}{C_b}\right)}$

$$= \sqrt{\frac{2(12{,}000)(25)}{0.50}\left(\frac{0.50 + 5}{0.50}\right)} = 1148.91$$

b. $S^* = Q^*\left(\frac{C_h}{C_h + C_b}\right) = 1148.91\left(\frac{0.50}{0.50 + 5}\right) = 104.45$

c. Max inventory $= Q^* - S^* = 1044.46$

d. $T = \frac{250Q^*}{D} = \frac{250(1148.91)}{12{,}000} = 23.94$ days

e. Holding $= \frac{(Q - S)^2}{2Q}C_h = \$237.38$

Ordering $= \frac{D}{Q}C_0 = \$261.12$

Backorder $= \frac{S^2}{2Q}C_b = \$23.74$

Total cost $= \$522.24$

The total cost for the EOQ model in Problem 4 was \$547.72; allowing backorders reduces the total cost

16. 135.55; $r = dm - S$; less than

18. 64, 24.44

20. $Q^* = 100$; Total cost = \$3,601.50

21. $Q = \sqrt{\frac{2DC_0}{C_h}}$

$$Q_1 = \sqrt{\frac{2(500)(40)}{0.20(10)}} = 141.42$$

$$Q_2 = \sqrt{\frac{2(500)(40)}{0.20(9.7)}} = 143.59$$

Because Q_1 is over its limit of 99 units, Q_1 cannot be optimal (see Problem 23); use $Q_2 = 143.59$ as the optimal order quantity

Total cost $= \frac{1}{2}QC_h + \frac{D}{Q}C_0 + DC$

$$= 139.28 + 139.28 + 4850.00 = \$5128.56$$

22. $Q^* = 300$; Savings = \$480

24. a. 500

b. 580.4

25. a. $c_o = 80 - 50 = 30$

$$c_u = 125 - 80 = 45$$

$$P(D \le Q^*) = \frac{c_u}{c_u + c_o} = \frac{45}{45 + 30} = 0.60$$

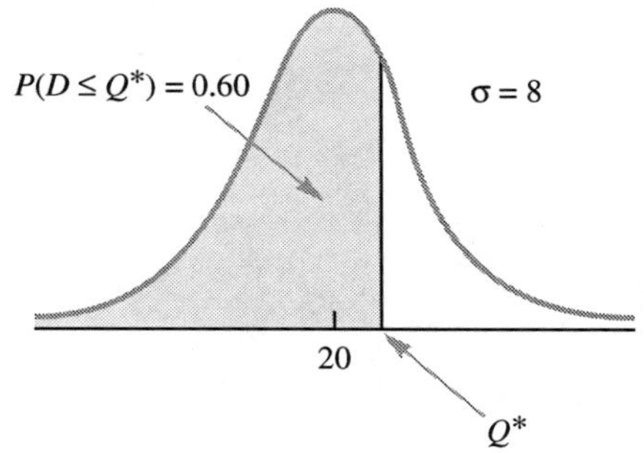

For an area of 0.60 below Q^*, $z = 0.25$

$Q^* = 20 + 0.25(8) = 22$

b. $P(\text{Sell all}) = P(D \ge Q^*) = 1 - 0.60 = 0.40$

26. a. \$150

b. \$240 − \$150 = \$90

c. 47

d. 0.625

28. a. 440

b. 0.60

c. 710

d. $c_u = \$17$

29. a. $r = dm = (200/250)15 = 12$

b. $\frac{D}{Q} = \frac{200}{25} = 8$ orders/year

The limit of 1 stock-out per year means that $P(\text{Stock-out/cycle}) = 1/8 = 0.125$

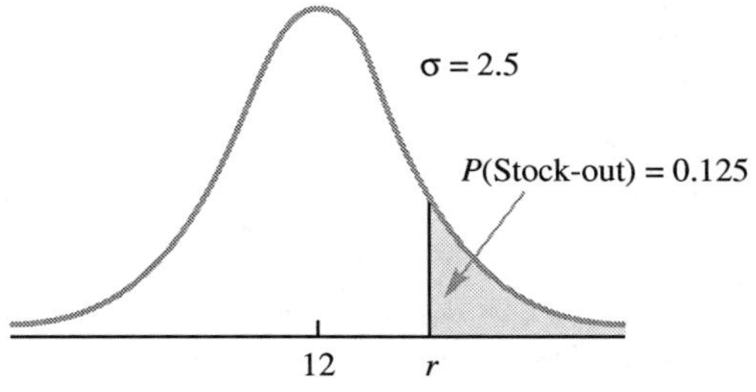

For area in tail = 0.125, $z = 1.15$

$$z = \frac{r - 12}{2.5} = 1.15$$

or

$$r = 12 + 1.15(2.5) = 14.875 \approx 15$$

c. Safety stock = 3 units

Added cost = 3(\$5) = \$15/year

30. a. 13.68 (14)
b. 17.83 (18)
c. 2, \$10; 6, \$30

32. a. 31.62
b. 19.86 (20); 0.2108
c. 5, \$15

33. a. 1/52 = 0.0192
b. $M = \mu + z\sigma = 60 + 2.07(12) = 85$
c. $M = 35 + (0.9808)(85 - 35) = 84$

34. a. 243
b. 93, \$54.87
c. 613
d. 163, \$96.17
e. Yes, added cost only \$41.30 per year
f. Yes, added cost would be \$4130 per year

36. a. 40
b. 62.25; 7.9
c. 54
d. 36

Chapter 14

2. a. 0.4512
b. 0.6988
c. 0.3012

4. 0.3333, 0.2222, 0.1481, 0.0988; 0.1976

5. a. $P_0 = 1 - \dfrac{\lambda}{\mu} = 1 - \dfrac{10}{12} = 0.1667$

b. $L_q = \dfrac{\lambda^2}{\mu(\mu - \lambda)} = \dfrac{10^2}{12(12 - 10)} = 4.1667$

c. $W_q = \dfrac{L_q}{\lambda} = 0.4167$ hour (25 minutes)

d. $W = W_q + \dfrac{1}{\mu} = 0.5$ hour (30 minutes)

e. $P_w = \dfrac{\lambda}{\mu} = \dfrac{10}{12} = 0.8333$

6. a. 0.3750
b. 1.0417
c. 0.8333 minutes (50 seconds)
d. 0.6250
e. Yes

8. 0.20, 3.2, 4, 3.2, 4, 0.80
Slightly poorer service

10. a. New: 0.3333, 1.3333, 2, 0.6667, 1, 0.6667
Experienced: 0.50, 0.50, 1, 0.25, 0.50, 0.50
b. New \$74; experienced \$50; hire experienced

11. a. $\lambda = 2.5; \quad \mu = \dfrac{60}{10} = 6$ customers per hour

$$L_q = \frac{\lambda^2}{\mu(\mu - \lambda)} = \frac{(2.5)^2}{6(6 - 2.5)} = 0.2976$$

$$L = L_q + \frac{\lambda}{\mu} = 0.7143$$

$W_q = \dfrac{L_q}{\lambda} = 0.1190$ hours (7.14 minutes)

$W = W_q + \dfrac{1}{\mu} = 0.2857$ hours

$$P_w = \frac{\lambda}{\mu} = \frac{2.5}{6} = 0.4167$$

b. No; $W_q = 7.14$ minutes; firm should increase the service rate (μ) for the consultant or hire a second consultant

c. $\mu = \dfrac{60}{8} = 7.5$ customers per hour

$$L_q = \frac{\lambda^2}{\mu(\mu - \lambda)} = \frac{(2.5)^2}{7.5(7.5 - 2.5)} = 0.1667$$

$W_q = \dfrac{L_q}{\lambda} = 0.0667$ hour (4 minutes)

The service goal is being met

12. a. 0.25, 2.25, 3, 0.15 hours, 0.20 hours, 0.75
b. The service needs improvement

14. a. 8
b. 0.3750
c. 1.0417
d. 12.5 minutes
e. 0.6250
f. Add a second consultant

16. a. 0.50
b. 0.50
c. 0.10 hours (6 minutes)
d. 0.20 hours (12 minutes)
e. Yes, $W_q = 6$ minutes is most likely acceptable for a marina

18. a. $k = 2$; $\lambda/\mu = 5.4/3 = 1.8$; $P_0 = 0.0526$

$$L_q = \frac{(\lambda/\mu)^2 \lambda\mu}{(k - 1)!(2\mu - \lambda)^2} P_0$$

$$= \frac{(1.8)^2(5.4)(3)}{(2 - 1)!(6 - 5.4)^2}(0.0526) = 7.67$$

$$L = L_q + \lambda/\mu = 7.67 + 1.8 = 9.47$$

$W_q = \dfrac{L_q}{\lambda} = \dfrac{7.67}{5.4} = 1.42$ minutes

$W = W_q + 1/\mu = 1.42 + 0.33 = 1.75$ minutes

$$P_W = \frac{1}{k!}\left(\frac{\lambda}{\mu}\right)^k \left(\frac{k\mu}{k\mu - \lambda}\right) P_0$$

$$= \frac{1}{2!}(1.8)^2\left(\frac{6}{6 - 5.4}\right)0.0526 = 0.8526$$

b. $L_q = 7.67$; Yes
c. $W = 1.75$ minutes

20. a. Use $k = 2$
$W = 3.7037$ minutes
$L = 4.4444$
$P_w = 0.7111$

b. For $k = 3$
$W = 7.1778$ minutes
$L = 15.0735$ customers
$P_N = 0.8767$
Expand post office

21. From Problem 11, a service time of 8 minutes has $\mu = 60/8 = 7.5$

$$L_q = \frac{\lambda^2}{\mu(\mu - \lambda)} = \frac{(2.5)^2}{7.5(7.5 - 2.5)} = 0.1667$$

$$L = L_q + \frac{\lambda}{\mu} = 0.50$$

Total cost = $\$25L + \$16$
= $25(0.50) + 16 = \$28.50$

Two channels: $\lambda = 2.5$; $\mu = 60/10 = 6$
With $P_0 = 0.6552$,

$$L_q = \frac{(\lambda/\mu)^2\lambda\mu}{1!(2\mu - \lambda)^2}P_0 = 0.0189$$

$$L = L_q + \frac{\lambda}{\mu} = 0.4356$$

Total cost = $25(0.4356) + 2(16) = \$42.89$
Use one consultant with an 8-minute service time

22.

Characteristic	A	B	C
a. P_0	0.2000	0.5000	0.4286
b. L_q	3.2000	0.5000	0.1524
c. L	4.0000	1.0000	0.9524
d. W_q	0.1333	0.0208	0.0063
e. W	0.1667	0.0417	0.0397
f. P_w	0.8000	0.5000	0.2286

The two-channel System C provides the best service

24. a. 0.0466, 0.05
b. 1.4
c. 11:00 A.M.

25. $\lambda = 4$, $W = 10$ minutes
a. $\mu = ½ = 0.5$
b. $W_q = W - 1/\mu = 10 - 1/0.5 = 8$ minutes
c. $L = \lambda W = 4(10) = 40$

26. a. 0.2668, 10 minutes, 0.6667
b. 0.0667, 7 minutes, 0.4669
c. \$25.33; \$33.34; one-channel

27. a. ⅔ hours = 0.25 per hour
b. 1/3.2 hours = 0.3125 per hour
c. $$L_q = \frac{\lambda^2\sigma^2 + (\lambda/\mu)^2}{2(1 - \lambda/\mu)}$$
$$= \frac{(0.25)^2(2)^2 + (0.25/0.3125)^2}{2(1 - 0.25/0.3125)} = 2.225$$
d. $$W_q = \frac{L_q}{\lambda} = \frac{2.225}{0.25} = 8.9 \text{ hours}$$
e. $$W = W_q + \frac{1}{\mu} = 8.9 + \frac{1}{0.3125} = 12.1 \text{ hours}$$
f. Same as $$P_w = \frac{\lambda}{\mu} = \frac{0.25}{0.3125} = 0.80$$
80% of the time the welder is busy

28. a. 10, 9.6
b. Design A with $\mu = 10$
c. 0.05, 0.01
d. A: 0.5, 0.3125, 0.8125, 0.0625, 0.1625, 0.5
B: 0.4792, 0.2857, 0.8065, 0.0571, 0.1613, 0.5208
e. Design B has slightly less waiting time

30. a. $\lambda = 42$; $\mu = 20$

i	$(\lambda/\mu)^i/i!$
0	1.0000
1	2.1000
2	2.2050
3	1.5435
Total	6.8485

j	P_j
0	1/6.8485 = 0.1460
1	2.1/6.8485 = 0.3066
2	2.2050/6.8485 = 0.3220
3	1.5435/6.8485 = 0.2254
	1.0000

b. 0.2254
c. $L = \lambda/\mu(1 - P_k) = 42/20(1 - 0.2254) = 1.6267$
d. Four lines will be necessary; the probability of denied access is 0.1499

32. a. 31.03%
b. 27.59%
c. 0.2759, 0.1092, 0.0351
d. 3, 10.92%

34. $N = 5$; $\lambda = 0.025$; $\mu = 0.20$; $\lambda/\mu = 0.125$
a.

n	$\frac{N!}{(N-n)!}\left(\frac{\lambda}{\mu}\right)^n$
0	1.0000
1	0.6250
2	0.3125
3	0.1172
4	0.0293
5	0.0037
Total	2.0877

$P_0 = 1/2.0877 = 0.4790$

b. $L_q = N - \left(\frac{\lambda + \mu}{\lambda}\right)(1 - P_0)$

$= 5 - \left(\frac{0.225}{0.025}\right)(1 - 0.4790) = 0.3110$

c. $L = L_q + (1 - P_0) = 0.3110 + (1 - 0.4790)$
$= 0.8321$

d. $W_q = \frac{L_q}{(N - L)\lambda} = \frac{0.3110}{(5 - 0.8321)(0.025)}$

$= 2.9854$ minutes

e. $W = W_q + \frac{1}{\mu} = 2.9854 + \frac{1}{0.20} = 7.9854$ minutes

f. Trips/day = (8 hours)(60 minutes/hour)(λ)
= (8)(60)(0.025) = 12 trips

Time at copier: 12 × 7.9854 = 95.8 minutes/day
Wait time at copier: 12 × 2.9854 = 35.8 minutes/day

g. Yes, five assistants × 35.8 = 179 minutes (3 hours/day), so 3 hours per day are lost to waiting
(35.8/480)(100) = 7.5% of each assistant's day is spent waiting for the copier

Chapter 15

2. a. c = variable cost per unit
x = demand
Profit = $(50 - c)x - 30{,}000$

b. Base: Profit = (50 − 20)1200 − 30,000 = 6,000
Worst: Profit = (50 − 24)300 − 30,000 = −22,200
Best: Profit = (50 − 16)2100 − 30,000 = 41,400

c. Simulation will be helpful in estimating the probability of a loss

4. a.

Number of New Accounts	Interval
0	0.00 but less than 0.01
1	0.01 but less than 0.05
2	0.05 but less than 0.15
3	0.15 but less than 0.40
4	0.40 but less than 0.80
5	0.80 but less than 0.95
6	0.95 but less than 1.00

b. 4, 3, 3, 5, 2, 6, 4, 4, 4, 2
37 new accounts

c. First-year commission = $185,000
Cost of 10 seminars = $35,000
Yes

5. a.

Stock Price Change	Interval
−2	0.00 but less than 0.05
−1	0.05 but less than 0.15
0	0.15 but less than 0.40
Stock Price Change	**Interval**
+1	0.40 but less than 0.60
+2	0.60 but less than 0.80
+3	0.80 but less than 0.90
+4	0.90 but less than 1.00

b. Beginning price $39
0.1091 indicates −1 change; $38
0.9407 indicates +4 change; $42
0.1941 indicates 0 change; $42
0.8083 indicates +3 change; $45 (ending price)

6. a. 0.00–0.83, 0.83–0.89, 0.89–0.94, 0.94–0.96, 0.96–0.98, 0.98–0.99, 0.99–1.00

b. 4 claims paid; Total = $22,000

8. a. Atlanta wins each game if random number is in interval 0.00–0.60, 0.00–0.55, 0.00–0.48, 0.00–0.45, 0.00–0.48, 0.00–0.55, 0.00–0.50

b. Atlanta wins games 1, 2, 4, and 6
Atlanta wins series 4 to 2

c. Repeat many times; record % of Atlanta wins

9. a. Base-case based on most likely;
Time = 6 + 5 + 14 + 8 = 33 weeks
Worst: Time = 8 + 7 + 18 + 10 = 43 weeks
Best: Time = 5 + 3 + 10 + 8 = 26 weeks

b. 0.1778 for A: 5 weeks
0.9617 for B: 7 weeks
0.6849 for C: 14 weeks
0.4503 for D: 8 weeks; Total = 34 weeks

c. Simulation will provide an estimate of the probability of 35 weeks or less

10. a.

Hand Value	Interval
17	0.0000 but less than 0.1654
18	0.1654 but less than 0.2717
19	0.2717 but less than 0.3780
20	0.3780 but less than 0.4797
21	0.4797 but less than 0.5769
Broke	0.5769 but less than 1.0000

b, c, & d. Dealer wins 13 hands, Player wins 5, 2 pushes

e. Player wins 7, dealer wins 13

12. a. $7, $3, $12

b. Purchase: 0.00–0.25, 0.25–0.70, 0.70–1.00
Labor: 0.00–0.10, 0.10–0.35, 0.35–0.70, 0.70–1.00
Transportation: 0.00–0.75, 0.75–1.00

c. $5

d. $7

e. Provide probability profit less than $5/unit

14. Selected cell formulas for the worksheet shown in Figure F15.14 are as follows:

Cell	Formula
B13	=$C$7+RAND()*($C$8−$C$7)
C13	=NORMINV(RAND(),$G$7,$G$8)
D13	=($C$3−B13)*C13−$C$4

a. The mean profit should be approximately $6000; simulation results will vary with most simulations having a mean profit between $5500 and $6500

FIGURE F15.14 WORKSHEET FOR THE MADEIRA MANUFACTURING COMPANY

	A	B	C	D	E	F	G	H
1	**Madeira Manufacturing Company**							
2								
3	Selling Price per Unit		$50					
4	Fixed Cost		$30,000					
5								
6	**Variable Cost (Uniform Distribution)**				**Demand (Normal Distribution)**			
7	Smallest Value		$16		Mean		1200	
8	Largest Value		$24		Standard Deviation		300	
9								
10	**Simulation trials**							
11		Variable						
12	Trial	Cost per Unit	Demand	Profit				
13	1	$17.81	788	($4,681)				
14	2	$18.86	1078	$3,580				
15								

b. 120 to 150 of the 500 simulation trials should show a loss; thus, the probability of a loss should be between 0.24 and 0.30

c. This project appears too risky

16. a. About 36% of simulation runs will show $130,000 as the winning bid

b. $150,000; $10,000

c. Recommended $140,000

18. Selected cell formulas for the worksheet shown in Figure F15.18 are as follows:

Cell	Formula
B11	=$C$4 + RAND()*($C$5−$C$4)
C11	=NORMINV(RAND(),$H$4,$H$5)
D11	=MAX(B11:C11)
G11	=COUNTIF(D11:D1010,"<750")
H11	=G11/COUNT(D11:D1010)

FIGURE F15.18 WORKSHEET FOR THE CONTRACTOR BIDDING

	A	B	C	D	E	F	G	H	I
1	**Contractor Bidding**								
2									
3	**Contractor A (Uniform Distribution)**					**Contractor B (Normal Distribution)**			
4	Smallest Value		$600			Mean		$700	
5	Largest Value		$800			Standard Deviation		$50	
6									
7									
8									
9									
10	**Simulation**					**Results**			
11		Contractor	Contractor	Highest		Contractor's	Number	Probability	
12	Trial	A's Bid	B's Bid	Bid		Bid	of Wins	of Winning	
13	1	$673.00	$720	$720		750	629	0.629	
14	2	$757.00	$655	$757		775	824	0.824	
15	3	$706	$791	$791		785	887	0.887	
16	4	$638	$677	$677					
17									

a. \$750,000 should win roughly 600 to 650 of the 1000 times; the probability of winning the bid should be between 0.60 and 0.65

b. The probability of \$775,000 winning should be roughly 0.82, and the probability of \$785,000 winning should be roughly 0.88; a contractor's bid of \$775,000 is recommended

20. a. Results vary with each simulation run
Approximate results: 50,000 provided \$230,000
60,000 provided \$190,000
70,000 less than \$100,000

b. Recommend 50,000 units

c. Roughly 0.75

22. Very poor operation; some customers wait 30 minutes or more

24. b. Waiting time approximately 0.8 minutes

c. 30% to 35% of customers have to wait

Chapter 16

2. a. 0.82

b. $\pi_1 = 0.5, \pi_2 = 0.5$

c. $\pi_1 = 0.6, \pi_2 = 0.4$

3. a. 0.10 as given by the transition probability

b. $\pi_1 = 0.90\pi_1 + 0.30\pi_2$ (1)

$\pi_2 = 0.10\pi_1 + 0.70\pi_2$ (2)

$\pi_1 + \pi_2 = 1$ (3)

Using (1) and (3),

$$0.10\pi_1 - 0.30\pi_2 = 0$$
$$0.10\pi_1 - 0.30(1 - \pi_1) = 0$$
$$0.10\pi_1 - 0.30 + 0.30\pi_1 = 0$$
$$0.40\pi_1 = 0.30$$
$$\pi_1 = 0.75$$
$$\pi_2 = (1 - \pi_1) = 0.25$$

4. a. $\pi_1 = 0.92, \pi_2 = 0.08$

b. \$85

6. a.

	City	Suburbs
City	0.98	0.02
Suburbs	0.01	0.99

b. $\pi_1 = 0.333, \pi_2 = 0.667$

c. City will decrease from 40% to 33%; suburbs will increase from 60% to 67%

7. a. $\pi_1 = 0.85\pi_1 + 0.20\pi_2 + 0.15\pi_3$ (1)

$\pi_2 = 0.10\pi_1 + 0.75\pi_2 + 0.10\pi_3$ (2)

$\pi_3 = 0.05\pi_1 + 0.05\pi_2 + 0.75\pi_3$ (3)

$\pi_1 + \pi_2 + \pi_3 = 1$ (4)

Using (1), (2), and (4) provides three equations with three unknowns; solving provides $\pi_1 = 0.548$, $\pi_2 = 0.286$, and $\pi_3 = 0.166$

b. 16.6% as given by π_3

c. Quick Stop should take

667 − 0.548(1000) = 119 Murphy's customers
and 333 − 0.286(1000) = 47 Ashley's customers
Total 166 Quick Stop customers

It will take customers from Murphy's and Ashley's

8. a. MDA

b. $\pi_1 = 1/3, \pi_2 = 2/3$

10. 3 − 1(0.59), 4 − 1(0.52)

11. $I = \begin{bmatrix} 1 & 0 \\ 0 & 1 \end{bmatrix} \quad Q = \begin{bmatrix} 0.25 & 0.25 \\ 0.05 & 0.25 \end{bmatrix}$

$$(I - Q) = \begin{bmatrix} 0.75 & -0.25 \\ -0.05 & 0.75 \end{bmatrix}$$

$$N = (I - Q)^{-1} = \begin{bmatrix} 1.3636 & 0.4545 \\ 0.0909 & 1.3636 \end{bmatrix}$$

$$NR = \begin{bmatrix} 1.3636 & 0.4545 \\ 0.0909 & 1.3636 \end{bmatrix}\begin{bmatrix} 0.5 & 0.0 \\ 0.5 & 0.2 \end{bmatrix} = \begin{bmatrix} 0.909 & 0.091 \\ 0.727 & 0.273 \end{bmatrix}$$

$$BNR = [4000 \quad 5000]\begin{bmatrix} 0.909 & 0.091 \\ 0.727 & 0.273 \end{bmatrix} = [7271 \quad 1729]$$

Estimate \$1729 in bad debts

12. 3580 will be sold eventually; 1420 will be lost

14. a. Graduate and drop out

b. P(Drop Out) = 0.15, P(Sophomore) = 0.10, P(Junior) = 0.75

c. 0.706, 0.294

d. Yes; P(Graduate) = 0.54
P(Drop Out) = 0.46

e. 1479 (74%) will graduate

Chapter 17

2. a. Let x_1 = number of shares of AGA Products purchased
x_2 = number of shares of Key Oil purchased

To obtain an annual return of exactly 9%:

$$0.06(50)x_1 + 0.10(100)x_2 = 0.09(50{,}000)$$
$$3x_1 + 10x_2 = 4500$$

To have exactly 60% of the total investment in Key Oil:

$$100x_2 = 0.60(50{,}000)$$
$$x_2 = 300$$

Therefore, we can write the goal programming model as follows:

$$\text{Min } P_1(d_1^-) + P_2(d_2^+)$$

s.t.

$$50x_1 + 100x_2 \le 50{,}000 \quad \text{Funds available}$$
$$3x_1 + 10x_2 - d_1^+ + d_1^- = 4{,}500 \quad P_1 \text{ goal}$$
$$x_2 - d_2^+ + d_2^- = 300 \quad P_2 \text{ goal}$$
$$x_1, x_2, d_1^+, d_1^-, d_2^+, d_2^- \ge 0$$

b. In the following graphical solution, $x_1 = 250$ and $x_2 = 375$

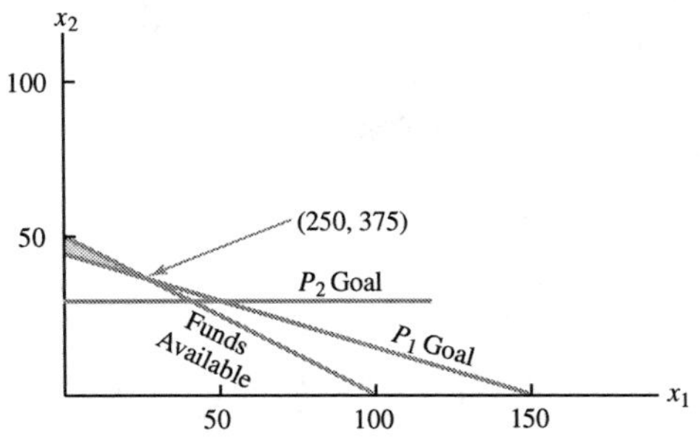

4. a. Min $P_1(d_1^-) + P_1(d_2^+) + P_2(d_3^-) + P_2(d_4^-) + P_3(d_5^-)$

s.t.

$$\begin{aligned} 20x_1 + 30x_2 - d_1^+ + d_1^- &= 4800 \\ 20x_1 + 30x_2 - d_2^+ + d_2^- &= 6000 \\ x_1 \qquad - d_3^+ + d_3^- &= 100 \\ x_2 - d_4^+ + d_4^- &= 120 \\ x_1 + x_2 \quad - d_5^+ + d_5^- &= 300 \end{aligned}$$

x_1, x_2, all deviation variables ≥ 0

b. $x_1 = 120, x_2 = 120$

6. a. Let x_1 = number of letters mailed to group 1 customers

x_2 = number of letters mailed to group 2 customers

Min $P_1(d_1^-) + P_1(d_2^-) + P_2(d_3^+)$

s.t.

$$\begin{aligned} x_1 \qquad - d_1^+ + d_1^- &= 40{,}000 \\ x_2 - d_2^+ + d_2^- &= 50{,}000 \\ x_1 + x_2 - d_3^+ + d_3^- &= 70{,}000 \end{aligned}$$

x_1, x_2, all deviation variables ≥ 0

b. $x_1 = 40{,}000, x_2 = 50{,}000$

c. Optimal solution does not change

8. a. Min $d_1^- + d_1^+ + e_1^- + e_1^+ + d_2^- + d_2^+ + e_2^- + e_2^+ + d_3^- + d_3^+ + e_3^- + e_3^+$

s.t.

$$\begin{aligned} x_1 \qquad + d_1^- - d_1^+ &= 1 \\ x_2 + e_1^- - e_1^+ &= 7 \\ x_1 \qquad + d_2^- - d_2^+ &= 5 \\ x_2 + e_2^- - e_2^+ &= 9 \\ x_1 \qquad + d_3^- - d_3^+ &= 6 \\ x_2 + e_3^- - e_3^+ &= 2 \end{aligned}$$

all variables ≥ 0

b. $x_1 = 5, x_2 = 7$

9. Scoring calculations

Criteria	Analyst Chicago	Accountant Denver	Auditor Houston
Career advancement	35	20	20
Location	10	12	8
Management	30	25	35
Salary	28	32	16
Prestige	32	20	24
Job security	8	10	16
Enjoyment of the work	28	20	20
Totals	171	139	139

The analyst position in Chicago is recommended

10. 178, 184, 151
Marysville

12. 170, 168, 190, 183
Handover College

14. a. 220 Bowrider (194)
b. 240 Sundancer (144)

16. Step 1: Column totals are $^{17}/_4$, $^{31}/_{21}$, and 12

Step 2:

Style	Accord	Saturn	Cavalier
Accord	$^4/_{17}$	$^7/_{31}$	$^4/_{12}$
Saturn	$^{12}/_{17}$	$^{21}/_{31}$	$^7/_{12}$
Cavalier	$^1/_{17}$	$^3/_{31}$	$^1/_{12}$

Step 3:

Style	Accord	Saturn	Cavalier	Row Average
Accord	0.235	0.226	0.333	0.265
Saturn	0.706	0.677	0.583	0.656
Cavalier	0.059	0.097	0.083	0.080

Consistency Ratio

Step 1:

$$0.265\begin{bmatrix}1\\3\\ ^1/_4\end{bmatrix} + 0.656\begin{bmatrix}^1/_3\\1\\ ^1/_7\end{bmatrix} + 0.080\begin{bmatrix}4\\7\\1\end{bmatrix}$$

$$\begin{bmatrix}0.265\\0.795\\0.066\end{bmatrix} + \begin{bmatrix}0.219\\0.656\\0.094\end{bmatrix} + \begin{bmatrix}0.320\\0.560\\0.080\end{bmatrix} = \begin{bmatrix}0.802\\2.007\\0.239\end{bmatrix}$$

Step 2: 0.802/0.265 = 3.028

2.007/0.656 = 3.062

0.239/0.080 = 3.007

Step 3: $\lambda_{max} = (3.028 + 3.062 + 3.007)/3 = 3.032$

Step 4: CI = (3.032 − 3)/2 = 0.016

Step 5: CR = 0.016/0.58 = 0.028

Because CR = 0.028 is less than 0.10, the degree of consistency exhibited in the pairwise comparison matrix for style is acceptable

18. a. 0.724, 0.193, 0.083
b. CR = 0.057, yes

20. a.

Flavor	A	B	C
A	1	3	2
B	$^1/_3$	1	5
C	$^1/_2$	$^1/_5$	1

b. Step 1: Column totals are $^{11}/_6$, $^{21}/_5$, and 8

Step 2:

Flavor	A	B	C
A	$6/11$	$15/21$	$2/8$
B	$2/11$	$5/21$	$5/8$
C	$3/11$	$1/21$	$1/8$

Step 3:

Flavor	A	B	C	Row Average
A	0.545	0.714	0.250	0.503
B	0.182	0.238	0.625	0.348
C	0.273	0.048	0.125	0.148

c. Step 1:

$$0.503\begin{bmatrix}1\\1/3\\1/2\end{bmatrix} + 0.348\begin{bmatrix}3\\1\\1/5\end{bmatrix} + 0.148\begin{bmatrix}2\\5\\1\end{bmatrix}$$

$$\begin{bmatrix}0.503\\0.168\\0.252\end{bmatrix} + \begin{bmatrix}1.044\\0.348\\0.070\end{bmatrix} + \begin{bmatrix}0.296\\0.740\\0.148\end{bmatrix} = \begin{bmatrix}1.845\\1.258\\0.470\end{bmatrix}$$

Step 2: 1.845/0.503 = 3.668
1.258/0.348 = 3.615
0.470/0.148 = 3.123
Step 3: $\lambda_{max} = (3.668 + 3.615 + 3.123)/3 = 3.469$
Step 4: CI = (3.469 − 3)/2 = 0.235
Step 5: CR = 0.235/0.58 = 0.415
Because CR = 0.415 is greater than 0.10, the individual's judgments are not consistent

22. a.

	D	S	N
D	1	$1/4$	$1/7$
S	4	1	$1/3$
N	7	3	1

b. 0.080, 0.265, 0.656
c. CR = 0.028, yes

24. Criteria: Yield and Risk
Step 1: Column totals are 1.5 and 3
Step 2:

	Yield	Risk	Priority
Yield	0.667	0.667	0.667
Risk	0.333	0.333	0.333

With only two criteria, CR = 0; no need to compute CR
Preceding calculations for Yield and Risk provide

Stocks	Yield Priority	Risk Priority
CCC	0.750	0.333
SRI	0.250	0.667

Overall Priorities:
CCC 0.667(0.750) + 0.333(0.333) = 0.611
SRI 0.667(0.250) + 0.333(0.667) = 0.389
CCC is preferred

26. a. Criterion: 0.608, 0.272, 0.120
Price: 0.557, 0.123, 0.320
Sound: 0.137, 0.239, 0.623
Reception: 0.579, 0.187, 0.046
b. 0.446, 0.162, 0.392
System A is preferred

INDEX